D0572871

Biology of the Seas of the U.S.S.R.

Biology of the Seas of the U.S.S.R.

PROFESSOR L. ZENKEVITCH

Professor at Moscow State University
Chairman of the National Oceanographical Committee of the U.S.S.R.
Vice-President of the Special Committee on Oceanic Research (SCOR)

TRANSLATED BY S. BOTCHARSKAYA

ILLUSTRATED

NEW YORK
INTERSCIENCE PUBLISHERS
a division of John Wiley & Sons, Inc.

Published jointly by
Interscience Publishers
a division of John Wiley & Sons Inc.
440 Park Avenue South
New York 16, New York

and

George Allen & Unwin Ltd.
40 Museum Street
London, W.C.1.

TRANSLATED FROM THE RUSSIAN
BY SOPHIA BOTCHARSKAYA

PRINTED IN GREAT BRITAIN

PREFACE

The present publication is a considerably amended and supplemented version of the second edition of my book *The Fauna and Biological Productivity of the Sea*, published in 1947. A large amount of new research has been gathered during the last fourteen years. Some bodies of water have considerably changed their hydrographical and biological aspect during that time.

I have found it necessary to add a section on 'The Far Eastern Seas', which was not included in the Russian edition. An Introduction has also been added. Since I did not wish to make any considerable increase in the size of the book I have shortened the sections on the Northern and Southern seas. Some illustrations have also been omitted.

I set myself the task of collecting in this book the results of research carried out in seas adjacent to the frontiers of the U.S.S.R., and only in the section 'The Far Eastern Seas, have I gone beyond the boundaries of the U.S.S.R. in order to give a summary of the results of Soviet deep-water explorations in the Pacific Ocean.

In the Russian edition of my book many problems of marine biology are included in the first volume and are not discussed in further detail in the second. These problems include, for instance, the conception of the biosphere, biological productivity, the problem of brackish-water environment, biogeographical zonation, the practical significance of marine organisms, the problems of acclimatization, and others. All these problems had to be excluded, the more so because of the addition of the large new section.

Unfortunately I have also been unable to include in the book a more detailed exposition of comprehensive and numerous monographic studies on individual groups of marine organisms, or of the large number of works on the ecology and biology of individual forms. These works form an abundant literature in Russian.

I have thought it essential to give a short physico-geographical introduction to the description of each sea. Although a zoologist, I have considered it expedient to include some botanical data, in order to give a more complete biological picture.

The land mass of Europe and Asia is distinguished from other land masses in that its shores are almost entirely bordered by coastal seas. This is particularly true of the Soviet Union; the south eastern coast of Kamchatka and the Kuril Islands alone being washed by ocean waters. It is not surprising that these coastal seas have been the subject of many different and complex marine research studies, and in particular the Azov, Caspian, Barents and Black Seas have been systematically explored. Equal attention has been given to the study of plankton, benthos and fish.

This book has a strongly quantitative approach. There are quantitative studies of the feeding habits of fish; similar investigations of the distribution of flora and fauna throughout the seasons make it possible for general conclusions about biological productivity to be drawn.

The author has taken part in many expeditions to both the northern and the southern seas and has devoted fourteen years to the study of the Far

Eastern seas. He is extremely pleased to see his book published in English. Original scientific papers in Russian have had little publicity outside the U.S.S.R. and quite often works on marine biology or biogeography have appeared in other languages purporting to offer a new interpretation of certain problems, when in fact they had already been examined and interpreted by Russian writers.

With this book a special effort has been made to make Russian work as widely available as possible to the foreign reader. The author believes that his treatise will be a reliable aid and guide to all who seek access to the rich literature of Russian marine biology.

L. ZENKEVITCH

CONTENTS

THE SOUTHERN SEAS OF THE U.S.S.R.

CONTENTS

INTRODUCTION

No country in the world possesses such an abundance and variety of bodies of water as the U.S.S.R. Its frontiers are about 60,000 km long. Only a small part of the seas of the U.S.S.R. is directly connected with the open ocean, most of its shores being encirled by the accessory seas of three oceans—the Arctic, the Atlantic and the Pacific.

A comparison with other continents, which are usually almost devoid of accessory seas, brings out clearly this characteristic of Eurasia.

Twelve of the seas of the U.S.S.R. have retained their link with the open oceans; two of its greatest lake-oceans—the Caspian and Aral Seas—are at present isolated from them.

The total area of these 14 seas composes about 5 per cent of the surface of the world-ocean; they astonish their investigators by the variety of their physico-geographical conditions, by the abundance and variety of their flora and fauna and by the complexity of their geological past, which has left its ineffaceable imprint on their composition, their biological peculiarities and their ranges of flora and fauna which provide huge resources of plant and animal raw material. The population of the seas of the U.S.S.R. is a very rich subject for scientific investigation.

The seas of the U.S.S.R. include such pygmies as the Sea of Azov, with depths no greater than 13·5 m, and such giants as the Bering Sea, with depths exceeding 5 km. Some of its seas have a full marine salinity, some are brackish, with a salinity of 12–10–8 parts per thousand and less. The composition of the salts of some sea-lakes, such as the Caspian and the Aral Seas, has changed considerably, and at present they differ greatly from that of the oceans. Some details are given in *Table 1*.

The Baltic and northern seas of the U.S.S.R. contain a most characteristic brackish-water relict fauna, the result of a considerable and protracted loss of salinity experienced during the Ice Age. Some representatives of this relict fauna moved southwards, penetrated into river systems and reached the Caspian Sea. The southern seas of the U.S.S.R. give shelter to a rich, brackish-water relict fauna—a remainder of the Pontic lake-sea fauna, which has in a large number of representatives penetrated into the river systems of the Black, Azov and Caspian Seas. No other seas contain such rich, brackish-water fauna of varied origin as those of the U.S.S.R. The penetration of representatatives of the Mediterranean (Atlantic) fauna eastward into the Caspian and even the Aral Seas is also most interesting.

During the recent millennia the Barents Sea and the adjacent Siberian seas have formed a broad route for the penetration of Atlantic fauna eastward, and of Pacific fauna westward. The great depths of the central depression of the Arctic basin with their original bathypelagic fauna are adjacent to the northern confines of the Siberian seas.

One of the greatest depths in the Pacific—the Kurile–Kamchatka Trench—lies immediately adjacent to the eastern boundary of the U.S.S.R.

*Table 1. Areas, volumes and depths of seas of the U.S.S.R.**

Name	Area $10^3 \times m^2$	Volume $10^3 \times m^3$	Mean depth m	Greatest depth m
Baltic Sea	386	33	86	459
White Sea	90	8	89	330
Barents Sea	1,405	322	229	600
Kara Sea	883	104	118	620
Laptev Sea	650	338	519	2,980
East Siberian Sea	901	53	58	155
Chukotsk Sea	582	51	88	160
Bering Sea	2,304	3,683	1,598	4,773
Sea of Okhotsk	1,590	1,365	859	3,657
Sea of Japan	978	1,713	1,752	4,036
Black Sea	423	537	1,271	2,245
Sea of Azov	38	0·3	9	13
Caspian Sea	370	77	197	980
Aral Sea	64	1·0	75	68
Total	10,644	8,285·3		

* Except for the Caspian and Aral Seas the data are taken from the *Nautical Atlas*, Volume II, 1953. The greatest depths of Far Eastern Seas are according to the latest *Vityaz* data.

The Caspian, White and Barents Seas have been an area of Russian fishery from ancient times. Fisheries were developed in the Azov and Black Seas somewhat later. In the seas of the Far East they were developed most recently. At present the U.S.S.R. occupies one of the leading places in marine fishery.

Hence the investigation of the flora and fauna of the seas of the U.S.S.R. is of exceptional interest.

The Russian people, who for centuries had lived by agriculture, were drawn to the sea at the time when antiquity changed into the Middle Ages. As early as the fifth century military expeditions took the Slavs down to the Black Sea. Two powerful states—Novgorod and Kiev—arose in the ninth century on the Volkhov and Dnieper, along the great water route from Varangians to the Greeks. Both states learned to use the water routes for trade and war alike. A high nautical culture developed in Novgorod state through the centuries. The Novgorod helmsmen ploughed, in their small boats, first the Baltic Sea, and then, from the beginning of the twelfth century, the White Sea and the Arctic Ocean. In the ninth and tenth centuries numerous Russian ships sailed to Byzantium. In the sixteenth and seventeenth centuries men of Novgorod and Kiev were good navigators. Marine communications with the west became more lively under Ivan III: English trade ships 'opened' the northern sea route to the White Sea in the middle of the sixteenth century. Venice led a lively trade with the south of Russia through the Black Sea. At first Russia's role was rather passive but, in the sixteenth century under Ivan the Terrible, there awoke a new striving for marine frontiers and an active struggle for the

Black, Baltic and Caspian Seas was begun, followed later by that for the coastline of the Pacific Ocean.

In the time of Peter the Great Russian science was enriched by the first data on the fauna of the seas which wash the shores of Russia. The eighteenth and the first quarter of the nineteenth century was a real epoch of great expeditions to explore the Russian seas. Eighteenth-century discoveries were connected with V. Bering's expedition and with the Great Northern expedition. Kruzenshtern and Lisyansky (1803–05), Kozebou (1816–17), Bellingshausen and Lazarev (1819–21) and Litke (1826–29) sailed round the world in the first quarter of the nineteenth century, bringing back from their voyages, for Russian and world science, the first geographical data on Russian seas and the first information on their populations.

Basic data on the Russian flora and fauna were gathered mostly during the second half of the last century. Marine expeditions left for every corner of Russia, laboratories and museums were enriched with collections of different groups of marine fauna, marine stations were opened, scientific conferences were organized, remarkable embryological investigations of marine fauna were carried out by E. Metchnikov and A. Kovalevksy. The first scientific and commercial expedition comprehensive both in the tasks it undertook and in the results obtained was that of Baer to the Caspian Sea, which lasted from 1853 to 1856.

Sevastopol Biological Station started its work in 1871–72, the Murman Biological Station in 1881, and the Scientific Fishery Station at Astrakhan on the Caspian Sea was opened in 1897. All these played an important role in the development of marine biological research in Russia.

In relation to the beginning of the present century the following should be noted: ten-year (1898–1910) research work done by the 'Expedition for Scientific-Industrial Research off the Murman Coast' on the ship *Andrei Pervozvanniy*, organized by the eminent Russian oceanographer N. M. Knipovitch, which discovered huge accumulations of commercial fish in the Barents Sea; Toll's expedition on the *Zarya* along the northern shores of Asia in 1900–1901, and P. Schmidt's (1900–01) expedition to Korea and Sakhalin.

Nordenskjöld's remarkable Swedish expedition on the *Vega*, the first to sail through the northeastern passage, in 1878–79, played a very important part in the study of the fauna of the northern seas of Russia.

N. Andrussov's and A. Lebedintzev's well-known expedition, which discovered the contamination of the deep waters of the Black Sea with hydrogen sulphide, worked in the early eighteen-nineties.

The excellent work of K. Derjugin in the Kola Guba, on the Murman Peninsula, and that of S. Zernov in the Black Sea, in the Sevastopol area, carried out in the first decade of the present century, should also be noted.

Biological research of the seas which wash the shores of the U.S.S.R. has progressed greatly during the last 35 years or so, owing to the organization of a large number of permanent marine institutions, carrying out a comprehensive survey throughout the seas of the U.S.S.R. (*Table 2*). These numerous institutions were under the authority of the Academies of Sciences of the U.S.S.R. and Ukrainian S.S.R., of the Fishery Administration, of the Chief Administration of the Hydrometeorological Service, the Ministry of Marine, the Ministry of Higher Education, Administration of Nature Reserve and some others. In the northern seas the efforts of the Marine Scientific Institute and its 20-year expeditions on the ship *Persey* and the work done by the Arctic Institute with its numerous expeditions on the ships *Chelyuskin*, *Sadko*, *Sedov*, *Rusanov* and others, were mostly responsible for this progress.

K. Derjugin's researches and the work of his expeditions on the ship *Rosinante* and others, and the organization of the Pacific Ocean Institutes of Fisheries and Oceanography at Vladivostok in 1925 were just as important for research in the Far Eastern Seas.

Knipovitch's expeditions and the work done by the Azov–Black Seas Institute of Fisheries and Oceanography (from 1921) have played an important role in the investigations in that area, while in the Caspian Sea important research was carried out by the three expeditions of Knipovitch (1904–15) and, during the Soviet period, in the nineteen-thirties, by scientific and industrial expeditions.

The Solovets Biological Station of the St Petersburg Society of Naturalists was set up in 1881. In 1899 this station was transferred to the town Aleksandrovsk (Kola Guba, on the Barents Sea); it remained there until 1929, when it was transferred to Murmansk. In 1933 it was reorganized together with the State Institute of Oceanography and the Institute of Fisheries into the Polar Institute of Fisheries and Oceanography. The Murman Marine Biological Institute in Dal'naya Zelenetskaya Guba mentioned in *Table 2* came into being in 1936, with no direct connection with the old Murmansk Station, but it is continuing the work of the latter.

Table 2. Institutions carrying on research on the marine flora and fauna of the U.S.S.R.

Department and name of Institution	Place	Date of foundation	Main expedition ships
(A) Academy of Sciences of the U.S.S.R.			
1. Zoological Institute	Leningrad		
2. Botanical Institute	Leningrad		
3. Murman Marine Biological Institute	Dal'naya Zelenetskaya Guba, Murmansk	1936	*Professor Derjugin*
4. Institute of Oceanology	Moscow	1941	*Vityaz*
5. Black Sea Station of the Institute of Oceanology	Gelendzhik		*Academician S. Vavilov*
6. Acoustic Institute	Moscow	1951	*P. Lebedev* *S. Vavilov*
7. Institute of Marine Hydrophysics	Moscow		*Lomonosov*
8. Black Sea Hydrophysical Station of the Institute of Marine Hydrophysics	Katsiveli, Crimea	1929	

Table 2—(contd.)

Department and name of Institution	Place	Date of foundation	Main expedition ships
(B) Academy of Sciences of the Ukrainian S.S.R.			
9. Sevastopol Biological Station	Sevastopol	1871–72	*Alexander Kovalevsky*
10. Odessa Biological Station	Odessa	1954	
11. Laboratory of the Odessa Biological Station	Vilkovo, Odessa Province	1954	
12. Karadag Biological Station	Karadag, Crimea	1914	
(C) Karelo-Finnish Branch of the Academy of Sciences of the U.S.S.R.			
13. White Sea Biological Station	Cape Kartesh, Chupa Guba, White Sea	1949	
(D) University Marine Stations			
14. Novorossiysk Biological Station of Rostov University	Novorossiysk	1921	
15. White Sea Biological Station of Moscow University	Velikaya Salma, Kandalaksha Gulf, White Sea	1938	
16. Peterhof Biological Institute of Leningrad University	Petrodvorets	1920	
(E) Institutes of Fisheries			
17. All-Union Institute of Fisheries and Oceanography (V.N.I.R.O.)	Moscow	1933 (1921*)	
18. Pacific Ocean Institute of Fisheries and Oceanography	Vladivostok	1929 (1925)	*Zhemchug* *Almaz* *Isumrud* *Ogon*
19. Kamchatka branch of the Pacific Ocean Institute of Fisheries	Petropavlovsk on Kamchatka	1932	*Ozlik* *and others*
20. Sakhalin Branch of the Pacific Institute of Fisheries	Antonovo, Chekhov District, Sakhalin	1932	
21. Amur Branch of the Pacific Ocean Institute of Fisheries	Khabarovsk	1945	

Table 2—(contd.)

Department and name of Institution	Place	Date of foundation	Main expedition ships
22. Polar Institute of Fisheries and Oceanography	Murmansk	1933 (1929)	*Sevastopol* *Knipovich* *Academician Berg* *Persey II* *Professor Masyatzev*
23. Baltic Institute of Fisheries and Oceanography	Kaliningrad	1945	*Alazan*
24. Azov–Black Seas Institute of Fishery and Oceanography	Kerch	1921	*Grot* *Donetz and others*
25. Azov Institute of Marine Fishery	Rostov-on-Don	1955	*Professor Vasnetzov*
26. Latvian Institute of Marine Fishery	Riga	1945	
27. Latvian Laboratory of Commercial Ichthyology	Riga	1945	
28. Estonian Laboratory of Commercial Ichthyology	Tallin	1944	
29. Caspian Institute of Fisheries and Oceanography†	Astrakhan	1897	
30. Azerbaijan Institute of Fishery‡	Baku	1912	
31. Georgian Scientific Experimental Laboratory	Batumi	1932	
32. Aral Institute of Fisheries and Oceanography	Aralsk	1929	
33. Scientific Research Laboratory for Seaweeds	Archangel	1930	
34. Kura Experimental Sturgeon Hatchery	Baku		
35. Institute of Lake and River Fisheries (VNIORKH)	Leningrad	1914	
36. Ob'-Tazov Branch of the Institute of Lake and River Fisheries	Tobolsk	1932	
37. Siberian Branch of the Institute of Lake and River Fisheries	Krasnoyarsk	1908	
38. Scientific Research Institute of Marine Fisheries of the Ukrainian S.S.R.	Odessa	1932	

* Emerged in 1933 when the Central Institute of Fisheries was united with the State Oceanographic Institute I.

† Up to 1917 the Astrakhan Ichthyological Laboratory.

‡ Up to 1917 the Baku Ichthyological Laboratory.

Table 2—(contd.)

Department and name of Institution	Place	Date of foundation	Main expedition ships
39. State Oceanographic Institute of the Hydrometeorological Administration* (GOI)	Moscow	1942	*Schokalsky Voejkov*
40. All-Union Arctic and Antarctic Institute of the Ministry of the Merchant Marine	Leningrad 1959	1919	
41. Kandalaksha State Nature Reserve	Kandalaksha (White Sea)	1939	
42. Astrakhan Nature Reserve	Astrakhan	1919	
43. 'Gassan-Kuli' Nature Reserve	Krasnovodsk	1933	
44. 'Kzil-Agach' Nature Reserve	Lenkoran'	1929	

Table 3. Major Russian monographs in the field of oceanography

The Acclimatization of Nereis in the Caspian Sea. Symposium, 1952.

ANDRIASHEV, A. P. *Essay on the Animal Geography and Origin of the Fish of the Bering Sea and Adjacent Waters*. 1933.

ANDRIASHEV, A. P. *The Fish of the Northern Seas of the U.S.S.R.* 1954.

ARKHANGELSKY, A. D. and STRAHOV, N. M. *Geological Structure and History of the Development of the Black Sea*. 1958.

BEREZKIN, V. A. *The Dynamics of the Sea*. 1938.

BERG, L. S. *The Aral Sea*. 1908.

BERG, L. S. *Fresh-water Fish of the U.S.S.R.* 1948–49.

BLINOV, L. K. *Hydrochemistry of the Aral Sea*. 1956.

BRODSKY, K. A. *Copepods*. 1950.

BRUJEVITCH, S. B. *Hydrochemistry of the Central and Southern Caspian*. 1937.

DATZKE, V. G. *Organic Substances in the Waters of the South Seas of the U.S.S.R.* 1959.

DERJAVIN, A. N. *The Caspian Mysids*. 1939.

DERJAVIN, A. N. *A Survey of the History of the Caspian Fauna and of the Bodies of Fresh Water of Azerbaijan and the Caspian Aquatic Fauna*, from the Symposium 'Azerbaijan Animal World'. 1951.

DERJUGIN, K. M. *The Fauna of the Kola Guba and Its Environment*. 1915.

DERJUGIN, K. M. *The Fauna of the White Sea and Its Environment*. 1929.

DERJUGIN, K. M. *The Mogil'noye Relict Lake*. 1926.

DJAKONOV, A. M. *The Echinoderms of the Barents, Kara and White Seas. Proceedings* of the Leningrad Society of Naturalists. 1926, **56**, 2.

* Was founded in 1942 separately from the State Oceanographic Institute (GOI N) which had been reorganized in 1933 into the All-Union Institue of Fisheries and Oceanography.

DJAKONOV, A. M. *Brittle Stars [Ophiuroidea] of the Seas of the U.S.S.R· Classification Keys to U.S.S.R. Fauna, No. 55,* 1954· Zoological Institute of the Academy of Sciences of the U.S.S.R.

ESIPOV, V. K. *The Fish of the Kara Sea.* 1952.

FILATOVA, Z. A. *Zoogeographical Zonation of the Northern Seas of the U.S.S.R. according to the Distribution of the Bivalves.* 1957.

GAEVSKAYA, N. S. (Editor). *Classification Keys to the Fauna and Flora of the Northern Seas of the U.S.S.R.* 1937.

GRIMM, O. A. *The Caspian Sea and Its Fauna.* (Works of the Aral–Caspian Expedition 1876–77.)

GURJANOVA, E. F., ZACHS, I. G. and USCHAKOW, P. V. *Das Litoral des Kola-Fjords.* 1928–30.

GURJANOVA, E. F. *Gammaridae of the Seas of the U.S.S.R. and Adjacent Waters.* 1951.

GURJANOVA, E. F. *The Gammaridae of the Northern Part of the Pacific Ocean.* 1962.

ISSATCHENKO, B. L. *Research on Arctic Ocean Micro-organisms.* 1914.

IVANOV, A. V. *Commercial Water Invertebrates.* 1955.

IVANOV, A. V. *The Pogonophora.* 1959, 1960.

JASHNOV, V. A. *Plankton Productivity of the Northern Seas of the U.S.S.R.* 1940.

JOUSE, A. P. *Stratigraphic and Geographical Investigations in the North-western Part of the Pacific Ocean.* 1962.

KLENOVA, M. V. *The Geology of the Sea.* 1948.

KLENOVA, M. V. (1960). *Geology of the Barents Sea.* Ac. Sci. U.S.S.R. (R.)

KLUGE, G. A. (1962). *Bryozoa of the Seas of the U.S.S.R.* Ac. Sci. U.S.S.R. (R).

KNIPOVITCH, N. M. *The Basis of the Hydrology of the European Arctic Ocean.* 1906.

KNIPOVITCH, N. M. *The Hydrology of the Sea of Azov.* 1927.

KNIPOVITCH, N. M. *Hydrological Research in the Sea of Azov.* 1932.

KNIPOVITCH, N. M. *Hydrological Research in the Black Sea.* 1932.

KNIPOVITCH, N. M. *The Hydrology of Seas and Brackish Waters.* 1938.

LINDBERG, G. U. *The Quaternary Period in the Light of the Biogeographical Data.* 1955.

MARKOVSKY, J. M. *Invertebrate Fauna in the Lower Stream of the Rivers in the Ukraine, its Environmental Conditions and its Utilization.* 1953–55.

MASLOV, N. A. *Bottom-living Fish in the Fishery Industry in the Barents Sea. Proceedings* of the Polar Institute of Fisheries and Oceanography, No. 8. 1944.

MEISNER, V. I. *Fisheries.* 1933. (Ed. 'Snabtechisdat' L.)

MILASHEVITCH, K. O. *The Molluscs of the Black and Azov Seas.* 1916.

MOISEEV, P. A. *Cod and Dab of the Far Eastern Seas.* 1933.

MORDUKHAI-BOLTOVSKOY, F. D. *The Caspian Fauna in the Azov–Black Sea Basin.* 1960.

MOROSOWA-WODJANITZKAJA, N. V. *Phytoplankton of the Black Sea.* 1940–57.

NAUMOV, D. V. (1960). *Hydroids and Hydromedusa in Seawater, Brackish Water and Fresh-water Basins of the U.S.S.R.* Ac. Sci. U.S.S.R. (R).

NIKITIN, B. N. *Vertical Distribution of Plankton in the Black Sea.* 1926–29 and 1938–45.

NIKOLSKY, G. V. *Fish of the Aral Sea.* 1940.

SAIDOVA, KH. M. (1962). *The Ecology of the Foraminifera and Paleogeography of the Far East Seas of U.S.S.R. and Northwestern part of the Pacific Ocean.* Ac. Sci. U.S.S.R. (R.)
SAMOILOV, N. V. *River Mouths.* 1952.
SCHIMKEVITCH, V. M. *Pantopoda. U.S.S.R. Fauna,* Parts 1 and 2, 1929, 1930.
SCHMIDT, P. J. *Pisces marium orientalium Imperii Rossici.* 1904.
SCHMIDT, P. J. *Fish of the Pacific Ocean.* 1948.
SCHMIDT, P. J. *The Migration of Fish.* 1947.
SCHMIDT, P. J. *Fish of the Sea of Okhotsk.* 1950.
SCHOKALSKY, J. M. *Oceanography.* 1917.
SCHOKALSKY, J. M. *Physical Oceanography.* 1933.
SCHORYGIN, A. A. *Nutrition and Nutrient Correlations of Caspian Sea Fish.* 1952.
SCHULEIKIN, V. V. *The Physics of the Sea.* 1932, 1937, 1941.
SINOVA, E. S. *The Algae of the Murman.* 1912–14.
SINOVA, E. S. *The Algae of the White, Black, Japan, Chukotsk Seas.* 1928–54.
SNEZHINSKY, V. A. *Practical Oceanography.* 1954.
SOLDATOV, V. K. and LINDBERG, G. U. *A Survey of the Fish of Far Eastern Seas.* 1930.
SOLDATOV, V. K. *Commercial Ichthyology.* Vol. I, 1934; Vol. II, 1938.
SOVINSKY, V. K. *An Introduction to the Study of the Fauna of Ponto–Caspian–Aral Sea Basin. Notes* of the Kiev Society of Naturalists. 1904, **18**.
SUVOROV, E. K. *The Foundations of Ichthyology.* 1948.
SVETOVIDOV, A. N. *Gadiforms, Fauna of the U.S.S.R. Fishes,* 1948, **9**, 4.
SVETOVIDOV, A. N. *Clupeidae, U.S.S.R. Fauna. Fishes,* 1952, **11**, 1.
USCHAKOV, P. V. (Editor). *The Fauna and Flora of the Chukotsk Sea.* 1952.
USCHAKOV, P. V. *Okhotsk Sea Fauna and Its Environment.* 1953.
USCHAKOV, P. V. *Polychaetae Worms of the Far Eastern Seas of the U.S.S.R.* 1955.
VINOGRADOV, A. P. *Chemical Composition of Marine Organisms.* (Works of the Biochemistry and Geochemistry Laboratory of the Academy of Sciences, U.S.S.R. 3—1935, 4—1936, 6—1944).
VINOGRADOV, A. P. *The Chemical Composition of Marine Organisms.* The Foundation for Marine Research, New Haven, 1953.
VIZE, V. YU. *The Seas of the Soviet Arctic.* 1948.
VOROBIEFF, V. P. *The Benthos of the Azov Sea.* 1945.
ZENKEVITCH, L. A. *Fauna and the Biological Productivity of the Sea.* Vol. I, 1947; Vol. II, 1951.
ZENKEVITCH, L. A. *The Seas of the U.S.S.R., Their Fauna and Flora.* 1951 and 1955.
ZERNOV, S. A. *Textbook on Hydrobiology.* 1934 and 1949.
ZERNOV, S. A. *The Problem of the Study of Life in the Black Sea.* 1913.
ZINOVA, A. D. *Classification Key for Brown Algae.* 1953.
ZINOVA, A. D. *Classification Key for Red Algae of the Northern Seas.* 1955.
ZUBOV, N. N. *Oceanographic Tables.* 1931 and 1940.
ZUBOV, N. N. *Sea Waters and Ice.* 1938.
ZUBOV, N. N. *Arctic Ice.* 1945.
ZUBOV, N. N. *Dynamic Oceanography.* 1947.
ZUBOV, N. N. *The Bases of the Study of the World-Ocean Straits.* 1950.
ZUBOV, N. N. *In the Centre of the Arctic.* 1948.

Table 4. The main Russian serials and proceedings of scientific institutes containing the results of research done in the field of marine biology

Contemporary	Year	Number of volumes or parts	Publications to which the present series are successors
Transactions of the Institute of Oceanology of the Academy of Sciences of the U.S.S.R.	1946–62	1–53	
Transactions of the Institute of Marine Hydrophysics of the Academy of Sciences of the U.S.S.R.	1948–58	1–24	
Transactions of the All-Union Institute of Marine Fisheries and Oceanography	1935–62	1–44	*Transactions* of the Scientific Institute of Fisheries, Vols. 1–4, 1924–30 *Transactions* of the Central Institute of Fisheries, Vols. 1–4, 1931–32 *Transactions* of the All-Union Institute of Fisheries, Vols. 1–3, 1933–34
			Transactions of the Floating Marine Scientific Institute, Vols. 1–2, 1926–1927 *Transactions* of the Marine Scientific Institute (*Berichte* des wissenschaftlichen Meeresinstituts), Vols. 3–4, 1928–30 *Transactions* of the State Oceanographical Institute (GOI N), Vols. 1–3, 1932–33
Transactions of the Sevastopol Biological Station of the Academy of Sciences of the U.S.S.R.	1936–62	1–14	
Transactions of the Murman Marine Biological Institute of the Academy of Sciences of the U.S.S.R.	1948–62	1–5	*Works* of the Murman Biological Station of the Academy of Sciences, U.S.S.R., Vols. 1–3, 1925–1929 (*Travaux* de la Station Biologique de Murman)
Transactions of the Karadag Biological Station of the Academy of Sciences of the Ukrainian S.S.R. (*Travaux* de la Station Biologique de Karadag de l'Académie des Sciences de l'U.R.S.S.)	1930–57	1–14	

Table 4—(contd.)

Contemporary	Year	Number of volumes or parts	Publications to which the present series are successors
Transactions of the Novorossiysk Biological Station	1937–38	1–3	
Transactions of the Aral Branch of the All-Union Institute of Marine Fisheries and Oceanography	1933–35	1–5	
Transactions of the Azov–Black Sea Institute of Fisheries and Oceanography	1940–62	1–19	*Transactions* of Kerch Ichthyological Laboratory, Vol. 1, 1926–27 *Transactions* of the Azov–Black Sea Scientific Fishery Station, Vols. 1–9, 1927–39 *Transactions* of the Azov–Black Sea Scientific and Commercial Expedition, Vols. 1–16, 1926–55 (*Bulletin* of the Pacific Scientific Institute of Fisheries and Oceanography)
Transactions of the Caspian Institute of Fisheries and Oceanography	1957	13–16	*Transactions* of the Ichthyological Laboratory attached to the Administration of the Caspian–Volga Fish and Seal Industries, Vol. 1, 1909
Transactions of the 'N. M. Knipovitch' Polar Institute of Sea Fisheries and Oceanography	1938–62	1–13	
Transactions of the Pacific Ocean Institute of Fisheries and Oceanography. (*Abhandlungen* der wissenschaftlichen Fischerei-Expedition im Asowschen und Schwarzen Meer)	1930–62	5–47	*Transactions* of the Pacific Ocean Scientific–Commercial Station, Vols. 1–4, 1928–29
Transactions of the State Oceanographical Institute	1947–62	1–65	
Fauna of the U.S.S.R. (published by the Zoological Institute of the Academy of Sciences of the U.S.S.R.)	1917–62		*Fauna of Russia and Adjacent Countries*, Vols. 1–26, 1911–17
Research on the Seas of the U.S.S.R. (published by the Zoological Institute of the Academy of Sciences of the U.S.S.R.)	1925–37	1–25	

Table 4—(contd.)

Contemporary	Year	Number of volumes or parts	Publications to which the present series are successors
Research on the Far Eastern Seas of the U.S.S.R. (published by the Zoological Institute of the Academy of Sciences of the U.S.S.R.)	1927	1–7	
Key to the Classification of the Fauna of the U.S.S.R. (published by the Zoological Institute of the Academy of Sciences of the U.S.S.R.) *Tableaux analytiques de la Fauna de l'U.R.S.S.* (publiés par l'Institut Zoologique de l'Académie de Sciences de l'U.R.S.S.)	1933–62		
Transactions of the Zoological Institute of the Academy of Sciences of the U.S.S.R.		1–28	
Transactions of the All-Union Hydrobiological Society	1949–62	1–12	
Russian Hydrobiological Journal (published by the Volga Biological Station, Saratov)	1921–28	1–7	
Zoological Journal (published by the Academy of Sciences of the U.S.S.R.)	1916–62	1–40	
Oceanology (published by the Academy of Sciences of the U.S.S.R.)	1961	1–2	
Problems of Ichthyology (published by the Academy of Sciences of the U.S.S.R.)	1961	1–2	
Transactions of the Arctic and Antarctic Institute	1959–62	226–56	
Transactions of the Arctic Institute	1933–59	1–225	

THE MAIN TRENDS OF RESEARCH ON THE BIOLOGY OF THE SEAS IN THE U.S.S.R.

The study of the seas of the U.S.S.R. has developed widely during the last 40 years in practically all areas, but to a lesser degree in the Laptev and East-Siberian Seas, which are hard of access. Marine research has been carried out in all the basic departments of oceanography, and for the most part has been of a comprehensive character.

Biological research has also been systematic and all-embracing, covering more or less uniformly both plant and animal populations throughout the sea column from its tidal zone to its abyssal zones. This started as a systematic study of the fauna and biogeographical characteristics of the seas, which covered, however, some ecological problems, as well as the seasonal cycles of development and the phenomena of biological productivity. The study of fish feeding and their use of plankton and benthos forms a considerable section of marine biological research. The results of biological research were used in dealing with the problem of acclimatization in new places of marine fish and the invertebrates used by them as food. The acclimatization of *Mugil auratus. M. saliens*, *Nereis diversicolor*, *Syndesmya ovata*, *Leander longirostris* and *L. squilla* in the Caspian Sea and *Clupea harengus membras* and *Leander squilla* in the Aral Sea were found most effective and interesting.

THE NORTHERN SEAS OF THE U.S.S.R.

1

General Characteristics of the Northern Seas

I. HYDROLOGICAL CONDITIONS

The link with the Atlantic and the Pacific Oceans

The Arctic Ocean is sometimes regarded as a kind of Inter-American-Eurasian Mediterranean Sea (North Polar Sea) which forms a supplementary body of water for the Atlantic Ocean. The Arctic Ocean is, however, so much a separate body of water with its own characteristic and independent climatic and hydrological conditions, that it can be considered as an independent ocean.

Nevertheless, this is not to deny that the Arctic Ocean and its fauna are at the present time exposed to the continuous and very powerful influence of the waters of the Atlantic Ocean, and to the comparatively insignificant influence of the waters of the Pacific Ocean.

The cross section of the Bering Strait is only 2·5 km^2 while that of all the straits between Greenland and the Scandinavian Peninsula is about 370 km^2. The maximum depth of the Bering Strait is 70 m but the minimum depth of the submarine ridge between Greenland and Scandinavia is about 440 m.

Approximately 8,000 km^3 of water (Kort, 1962) enter the Arctic Ocean annually through the Bering Strait, but no less than 400,000 km^3 of Atlantic waters enter the Arctic Ocean from the south. No less than 436,300 km^3 of water are carried out by the Arctic currents into the Atlantic Ocean including approximately 6,000 km^3 in the form of floating ice. Thus the Arctic Ocean exercises a great influence on the Atlantic Ocean and on the climate of North America. The amount of heat brought into the Arctic basin* with the warm Atlantic waters is enormous. The heat liberated by cooling these waters merely by 1° would be sufficient to raise the temperature of a 4 km layer of air over the whole of Europe by 10°.

The warm Atlantic waters, acting as a special kind of heating system, heat the Arctic and bring warm-water fauna far to the northward.

The surface layer of water with a lower salinity and the great extent of floating ice, which in winter is about 11×10^6 km^2, and in summer about 8×10^6 km^2 (60 to 80 per cent of the total surface), cover the warm Atlantic waters like an insulator, and the thermal action of these waters is felt at a depth of 300 to 900 m.

As will be shown below, the nature of the interaction of the faunas of the three oceans, the strong influence of the faunas of the Atlantic and Arctic Oceans upon each other, and the slight interaction between the faunas of the Arctic and Pacific Oceans, are completely in keeping with the systematic interchange of water between the Arctic and its two neighbouring oceans.

This, however, is only true, of course, for the position at the present time.

* The expression Arctic basin is commonly used, and we shall use it here in the same sense as the North Polar Ocean.

The relationships differed to a considerable degree in the Quaternary Period, and even more during the Tertiary Period, not to mention the Mesozoic era.

The seas lying within the Soviet sector of the Arctic basin

More than half of the coastline of the Arctic basin (North Polar Ocean) belongs to the Soviet Union. From the chart (Fig. 1A) it will be seen that a wide belt of shallow water, 500 to 1,000 km in width, adjoins the coast of the U.S.S.R., forming a system of separate, more or less open seas. Most of them could be

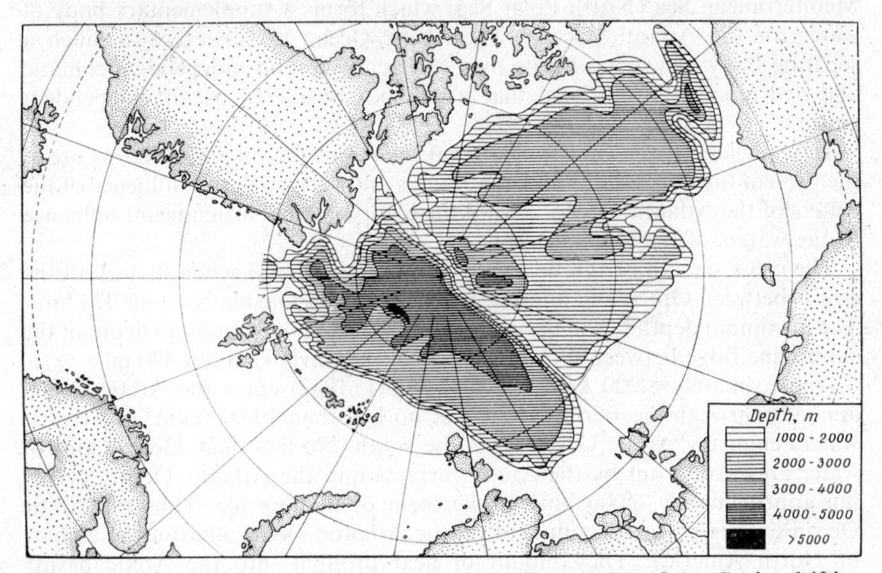

FIG. 1A. Arctic basin bottom topography according to data from Soviet drifting observation stations.

called inlets of the Arctic Ocean, rather than individual seas.* The most westerly of them, the Barents Sea, is limited to the north by Spitsbergen and Franz Joseph Land, and to the east by Novaya Zemlya. On the west the natural boundary of the Barents Sea is formed by the edge of the continental shelf at a depth of 500 m. To the south the White Sea adjoins the Barents Sea. The Kara Sea extends from Novaya Zemlya to the Severnaya Zemlya archipelago, and between the Severnaya Zemlya and the Novosibirsk Islands lies the Laptev Sea. Beyond as far as Wrangel Island there is the East Siberian Sea, and lastly the Chukotsk Sea lies between Wrangel Island and the Bering Strait. All these seas, except for the western half of the Barents Sea, and part of the Chukotsk Sea adjoining America, lie within the boundaries of the U.S.S.R. Whereas the eastern and western boundaries of these seas can be defined fairly accurately,

* The epicontinental bodies of water composing the Arctic Ocean form about 37 per cent of its whole area, whereas the continental self of the world-ocean forms only 8 per cent of its area.

to the north precise boundaries do not exist, and the edge of the continental shelf is taken to be the boundary.

Huge European and Siberian rivers—the Northern Dvina, Pechora, Ob, Yenisei, Khatanga, Lena, Yana, Indigirka, Kolyma—bring into the Arctic basin large masses of river water (up to 3,000 km³ a year) lowering the salinity of the adjoining areas of sea water, especially that of the White Sea and of the Laptev and East Siberian Seas, and likewise the surface waters of the whole Arctic Basin.

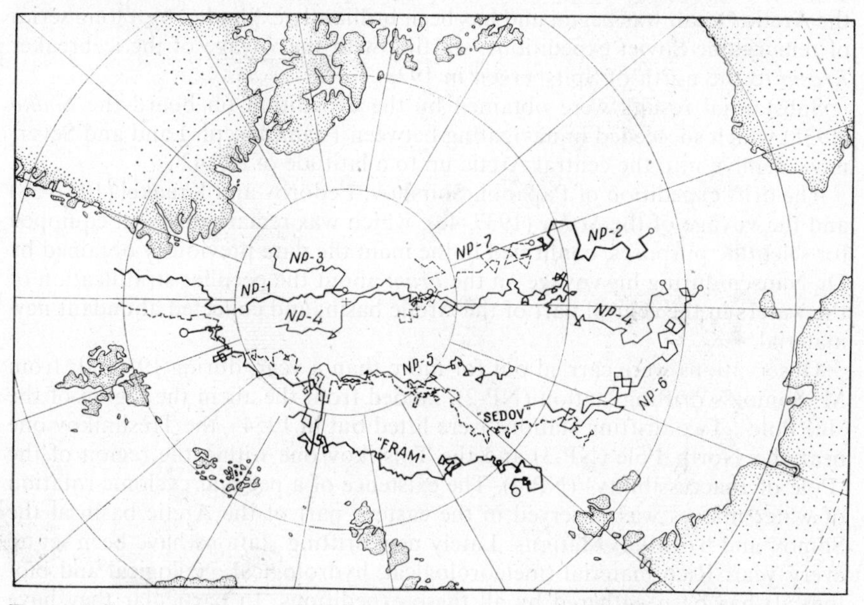

FIG. 1B. Course of *Fram* and *Sedov* and Soviet drifting observation stations NP-1 to NP-7.

Size

The total area of the Arctic Ocean is about 13×10^6 km², while its central part is $4{\cdot}891 \times 10^6$ km². This latter is in the main more than 2,000 m deep, i.e. it consists of an abyssal zone (70 per cent), while only a third of it (30 per cent) is composed by the continental shelf (200 to 2,000 m). The expedition on board the *Sedov* in 1939 established that the greatest depth of the Arctic Ocean—5,180 m—lies to the north of Franz Joseph Land.

Ice-floes

The climatic conditions of our northern seas, except for the southwestern half of the Barents Sea and the southern half of the Chukotsk Sea, are very severe. Even during the warmest season of the year—in August—a great part of the sea surface is usually covered with ice-floes (Fig. 1B). Polar ice can, perhaps, be considered the most characteristic feature of the Arctic basin, determining many aspects of its hydrological and biological conditions.

History of exploration

The remarkable voyage of Dr F. Nansen's *Fram* (1896) marked the beginning of the comprehensive exploration of the central part of the Arctic Ocean. The honour of the discovery of the great oceanic depths of the central depression belongs to Dr Nansen, and it was he who first put forward a theory about the stratification of, and the forces exerted by, the waters of the Arctic basin and the causes of these phenomena.

After an interval of 32 years the intensive exploration of the central areas of the Arctic Ocean was begun and has been brilliantly expanded by a long series of remarkable Soviet expeditions, starting with the voyage of the icebreaker *Krasin* to the north of Spitsbergen in 1928.

Substantial results were obtained by the expedition on board the *Sadko* (1935) which succeeded in navigating between Franz Joseph Land and Severnaya Zemlya into the central Arctic up to a latitude of 82° 42′.

The drift expedition of Papanin, Shirshov, Fedorov and Krenkel (1937–38) and the voyage of the *Sedov* (1937–40), which was remarkably well equipped for scientific purposes, confirmed in the main the data previously obtained by Dr Nansen during his voyage on the *Fram* about the peculiar stratification of the waters in the central part of the Arctic basin, and collected abundant new material.

Observations were carried out for more than a year, during 1950–51, from M. Somov's drifting station (NP-2), landed from the air in the region of the 'Ice Pole'. Two drifting stations were fitted out in 1954—the Treshnikov one near the North Pole (NP-3) and the Tolstikov one within the region of the 'Pole of Inaccessibility' (NP-4). The existence of a peculiar cyclonic rotation of water masses was observed in the eastern part of the Arctic basin at the Somov and Tolstikov stations. Lately new drifting stations have been set up every year. Rich material (meteorological, hydrological, geological and biological) has been gathered by all these expeditions. In particular they have shown that the central part of the polar basin is divided into two independent depressions by a huge submarine range, which has been named the Lomonosov range. It stretches from the Novosibirsk Islands to Ellesmere Island, rising from a depth of 4 km to within 1,000 m of the surface at its summit.

Stratification of waters

Throughout the central part of the Arctic basin (Fig. 2), underneath the shallow surface layer (100 to 150 m) of water with low salinity* (30 to 32‰) and of low temperature (from −1·5 to −1·7°) there is a second layer with normal salinity (34‰) but of low temperature (−1·0°) and beneath it lies a 600 m deep layer of warm (up to 2·0 to 2·5°) Atlantic water with high salinity (34·7 to 34·9‰). Deeper down and extending to the sea bottom the salinity remains the same as that of the layer immediately above it, but its temperature is low. In the higher levels of the eastern sector of the Arctic basin waters are observed which have penetrated from the Bering Sea.

* Salinity, symbol *S*, will be quoted in grammes per kilogramme (denoted ‰) throughout this text.

The surface layer results from the lowering of salinity by river waters. The saline, cold layer deeper down is produced by the mixing of the lower-lying Atlantic waters with the cold surface waters.

The deep-lying masses of fully saline, cold waters are the cooled Atlantic waters. Dr F. Nansen assumed that they were formed by the cooling and sinking of surface water in winter time in the northern part of the Greenland Sea. Most probably, however, they result from a local cooling and downward

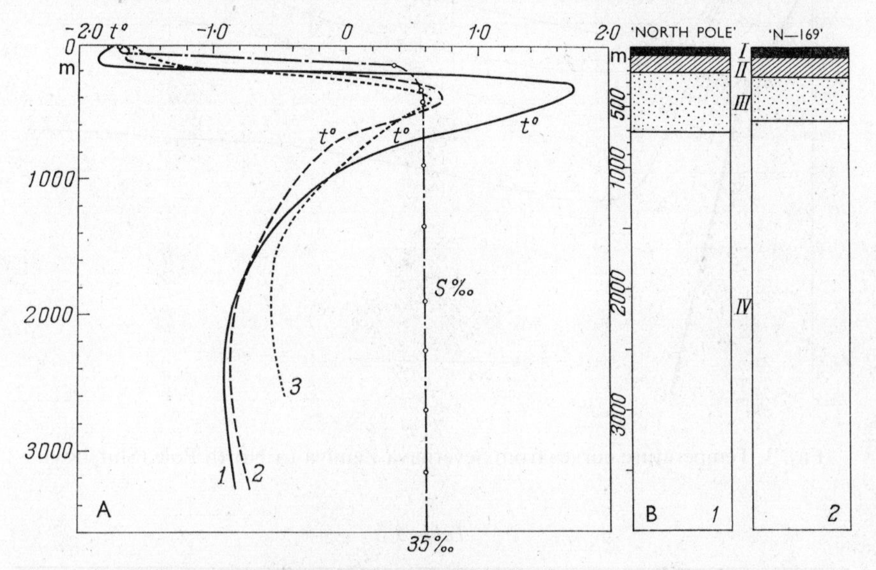

FIG. 2. A. Salinity and temperature curves (Shirshov).

1 Station 28 of 'North Pole' expedition;
2 near North Pole according to data of 'North Pole' expedition;
3 within region of 'Pole of Inaccessibility', according to data of Libin–Cherevichny expedition aircraft 'N-169'.

B. Diagram of distribution of four layers (Stockmann).

1 according to data of 'North Pole' expedition;
2 according to data of Libin–Cherevichny expedition.

movement along the declivities of part of the cold, saline water, formed on the surface in winter time as a result of freezing.

This singular stratification is best seen in the light of the comparison between the waters of the central part of the Arctic basin and those of the northern part of the Greenland Sea situated somewhat more to the south, where the warm Atlantic waters still remain on the surface (*Table 5*).

Warm Atlantic waters, passing over the Nansen ridge, enter the Arctic basin and spread northwards and eastwards and being heavier sink below the less saline surface layer (Figs. 3 and 4). The comparative thickness of the four layers changes gradually with their movement northward and eastward away from the regions adjacent to the outlets to the Atlantic; this can be seen in

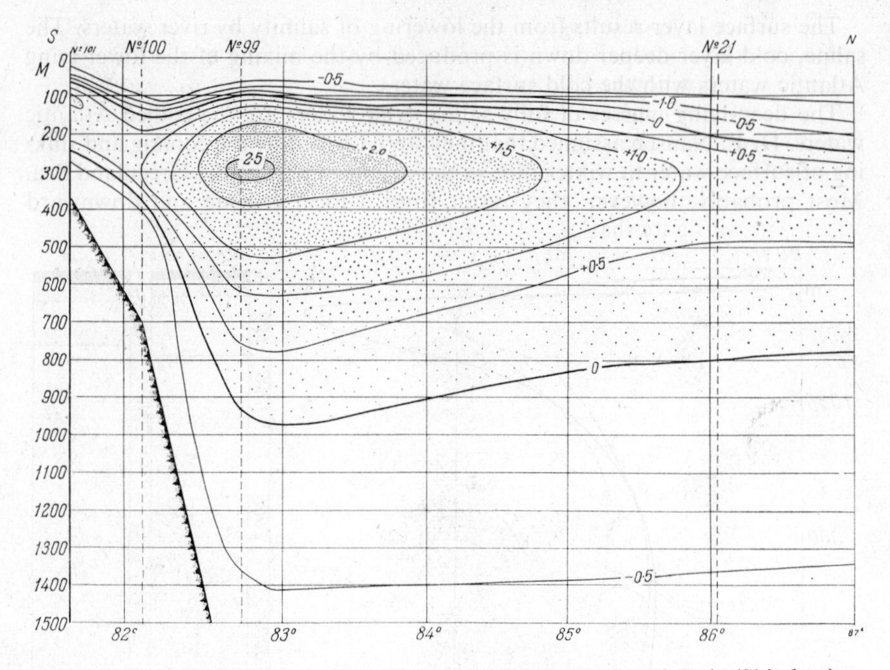

FIG. 3. Temperature curves from Severnaya Zemlya to North Pole (Shirshov).

Table 5

Depth m	Greenland Sea 76° 20′ N lat. 2° 17′ E long. *Sadko*, 1935		Arctic basin northeast of Franz Joseph Land 82° 41′ N lat. 87° 03′ E. long. *Sadko*, 1935		Arctic basin northeast from Severnaya Zemlya 78° 31′ N lat. 118° 18′ E long. *Sedov*, 1937	
	t°	*S*‰	*t*°	*S*‰	*t*°	*S*‰
0	3·90	34·97	−1·70	31·60	−1·46	30·32
25	3·93	35·03	−1·70	32·43	−1·70	31·58
50	1·62	35·03	1·74	33·98	1·77	33·68
75	1·40	35·03	−1·34	34·20	−1·74	33·95
100	1·30	35·03	−0·34	34·33	−1·65	34·51
150	0·70	34·96	1·91	34·74	—	—
200	—	—	—	—	1·09	34·65
250	−0·5	35·08	2·12	34·83	—	—
300	—	—	—	—	1·34	34·70
500	−0·44	34·92	1·58	34·90	0·80	34·70
800	—	—	—	—	0·01	34·72
1,000	−0·67	34·94	−0·16	34·85	−0·30	34·72
2,000	−0·99	34·94	−0·67	34·85		

Fig. 2. The two upper layers become thicker, while the warm Atlantic layer, on the contrary, gradually loses its heat, mixes with the water layers above and below, and becomes thinner.

A comparison of the changes of temperature with depth at three points in the central part of the Arctic basin—north of the Greenland Sea, near the North Pole and within the region of the 'Pole of Inaccessibility' (station No. 3 Libin–Cherevichny air expedition, 1941, 3)—is given in Fig. 2. It is perfectly clear from that figure that as one moves farther up the basin and towards the

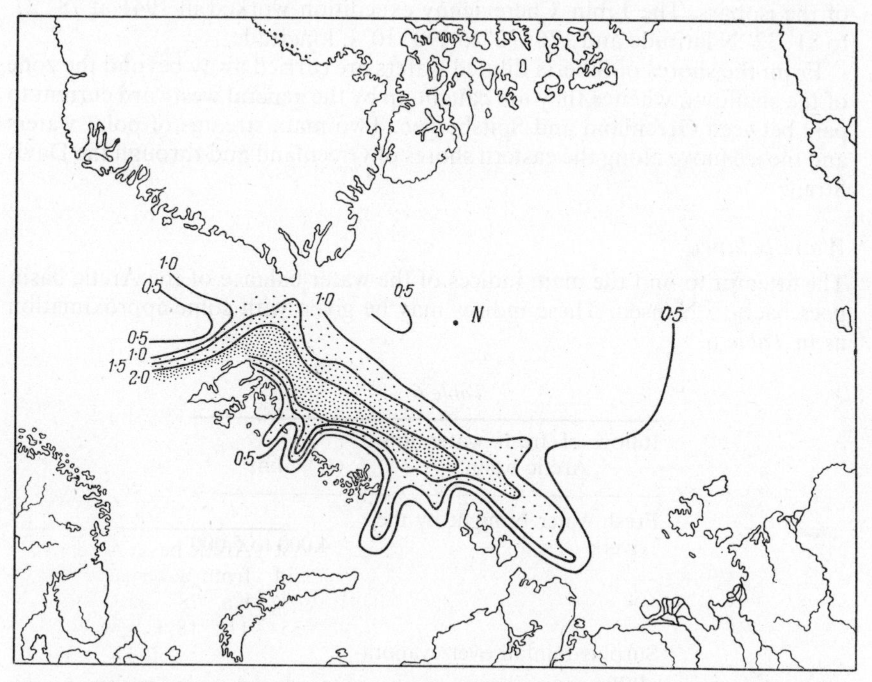

FIG. 4. Distribution of isotherms at depth of 300 m (isothermobaths). Penetration of deep Atlantic waters into northern parts of Barents, Kara and Laptev Seas is clearly shown (Dobrovolsky, after Shirshov).

Bering Strait the upper cold layer becomes somewhat warmer, the intermediate Atlantic one loses some of its heat and the cold abyssal one becomes somewhat warmer. This is the result of a gradual intermixing of the intermediate warm layer with the adjacent colder lower and upper layers. According to A. Dobrovolsky's computation the course of the Atlantic waters from Spitsbergen to Kara Sea takes two years; in one year more they reach the Laptev Sea and two years later they penetrate the Chukotsk Sea. It takes the Atlantic waters three years to cover the distance from Lofoten to Spitsbergen.

It is evident from *Table 5* that the deep waters of the Arctic basin are warmer than those of the Greenland Sea.

The drift of polar waters

The direction of the drift bringing masses of surface waters and ice-floes out of the eastern sector of the Arctic basin was charted by the voyage of the *Fram* and, with greater precision, by the later Soviet expeditions—that of Papanin on drifting ice and by the icebreaker *Sedov* (1937–39). As was shown by N. Zubov in 1937–39 (Nansen had noted it earlier) the movement of the Arctic basin surface water and of the ice-floes on it is occasioned by the prevailing winds; the direction the Arctic Ocean's currents corresponds to the direction of the isobars. The Libin–Cherevichny expedition worked in 1941 at 78° 27′ to 81° 32′ N latitude and 176° 32′ to 190° 10′ E longitude.

From the shores of Siberia diluted waters are carried away beyond the zone of the shallows, whence they are caught up by the general westward current to pass between Greenland and Spitsbergen. Two main streams of polar waters and the ice move along the eastern shores of Greenland and through the Davis Strait.

Water balance

The attempt to find the main indices of the water balance of the Arctic basin goes back to Nansen. These indices may be given with some approximation as in *Table 6*.

Table 6

Inflow of fresh water into Arctic basin	km^3
Fresh water brought by the rivers	4,000 to 5,000
Surplus rainfall over evaporation about	2,000
On account of exchange through the Bering Strait about	2,000
Total about	8,000 to 9,000

The present Arctic basin water balance is probably most unstable. During the Ice Age the Arctic basin waters became greatly diluted, and in the succeeding millennia the reverse process of increase of salinity must have gone on. It is clear that the salinity of the Arctic waters always largely depends on the inflow of river water, the amount of ice carried out (two factors greatly affected by seasonal changes) and the nature of the water exchange with the Atlantic Ocean (depending on the bottom topography of the passages connecting the Arctic basin with the Atlantic Ocean).

This undoubtedly points to the instability of the saline conditions of the surface waters of the whole of the Arctic basin and of the seas included in it.

In addition, the climate of the Arctic does not remain unchanged.

Increase in temperature of the Arctic

A considerable rise of temperature has been observed in the Arctic and the adjacent temperate latitudes during the last 40 years; it was first noted by N. Knipovitch for the Barents Sea in 1921. In Spitsbergen during the five months November to March of the period 1916–20 the mean temperature was −17·6°, whereas in 1931–34 it was −8·6°, i.e. 9° higher.

A graphic illustration of the increase in temperature of the Arctic is given by K. Badigin. It is evident from a comparison of the mean monthly temperature readings taken on the voyage of the *Fram* (1895) with those taken on the *Sedov* (1939–39) that during the coldest months the average temperature of the air is now almost 10° higher than it was 43 years ago (*Table 7*).

Table 7

Months	*Fram* 1895–96	*Sedov* 1938–39
September	−9·6	−4·1
October	−21·2	−12·8
November	−30·9	−21·7
December	−32·7	−22·5
January	−34·7	−31·1
February	−34·7	−30·2

The mean annual temperature at Archangel between 1891 and 1915 was 0·2° and between 1931 and 1934, 1·6°. In the Yugorsky Shar the mean annual air temperature was −8·4° between 1914 and 1919, whereas from 1920 to 1935 it was +2·2°. In Franz Joseph Land (Tikhaya inlet) between 1873 and 1914 the temperature was −13·9° and from 1929 to 1936, +3·4°. In Spitsbergen the annual mean temperature was 1·7 to 1·8° above normal during the period from 1923 to 1933. The mean winter temperature in Spitsbergen has gradually risen over the years, *Table 8*.

Table 8

Period	1916–20	1921–25	1926–30	1931–35
Mean winter temperature, °C	−17·6	−12·5	−13·9	−8·6

There are many other indications of a rise of temperature in the Arctic in the course of recent decades:* the retreat of glaciers which covered the Arctic

* Willet (1950) thinks that the increase in the temperature of the Arctic began in 1885.

islands, the warming up of the Polar waters, a decrease in icing and easier navigation for shipping in high latitudes.

As early as 1921–26 (taking average annual data) a rise of almost 1° degree, as compared with 1900–01, was observed in the temperature of the bottom layers of water along the meridian of Kola; the rise in the temperature of the upper 200 m layer was on the average almost 2°. During that time the ice in the Barents Sea decreased considerably (by 13 per cent).

The waters of the Kara Sea have been affected by a no less sharp rise in temperature. This made possible the voyage in 1939 of the *Sibiryakov*, when she rounded Severnaya Zemlya from the north, reaching a latitude of 80° N in one season. On her passage from Cape Zhelaniye to Wiese Island and on to the Pioner Island in 1933 the *Taimyr* never encountered a surface temperature below zero, while in some places the temperature of the water reached 4·5°.

The sea fauna, that extremely sensitive indicator of changes of temperature, reacts to climatic changes, by changes both qualitative and quantitative in its composition. Many warmth-loving sea dwellers new to the Arctic penetrate far into it, while, on the other hand, forms characteristic of cold waters move deeper into it from the more southerly parts of the Arctic regions. This concerns not only individual forms; whole communities change their composition both qualitatively and quantitatively. All aspects of the biology of Arctic flora and fauna are influenced by this general change towards a warmer climate; the Arctic's outposts—the Barents and Kara Seas—are particularly affected by it. Fisheries are also affected since the regions of the shoaling of commercial fish—cod, haddock, herring, bass, cambala—have moved east and north. The Danish scientist Ad. S. Jensen (1939) thinks that the great development of cod fishing off the southwestern shores of Greenland is due to the mass arrival of cod in this region as a result of the increase in temperature of the Arctic. The annual catch of this industry has increased since the 1920s from 400 to 8,000 tons.

Moreover Ad. S. Jensen notes that fish which were either absent or rare off the western shores of Greenland have now become common there. This includes haddock (*Gadus aeglefinus*), brismak (*Brosmius brosme*), sea pike (*Molva vulgaris*) and others. Cod, herring, coalfish, salmon and others have become common and are even fished there. Halibut and caplin are widely distributed and, finally, some fish, e.g. bass, have begun to spawn there. Hence according to Ad. S. Jensen's data, the fish of the Davis Strait have undergone a complete change owing to the warming up of its waters. Among others the common asterid (*Asterias rubens*) is widely propagated there. On the other hand many forms have moved from the south to the northern parts of the Davis Strait and Baffin Bay. The main shoaling of *Delphinapterus leucas* and such fish as the fjord cod (*Gadus ogac*) and Greenland flatfish (*Reinhardtius hippoglossoides*) have moved.

All these far-reaching changes in the composition and distribution of the fauna of Greenland's western shores are the result of the intensification of the stream of Atlantic water entering the Davis Strait from the south and of the general 1° to 2° rise in the temperature of the waters. A comparison of water temperatures at various depths in one of the fjords on the southern point of Greenland is given in *Table 9*.

Table 9

Depth m	Temperature of water in °C	
	22.8.'09	16.8.'34
0	3·85	5·20
10	1·45	3·65
50	0·62	1·36
100	0·07	1·09
200	0·61	1·50

Similar changes in the fauna and especially in the fish population have taken place in the waters of Iceland.

Many fish, such as caplin, herring and cod, the great bulk of which have hitherto inhabited the warmer southern and western shores of the island have migrated to the northern shores and begun to spawn there. Fish formerly rare in Icelandic waters have now become common. They include tuna, mackerel, *Selache maxima*, *Scombresox saurus*, *Orthogoriscus mola*, *Paralepis kroyeri* and many others. Such southern forms as, for instance, *Notidanus griseus*, *Xiphias gladius* and *Caranx trachurus*, which have never before been observed in Icelandic waters, have been found there in recent years.

The same can be said about the invertebrates. Formerly unknown off the shores of Iceland, there have now appeared there *Echinus esculentus*, *Aphrodite aculeata*, *Lithodes maja*, and the huge south boreal polychaetes (*Nereis virens*), which, by the way, was found in the White Sea in recent years (Annenkova and Palenichko, 1946) and was undoubtedly absent from those waters before.

Not only marine animals but birds are extending their habitats northwards because the climate is becoming milder. Some North-European gulls (*Larus ridibundus*, *L. fuscus* and *L. argentatus*), which used to be rare in these parts, have in recent years appeared in great numbers in Iceland.

Ice has disappeared from the northwestern, northern and eastern shores of Iceland in recent years, the winter has become very mild, the average air temperature in February and March has risen by 4° to 7° above the former average, while the temperature of the surface waters along the northern and western shores has risen by 0·5° to 4°. This rise in temperature is felt to depths of 200 to 400 m; hence the difference between the temperatures of the northern and southern shores of Iceland has practically disappeared. The same phenomena are observed at Jan Mayen I., Spitsbergen and in Arctic bodies of water situated to the east of them. In the 1870s and 1880s there was a fairly good catch of cod and haddock along the western shores of Spitsbergen. Later this fishing stopped completely to begin again in the third decade of the present century. About 200 small Norwegian trawlers fishing in these waters in 1935 obtained a total catch of 4,500 tons of fish. N. Tanassijcuk

(1929) notes that in recent years fish which had hitherto been very rare along the Murman coast have begun to appear there, such as *Lamna cornubica*, *Microstomus microcephalus*, as well as *Gadus merlangus*, *Trachypterus arcticus* and others; Yu. Boldovsky (1937) has noted the finding of *Gadus esmarki* and *G. poutassou* in Murman waters.

Some boreal forms which formerly were never or very rarely found in the plankton of the Barents Sea have become common there. Among them may be mentioned the cephalopod *Ommatostrephes todarus*, the siphonophore *Physophora hydrostatica*, the polychaete *Tomopteris helgolandica* and a series of others. Sometimes the warm-water pteropod mollusc *Limacina retroversa* drifts in great numbers into the southwestern part of the Barents Sea.

Meganyctiphanes norvegica (Euphausiacea), rare in the Barents Sea at the beginning of this century, has now become a common form there. Still more examples could be given as regards benthos. The boreal sea urchin *Schizaster fragilis*, which according to K. Derjugin (1915) was absent in the Kola Guba in 1908–09, has in recent years become a mass form there. The mollusc *Cardium echinatum* was also unknown there. Another boreal sea urchin *Echinus esculentus* has become common on the western Murman coast. A whole series of boreal molluscs has become common in the Kola Guba and the adjacent area of the Barents Sea; as for example *Cardium edule*, *C. fasciatum*, *C. elegantulum*, *Acera bullata*, *Doto coronata*, *Gibbula tumida*; of crustaceans *Eupagurus bernhardus*, *Munida rugosa* and others may be mentioned. At the same time Arctic forms are receding eastward. The cold-water mollusc *Serripes groenlandicus* which at the time of K. Derjugin's explorations (1910 to 1914) was a mass form in the Kola Guba has at present (V. Zatzepin, 1946) become a rarity there, and the cold-loving pteropod mollusc *Limacina helicina* has been driven out into the eastern part of the sea.

The appearance of a whole series of warm-water fish off the shores of Novaya Zemlya and in the Kara and White Seas has been observed (L. Berg, 1939). In 1883 the warm-water fish *Scombresox saurus* was very rarely caught off the North Cape, but in 1937 it was caught at Matochkin Shar. Moreover, herring, mackerel, haddock and coalfish were found off the shores of Novaya Zemlya. Cod and coalfish have apparently begun to multiply there.

Haddock, coalfish and bass have appeared in the White Sea; Atlantic herring and Barents Sea cod have penetrated into the Kara Sea.

The quantitative and qualitative composition of the population of the Arctic basin has substantially changed as a result of the warming up of the water by a few degrees. The changes are in three directions: first of all there is a change in the composition of the population, that is in the structure of the biocoenoses; then there is migration not only of separate forms, but of whole groups (biocoenoses) from south to north—the Arctic communities recede, the boreal advance; finally there is also a change in the quantitative indices of the density of the population. This colossal process of the general change of the Arctic basin fauna proceeding in a definite direction and taking whole decades to develop deserves most careful investigation.

II. GENERAL CHARACTERISTICS OF THE FAUNA OF THE EASTERN SECTOR OF THE ARCTIC BASIN

Impoverishment of the fauna towards the north and east

The farther one moves east from the southwestern parts of the Barents Sea, the greater is the distance from the sphere of influence of the warm, saline Atlantic waters and the poorer the quality of the flora and fauna. The flora and fauna of the littoral and of the highest level of the sublittoral are particularly affected by this process of impoverishment.

In the northern and eastern parts of the Barents Sea the littoral population has almost vanished already. Only three or four of its hardiest representatives (*Fucus vesiculosus*, *Littorina rudis* and *Balanus balanoides*) are found on the seashore at low tide, and some species (*Mytilus edulus*, *Fabricia sabella*, *Balanus balanoides* and others) have moved from the littoral into the sublittoral. These last remains of the littoral fauna are hardly ever found east of Novaya Zemlya. The extreme ice conditions during the eight to nine winter months are particularly destructive of the littoral fauna.

Although the study of the bottom fauna of the Siberian seas has so far been extremely inadequate, the quantitative and qualitative poverty of both flora and fauna are beyond doubt. The impoverishment of the fauna is particularly clearly marked as one travels eastward, comparing the Barents Sea with the Laptev Sea. A comparison of the number of species of some basic groups is given in *Table 10*.

Table 10

Group	Approximate number of known species of fauna groups in		
	Barents Sea	Kara Sea	Laptev Sea
Polychaeta	about 200	about 150	40
Echinodermata	62	47	33
Amphipoda	262	225	87
Decapoda	25	14	5
Lamellibranchiata	87	about 100 (Lamellibranchiata and Gastropoda)	23
Gastropoda	150		32
Tunicata	50	31	24
Pisces	144	54	37
Total bottom fauna	about 1,300	about 1,200	about 500

A. P. Andriashev (1954) has recorded 204 species and sub-species of fish in the northern seas of the U.S.S.R. from the Barents Sea to the Chukotsk Sea. As one moves eastwards, the number of species and their composition for the six families with the greatest number of species undergoes characteristic changes (*Table 11*).

Moreover, not only a qualitative impoverishment but also a considerable admixture of brackish relict and fresh-water families, Salmonidae, Gadidae and Cottidae, is characteristic of the Kara Sea and farther east.

Table 11

Family	Total No. of species	Barents Sea	White Sea	Kara Sea	Laptev Sea	East Siberian Sea	Chukotsk Sea
Gadidae	20	19	6	4	2	2	2
Ragidae	7	7	1	0	0	0	0
Salmonidae	17	7	5	7	7	8	7
Zoarcidae	23	14	4	11	7	2	5
Cottidae	15	12	6	9	9	6	9
Pleuronectidae	13	9	4	2	1	1	4
Total	95	68	26	33	26	19	27

Qualitatively rich fauna, in a series of groups almost as varied as Barents Sea fauna, is found only at the northern boundary of the Siberian seas at the edges of the continental shelf, washed at the depth of some hundreds of metres by the warm intermediate layer of Atlantic water, and in the deep trenches entering the Kara and Laptev Seas from the north.

The richest benthos as regards numbers is found in the southeastern, shallower part of the Barents Sea, in its central shallows and on the southern and eastern slopes of the Spitsbergen shallows. The southwestern half of the Barents Sea has quantitatively the richest plankton. A sharp decrease of the biomass and an impoverishment of the qualitative composition of benthos and plankton can be observed as one moves into the northern part of the Barents Sea and eastward beyond Novaya Zemlya.

The southeastern part of the Kara Sea, the Laptev and East Siberian Seas are probably the poorest in benthos and plankton, and the biomass of plankton and benthos increases again only in the eastern part of the Chukotsk Sea.

The high salinity and the strong vertical circulation of the Barents and Chukotsk Seas ensure richness of pelagic and bottom life. In the seas situated between Novaya Zemlya and Wrangel Island the aeration of the bottom layer and of the whole water column is, at any rate in certain seasons of the year, impeded by the considerable desalting of the surface layer; this has an adverse effect on the development of life. The latter perhaps suffers even more from the extremely severe climatic conditions of these seas, which are only free from their ice cover for a short period, from the almost complete suspension of the growth of phytoplankton for ten months of the year, and finally from the considerable lowering of salinity in the southern part of the whole chain of Siberian epicontinental water bodies. Their productivity must be many times lower than that of the Barents Sea. Since the biomass in these seas in summer, when it is flowering, is three to five times, or perhaps even eight to ten times smaller than that of the Barents Sea, its annual production must be much less.

The process of growth can serve as an indicator of the comparatively slow rate of the biological processes in the northern seas as compared to those taking place in the southern ones. Thus, for example, the fouling process in

Kola Guba, thermally one of the most favourable regions of the Barents Sea, attains appreciable intensity during two months—July and August—only at a temperature of 9° to 12° C. Even then growth hardly reaches 700 to 800 g/m², whereas in the Black Sea the fouling process is continuous almost throughout the whole year, and as a result of it during the same two months an animal fouling is obtained weighing 8 to 10 kg/m².

Phytoplankton

P. Usachev (1947) in his reference work on the phytoplankton of the seas of the U.S.S.R. notes, from data obtained for August and September, the impoverishment of the qualitative composition of the plankton seaweeds in all their component groups, as one moves from the Barents Sea east and northward into the central part of the Arctic Ocean (*Table 12*).

Table 12

Region	Total number of phytoplankton	Diatoms	Peridineans	Flagellates, silicoflagellates and green algae
Central part of Arctic basin	53	40 (76%)	10 (19%)	3 (5%)
Western part of Barents Sea	179	92 (51%)	69 (39%)	18 (10%)
Eastern part of Barents Sea	110	56 (51%)	47 (43%)	7 (6%)
White Sea	106	61 (58%)	29 (28%)	16 (14%)
Kara Sea (central part)	78	52 (67%)	20 (25·6%)	6 (7·7%)
Laptev Sea (central part)	95	61 (64%)	28 (30%)	6 (6%)

As shown in *Table 12* the relative variety of species of the diatomaceous algae increases from 51 to 76 per cent while that of peridineans decreases from 39 to 11 per cent. This shows the Arctic aspect of the diatoms and the boreal character of the peridineans.

The character of the two main groups of phytoplankton appears even more clearly in the biomass. The diatoms have a preponderant influence, while the peridineans play a very modest part (*Table 13*).

The considerable increase of the role of the flagellates in the plankton biomass of the Barents, and partly of the Kara, Sea is caused by a mass development of Phaeocystis and Dinobryon, which is sometimes observed even in the form of 'bloom' in the Barents Sea and to a lesser degree in the northern part of the Kara Sea.

The development of the phytoplankton of the Arctic basin is closely bound up with ice conditions. The mass development of the spring plankton (mainly diatoms) coincides with melting of the ice and the penetration of light into the

Table 13

Region	Percentage of total phytoplankton biomass			
	Diatoms	Peridineans	Flagellates	Green algae
Eastern half of Barents Sea	79	8	10	3
Kara Sea (central part)	87	6	5	2
Laptev Sea (central part)	94	4	1	1
North Pole	98	2	—	—

water column. The nearer the Pole, the weaker is the vernal outburst and the sooner it passes. In the seas adjacent to the Pole this lasts no more than a month (August), but farther south the vegetation period is longer: in the central part of the Kara Sea it lasts nearly three months, while in the south-west of the Barents Sea it continues for about eight months (Fig. 5).

Although in the circumpolar part of the Arctic basin there is only a 'spring' in the development of phytoplankton, in the Kara and Laptev Seas there is also a 'summer', while in the Barents Sea there is an 'autumn', and the vegetation period lasts from April till November.

However luxuriant the development of phytoplankton, if its vegetation period is of short duration, its production will be small. The maximum phytoplankton biomass at any single time in our Arctic seas may sometimes be expressed by very high rates—from 6 to 14 g/m^3 even in the East Siberian and Laptev Seas. Nevertheless this cannot in any way be considered as a measure of the high productive capabilities of these bodies of water. The average values for a layer thirty metres thick are more truly indicative. The true value of annual production is well demonstrated by a conventional index (the product of the average biomass during observations times the length of the vegetation period in months, divided into 12 months—*Table 14*) introduced by P. Usachev, especially in comparison with similar indices for the southern seas.

Table 14

Region	Length of vegetation period, months (*A*)	Phytoplankton biomass during vegetation period: average values for 0–30 m layer, g/m^3 (*B*)	Conventional index $(A \times B)/12$
Central part of Arctic basin	1	0·12	0·01
Laptev Sea	4·5	0·6	0·20
Kara Sea	4	0·6	0·20
East Siberian Sea	4–5	0·6	0·20
Northeastern part of Barents Sea	5	0·5	0·20
Sea of Azov	9·5	4·0	3·20

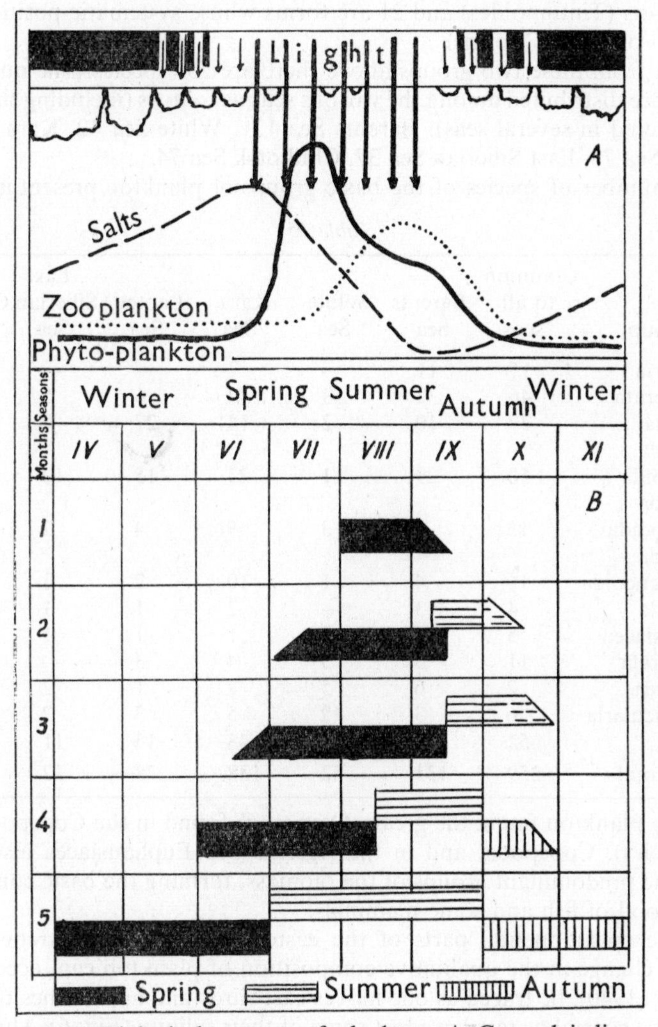

FIG. 5. Biological seasons of plankton. A General indices (Bogorov). B Phyto-plankton development (Usachev). *1* Circumpolar part of Arctic Ocean, *2* Central region of Kara Sea, *3* Laptev Sea, *4* Northern part of Barents Sea, *5* Southwestern part of Barents Sea.

Zooplankton

According to V. Bogorov's estimate, the zooplankton of our northern seas on the basis of existing data includes 321 species* of which 41 species are

* It must be borne in mind that the populations of separate seas and parts of them have not been studied equally well, as regards the qualitative variety of the fauna and flora. The Kara Sea plankton is probably as varied as that of the Barents Sea, but the former has been the subject of a more comprehensive survey.

infusorians (Tintinnoides) and 21 are forms whose systematic position is not clear ('problematic' forms).

Apart from these two groups above there are 259 species. The numbers of species are distributed among the various seas as follows (including the species encountered in several seas): Barents Sea 131, White Sea 62, Kara Sea 138, Laptev Sea 78, East Siberian Sea 37, Chukotsk Sea 74.

The number of species of the basic groups of plankton present in various seas is:

Table 15

Group	Common to all seas	Barents Sea	White Sea	Kara Sea	Laptev Sea	East Siberian Sea	Chukotsk Sea
Radiolaria	15	11	—	7	—	—	—
Coelenterata	46	32	18	19	6	5	15
Rotatoria	37	10	2	14	27	—	5
Copepoda calanoida	50	29	11	27	15	10	22
Copepoda hyclopoida	15	5	3	9	4	2	5
Copepoda karpacticoida	16	4	1	10	2	3	6
Ostracoda	4	3	—	2	1	1	—
Euphausiacea	5	5	2	1	1	1	2
Amphipoda	11	5	5	4	3	—	2
Mysidacea	2	6	5	7	1	2	1
Appendicularia	6	3	2	5	3	2	1
Other	52	18	13	43	15	11	11
Total	259	131	52	138	78	37	74

In the plankton fauna the greatest variety is found in the Copepoda group (81 species). Copepoda, and in the Barents Sea Euphausiacea also, are as usual the predominant groups of the biomass, forming the basic components of the food of fish and some mammals.

In the epicontinental parts of the eastern sector of the Arctic basin a definite change in the qualitative composition of plankton can, according to Jashnov (1940), be traced as one moves eastwards and approaches the shores where the coastal waters have lost some of their salinity (Fig. 6). Throughout the southern part of the Barents Sea, to the west and north of Spitsbergen, i.e. in the regions most subject to the influence of the Atlantic waters, nine-tenths of the plankton consists of *Calanus finmarchicus* (I)* and contains many boreal forms of Copepoda: *Metridia lucens*, Euphausiacea: *Limacina retroversa* and others. The average plankton biomass of these regions is equal to 230 mg/m³. In the northern part of the Barents Sea besides *Calanus finmarchi-*

* V. A. Jaschnov (1957, 1958) distinguished and singled out *Calanus finmarchicus* s.l. species *C. glacialis*. The area of the latter's dwelling covers the entire Arctic Basin, the waters adjoining from the east and west and extending towards North America up to Newfoundland in the southern direction. This area included also the Bering and the Okhotsk Seas. From the south its area links up with the areas in the Pacific Ocean *C. pacificus* and in the Atlantic Ocean *C. finmarchicus* s.str.

cus there are large amounts of *Metridia longa* (II). These two species together form 90 per cent of the total plankton biomass. The total biomass is about 90 mg/m^3.

In the upper layers of the northern part of the Kara and Laptev Seas *Calanus finmarchicus* (not exceeding 60 per cent of the total biomass) is still the main constituent of the plankton, but *C. hyperboreus* (III) is mixed with it to a considerable extent and, what is of special interest, in the deeper layers there is a considerable admixture of forms penetrating from the north along the troughs from the warm intermediate layer of the Arctic basin, such as

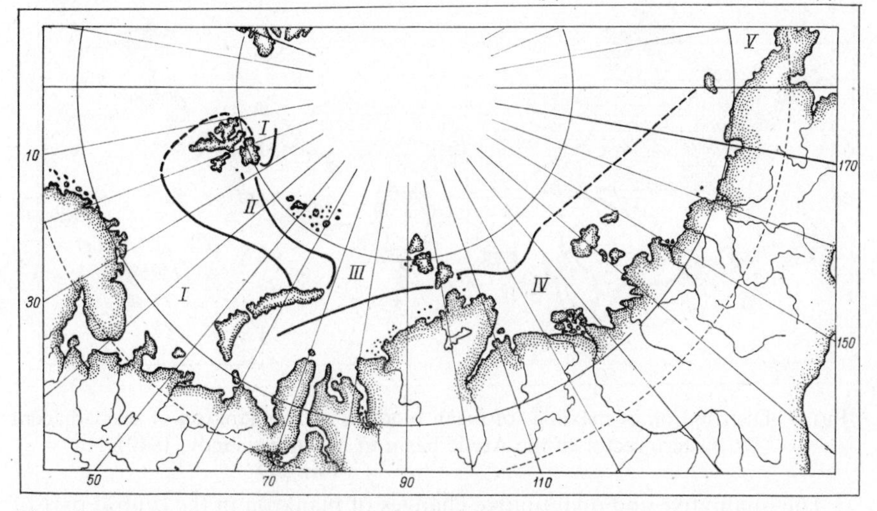

FIG. 6. Distribution of main types of zooplankton in northern seas (Jashnov, with certain alterations).

I, II Pronounced predominance of *Calanus finmarchicus* (90 per cent of biomass; many boreal forms present); *III* Predominance of *Calanus finmarchicus* (not more than 60 per cent of total biomass) and *C. hyperboreus*; a considerable admixture of Atlantic forms from intermediate layer; *IV* Predominance of *Pseudocalanus elongatus* and a selection of brackish-water forms; *V* Same as *IV* but with an admixture of Pacific Ocean forms.

Pareuchaeta norvegica and *P. glacialis, Conchoecia elegans, Themisto abyssorum, Eukrohnia hamata, Diphyes arctica* and others. The plankton of the less saline littoral waters of the bordering seas is characterized by the great predominance of brackish forms. The sea form of Pseudocalanus and brackish-water *Limnocalanus grimaldi, Drepanopus bungei* and *Derjuginia tolli* (IV) are predominant here. All these copepoda crustaceans comprise 60 per cent of the plankton biomass. About 20 per cent of the plankton consists of *Sagitta elegans*, mixed with a considerable quantity of fresh-water forms.

Finally in the southern part of the Chukotsk Sea, as a result of an increase of salinity, the brackish-water forms are becoming rare. Pacific Ocean forms are found here but, as has been noted by V. Jashnov (1940), they do not play any substantial role in the biomass (V).

The general picture of the quantitative distribution of zooplankton in the Arctic basin is similar to that of benthos. According to V. Jashnov's work (1940) high indices of plankton biomass are obtained only within the boundaries of the Barents Sea, while for the other Seas of the northern coasts of Siberia the indices are much lower (Fig. 7).

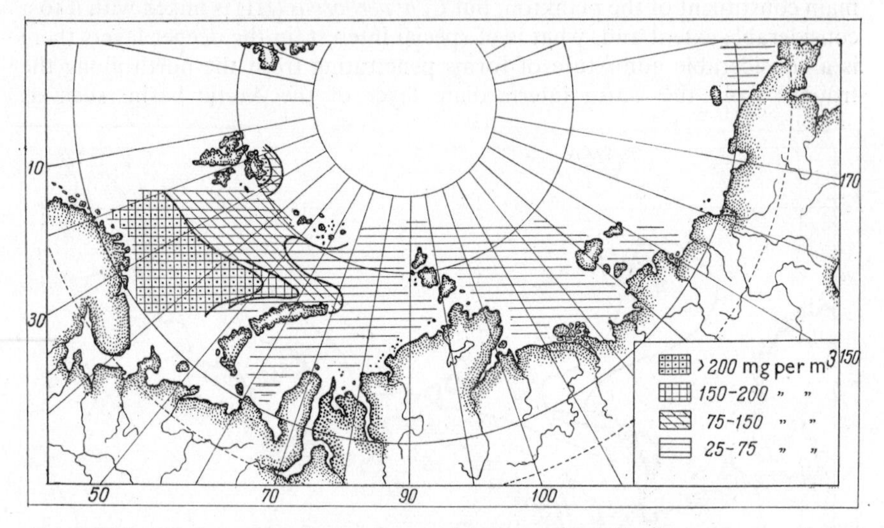

FIG. 7. Distribution of maxima of mean biomass of zooplankton of seas adjacent to eastern sector of the Arctic basin in mg/m³ (Jashnov, 1940).

The qualitative and quantitative changes of plankton in the central part of the Arctic basin are given in *Tables 16* to *20*.

Table 16. Maximum values of mean plankton biomass for various areas of the Arctic basin (V. Jashnov), mg/m³

Area	Depth of layer, m				
	0–25	25–50	50–100	100–300	500–2,500
Southwestern part of Barents Sea	1,000	400	170	110	—
Northern half of Barents Sea	140	110	100	60	—
Area southeast of Franz Joseph Land	30	70	90	50	—
Central part of Arctic basin in Spitsbergen area	200	160	160	50	—
Same basin, area of Severnaya Zemlya	100	120	90	70	—
White Sea	200	100	70	50	—
Kara Sea	50	40	50	60	—
Laptev and East Siberian Seas	70	—	—	—	—
Chukotsk Sea	60	—	—	—	—
Arctic basin, area of abyssal depths	—	10	—	10–30	4–7

Table 17. Percentage content of zooplankton biomass in the Greenland Sea, July 1935 (Jashnov)

Plankton content composition	Depth of layer, m					
	0–200		200–500		500–745	
Calanus finmarchicus	67·1	} 78	67·2	} 79·2	17·4	} 30·4
Metridia longa / *Calanus hyperboreus* / *Pareuchaeta norvegica* / Other Copepoda	10·9		12·0		13·0	
Amphipoda	9·4		9·9		—	
Chaetognatha	11·0		7·6		21·8	
Coelenterata	—		2·2		34·8	
Mollusca	—		—		4·3	
Others	1·6		1·1		8·7	

Table 18. Percentage content of zooplankton biomass within the area north of Spitsbergen, August 1935 (Jashnov)

Plankton content composition	Depth of layer, m		
	0–100	100–200	200–600
Calanus finmarchicus	63·0	58·0	20·8
Other Copepoda	28·0	13·7	18·9
Amphipoda	0·3	4·6	10·2
Chaetognatha	3·0	18·3	29·7
Coelenterata	2·4	—	13·0
Others	3·3	3·4	7·4

Table 19. Percentage content of zooplankton biomass between Franz Joseph Land and Severnaya Zemlya (Jashnov)

Plankton content composition	Depth of layer, m					
	0–100		100–200		200–500	
Calanus finmarchicus	57·3		35·0		30·8	
Metridia longa	8·2	} 17·7	27·3	} 34·5	22·8	} 33·1
Other Copepoda	9·5		7·2		10·3	
Amphipoda	0·9		4·4		12·5	
Chaetognatha	15·7		7·8		11·8	
Coelenterata	2·9		16·6		8·1	
Others	5·5		1·7		3·7	

Table 20. Percentage content of zooplankton biomass in northwestern part of Laptev Sea (Jashnov)

Plankton content composition	Depth of layer, m				
	0–50	50–150	150–250	250–300	300–800
Calanus finmarchicus	70	50	*Calanus finmarchicus* disappears. The Atlantic forms of Copepoda: *Scaphocalanus magnus, Gaigius tenuispinus, Heterorhabdus norvegicus, Montonilla minor* and others and the Polychaeta: *Thyphloscolex mullerri, Pelagobia longicirrata* become sharply preponderant		
Metridia longa *Pareuchaeta glacialis* *Calanus hyperboreus*		30			

From the above tables it can be seen that *Calanus finmarchicus* preponderates in the 200 m surface layer (colder and less saline), whereas Chaetognatha and Coelenterata are more abundant in deeper layers. Sometimes various Atlantic forms of crustaceans greatly preponderate in this deep layer (200 to 800 m) which is warmer and more saline than the surface layer.

All the data given refer, however, to sections of the Arctic basin exposed to the influence of coastal waters. It may be supposed that as one penetrates farther into the depths of the central part of the basin there is a significant decrease of zooplankton biomass, and in this connection the collections made aboard the *Sadko* in September 1935, northeast of Franz Joseph Land at depths up to 2 km, are of great interest. Only 12 mg/m^3 of plankton biomass was obtained by the first catch at a depth of up to 100 m (50 per cent of it consisted of *Calanus finmarchicus*). In a lower layer (100 to 500 m) the biomass content was found to be higher—29mg/m^3, but the amount of *Calanus finmarchicus* was limited to 20 per cent. Other Copepoda, namely *Metridia longa, Pareuchaeta norvegica, P. glacialis* (approximately 3 per cent), preponderate here. Of the other forms Coelenterata (*Aglantha digitale*), Ostracoda, Amphipoda and Polychaeta are the most important. At the lowest level (500 to 2,350 m) most of which lies in the abyssal cold layer (below 800 m) the biomass was 7 mg/m^3.

The *Sadko* data on the plankton in the central regions of the Arctic were supplemented in 1937–40 during the famous drift of the *G. Sedov* (B. Bogorov, 1946) and by the researches of the drifting polar stations North Pole 2, 3 and 4 (K. Brodsky, 1956). In all, 73 species of zooplankton were found in this plankton; this includes 40 Calanoida species, 5 Amphipoda and 3 Appendicularia. In direct contrast with the benthos, the majority of zooplankton species are common in the Greenland Sea and northern Atlantic. The comparison between the number of species and the number of plankton specimens for different regions of the Pacific Ocean and Arctic Seas, drawn by K. Brodsky (1956), is of great interest (Fig. 8). The diversity of forms continuously diminishes as one moves from the Pacific Ocean to the Chukotsk Sea and only rises

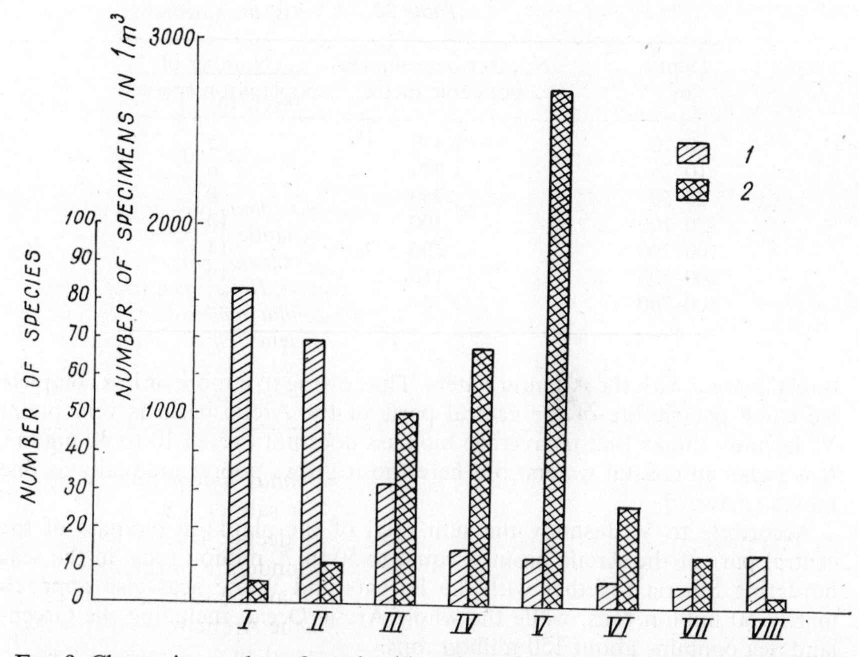

FIG. 8. Change in number of species (*1*) and number of specimens (*2*) per m³ from tropical part of Pacific Ocean (*I*) through northern part of the Pacific (*II*, *III*), Bering Sea (*IV*, *V*), Chukotsk Sea (*VI*, *VII*) and Arctic basin (*VIII*) (K. Brodsky, 1956).

again, on account of the Atlantic forms of the intermediate warm layer, in the western sector of the polar basin. On the other hand the biomass increases up to the Bering Sea, decreasing sharply in the polar basin. However, the zooplankton of the polar basin contains some endemic forms and very few Pacific ones (*Table 21*).

Table 21. Number of Atlantic, Pacific and endemic forms of Calanoida in the Arctic basin (percentage)

Area	Atlantic species	Pacific species	Endemic species
Nansen Ridge	60	0	0
Arctic basin	48–50	1	13

Most typical of the endemic forms are the deep-water ones described by K. Brodsky (1956): *Pseudagaptilus polaris*, *Pareuchaeta polaris*, *Lucicutia anomala*, *L. polaris* and others. The quantitative and qualitative vertical sequence of plankton in the central parts of the Arctic basin, illustrated in the following manner by V. Jashnov (1940) (*Table 22*), is most significant.

The greatest density of plankton is related to the less saline surface layer of water, while the greatest quantitative variety is found in the deep layers in

Table 22

Depth m	Number of specimens per cubic metre	Number of zooplankton species
0–10	2,430	5
10–25	1,870	6
25–50	750	8
50–100	300	10
100–200	200	14
200–500	110	19
500–700	4	22

direct contact with the Atlantic waters. Thus owing to a more or less complete ice cover pelagic life of the central parts of the Arctic basin is very poor; V. Jashnov thinks that its average biomass does not exceed 10 to 30 mg/m³. It is richer in coastal waters, but here too it grows poorer gradually as one moves eastward.

According to V. Jashnov the sum total of the plankton biomass of the central part of the Arctic basin is equal to 50 to 70 million tons, in the seas bordering Siberia together with the Barents and White Seas also approximately 50 million tons, while the whole Arctic Ocean including the Greenland Sea contains about 150 million tons.

Exceedingly interesting observations on the seasonal changes in the composition of biomass and of the plankton of our Polar seas were carried out by V. Bogorov during the remarkable cruise of the icebreaker *Litke* in 1934, when all the Siberian seas beginning with the Chukotsk Sea and ending with the Barents Sea were traversed in a single voyage (3 July to 18 September).

Biological seasons of plankton

As V. Bogorov has shown (1938, 1939) it is difficult to establish a direct connection between the distribution of the plankton biomass in the seas on the edge of the Arctic basin and the variations of temperature and salinity observed in them. On the other hand at the ice fringe there can be observed everywhere a very rich development of plankton and a huge preponderance of phytoplankton (bloom) over zooplankton (Fig. 5). But in the region of solid ice zooplankton always preponderates over phytoplankton. In open water, sufficiently far from the ice fringe and from the mouths of rivers, the animal and vegetable parts of the plankton biomasses are almost equal. At the mouths of rivers where fresh and saline waters meet, a huge development of plankton, with a preponderance of its vegetable part, is observed.

Leaving aside this last increase of plankton at the mouths of rivers, caused by the outflow of a mass of plant food and detritus in the river waters, the regularity of the quantitative development of plankton and its two main parts in the Arctic seas is determined, according to V. Bogorov, by the change of the three main seasonal phases in the annual cycle of plankton. During the period of 'biological winter' plankton is poor (less than 200 mg/m³) and the animal part preponderates over the vegetable one. With the advent of 'biological spring' phytoplankton begins rapidly to predominate over the zooplankton, and the total amount of plankton rises to 2,000 mg/m^3. 'Biological summer' is characterized by a decrease of the plankton biomass (about 1,000 mg/m^3) with an increase of zooplankton; moreover the phyto- and zooplankton components become almost equal. This change is illustrated by the data given in *Table 23.*

Table 23. Plankton biomass, mg/m^3

Biological season	Zooplankton	Phytoplankton	Total biomass	Ratio of vegetable to animal mass
Winter	52	41	93	0·8
Spring	122	2,470	2,592	20·0
Summer	230	560	790	2·5

Thus the zooplankton biomass is doubled between 'winter' and 'spring', and is increased almost five times by the 'summer', while phytoplankton increases 60 times between 'winter' and 'spring', and decreases five times by 'summer'. The composition of plankton also changes. In 'winter' zooplankton consists mainly of adult wintering stages, in the spring the plankton teems with eggs and larvae of the pelagic forms, infusoria, rotifers and fritillaries. More adult stages of Copepoda and the larvae of bottom forms are predominant in the 'summer'. Under Arctic conditions, 'biological spring' arrives at the time of melting of the ice and the appearance of open water; it develops at the edge of floating ice where the abundant bloom of phytoplankton is always encountered. 'Biological summer' is observed in plankton in places which have been free of ice for some time.

Thus different phases of plankton development may be observed at the same time in different regions of the sea or, on the other hand, the very same phases of its development at different times. The microclimate causing the transition from one phase of plankton development to another is determined by the ice conditions. It is possible that, depending upon the ice, an approaching phase may be broken off and started again with the recurrence of better conditions.

V. Wiese (1943) notes that as it were the 'continuous' temperature and saline front of the Arctic waters gets broken near the fringe of polar ice and certain special conditions set in there, determined in winter by the formation of a mass of floating ice and in summer by its melting.

These special conditions created near the ice fringe are reflected in hydrological, hydrochemical and biological phenomena. In summer a reduction of salinity, an increase of specific alkalinity, a fall in carbon dioxide pressure and a rise in the hydrogen ion concentration and in oxygen content are observed at the ice fringe. The phosphate and nitrate contents of the surface layer decrease. Almost all these characteristics are connected with a vigorous development of phytoplankton.

The existence of a single phytoplankton maximum, as Bogorov noted, is characteristic of the normal cycle of plankton development in the seas of the high Arctic sub-region. There is no autumn maximum there, as there is in the seas of the lower Arctic region and in more southerly seas.

This led Bogorov (1938, 1939) to the idea of using the seasonal state of plankton as an indicator of ice conditions and, in particular, for ice forecasts for Arctic passages; he has repeatedly done this with great success.

A number of investigators both at home and abroad have taken a keen interest in luxuriant plankton development near the fringe of polar ice. The names of Gran, V. Bogorov, P. Usachev, P. Shirshov and others may be mentioned.

Usachev (1935) saw that the mass development of phytoplankton at the fringe of melting ice was caused by the special concentrations of carbonates formed as a result of melting. N. Zubov (1938) points out the possibility of the influence on seaweed development of 'trihydric' molecules abundant in melt water. Shirshov (1936, 1937) and Bogorov consider the mass development of phytoplankton as a temporary, seasonal condition in the regions of melting winter ice.

In the course of a year plankton passes through distinct successive stages. 'When light penetrates into water a rapid growth of algae begins. In polar seas this occurs during the light period of the year, when the surface of the sea is free of solid ice. This phase of biological spring is followed by the summer phase, which in its turn passes first into the autumn and then the winter phases. The succession of the biological seasons is a definite phenomenon' (V. Bogorov, 1939). 'The phytoplankton bloom among the ice is not at all a direct function of its melting; it is the usual spring maximum' (P. Shirshov, 1937).

Phytobenthos

Among the bottom macrophytes of the Arctic Ocean there is a certain predominance of the orders Laminariales (Laminaria and Alaria) and Fucales (Fucus, Ascophyllum) among the brown algae and Ulvacea (Enteromorpha and Monostroma) among the green ones. These algae attain their highest growth in the warmest parts of the Arctic basin—the southern part of the Barents Sea and the southeastern part of the Chukotsk Sea. In other parts of the Arctic the bottom macrophytes are only slightly developed largely owing to the weak development or even absence of the littoral population and of the population of the upper level of the sublittoral.

Qualitatively the Arctic basin macrophytes lack individuality. They all belong to the typical Atlantic flora which has penetrated into the cold regions of the north. The same may be said about the fauna of the littoral and the upper level of the sublittoral. The peculiar characteristics of the fauna increase with the depth of its habitat.

This phenomenon can be explained by the fact that the deterioration of climatic conditions in the Ice Age naturally had more effect on the population of the shallows, all of which inevitably perished; in deeper layers the fauna could more easily endure harsh conditions and survive.

Zoobenthos and the history of its formation

The fauna of the Arctic basin, including the Greenland and Norwegian Seas, can be divided into the following main groups (according to E. F. Gurjanova, 1939, with some alterations):

I. The Arctic autochthonous forms
   1. Species endemic in the Arctic region
      (a) Eurybiotic circumpolar species
      (b) High Arctic epicontinental species
      (c) Forms of the depths of the Arctic basin
   2. Brackish-water relicts
   3. Arctic boreal species (partly)

II. Immigrants from the North Atlantic
   1. Post-glacial and contemporary immigrants (part of the Arctic boreal species)
      (a) Littoral boreal species
      (b) North Atlantic forms of the continental shelf
   2. Relicts of the Littorina period

III. Immigrants from the Northern Pacific
   1. Post-glacial and modern immigrants
   2. Pliocene relicts

L. Berg (1934), as has been mentioned before, thinks that in the Pliocene Period the Arctic basin was widely connected with the Atlantic and Pacific Oceans, and that its climate was considerably warmer. At that time a large exchange of fauna between the two oceans must have taken place via the Arctic basin, and the fauna of these three water bodies was very similar. As early as the Pliocene Period, before the closing up of the Bering Strait, the fauna inhabiting the Arctic basin began to be pushed southwards into the Atlantic and Pacific Oceans under the influence of the continuous cooling of this basin. In the opinion of L. Berg the main stock of amphyboreal forms were evolved at that time.

E. Gurjanova (1938, 1939) gives a somewhat different explanation for this phase of the history of the Arctic fauna. In her opinion the endemic character of the Arctic fauna is so clearly reflected not only in its species but also in its genera (Acanthostepheia, Onisimus, Pseudalibrotus, Mesidothea) that the formation of the main autochthonous stock of the Arctic basin should be ascribed to a period earlier than the Pliocene. The warming up during the Pliocene Period gave the Pacific fauna as a whole the opportunity to penetrate into the Arctic, but its autochthonous stock had already been formed. Later during the Ice Age the Pacific fauna, which had penetrated into the Arctic basin, 'was almost completely destroyed and replaced by a new high Arctic fauna, which had developed mostly from the ancient autochthonous fauna of the Arctic'.

A. M. Djakonov (1945) also thinks that the Pliocene fauna of the Arctic basin perished in the Ice Age, except for the species which moved into the depths and there survived the period of unfavourable climate. The repopulation of the Arctic by Pacific forms took place as early as the post-glacial period.

The genesis of the Arctic basin fauna is closely connected with its geological past, which so far is insufficiently known.

Some geologists (Du Toit, 1939) assume the formation of the central part of the Arctic basin in the Mesozoic and Tertiary periods.

Others (D. Panov, 1945) think that a depression (900 to 1,000 m deep) was formed in the Tertiary Era and that this only became deeper in the Ice Age.

Finally, according to Wegener's theory (1922) the depression of the polar basin as it exists now was formed in the Quaternary Era.

In spite of the obscurity surrounding the geological past of the Arctic basin it can be assumed that some components of the modern Arctic fauna were evolved in preglacial times. Considering the orographic, climatic and hydrological changes of the Quaternary Era with its most unfavourable conditions for the life of sea fauna, we can only accept the genetic descent of the modern fauna from the Tertiary one on the assumption that the latter survived the Ice Age only in certain parts of the North Atlantic. The formation of the main autochthonous fauna community of the Arctic basin should probably be connected with the fall in temperature characteristic of the Ice Age.

The high Arctic aspect of the present fauna is a result of it. So far it is not known whether it was formed inside the polar basin or at the 'approaches' to the ice barriers of the Quaternary Arctic, but considerable geographical movement of this fauna during the Ice Age must be accepted.

Among the most typical and ancient endemic genera of crustaceans of the Arctic region it is possible to establish a most curious division into species, adapted to specific conditions of life. First of all we could single out groups of species adapted to various degrees of salinity. Changes in the salinity of the Arctic basin during the glacial and post-glacial periods played the main part in the formation of these groups. If at the end of the Tertiary and especially during the Quaternary Era there were long intervals when the Arctic basin was completely or partially enclosed, then under the conditions of a temperate or cold climate its waters must have lost much of their salinity. If this was accompanied by the formation of brackish or fresh-water seas, they may have acquired the character of whole interconnected systems. In the complex system of transgressions and regressions these systems of semi-closed bodies of water may have been connected at some time with the Atlantic, at other times with the Pacific, becoming more saline once more and receiving some sea fauna communities and later again losing some of their salinity. The bottom topography of the epicontinental water bodies of the Arctic basin is such that even a slight rise of the floor would have led to the formation of closed or semi-closed bodies of water (Figs. 9 and 10). What effect would these changes of salinity have had on the marine fauna? The original fauna had either to die during the decrease of salinity or to adapt itself to the new environment. Nearly all the original fauna died out, but a definite number of species, mostly crustaceans and fish, two groups most resistant to a decrease in salinity, adapted themselves to life in less saline water. During the subsequent phase of increasing salinity these forms were concentrated in the areas of the river mouths and their further penetration into continental waters is easy to imagine From this angle we can easily understand the genesis of the so-called ice-sea relicts: Mysis, Mesidothea, Pontoporeia, Limnocalanus, Eurythemora, Gammaracanthus, Pallasea, Pseudalibrotus, Myoxophalus, Lota, and a number of the species of the families Salmonidae, Coregonidae and Osmeridae in the areas of river mouths of the Arctic basin, forming the dominant group both as regards number of species and biomass. The crustacean *Mysis relicta* (Fig. 11) may be cited as an example. In a number of crustaceans which

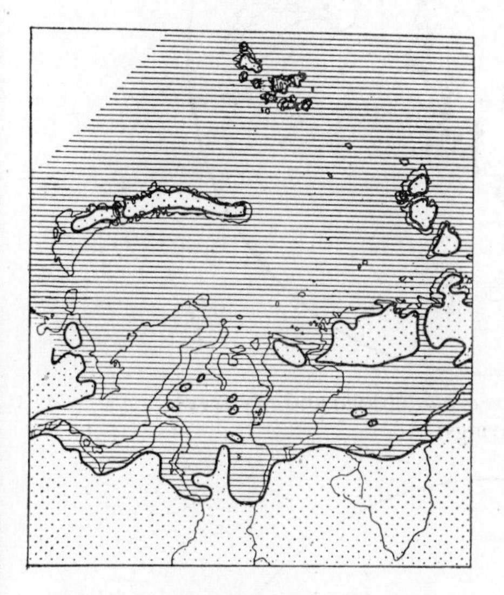

FIG. 9. Limits of greatest sea-transgression in Quaternary Era (Zachs, 1945, 1948).

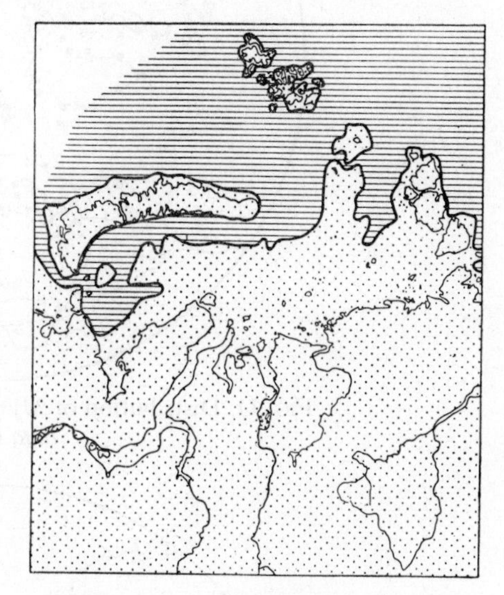

FIG. 10. Limits of the greatest sea-regression in the Quaternary Era (Zachs, 1495, 1948).

completely migrated into fresh water (*M. relicta*) the original forms, inhabiting the brackish waters of the river-mouth zones, are known (*M. oculata*).

From this point of view the biology and distribution of the above-mentioned fish are of interest. In the high Arctic sub-region of the Arctic basin the Gadidae, a typical marine family, has five representatives: burbot, Arctic cod, navaga and two species of the genus Arctogadus (Fig. 12). The other 50 species are not inhabitants of the Arctic region. Of the five Arctic species of Gadidae, one (burbot) has completely migrated into fresh waters, the others are more or less connected with it during their spawning period. These five species probably survived the Quaternary Era somewhere in the Arctic basin itself and the phases of its loss of salinity are reflected in their biology.

The salmon family (including Coregonidae and Osmeridae), the most typical of the Arctic basin and so closely connected with fresh water in its distribution and biology, is still more significant (Fig. 13). There is no doubt that most species of this family (which includes more than 80 species) survived the Ice Age in the Arctic basin itself. The specific richness of Salmonidae

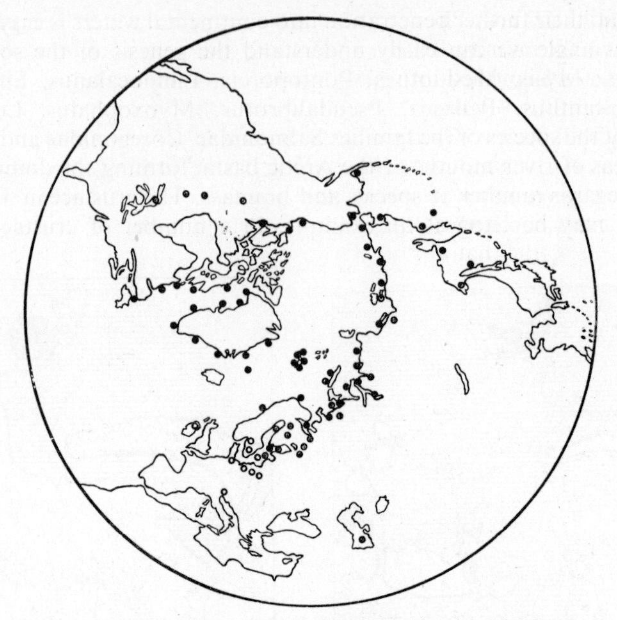

FIG. 11. Distribution of *Mysis oculata* (dots) and *Mysis relicta* (rings).

FIG. 12. Distribution of family Gadidae. Intensity of shading corresponds to number of species inhabiting a given area (Zenkevitch, 1933).

developed in the post-Pliocene period, while the original Pliocene forms were few. When the salinity of the waters had increased again the main mass of Salmonidae was pushed into the estuaries of the rivers and into river systems and within this new habitat they went through the process of rapid formation of species. If the pre-Quaternary ancestors of the Salmonidae had already possessed the original type of anadromous migration, then the system of migration, as we know it now, developed as a result of the above-mentioned palaegeographic changes.

It is remarkable that all this relict ice-marine fauna has in its distribution a

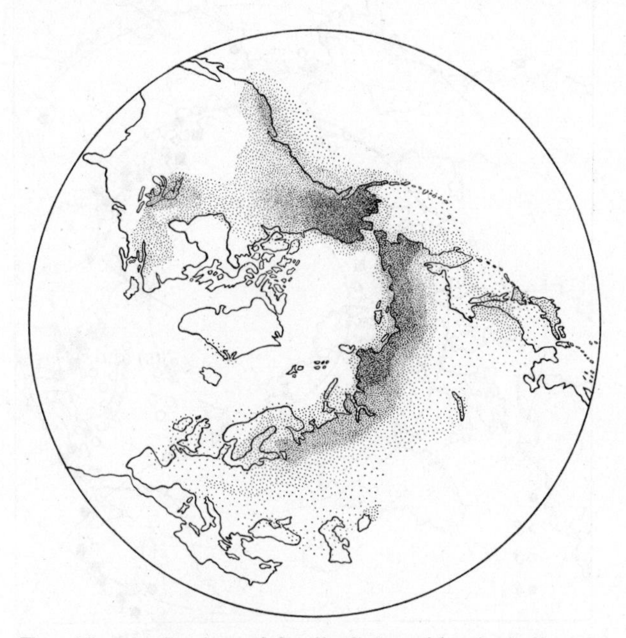

FIG. 13. Distribution of family Salmonidae including the Coregonidae and Osmeridae (Zenkevitch, 1933).

clearly manifest character of stages, linked with its adaptation to definite salinity.

A. Svetovidov (1952, 1954) has expressed some very interesting ideas about the distribution of Clupeidae and Salmonidae in the Arctic. It is known that both groups in their origin are connected with the northern half of the Atlantic Ocean. Svetovidov thinks that in the case of both families only a few representatives of the northern ocean have penetrated into the Pacific Ocean from the Arctic basin and are represented by cold-living forms. The endemic, small herring with a few vertebrates which are representatives of the Arctic herrings are *Clupea harengus pallasi n. maris albi* (White Sea) and *Cl.h.d.n. suvorovi* (Cheshsko-pechora). The origin of the Arctic sub-species of herring is no doubt connected with the Atlantic sub-species *Cl. harengus harengus*. Having migrated to the Pacific Ocean herring has formed there a variety with few vertebrates; it is apparently a large form of *Cl. harengus pallasi*, which later moved eastward again across the Arctic basin and reached the White Sea.

The Pacific cod *Gadus morhua macrocephalus*, according to Svetovidov (1948), is a descendant of the Greenland cod *G.m. ogac* which came through the Arctic along the American side of the polar basin. The Pacific navaga (*Eleginus gracilis*), a descendant of the Arctic *E. navaga*, but of a larger size, penetrated into the Pacific along the Siberian side of the polar basin. At present

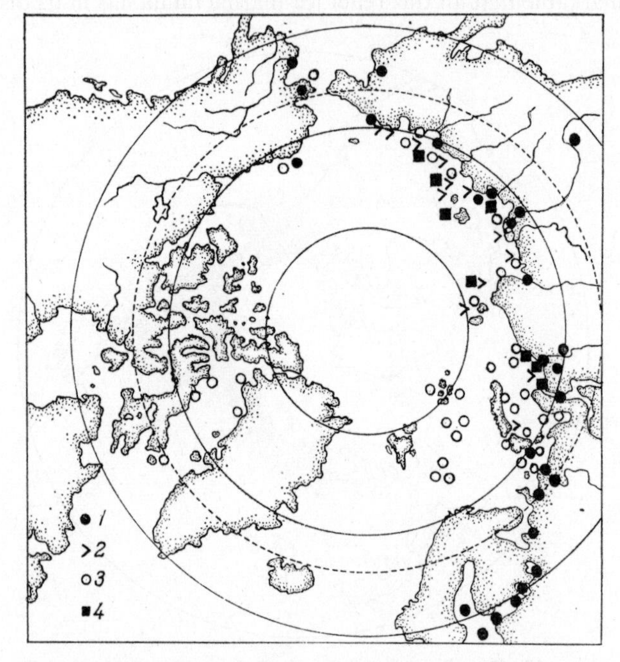

FIG. 14. Distribution of genus Mesidothea (Gurjanova, 1934). 1 *Mesidothea entomon*; 2 *M. sibirica*; 3 *M. sabini*; 4 *M. sabini* v. *robusta*.

both the original forms *G. morhua ogac* and *E. navaga* live mostly in the White and Kara Seas, in the Hudson Strait and Hudson's Bay. Svetovidov, noting that the Arctic basin cod mentioned above and representatives of the genera Boreogadus and Arctogadus favour greatly diluted waters of much lowered salinity during their spawning, sees in this their longing for warmer river waters. However, it now seems that desire for less saline waters and for spawning at the coldest time of the year is evidence of prolonged existence in waters of much lower salinity of the polar basin during the Ice Age.

The genus Mesidothea (Fig. 14) can also serve as a good illustration of a group of closely related species, adapted to various degrees of salinity (step-by-step distribution). *M. sabini sabini* lives in waters of normal salinity. Other forms, *M. sabini robusta* and *M. sibirica*, live mainly in the outer part of the brackish zone. *M. entomon* is a typical inhabitant of this zone and of the fresh waters of many closed bodies of water of the Arctic basin.

E. F. Gurjanova (1938) considers that in the Ice Age many forms acquired the capacity for a wide vertical distribution, and thus deep-water species were formed which inhabited the depressions of the Arctic basin and in this way escaped the surface loss of salinity. Some of these series are given in *Table 24*.

Table 24. Series with capacity for wide vertical distribution (after E. F. Gurjanova)

Deep-water species	Shallow-water species			
	Normal salinity	Lowered salinity	Brackish water	Fresh water
Mesidothea megalura	*M. sabini sabini*	*M.s. robusta* *M. sibirica*	*M. entomon glacialis* *M. entomon entomon*	*M. entomon vetterensis*
Onisimus sextoni	*O. brevicaudatus*	*O. affinis*	*O. botkini*	
O. turgidus *O. leucopis*	*O. caricus* *O. dubius* *O. edwardsi* *O. derjugini* *O. sibiricus* *O. plautus* *O. normanni*	*O. dubius* *O. sibiricus*		
	Pseudolibrotus glacialis *Ps. nanseni*	*Ps. littoralis*	*Ps. caspius birulai*	*Ps. caspius* *Ps. platyceras*
	Pontoporeia femorata	*P. femorata* *P. sinuata* *P. weltneri*	*P. sinuata* *P. affinis*	*P. affinis affinis*

This distribution indicates that the formation of species adapted to various degrees of salinity proceeded through several stages, and that the process of the salinity change had a step-by-step character. This suggestion is confirmed (E. F. Gurjanova, 1939) by the fact that 'all the links of this chain of species from the typical marine stenohaline species to the fresh-water ones exist simultaneously in the same basin (Kara and Laptev Seas). This indicates that the formation of the present Arctic fauna, accompanied by the division of the autochthonous genera into shallow-water species of a different stage of brackishness and into deep-water species, took place there and that, consequently, the region of the Kara and Laptev Seas is not only the centre of the development of the modern young (Ice Age) high Arctic fauna of the continental shelf but also its place of origin.' The high Arctic endemic forms of the Arctic show usually a characteristic break in their circumpolar habitat in the region of the Greenland Sea, the Norwegian Sea and the western part of the Barents Sea.

On the other hand, many species of this autochthonous fauna having acquired a capacity for a wide vertical propagation, and being marked with considerable eurybiotic capacities, have moved far beyond the boundaries of the Arctic basin. Thus some species of the genus Onisimus along the slopes of the Greenland Sea penetrate through the trenches far to the south to the Skagerak and Kattegat, and travel along the Asian coast into the Bering and Okhotsk Seas.

Most of the forms included in the group of Arctic boreal species are descendants of the eurybiotic part of the autochthonous Arctic fauna. In the

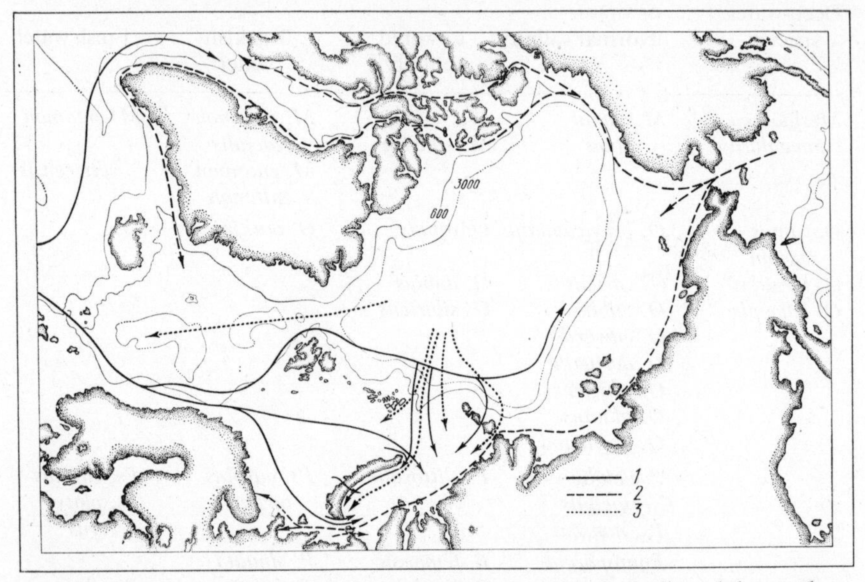

FIG. 15. Routes of exchange between the faunas of the Arctic Basin and the northern parts of the Atlantic and the Pacific (Gurjanova). *1* Atlantic fauna; *2* Pacific fauna; *3* Arctic deep-water fauna.

Atlantic Ocean they come southward to the North Sea, and in the Pacific to the Sea of Japan. At the same time they go down into the depths and become smaller in size. At present there is constant exchange between the Arctic basin fauna and the Pacific and Atlantic ones via the straits. The main routes of this exchange are given in Fig. 15.

The Arctic basin is now being rapidly populated by the more thermophilic forms from the Atlantic Ocean. G. Gorbunov (1939) points out a very interesting phenomenon of 'the presence, as a rule, of a particularly high Arctic fauna along the continental shores of the Siberian Seas. As one moves northwards, thermophilic forms are more and more mixed with it and gradually the high Arctic forms disappear; finally on the slopes of the continental shelf the high Arctic forms are represented only by some single species, while the main mass consists of the low Arctic and Arctic boreal forms, and even some near-boreal forms make their appearance. This is explained by the Arctic basin at certain depths being full of warm waters from the Atlantic which in part reach the surface in the shallows of the Siberian Seas carrying their fauna with them.'

The greatest variety of species was found here near the fringe of the shallow plateau of the Siberian Seas. Gorbunov notes that one of the *Sadko* stations obtained more than 200 species of different animal forms at the fringe of a shallow bank of the Kara Sea, at a depth of 698 m.

A considerable number of more thermophilic forms penetrated into the Arctic from the Atlantic Ocean during the warm phase of the Littorina period, and a part of them survives in the Arctic as relicts, as for example the sea grass Zostera in the White Sea.

Bathyal and abyssal fauna of the Arctic basin

The collections of the latest Soviet polar expeditions have made it possible for us to look into the interesting and hitherto closed world of the bathyal and abyssal fauna of the Arctic basin.

The bathyal fauna has risen so much at the shallow northern fringe of the Siberian Seas that at depths of 100 to 200 m, as has been pointed out by G. Gorbunov (1946), the fauna has a completely bathyal character.

In the Barents Sea there is pseudo-abyssal fauna at depths of more than 200 m, while in the Novosibirsk shallows it rises to 40 to 50 m.

The Novosibirsk shallows have a rich fauna of more than 800 species mainly of the foraminifera, polychaetes, bryozoa, amphipoda and molluscs. As has been noted by G. Gorbunov (1946) this fauna consists mainly of high Arctic, Arctic and Arctic boreal forms. In this region it is very difficult to draw the line between the abyssal and the bathyal, and between this latter and the sublittoral, since for a variety of reasons that have been discussed, the sublittoral forms go down more easily into the bathyal and the abyssal and the bathyal fauna rise easily to the sublittoral.

Collections made at 300 to 400 m and sometimes higher should (according to G. Gorbunov, 1946) be included in the bathyal fauna of the Arctic Ocean, owing to a general rise to higher levels.

In the bathyal fauna of the high-latitude collections made by the *Sadko* and *Sedov* expeditions Gorbunov includes 528 species of bottom animals; hence, in general, it contains four times more forms than the abyssal one. With the exception of some groups, this author gives the analysis of bathyal fauna of the Siberian shallows set out in *Table 25*.

Hence the bathyal fauna contains 72 per cent of sublittoral forms; 80 of these are really bathyal forms and 59 are endemic forms of the Arctic Ocean. Gorbunov includes the typical bathyal forms *Leucon spinulosus* among the Porifera, *Umbellula encrinus* among the Octocorallia, *Phascolosoma glaciale* among the Sipunculids. As regards Amphipoda these are represented by *Halirages elegans*, *Cleppides lomonosovi*, *Amathillopsus spinigera*, *Bythocaris payeri*; there are *Poliometra prolixa* from the Crinoidea, and as regards fish *Lycodes eudipleurosticus*. On the whole the fauna of the bathyal part of the Siberian sector of the Arctic can be considered as 81 per cent endemic and genetically linked with the abyssal fauna of the Atlantic Ocean but, unlike

Table 25

Endemic forms of Arctic Ocean	No. of species	Per cent
Deep-water species:		
Abyssal	29	7
Bathyal	59	14
Sublittoral species	128	30
Species of wider distribution		
Deep-water species:		
Abyssal	8	2
Bathyal	21	5
Sublittoral species	184	42
Total	429	100

the sublittoral fauna, Pacific elements are absent from it. The bathyal fauna of the central part of the polar basin consists mostly of the pan-Arctic and Arctic boreal forms.

Collections made by the *Sadko* in 1935 and 1937–38 give some idea of the abyssal fauna of the central part of the Arctic Ocean north of the Novosibirsk Islands. Members of 98 species were obtained by nine deep-water casts of the trawl at depths of 1,180 to 3,800 m, among them 26 Foraminifera, 4 Porifera, 4 Coelenterata, 13 Polychaeta, 1 Pogonophora, 1 Copepoda, 1 Cirripedia, 1 Cumacea, 6 Isopoda, 10 Amphipoda, 2 Decapoda, 1 Pantopoda, 19 Mollusca, 8 Echinodermata, 1 Pisces, and including also the typical abyssal species like *Astrorhiza crassatina* and *Ammodiscus incertus* of the Foraminifera, *Myriochele danielsseni*, *Gorbunovia malmgreni* of the Polychaeta, Pogonophora, *Lamellisabella gorbunovi*, among Cumacea—*Diastylis polaris*, among Isopoda *Ilyarachna derjugini*, *Eurycope ratmanovi*, *Mesidothea megalura* v. *polaris*, among Amphipoda—*Halirages gorbunovi*, *Melita pallida*, and *Dulichia cyclops*, among Decapoda—*Hymenodora glacialis*, *Bythocaris leucopis*, among Mollusca—*Ganesa bujnitzkii*, *Natica bathybia*, *Sipho danielsseni*, *Tindaria derjugini*, *Neilonella kolthoffi*, *Ledella tamara*, *Propeamussium frigidum*, *Thyasira ottoschmidti*, *Lyonsiella jeffreysi*, *L. uschacovi*, and among Echinodermata—*Kolga hyalina*. Most of the above-mentioned species are endemic forms of the Arctic Ocean. Besides these forms 20 abyssal species come into the bathyal, and 28 abyssal species were found only in the bathyal. Thirty-seven species caught in the abyssal are immigrants from the sublittoral. The vertical propagation of the forms found in the abyssal is given in *Table 26*.

A complete absence of bryozoans is a characteristic feature of the Arctic Ocean fauna. Sixty per cent of this fauna is endemic and, of the purely abyssal species, 89 per cent is endemic.

In Gorbunov's opinion (1946) based on the presence of a number of endemic

Table 26

Endemic forms of Arctic Ocean	No. of species, except Foraminifera
Deep-water species:	
Purely abyssal	24
Abyssal eurybathic	32
Bathyal	5
Shallow eurybathic	7
More widely propagated species	
Deep-water species:	
Purely abyssal	3
Abyssal eurybathic	8
Bathyal	0
Shallow-water eurybathic	15
Total	94

species and even endemic genera, the abyssal fauna of the Arctic Ocean is ancient, going back at least to Tertiary genesis.

On the other hand, E. F. Gurjanova (1938) thinks that all this fauna originated from the forms inhabiting the shallow zones of the Arctic in the postglacial period. This fauna consists partly of the same species which still live in the shallows, and partly of species developed from these latter. On the basis of her data Gurjanova considers the Arctic basin as very young,* but this is difficult to accept. If the deep-water fauna did exist here during preglacial times, it might have perished totally or partially during the Ice Age as a result of a considerable loss of salinity of the surface layers of the sea or perhaps throughout the whole basin as occurred in the Sea of Japan.

As regards the pelagic fauna of the Arctic basin V. Jashnov (1940) has also come to the conclusion that specific abyssal pelagic fauna of the Arctic basin does not exist. Of the 46 species of Copepoda found in the depths of the Arctic basin, the Norwegian and Greenland Seas and Baffin Bay, 42 are known also in the rest of the Atlantic. The same may be said about the coastal vegetation (macrophytes) of the Arctic basin. It has no peculiar features, it is simply an impoverished Atlantic flora.

A remarkable phenomenon was observed by the latest Soviet high-latitude expeditions—many members of the abyssal fauna of the Arctic basin have risen into the comparatively shallow zones along its fringes in seas with high Arctic conditions. This is particularly evident in the northern part of the Kara Sea and the northwestern part of the Laptev Sea, where great depths approach closely and where there are trenches (200 to 400 m) running from them.

* It must, however, be borne in mind that the abyssal fauna of the central part of the Arctic Ocean is as yet practically uninvestigated. So far explorers have only penetrated along the continental slopes of the northern part of the Kara Sea and the Novosibirsk shallows.

The rise of the mass of abyssal forms to depths unusual for them (80 to 100 m), which does not occur anywhere in the southern part of the Arctic basin (at the outlet into the Atlantic) may be explained by the following four causes: (*1*) low temperature of surface water of high Arctic; (*2*) small annual temperature fluctuations; (*3*) comparatively low transparency of water; (*4*) obscuration caused by the ice cover which lasts almost all the year round.

Hence the deep-water fauna with a sharply expressed cold-water stenothermy and a negative phototropism finds no obstacles here for expanding into comparatively higher levels.

III. ZOOGEOGRAPHICAL ZONATION OF THE ARCTIC REGION

All our Arctic seas, except for the most southwestern corner of the Barents Sea, belong to the Arctic region, which is limited by about 70° N latitude and only comes down to 60° N in the Norwegian and Greenland Seas. The boundaries of the Arctic and boreal regions in the North Atlantic are not the same for the bottom and the pelagic fauna.

Ortmann noted this general phenomenon as early as 1896. Pelagic organisms, easily carried around by currents and with life cycles shorter than those of the bottom organisms, form more mobile zoogeographical boundaries than the slowly growing benthos organisms liked with the bottom. The boundaries given in Fig. 16 refer mainly to benthos. Sea currents would widen these boundaries more for plankton than for benthos. The boundary between the Arctic and boreal plankton along the shores of Norway and in the western part of the Barents Sea would (in relation to the boundary for benthos) therefore lie considerably farther north and east, possibly as far as the central parts of the Barents Sea. Along the eastern coasts of Greenland, on the other hand, this boundary would be found such farther south, towards Newfoundland. In exactly the same way fresh river waters carry fresh-water plankton out into the sea and, in spreading outwards, move the boundary between the sea and brackish plankton away to the north. Conversely, in the near-bottom layers, the saline waters together with the bottom population move towards the shore, often entering the estuarial zones, so that the surface layer frequently has a completely fresh-water fauna, and the near-bottom one a sea fauna. This can be seen by comparing the boundaries in Figs. 13 and 14.

The littoral fauna provides another case of the boundaries for different groups of the population of the northern seas not being coincident. Owing to a number of conditions which have already been mentioned the boreal littoral fauna has been moved far to the east, covering all the Murman coast and White Sea, i.e. regions where the fauna of the sublittoral, and the plankton too, have a true Arctic character.

The Arctic region may be divided into three sub-regions (Fig. 16). First of all there is the abyssal Arctic sub-region, embracing the three depressions (Norwegian, Greenland and Central Arctic) of the Arctic basin and separating them from the abyssal of the Atlantic Ocean proper. Species of the genus Themisto can serve as an excellent example of the sharp fauna distinction between the Arctic and Atlantic abyssal forms.

The sublittoral fauna of the Arctic region, which differs fairly sharply from the abyssal, may in its turn be divided into two sub-regions—the shallow, lower Arctic one, including the Barents and White Seas (the White Sea–Spitsbergen province of the Arctic region, according to Gurjanova), and the shallow, high Arctic sub-region, including all the other seas of the Soviet and American sectors (the Siberian province and the North American–Greenland province of the Arctic region, according to E. Gurjanova). Again,

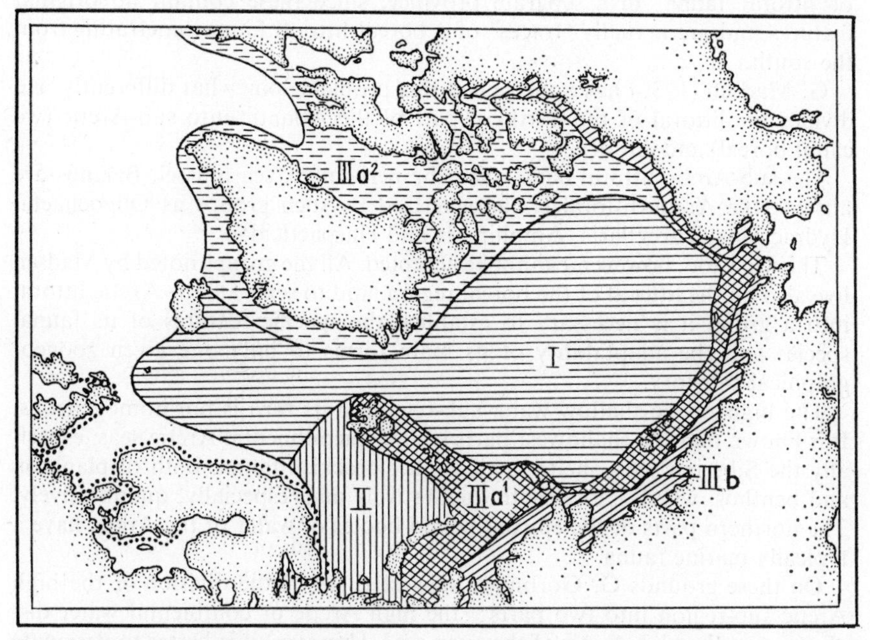

FIG. 16. Zoogeographical zonation of the Arctic region (according to various investigators). *I* Abyssal Arctic sub-region; *II* Lower-Arctic, shallow sub-region; *III* High Arctic, shallow sub-region; *IIIa* Shallow marine province; *IIIb* Shallow brackish-water province; *IIIa*¹ Suberian region, *IIIa*² North American Greenland region. The propagation of the boreal littoral fauna northwards and eastwards is marked by a dotted line (Zenkevitch, 1947).

as has been stated above, the littoral fauna and to a certain extent the fauna of the upper level of the Murman sublittoral and that of the western part of the White Sea has a distinctly boreal character. E. F. Gurjanova, I. Zachs and P. Ushakov (1925) attributed a sub-Arctic nature to it; however, this littoral fauna, changing but little, reaches the shores of Brittany. On the other hand it is evident that in the Ice Age and the Yoldian stage the Murman and White Sea littoral was in the same state as it is at present in the high Arctic regions, i.e. it was practically absent and only later, with the rise of temperature, could the littoral fauna move northward and eastward. The absence of littoral fauna is, in fact, characteristic of the high Arctic.

Movement far to the north and to the east is made possible for the boreal littoral fauna by specific conditions of the littoral microclimate. Some authors divide the Arctic littoral region into two provinces—the high Arctic one (Kara–Siberia) with its uninhabited littoral zone, and the Arctic one with its traces of littoral fauna and flora (Matochkin Shar, Spitsbergen). But it is impossible to accept either of these divisions. The separation of an uninhabited littorial zone into a zoogeographical province is not justified since animal life is absent from it. Again there are no grounds for placing 'traces of littoral fauna' in a separate province, since these contain no original features and are actually 'traces' of a boreal littoral fauna penetrating from the south.

G. Madsen (1936) has approached this problem somewhat differently. He divides the littoral of the northern part of the Atlantic into sub-Arctic (we call it boreal) and Arctic.

The sub-Arctic littoral ends when the periwinkle, sea mussel, Balanus are absent; the Arctic littoral is characterized by such groups as Oligochaeta, Hydracarina, Turbellaria, Amphipoda and Harpacticidae.

This view too, however, cannot be accepted. All the groups noted by Madsen live also on the littoral of the boreal region, and to separate the Arctic littoral into a group it is necessary to establish the specific features of its faunal species and the adaptability of its main forms to only one given zoogeographical category.

The high Arctic shallow-water sub-region in its turn is not homogeneous. It is known that the shallowest parts of the epicontinental Arctic seas, especially the Siberian seas, shelter a rich relict brackish fauna, both of plankton and benthos, which is rich both qualitatively and, especially, quantitatively. The northern parts of the epicontinental bodies of water of the Arctic have a typically marine fauna.

On these grounds G. Gorbunov suggested (1941) the division of the high Arctic sub-region into two parts: 'the high Arctic or continental water discharge and the high Arctic of the open sea'. However, it is better to designate them differently and to divide the high Arctic shallow-water sub-region into sea-water and brackish-water provinces, thus marking the most characteristic difference in the fauna of both parts. The brackish-water province could probably be further divided into several zones according to their degree of salinity and the fauna corresponding to them. Evidently the outer circle of the brackish-water province, adjacent to the sea province of the shallow high Arctic sub-region, is the zone so clearly defined by G. Gorbunov (1941) as that of the distribution of the bivalve, *Portlandia arctica* (Fig. 17), comparing it with that of the distribution of another high Arctic mollusc, *Propeamussium* (Pecten) *groenlandicum major*.

Unlike *P. arctica* this mollusc cannot endure a lowering of salinity and lives outside the zones influenced by river waters.

The two molluscs exclude each other, as it were, and are very rarely found in large quantities in the same place.

Although *P. arctica* can live under conditions of full sea-salinity, the zones of its mass development are connected with regions exposed to a greater or lesser extent to river discharge.

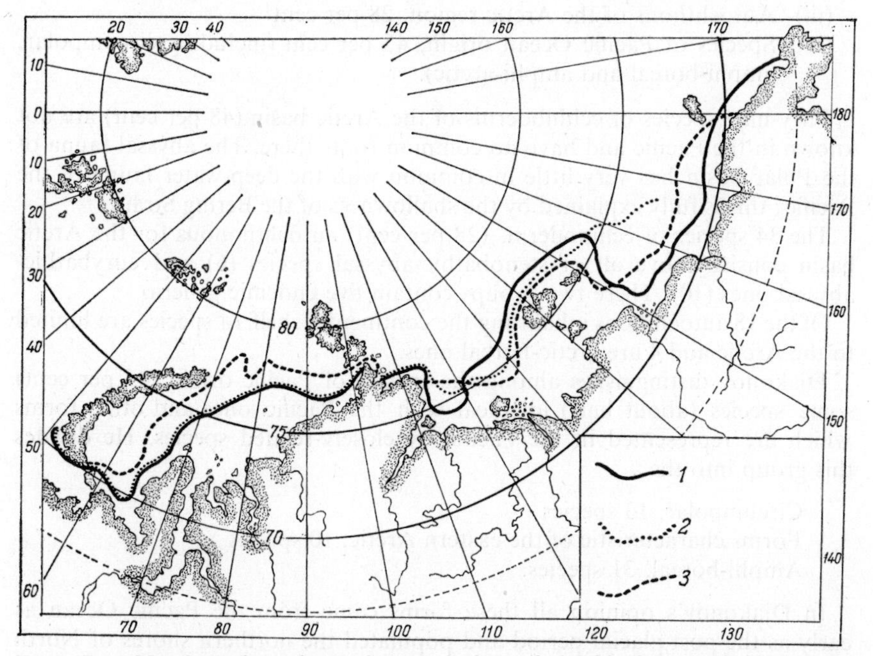

FIG. 17. *1* Northern boundary of propagation of the bivalve *Portlandia arctica* (brackish-water province); *2* Southern boundary of propagation of the bivalve *Pecten* (Propeamusium) *groenlandicum* (marine province, according to Gorbunov, 1941); *3* Northern boundary of propagation of brackish-water plankton Crustacea *Limnocalanus grimaldi* and *Dropanopus bungei* (Bogorov, 1944).

Hence on the whole the following scheme of zoogeographical subdivision is obtained for the Arctic region (Fig. 16):

Region	Sub-region	Province	Regions
Arctic	I. Abyssal		
	II. Shallow lower Arctic		
	II. Shallow high Arctic	(*1*) Sea (*2*) Brackish-water	(*a*) Siberian (*b*) North American-Greenland

The echinoderm group, as one of the best studied, may be cited as an example of the zoogeographical analysis of the Arctic basin fauna. According to A. M. Djakonov (1945) the following* groups can be distinguished among the 121 species of Echinodermata known in the Arctic Ocean.

(i) Cosmopolitan species, 4 per cent
(ii) Boreal species, immigrants from the Atlantic, 23 per cent

* Species were not taken into account when the percentage (23, 28 and 45) were calculated.

(iii) Autochthons of the Arctic region, 28 per cent
(iv) Species of Pacific Ocean origin, 45 per cent (including circumpolar, amphi-boreal and amphi-arctic).

Fifty-nine species of echinoderms of the Arctic basin (48 per cent) are not known in the Pacific and have no common roots there. The abyssal fauna of the Polar basin has very little in common with the deep-water fauna of the Pacific; this is fully explained by the shallowness of the Bering Strait.

The 34 species of echinoderms (28 per cent) autochthonous for the Arctic basin consist above all of stenobathic-abyssal species (6) and eurybathic-abyssal ones (10). These two groups contain five endemic genera.

Of the 18 autochthons inhabiting the continental shelf 14 species are limited to the Arctic and 4 are arctic-boreal ones.

Djakonov distinguishes among the species of Pacific origin (45 per cent) some species (about half) identical with the Pacific ones and other forms which are represented in the Pacific by closely-related species. He divides this group into the:

Circumpolar, 13 species
Forms characteristic of the eastern Arctic, 10 species
Amphi-boreal, 31 species.

In Djakonov's opinion all these forms came from the Pacific Ocean as early as the post-glacial period and populated the northern shores of North America.

As an example Djakonov gives the distribution of species of the genus Leptasterias:

Region	No. of Leptasterias species
Northern part of Pacific	27
Off the northeastern shores of North America	5
Off Greenland	2
Off Scandinavia	3
Circumpolar	1

The way described here in which the Arctic was populated by Pacific Ocean forms is considered by several authors as basic.

IV. TYPOLOGY OF THE BODIES OF WATER OF THE ARCTIC BASIN AND THE NORTHERN ATLANTIC

A quantitative survey of the marine fauna leads to the problem of the typology of the bodies of water based on biological productivity.

Beside the fact of it belonging to one or another biogeographical region, characterized by a certain specific population, the most important features which condition the whole type of a body of water and that of the biological productivity developed in it are:

(*1*) the nature of the connection between the body of water and the ocean (open bodies of water on the one hand, and closed or semi-closed on the other)

(*2*) the vertical characteristics of the body of water (deep-water and epicontinental bodies of water) and
(*3*) the general character of the hydrological conditions, and in particular, the formation of an ice cover in winter.

In fact the character of the hydrological conditions (salinity, temperature, the presence of gas, etc.), water circulation, the supply of nutritive substances and other factors influencing biological production differ greatly in each of the above-mentioned types of bodies of water.

In high latitudes, in closed and semi-closed bodies of water, a loss of salinity inevitably takes place, leading to the disappearance of a number of typical sea forms, and sometimes of whole groups of organisms. In connection with this either a lowering of the biomass is observed or, in the presence of favourable feeding conditions, quantitatively rich communities of either meso- or oligo-mixed type are developed; whereas polymixed communities are characteristic of the fully saline open sea.

It is likewise easily shown that the course of the hydrological processes and also a whole series of factors directly determining the character of the biological productivity—most important being the supply of nutritive substances—differ greatly in near-bottom bodies of water on the one hand and epicontinental ones on the other.

The pre-polar parts of the Arctic basin, approximately within the limits of the high Arctic sub-region, with Novaya Zemlya, the northern part of the Barents Sea and the shores of Spitsbergen and Greenland as its boundaries on the Atlantic side, and to the east the parts of the Bering Sea adjacent to the Bering Strait, have four main characteristic features: (*1*) lowered salinity in their upper 200 m layer and a considerably greater salinity of the deep waters (saline stratification), (*2*) a vertical circulation rendered difficult in consequence, (*3*) a very low (usually below $-1°$ C) temperature, except for a short and slight summer heating of the surface layer, and (*4*) a cover of floating ice usually throughout most of the year and sometimes during the whole of it. As regards its fauna and palaeoclimatic conditions this region has the following characteristics: (*a*) a preceding much colder phase connected with the Ice Age and post-glacial period, (*b*) a comparatively short phase of higher temperature during the Atlantic period, (*c*) a notable increase now of penetration of forms more adapted to warm waters, and (*d*) the saturation of the region of lower salinity by brackish relict fauna.

All the factors mentioned explain the low indices of biomass usually obtained for the high Arctic sub-region (less than 50 g/m^2) while in the circumpolar zone the productivity rate is low. The poor quality of the population for an undoubtedly mesomixed community, and a tendency of passing over at some points to the oligomixed one, are also characteristic.

In the summer season plankton biomass in the surface layer comprises 100 to 3,200 mg/m^3, but the amount of zooplankton is usually about 50 to 230 mg/m^3; zooplankton biomass rises to 400 mg/m^3 only in inlets and river mouths. Rotatoria, Cladocera and among the Copepoda, *Pseudocalanus elongatus* become significant in the plankton as a result of a considerable loss of salinity, especially near the river mouths. Only one period of phytoplankton bloom is observed in the spring; the autumn one is absent.

The circumpolar zone with its numerically rich fauna and its considerably increased productivity forms a belt round this pre-polar zone of the northern hemisphere which has an impoverished fauna and a lowered productivity; this belt passes through the northern Atlantic and the northern Pacific. Hydrologically this zone has the following characteristics: (*1*) the most favourable conditions for vertical circulation, approaching uniformity of temperature and salinity, (*2*) a temperature of more than 0°, and (*3*) a normal sea salinity. The main meeting place of the warm waters moving from the south with the local cold ones is situated in this zone, hence the phenomenon of the 'polar front' develops here with all its consequences. To this given combination of hydrological factors which determine the best conditions for feeding and life processes, there corresponds an increased biomass (for benthos more than 100 to 200 g/cm^2), a considerable productivity and polymixed communities. Zooplankton biomass, consisting mainly of *Calanus finmarchicus*, is subject to great fluctuations (from 1·5 to 3,843 mg/m^3) and for the southwestern part of the Barents Sea it is, on the average, about 230 mg/m^3 in August. Two maxima of bloom—the spring and autumn ones—are observed in the development of phytoplankton.

Moving farther south, beyond the influence of the polar front, we reach a zone with different hydrological and biological characteristics. The hydrological conditions of this zone are: (*1*) a considerably higher temperature of the upper layer of water which creates a thermal stratification in the warm parts of the ocean in such marked degree that the whole nature of the biological processes is determined by it, and (*2*) restricted vertical circulation. These regions are characterized by the rich qualitative composition of their population and their decreased biomass. Conditions for increased biomass and productivity are created only in places with favourable circulation and in the shallows.

Table 27 gives a typological scheme for the zonation of the northern Atlantic and the polar basin, for the upper layer of the sea (200 to 300 m) due to M. J. Dunbar (1951, 1953). It is drawn up according to particular characteristics, both biological (the composition of the population and the peculiarities of biological productivity) and hydrological (temperature, mixing). The northern boundary of Dunbar's boreal region coincides with that given by most of the biologists, except that Finmark and the western part of the Murman coast are usually included in the boreal region. Dunbar divides the region to the north of this boundary into Arctic and sub-Arctic zones of life. These two zones on the whole correspond to the division generally accepted in the U.S.S.R. for the Arctic region: the high Arctic sub-region (Dunbar's Arctic) and lower Arctic one (Dunbar's sub-Arctic). We think that there is not sufficient ground to call these two sub-regions independent ecological zones of life on the regional scale. Their population does not possess sufficiently sharp distinctive characteristics allowing them to be separated into categories of a higher order.

The boundary between the Arctic and sub-Arctic of Dunbar differs in some

Table 27. Scheme for typological division of the bodies of water of the Arctic, sub-Arctic and boreal regions

Arctic	Open	1. High Arctic epicontinental (Kara and Laptev Seas, etc., up to Crown Prince Gustav Sea and the shallow parts of Baffin Bay)
		2. High Arctic deep-water (Arctic basin, deep parts of the Greenland Sea and Baffin Bay)
		3. Lower Arctic epicontinental (Barents Sea, waters off northern Iceland, and southern Greenland coastal waters)
		4. Lower Arctic deep-water (Davis Strait)
	Semi-closed	5. High Arctic epicontinental (White Sea and Hudson's Bay)
Sub-Arctic	Open	6. Sub-Arctic epicontinental (north Norwegian coastal waters, south Icelandic waters)
		7. Sub-Arctic deep-water (Norwegian Sea)
	Semi-closed	8. Sub-Arctic epicontinental deep-water (deep part of Baltic Sea)
Boreal	Open	9. Boreal epicontinental (Faroe waters, North Sea waters around the British Isles, epicontinental parts of the Bering and Okhotsk Seas and the Sea of Japan)
		10. Deep-water boreal (Bay of Biscay, the depths of the northern Atlantic, deep parts of the Bering and Okhotsk Seas and the Sea of Japan)
	Semi-closed	11. Boreal epicontinental (Kattegat, Sounds, Belts, the surface layers of the Baltic Sea)

detail from that drawn by us between the lower Arctic and high Arctic sub-regions, specially for the Kara Sea. The southern half of the Kara Sea undoubtedly should be referred to the high Arctic sub-region (Dunbar's Arctic). Moreover the White Sea could not, from Dunbar's point of view, be included in the sub-Arctic, since it is not a zone of the mixed polar and non-polar waters, neither is the southern half of the Kara Sea.

2

The Barents Sea

The Barents Sea is an open epicontinental fully saline body of water, mainly of Arctic character, covered in its northern and eastern parts with floating ice during the winter season. As the warm Atlantic waters flowing from the west enter this sea they are cooled (from 8° to −1·8° C); thus a complex system of horizontal circulation is set up, consisting of several main cyclonic revolutions. The Sea is well aerated.

On the slopes of the shallows warmer and more mobile masses of Atlantic waters meet cold and stagnant 'local' waters; this causes strong vertical circulations and other phenomena covered by the term polar front. In these regions—where plant food is accumulated—the amount of benthos biomass is 150 to 600 g/m² or more. In the regions of increased vertical circulation, benthos biomass falls to 20 to 50 g/m² or less. This occurs in the most westerly and especially in the northern part of the Sea, where brown mud is widely distributed and owing to the insufficiently brisk vertical circulation large amounts of carbon dioxide may accumulate in the bottom layers. Marine fauna and flora with a preponderance of bivalve molluscs, echinoderms, polychaetes, crustaceans, sponges, hydroides, bryozoans and sipunculids are characteristic of this Sea.

Bottom communities of the polymixed type belong, except for the littoral, to the high and low Arctic sub-regions of the Arctic. The main mass of the coastal vegetation is concentrated in the south of the Sea at zero depth, with a biomass of up to 24 to 28 kg/m² (Laminaria, Ascophyllum, Fucus). At lower levels the mass of macrophytes decreases greatly. The typical boreal littoral, well represented in the warmer part of the Sea, disappears in regions which remain under ice for a long time.

As a rough calculation for the main groups the following ranges may be taken as typical *P*/*B* coefficients:* for littoral and sublittoral vegetation approximately 1; for zoobenthos about 0·25 to 0·2; for zooplankton approximately 1; for phytoplankton approximately 50; for fish on the average not more than a sixth. The quantity of organic matter present on the sea bottom is low and depends on its mechanical composition. In the north, where soft bottoms predominate, there is 1 to 2 per cent carbon, 0·1 to 0·3 per cent nitrogen; in the south (south of 72° N) there are 0·3 to 0·8 per cent carbon and 0·05 to 0·15 per cent nitrogen. The C/N ratio in the sea bed is 5·5 to 8·0.

The trawling industry both Soviet and foreign is highly developed in the Barents Sea, the main catch being cod, haddock and bass. In that part of the sea adjacent to the Murman coast herring fishing has been greatly developed in Soviet times.

* Ratio of annual production/average annual biomass.

I. HISTORY OF EXPLORATION

The first period

The first observations on the fauna of the Barents and White Seas, mainly on fish and marine mammals, were collected by the Russian inhabitants of the White Sea coast and by the Novgorod merchants, beginning in the twelfth century. Sea fisheries existed here in the sixteenth and seventeenth centuries. The first data on the Barents Sea fauna to appear in the literature were given

FIG. 18. Professor N. M. Knipovitch.

by the academician K. Baer, after his famous voyage to Novaya Zemlya in 1837. He collected about 70 species of various animals from those shores.

The fauna of the Murman coast was first studied during the voyages of the St Petersburg zoologist F. Jarzhinsky (1869–70), S. Herzenstein (1880–84), Grigoriev (1887) and others.

In the open parts of the Barents Sea and in its northern parts zoological data were collected in the last century by the expeditions of Peyr and Vaiprecht (1872–74), Baron E. Nordenskjöld (1875–76 and 1878–79) and others.

The second period

A comprehensive study of the Barents Sea fauna was begun during the present century and is first of all connected with the work done by the expedition for the Murman scientific fishery survey, organized in 1898 and operating for ten years under the direction first of N. M. Knipovitch and later of L. Breitfuss. A year later the biological station of the St Petersburg Natural History Society, named the Murman Biological Station, was transferred from the

FIG. 19. Professor I. I. Mesiacev.

Solovetsk Islands to the Ekaterininskaya Bay of the Kola Guba. This scientific and industrial expedition made a basic survey of the hydrological conditions of the Barents Sea and of the commercial fish, and the Murman station carried out a careful examination of the fauna of the Kola Guba. Like the Sevastopol station of the Academy of Sciences, the Murman station was the centre of research by Russian and Soviet biologists into marine fauna and flora. It was here that K. Derjugin collected the data for his large monograph on the fauna of the Kola Guba.

It should be noted that N. M. Knipovitch had a special vessel the *Andrey Pervozvanniy* built for his Murman expedition, equipped also as a fishing trawler. It was the first experiment of this sort and a most fruitful one for the practice of sea exploration. N. M. Knipovitch proved the practicability of trawling in the Barents Sea.

The third period

The third period in the study of the fauna of the northern seas belongs to the Soviet epoch. There was no sea in which the survey work was developed over

FIG. 20. Professor K. M. Derjugin.

so wide an area and to such a depth as that carried out in the Barents Sea in the twenties and thirties. Almost at the same time (1919–21) there came into existence three central institutes which carried out the exploration of this region: the Northern Scientific-Industrial Expedition (later the All-Union Arctic Institute), the State Hydrological Institute, and the State Oceanographic Institute, organized by I. Mesiacev (now the All-Union Institute of Sea Fisheries and Oceanography, VNIRO). A little later the Chief Directorate of the Northern Sea Route was created and its expeditionary activity placed the names of Russian explorers in the first rank of explorers of the polar regions. As a result the Barents Sea may be considered one of the best surveyed seas in the world. The research vessel *Persei* of the State Oceano-

FIG. 21. *Persei*, research vessel of State Oceanographic Institute (1923 to 1940).

graphic Institute (1923 to 1940) (Fig. 21) has played a particularly important role in the exploration of the Barents Sea.

Continuous research work on the fauna of the Barents Sea is now being carried out by the N. M. Knipovitch Polar Institute of Sea Fisheries and Oceanography in Murmansk (mainly by way of scientific and commercial researches) and by the Murman biological station which was organized in 1936 on the Dalne-Zelenetskaya Guba by the Soviet Academy of Sciences.

II. PHYSICS, GEOGRAPHY, HYDROLOGY, HYDRO-CHEMISTRY AND GEOLOGY

Boundaries

The Barents Sea (Fig. 22) is the first of the system of boundary epicontinental bodies of water of the Arctic basin, which we enter in our voyage round northwest Europe. It is a kind of approach to the outposts of the Arctic, which have been conquered by the warm Atlantic waters. The Barents Sea is bounded on the north by the Archipelagoes of Spitsbergen and Franz Joseph Land, to the east by Novaya Zemlya, while to the west a slope towards the great depths of the Greenland Sea serves as a boundary.

Size

Within these boundaries the area of the Barents Sea is 1,405,000 km^2, the average depth of the Sea is 229 m, and its volume is 322,000 km^3. Depths below 400 m are rare; they are found in the western and northeastern parts of the Sea lying adjacent to the great depths of the Greenland Sea and the Arctic basin.

N. Zubov (1932) has calculated the distribution of depths in the Barents Sea in percentages as given in *Table 28*.

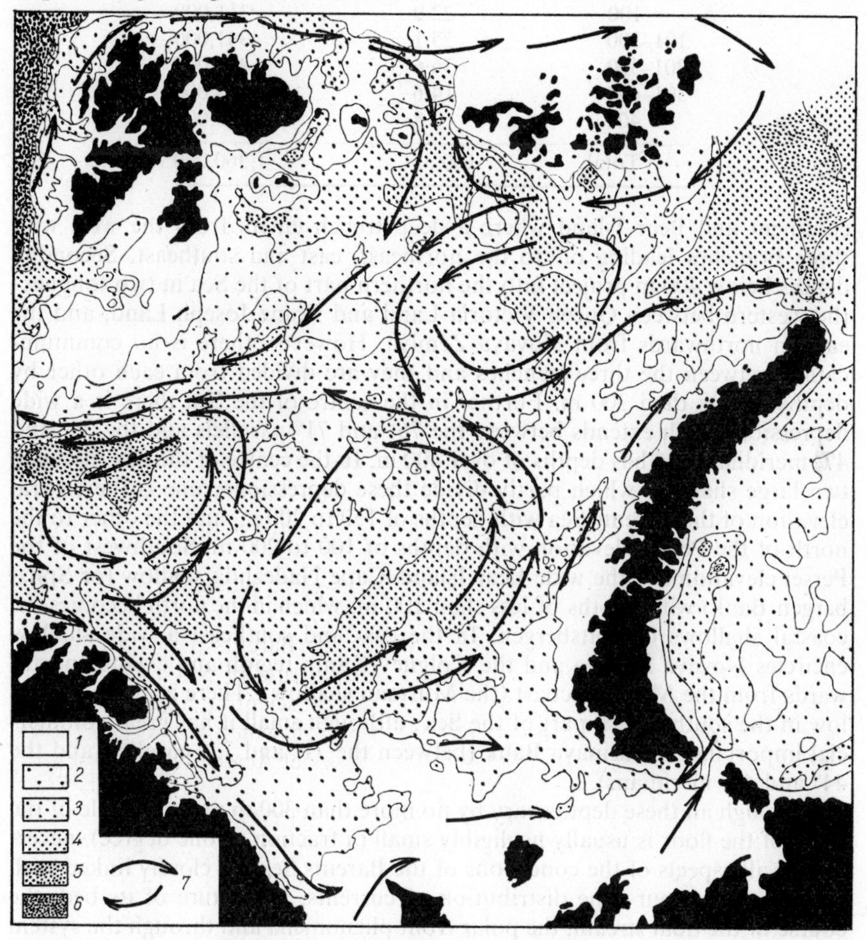

FIG. 22. Chart of Barents Sea, showing depths (Zubov) and currents (Zaytsev). *1* 100 m; *2* 100 to 200 m; *3* 200 to 300 m; *4* 300 to 400 m; *5* 400 to 500 m; *6* >500 m; *7* Main directions of currents.

In the opinion of F. Nansen (1922) the floor of the Barents Sea is an elaborate system of river valleys sunk under the sea surface. In fact if the sea-level were lowered 500 m the whole of the Barents Sea would become dry land.

Bottom topography

The bottom topography of the Barents Sea has the following features (Fig. 22). In three places troughs below 400 m enter the sea, the first lying between the

Table 28

Depth m	Depth as % of total sea	Area km²
100	22·9	311,000
101–200	25·1	341,000
201–300	36·6	470,000
301–400	14·6	199,000
400	2·8	39,000
Total	100	1,360,000

continent and Bear Island where a deep trench enters from the west with three branches leading off to the northeast, east and southeast. Secondly, depths below 400 m project into the northern part of the Sea in two tongues: the western between Queen Victoria Land and Franz Joseph Land, and the eastern northwards from Novaya Zemlya. However, there is no communication between the three trenches and they are divided from each other by depths of less than 300 m. Further in the centre of the Sea there is a wide depression which extends between the 76° and 71° parallels and the 35° and 47° meridians and has depths of over 400 m. In the centre of the Sea there are two large shallows which partly divide these depressions: one is the central elevation of the Barents Sea with depths of 150 to 200 m, and the other to the north of the Persei elevation with depths of 100 to 200 m. Southwest of the Persei elevation lies the wide Bear Island–Cape Nadezhda shallow (or Spitsbergen Bank) with depths of less than 100 m, which in the north becomes the coastal shallows of Spitsbergen. In the east and southeast a wide shallow encircles Novaya Zemlya and the Kolguev-Kanin region and extends northwards from the Murman coast (the Murman shallow). There is another shallow in the southeastern part of the Sea; although small it has great commercial importance—Gusinaya Bank (between the 71° and 72° parallels and the 44° and 48° meridians).

Although all these depths vary by no more than 300 m and the angle of the slope of the floor is usually negligibly small (a fraction of one degree), nevertheless all aspects of the conditions of the Barents Sea are closely linked with its bottom contour—the distribution of currents, the nature of its bed, the course of the tidal stream, the polar front phenomena and through the system of horizontal and vertical circulation of water the distribution of densities of bottom population and the concentration of commercial fish; all this in the final analysis is primarily determined by the bottom topography.

Currents

A powerful stream of Atlantic waters, skirting the North Cape, enters the Barents Sea from the west through the broad passage (128 km across) between the North Cape and Bear Island (Fig. 22).

Warm Atlantic waters penetrate into the Barents Sea not only from the west, to the south and north of Bear Island, but also from the north through the straits off the eastern and western coasts of Franz Joseph Land.

The North Cape current enters the Barents Sea in two streams a little to the north and south of 72° N latitude. The southern stream is slightly less saline owing to the coastal dilution of water (34·2 to 35·2‰), its speed being slightly greater (about 4 to 4·5 cm/sec). The northern stream consists of fully saline Atlantic waters (35·0 to 35·2‰) and travels slower than the southern one (about 2 cm/sec).

The chart of the currents of the Barents Sea was first compiled by N. M. Knipovitch at the very beginning of this century (1902–06). In his opinion (later developed in detail by L. Breitfuss and Gebel), the North Cape current entering between Bear Island and the continent breaks into four main branches, corresponding, as Knipovitch supposed, to the four deeper trenches in the floor. In this conception the Barents Sea appeared as a kind of flowing water mass, the movement being from west to east and north, and with more or less rectilinear currents. According to Knipovitch cold and slightly saline polar water lies on the ridges and shallows between the warm branches of the stream. L. Breitfuss even assumed the presence of cold countercurrents moving to meet the warm water and dividing into separate branches.

A different point of view on the circulation of the Barents Sea waters was expressed about the same time. As early as 1902 F. Nansen and later Helland-Hansen (1912) represented the movement of water in the Barents Sea as one huge cyclonic vortex breaking up into several smaller ones. Over shallows and depressions, round which cyclonic eddies are formed, cold local polar water becomes stagnant. Nansen and Helland-Hansen's theory was completely confirmed by N. Zubov (1932) and A. Sokolov (1932), when they applied the dynamic method in their treatment of the extensive new data on the hydrology of the Barents Sea. In the western part of the Sea (30° to 35° W) the North Cape current is broken up by the influence of the floor contour into separate branches, of which the least saline (34·6‰) but warm (average annual temperature 4·3° C) branch moves along the north of Norway and the Murman coast. This is the so-called Ruppinovsk branch, which is of great significance for the distribution of the littoral fauna. The second branch flows along the meridian of the Kola Guba between 71° 51′ and 72° 45′ N, the third at 73° 15′ N and the fourth at 75° 15′ N. The North Cape streams become cooler and less saline the farther north they move.

Thus the southwestern part of the Sea as far as the Kola meridian to the east and as far as 73° N have, except for the section next to the coast, a salinity of about 35‰, and a temperature of not less than 3° C in the main depth of the water column and 2° C in the bottom layer. These conditions make it possible for the warmer-water fauna to exist there.

Water balance

The following quantitative characteristics of the waters flowing into the Barent Sea were given for the summer of 1931 by A. Sokolov and V. Lednev (1935):

North Cape–Bear Island	163·3 km³/day
Spitsbergen–Franz Joseph Land	38·0
Franz Joseph Land–Novaya Zemlya	49·2
Total	250·5

The amount of water flowing in and out through the above-mentioned straits can change and create sometimes a positive, sometimes a negative balance. Thus for July 1927 A. Sokolov gives the following data:

	Flowing into the Barents Sea	Flowing out of the Barents Sea
North Cape–Bear Island	127·7 km^3/day	97·6 km^3/day
Spitsbergen–Franz Joseph Land	38·0	68·3
Franz Joseph Land–Novaya Zemlya	49·2	43·2
Total	214·9	209·1

So we may accept that in one year 40 to 70 thousand cubic kilometres of water flows into the Barents Sea from the southwest between the North Cape and Bear Island, i.e. a little more than one-third of the water which, according to Helland-Hansen's calculations, flows into the Norwegian Sea from the south. Thirty-five to 60 thousand cubic kilometres flows out towards the south from Bear Island back into the Norwegian Sea. At the north tip of Novaya Zemlya 5 to 15 thousand cubic kilometres of water flows out of the Barents Sea. According to Sokolov, the total volume of water flowing annually into the Barents Sea is 75 thousand cubic kilometres, i.e. about a quarter of the volume of the Sea.

Vertical circulation and polar front

Atlantic waters with a temperature of 4° to 12° and a salinity of 34·8 to 35·2‰, entering from the west, get gradually cooler as they move east and north, and acquire the character of the local polar waters. Under the influence of the floor contour, the Atlantic waters press against the shallows and, meeting the local less saline and colder waters, are cooled and sink. Water from the depths wells up in their place. Hence in precisely the same way as at the meeting point of the warm saline Atlantic waters and the cold less saline East Greenland waters in the Greenland Sea, the phenomena of intensified vertical circulation occur in certain areas of the Barents Sea. As a whole these phenomena are known as the polar front. It brings to the surface nutrient salts accumulated in deep layers of the Sea and causes the ventilation of the bottom layers. As a result the shallow Barents Sea is found to be very favourable for a rich development of plankton and bottom life and for the feeding of a huge amount of commercial fish (Fig. 23).

Tides

Widely open on the side of the Atlantic Ocean, the Barents Sea is greatly exposed to the influence of tides. In the southern part of the Sea on the Murman shores, the tidal range is more than 4 m, and when the tide goes out part of the bottom populated by a very rich littoral fauna is laid bare. The tides become weaker as we travel east and north (except for the eastern Murman coast and the entrance to the White Sea) and are reduced to 1m or less.

Temperature and saline conditions

In the western part of the Barents Sea (Fig. 24) where the warm Atlantic waters enter, the whole water column has a temperature above zero even in winter time. Following the bottom contour the Atlantic waters penetrate into the Barents Sea in four streams—the northern one at 80° N, the middle one along the 75° parallel, the main and most powerful stream between the 71° and 72° parallels while the fourth stream flows close to the Murman coast. In

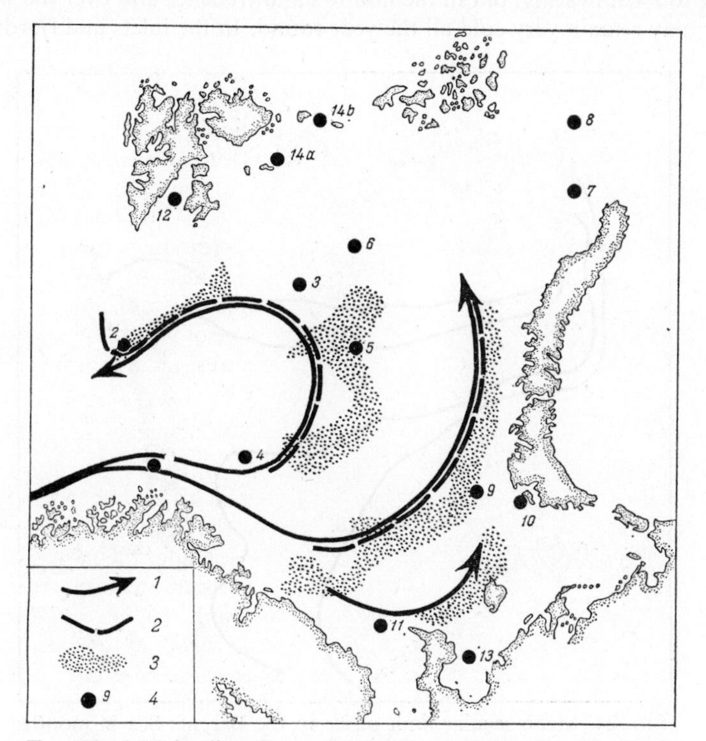

FIG. 23. *1* Main directions of currents; *2* Zone of polar front; *3* Regions of increased biomass and feeding aggregations (Zenkevitch).

the north, east and southeast of the Sea these waters are cooled and remain below zero from surface to floor all the year round. This is clearly shown from the annual averages of temperature ranges at different levels (Fig. 25).

Thus a considerable change of the warm Atlantic waters which have flowed into the cold local ones takes place in the Barents Sea. In the middle of the Sea in its northern and eastern regions only a thin surface layer is heated in summer. At depths of 10 to 25 m the temperature is already below zero. Only in the most northeasterly part, between Novaya Zemlya and Franz Joseph Land, at depths of 200 to 250 m can a temperature above zero (+1° C) be observed at a high salinity (35‰). These are Atlantic waters which penetrate from the northeast along the trenches from the centre of the polar basin (Fig. 4). In addition there is another very interesting phenomenon to be observed throughout the Barents Sea. In summer the lowest temperature remains at a depth of 50 to 75 m. This is considerably cooled and saline 'winter' water which has sunk down. It is called the intermediate cold layer. In the coastal areas of the southern part of the Sea, in its more or less isolated parts, the temperature of the surface layer in summer may be fairly high, owing to local heating, but in the hollows and trenches and over the shallows water may remain very cold all the year round. In the inlets and fjords of the

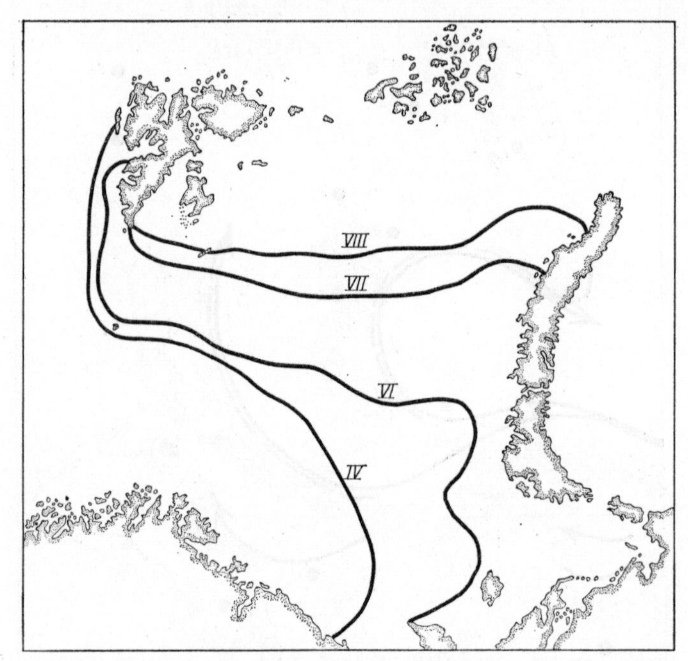

FIG. 24. Mean secular limit of ice in the Barents Sea in months from April to August (data from Meteorological Institute of Denmark).

northern part of the Sea, if they are separated from the open sea by shallow ridges, cold, low-salinity surface water remains even in summer, as, for example, in Stur-fjord in Spitsbergen. In winter, however, owing to formation of ice in bays and fjords, homothermia and homohalinity may be observed at a temperature below zero and in the presence of high salinity (35 to 37‰).

The Murman coastal area has a considerably higher temperature (Fig. 26) in summer, but in winter its temperature is above zero.

The Atlantic waters with a salinity of about 35‰ at their entrance into the Barents Sea retain the same salinity in the deep layers as they move north and east, while in the surface layers this goes down to 32 to 34‰, and only farther up the inlets do they get considerably diluted.

Ice conditions

The thick pack ice formed on the Barents Sea in winter disappears each summer, only remaining in the northern part of the Sea after a more severe winter (Fig. 24). The ice reaches its southerly extreme in April, and recedes farthest to the north in August–September.

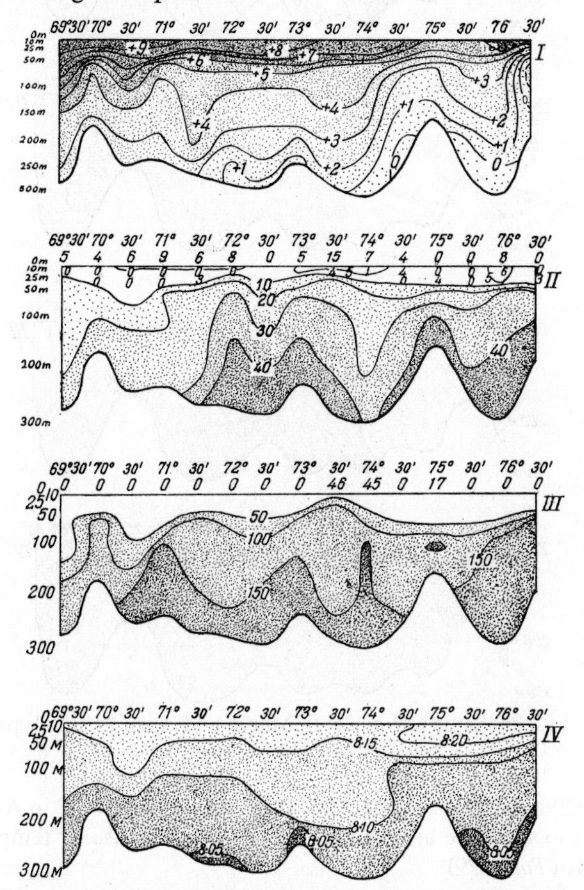

FIG. 25. Vertical distribution of temperatures (*I*), phosphates (*II*), nitrates (*III*), and concentration of hydrogen ions (*IV*) along the Kola meridian of the Barents Sea (33° 30′—in August 1930) (Kreps and Verzhbinskaya).

Data on the temperature conditions along the Kola meridian and on the ice conditions of the Barents Sea accumulated through years of work have been very successfully used by N. Zubov (1932) for a system of ice prediction for the Barents Sea, and therefore, to a certain extent, for other seas lying to the east of it. Zubov has found that the extension of the winter ice cover of the Barents Sea is closely connected with the average temperature along the Kola meridian during the preceding summer. This average temperature for three

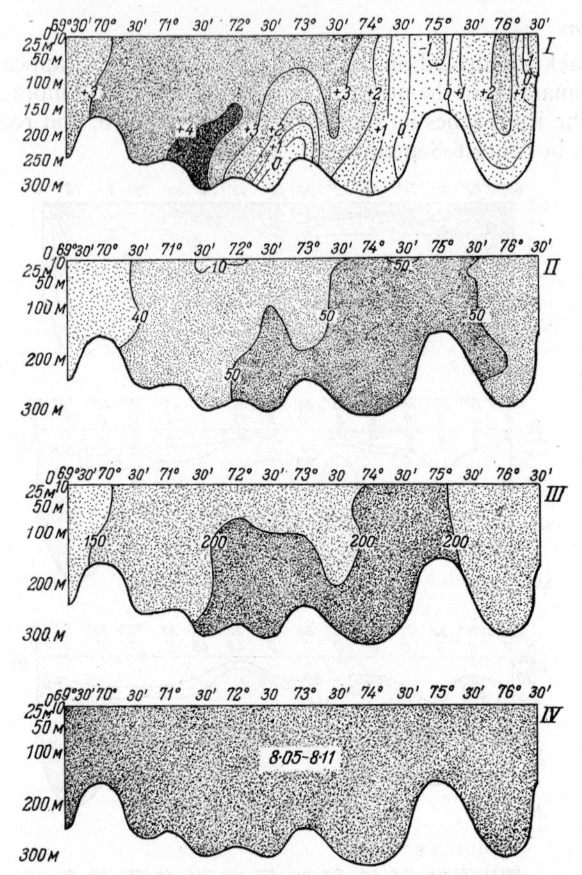

FIG. 26. Same as Fig. 25, in March and April 1930 (Kreps and Verzhbinskaya, 1930, 1932).

decades (1920 to 1950) is about 2·62° C in May and 4·41° C in August; moreover, here too we have an example of the gradual rise in temperature over long periods (*Table 29*).

Table 29

Period	May	August
Average for 1900–06	2·16°	3·94°
Average for 1921–34	2·84°	4·64°
Difference	+0·68	+0·70

The waters of the western part of the Barents Sea have definitely been getting warmer recently. This corresponds closely with the data on the ice condition of the sea (*Table 30*).

Table 30

Period	Ice cover, %
Average for 1901–06	57
Average for 1921–31	44
Difference	– 13

Oxygen

The Barents Sea, as has already been mentioned, is on the whole well aerated. In summer the oxygen content of the surface layer is usually slightly above 100 per cent of saturation, on the average 105 per cent. In summer the 10 to 25 m layer contains the maximum amount of oxygen where it sometimes reaches 123 per cent of saturation, which corresponds to the maximum development of phytoplankton. In the autumn when the photosynthesis process becomes weaker, while the vertical circulation increases, the amount of oxygen in the upper layer is somewhat below 100 per cent of saturation (90 to 100 per cent). The average minimum amount of oxygen is rarely below 85 per cent of saturation. Smaller oxygen contents were recorded in the deep trough south of Novaya Zemlya (down to 70 per cent). The amount of oxygen in the bottom layer is usually about 90 per cent. These data, however, do not cover the actual bottom layer, since during the so-called 'bottom' sampling the bathymeter remains at some distance from the sea floor. We shall revert to this problem later in connection with the quantitative distribution of benthos.

Nutrient salts

The distribution of nutrient salts, most important for the development of vegetable plankton, is correlated with the system of vertical circulation. A very full picture of the annual cycle of the changes of nutrrient salts in the Barents Sea is given by the excellent research carried out by E. Kreps and N. Verzhbinskaya (1930, 1932). The Arctic waters are slightly richer in nutrient salts than the Atlantic ones. Owing to the vigorous development of phytoplankton in the photosynthesis layer, the amount of phosphates present gradually decreases in the spring and during the summer. An accumulation of nutrient salts in the abyssal layers proceeds simultaneously and, by August, a definite stratification (Fig. 27) which also coincides with the period of the highest temperature is established. At that time the nitrates are absent from the upper layer, while their amount increases with depth and in the bottom layer reaches 200 mg/m³. The summer shortage of phosphates is particularly marked in the upper layer, from which they are absent during that season, but in the bottom layer the quantity reaches 60 mg/m³.

With the arrival of the autumn circulation and during the winter, when the whole water column gets mixed, the nutrient salts are brought up from the lower levels and a uniform distribution of them is established. The most uniform distribution is observed in March (Fig. 26)—a period of most marked homothermic conditions. At that time the amount of nitrates in the water varies from 150 to 250, and of phosphates from 40 to 60 mg/m³. The nitrate and phosphate contents increase slightly from south to north and in the northern parts of the Sea the amount of nitrates in bottom layers reaches 450 to 460 mg/m³. The off-shore waters are, on the contrary, appreciably poorer in nutrient salts. Their nitrate content may fall to 100 mg (and below) and that of phosphates to 14 to 15 mg/m³. The Arctic waters are on the whole richer in nutrient salts than the Atlantic ones. Careful all the year round observation has allowed Kreps and Verzhbinskaya not only to draw a full picture of the annual cycle of nutrient salts but to come to some interesting conclusions on biological productivity.

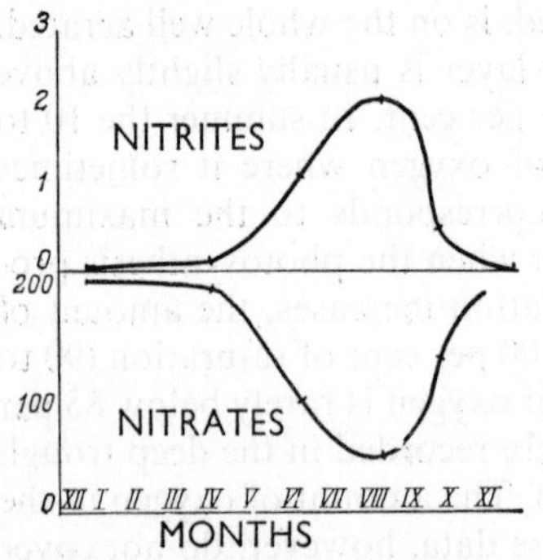

FIG. 27. Seasonal changes in nitrite and nitrate content in 0 to 100 m layer in Barents Sea in 1930, on the 72° to 72° 30′ latitude along the Kola meridian (33° 30′) (Verzhbinskaya, 1932).

First of all it was found possible to determine the total amount of phosphorus used up during the multiplication period of 1930–31 in the region near the Kola meridian. Knowing the amount of phosphorus contained in phytoplankton (0·15 per cent of the wet weight) it is possible to calculate the amount of phytoplankton which could develop at the expense of a given amount of phosphates. It was established that 3,000 to 5,000 tons of the wet mass of phytoplankton could be formed for each square kilometre of sea surface at the expense of the phosphates present through the whole depth of the Barents Sea. This amount is about double that of the annual phytoplankton production calculated by Atkinson for the English Channel (1,400 tons) and for the Oslofjord by Gran (1,600 tons/km²).

Interesting data on the distribution of nitrites in the Barents Sea are given by S. P. Brujevitch (1931). In summer nitrites are absent from the photosynthesis layer; the largest amount is accumulated under it, at a depth of 50 m or more.

The amount of nitrites is rarely above 10 mg/m³. Usually it is a few milligrammes. Nitrites are present in such amounts usually only at the end of the summer and in the autumn. They generally disappear after the period of vertical circulation in winter. Hence accumulation of nitrites takes place under the zone of the highest production of plankton by the end of the photosynthesis period. Brujevitch notes a decrease of oxygen content in the layer of the highest concentration of nitrites. The concentration of nitrites and the decrease of oxygen content are the results of oxidation processes accompanying the disintegration of the organic substances of defunct plankton, which decomposes to amino-acids and ammonia. The fact of the rapid summer and autumn accumulation of nitrites followed by their oxidation to nitrates was also noted by Harvey for the Atlantic Ocean. The nitrites are considered by most investigators to be an intermediate phase of the process of ammonia and amino-acid oxidation to nitrates. On the other hand, V. Butkevitch considers that the nitrites accumulate under the photosynthesis layer as a result of the reduction of nitrates, since no nitrifying bacteria have been found in the surface layers of sea water.

Quantitative correlation between the nitrates and nitrites is evident from Fig. 27, drawn by Verzhbinskaya (1932) for the Barents Sea. Ammonia is formed during the decomposition of organic substances. Nitrogen content in the form of ammonia is low in the upper layer of the Barents Sea—no more than 10 to 20 mg/m^3. Below the photosynthesis layer (50 m) the amount of ammonia decreases with depth and at the bottom it is 3 to 5 mg/m^3. Similar results were obtained for the Danish Strait by the *Meteor* expedition.

There is no shortage of silica in the Barents Sea even in the period of the highest increase of photosynthesis, and therefore it is not a limiting factor in the development of phytoplankton. The silica content in the waters of the western part of the Barents Sea reaches 1,000 mg/m^3. Within the region of the Kola meridian the amount of silica in the winter varies between 400 and 800 mg/m^3. By the end of summer, as a result of phytoplankton development, the silica content in the upper layers of water falls to 200 mg/m^3, and in the bottom layer rises to 600 to 800 mg/m^3.

Sea soils

M. Klenova (1940, 1961), who has for many years investigated the sea-bed of the Barents Sea, points out that its sediments consist of grains of greatly varying sizes, mostly of mineral origin, from a thin silt to large boulders (Fig. 28). Sandy silt (10 to 30 per cent; about 21 per cent of the fine fraction*) is the preponderant soil of the Barents Sea, occupying about 4 per cent of its bottom area. Fifteen per cent of the bottom area is covered with sand or sandy silt, the remaining 25 per cent with silts. Clayey mud forms only 1 per cent of the bottom area. There is a great predominance of silica and alumina in the chemical composition of typical Barents Sea soils (*Table 31*).

Table 31. Typical percentage compositions of floor of Barents Sea

Constituent	Sand	Silty sand	Sand and silt	Silty clay
Silica (SiO_2)	84·21	79·88	70·34	58·21
Titania (TiO_2)	0·29	0·26	—	—
Alumina (Al_2O_3)	7·00	8·78	12·99	19·78
Iron oxide (Fe_2O_3)	1·32	2·16	3·84	4·97
Calcium oxide (CaO)	2·43	2·76	1·54	1·76
Magnesium oxide (MgO)	0·78	0·55	2·24	2·62
Sulphuric anhydride (SO_3)	—	—	0·68	—
Losses in calcination	2·66	3·18	4·61	8·11
Water (hygroscopic)	0·65	0·95	2·55	3·67

* Bottom sediments formed of grains less than 0·01 mm in diameter are called the fine fraction.

The brown colour of the surface layer of the sandy silt and silt is a well-known and interesting phenomenon characteristic of the floor of various oceans and seas, and widespread in the Barents Sea.

The northern part of the Barents Sea and the trough south to Novaya Zemlya have brown mud bottoms. The floor of the whole White Sea depression, most of the Kara Sea and that of the Arctic basin are covered with

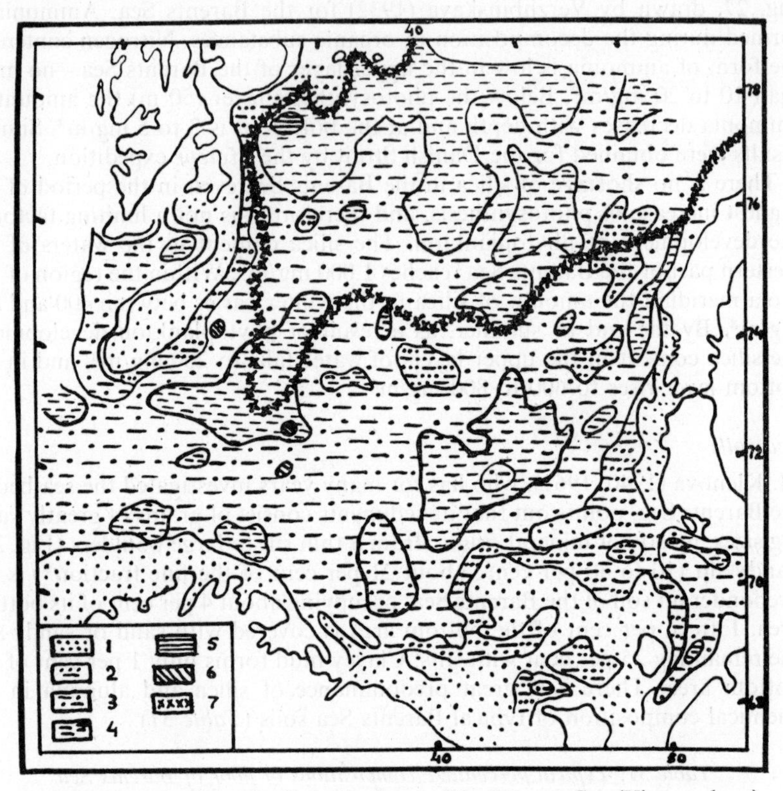

FIG. 28. Distribution of soils in the floor of the Barents Sea (Vinogradova). *1* Sand; *2* Silty sand; *3* Sandy silt; *4* Mud; *5* Clay–silt; *6* Clay; *7* Limit of brown soils.

brown mud. A brown tint of the often very thin surface layer of the sea-bed is commonly found on different kinds of bottom, even on sand. This brown colour is due to the presence of ferric and manganic hydroxides; and its presence leads to the suggestion that the bottom layer contains sufficient oxygen for their oxidation. However, brown mud beds are undoubtedly situated mainly either in depressions or within the regions of unfavourable aeration and of considerable accumulation of free carbon dioxide in the bottom layer; brown mud is not formed under conditions specially favourable for aeration. M. Klenova (1938, 1940) suggests that the brown colour of this soil may disappear as a result of a plentiful benthos population which would create a reducing medium. The fauna of brown mud is usually very scarce, hence the oxidizing medium is retained. The conditions under which the brown mud is created are undoubtedly unfavourable for the growth of benthos; Hessle has also pointed this out in relation to the Gulf of Bothnia. The problems of brown muds await further investigations.

Plant foods in the sea-bed

T. Gorshkova (1958) has analysed the organic matter present in the bottom sediments of the Barents Sea. Their carbon content varies over all

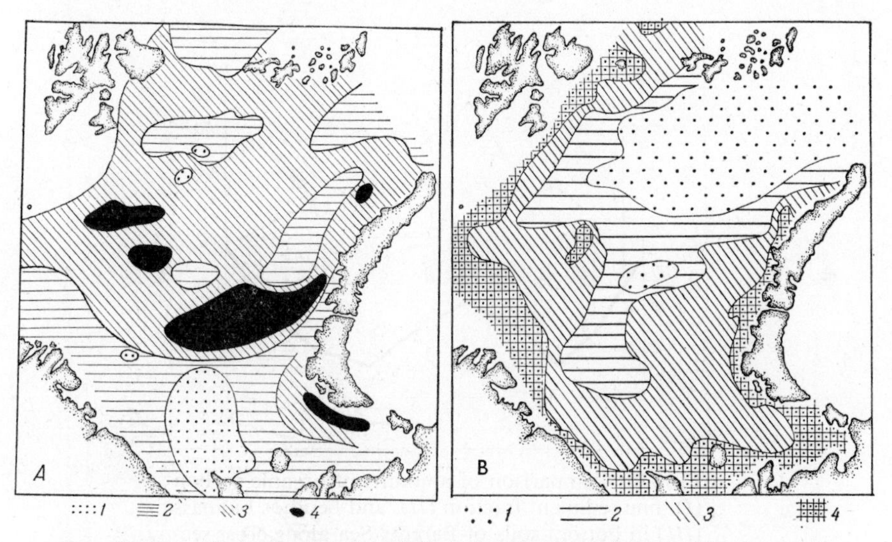

FIG. 29. Organic carbon content (A) and carbonates (B) in soils of Barents Sea bottom (Gorshkova).

A. *1* 0·5%; *2* 0·5 to 1·0%; *3* 1·0 to 2·0%; *4* 2·0 to 3·0%.

B. *1* 0·25% *2* 0·25 to 0·5%; *3* 0·5 to 1·0%; *4* 1·0% and more.

from 0·15 to 3·12 per cent, that of nitrogen from 0·02 to 0·42 per cent, and the ratio of the first to the second from 5 to 8·7 (average 7). These values are close to those obtained for the shallow parts of the Atlantic Ocean. They indicate the origin of the organic matter in sedimentation as mainly due to plankton. The range of organic carbon in the upper layer of the Barents Sea sediment is shown in Fig. 29. No simple relationship can be established between the bed's content of organic substances and some definite factor of the media; it is found to be much too complex.

The most constant relationship has been observed between the organic matter content and the mechanical properties of marine sedimentation. As a rule the larger the amount of the fine sediment fraction, the richer its organic matter content (Fig. 30). This is clearly shown by a comparison of the organic carbon content of the brown silts of the northern part of the Barents Sea (T. Gorshkova, 1957).

Clayey silt	1·78 per cent carbon
Ooze	1·31 per cent carbon
Sandy silt	0·97 per cent carbon
Silty sand	0·59 per cent carbon

In other words, in regions with favourable conditions for deposition of the fine-grained fraction, large amounts of detritus are also deposited, but on the other hand these regions are usually unfavourable for the development of

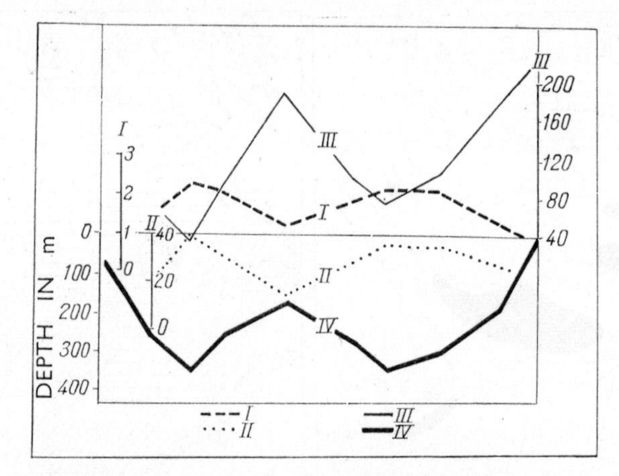

FIG. 30. Comparison of amounts of organic carbon (*I*), fine sediment fraction (*II*), and benthos biomass (*III*) in bottom soils of Barents Sea along cross section from 75° 50′ N latitude and 25° 00′ E longitude approximately along 74° parallel towards coast of Novaya Zemlya. (*IV*) Depth, m (Gorshkova, 1958).

bottom life. However, in the northern parts of the sea on soft brown sediments life is scarce and the amount of organic matter low. Finally, many regions with sandy bottoms and a rich life may have a low content of organic matter. Good vertical and horizontal water circulation prevents the accumulation of organic matter on the bottom, sweeping it again and again into a vortex.

Hence, although on one hand one may accept the rule that seas rich in life have more organic matter in their soils, in some of them a reverse relationship between the amount of bottom life and of organic matter in the sea-bed may be created. The comparison of benthos biomass and carbon content in the sea-bed, given in Fig. 30, may serve as an illustration of this. The picture of the relationship between the biomass density and the carbon content of the sediment may also be obscured by the quantitative distribution of plankton and its role in the formation of organic matter in the sea-bed.

Thus the accumulation of organic matter in the bed depends on the abundance of plankton and benthos life, which is its source, and on the conditions favouring its deposition on the sea-floor; the two factors, however, may act in the reverse direction.

The C/N ratio for the Barents Sea, close to 7, characteristic for planktogenetic organic substance, indicates a sufficient aeration of the whole water column and the very limited role of the littoral vegetation on the genesis of organic matter. From this point of view the data of T. Gorshkova (1939) on the Motovsky Gulf are most interesting. Although the shores are close to each other the ratio of C/N is here also about 7. There is no increase of organic carbon which remains constant at 0·15 to 2·76 per cent, so that even near the shores the littoral vegetation does not affect the amount and nature of the organic matter in the sea-bed. The closeness of the shores affects only the chlorophyll content, which is higher here than in regions farther removed from a shore.

III. FLORA AND FAUNA: GENERAL CHARACTERISTICS

The fauna of the Barents Sea, in spite of a complete or partial absence of a number of groups which are characteristic of warmer seas (radiolarians, Siphonophorae, corals, cephalopod molluscs, crabs, salpes, pyrosomes and some others), is both varied and abundant and consists mainly of bivalves and gastropods, polychaetes, echinoderms, lower and higher crustaceans, Porifera, hydroids, bryozoans, ascidians and Foraminifera (Fig. 31).

The number of animal species living in the Barents Sea is, probably, not less than 2,500. At present, however, owing to an insufficiently systematic study of many groups of the Barents Sea population, only an approximate estimate of the number of its species is possible.

Plankton

The composition of phytoplankton. The Barents Sea phytoplankton has not yet been adequately investigated, especially as regards its productivity. According to I. Kisselev (1937) the plankton of the Barents Sea includes:

Green algae	9 forms
Diatomaceous algae	92 forms
Peridinean algae	69 forms
Flagellatean algae	7 forms
Others	2 forms
Total	179 forms

The actual number of phytoplankton forms is probably above 200.

However, in this fairly rich stock only a few are of importance, among the diatoms the following: *Chaetoceras diadema*, *Coscinodiscus subbulliens*, *Corethron criophilum*, *Sceletonema costatum*, and two species of Rhizoselenia–*R. styliformis* and *R. semispina*. Of the green algae only *Halosphaera viridis* is very widely distributed; of the peridineans *Peridinium depressum*, *P. ovatum*, *P. pallidum*; and the three species of Ceratium—*C. longipes*, *C. arcticum* and *C. fusum*, that is 13 forms in all.

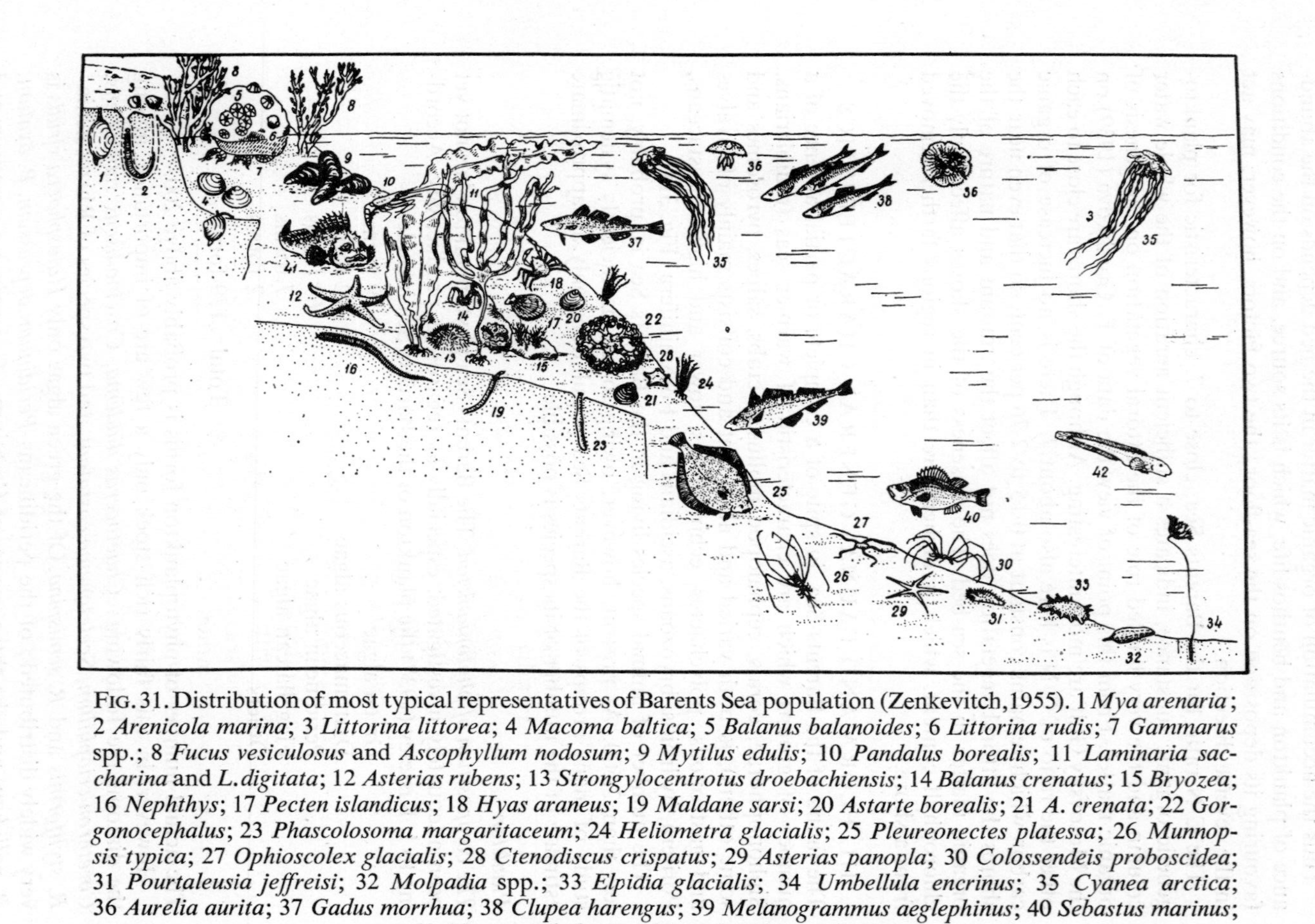

FIG. 31. Distribution of most typical representatives of Barents Sea population (Zenkevitch, 1955). 1 *Mya arenaria*; 2 *Arenicola marina*; 3 *Littorina littorea*; 4 *Macoma baltica*; 5 *Balanus balanoides*; 6 *Littorina rudis*; 7 *Gammarus* spp.; 8 *Fucus vesiculosus* and *Ascophyllum nodosum*; 9 *Mytilus edulis*; 10 *Pandalus borealis*; 11 *Laminaria saccharina* and *L. digitata*; 12 *Asterias rubens*; 13 *Strongylocentrotus droebachiensis*; 14 *Balanus crenatus*; 15 *Bryozea*; 16 *Nephthys*; 17 *Pecten islandicus*; 18 *Hyas araneus*; 19 *Maldane sarsi*; 20 *Astarte borealis*; 21 *A. crenata*; 22 *Gorgonocephalus*; 23 *Phascolosoma margaritaceum*; 24 *Heliometra glacialis*; 25 *Pleureonectes platessa*; 26 *Munnopsis typica*; 27 *Ophioscolex glacialis*; 28 *Ctenodiscus crispatus*; 29 *Asterias panopla*; 30 *Colossendeis proboscidea*; 31 *Pourtaleusia jeffreisi*; 32 *Molpadia* spp.; 33 *Elpidia glacialis*; 34 *Umbellula encrinus*; 35 *Cyanea arctica*; 36 *Aurelia aurita*; 37 *Gadus morrhua*; 38 *Clupea harengus*; 39 *Melanogrammus aeglephinus*; 40 *Sebastus marinus*; 41 *Myoxocephalus quadricornis*; 42 *Lycedes* spp.

In the spring the diatoms are most important, developing rapidly and giving an appearance of 'bloom' in some parts of the Sea. In the autumn diatoms are superseded in importance by the peridinean mass, then showing maximum development.

The course of phytoplankton development, with its two maxima, which is characteristic of the whole temperate zone of the oceans of the world, is well defined in the southwest of the Barents Sea (Fig. 32). The first maximum in the coastal waters is in May and is connected with the mass bloom of Phaeocystis (Cryptomonidinae) and to a much lesser degree with that of the diatomaceous Chaetoceras and Sceletonema. The second, smaller maximum (July to September) is conditioned by the mass development of peridineans.

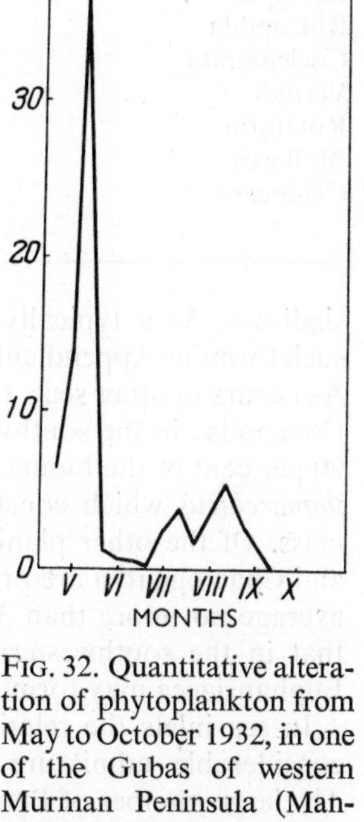

FIG. 32. Quantitative alteration of phytoplankton from May to October 1932, in one of the Gubas of western Murman Peninsula (Manteufel, 1939). The ordinate gives the number of cells in millions in a 40 m column of water of 50 cm² cross section.

Composition of zooplankton. Zooplankton in the Barents Sea (V. Bogorov, 1946) is fairly poor in its numbers; of the groups composing it only Infusoria, Copepoda and Coelenterata (*Table 32*) stand out.

The Barents Sea zooplankton contains the oceanic and neritic forms and forms distributed equally in the coastal areas in the open sea. M. Virketis (1928) includes in the first category the main forms of Copepoda genera—Calanus, Pseudocalanus, Metridia, Oithona, Euchaeta, Microsetella; salps—*Oikopleura medusa, Aglanta digitalis*: and in the second the Daphnidae Evadne and Podon, the Copepod *Temora longicornis*, and the salps *Fritillaria borealis* and *F. medusa Rathkea octopunctata*.

On the other hand the permanent inhabitants of the Barents Sea may be distinguished from the more or less temporary visitors. The latter forms of one origin or another may often appear in large numbers carried in by the waters, and rapidly disappear with a change of hydrological conditions. Thus it is possible to observe the seasonal change of zooplankton composition, which is not possible with benthos forms. Virketis includes *Calanus finmarchicus, Metridia longa, Oithona similis* and others among the main permanent inhabitants of the Barents Sea.

The more thermophilic forms of western origin keep mostly in the warm streams of the North Cape current. They move eastward in summer and westward in winter. Their numbers are higher in warmer years than in colder.

In contrast to the thermophilic forms, the arctic ones attain their highest development in winter and spring. In summer they travel far to the north, or keep to the cooler abyssal layers or the colder waters remaining over the

Table 32

Group	No. of species	Group	No. of species
Radiolaria	11	Copepoda	38
Infusoria	21	Ostracoda	3
Rhizopoda	2	Euphausiacea	5
Coelenterata	32	Amphipoda	5
Vermes	3	Mysidacea	6
Rotatoria	10	Decapoda	1
Mollusca	3	Appendicularia	3
Cladocera	2		
		Total	151

shallows. As a typically arctic component of plankton, one may mention such forms as Appendiculariidae *Oikopleura labradoriensis* and *O. vanhoeffeni*. As occurs in other seas, the main part of Barents Sea zooplankton consists of Copepoda: in the southwest of the sea (V. Jashnov, 1940) they form almost 90 per cent of the biomass: moreover the most important of them is *Calanus finmarchicus* which constitutes on average 30 per cent of the plankton biomass. Of the other plankton components only Euphausiacea (5·3 per cent) and Chaetognatha are prominent (3·2 per cent). All the others taken together average not more than 3 per cent (by biomass). B. Manteufel (1941) thinks that in the southwestern parts of the Sea at certain seasons of the year, Euphausiacea may form about half of the whole plankton biomass.

In sea inlets the relative number of Copepoda is smaller, and there is a considerable admixture of Cladocera and Cirripedia larvae (*Table 33*). The large number of Pteropoda is more or less accidental; in 1931 they were very numerous (25 per cent of the biomass), and in 1932 they were entirely absent. It is of interest to note that during both years of investigation in Motovsky Gulf *Calanus finmarchicus* constituted about the same percentage of

Table 33

Form	Average percentage composition of plankton in annual biomass	
	Southwestern part of Barents Sea	Motovsky Gulf
Calanus finmarchicus	80·46	63·5
Other Copepoda	7·80	7·0
Euphausiacea	5·32	5·6
Chaetognatha	3·22	1·4
Coelenterata	1·51	2·0
Balanus nauplii	—	3·3
Limacina retroversa	—	12·0
Cladocera	—	3·3
Others	1·65	6·2

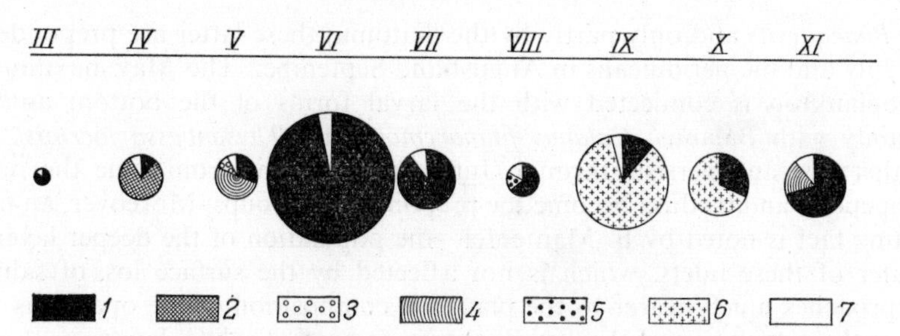

FIG. 33 Quantitative and qualitative changes (mg/m³) of zooplankton in the Motovsky Gulf in 1931 (Manteufel). *1 Calanus finmarchicus*; *2* Balanus larvae; *3* Decapoda larvae; *4 Thysanoessa inermis*; *5* Copepoda (summer community); *6 Limacina retroversa*; *7* Varia.

plankton (64 and 63 per cent) and that the relative amounts of some other groups present in the open sea and in the gulf were also constant (other Copepoda, Euphausiacea and Coelenterata).

In large inlets and fjords widely open to the sea, the composition of plankton is intermediate between that of the open sea and of the closed bays and inlets. Copepoda (and particularly *Calanus finmarchicus*) constitute, as mentioned above, the preponderant part of the plankton (Fig. 33). The June maximum of zooplankton is connected actually with the development of *C. finmarchicus*. For a biomass of almost up to 300 mg/m³ (1931) the zooplankton consists of 92 per cent *Calanus finmarchicus*.

In small bays and inlets, more or less isolated form the open sea, the neritic character of the plankton is most strongly marked (Fig. 34). The May maximum of the phytoplankton is controlled here also by the mass development

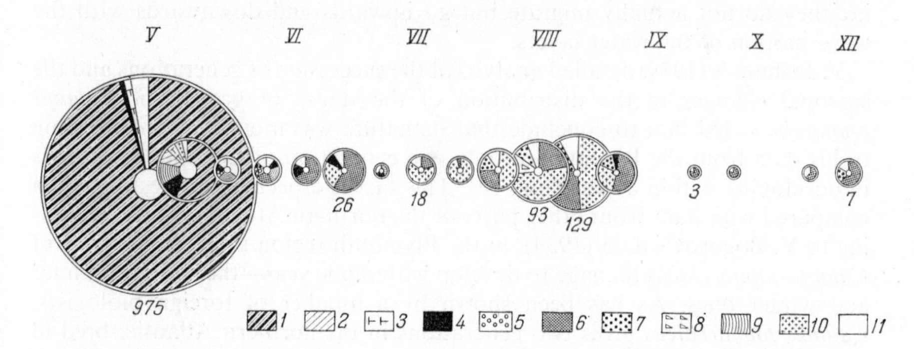

FIG. 34. Changes of zooplankton biomass (mg/m³) in one small isolated Guba of the western Murman Peninsula in a layer of 10 to 25 m (Manteufel). The area of the circle corresponds to the biomass represented by the numerals. *1* Nauplii–Cirripedia; *2* Polychaeta larvae; *3* Decapoda larvae; *4 Calanus finmarchicus*, *5 Fritillaria borealis*; *6* Neritic Copepoda; *7 Pseudocalanus elongatus*; *8* Cladocera; *9* Euphausiacea larvae; *10* Medusae; *11* Varia.

of *Phaeocystis* and only partly by the diatoms; these latter are preponderant in July and the peridineans in August and September. The May maximum of zooplankton is connected with the larval forms of the bottom animals, mainly with Balanus, *Calanus finmarchicus* and *Thysanoessa inermis*; it is rather low and persists through June only. Starting from June the neritic Copepoda and medusa become the preponderant groups. Moreover, an interesting fact is noted by B. Manteufel—the population of the deeper layers of water of these inlets, which is not affected by the surface loss of salinity, approaches much nearer to the plankton composition of the open seas than does the population of the upper, always somewhat saline, layer.

Vertical migrations and seasonal variations. As was shown by V. Bogorov (1932) and V. Jashnov (1939) for a number of the highest mass forms of Copepoda during their young stages they keep to the surface layer of water (in the south of the Sea mainly at a depth of 10 to 25 m and in the north at 25 to 75 m); the adult forms, however, descend into deeper layers (75 to 300 m).

It is most curious that under the conditions of a polar day the Copepoda remain on the same level at different hours of the day and night (V. Bogorov, (1938); they do not migrate vertically every 24 hours, as they do in other latitudes with the change of day to night. However, as we have noted in our general section, owing to the presence of the deep waves, the layers of water are subject to 24-hourly vertical oscillations, sometimes of several tens of metres. Evidently, Copepoda, in order to keep their position within the same intensity of light, are forced to travel in the opposite direction to the wave motion. Hence the purpose of the known vertical semidiurnal migrations of Copepoda is to remain at a constant level. V. Bogorov has observed the same phenomenon in other plankton. In the autumn with the alternation of day and night Copepoda begin their daily vertical migration of the usual type. On the other hand, some organisms change their position of greatest density twice daily, i.e. they do not actually migrate but go upwards and downwards with the wave motion of the water layers.

V. Jashnov's (1939) detailed analysis of the succession of generations and the seasonal changes in the distribution of the stages of growth of *Calanus finmarchicus* led him to conclude that its nature was monocyclic. According to his data from the Barents Sea only one generation of Copepoda succeeds in developing within a year (Fig. 35). This fact is especially interesting when compared with data from other parts of the northern Atlantic. Thus, according to V. Bogorov's data (1934), in the Plymouth region three generations of *Calanus finmarchicus* manage to develop within one year—the spring, summer and winter ones. As has been shown by a number of foreign biologists, *Calanus finmarchicus* gives two generations in the northern Atlantic, bred in the spring and by the end of the summer (Scotland, the western shores of Norway, etc.). However, a very circumstantial survey by M. Kamshilov (1955), carried out almost fifteen years later, has led him to the conclusion that in the eastern part of the Barents Sea *Calanus finmarchicus* breeds twice a year. The first breeding period begins in April, and at the end of June or the beginning of July there appears the second brood, with considerably bigger females.

These females breed another summer generation. Moreover, Kamshilov notes the considerable variation in the size of *Calanus finmarchicus* in the Barents Sea, depending on temperature conditions. Large forms develop at a low temperature, small ones at a high temperature. The large size, high breeding capacity and other characteristics of the Barents Sea Calanus, do not enable us, according to Kamshilov, to regard it as a special race different from the Atlantic one. This difference between the data obtained by Jashnov and by Kamshilov, separated by an interval of almost twenty years, might, possibly, be explained by the warming-up of the Barents Sea waters. B. Manteufel

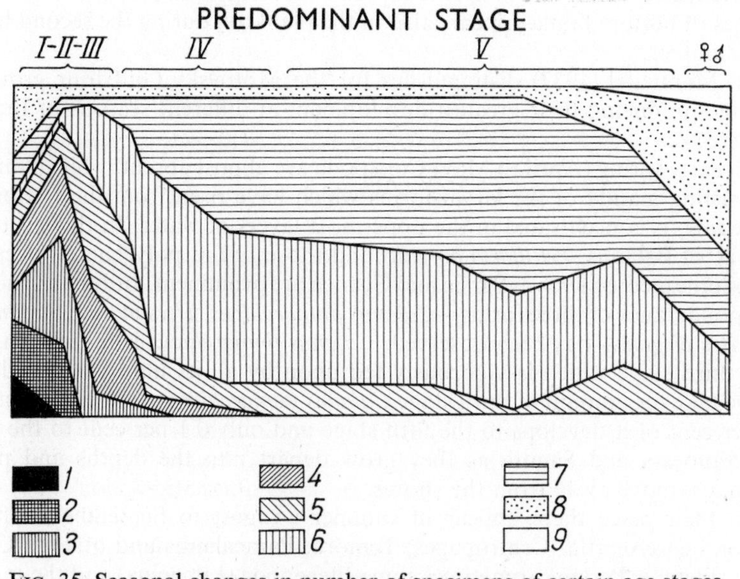

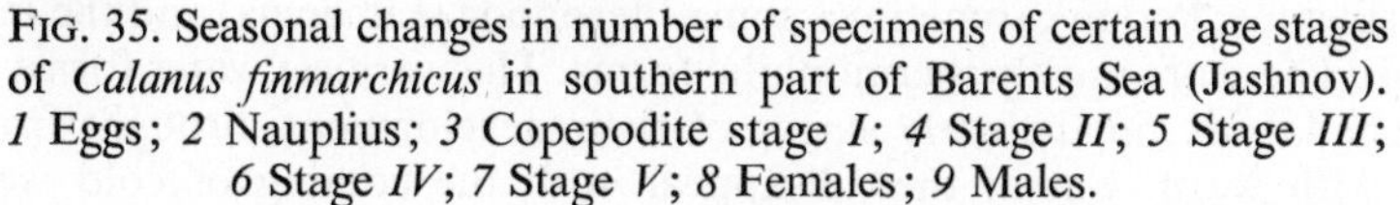

FIG. 35. Seasonal changes in number of specimens of certain age stages of *Calanus finmarchicus* in southern part of Barents Sea (Jashnov). *1* Eggs; *2* Nauplius; *3* Copepodite stage *I*; *4* Stage *II*; *5* Stage *III*; *6* Stage *IV*; *7* Stage *V*; *8* Females; *9* Males.

(1939) recorded a second generation of *Calanus finmarchicus* brought into the southwest of the Barents Sea from the west.

Calanus finmarchicus males never rise above the 75 m level, while the females are more uniformly distributed. Late in the autumn and in the winter the growing *Calanus finmarchicus* go down to the deeper layers of the sea. 'Before the coming of spring,' writes V. Jashnov, '*Calanus finmarchicus* begins to rise in a mass into the upper layers, and the newly bred young stages begin to appear then.' Thus *Calanus finmarchicus* serves as a good example of a plankton organism making seasonal vertical migrations during the year.

The large pelagic crustaceans—Meganyctiphanes, Themisto, Thysanoessa—have a biennial life cycle. Some of them breed twice a year, in the spring and summer, others only in the summer. The picture of the vertical propagation of these crustaceans is similar to that of *Calanus finmarchicus*: the immature forms keep mostly to the surface layer, the adults to the depths. They likewise prefer the deep layers in the summer and the surface ones in the winter; this is an example of a peculiar type of migration conditioned by phototropism but adapted not to the daily change of light, but to the yearly alternation of the polar day and night.

A certain change of the qualitative composition of plankton is observed during the year and is particularly marked in inlets.

In the spring and early summer, the oceanic forms of plankton are dominant, while in the second half of the summer and in the autumn there is a considerable admixture of neritic forms. A considerable amount of the larval stages of bottom fauna appears also in the plankton during the second half of the summer.

B. Manteufel (1937) distinguishes for the Motovsky Gulf four groups of forms, producing their greatest development at different seasons of the year (Fig. 33).

In early spring (April to May) Copepoda are almost absent, while plankton, consisting mainly of the larval forms which have risen from the bottom for breeding, is concentrated in the uppermost layers of water. In this group the larvae of Balanus, *Fritillaria borealis* and those of the polychaetes, decapods and some medusa such as Sarsia and Cyanea are prominent. In June the notable preponderance of three forms—*Calanus finmarchicus*, *Thysanoessa inermis* and *Sagitta elegans*—has been observed. *Calanus finmarchicus* is found mainly in the third stage which is vigorously fed upon by all its numerous predators. It we take the amount of third stage *Calanus finmarchicus* as the unit, then only 9 per cent of it develops to the fifth stage and only 0·1 per cent to the sixth. Thysanoessa and Sagitta as they grow depart into the depths and partly, perhaps, move away from the shores.

In their place there appear in summer (August to September) different Copepoda (Acartia, Centropages, Temora, Paracalanus and others), Cladocera (Evadne, Podon), sometimes some Pteropoda (Limacina) and the mollusc larvae. These are mostly thermophilic forms. The warmest water forms (some Copepoda) are, in the early stages of their development, brought from the west with warm water; they disappear with the coming of cold weather. Others (Cladocera) live through the winter in the stage of resting eggs.

Finally, in the late autumn and in the winter the fourth group develops significantly.

This group contains a whole series of Copepoda (Metridia, *Calanus hyperboreus*, Euchaeta, Oithona and others), Euphausiacea (Thysanoessa, Meganyctiphanes), *Oikopleura labradoriensis* and *Aglantha digitale*. In the spring their number is greatly reduced and in summer they are met only in the deepest parts of the inlet, and then only in small numbers.

In the open sea the seasonal changes of plankton are not so sharply defined, *Calanus finmarchicus* and Euphausiacea are, however, sharply predominant even in June, and different Copepoda and other Euphausiacea in December.

Quantitative distribution of plankton. It is possible to obtain an idea of plankton productivity in the southwesterly half of the Barents Sea, southwest of a line

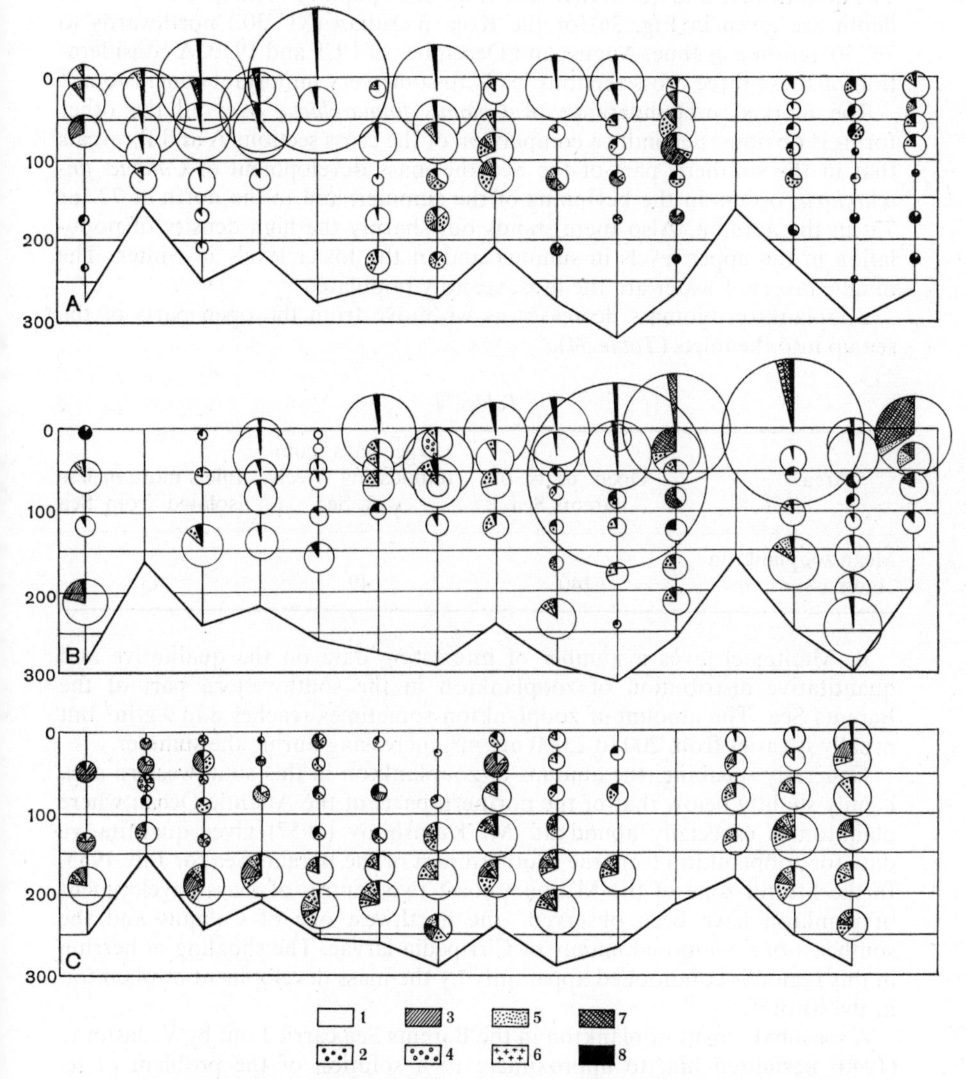

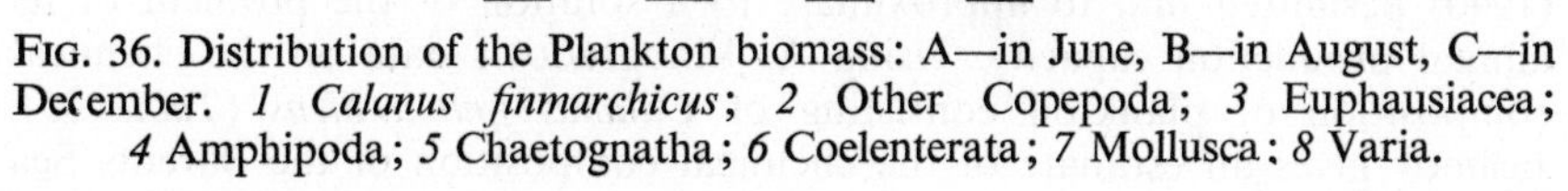

FIG. 36. Distribution of the Plankton biomass: A—in June, B—in August, C—in December. *1 Calanus finmarchicus*; *2* Other Copepoda; *3* Euphausiacea; *4* Amphipoda; *5* Chaetognatha; *6* Coelenterata; *7* Mollusca; *8* Varia.

connecting Vaigach Island with Stur-fjord in Spitsbergen, from the work of V. Jashnov (1939), B. Manteufel (1939) and M. Kamshilov (1956, 1957). The quantitative and qualitative distribution of plankton and its changes with depth are given in Fig. 36 for the Kola meridian (33° 30′) northwards to 76° 30′ latitude in June, August and December of 1929 and 1930. A consideration of these three cross sections leads to some very important conclusions.*

The marked preponderance of *Calanus finmarchicus* over all the other forms is obvious. Secondly a comparison of the cross sections A and B reveals that in the southern part of the Sea the mass development of *Calanus finmarchicus* occurs in the beginning of the summer, and to the north of 72° or 73° in the autumn. Also there stands out sharply the high density of population in the upper levels in summer and in the lower levels in winter. The middle layers of water are the most scantily populated.

Zooplankton biomass decreases as we move from the open parts of the sea up into the inlets (*Table 34*).

Table 34

Area	Open parts of Barents Sea	Large bays communicating freely with Sea	Inlets more or less isolated from Sea
Mean zooplankton biomass, mg/m³	140	49	43

B. Manteufel gives a number of interesting data on the qualitative and quantitative distribution of zooplankton in the southwestern part of the Barents Sea. The amount of zooplankton sometimes reaches 8 to 9 g/m³ but usually it varies from 200 to 2,000 mg/m³, increasing during the summer.

Generally speaking, the amount of zooplankton in this southwestern area is only slightly below that of the northern parts of the Atlantic Ocean where plankton is especially abundant. M. Kamshilov (1957) gives quantitative data for zooplankton from the southern part of the Barents Sea for July 1953. In the littoral zone of the Murman coast two centres of mass development of plankton have been observed—the northwest one of Calanus and the southeast one composed mainly of Cirripedia larvae. The shoaling of herring in this region is conditioned apparently by the mass development of plankton in the littoral.

A seasonal census of plankton in the Barents Sea carried out by V. Jashnov (1940) permitted him to approximate to a solution of the problem of its annual production capacity. Using A. Vinogradov's data on the chemical composition of plankton consisting of *Calanus finmarchicus* (*Table 35*), Jashnov gives an estimate of the chemical composition of the Barents Sea plankton as a whole, in millions of tons (*Table 36*), expressing the total production of the Sea by the amount of food required by the whole mass of

* Total plankton biomass is represented by the area of the circle, while the biomass of different plankton components is shown by sectors.

Table 35

% wet weight		Loss of weight	% dry weight					Calories, cal/g
Plankton from	Dry residue	on drying	Ash	Chitin	Albumen	Fat	Total Nitrogen	dry basis
Motovsky Gulf 1	13·3	86·7	14·04	3·72	62·56	19·3	10·21	5,742
Motovsky Gulf 2	14·3	85·7	16·10	2·99	64·38	14·8	10·48	5,339
Barents Sea	15·2	84·8	14·64	3·48	61·00	21·5	9·98	—
Average	14·3	85·7	14·93	3·4	62·65	18·5	10·22	5,540

Calanus finmarchicus. The amount of oxygen used by this crustacean in the adult state is assessed on the basis that 1,000 specimens require 0·33 m³/hour in the summer.

On the other hand, knowing the chemical composition of *Calanus finmarchicus*, it may be calculated that 222 g of oxygen is required for the oxidation of 1 kg of its wet material. Using these data, V. Jashnov has calculated that the amount of food needed for *Calanus finmarchicus* in the Barents Sea must be 290 to 480 tons under every 1 km² of the sea surface; and since *Calanus finmarchicus* feeds mainly on phytoplankton, it is possible to estimate the minimum value of the production of phytoplankton in the Barents Sea, although its true value must be considerably higher. Let us remember that the estimation of the annual production of phytoplankton by the consumption of phosphates, carried out by Kreps and Verzhbinskaya, gave a quantity of the order of 3,000 to 5,000 tons of wet weight under every 1 km² of the sea surface, and that even this figure, as we have said, must be recognized as considerably lower than the actual one.

On the other hand, since *Calanus finmarchicus* is a one-year animal, we can assume that the P/B ratio for the Barents Sea is about 1.

Nutritional value of plankton. As in other seas of the world ocean, *Calanus finmarchicus* of the Barents Sea is, as a mass form of Copepoda, one of the main links in the food chain of the pelagic region. Huge masses of herrings, haddock and the fry of various fish are fed on this crustacean medusa and ctenophores, which devour enormous numbers of *Calanus finmarchicus* and are great rivals of theirs.

As stated above, *Calanus finmarchicus* breeds once a year in the Barents

Table 36. Average chemical composition of Barents Sea plankton in millions of tons after V. Jashnov.

Wet weight	38·6	Fat	1·1
Dry weight	6·4	Chitin	0·2
Protein	3·9	Ash	1·2

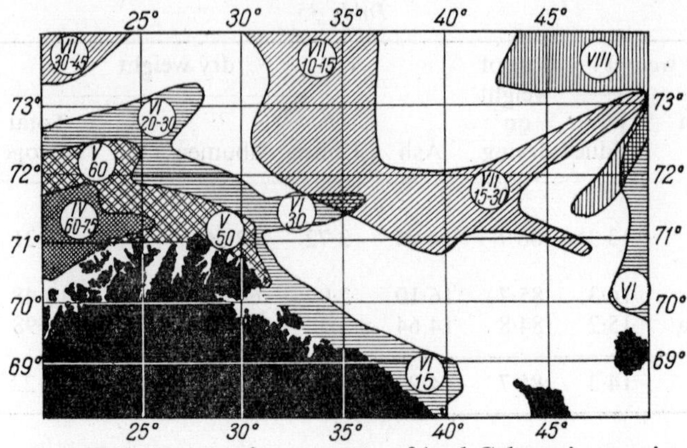

FIG. 37. Sequence of occurrence of 'red Calanus' zones in Barents Sea (Manteufel). Months of occurrence are shown in Roman numerals and days of life in Arabic numerals.

Sea. A second generation appears only in the extreme southwestern part of the Sea brought in from the west. The so-called 'red Calanus' (fourth to fifth Copepoda stages) which acquires the red tint as a consequence of colouring by some oil drops, has the highest nutritional value. In summer, as reported by B. Manteufel (1941), a kind of wave of the red Calanus passes from the west to the east and north. Calanus reaches sexual maturity in the western part of the Sea in April (Fig. 37) and in the eastern part in August. Moreover the life span of red Calanus decreases from 65 to 75 days in the west to 15 to 30 days in the east and its numbers also decrease from west. The herring's most abundant Calanus feeding ground is in the 0 to 25 m layer in the southwestern part of the Sea.

In some years even with a slight rise of temperature and some decrease in salinity of the upper layers of the southwestern part of the Barents Sea Ctenophora, *Bolinopsis infundibulum* and some medusae (Cyanea, Aurelia, Staurophora) develop in large numbers in July, August and September. If their period of mass development coincides with that of the red Calanus it is devoured in large numbers by Ctenophora and medusa, and its amount may be decreased so much that the herring would not find enough food in such feeding grounds. Coelenterata devour not only Copepoda and other plankton, but they clear masses of water of all living matter. In some years (for instance in 1938) the number of Ctenophora was so great that it is actually possible to assume that all the water of the layer inhabited by the Ctenophora was cleared of the main mass of zooplankton by them. The quantitative ratio of Ctenophora and Calanus in various regions of the sea in 1938 is shown in *Table 37*.

Table 37

Regions	1	2	3	4
Bolinopsis infundibulum	None	Small number	Large number	Masses
Calanus finmarchicus	Many	Fair amount	Small number	Very few

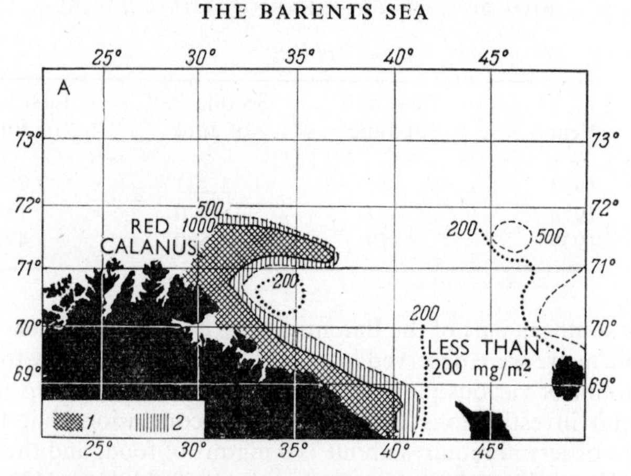

FIG. 38. Distribution of plankton wet weight in 0 to 25 m layer of water, mg/m³. A—in second half of June 1937 (Manteufel). *1* Plankton biomass above 1,000 mg/m²; *2* Plankton biomass 500 to 1,000 mg/m².

The mass destruction of Calanus by Ctenophora in 1938 becomes particularly conspicuous from a comparison of the quantitative distribution of this crustacean in 1937 and 1938 (Figs. 38 and 39) with the wet weight of plankton in the 0 to 25 m layer of the southwestern part of the Barents Sea, expressed in mg/m³ (*Table 38*).

M. Kamshilov (1957) has elucidated some most interesting details of the role of Ctenophora in the development of plankton. Three species of Ctenophora, *Bolinopsis infundibulum*, *Pleurobrachia pileus* and *Beroe cucumis*

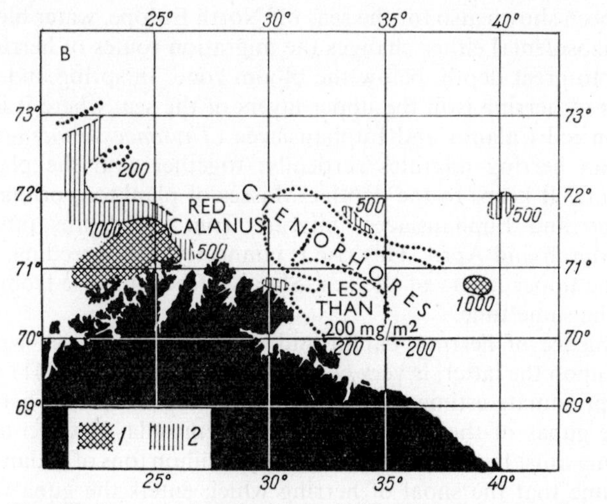

FIG. 39. In second half of June 1938—the same notation as in Fig. 38.

Table 38

Year	First half of June	Second half of June	First half of July
1937	—	1,233	2,258
1938	437	270	133
1939	819	1,580	491

inhabit the southern part of the Barents Sea. Up to 123 specimens of Bolinopsis per cubic metre were observed in July. This most predatory form destroys a huge amount of various plankton organisms, mainly *Calanus finmarchicus*. Experimental investigations have led to the conclusion that the mass of Ctenophora observed requires about 170 mg/m³ of food, and the annual production of Ctenophora was, according to the 1950–54 data, 343 mg/m³.

In the second half of June 1938 the total amount of plankton in the southwestern part of the Barents Sea was 1·5 million tons less than in 1939 and 1·1 million tons less than in 1937. Evidently such considerable fluctuations in plankton development and, in particular, in that of Calanus and Ctenophora would cause considerable fluctuations in the quantitative distribution of herring and other plankton-eating fish.

Previously, 1935 was an equally unfavourable year for the feeding of herring and other plankton-eating fish. The distribution of herring in the Barents Sea and the routes of their horizontal migration depend to a great extent on the composition and distribution of plankton: in summer, herrings move to the east with the mass of the growing plankton. Herring fattens up mainly in the southwestern part of the Sea. By the end of the winter it moves in the opposite direction.

As has been shown also for the seas off North Europe, water bloom (Phaeocystis, Rhizosolenia) either changes the migration routes of herring or makes them sink to great depth, below the bloom zone. In spring and summer the main mass of herring is in the upper layers of the sea, where it is intensively fattened on red Calanus and Euphausiacea (*Thysanoessa inermis*). In spring and autumn herring migrates vertically, together with the plankton (Fig. 40): in winter it keeps to the depths. Masses of plankton, primarily *Calanus finmarchicus* and Euphausiacea, migrate from the depths into the upper layers in March and April. This rise is connected with breeding, which takes place in the upper layers of the sea. Shoals of herring rise from the bottom layers at the same time.

The influence of herring, caplin and the fry of other fish which feed on plankton, upon the latter, is very considerable. Manteufel (1941) gives the following approximate estimate: in 1934 about 200,000 tons of herring entered one of the gubas of the western Murman Peninsula. In the course of a year these herring must have eaten not less than 4 million tons of Calanus plankton. If we assume that the shoal of herring which enters the guba forms only a small part of the total amount of Barents Sea herring, and that about the same amount of plankton is eaten by caplin and that the other plankton-eating

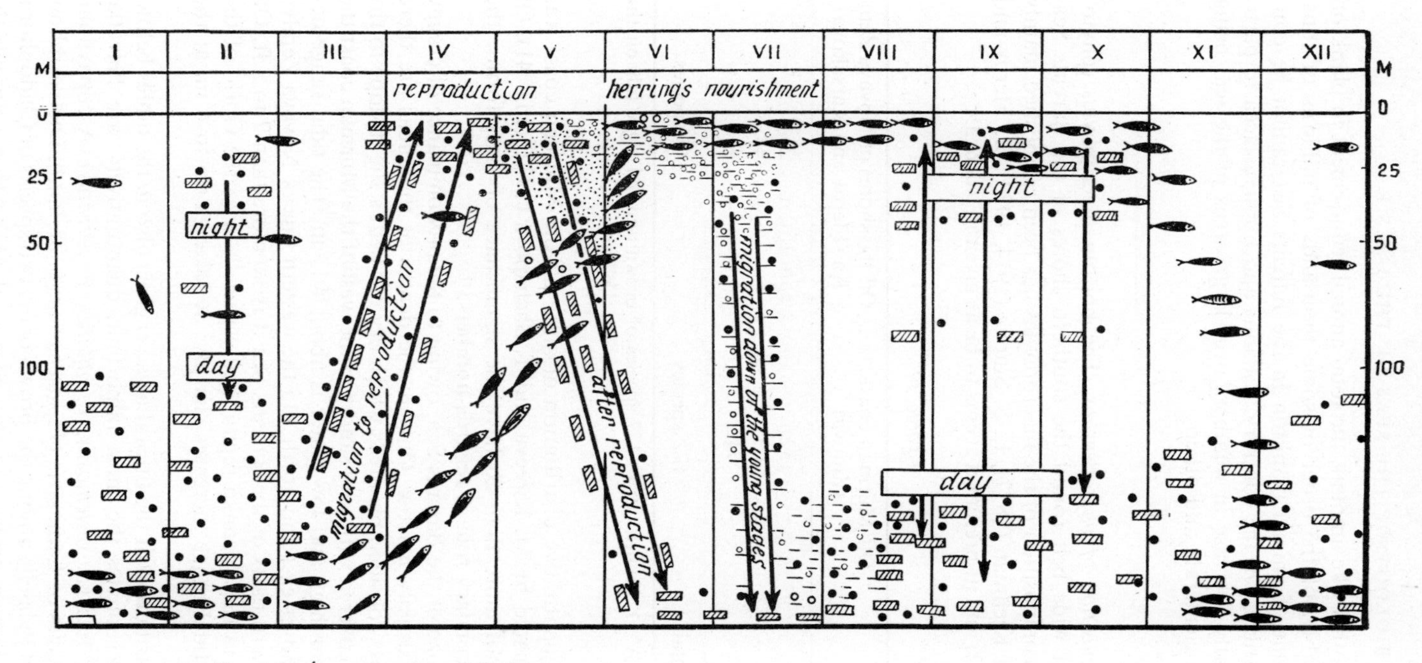

Fig. 40. Diagram of vertical migration of immature herring and of its food (Calanus and Euphausiaceae) within the region of Murman Bank (Manteufel, 1941). The direction of plankton migration is shown by the arrows, daily vertical plankton migrations are shown by double-ended arrows. *1 V* to *VII* Copepoda stages of *Calanus finmarchicus*; *2 I* to *V* Copepoda stages; *3* Adult Thysanoessa; *4* Thysanoessa larvae; *5* Herring; *6* Water-bloom.

fish consume another like amount, the total annual requirement in plankton would be, probably, of the order of some thousands of millions of tons. Hence the amount of animal plankton in the Barents Sea cannot be considered inexhaustible. On the contrary, Calanus and Euphausiacea in particular might greatly decrease in numbers over large areas of the sea, being eaten by fish, Coelenterata and others.

Benthos

Qualitative composition of phytobenthos, The bottom macrophytes (phytobenthos) form a wide belt round the southern shores of the Barents Sea. The qualitative composition of the macrophytes has been established mainly by the survey of Kjellman (1877), E. S. Sinova (1914, 1923), B. Flerov and Karsakova (1932) and at present it seems to be as given in *Table 39.*

Table 39

Algae	Off Murman coast (Zinova)	Off the shores of Novaya Zemlya (Flerov and Karsakova)
Green	32	26
Brown	69*	48
Red	71	41
Total	172 species	115 species

* According to A. D. Zinova (1950) 177 species of brown and red algae inhabit the Barents Sea.

The vertical quantitative distribution of algae off the Murman coast was carefully investigated by M. Kireeva and T. Shchapova (1932) (Fig. 41). Of the 172 forms not more than 20 have the significance of mass forms, the others play a secondary role as regards numbers.

The littoral zone of the Barents Sea, owing to the predominance of craggy steep shores, is usually narrow. Only in the depths of the gubas are there some more or less considerable areas which dry out with a slight slope to the bottom and are covered with silty sand. On the west of the Murman coast the difference between high and low water is about 4·17 m. The tidal range decreases as one moves east and north. On the western side of Novaya Zemlya and in the northern parts of the Barents Sea it is no more than 2 to 3 ft. On the other hand, in the Voronka region and especially near the Gorlo of the White Sea, the tidal range increases sharply: at Iokanga up to 6 m, at the Gorlo to 8·5 m.

The zonal distribution of the littoral algae is given also in the tables below. Among the macrophytes the most important, quantitatively, are Pelvetia, three species of fuci (*F. vesiculosus, F. inflatus, F. serratus*), Ascophyllum, Chorda; two species of Laminaria (*L. saccharina, L. digitata*), Dictyosiphon, Desmarestia and Pylaiella among the brown ones; two species of Cladophora, two species of Enterimorpha and two species of Monostroma among the green ones; and among the red ones *Rhodymenia palmata, Odonthalia dentata, Ptilota plumosa, Delesseria sanguinea*, Phyllophora, Brodiaei and Lithothamnion.

Quantitative distribution of phytobenthos. On the littoral, among the species cited, *Ascophyllum nodosum, Fucus vesiculosus, F. inflatus, F. serratus* and on the upper level of the sublittoral both species of Laminaria are much in

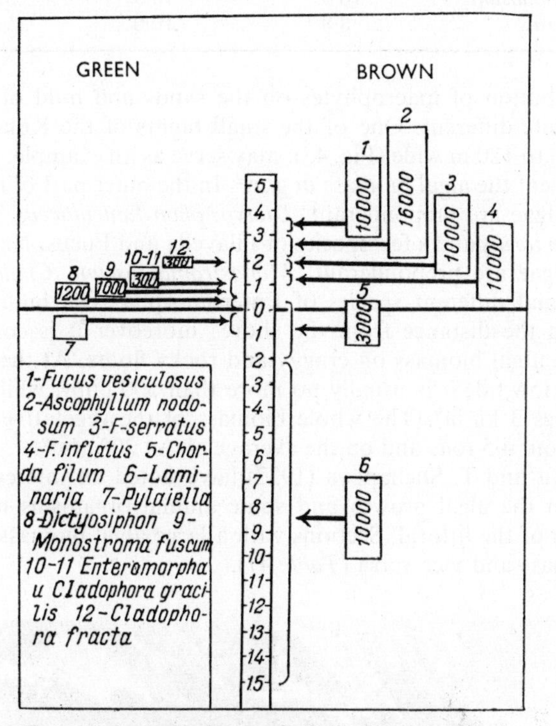

FIG. 41. Quantitative vertical distribution of main forms of phytobenthos on rock and stone soils off the western Murman coast, g/m³ (Zenkevitch). (The vertical series of numerals denotes metres from zero depth.)

evidence. Moreover, it is remarkable that the mean biomass indices of all these forms are very stable not only for different regions of the western Murman coast, but also for a much wider area (*Table 40* and Fig. 41).

In the Ascophyllum bed (Fig. 42) a biomass of as much as 28 kg/m² has been observed, while fuci do not produce more than 12 kg/m². According to the estimates of the above-mentioned workers, 39 tons of wet algae can be obtained from a portion of a craggy or rocky littoral of 1 to 15 m wide and 1km in length, while from the whole Murman coast more than 500,000 tons can be obtained.

Table 40

Species	Average biomass, kg/m²		
	Western Murman		Gulmarfjord (Sweden) (Gislen, 1930)
	Craggy cliffs	Rocky shale	
Ascophyllum nodosum	16·0	16·5	16·0
Fucus vesiculosus	8·8	10·0	9·0

The distribution of macrophytes on the sands and mud of the Murman littoral is quite different. One of the small bights of the Kola Inlet, 220 m long and 100 to 120 m wide (Fig. 43), may serve as an example. The figures on the map present the algal biomass in g/m². In the outer part of the tidal range the brown algae are preponderant, *Dictyosiphon funiculaceus*, *D. mesogloja*, *Stictyosiphon torilis* and a few species of Pilavella and Fucus. Nearer the shore the green algae are preponderant, *Monostroma fuscum*, *Cladophora fracta*, *Cl. gracilis* and different species of Enteromorpha. The biomass decreases sharply with the distance from the shore; moreover it is considerably inferior to the algal biomass on craggy and rocky floors. At the inner part of the beach at low tide it is usually no more than 500 g/m², while at the outer one it reaches 3 kg/m². The whole biomass of the vegetative cover of this littoral is about 4·5 tons and on the average about 200 g/m².

M. Kireeva and T. Shchapova (1937) have noted an interesting relationship between the algal growth and some animal organisms inhabiting the same section of the littoral. Sections with a large algal biomass have a small mussel biomass and vice versa (*Table 41*).

FIG. 42. A belt of brown algae Ascophyllum and Fucus on the rock littoral of Murman coast (Gurjanova, Zachs and Ushakov).

The main bulk of the macrophyte growth of the sublittoral upper level (0·5 to 15 m) of the Murman coast and the shores of Novaya Zemlya is formed by two species of Laminaria, *L. saccharina* and *L. digitata* with their numerous forms. *Alaria esculenta* and still more *Chorda filum* and *Desmarestia aculeata* are considerably inferior to them in numbers. Among the

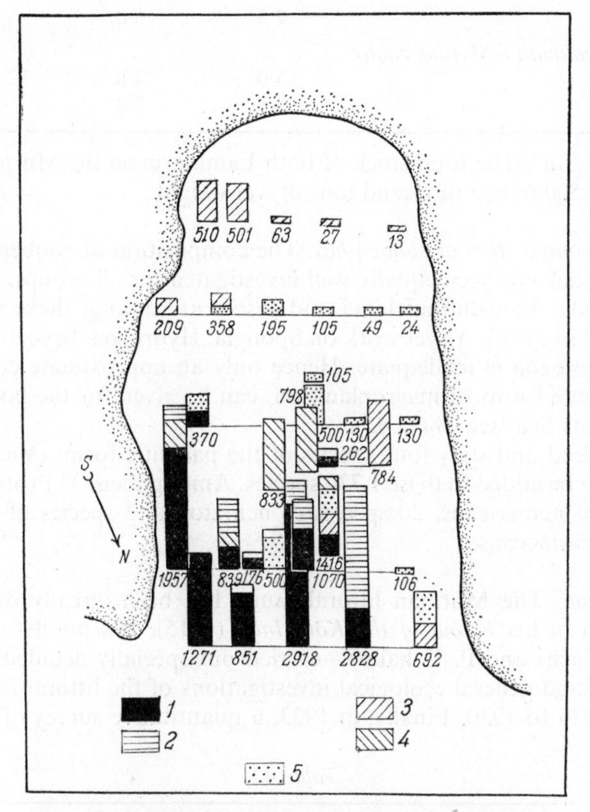

FIG. 43. Qualitative and quantitative distribution of macrophytes on the silty-sand littoral of one of the bays of Kola Guba (Kireeva and Shchapova). The height of the columns and the associated numerals represent the biomass in g/m².

red algae the most common here are *Ptilota plumosa*, *Odonthalia dentata*, *Delesseria sinuosa* and *Phyllophora brodiaei*, usually fastened to the Laminaria stalks and rhizoids.

The uppermost horizon of the sublittoral (1 to 2 m) is occupied by a belt of *Chorda filum* with an average biomass of 1 to 3 kg/m³. The average Laminaria biomass is about 10 kg/m³, and it sometimes attains 27 kg/m³. The admixture of red algae is noticeable from the depth of 5 m; however, on average it never

Table 41

Nature of bed	Total biomass kg/m²	Algae biomass kg/m²	Biomass kg/m²
Fucus serratus + Mytilus edulis			
1 sector	11·25	2·75	8·5
2 Sector	7·5	5·0	2·5
Rhodimenia palmata + Mytilus edulis			
1 sector	15·0	4·6	10·4
2 sector	8·8	7·8	1·0

exceeds 100 g/m². The total stock of both Laminaria on the Murman coast is reckoned as 500 to 600 thousand tons of wet weight.

Qualitative composition of zoobenthos. The composition of zoobenthos in the Barents Sea has not been equally well investigated for all groups. Echinodermata, Isopoda, Lamellibranchiata and Pisces are among those which have been studied in detail. As yet work on Spongia, Hydrozoa, Bryozoa and some forms of Protozoa is inadequate. Hence only an approximate composition, including some forms of macroplankton, can be given for the bottom fauna of the Barents Sea (see *Table 42*).

One hundred and sixty-four species of the parasitic forms (Yu. Poljansky, 1955) should be added to these 1,730 species. Among them 33 Protozoa forms, 68 species of nemerteans, 20 species of nematodes, 3 species of leeches, 21 species of crustaceans.

Littoral fauna. The Murman littoral fauna has been already described by K. Derjugin in his *Fauna of the Kola Inlet* (1915). His pupils—E. F. Gurjanova, I. Zachs and P. Ushakov—carried out specially detailed qualitative biocoenotic and general ecological investigations of the littoral fauna during the years 1925 to 1930. Finally, in 1933, a quantitative survey of the littoral

Table 42

Name	No. of Species	Name	No. of Species	Name	No. of Species
Foraminifera	115	Echiuroidea	2	Pantopoda	24
Cornacuspongia	91	Oligochaeta	8	Lamellibranchiata	87
Hydrozoa	119	Polychaeta	200	Gastropoda	150
Anthozoa	20	Brachiopoda	4	Amphineura	8
Turbellaria	27	Bryozoa	272	Scaphopoda	2
Nematoda		Cirripedia	6	Cephalopoda	3
(Enopliidae)	97	Cumacea	32	Echinodermata	62
Nemertini	20	Amphipoda	262	Ascidia	50
Priapuloidea	2	Isopoda	42	Pogonophora	1
Sipunculoidea	6	Decapoda	25		
				Total	1,738

fauna of the western Murman Peninsula was made by the author and his collaborators (1945), while the eastern Murman was surveyed in 1939 by N. Sokolova (1940), T. Gurjeva (1948) and T. Matveeva (1948).

A difference in the length of its drying-out period, its temperature and salinity oscillations, and finally, the variety of the littoral zone soils made it possible for us to divide it fractionally into a system of horizons and zones.

E. F. Gurjanova *et al.* (1928) gave a system of subdivisions for the cliffs and the rocks of the littoral of the western Murman coast (*Table 43*).

Table 43

Horizon	Floor	Form		Depth, ft
I	1		Lichens	4·1
	2		*Pelvetta canaliculata*	3·7
II	1	*Littorina rudis*	*Fucus vesiculosus*	3·4
	2	*Balanus balanoides*	*Ascophyllum nodosum*	2·5
	3	*Mytilus edulis*	*Fucus inflatus*	2·0
			Cladophora, Spangomorpha, Monostroma, Rhodymenia	1·3
III	1		Halosaccion, Ectocarpus, Pylatella	0·5
	2	*Balanus crenatus*	crust-Lithothamnion	0

The littoral and its fauna change considerably with the distance from the open sea and the nature of the connection with it. This enables us to distinguish the following six main bionomic types* for the Murman littoral.

(*1*) Open shore, exposed to heavy swell
(*2*) Quiet bays situated near the open sea, but protected against the buffeting of the waves
(*3*) Narrow straits, protected against the swell, but washed by very strong currents
(*4*) Deep-cut gubas at some distance from the open sea, without any swell or currents and with a somewhat lowered salinity
(*5*) Gubas of greatly reduced salinity remote from the open sea, without swell or current
(*6*) Estuaries of low salinity and an absence of currents.

Every bionomic type is characterized by its own peculiar composition and its own distribution of organisms. Many littoral biocoenoses are found in all the bionomic types, but they undergo definite changes in their vertical position, in their composition and in the relative significance of their separate components.

In the seas of the Arctic basin, where for the greater part of the year floating ice is piled up at the shores, life is very scarce in the littoral and the upper

* A term introduced by de Beauchamp and Zachs in 1913 for a definite combination of conditions of existence, determining the character of the biocoenoses.

level of the sublittoral, and part of the typical littoral forms sink down to the sublittoral. On the western and southern shores of Novaya Zemlya and off the shores of Spitsbergen, where the abrasive effect of ice and the winter cold is not so severe as in the high Arctic region, a very much impoverished flora and fauna can be observed on the littoral. The littoral fauna of the White Sea is fairly varied, it is a somewhat impoverished version of the fauna of the Murman coast littoral; this latter, however, is very rich. Farther west, along the shores of Norway and the North Sea, the main components of the littoral fauna remain the same but become more varied still, and a number of forms absent in the north are added to it.

In the Barents Sea the littoral fauna reaches its most luxuriant development on the western Murman coast—on its cliffs, shale deposits, silty sand and sandy mud, in the depth of well-protected fjords, on wide beaches, provided only that their salinity is not too much reduced.

The littoral fauna is at its richest in the autumn. In winter, owing to the sharp deterioration of climatic conditions, a considerable regrouping of the population of the littoral takes place; some of it migrates to the sublittoral, some sinks into a quiescent condition. The abundance of light in the summer (the polar day on the western Murman Peninsula lasts from 22 May to 23 July) and its absence in winter (the polar night lasts from 30 November to 13 January) and extremely sharp seasonal fluctuations of temperature and salinity are characteristic of the Murman littoral.

For the cliff facies with their overgrowth of fucoids besides *Mytilus edulis* and two species of Balanus—*B. balanoides* and *B. crenatus*—the following animal organisms are likewise particularly characteristic; gastropods: *Littorina rudis, L. littorea L. palliata, Acmaea testudinalis, Purpura* (*Nucella*) *lapillus, Limapontia capitata, Rissoa aculeus*; crustaceans: *Gammarus locusta, Idothea granulosa, Jaera albifrons*; Bryozoa: *Flustrella hispida, Alcyonidium hirsutum, Sertularia pumilla*, and others. All these cliff fauna can be grouped into five basic biocoenoses: (*1*) *Balanus balanoides*; (*2*) *Mytilus edulis*; (*3*) *Ascophyllum nodosum*, Sertularia and Flustrella; (*4*) red algae and (*5*) Sphacellaria with the fauna of worms and small molluscs.

On the rocky shale, usually partly sunk into the soft sea-bed, among the fucoids, on the sides and lower parts of the rocks and between them and on the floor under them the fauna is usually abundant. Here the most characteristic groups are actinians: *Actinia equina*; the sponge: *Halichondria tenuiderma*; the nemerteans: *Lineus gesserensis* and *Amphiporus lactifloreus*; the molluscs: *Cyamium minutum*, and Lacuna; the crustaceans: *Gammarus locusta, G. marinus, Jaera marina*; the fish: *Pholis gunnellus* and *Encheliopus* (Zoarces) *viviparus*.

Bryozoa: *Flustrella hispida*; hydroids: *Dynamena pumilla, Gonothyrea loveni* and *Obelia longissima, O. loveni*; three types of Littorina (*L. rudis, L. littorea* and *L. palliata*); *Balanus balanoides*; a large number of molluscs: *Acanthodoris pilosa, Dendronotus frondosus, Lamellidoris muzicata* and *L. bilamellata, Coryphella rufibranchialis, Limapontia capitata*; some species of polychaetes: Spirorbis; and the mollusc *Chiton marmoreus* settle on the algae. There are some worms in the groups under the rocks, such as *Priapulus caudatus*,

Halicryptus spinulosus, *Scoloplos armiger*, *Capitella capitata*, *Ophelia limacina*, *Travisia forbesi*, *Nephthys ciliata*, *Glycera capitata*, *Lineus gesserensis*, and *Amphiporus lactifloreus*.

In the rocky shale facies besides the above-mentioned the following biocoenoses can be distinguished: *Fucus serratus*, *Spirorbis borealis* and *Lacuna pallidula*; fauna: the polychaetes *Amphitrites johnstoni*, *Phyllodoce maculata*, together with nemerteans and oligochaetes.

The biocoenoses of *Balanus balanoides* and *Mytilus edulis* are most important for the facies of cliff, boulders and large rocks. The first of these forms is most developed at a level of 2·5 to 3·5 m above zero depth, within the zone of the luxuriant fucoid development. A narrow band of *Fucus vesiculosus* (20 to 30 cm in width) extends over all; under it there is a one-metre band of *Ascophyllum nodosum*. Below this there is a band of *Fucus inflatus* and *F. serratus*. Numerous animals find excellent protection from drying out under the large fronds of Ascophyllum when the tide is low.

Fucus vesiculosus gives a comparatively small biomass of 4 to 7 kg/m^2. *Ascophyllum nodosum*, which gives the largest biomass of all the fuci, may yield 10 to 18 kg/m^2. As a rule the population of *Balanus balanoides* is most dense directly under the fucus border, where they form a solid white band 10 to 20 cm in width and clearly visible even from a distance. The number of young balanus settled on the rocks may reach up to 100 to 200 thousand per square metre, and their biomass up to 1 kg/m^2. The total biomass of the animal biocoenosis of Balanus on the Murman coast is as high as 3·2 kg/m^2 and sometimes even higher (up to 10 kg/m^2). The quantitative composition of the given biocoenosis is set out in *Table 44*.

With the growth of the young recently-settled balanus, their number considerably decreases: during the period from May to September, the loss in

Table 44

Biocoenosis composition of *B. balanoides*	Mean No. found per 1 m^2	Mean biomass g/m^2	Mean biomass of total biomass per cent	Maximum biomass g/m^2
B. balanoides over 1 year old	253	136·30	9·08	10,000
B. balanoides young-of-the-year	12,493	1,049·00	69·93	—
Littorina rudis	2,413	223·30	14·90	—
L. palliata	253	86·90	5·79	—
Acmaea testudinalis	16	1·50	0·10	—
Gammarus spp.	162	1·60	0·12	—
Jaera marina	202	1·00	0·07	—
Idothea baltica	7	0·20	0·01	—
Total	15,799	1,499·80	100·00	

the number of specimens is no less than 85 to 90 per cent, whereas the total sum of the biomass increases two to three times. The winter frosts are also destructive of the settled balanus; their mortality during the winter may be 95 to 98 per cent.

Somewhat below the layer of highest balanus development in the second and third zones of the middle horizon, 1·3 m above zero depth, lies the Mytilus biocoenosis—*Mytilus edulis*. Mytilus attains its highest development in places where there is little swell, on cliffs and rocks and on rising ground on the silty sand beaches. On cliffs and rocks the amount of Mytilus reaches 7 to 10 thousand specimens with a biomass of 10 to 15 kg/m², and sometimes up to 13 thousand specimens with a biomass of 19 to 25 kg/m². Among the fuci the quantity of Mytilus is smaller (2·5 to 3 kg/m²) and they themselves are smaller in size.

The Mytilus biocoenosis is characterized also by the presence of a large amount of *Nucella lapillus*, *Acmaea testudinalis*, molluscs, hydroids and bryozoans and, in the lowest levels in autumn, of asterids *Asterias rubens* and gastropods *Buccinum undatum* (*Table 45*).

Table 45

Composition of Mytilus biocoenosis on cliffs and rocks of Murman coast	Maximum/m²		Average/m²	
	No. of specimens	Biomass g	No. of specimens	Biomass g
Mytilus edulis	13,000	25,000	8,200	4,806
Littorina rudis	800	170	360	95·4
L. palliata	900	385	240	92
L. littorea	300	130	60	26
Nucella lapillus	200	325	60	84
Acmaea testudinalis	200	35	60	7·2
Gammarus spp.	—	—	620	10·4
Jaera marina	—	—	360	1·9
Nemerteans (Lineus + Amphiporus)	—	—	160	4·5
Total			10,120	5,127·4

On silty sand of the lower littoral zone dense Mytilus colonies are common (the so-called Mytilus banks); they form a kind of defensive border to the littoral. The total amount of Mytilus on such banks is somewhat smaller than on the cliffs, but it also can reach 19 to 21·5 kg/m² and may be more than 10,000 specimens (*Table 46*). Thus here a considerable part of the population is represented by the Macoma community.

The main gatherings of Mytilus, forming powerful biofilters, are situated within the lower level of the littoral and in the upper (1 to 3 m) level of the sublittoral.

Table 46

Composition of Mytilus biocoenosis on silty-sand littoral of Murman coast	Average/m²		Maximum/m²	
	No. of specimens	Biomass g	No. of specimens	Biomass g
Mytilus edulis	2,624	4,651·2	—	—
Macoma baltica	460	114·7	3,380	555
Littorina rudis	241	25·8	1,200	106
Arenicola marina	8·4	14·65	—	—
Gammarus sp. sp.	233	7·54	—	—
Priapulus caudatus	11·7	2·3	392	19·6
Halicryptus spinulosus	3·2	0·3	220	16·5
Lineus gesserensis	39	1·8		
Amphiporus lacteus	3	0·25		
Phyllodoce maculata	53	0·6		
Actinia equina	3·6	1·45		
Others	38·1	3·06		
Total	3,718	4,823·65		

The newly-born Mytilus settle in masses on conferva and green algae beds right at the water's edge.

As has been shown by the quantitative estimate of the cliff and rock littoral fauna of the great Kharlovsky Island (eastern Murman, Seven Islands) carried out by N. Sokolova in 1941 (1957), the basic forms here are *Balanus balanoides, Littorina rudis* and *Mytilus edulis* which form 98·8 per cent of the total biomass (*Table 47*).

The littoral fauna of Kharlovsky Island is considerably impoverished by reason of the swell. This bionomic phylum lies between the first and the second phyla of the classification given above.

Table 47. Mean biomasss in cross section of rock littoral off Kharlovsky Island, g/m

Form	No. of specimens	Mean biomass	Highest biomass
Balanus balanoides	2,070	617·3	7,800·0
Littorina rudis	896	94·63	425·0
Mytilus edulis	53	17·53	75·2
Turbellaria	209	3·68	45·0
Acmaea testudinalis	4	3·12	32·0
Oligochaeta	558	0·72	7·84
Jaera albifrons	193	0·131	0·98
Various	—	1·00	—
Total	3,983	738·11	8,386·0

The most dense population is found on the rocks and cliffs in the middle horizons of the intertidal zone.

The succession of the maximum development of individual forms proceeds in the order given in *Table 48*.

Table 48

Form	Level above zero depth m	Form	Level above zero depth m
Oligochaeta	2·68	*Jaera albifrons*	1·30
Littorina rudis	2·21	*Acmaea testudinalis*	0·10
Balanus balanoides	1·52	Membranipora sp.	0·10
Mytilus edulis	1·45	Nemertini g. sp.	0·10
Turbellaria	1·30		

Like the western Murman coast the littoral is inhabited by a large number of gammarids which serve as food to the numerous fish during low tide; their numbers, however, have not been estimated so far, owing to the difficulty of collecting them. When the stones under which they hide during low tide are turned over they scatter with astonishing speed and agility.

The biomass is somewhat lower (647·34 g/m^2) on the cliffs and rocks of the littoral entirely exposed to the pounding of the waves on Kharlovsky Island. As before, *Mytilus edulis*, *Balanus balanoides* and *Littorina rudis* are preponderant, but the dominant role is transferred to *Mytilus edulis* (forming about 67 per cent of the total biomass). In the inlets on the southern side of this island which are protected from the action of the swell, the littoral fauna biomass increases sharply from 1·3 to 9·3 kg/m^2; this is contributed by *Mytilus edulis* and *Balanus balanoides*.

Littorina rudis, which inhabits the upper horizon of the littoral, is found in the supralittoral too. This is one of the most enduring forms of the intertidal zone. It can exist for a long time without water and easily tolerates fresh water. *Littorina rudis* prefers to inhabit cliffs and rocks. *Balanus balanoides* also thrives in cliffs and rocks; however, it does not rise beyond the limits of the littoral. Downwards it extends farther than Littorina. The third and most typical form of the intertidal zone sea mussel is usually found in the shape of brushes or bunches and is adapted mainly to the lower part of the littoral. The number of sea mussels decreases from west to east. According to Wollenberg the amount of sea mussels on the mussel grounds of Helgoland reaches 75 kg/m^2; in the western Murman coast it is only 30 to 40, and in the eastern it does not exceed 8 to 9 kg/m^2. The amount of it in the White Sea is smaller.

Algal biomass increases in the littoral and the quantitative ratio of its groups and forms changes as we move into the inlets of the eastern Murman coast. T. Gurjeva (1948) provides demonstrative material derived from experiments for the Dal'ne Zelentzkaya Guba (*Table 49*).

Table 49

Location	In the depth of the Guba	In the Strait	At Cape Vykhodnoy
Mean plant biomass	18,818	14,672	7,029
Mean animal biomass	1,702	778	2,604
Total biomass	21,520	14,450	9,633

T. Gurjeva notes that on sectors open to a heavy swell some forms of the littoral fauna rise to higher levels, passing even into the supralittoral; others, on the contrary, disappear. Thus in places where the swell is violent, *Ascophyllum nodosum* disappears almost completely, and is replaced by *Rhodymenia palmata.* It is interesting that the biomass is considerably increased by sea mussel both in places of a strong swell and on protected sectors. T. Gurjeva assumes the existence of two biological races of sea mussel.

T. Matveeva gives some interesting data on the seasonal changes of the population of the rock littoral. The growth of the young in the summer months is first to be noted. It is natural that the highest fluctuations (two or three times) are given by the algae. In autumn and winter the number of Littorina decreases considerably; only a few forms such as *Asterias rubens* and *Buccinum groenlandicum* migrate into the sublittoral. According to T. Matveeva's observations, by the end of the summer many gastropods, *Margarita helicina*, *Lacuna divaricata*, *Trophon truncatus*, *Natica clausa*, and the crab *Hyas araneus* migrate to the sublittoral. About the same time Nudibranchiata (*Doto coronata*, *Coryphella rufibranchialis*, *Dendronotus frondosus*, *Acatodoris pelosa*) appear in large numbers. Many components of the littoral fauna go under cover in winter, hiding under rocks or even burrowing into the bottom, as for example *Nucella lapillus*, *Rissoa aculeus* and others.

The winter weakening in the growth of laminaria and the change of conditions bring about the migration of some inhabitants of the upper level of the sublittoral into the deeper layers. For instance, the mollusc *Lacuna vincta* (V. Kuznetzov, 1948) is apt to perform such seasonal migrations.

In the soft soils of the intertidal zone of the western Murman, the burrowing bivalves and annelid worms in various forms inhabit the sea-weeds covering the beach (Enteromorpha, Monostroma and others). Among the members of onfauna* *Iaera marina*, *Gammarus locusta*, *Littorina rudis*, *Skenea planorbis*, *Hydrobia ulvae*, *Limapontia capitata*, *Mytilus edulis* may always be found here. The upper layer of the soil and the turf-like seaweed beds are inhabited by innumerable minute *Fabricia sabella* and *Manayunkia polaris* and by large *Cardium edule*. The polychaetes *Pygospio elegans*, *Arenicola marina*, *Polydora quadrilobata*, *Scoloplos armiger*, *Ophelia limacina*, *Travisia forbesi*, *Terebellides strömi*, the hypherian *Priapulus caudatus* and *Halicryptus spinulosus*, and the

* Danish and English authors use the terms onfauna and infauna to distinguish the fauna living on the bed and in the bed.

bivalves *Macoma baltica*, *Mya truncata* and *M. arenaria*. The main biocoenosis of the infauna Macoma, Arenicola, Phygospio, Polydora, Terebellides and Scoloplos may form fairly individual biocoenotic groupings.

Large numbers of oligochaetes and especially enhytreides such as *Pachydrillus lineatus*, *P. profudus*, *Enchytreus albidus* and *Marionina crassa* sometimes swarm under the rocks and washed-up sea-weeds.

The sea mussel communities Fabricia, Manayunkia and *Littorina rudis* may be distinguished among the onfauna.

The zonation in the distribution of the fauna of silty sand littoral on the western Murman coast may be illustrated by *Table 50* from the paper of Gurjanova, Zachs and and Ushakov (1930).

Table 50

Horizon	Zone	Form	Depth, m
I		Masses of washed-up seaweed. A mass larvae of fly and of Oligochaeta	14·1
II	1 *Fabricia sabella* +Manayunkia (zones 1–3)	Oligochaeta	2·4
	2	Oligochaeta, *Macoma baltica*, *Enteromorpha intestinalis*, *Urospora penicilliformis*	2·1
	3	*Mytilus edulis*, *Halicryptus spinulosus*, *Priapulus caudatus*, *Macoma baltica*, *Arenicola marina*	1·3
III	1 *Pygospio elegans*	*Macoma baltica*, *Scoloplos armiger*, *Pygospio elegans*, *Ophelia limacina*, *Travisia forbesi*, *Terebellides strömi*	0·5
	2	*Mya truncata*, *Axinus flexuosus*, *Macoma baltica*, *Chiridota laevis*, *Echiurus pallasi*	0

A census of the fauna of the soft bed soils of the Kola Inlet littoral reveals a marked preponderance of a few forms (*Tables 51* and *52*).

The contamination of the littoral is easily endured by Macoma while Littorina and Priapulus even increase their numbers in it.

Arenicola and Cardium have a negative reaction to contamination. The qualitative distribution of the dominant forms of the littoral fauna is given in Figs. 44 and 45. As shown by the isobenths given, the biomass increases gradually towards the sea, and then falls again towards zero depth.

The total benthos biomass of this small section of the littoral, of about 25,000 m^2, is about 13·6 tons, of which 4·5 tons is attributed to plants and 9·1 tons to animals. The onfauna and infauna are represented about equally: 4·6 tons of onfauna and 4·5 tons of infauna. The average benthos biomass is 422 g/m^2, that is approximately double that of the macrophytes.

During high tide a considerable amount of fish enters the littoral zone to feed; this was pointed out by us for the Kola Inlet as early as 1933. This

Table 51

Macrofauna forms	Littoral remote from human habitation not contaminated			Largest numbers encountered		Littoral open to contamination of human habitation			The largest numbers encountered	
	No. of specimens/m²	Biomass g/m²	% total biomass except sea mussel	No. of specimens/m²	Biomass g/m²	No. of specimens/m²	Biomass g/m²	% total biomass except sea mussel	No. of specimens/m²	Biomass g/m²
Onfauna										
Mytilus edulis	823	1,409·0	—	—	—	191	244·6	—	—	—
Littorina rudis	44	4·8	2·3	624	66·8	256	18·8	9·8	1,816	104·6
Gammaridae	39	1·5	0·7	—	—	42	0·8	0·4	—	—
Infauna										
Macoma baltica	750	167·8	81·3	2,596	458·8	1,364	152·5	70·8	3,400	554·8
Cardium edule	1	8·9	4·3	16	148·8	—	—	—	—	—
Arenicola marina	11	16·2	7·9	44	67·2	—	—	—	—	—
Priapulus caudatus	7	1·2	0·6	28	5·36	142	6·9	3·6	484	19·6
Halicryptus spinulosus	24	1·2	0·6	220	16·48	0·5	0·1	0·06	8	3·48
Remainder	56	4·8	2·3	—	—	58	11·9	6·34	—	—
Total	1,755	1,615·4	100·0	—	7,924·28	2,053·5	435·6	—	—	5,506·2
Except sea mussel	—	206·4	—	—	478·24	—	191·0	—	—	593·16

Table 52

Microfauna form	Mean no. of specimens	Microfauna form	Mean no. of specimens
Fabricia sabella	116,950	Foraminifera	11,225
Manayunkia polaris	34,250	Iaera	12,650
Pygospio elegans	48,000	Harpacticidae	12,550
Polychaeta varia	650	Ostracoda	700
Oligochaeta	92,600	Hydracarina	150
Nematoda	218,350	Chironomidae	16,050
Turbellaria	1,250	Total	564,175

phenomenon was noted by H. Thamdrup (1935) and O. Linke (1939) for the North Sea littoral.

The following method was used in our investigation of the importance of the Murman littoral fauna as food. On a section of the littoral suitable by its configuration and at high tide, the exit into the sea was completely closed by seines. When the tide went down all the fish caught were counted, weighed and the contents of their stomachs were analysed. These observations showed that a fish is hungry when it enters the littoral and that it feeds there vigorously. A large number of young cod, haddock, coalfish, flounder, goby and viviparous blenny swims into the littoral. No less than 100 kg of fish concentrated

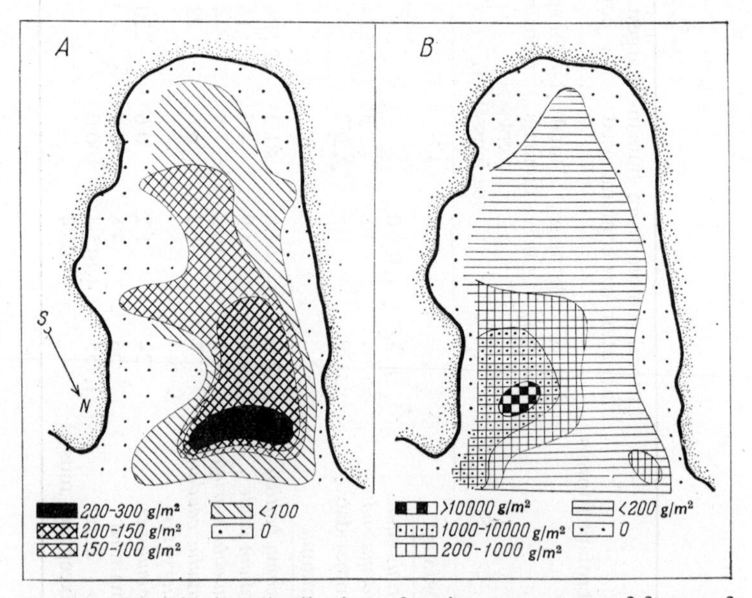

FIG. 44. Quantitative distribution of main components of fauna of the littoral of one of the gubas of western Murman (g/m²). A *Mytilus edulis*; B *Macoma baltica* (Zenkevitch, Zatzepin and Filatova, 1948).

near high tide in the comparatively small section of the littoral investigated (25,000 km²).

The most commonly consumed marine organisms (Fig. 46) on the littoral were in order of declining significance: Gammaridae, *Macoma baltica, Littorina rudis, Mytilus edulis, Priapulus caudatus*. Cod, coalfish, viviparous blenny and goby feed there almost exclusively on gammarus with a small

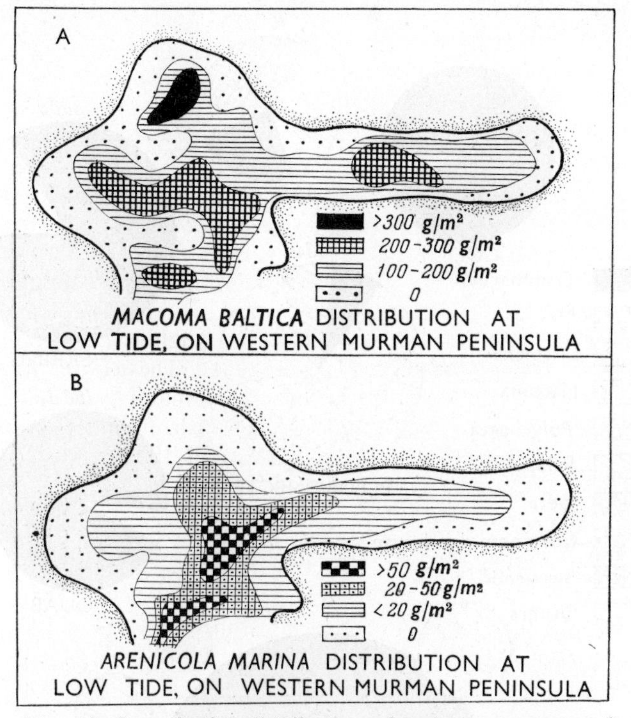

FIG. 45. Quantitative distribution of main components of fauna of littoral of one of the gubas of western Murman (g/m²) (Zenkevitch, Zatzepin and Filatova, 1948).

admixture of other animals; haddock and dab retain here their true benthophagous nature. Haddock eats a little of everything, even a fairly large amount of seaweed. On the whole the flounder feeds on bivalves (see mussel and Macoma) and on Gastropoda (Littorina) molluscs but seizes everything else too, in passing. Its indices of repletion are fairly high (100 to 340).

A quantitative comparison of the mass of littoral organisms and the intestine contents (Fig. 46B) of the fish visiting the littoral shows that at every flood-tide, i.e. twice a day, the fish consume about 0·03 per cent of the whole fauna.

From corresponding investigations at low tide the amount of animal forms eaten in a year is about 1·5 to 2·0 tons, i.e. about 17 per cent of the whole population; moreover, in the main, only certain groups are being eaten, so that the percentage of consumption for the groups consumed must be much higher.

The littoral fauna grows poorer both in quality and numbers as we travel eastward along the Murman coast. This decline is accelerated by the deterioration of the climatic conditions and the absence of deep bays and inlets well protected against the tides on the eastern Murman coast. According to

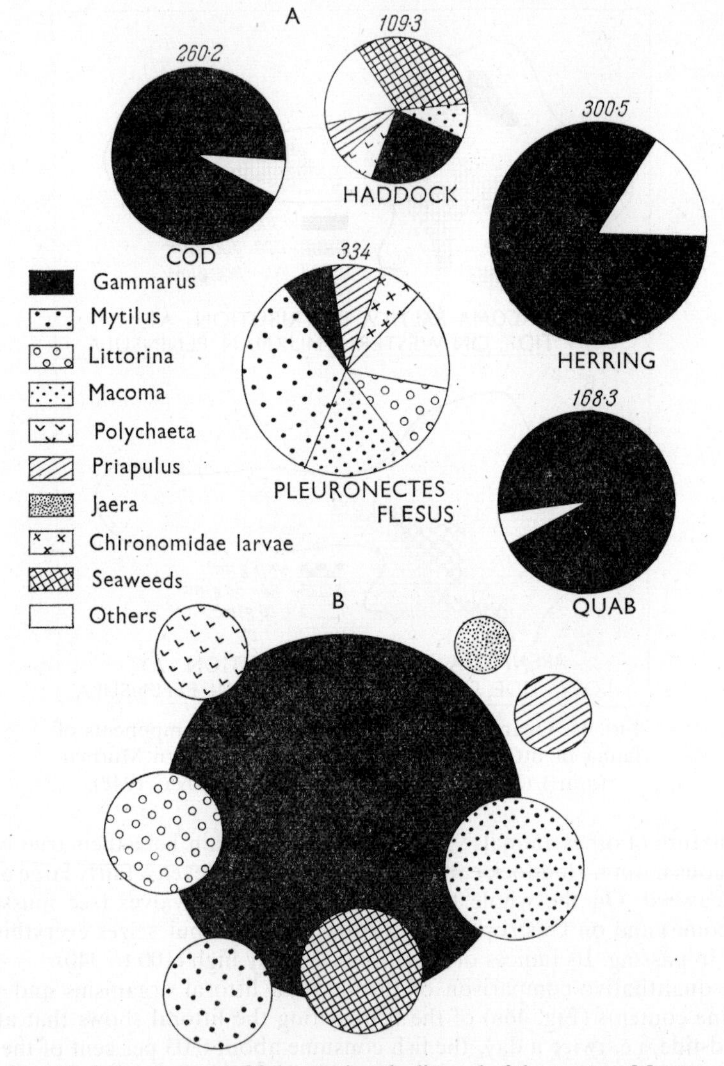

FIG. 46. A Food range of fish entering the littoral of the western Murman for feeding. Mean repletion indices are shown by numerals above circles. B Comparative food value between inhabitants of littoral and fish entering the littoral (Zenkevitch, Zatzepin and Filatova, 1948).

E. Gurjanova's data (1928) farther east in the Cheshskaya Guba, some littoral forms such as *Balanus balanoides*, *Mytilus edulis*, *Acmaeo testudinalis*, *Littorina rudis*, *Arenicola marina* and *Macoma baltica* are retained in places where there are rocks sparsely covered by seaweed.

In the southern bays of Novaya Zemlya (E. Gurjanova and P. Ushakov, 1928) *Mytilus edulis*, *Littorina rudis*, *Rissoa aculeus*, *Margarita helicina* v. *major*, *Gammarus locusta* and others may still be found on the littoral. At the Matochkin Shar (P. Ushakov, 1931) and farther northwards the littoral fauna dwindles almost to nothing. It is represented only by *Gammarus locusta Pseudalibrotus littoralis* and by the rare and small-sized *Mytilus edulis*. In some places on the eastern coast of Spitsbergen colonies of small-sized *Balanus balanoides* have been found on the rocks.

Sublittoral fauna. A qualitative biocoenotic description of the sublittoral fauna was given by K. Derjugin in his monograph on the Kola Inlet (1915), and later by his pupil E. F. Gurjanova for Cheshskaya Guba (1929) and by E. F. Gurjanova and P. Ushakov (1928, 1931) for the shores on Novaya Zemlya (Chernaya Guba and Matochkin Shar). Finally the benthos along the Kola meridian has been under constant, careful investigation (K. Derjugin, N. Tanassijchuk and others). In 1924 large-scale quantitative fauna surveys were begun by the State Institute of Oceanography (Zenkevitch, Brotzkaya, Idelson, Leibson, Filatova and Zatzepin) (1924 to 1939).

As depth increases and biotopic variety correspondingly decreases, so also the range of animal and vegetable groups is reduced. Thus E. F. Gurjanova, I. Zachs and P. Ushakov (1925 to 1930) have distinguished on a comparatively small area of the Murman coast littoral more than fifteen basic biocoenoses. About the same amount of biocoenoses was found by K. Derjugin (1915) on the Kola Inlet sublittoral, on an area of about 130 km^2. Finally no more than ten more basic benthic groups were noted by the quantitative surveys on the huge bottom area of the open parts of the Barents Sea. The largest variety of species is adapted to the middle and lower levels of the sublittoral. As has been mentioned above, Derjugin introduced also a pseudo-abyssal zone, at depths below 250 m, in his description of the Kola Inlet fauna. There are no plants at all here, while a considerable number of forms with fairly sharply expressed abyssal characteristics (loss of pigmentation, extended extremities, adjustments for inhabiting very soft floors, etc.) are accumulated.

For several years (1903, 1908, 1909) K. Derjugin studied in great detail at the Murman Biological Station (Fig. 47) the distribution of the Kola bottom fauna. As a result of his investigation a fundamental work appeared, *The Kola Inlet Fauna and the Conditions of Its Existence* (1915). It still retains its scientific importance as one of the greatest surveys of this type in world literature.

Kola Inlet (Fig. 48), the largest inlet on the Murman coast, extends from north to south for about 55 km and has a mouth about 6 km wide. It is a typical fjord in its contour; it has great depths (down to 380 m) and, unlike the nearby Motovksy Bay, it is separated from the open sea by a submarine barrier with depths not exceeding 150 m. As a result the conditions of the Kola Inlet are on the whole more severe than those of the well-washed, comparatively shallow Motovsky Bay.

The northern part of the Kola Inlet has depths down to 350 to 380 m, the middle part down to 200 m and the southern part has depths mostly less than 50 m. The precipitous rocky, granite shores (to 150 m) frequently lead under water into steep bottom slopes and the type of environment of submarine cliffs is very prominent indeed.

Almost all the deep parts of the bay are filled with ooze, sandy bottoms appear only in the southern and middle parts of it. Rocky floors strewn with large boulders are widely distributed over the whole inlet.

Everywhere, especially in the north of the inlet, there are extensive beds of several species of calcareous algae or of the Lithothamnion genus (red algae group) which are found in individual patches. Branching Lithothamnion

FIG. 47. Murmansk Biological Station of the Petersburg Society of Naturalists (1914).

grows only in places where there are rapid currents, on steep cliff slopes, on the cliff barriers at the mouth of the bay, and in narrow channels.

The considerable north to south extent of the Kola Inlet, the inflow of two large rivers—Kola and Tuloma—into its southern part, and additionally the heating effect of the warm Atlantic waters (Ruppin branch) flowing along the Murman coast make the Kola waters heterogeneous both in their salinity and temperature.

In summer the temperature in the northern part of the inlet is 5° to 13·5° on the surface, and at a depth of 300 m it is only 1·3° to 2·0°. The temperature falls rapidly from the surface to a depth of 50 to 100 m (down to the thermocline layer); at greater depths it changes but little.

A homothermic state (0° to 1°) is established by the end of the coldest season of the year. The 'hydrological summer' comes to the surface layers of Kola Inlet waters in July and August and the winter in January and February.

In summer there is a characteristic fall of salinity in the surface layer of the Kola Inlet waters. Even in the northern part of the inlet up to 8·3‰ salinity has been observed. However, even at a depth of 5 m salinity is never below 30‰; it increases still more lower down (up to 30 to 34·5‰), and its seasonal changes in the deep zones are negligible. In winter the surface waters also attain 30 to 34‰ salinity. In spring, during the melting of the large masses of snow which have fallen through the winter, the amount of fresh water entering the inlet increases considerably and the surface layer is diluted even more.

In summer, in the middle of the southern part of the inlet, the salinity in the upper surface layer fluctuates from zero to 16·5‰, at a depth of 3 m from 2 to 31‰, at 5 m from 5 to 33‰, and at greater depths fluctuation is still further increased.

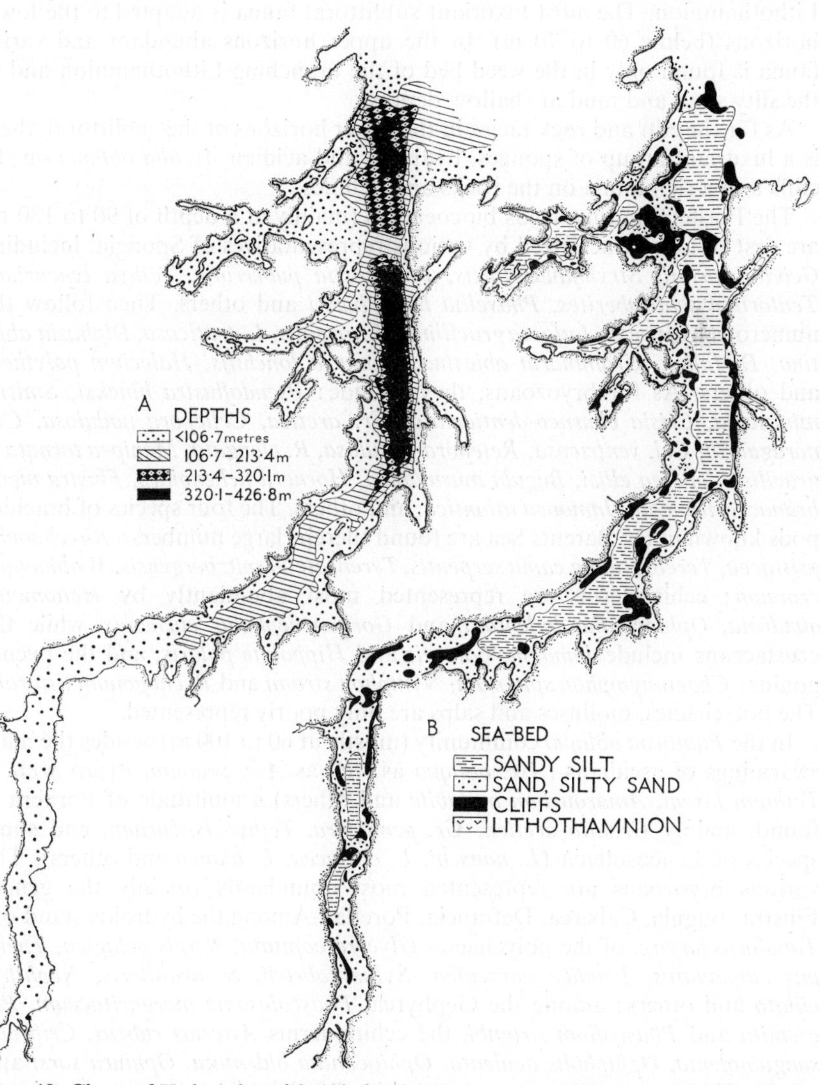

FIG. 48. Chart of Kola Inlet with (A) depths (fathoms) and (B) composition of sea-bed (Derjugin).

'The general picture of the Kola Inlet obtained from topographical, hydrographic and geological surveys, is very much of the same type as that obtained for the neighbouring Norwegian fjords', writes Derjugin. 'The side parts of the main fjord are usually connected with the main straits, cut through the ancient moraines. There is always a main deep channel with an ooze bed, with ravines or shores at its sides; the side pans are determined by submarine barriers.'

K. Derjugin has distinguished five main biotopes (facies) in the Kola Inlet sublittoral, namely cliffs and rocks, sand, shell, ooze and the branching Lithothamnion. The most luxuriant sublittoral fauna is adapted to the lower horizons (below 60 to 70 m). In the upper horizons abundant and varied fauna is found only in the weed bed of the branching Lithothamnion and in the silty sand and mud at shallow depths.

As for the cliff and rock facies in the lower horizons of the sublittoral, there is a luxuriant group of sponges, hydroids and acidian *Ascidia obliqua* on the cliffs and a rich fauna on the rocks and pebbles.

The Porifera and hydroids biocoenoses (mainly at a depth of 90 to 180 m) are first of all characterized by various representatives of Spongia, including *Geodia baretti*, *Stryhhanus fortis*, *Polymastia puberrima*, *Tethya lyncurium*, *Tentorium semisuberites*, *Phavellia bowerbanki* and others. Then follow the numerous hydroids: *Lafosea gracillima*, *L. grandis*, *L. fruticosa*, *Diphasia abietina*, *D. fallax*, *Grammaria abietina*, *Thuiaria lonchitis*, *Halecium polytheca* and others. As for bryozoans, they include: *Pseudoflustra hincksi*, *Smittia minuscula*, *Crisia eburneo-denticulata*, *Cr. arctica*, *Cellepora nodulosa*, *Cel. nordgaardi*, *Cel. ventricosa*, *Retepora cellulosa*, *R. elongata*, *Menipea tornata* v. *gracilis*, *Caberea ellisi*, *Bugula murmanica*, *Hornera lichenoides*, *Flustra membranaceo-truncata*, *Idmonea atlantica*, and others. The four species of brachiopods known in the Barents Sea are found therein large numbers: *Rhychonella psittacea*, *Terebratulina caput serpentis*, *Terebratella spitzbergensis*, *Waldheimia cranium*; echinoderms are represented most abundantly by *Heliometra quadrata*, *Ophiocantha bidentata* and *Gorgonocephalus eucnemis*, while the crustaceans include *Pandalus borealis* and *Hippolyte polaris*, and the pycnogonids: *Chaetonymphon spinosum*, *Nymphon stromi* and *Pycnogonum littorale*. The polychaetes, molluscs and salps are only poorly represented.

In the *Phallusia obliqua* community (mostly at 60 to 100 m) besides the mass swarmings of ascidians (*Asc. obliqua* as well as *Asc. prunum*, *Pyura arctica*, *Tethium loveni*, *Amaroucium mutabile* and others) a multitude of Porifera is found, mainly *Grantia arctica*, *Gr. pennigera*, *Tethya lyncurium*, and some species of Leucosolenia (*L. nanseni*, *L. coriacea*, *L. blanca* and others). The various bryozoans are represented most abundantly (mainly the genera Flustra, Bugula, Caberea, Defrancia, Porella). Among the hydroids stand out *Tubularia larynx*, of the polychaetes *Glycera capitata*, *Nereis pelagica*, *Thelepus cincinnatus*, *Leodice norvegica*, *Syllis fabricii*, *S. armillaris*, *Nephthys ciliata* and others; among the Gephyrea, *Phascolosoma margaritaceum*, *Ph. eremita* and *Phascolium strombi*, the echinoderms *Asterias rubens*, *Cribrella sanguinolenta*, *Ophipholis aculeata*, *Ophiocantha bidentata*, *Ophiura sarsi* and others. The crustaceans are represented by *Pandalus borealis*, some species of Spirontocaris and some other Decapoda. The molluscs are also varied and numerous, first of all *Onchidiopsis glacialis*, *Trochus occidentalis*, some species of Velutina (*V. haliotoides*, *V. lanigera*, *Undata g. expansa*, *Columella rosacea*, *Marsenina micromphala*) and others.

On sand facies a more or less abundant life on the sublittoral develops only with silting. Life is very poor on large-grain sand and gravel. Only the so-called Dentalium sand (40 to 69 m), consisting mainly of finely ground mollusc shells, is abundantly populated by a rich fauna of molluscs (up to 60 species) *Dentalium entalis* and species of the genera Bela, Philine, Solariella, Cylichna, Astarte, Cardium, Mactra and others. Other groups of animals are rather scantily represented here.

An abundant fauna of polychaetes, echinoderms and molluscs grows on silty sands at shallow depths (4 to 15 m). Among the first-mentioned the most frequent here are *Ophelia limacina*, *Nephthys ciliata*, *Harmothoe imbricata*, *Nychia cirrosa* and *Travisia forbesi*; of secondary importance are *Chiridota laevis*, *Strongylocentrotus droebachiensis* and *Asterias rubens*. The molluscs most frequently found include *Nucula tenuis*, *Cardium ciliatum*, *Leda pernula*, *Astarte banksi*, *A. borealis* and *Pecten islanidcus*, and of the crustaceans *Hyas araneus* v. *hoeki*, *Eupagurus pubescens* and others.

The fauna of the facies of large-size shell gravel at shallow depths (20 to 30 m) is not typical and on the whole very poor. Much deeper (50 to 140 m) finer coquina accumulate, giving shelter to an extremely abundant fauna, consisting mainly of sponges, polychaetes, bryozoans, echinoderms and crustaceans (amphipods). The Porifera are especially well represented here (up to 26 species): in the first place—*Phavellia bowerbanki*, *Geodia baretti*, *Grayella pyrula*, *Trichostemma hemisphaericum*, *Tentorium semisuberites*, *Tedania suctoria*, *Tethya lyncurium*, and others. Among the polychaetes *Onuphis conchylega*, *Glycera capitata*, *Maldane sarsi*, *Nicomache lumbricalis*, *Nereis pelagica*, *Leodice norvegica*, *Protula media*, *Placostegus tridentatus*, *Flabelligera affinis*, *Filigrana implexa*, *Lumbrinereis fragilis*, *Thelepus cincinnatus*, *Sabella fabricii*, *Nephthis ciliata*, *Brada granulosa* and others should be noted.

Of the Sipunculoidea there are many *Phascolion strombi*. The bryozoans are represented here by *Flustra membranaceo-truncata*, *Fl. securifrons*, some species of Retepora, *Idmonea atlantica*, *Menipea ternata* v. *gracilis*, *Bugula murrayana*, and others.

Of the echinoderms the most frequent here are young *Heliometra quadrata*, and *Cribrella sanguinolenta*, *Pteraster pulvillus*, *Solaster endeca*, *Ophiocantha bidentata*, *Ophiopholis aculeata*, *Ophiura sarsi*, *Strongylocentrotus droebachiensis*, and others. *Haploops tubicola*, *Socarnes vahlii*, *Pardalisca cuspidata* and others are the characteristic amphipods. Other groups are scarcer on coquina.

The fauna of the facies is both peculiar and rich. The clayey-sandy mud of shallow depths (12 to 60 m) is inhabited by numerous burrowing fauna of polychaetes, holothurians, molluscs, Cumacea and amphipods. The main polychaetes are *Pectinaria hyperborea*, *Nephthys ciliata*, *Brada villosa* and *Scoloplos armiger*. There are huge numbers of *Myriotrochus rinki* and *Chiridota laevis* among Holothuriae. As for the other echinoderms there are many *Ophiura sarsi* and *Strongylocentratus droebachiensis*.

The most characteristic molluscs are *Joldia hyperborea*, *Cardium groenlandicum*, *C. ciliatum*, *Nucula tenuis*, *Axinus flexuosus*, *Leda pernula*, *Mya truncata*, *Macoma calcarea*. *Diastylis rathkei* and amphipod *Byblis gaimardi* are very numerous here.

The fauna of the sublittoral sandy silt and of the pseudo-abyssal, middle and great depths (60 to 360 m) is especially rich. The bottom fauna of the so-called 'trawling hole' with its typical Foraminifera *Hyperammina subnodosa*, polychaetes *Onuphis conchylega*, *Nicomache lumbricalis*, *Maldane sarsi*, *Pectinaria hyperborea*, *Polycirrus albicans*, Gephyrea *Phascolium strombi*, bryozoans *Defrancia lucernaria*, *Alcyonidium gelatinosum*, echinoderms *Ctenodiscus crispatus*, *Asterias lincki*, *Ophiura sarsi*, crustaceans *Calathura carinata*, has been thoroughly studied. Among the molluscs *Astarte crenata* and *Arca glacialis* are found here in large numbers.

At the greatest depths, down to 400 m (pseudo-abyssal), certain Porifera are added to this community, as for instance *Myxilla brunnea*, brachiopods Terebratulina and Rhynchonella, the deep-sea echinoderm *Rhegaster tumidus*, the crustacean *Pontophilus norvegicus*, and the molluscs *Buccinum hydrophanum* and *Pecten groenlandicus*.

There is an extremely original and rich life in the facies of the branched Lithothamnion (calcareous algae of the Rhodophyta) forming abundant clusters at places of strong water-circulation at depths of 10 to 40 m. Owing to the large number of its branches and to the presence of voida (similar to coral reefs) the Lithothamnion algae present exceptional facilities for the multiplying of specific fauna, partly hidden inside the Lithothamnion, partly connected with its surface. Inside the Lithothamnion thrive innumerable Lucernaria (*Lucernaria quadricornis*), nemerteans (Amphiporus, Cerebratulus) polychaetes (Nereis, Glycera and others), Gephyrea (*Phascolosoma eremita*, *Ph. margaritaceum*), Ophiuroidea (*Ophiopholis aculeata*), holothurians (*Phyllophorus pellucidus*), young sea urchins, asterids and molluscs (*Saxicava arctica*, *Modiola modiolus*). Ascidians (*Ciona intestinalis*, *Pyura aurantium*, *P. arctica*, *Sarcobotriloides aureum* and others), actinium (*Metridia dianthus*), polychaetes (*Chone infundibuliformis*, *Leaena abranchiata*, *Myxicola steenstrupi* and *Sabella fabricii*) are attached to the surface of Lithothamnion. Numerous echinoderms (*Ophiopholis aculeata*, *Cucumaria frondosa*) and molluscs (*Acmaea virginea*, *Margarita groenlandica*, *Chiton ruber*, *Ch. marmoreus*, *Ch. albus*, *Velutina haliotoides*, *Anomia squamula*, *Pecten islandicus*) crawl over the Lithothamnion. The crustaceans (especially some species of Spirontocaris—*S. turgida*, *S. gaimardi*, *S. spinus* and *S. polaris*), *Sclerocrangon boreas*, *Eupagurus pubescens*, *Hyas araneus* are also numerous on the Lithothamnion.

Almost 30 years after K. Derjugin's explorations, V. Zatzepin (1962) carried out careful investigations on the quantitative distribution of bottom fauna (1934 to 1936). First of all this worker remarks that the species composition and the distribution of the bottom biocoenoses are on the whole the same as those given by K. Derjugin. The change in the species composition can be easily explained first of all by the rise of temperature, which therefore affected mostly the cliffs, rocks and sandy floors of the northern part of the bay (in particular the mass population of the urchin *Brisaster fragilis*) and the southern part of the bay, from which a number of cold-water forms (for instance *Serripes groenlandicus*) have disappeared.

With a wide variation of species the Kola Inlet fauna has only 20 to 30 species of polychaetes, bivalves, echinoderms and Gephyrea composing the basic mass of its population.

As in the open parts of the Barents Sea polychaetes are preponderant at great depths and on softer bottoms and the bivalves at lesser depths and on harder floors.

The communities of the deep ooze and sand-ooze bottoms are very similar in their composition to those of the adjacent open parts of the Barents Sea (group II, see below).

In the Motovsky Bay, owing to its wide and free connection with the open sea, before it joins the bight of the Kola Inlet and in its northern part, the communities Cyprina, Macoma and Mactra, which inhabit warmer water, are strongly developed; a large number of warm-water boreal species are found here. The cold-water species are concentrated in the south of the Inlet.

Up to 80 per cent of the deep part of the Kola Inlet (Fig. 49) is occupied by a typical Barents Sea biocoenosis with a preponderance of Spiochaetopterus, Maldane, Astarte, Ctenodiscus, Phascolosoma and Strongylocentrotus (see below).

Zatzepin has distinguished in the deep part of the Kola Inlet, from north to south, five variations of the above-mentioned biocoenoses; for four of them data are given in *Table 53*, and their distribution is shown in Fig. 49. These four variations are distinguished by the preponderance of individual forms in the biocoenoses components, but the basic composition remains unaltered. Towards the south the dominant forms change. At first we find *Astarte crenata* and *Maldane sarsi*, then *Onuphis conchilega*, *Strongylocentrotus droebachiensis*, *Nicomache lumbricalis*, and finally in the southern part of the Inlet *Cardium ciliatum* and *Cyprina islandica*. In the shallow holes of the Kola Inlet another variant with the leading forms of *Cardium ciliatum*, *Macoma calcarea* and *Maldane sarsi* is formed on sandy silt. Moreover of the characteristic forms widely distributed throughout the whole Barents Sea there are worms *Spiochaetopterus typicus*, *Myriochele oculata*, *Nephthys ciliata*, *Lumbriconereis fragilis*, *Phascolosoma margaritaceum*, *Phascolion strombi*, *Rhodine gracilior*, molluscs *Portlandia lenticula*, *P. intermedia*, *Arca glacialis*, *Pecten islandicus*, *Yoldia hyperborea*, *Nucula tenuis*, echinoderms *Ctenodiscus crispatus*, *Ophiura sarsi*, with *Ophiopholis aculeata* and *Terebratulina septentrionalis* among the branchiopods. The sandy bed of the southern part of the bay is inhabited by the biocoenoses *Cardium ciliatum* and *Cyprina islandica*. Among the characteristic forms the polychaetes *Scoloplos armiger*, *Pectinaria hyperborea*, *Myriochele oculata* and *Lumbriconereis fragilis*, the molluscs *Yoldia hyperborea*, *Macoma calcarea* and *Axinus flexuosus* and the echinoderms *Ctenodiscus crispatus* and *Myriotrochus rincki* should be mentioned.

With all its qualitative changes within the limits of the two communities considered, the biomass is not large (Fig. 49A); it varies from 25 to 200 g/m^3, rarely reaching this upper limit.

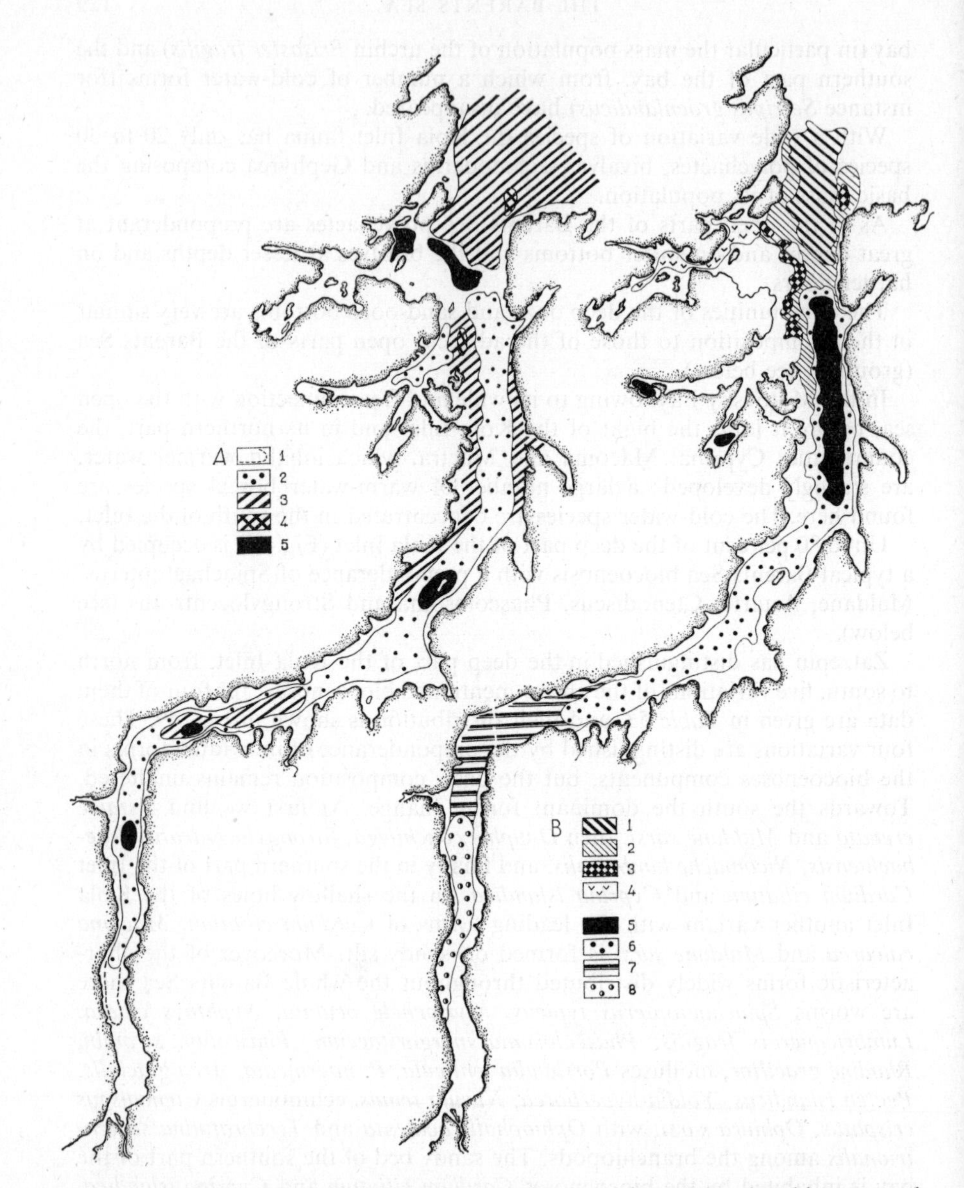

FIG. 49. Chart of Kola Inlct showing distribution of total benthos biomass and main bottom biocoenoses (Zatzepin): A Biomass: *1* 25; *2* 25 to 50; *3* 50 to 100; *4* 100 to 150; *5* 150 g/m² and over. B Bottom biocoenoses: *1* Astarte–Maldane; *2* Porifera–Brachiopoda–Bryozoa; *3 Ascidia obliqua*; *4* Maldane–*Cardium ciliatum*; *5* Maldane–Astarte; *6* Astarte–Onuphis; *7 Strongylocentrotus–Nicomache*; *8* Cardium–Scolopolos–Pectinaria.

Table 53

Communities	Depth of occurrence m	No. of species	Mean total biomass g/m³	Biomass, per cent Infauna	Epifauna	Bottom feeders	Seston feeders
1) Variations of the basic communities of the Kola Guba depths on soft bed:							
Astarte–Maldane	150	83	83·6	84	16	89	11
Maldane–Astarte	200	73	48·9	88	12	90	5
Astarte–Onuphis	80–200	101	79·7	71	29	76	4
Strongylocentrotus–Astarte–Nicomache	20–50	112	162·3	45	55	75	20
2) Cardium–Cyprina community	25–60	65	77·2	87	13	89	4

V. Zatzepin (1939) compared the consecutive changes of the total biomass of the epi- and in-fauna of the depths for a stretch of the Kola Inlet 50 km long and 1½ to 4½ km wide. On the two submarine bars of the outer part of the Inlet the epifauna is fed on the dying plankton and the organic detritus, and is developed abundantly. In the hollow between the bars the infauna is preponderant, mainly detritus-eaters, living on detritus settled on the floor. Farther into the Inlet the infauna increases as well as the epifauna because of the presence of partly suspended detritus brought out by the rivers.

Changes in the individual groups of the bottom population from north to south are given in *Table 53*. The benthos of the cliff and rocky floor of the sublittoral of the northern part of the Kola Inlet is different in its character.

Table 54

Community	Ratio of component groups in biomass, per cent Lamellibranchiata	Polychaeta	Echinodermata	Sipuncuoloidea	Brachiopoda
Astarte–Maldane					
Variation 1	56·3	24·6	6·6	7·12	1·45
Variation 2	19·4	46·1	20·3	7·4	3·6
Variation 3	23·4	45·6	14·5	10·2	2·8
Variation 4	42·8	13·5	36·8	4·3	—
Cardium–Cyprina	67·0	14·6	16·0	—	—

Epifauna is preponderant and the total biomass is much higher. Several most typical communities may be distinguished there (Fig. 49A and B).

First of all there is the Porifera–Brachiopoda–Bryozoa community very similar to the one so widely distributed in the open southwestern parts of the Barents Sea shores and with the same main organisms (see below).

In separate patches among the above community, and often on more shallow sites, the peculiar communities of the Salpa *Ascidia obliqua* (50 to

FIG. 50. Murman Biological Station of the Academy of Sciences of the U.S.S.R. in the Dal'naya Zelenetskaya Guba on the Murman Peninsula coast (1938).

100 m) and the population of the branched Lithothamnion are found everywhere. Both these communities are peculiar to places with vigorous water movement; the polychaetes *Thelepus cincinnatus*, *Eunice norvegica*, the molluscs *Astarte elliptica*, *A. crenata*, *A. sulcata*, *Cardium fasciatum*, *C. elegantulum*, bryozoans of the genera Retepora, Flustra and Defrancia, Porifera of the genera Tethya and Tenthorium, and *Ophiopholis aculeata* are peculiar to the first one. This community includes quite a number of warm-water forms.

Among the population of the branched Lithothamnion the following are of significance as regards their numbers—of the echinoderms *Ophiopholis aculeata*, *Strongylocentrotus droebachiensis*, *Cucumaria frondosa*, of the molluscs *Pecten islandicus*, *Saxicava arctica*, *Modiola modiolus*, of the tunicates *Cyona intestinalis*, *Pyura aurantium*, of the crustaceans *Balanus porcatus* and *Eupagurus pubescens*.

The basic quantitative indices for the three above-mentioned communities are given in *Tables 55 and 56*.

When moving east along the Murman coast and north along the Novaya Zemlya coast the fauna suffers considerable impoverishment; a large number of boreal and sub-Arctic forms disappear, and a series of high Arctic species are

Table 55

Community	Depth of occurrence m	No. of species	Mean total biomass g/m²	Biomass, per cent			
				Infauna	Epifauna	Bottom feeders	Seston feeders
Porifera–Brachiopoda–Bryozoa	100–200	131	170	23·3	76·7	41·3	54·3
Ascidia obliqua	50–100	93	524	4·3	95·7	7·4	91·1
Population of branched Lithothamnion	5–75	—	321	0	100	—	—

Table 56

Communities	Ratio of component groups in biomass, per cent								
	Lamelli-branchiata	Polychaeta	Echinodermata	Gephyrea	Brachiopoda	Porifera	Bryozoa	Cirripedia	Tunicata
Porifera–Brachipoda–Bryozoa	11·8	10·5	20·8	6·1	4·5	36·9	2·4	2·6	—
Ascidia obliqua	4·1	4·2	1·0	0·4		2·8	—	—	85·1
Population of branched Lithothamnion	7·6	—	75·9	—		—		1·6	5·6

added instead. A good illustration of this can be found in the papers of E. Gurjanova and P. Ushakov on the fauna of Chernaya Guba in the Novaya Zemlya (1928), of E. Gurjanova on the fauna of the Cheshskaya Guba (1929) and of P. Ushakov on the Matochkin Shar (1931).

The Chernaya Guba fauna has a sharply pronounced Arctic character, but side by side with it a whole series of boreal and warm-water forms have been discovered. These latter include *Acmaea rubella*, *Hydrobia ulrae*, *Rissoa aculeus*, *Littorina rudis*, *Cuthona distans*, *Corophium conelli* and some others. Of the Arctic forms the most characteristic are: among the molluscs *Venus fluctuosa*, *Pandora glacialis*, among the polychaetes *Harmothoe impar*, *Axionice flexuosa*, *Castalia arctica*, among the crustaceans *Acanthostepheia malmgreni*, *Gammaracanthus loricatus*, *Orchomene tschernyschevi*, *Socarnes bidenticulateus*.

Table 57 (p. 145) gives the composition and distribution of the fauna of the Chernaya Guba in its main sectors.

Some warmth-loving forms can find conditions suitable for their existence in some other parts of the Barents Sea. Cheshskaya Guba, for instance, is one of them. In winter, it is true, Cheshskaya Guba undergoes long and severe spells of cold weather, but in the summer the whole column of water is heated, sometimes to 14° at a depth of 10 to 15 m, and to 5° at a depth of 38 m. Evidently a number of forms can endure severe winter conditions, if in summer time a temperature high enough for breeding is attained at least for a short period. Among them we may point out *Buccinium undatum*, *Neptunea despecta typica*, *Acmaea testudinalis*, *Lacuna divarivata*, *Littorina palliata*, *Modiola modiolus*, *Mytilus edulis*, *Eumida sanguinea*, *Castalia punctata*, *Syllis armillaris*, *Balanus crenatus Apherusa tridentata*, and *Erialus gaimardi gaimardi*.

Some of these forms have possibly already broken away from their basic habitat and can be considered as warm-water relicts in the Cheshskaya Guba.

Similar phenomena are known for the inhabitants of the White Sea.

E. Gurjanova's indication (1929) of a whole series of high Arctic forms which do not visit the Cheshskaya Guba (*Acanthostepheia malmgreni*, *Synidothea bicuspida*, *Anonyx nugax*, *Neptunea despecta* v. *borealis*, *Buccinium glaciale*,

B. ciliatum, *Bela morchi*, *Dendronotus frondosus* v. *dalli* and some others) is also of great interest.

Sharp seasonal fluctuations of temperature in the Cheshskaya Guba, its severe winter, and comparatively warm summer have led to the development mainly of a eurytopic stable fauna.

Some peculiarities of benthos distribution. With the changes of the Barents Sea conditions from west to east, a vertical displacement of either the zones or individual forms is observed in its fauna range. In the White Sea the boundaries of the vertical zones rise upwards considerably as compared with those of the Barents Sea.

A number of typical Murman littoral forms in the eastern part of the Barents Sea and off the coast of Novaya Zemlya go down into the upper levels of the sublittoral. This is caused by severe climatic conditions, and chiefly by the grinding effect of ice in winter. This was noted by a series of workers, beginning with Stuxberg (1882, 1887). Thus in the Cheshskaya Guba *Mytilus edulis* and *Balanus crenatus* form thick growths at depths down to 30 m. The polychaete *Fabricia sabella*, so typical for the littoral, sinks down to a depth of 5 to 10 m in Belushja Guba. On the other hand, many forms typical of the sublittoral lower horizons move upwards in the eastern parts of the Sea. Ushakov, for instance, caught (1931) in Matochkin Shar at a depth of 3 to 7 m such forms as *Yoldia hyperborea*, *Leda pernula*, *Pecten groenlandicus*, *Pandora glacialis*, different species of Astarte and other forms which thrive at great depths in the western parts of the Sea. The asterid *Asterias panopla* and the mollusc *Cardium ciliatum* become also comparatively shallow-water forms in the east. According to Stuxberg *Gammarus locusta* lives in the Kara Sea at a depth of 6 m and *Ophiura sarsi*, *Ophiocten sericeum* and *Asterias panopla* which in the Kola Inlet live in deep water are here encountered at 10 to 20 m. This sinking down of the littoral fauna in deep inlets is due not only to the above-mentioned cause, but may also be the consequence of a considerable loss of salinity in the surface waters. The rise of the boundaries of the other zones is controlled in the east by the low temperature of the surface layers of the Sea, which allows the rise of cold-water bathypelagic fauna to higher levels. This explains the migration of the many Barents Sea forms into the colder deeper layers as they travel towards the more southerly parts of the Atlantic. But observers have also noted the withdrawal to considerable depths of the sublittoral of a number of typical littoral forms of the north-western European shores, as they travelled into the Barents Sea (*Pycnogonum littorale*, some species of Chiton, *Margarita helicina*, *M. groenlandica*, *Anomia squamula* and others). K. Derjugin was inclined to explain this, as yet incomprehensible, phenomenon by biocoenotic correlation.

The warm-water fauna travelling from the west differs from that of the cold local waters of the Barents Sea. It has been shown by K. Derjugin his collaborators that the distribution of a number of forms in the warm and cold waters can be established by collecting the bottom fauna along the Kola meridian.

The dominant forms in the warm waters consist of the coral polyps

Virgularia mirabilis and *Planularia arctica*, the polychaetes *Placostegus tridentatus* and *Potamilla neglecta*, the urchins *Echinus esculentus* and *Brisaster fragilis*, the asterids *Psilaster andromeda*, the cirripiedia *Scalpellum strömi*, the amphipods *Menigrates obtusifrons*, *Harpinia antennaria*, *Erichthonius brasiliensis*, Pantopods *Pycnogonum littorale*, the molluscs *Dentalium entale*, *Poromya granulata*, *Astarte sulcata*, *Scaphander punctostriatus*, *Triops laser*, and others. The following forms are just as characteristic of the cold waters: the bottom medusa *Ptichogastria polaris*, the polychaete *Glurhanostomum pallescens*, the asterid *Asterias lincki*, the brittle star *Stegophiura nodosa*, the amphipods *Stegocephalopsis ampulla*, *Acanthostepheia malmgreni*, *Lepidopecreum umbo*, *Rozinante fragilis*, *Socarnes bidenticulatus*, *Pseudalibrotes nanseni*, *Aegina echinata*, the mollusc *Acanthodoris sibirica* and others. Somewhat earlier N. M. Knipovitch (1906) established a similar distribution of bottom-fish of the genera Lycodes and Lycenchelys; some of them are adapted to cold waters, some to warm. Linko (1907, 1913) gives a very similar picture of some plankton forms Halosphaera, Rhizosolenia, Ceratium, Globigerina and especially the amphipods Hyperia and Euphausiaceae.

Later M. Virketis (1928) and Kisselev (1928) have also shown that a number of warm-water forms of the zoo- and phyto-plankton are adapted to the streams of Atlantic waters. Among the vegetable forms the following should be noted: *Rhizosolenia styliformis*, *Rh. shrubsolei*, *Rh. faerocensis*, *Rh. alata*, *Corethron criophilum*, *Ceratium tripos*, *Thalassiosira decipiens*, *Chaetoceras constrictum*, *Ch. curvisetum*, *Coscinodiscus centralis*, *Nitzschia delicatissima* and others, and among animal forms: *Euchaeta norvegica*, *Microcalanus pusillus*, *Temora longicornicus*, *Metridia lucens*, *Oithona plumifera* v. *atlantica* and others.

General distribution of benthos biomass in the open parts of the Sea. The bottom of the Barents Sea is not homogeneous as regards the benthos biomass, both of the total benthos and of its separate component groups (molluscs, worms, echinoderms) (Figs. 51 and 52).

Areas with particularly small biomass (10 to 25 g/m^2) stretch in the Barents Sea from the west to 30° E longitude, extending farther in two tongues—one southeastern and one northeastern; they also occupy a large area of the depths between the northern part of Novaya Zemlya and Franz Joseph Land; furthermore the biomass here is still lower than in the western part of the Sea. In contrast to these impoverished areas there are some areas with a most abundant bottom fauna. Five such areas with accumulations of organic matter as living organisms may be pointed out:

(*1*) The southeastern slope of the Spitsbergen bank—shallow with biomass up to 1 kg/m^2 or more.
(*2*) Separate patches with an increased biomass (300 to 500 g/m^2 or more) on the shores of the northern part of Norway (mostly epifauna).
(*3*) The central part of the Barents Sea with a biomass of up to 150 g/m^2.
(*4*) The Kanin–Kolguev–Pechora shallow with an exceptionally dense patch of benthos near Kanin Nos (up to 300 g/m^2).

(*5*) Novaya Zemlya shallow with separate patches of biomass exceeding 500 g/m².

In many parts of the shores of the Murman Peninsula, Novaya Zemlya and the Arctic archipelagoes, in inlets, gubas and fjords patches with very much

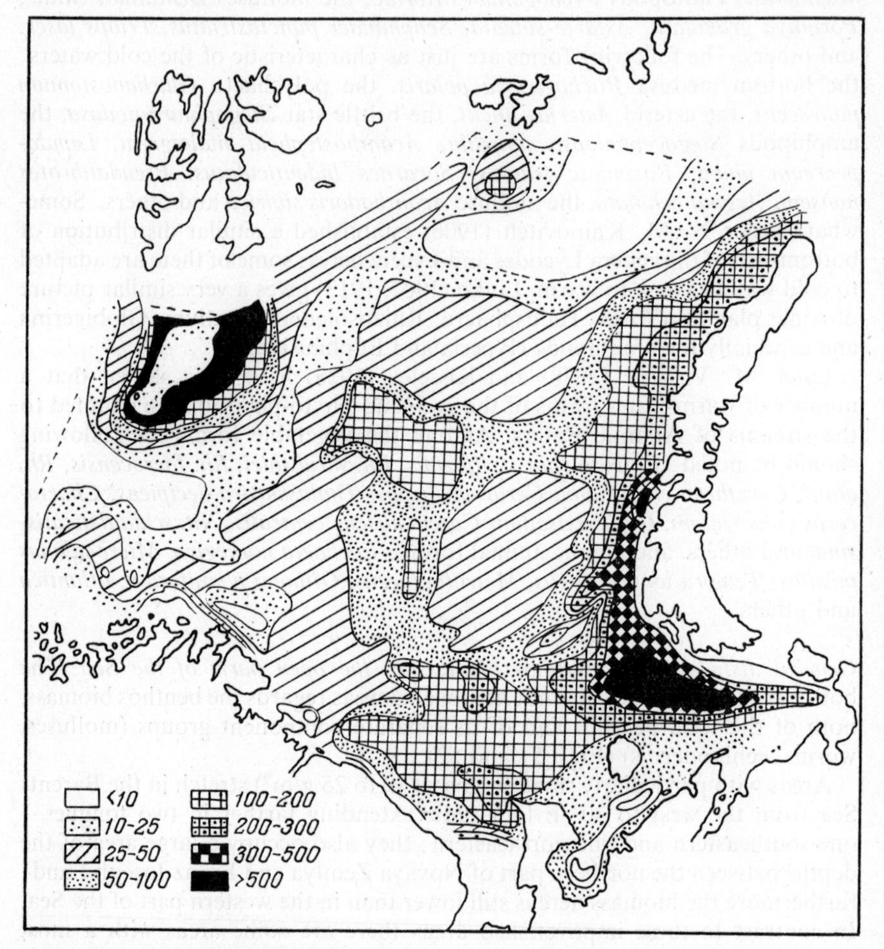

FIG. 51. Distribution of benthos biomass of Barents Sea (g/m²) (Brotzkaya and Zenkevitch with additions by Filatova).

increased biomass are found. Thus in the inner parts of Sturfjord the average biomass reaches 500 g/m², in Mashigina Guba it exceeds 3 kg/m², and on some patches in the Kola Inlet and Motovsky Bay it exceeds 200 g/m². In general a certain increase of the biomass is observed in shallow regions, partly on the shores, partly at the edges of banks. Moreover the benthos biomass of the large and deep bays like the Kola Inlet, Motovsky Bay and Cheshskaya Inlet is smaller in their central parts when the aeration of the bottom layer is impeded. Thus in the main area of the Motovsky Bay and Kola Inlet the biomass is 25 to 50 g/m², whereas at their entrances it is 50 to 100 g/m² or more. On average, as shown by M. Idelson (1934) for the whole benthos of the Barents Sea the change of biomass is as follows:

At depths of 0 to 100 m	311 g/m²
At depths of 100 to 200 m	168 g/m²
At depths of 200 to 300 m	93 g/m²
At depths of 300 to 400 m	48 g/m²

However, since as a rule any increase of depth is associated with a decrease of food supplies and a progressive worsening of air conditions in the bottom layer of water, it is difficult to say whether the fall of biomass can be explained by the increase of depth alone. On the contrary it is possible to see from some separate cross sections of the Barents Sea that the inverse dependence of the change of biomass on depth is only partly valid. The degree of upwelling of water is, as was pointed out above, a much more important factor in the distribution of the total benthos biomass. Moreover since in the Barents Sea the

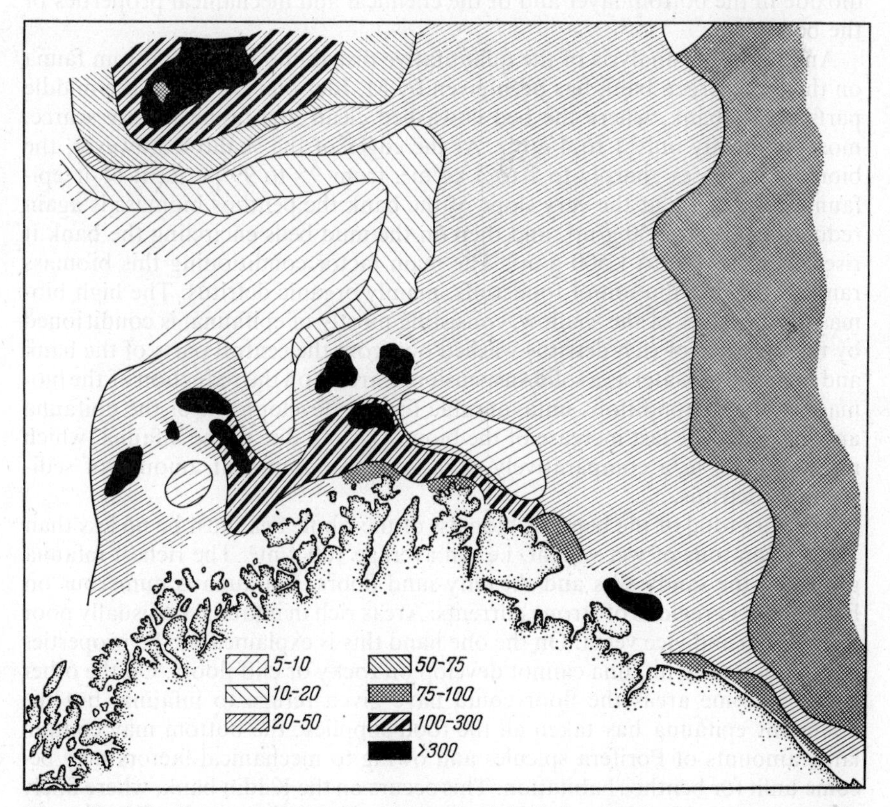

FIG. 52. Distribution of benthos biomass (g/m²) in southwestern Barents Sea (Filatova, 1938).

regions of the most active mixing of waters coincide with the coolest parts of the sea, an erroneous idea of an inverse dependence between the benthos biomass and temperature might be formed, since the line of the polar front coincides with a bottom temperature of from 0° to 1°. The cause of the fall of biomass towards the west should be sought in the more and more difficult upwelling and in the shortage of food, rather than in the rise of temperature.

As has been noted above, the areas of abundant biomass lie on the lines of the polar front. This is confirmed by a comparison of the charts of currents and of the biomass. The main areas of low biomass (the western and northern parts of the Sea and its central depression) are situated within the centre of the three great zones of cyclonic rotation, but at the meeting place of the alien warm waters and the local cold ones the biomass increases sharply. However, some other interlinking factors are active here. The horizontal circulation is conditioned by the bottom contour; halistatic areas are formed over the depressions and soft mud sediments are deposited there. Poor development of life is the result of somewhat impeded upwelling, an accumulation of carbon dioxide in the bottom layer and of the chemical and mechanical properties of the bed.

An interesting analysis of the quantitative distribution of the bottom fauna on the Spitsbergen bank has been given by M. Idelson (1930). On the middle parts of the bank, where the bed is washed clean, the fauna is very scarce, most frequently only 1 to 4 g/m². At the edges of the shallow, however, the biomass increases sharply to 1 to 3 kg/m², from 95 to 99 per cent of it epifauna. Farther on at the very slope of the bank the benthos biomass is again reduced to 150 to 350 g/m², and then on the mud beds encircling the bank it rises again to 500 to 1,500 g/m². The main factor conditioning this biomass range is the distribution of foodstuffs, mainly organic detritus. The high biomass at the edges of the shallow, consisting mostly of epifauna, is conditioned by the presence of rich detritus washed out from the central parts of the bank and brought by water as a solid suspension. Farther on the reduction of the biomass is due to conditions unfavourable for the development of the epifauna and infauna. The last increase of the biomass is not due to the infauna, which receives here, in a comparatively calm zone, an abundant amount of sedimentary detritus.

The sum total of the benthos biomass of the whole Sea must be no less than 150 million tons of wet weight, i.e. on average 100 g/m². The richest infauna grows on the sandy silts and the silty-sand floors. Epifauna is numerous on hard floors in regions of strong currents. Areas rich in infauna are usually poor in epifauna and vice versa. On the one hand this is explained by the properties of the floor since infauna cannot develop on rocky or cliff floors. On the other hand, in some areas the floor could have given refuge to infauna, but the abundant epifauna has taken all the food supplies; the bottom may contain large amounts of Porifera spicules and owing to mechanical factors may become unfit for benthos habitation. This occurs on the Kildin bank, where finely cartilaginous and sufficiently silted floors give refuge to a rich epifauna, and are almost devoid of infauna. The same picture is observed in the wide belt adjacent to Finmark. Porifera and Brachiopoda are predominant in these regions.

The third region of greatly increased epifauna biomass lies on the southeastern slopes of the Spitsbergen shallow. The patch of increased biomass in the north of the Barents Sea, southwest from Franz Joseph Land, corresponds to a considerable rise of the bottom, and likewise consists mostly of epifauna. In the central part of the Barents Sea considerable quantities of epifauna extend in a wide meridional band along 37° and 38°, on the shallow crest which separates the western depth of the Sea from its central depressions

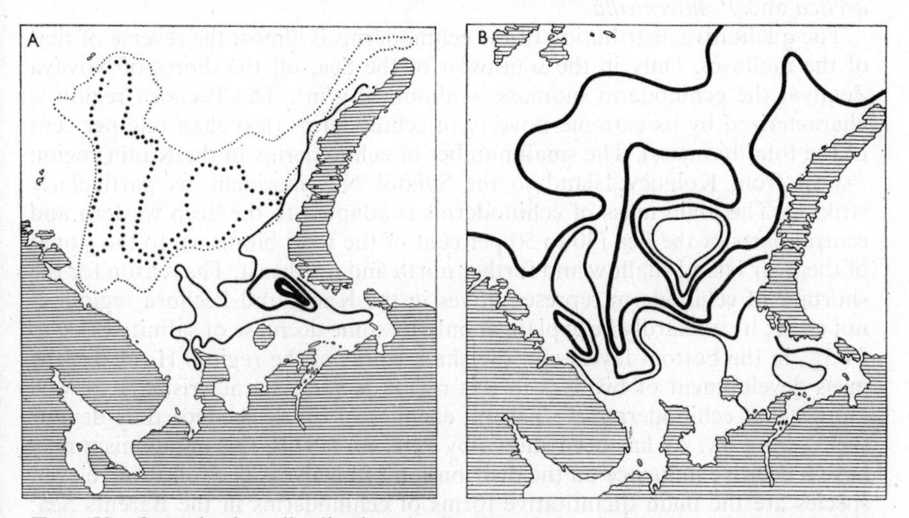

FIG. 53. Quantitative distribution in Barents Sea: A Bivalves (full line) and polychaetes (dotted line); B Echinoderms. Thicker lines denote greater biomass (Brotzkaya and Zenkevitch, 1939).

passing at the north into the central shallow. In the east an abundant epifauna thrives north of Kolguev Island and especially on the Gusinaya bank and farther along the shallows off Novaya Zemlya. In these regions the echinoderms are preponderant (Strongylocentrotus, Ophiopholis, Psolus) and some molluscs (Saxicava, Pecten, Buccinidae), crustaceans (Balanus and Eupagurus) and polychaetes (Thelepus). The biomass of the central depression with its great depths is comparatively poor. Coarse sand and gravel floors are very poorly populated. They are practically without life. Such regions are found in the Voronka of the White Sea southwest of Kanin Nos.

The main groups of the benthos—echinoderms, bivalves, polychaetes and sipunculids—play different roles in furnishing the common biomass in different areas of the sea (Fig. 53).

Lamellibranchiata are adapted mainly to fairly shallow (<150 m) silty-sand bottoms with a large detritus content. The largest accumulations of bivalves are found off the coast of Novaya Zemlya, in the Pechora region and, mainly, between Kolguev Island and Novaya Zemlya where their biomass reaches 600 g/m², forming more than 75 per cent of the total benthos. The Pechora region and the shallow off Novaya Zemlya must obtain large amounts of detritus from the abundant sea-weed growths off the southern coast of Novaya Zemlya, and from the outflow of the waters of the Pechora, the Novaya Zemlya rivers and from the Gorlo of the White Sea.

The following thirteen species are preponderant among the biomass of bivalves of the open parts of the Barents Sea: *Astarte crenata*, *A. borealis*, *A. montagui*, *A. elliptica*, *Cardium ciliatum*, *C. groenlandicum*, *Macoma calcarea*, *Arca glacialis*, *Leda pernula*, *Yoldia hyperborea*, *Nucula tenuis*, *Portlandia arctica* and *P. intermedia*.

The qualitative distribution of the echinoderms is almost the reverse of that of the molluscs. Only in the southwest of the Sea, off the shores of Novaya Zemlya, the echinoderm biomass is about 50 g/m². The Pechora region is characterized by its extreme poverty in echinoderms (less than one per cent of the total biomass). The small number of echinoderms in the Kanin region —west from Kolguev Island to the Sviatoi Nos meridian—is particularly striking. The main mass of echinoderms is adapted to the deep western and central parts of the Sea (30 to 50 per cent of the total biomass), to the slopes of the Bear Island shallow and farther north and northeast. The reason for the shortage of echinoderm representatives in the Kanin and Pechora regions is not clear; it can hardly be explained only by some decrease of salinity (33·0 to 34·5‰ in the bottom layer) and the shallowness of the region. However, the mass development of bivalves in this region is very characteristic. It is well known that echinoderms are natural enemies of bivalves, since they devour their young fry. As has been shown by Petersen (1913), this antagonism may have a decisive influence on the distribution of bivalves. The following eleven species are the main quantitative forms of echinoderms in the Barents Sea: *Ctenodiscus crispatus*, *Strongylocentrotus droebachiensis*, *Brisaster fragilis*, *Molpadia* sp., *Ophiura robusta*, *O. sarsi*, *Ophiopholis aculeata*, *Ophiopleura borealis*, *Ophiocantha bidentata*, *Ophioeten sericeum* and *Stegophiura nodosa*.

The picture of quantitative distribution of polychaetes is different from that of the molluscs and echinoderms. The greatest gathering of polychaetes is adapted mainly to the halistatic regions and the softer floors connected with them. The deeper western part of the Sea, so rich in echinoderms, is particularly poor in polychaetes. Its main polychaete forms are: *Spiochaetopterus typicus*, *Maldane sarsi*, *Pectinaria hyperborea*, *Onuphis conchylega*, *Thelepus cincinnatus*, *Myriochele oculata*, *Owenia assimilis* and *Scoloplos armiger*.

Of all the remaining fauna the large sipunculids *Phascolosoma margaritaceum* should be distinguished; in the central parts of the Sea and on the slopes of the southern island of Novaya Zemlya it forms dense colonies (15 to 65 g/m²) and frequently forms more than 50 per cent of the total benthos biomass.

The distribution in depth of the three main above-mentioned groups of Barents Sea benthos shows substantial differences (Fig. 54). The bivalves are considerably reduced with depth, the echinoderms, on the contrary, increase in numbers, while the polychaetes remain essentially unchanged. The same relationship in the vertical distribution of the three main groups of benthos has been established by R. Leibson (1939) for the Motovsky Gulf and the general character of the distribution of echinoderms, bivalves and polychaetes in the whole of the Barents Sea may be explained partly by these relationships.

Distribution and composition of the main communities of the open sea. Intensive quantitative investigations carried out for ten years make it possible to distinguish six basic communities in the bottom fauna of the Barents Sea and about forty secondary variations of these communities (Figs. 55 and 56). It must be kept in mind that these data, obtained by means of a bottom-grab, do not give a sufficiently complete picture of the epifauna, and its actual biocoenosis range must be wider. For the Barents Sea, however, with its soft

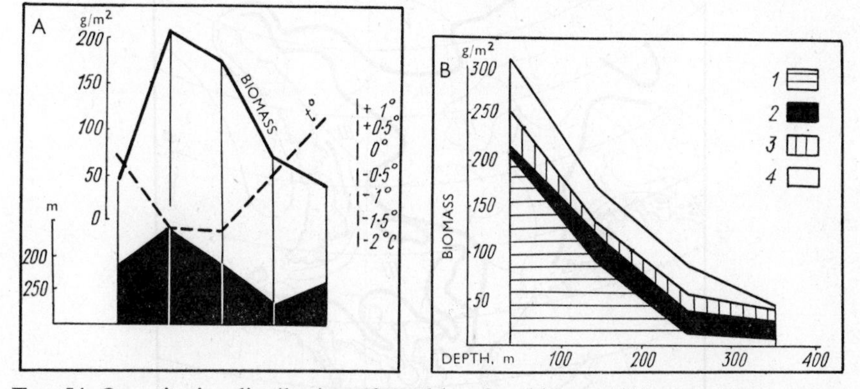

FIG. 54. Quantitative distribution of total benthos biomass (A) with depth and (B) bivalves, echinoderms and polychaetes on ooze soils of Barents Sea (Idelson). A: Benthos biomass and bottom temperature at the Central Elevation of the Barents Sea (along meridian 35° E). B: *1* Lamellibranchiata; *2* Echinodermata; *3* Polychaeta; *4* Other groups.

bottom, and therefore a preponderance of infauna, data of this type may be considered sufficient.

In the most southwesterly part of the Sea, open to considerable influence of thermophilic Atlantic fauna, a large biocoenosis diversity is observed on shallows of the continent. As has been shown by Z. Filatova (1938) the population of the littoral sand and rock floor at depths of 60 to 100 m along west and east Finmark loses some of its boreal forms, and they are replaced by Arctic ones as we move eastward. Epifauna consisting of different planktophages is here luxuriantly developed. To the west of the North Cape a mass development of warm-water forms is observed: bryozoans *Hornera lichenoides, Idmonea atlantica, Flustra foliacea,* soft coral Eunephthya, and the polychaetes *Placostegus tridentatus, Hydroides norvegica, Eunice norvegica, Pista cristata* and *Goniada maculata.* The boreal forms of echinoderms and especially sea-urchins *Echinus esculentus, Spatangus raschi, Brisaster fragilis, Echinocyamus pusillus, Echinocardium flavescens* are very typical. Among the molluscs *Astarte sulcata, Pecten auratus, Modiola barbata, Mactra elliptica, Cardium fasciatum*, *Gibbula tumida*, *Trichotropis conica* and others may be pointed out and among the Brachiopoda *Waldheimia cranium*.

To the east of the North Cape the boreal forms are considerably decreased and replaced by representative forms of the colder-water fauna. Instead of the above-mentioned sedentaria, *Protula media*, *Filigrana implexa*, *Pseudopotamilla reniformis*, *Potamilla neglecta* begin to preponderate here; *Waldheimia cranium* is replaced mainly by *Terebratulina septentrionalis* and *Rhynchonella psittacea*. Among the warm-water sea-urchins *Brisaster fragilis* and *Echinus*

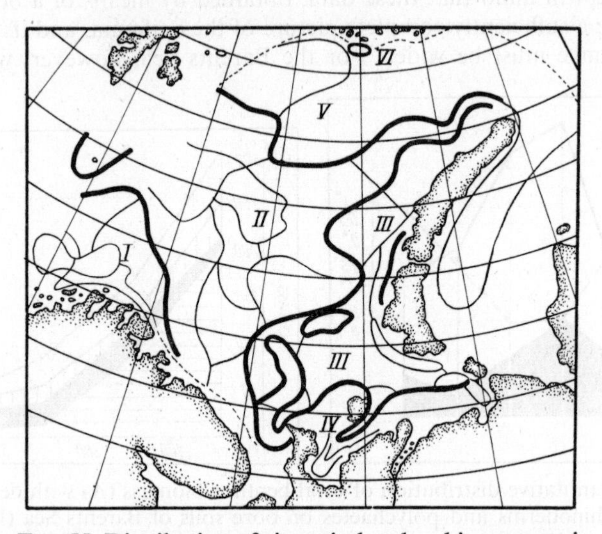

FIG. 55. Distribution of six main benthos biocoenoses in Barents Sea: *I* Southwestern; *II* Central; *III* Eastern shallows; *IV* Eastern (coastal); *V* Northern (deep); *VI* Northern (shallows) (Brotzkaya and Zenkevitch with Filatova's additions).

esculentus still remain and of the molluscs *Astarte montagui* and *Saxicava arctica* begin to prevail here.

East of North Cape a number of boreal forms are found in large amounts as mollusc shells.

The benthos biomass of the littoral sand and rock floors varies from 120 to 400 g/m².

Of the shallow (not deeper than 80 to 100 m) benthic groups of the Murman sublittoral the biocoenosis of the large bivalves *Modiola modiolus*, *Pecten islandicus* and *Mactra elliptica* are of great interest; they have a definite north-boreal character and in the last few years they have developed greatly on the Murman coast owing to a considerable rise in temperature.

They reach their highest development in Danish waters and off Iceland and the Faroe Islands. These communities grow poorer in quality and quantity as one proceeds northwards and eastwards. Off the Murman shores both communities reach the edge of their habitat; they are absent from the eastern and northern parts of the Barents Sea.

In the biocoenosis *Modiola modiolus–Pecten islandicus*, the polychaetes *Thelepus cincinnatus*, the Ophuroidea *Ophiopholis aculeata*, *Balanus balanus*, the sea-urchin *Strongylocentrotus droebachiensis* and some Bryozoa are the

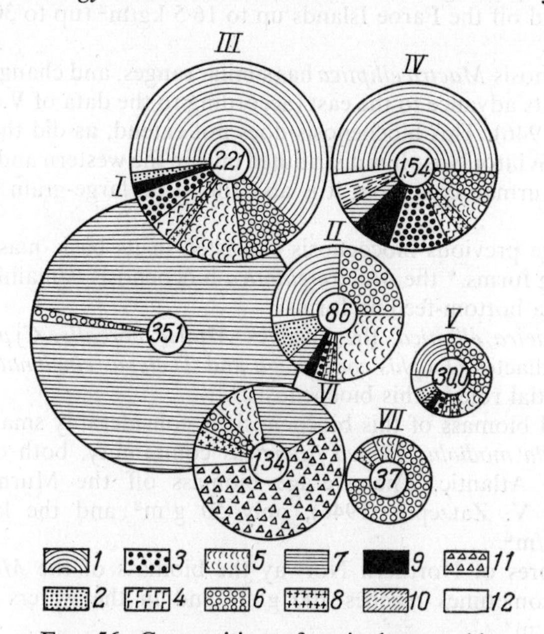

FIG. 56. Composition of main bottom biocoenoses of Barents Sea (Brotzkaya, Zenkevitch and Filatova). *I* Porifera; *II* Central; *III* Eastern (medium depths); *IV* Eastern littoral; *V* Northern littoral; *VI* Northern (deep water); *VII* Waldheimia–Brisaster. *1* Lamellibranchiata; *2* Gephyrea; *3* Crustacea; *4* Coelenterata; *5* Polychaeta; *6* Echinodermata; *7* Porifera; *8* Sipunculoidea; *9* Gastropoda; *10* Tunicata; *11* Brachiopoda; *12* Varia. Average biomass is given in numerals (g/m²).

most important. This biocoenosis is distributed mainly over large-grain sand and shale gravel, in zones of the constant ebb and flow of tidal streams.

V. Zatzepin and Z. Filatova (1945) have noted that in summer these communities keep to waters of 6° to 10° and in winter to 0·5° to 2·5°; large growths of macrophytes are frequently met, among them the branched Lithothamnion (red algae). On the Murman coast the biomass of Modiola biocoenosis reached 1 to 1·5 kg/m² (an average of 350 g/m²). Proceeding westward and southward the biocoenosis changes its qualitative composition—its cold-water forms such as the molluscs *Saxicava arctica*, *Pecten islandicus* and *Astarte elliptica*, polychaetes *Onuphis conchylega*, *Thelepus cincinnatus* and *Nephthys ciliata*, and the brittle stars *Ophiocantha bidentata* are reduced in numbers. They are gradually replaced by the thermophilic forms of echinoderms, molluscs and worms. At the same time the biocoenosis biomass increases, reaching 10 kg/m^2 in Danish waters, in Gulmarfjord (S. Sweden) up to 7 kg/m^2 and off the Faroe Islands up to 16·5 kg/m^2 (up to 300 specimens/m^2).

The biocoenosis *Mactra elliptica* has similar ranges, and changes in the same manner with its advance to the east (according to the data of V. Zatzepin and Z. Filatova, 1946). This biocoenosis does not extend, as did the former one, eastwards to Sviatoi Nos; it is distributed only in the western and along part of the central Murman coast, but it is also found on large-grain sand and fine gravel.

Whereas the previous biocoenosis consisted in its basic mass of epifauna seston-feeding forms,* the *Mactra elliptica* biocoenosis is mainly represented by the infauna bottom-feeding forms.

Besides *Mactra elliptica*, the bivalves *Astarte borealis*, *Cyprina islandica* and the polychaetes *Onuphis conchylega* and *Thelepus cincinnatus* and others play an essential role in this biocoenosis.

The quoted biomass of this biocoenosis is considerably smaller than that of the *Modiola modiolus–Pecten islandicus* community, both on coasts and in the north Atlantic. The average biomass off the Murman coast is, according to V. Zatzepin (1946), only 50 g/m^2 and the largest hardly reaches 100 g/m^2.

On the shores of Northern Norway the biomass of the *Mactra elliptica* biocoenosis sometimes reaches 200 g/m^2 and in the waters of Iceland it reaches 270 g/m^2.

Zatzepin confirms R. Spärck's (1936) opinion that the *M. elliptica* biocoenosis of the Faroe and Iceland waters (and according to Zatzepin's data, those of the Murman coast as well) should be considered as colder-water north-boreal modifications of the south-boreal groups of the Venus sand biocoenosis.

Among the biocoenoses peculiar to Murman coastal waters, it is possible to distinguish other north-boreal ones with ranges similar to the two previously mentioned. Such are the biocoenoses *Cyprina islandica*, *Pseudopotamilla reniformis*, *Brisaster fragilis*, *Waldheimia cranium* and others.

At great depths (150 to 350 m), on slightly silty sand floors containing rocks, the Brachiopoda *Waldheimia cranium* community is greatly developed; it stretches east almost to the Rybachiy Peninsula. Waldheimia, a typical planktophage, forms mass accumulations of some hundreds of grammes per m^2 in sectors with strong currents. In this community Waldheimia comprises, on the average, more than 50 per cent of the whole population. Moreover, there is an abundance of Porifera (*Geodia baretti*, *Craniella cranium*, Thakellia and others), polychaetes *Placostegus tridentatus* and *Eunice norvegica*, molluscs *Astarte sulcata*, *Anomia squamula*, sea-urchin *Brisaster fragilis*, asterid *Cribrella sanguinolenta*, crab *Hyas coarctatus* and others. In the west

* Zatzepin's terms.

this community passes over gradually into the communities *Placostegus–Modiola barbata*, and farther on, at Lofoten, into the community of the madreporarian coral *Lophophelia prolifera*. The average biomass of the *Waldheimia cranium* community is 133 g/m² (from 60 to 400 m.) Epifauna is sharply predominant in this community forming about 94 per cent of the total biomass (*Table 57*).

Table 57. Composition of the Waldheimia cranium *community according to groups*

Group	Biomass g/m²	Percentage of total biomass
Brachiopoda	78·2	58·3
Porifera	25·5	19·2
Polychaeta	10·9	8·2
Bryozoa	6·3	4·7
Echinodermata	5·5	4·0
Bivalvia	3·2	2·4
Ascidia	3·0	2·3
Others	1·1	0·9
Total biomass	133·7	100

The above-mentioned community in various places passes to the west, north and east into the Porifera community, which frequently forms 95 to 98 per cent of the total benthos biomass. Proceeding from west to east one observes that the thermophilic forms of this community are replaced by the less thermophilic ones. Only the three areas of the greatest accumulation of Porifera are marked on the chart; lesser gatherings are met everywhere off Finmark and the Murman coast on mixed rock bottoms. On bottom sectors occupied by this community the work of trawlers is made difficult since Porifera fill the trawl sometimes up to many tons and spoil the fish. On the other hand, hunge amounts of dead Porifera spicules mix with the bed deposits in such quantities that it becomes almost completely unfit for infauna habitation; after a little washing it appears as a compact felt made of spicules (the silica–Porifera floor). Here infauna forms usually 1 to 3 per cent of the total fauna biomass.

The development of other representatives of epifauna is also restricted by the mass growth of Porifera, since these latter, loose powerful filters, are the first to take out of water all the nutrient substances (detritus and plankton and, possibly, the dissolved organic substances). Manteufel (1938) has suggested that the warm-water plankton brought from the west and destroyed at the entrance to the Barents Sea may serve as a considerable source of food for Porifera off the shores of Finmark and the western Murman coast, and cause its luxuriant development.

The biomass of the Porifera community reaches 5 to 6 kg/m², and on the average on the huge patch opposite Nordkyn, 350 g/m². The mass forms of

Table 58

Group	Biomass g/m²	Percentage of total biomass
Porifera	336·9	86
Echinodermata	6·8	2
Polychaeta	2·4	
Brachiopoda	2·2	
Bivalvia	1·4	2
Bryozoa	0·8	
Others	0·8	
Total biomass	351·3	100

Porifera are *Geodia baretti*, *Craniella cranium* and *Thenea muricata*. It is interesting to note that these Porifera usually lie free on the bottom and therefore can develop in masses on a comparatively soft floor (sand and silty sand). Many mass forms of the previous community are of secondary significance here (Waldheimia, Retepora, Placostegus, Eunice, Asyches and others). Moreover among the characteristic forms here one may note *Astarte crenata*, *Nephthys coeca*, *Ophiocantha bidentata*, *Maldane sarsi*, *Lumbriconerbis fragilis*, *Ophiura sarsi* and a number of asterids Ceramaster, Leptychaster, Cribrella, etc. This particular group has the following composition (*Table 58*).

Farther east, in the Rybachiy Peninsula shallow, the admixture of cold-water forms, such typical inhabitants of the Barents Sea as *Myriochele oculata*, *Macoma calcarea*, *Spiochaetopterus typicus* and others, is felt even more strongly.

The Waldheimia and Porifera communities described above are gradually replaced by the *Brisaster fragilis* community which inhabits silty sand bottoms (200 to 300 m deep), with a mass Foraminifera Astrorhiza and Rhabdammina. High salinity (35 to 35·5‰) and a temperature of 3° to 4° turn it into a suitable habitat for a large number of warm-water forms. The average biomass of this community is not high—37 g/m² (from 20 to 80 m deep). The infauna there already accounts for a biomass of about 90 per cent of the whole fauna with a sharp preponderance of echinoderms and polychaetes (*Table 59*).

Table 59

Group	Biomass g/m²	Percentage of total biomass
Echinodermata	26·2	71·6
Polychaeta	4·8	13·5
Bivalvia	2·3	6·4
Coelenterata	0·9	2·5
Others	2·4	6·0
Total biomass	36·6	100

Brisaster fragilis (on the average 60 per cent of the total biomass) is the dominant form of this community. Among the characteristic forms one may point out the molluscs *Astarte crenata*; of the echinoderms *Ctenodiscus crispatus*, *Leptychaster arcticus*, *Ophiura sarsi*, *Trochostoma boreale*; among the polychaetes *Asychis biceps*, *Myriochele oculata*, *Owenia assimilis*, *Spiochaetopterus typicus*, *Praxilella praetermissa*, crustaceans *Pandalus borealis* and *Hyas coarctatus*, and the brachiopods *Waldheimia cranium* and *Terebratulina caputserpentis*.

The vast Spitsbergen shallow, extending southwards to 74° N latitude in its central part and especially between Bear Island and Nadezhda Island, is less than 50 m deep and has a hard floor. Sections of cleanly washed pebble and deposits of broken shells and fragments of Balanus with a small admixture of sand are extremely unfavourable for the development of life. The benthos biomass is here calculated (M. Idelson, 1930) as a few grammes or even fractions of a gramme per m^2. The population consists of small bivalves and gastropod molluscs, polychaetes and crustaceans. In areas where the sea-bed has finer structure, the epifauna is fairly abundant, forming sometimes hundreds and even thousands of grammes per m^2 mainly consisting of *Cucumaria frondosa*, *Strongylocentrotus droebachiensis*, *Balanus balanus* and *Alcyonidium gelatinosum*. Only *Cyprina islandica* is distinguished by its biomass among the infauna. On the silty sand and sandy silt bottoms surrounding Spitsbergen shallow from the east and south dwells the fauna described above in other communities.

Porifera and Brisaster communities extending from the northwest are replaced by communities peculiar to the western trough, which is 400 m deep and more, and is filled with soft ooze with a huge number of Foraminifera *Rhabdammina abyssorum* cases. The population of the western trough represents the change-over from Porifera and Brisaster communities to typical central Barents Sea low Arctic communities. The total biomass here is only 13·4 g/m^2. This is explained by a shortage of food (*Table 60*).

In the cold waters of the northern part of the trough off the Bear Island

Table 60

Group	Total biomass g/m^2	Percentage of total biomass
Echinodermata	4·1	31·0
Polychaeta	3·4	25·5
Bivalvia	1·9	15·0
Porifera	1·1	9·0
Coelenterata	0·9	7·0
Crustacea	0·8	5·5
Bryozoa	0·6	5·0
Others	0·6	3·0
Total	13·4	100
Epifauna	5·2	40·1
Infauna	8·2	59·9

shoal, forms typical of the middle part of the Barents Sea are highly developed —*Spiochaetopterus typicus*, *Maldane sarsi*, *Ctenodiscus crispatus*, *Astarte crenata*, and *Arca glacialis*. In the southern parts of the trough the waters are warmer and the warm-water *Asychis biceps*, *Arca pectunculoides*, *Pecten imbrifer*, *Dentalium striolatum* and others are predominant. In the deepest parts of the trough (400 m) the benthos biomass decreases to 5 to 8 g m^2 and less, consisting entirely of infauna forms feeding on ooze.

Thus in the northern part of the west trough (400 m) and to the east of the Brisaster community, the middle Barents Sea benthic community comes into full development; it occurs mainly on sandy silt and to a lesser extent on silt and silty sand, at depths of 100 to 350 m.

The dominant forms of this community are: the polychaete *Spiochaetopterus typicus*, the sipunculid *Phascolosoma margaritaceum*, the molluscs *Astarte crenata* and *Arca glacialis*, the echinoderms *Ctenodiscus crispatus* and *Psolus phantapus*. Besides this the characteristic forms of the first order are the polychaetes *Lumbriconereis fragilis*, *Nicomache lumbricalis*, *Myriochele oculata*, *Maldane sarsi*, the molluscs *Cardium ciliatum*, *Macoma calcarea*, *Saxicava arctica*, *Axinus flexuosus*, the echinoderms *Ophiopholis aculeata*, *Ophiocantha bidentata*, *Ophiura sarsi* and Molpadia species. This multiform community, occupying a huge area, can be subdivided into ten variants, differing in their combinations of the above-mentioned forms, and sometimes by the absence of a series of forms, but retaining, nevertheless, an inherent unity. The average biomass of this community is not large—85·5 g/m^2—and has the following group composition (*Table 61*).

Table 61

Group	Biomass g/m^2	Percentage of total biomass
Bivalvia	21·2	24·8
Polychaeta	21·4	25·9
Echinodermata	21·7	25·3
Sipunculoidea	11·0	12·8
Porifera	4·3	5·3
Coelenterata	1·5	1·8
Others	4·5	5·1
Total	85·5	100
Epifauna	17·8	20·8
Infauna	67·7	79·2

To the east and southeast of the Novaya Zemlya shoal and in the Pechora region, forming a wide belt round the previous community, there lies in the silty sand at shallow depths (50 to 250 m) a community with a preponderance of bivalves. The dominant forms in this belt are: among the molluscs, *Astarte borealis*, *A. montagui*, *Macoma calcarea*, *Cardium ciliata*, *Yoldia hyperborea*, *Cardium groenlandicum*, and among the echinoderms: *Ophiopholis aculeata* and *Strongylocentrotus droebachiensis*. The characteristic forms include a number of the dominant forms of the middle Barents Sea community. This community can also be divided into nine variations. Among them is the grouping to the east of Kolguev Island, on the silty sand at shallow depths (50 to 70 m) with a sharp preponderance of *Pectinaria hyperborea* and *Yoldia hyperborea*, with a considerable deviation from the ordinary phylum; so also is the grouping in the Novaya Zemlya trough on silty sand and at depths of 50 to 200 m. This trough shelters a very large population of a relict mollusc *Portlandia arctica*.

The composition of this community, the richest in its biomass, is given by groups in *Table 62*.

Table 62

Group	Biomass g/m²	Percentage of total biomass
Bivalvia	133·65	60·6
Polychaeta	25·41	11·4
Echinodermata	25·52	11·5
Sipunculoidea	9·64	4·4
Gastropoda	2·73	1·2
Crustacea	11·60	5·2
Others	12·14	5·7
Total	220·69	100
Epifauna	40·30	18·2
Infauna	180·39	81·8

On the coastal sands of the eastern and southeastern parts of the Sea and in the shallows of the open sea (Gusinaya bank, Kanin shallow) there thrives at depths of 9 to 100 m a hard-bed community mainly on various types of sand, from the slightly silty to the coarse-grained. This community gives a considerable admixture of shallow-water high Arctic forms, and consists half of epifauna. Its dominant forms include among the molluscs: *Astarte borealis*, *Macoma calcarea* and *Serripes groenlandicus*; among the bryozoans: *Pelonaja corrugata*; the crustaceans: *Eupagurus pubescens* and Balanus; and among the echinoderms, Strongylocentrotus.

Among these characteristic of the first order are *Alcyonidium disciforme*, *Travisia forbesi*, *Pectinaris hyperborea*, *Owenia assimilis*, *Sabellides borealis*, *Ampharete vega*, *Ophelia limacina*, *Ophiura nodosa*, *Myriotrochus rincki*, *Cucumaria calcigera*, *Cyprina islandica*, *Astarte elliptica*, *A. montagui*, *Saxicava arctica*, *Mya truncata*, *Diastylis rathkei*, *Hyas araneus* and *Balanus balanus*.

The fauna of the hard sea-floor (13 to 45 m deep) in the Cheshskaya Inlet have a special aspect.

The dominant forms here are *Mytilus edulis* and *Balanus crenatus*. The mass descent into the sublittoral of such a typical littoral form as sea mussel is of special interst. This community has the following group composition (*Table 63*).

Table 63

Group	Biomass g/m²	Percentage of total biomass
Bivalvia	79·0	51·3
Gastropoda	11·5	7·5
Polychaeta	10·0	6·5
Crustacea	24·0	15·6
Echinodermata	10·0	6·5
Ascidia	8·0	5·2
Bryozoa	4·0	2·7
Porifera	4·0	2·7
Coelenterata	3·0	2·0
Others	0·3	—
Total	153·8	100
Epifauna	79·5	51·7
Infauna	74·3	48·3

The northern part of the Barents Sea and the central parts of the Kara Sea, with its soft brown silts and depths of 200 to 450 m, are occupied by a biocoenosis with a large admixture of high Arctic forms. The dominant ones are *Astarte crenata* and *Ophiopleura borealis*, the characteristic members of the first order being *Ophiocantha bidentata* and *Molpadia* sp. (a high Arctic species different from Molpadia of the southwestern part of the Sea). The biomass here is very small—inferior only to that of the Atlantic trench (*Table 64*).

The nine biocoenoses examined are, of course, not all the biocoenotic variety of the open parts of the Barents Sea, especially as regards its epifauna.

Distribution and composition of bottom communities of certain inlets and gubas. A quantitative investigation of the benthos of the Motovsky (R. Leibson, 1939)

Table 64

Group	Biomass g/m²	Percentage of total biomass
Echinodermata	11·5	38·3
Bivalvia	7·3	24·3
Polychaeta	4·9	16·3
Sipunculoidea	1·3	4·3
Crustacea	1·2	4·0
Coelenterata	1·1	3·7
Bryozoa	1·0	3·3
Total	30·0	100
Epifauna	24·77	82·6
Infauna	5·23	17·4

and Kola (V. Zatzepin, 1939)* Inlets showed that the principal deep parts of both inlets have a reduced benthos biomass as compared to the adjacent parts of the Sea. In front of the entrance into both these inlets and in the seaward part of the Kola Inlet a benthos biomass of 50 to 100 g/m^2 is the rule, whereas all the central and abyssal part of the Motovsky Gulf has a benthos biomass of less than 25 g/m^2, and the corresponding parts of the Kola Inlet about 25 to 50 g/m^2. This impoverishment should be attributed to the development of the stagnation phenomena and to greater silting in the deeper parts of the inlet than in the open sea. Considerable areas of the Barents Sea, as we have seen, are occupied by a biomass of more than 300 g/m^2, consisting chiefly of infauna; on the Spitsbergen bank the biomass frequently reaches several kilogrammes per m^2. Such biomass indices have not been observed either in the Motovsky or Kola Inlets, except for the littoral zone. Even the *Ascidia obliqua* beds, the richest in fauna, have an average biomass of 520 g/m^2, exceeding 1 kg/m^2 only in a few individual cases.

R. Leibson (1939) examined the dependence of the infauna biomass on the amount of organic matter, and gave the following average data (for silt sea bottoms only), expressed in percentages of organic carbon content (*Table 65*).

Table 65

Carbon per cent	1·0	1·0–1·5	1·5–2·0	2·0–3·0
Infauna biomass	58·8	64	77	128

As usual, the quantitative distribution of the epifauna and infauna in the inlets gives a contrasting picture (Fig. 57). The largest accumulation of infauna is found in the depth of the Motovsky Gulf, and the epifauna is found in the coastal waters and the interior part. The total biomass increases farther up the inlet. As for the bottom fauna communities all the middle parts of both inlets are inhabited by the same central Barents Sea community mentioned above; the whole composition of the dominant and characteristic forms is the same, only in a somewhat different combination. In the inlets the polychaete *Maldane sarsi* is the most significant (Fig. 58), whereas in the most southern part of the Kola Inlet *Maldane sarsi*, *Spiochaetopterus typicus*, *Ctenodiscus crispatus* and *Phascolosoma margaritaceum* disappear. The depths there are 20 to 60 m; the floor consists of slightly silty sand and the salinity is somewhat reduced. The interior part of the Kola Inlet forms a different ecological ranges are encountered, comprising qualitatively and quantitatively a fairly rich fauna. Among the echinoderms are *Strongylocentrotus droebachiensis* and *Brisaster fragilis*; there are large colonies of *Gorgoncephalus arcticus*, *Asterias lincki*, *Ophiura sarsi*, *Ophiopholis aculeata*; the polychaetes include *Nicomache lumbricalis*, *Myriochele oculata*, *Nephthys ciliata*, *Lumbriconereis fragilis*, *Trophonia plumosa* and side by side with them *Aphrodite aculeata*;

* The quantitative composition of the benthos of the Kola Inlet has been discussed above.

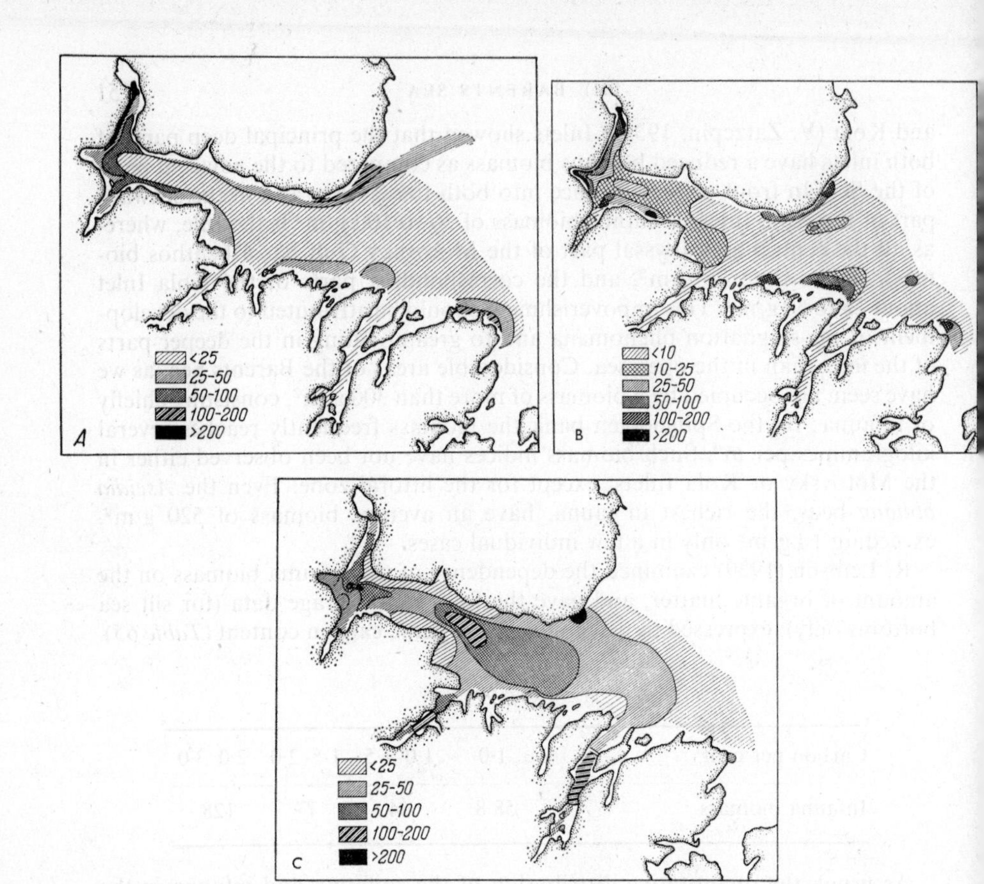

FIG. 57. Distribution of bottom fauna in Motovsky Gulf (Leibson, 1939)
A Total biomass, g/m²; B Biomass of infauna; C Biomass of epifauna.

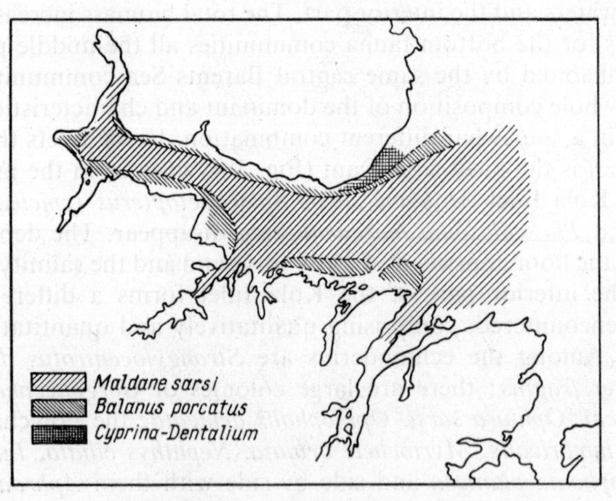

FIG. 58. Distribution of main benthos biocoenoses in Motovsky Gulf (Leibson, 1939).

also present are the molluscs *Astarte crenata*, *Cardium ciliatum*, *C. groenlandicum* and *Pecten islandicus*. Still farther into the inlet this rich fauna grows poorer, many forms are not found and a series of forms peculiar to sandy shallows make their appearance—*Scoloplos armiger*, *Cyprina islandica*, *Yoldia hyperborea*, *Macoma calcarea* and others.

On the cliffs and rock floors of the great depths of the outer parts of both inlets, especially in the Kola Inlet, lives the community Porifera–Brachiopoda–Bryozoa, and slightly above it lives the great community *Ascidia obliqua*, often with a biomass of more than 1 kg/m^2. Still higher is the Balanus belt, with *Balanus balanas*, *Ophiopholis aculeata*, *Thelepus cincinnatus*, *Pseudopotamilla reniformis*, *Modiola modiolus*, *Pecten islandicus*, *Rhynchonella psittacea*, and containing a mass of bryozoans and hydroids.

In the outer parts of the Motovsky and Kola Inlets and east of the Gavrilov Islands, on the sandy beaches of the sublittoral of the upper horizon is recorded an original fauna, developed in large numbers, primarily the molluscs: *Cyprina islandica*, *Mactra elliptica*, *Dentalium entalis*, *Macoma calcarea*, *Astarte crenata*, *A. montagui* and others.

A large number of warm-water boreal species are encountered there, and there is a considerable similarity with the sublittoral communities of the Norwegian coast. As we have seen above, the littoral fauna there has a more sharply pronounced warm-water character. On the other hand in the great depths of the inlets, in the zones of a weak vertical circulation and cold stagnant waters some cold-water Arctic forms have found shelter, and as one moves farther up the inlet, the higher do the cold-water forms ascend. Hence considerable summer heating of the surface waters of the enclosed parts of the inlets, and the presence of cold stagnant waters at shallow depths, results in a sharp vertical zonation of the fauna. Many representatives of the shallow-water, littoral and upper sublittoral boreal fauna find here their extreme limit of propagation to the east, and the Arctic fauna their extreme westerly limit. A vertical displacement of fauna of different thermophilic aspects at the border-line of their habitats is a common phenomenon. As has been pointed out by V. Zatzepin (1939), in some individual bights of the Motovsky Gulf (Ara, Ura, Zap. Litza), as a sequence of the submarine barriers, the depths are filled with cold stagnant waters, inhabited by cold-water species. By contrast, in bights not separated from the sea by submarine barriers, and not having a deep stagnant zone (as, for example, Teriberka, Yarnyshnaya), most of the sublittoral is inhabited by warm-water communities represented by such forms as *Cyprina islandica*, *Mactra elliptica*, *Cardium fasciatum*, *C. elegantulum*, *C. echinatum* and *Modiola modiolus*. The central parts of the inlets are, however, inhabited by cold-water forms such as *Pandora glacialis*, *Lyonsia arenosa*, *Serripes groenlandicus*, *C. ciliatum*, *Pelonaia corrugata* and others.

The bottom population of Sturfjord to the east of Spitsbergen is quite peculiar (V. Brotzkaya, 1930). This very wide and shallow (25 to 100 m) inlet with its negative bottom temperature is climatically one of the most inclement corners of the Barents Sea. Sturfjord is free for only a very short time of the sea ice and icebergs which usually block it. Numerous glaciers come right down to the water so that even in the warmest season of the year, the waters of the inlet are only slightly warmed. The floor of the fjord is covered by a homogeneous bed—a very soft green-grey silt, with a few boulders. There is no submarine barrier at the outlet of the gulf and the whole column of water is very well aerated. Owing to the homegeneity of its bed and to the hydrological conditions, the Sturfjord bottom fauna likewise is very varied. The dominant forms are *Astarte borealis*, *A. montagui*, *Macoma calcarea*, *Nucula tenuis*, *Maldane sarsi*, *Ophioeten sericeum* and *Strongylocentrotus droebachiensis*. Among the characteristic forms the following must be noted: *Leda pernula*, *Axinus flexuosus*, *Turitella reticulata*, *Amphiura sundevalli*, *Nephthys malmgreni* and *Chaetozone setosa*.

Off the shore of the inlet lives the mollusc *Portlandia arctica*, probably in large numbers, as if emphasizing the high Arctic character of the fjord. The high Arctic *Stegophiura nodosa* is also found there. The number of bivalves and the general biomass increase considerably as one moves deeper into the fjord, the latter increasing from 126 g/m^2 (average for the outer part of the fjord) to 468 g/m^2 (in its inner part); epifauna is markedly preponderant.

At some individual stations a considerably higher biomass was encountered. The presence of the community *Onuphis conchylega*, *Pecten groenlandicus* and *Arca glacialis* common in other parts of the Barents Sea is to be expected here. It is difficult to say what factors condition the high benthos biomass in Sturfjord and what are its main sources of nourishment under such severe climatic conditions.

For the sake of comparison one might mention the exceptionally high biomass recorded in 1926 in the Mashigina Guba in Novaya Zemlya. Its climatic conditions are also very severe and glaciers come right down to the waters of the guba. The benthos biomass on the soft silt bottom was found to be 3,394 g/m^2, consisting mostly of infauna. This is, probably, the highest infauna biomass ever registered in the sea. It consists mainly of *Saxicava arctica*, which here is one of the infauna components, *Mya truncata* and *Cardium ciliatum*.

Comparison of the Barents Sea bottom communities and those of other regions of the North Atlantic. The Barents Sea biocoenoses are very similar in their composition to those of Greenland waters. Almost identical groupings are observed there.

The bottom biocoenoses of Icelandic waters, while retaining a great similarity with those of the Barents Sea, present a transition from Arctic groupings to north-boreal ones.

Although the bottom biocoenoses of the Faroe Islands produce a series of typical forms like those of the Barents Sea, their general aspects are different: Faroe waters are a place where the north-boreal species preponderate markedly. Only littoral fauna retain their qualitative uniformity over all the huge distance from the North Sea to the White Sea.

A comparison of a number of forms of the highest biomass of the Barents Sea and of that of other bodies of water of the northern Atlantic (Greenland, Iceland, Faroe Islands) is of interest.

As shown in this comparison (*Table 66*), the biomass indices of the Barents

Table 66

Benthos biomass epifauna preponderant	Barents Sea	Faroe Islands	Icelandic waters	West Greenland	Danish waters
Biocoenosis *Modiola modiolus*					
Mean biomass	400	6,380	625	—	2,380
Highest biomass	1,568	17,259	1,932	—	10,320
Benthos biomass infauna preponderant					
Biocoenosis *Macoma baltica*					
Highest biomass	693	1,136	1,280	744	—
Biocoenosis *Mactra elliptica*					
Mean biomass	46	38	105	—	—
Highest biomass of some individual forms					
Astarte borealis	457	—	—	540	—
A. elliptica	173	—	—	307	—
Macoma calcarea	243	642	1,725	—	10,000
Cardium ciliatum	222	—	243	—	—
Modiola modiolus	1,080	165,000	1,725	—	10,000
Mactra elliptica	40	117	266	—	—
Mytilus edulis	25,000	—	—	—	49,500 (Güllmarfjord)
Ophiopholus aculeata	74	441	48·5	—	—
Ophiopleura borealis	36	—	—	57	—

Sea are lower than those in many other sectors of the northern Atlantic (the data are given in g/m^2).

Dominant and characteristic species. The quantitative, biocoenotic investigations carried out in the Barents Sea have provided a possibility of distinguishing the total number of dominant and characteristic benthos forms (*Table 67*).

Ecological characteristics of individual species. A. Schorygin (1928) has worked out, on the basis of the Barents Sea echinoderms, an interesting statistical method for studying the life conditions of organisms by comparing the frequency of occurrence of a species with the indices of temperature (thermopathy), salinity (halopathy), depth (bathopathy) and the bottom constitution (edaphopathy). As a result of it he gives four curves for each echinoderm species, characteristic for its degree of adaptation to the main factors of its environment (Figs. 59 and 60). Schorygin's method was later used by I. Mesiacev in his monograph on bivalves of the Barents Sea (1931).

Finally, V. Brotzkaya and L. Zenkevitch (1937) worked out, by analogy with the Barents Sea fauna, a method of charting quantitative ecological habitats which makes it possible to establish the optimum conditions for the existence of a given form in the Sea. In order to construct his graph Schorygin

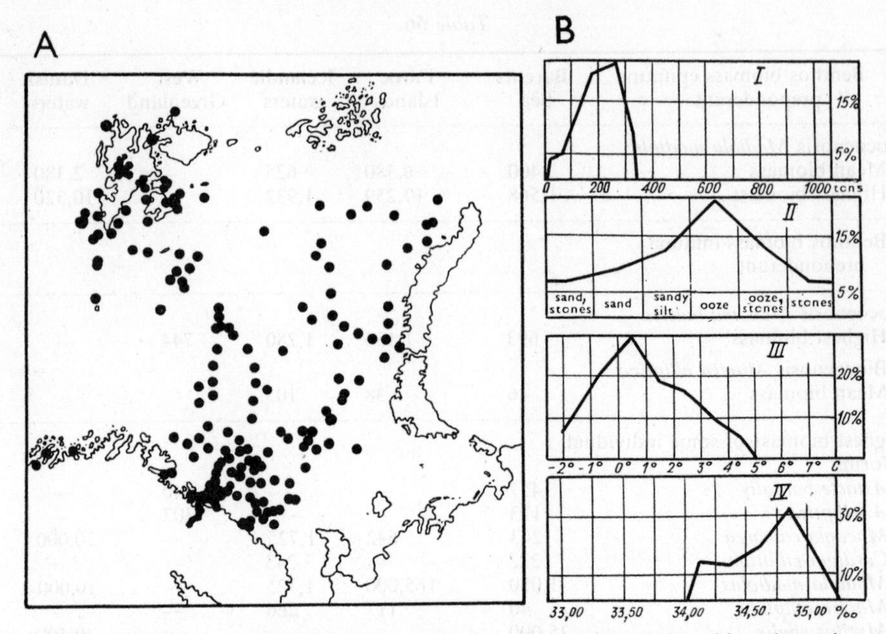

FIG. 59. Distribution of starfish *Asterias lincki* in Barents Sea (A) and its adaptation to different factors of the medium (B) (Schorygin, 1928). *I* Bathopathy; *II* Edaphopathy; *III* Thermopathy; *IV* Halopathy.

used the frequency of occurrence while Brotzkaya and Zenkevitch used the biomass (Fig. 61). Ecological habitats show a quantitative adaptability of a form to a combination of two factors of the habitat, in this case to temperature and depth.

Table 67

Group	Predominant forms	Characteristic forms of first order	Characteristic forms of second order	Total
Lamellibranchiata	13	7	7	27
Gastropoda	—	1	6	7
Scaphopoda	1	—	1	2
Amphineura	—	—	1	1
Echinodermata	8	8	2	18
Polychaeta	5	14	11	30
Gephyrea	1	—	3	4
Crustacea	3	3	3	9
Bryozoa	—	2	2	4
Brachiopoda	1	1	1	3
Tunicata	2	—	1	3
Total	34	36	38	108

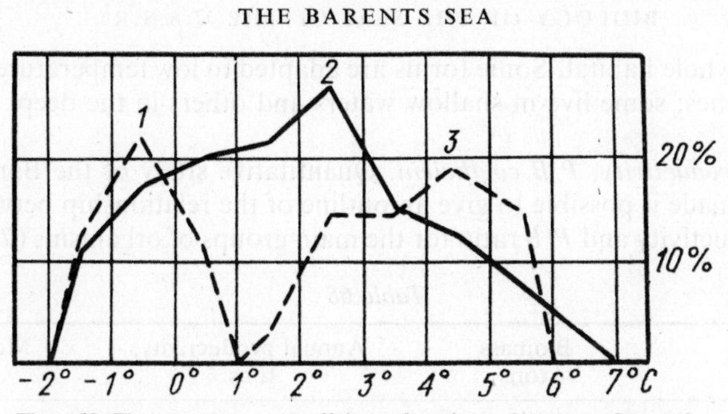

FIG. 60. Temperature conditions for the existence of certain echinoderms in the Barents Sea (Schorygin, 1928). 1 *Ophiopleura borealis*; 2 *Ophiura sarsi*; 3 *Leptychaster arcticus*.

It is interesting to note that some forms have a centre within the limits of their ecological habitat and the biomass decreases with the distance from this centre to the periphery (*1, 2, 3, 4*). Other forms are uniformly distributed

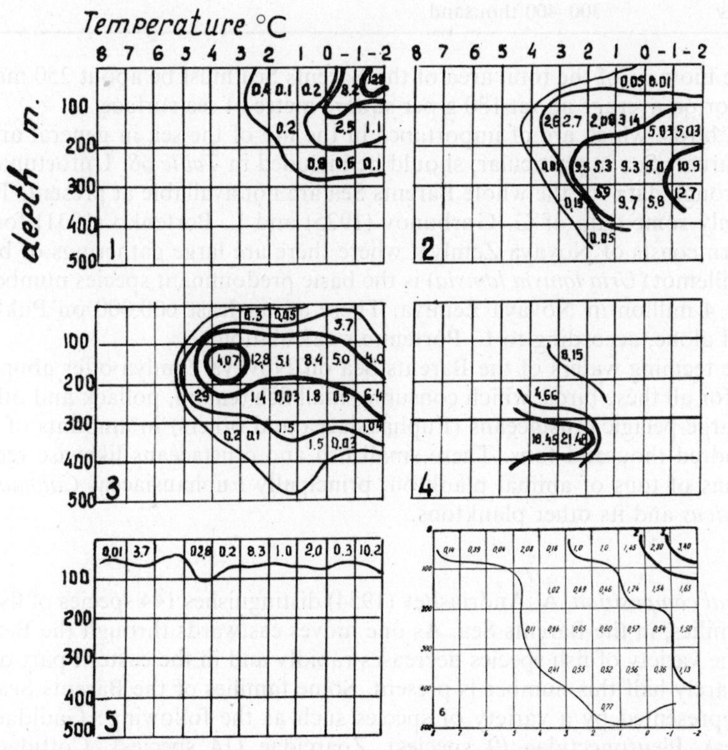

FIG. 61. Ecological habitats of some bottom animals of the Barents Sea (Zenkevitch and Brotzky, 1939). 1 *Astarte montagui*; 2 *Spiochaetopterus typicus*; 3 *Astarte crenata*; 4 *Brisaster fragilis*; 5 *Serripes groenlandicus*; 6 Average ecological habitat for 60 mass benthos forms.

within the whole habitat. Some forms are adapted to low temperatures, others to higher ones; some live in shallow waters and others in the deep.

Biomass, productivity, P/B coefficient. Quantitative study of the Barents Sea fauna has made it possible to give an outline of the relationship between biomass, productivity and *P/B* ratio for the main groups of organisms (*Table 68*).

Table 68

Group of Organisms	Biomass tons	Annual productivity, tons	Mean *P/B* ratio
Bacteria in water column	1 million	Hundreds of millions	Above 100
Bacteria in sea-bed	10 millions	?	?
Phytoplankton	Some millions	100–200 millions	About 50
Phytobenthos	Some tens of millions	Some tens of millions	About 1
Zooplankton			
Zoobenthos	140–150 millions	25–30 millions	$\frac{1}{4}$ to $\frac{1}{5}$
Fish	Some hundreds of millions	Some millions	$\frac{1}{6}$ to $\frac{1}{8}$
Sea animals	300–400 thousand		

The biomass of the total area of the Barents Sea must be about 250 million tons, or on average about 180 g per square metre of sea surface.

Sea birds, which are of importance in the life of the sea in general and of the Barents Sea in particular, should be included in *Table 68*. Unfortunately, even rough data for the whole Barents Sea are not available at present. There are only some data of G. Gorbunov (1925) and L. Portenko (1931) for the western coasts of Novaya Zemlya, where there are large gatherings of birds.

Guillemot (*Uria lomvia lomvia*) is the basic predominant species numbering about 4 million in Novaya Zemlya. There are at least 600,000 on Pukhovy Island alone, according to L. Portenko's calculations.

The teeming waters of the Barents Sea off Novaya Zemlya offer abundant food for all these birds, which consume small fish (caplin, pollack and others) and large pelagic crustaceans (Euphausiacea and others) in amounts of over a hundred thousand tons. These small fish and crustaceans likewise require millions of tons of animal plankton, principally Euphausiacea, *Calanus finmarchicus* and its other planktons.

Fish

General composition. A. Andriashev (1954) distinguishes 144 species of fish, of 52 families, in the Barents Sea. As one moves eastwards through the Barents Sea the variety of fish species decreases rapidly and in the eastern part of the Sea barely half this number is present. Some families of the Barents Sea fish are represented by a variety of species such as the following: Gadidae (19 species), Pleuronectidae (9 species), Zoarcidae (14 species), Cottidae (12 species), Rajidae (7 species) and Salmonidae (7 species). Most families, however, are represented by one or two species. Herring and bass, so important in fisheries, are among these latter.

Fish of commercial importance. Not more than 20 species could be included in a list of commercial fish in the Barents Sea, and among them only ten are of essential importance to the trawling industry. In this industry cod (*Gadus callarias*), haddock (*Gadus aeglefinus*) and bass (*Sebastes narinus*) are the most prominent.

The commercial importance of these three groups of fish changes from year to year, as is evident from *Table 69*.

Table 69. Percentage significance of individual races of fish in the catch of Barents Sea trawlers

Year	Cod	Haddock	Bass	Others
1923	74·0	22·0	0·6	3·4
1926	67·0	21·0	7·0	5·0
1930	47·5	20·7	24·2	7·6
1936	85·1	9·9	2·0	3·0
1938	56·7	37·0	3·5	2·8

Blue sea catfish and catfish (*Anarrhichas minor* and *A. lupus*), long rough dab (*Drepanopsetta platessoides*), sea dab (*Pleuronectes platessa*), halibut (*Hippoglossus hippoglossus*), coalfish (*Gadus virens*) and shark (*Somniosus microcephalus*), are of a secondary commercial importance in the industry.

In the last few years herring (*Clupea harengus harengus*) has acquired great importance in the Barents Sea fish industry.

It is remarkable that all the main commercial fish—cod, haddock, bass, coalfish and herring—occur in the Barents Sea at the extreme limit of their distribution while they breed mainly outside the Barents Sea in the coastal waters of Norway, where even in the deep floor layers the temperature does not fall below 5° to 6°. The Barents Sea, with its spawning–feeding migrations, is basically a feeding place for all these fish; they breed here only partially (mainly in the coastal waters) (Fig. 62).

The trawling yield is steadily increasing from year to year. In 1921 it was 39 thousand centners (1 centner=100 kg), in 1930—350 thousand, in 1934—772 thousand, in 1936—1·75 million, in 1950—2·3 million, and in 1956—5·5 million centners.

The catch of herring (*Clupea harengus harengus*) is still subject to great fluctuations, but in some years it reaches a million centners. In 1956 the herring catch was only 100,000 centners.

In 1955 the catch of the trawling fleets of the U.S.S.R., Britain and the German Federal Republic was 7·5 million centners in the south of the Barents Sea, in the Bear Island–Spitsbergen region (mainly the catch of Britain and the German Federal Republic) it was 1·6 million centners, while off the north-western coast of Norway it was 1·2 million centners. Furthermore the coastal catch of Norway and the U.S.S.R. (from Lofoten to the eastern Murman coast) in 1955 was 2·1 million centners, and the total for the Barents Sea was approximately 10 million centners.

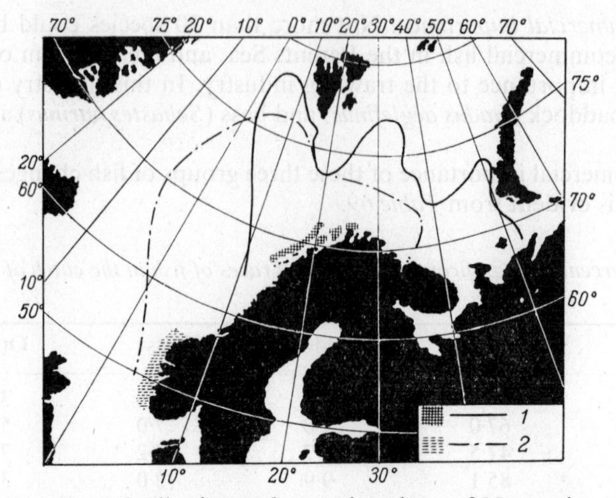

FIG. 62A. Distribution and spawning places of Norwegian and Murman herring (Tikhonov, 1939). *1* Murman herring; *2* Norwegian herring.

Fish feeding. The quantitative method of analysis of fish feeding for the Barents Sea was first worked out at the Oceanographic Institute, and later applied to other bodies of water of the Union. Before this there had been only qualitative evaluations of the diet of fish in the Barents Sea. At present we have a fairly complete quantitative analysis of the feeding of cod, haddock, herring, caplin, launce, long rough dab, catfish and a series of abundant, non-commercial fish.

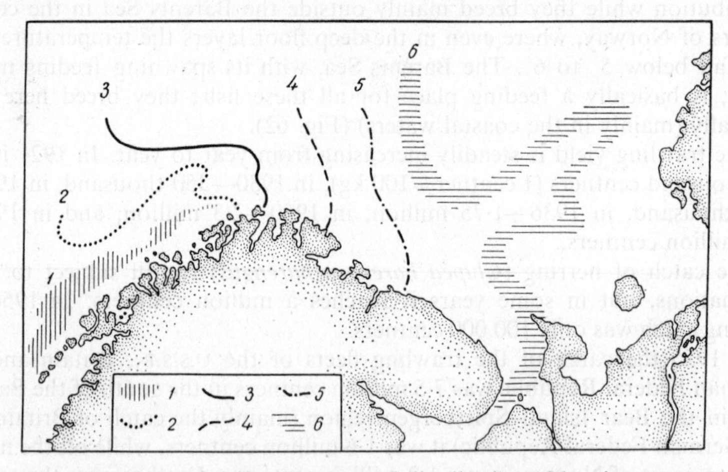

FIG. 62B. Chart of drift of larvae and distribution of herring young-of-the-year in the Barents Sea (Marti, 1939). *1* Spawning sites; *2* Larvae up to 20 mm; *3* Up to 30 mm; *4* Up to 40 mm; *5* Up to 50 mm; *6* Young-of-the-year.

The diet of the different main breeds of fish varies from purely benthos-feeding (sea dab, haddock) to typical plankton eaters (herring, bass) (Fig. 63). Such fish as long rough dab and ray have a mixed diet, feeding almost equally on pelagic and bottom organisms.

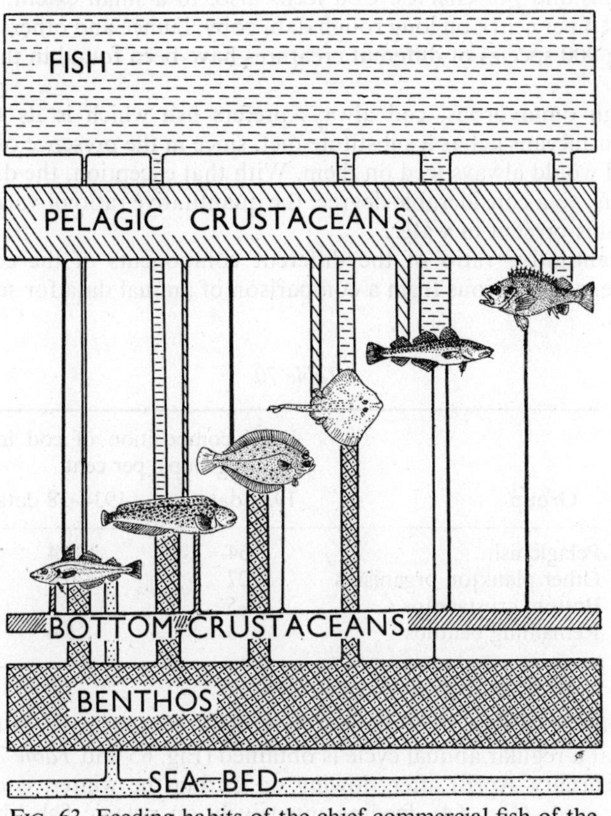

FIG. 63. Feeding habits of the chief commercial fish of the Barents Sea in order: haddock, Anarhichas, sand dab, ray, cod, sea bass (Zenkevitch, 1931).

The feeding of cod. The diet of cod has been investigated most fully. Exhaustive information is given in the extensive study by V. Zatzepin and N. Petrova (1939). The cod's diet consists basically of small pelagic fish—herring, caplin, young cod, haddock and finally, in the northern and western parts of the Sea, polar pollack (*Boreogadus saida*). Fish forms 60 per cent of the diet of the cod. Next come other pelagic organisms (more than 20 per cent), mainly the crustaceans: Euphausiacea and Hyperiidae (14 per cent), and prawns: *Pandalus borealis*, *Sabinea septemcarinata* (4·4 per cent), and other members of the Crangonidae and Hippolytidae families. Sometimes, especially in the west of the Sea, ctenophores, jellyfish, appendicularians and other plankton organisms form a considerable admixture to this diet (up to 2 per cent). In the eastern part of the Sea the bottom fauna plays a considerable role. This consists mainly of bottom crustaceans (about 5 per cent), *Hyas araneus*, *Eupagurus pubescens* and different Amphopoda, Isopoda and Cumacea. Among the other invertebrates (about 5 per cent) the most important are the molluscs, echinoderms and polychaetes. Cod feeds also, to a small extent, on bottom fish (about 4 per cent), on long rough dab, goby, launce and others. In general more than 200 species of different creatures have been found in the stomachs of cod.

Although omnivorous, cod always prefers fish which is its main food. Pelagic crustaceans act as a substitute diet, since in the presence of herring or caplin cod would always feed on them. With that exception, the diet range of cod reflects, to a considerable degree, the quantitative ratio of various groups of organisms present in water.

The quantitative ratio of the different components of the cod's diet is very stable, as is obvious from a comparison of annual data for several years (*Table 70*).

Table 70

Group	Food composition of cod in groups, per cent	
	1939 data	1934–38 data
Pelagic fish	64	62·4
Other plankton organisms	27	20·4
Bottom crustaceans	5	5·2
Remaining benthos	3	5·4

In the course of a year cod feeds differently in various parts of the Barents Sea, so that a regular annual cycle is obtained (Fig. 65 and *Table 71*). In early spring (February–April) after slowing up during the winter, cod begins to move eastwards (Fig. 64), feeding intensively on pelagic fish—herring and caplin. The cod which have spawned off Lofoten arrive rather later and likewise feed on fish. In summer in the central commercial fishery areas it feeds on the higher crustaceans (Euphausiacea and Hyperiidae). In autumn cod assembles in shoals in the eastern parts of the Sea, and in the absence of herring and caplin, turns quite extensively to bottom food—large crustaceans such as crabs and hermit crabs, and molluscs. While starting its westward movement cod reverts to a diet of fish (the young of both cod and haddock, herring, caplin). Those cod which travel westward to spawn in the Lofoten region (January–April) stop eating, at first partially and then completely; off Lofoten they are always caught with empty stomachs. The young cod, which winters in the southwestern part of the Sea, also eats considerably less. After intensive spring feeding the cod may pass through a period of compulsory starvation, when the pelagic fish (herring and caplin) migrate from the regions where cod dwell.

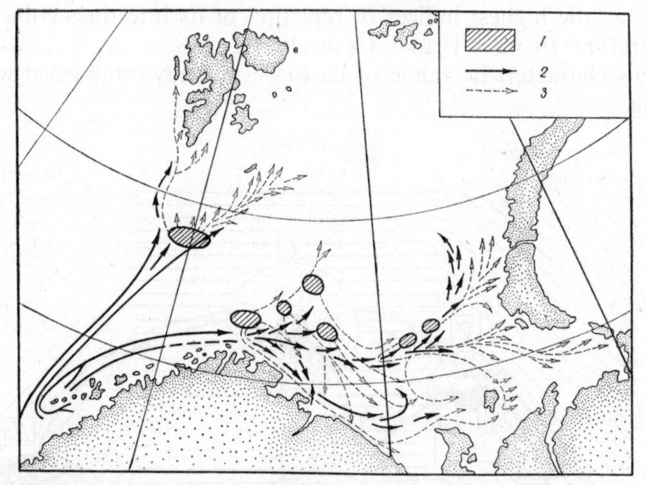

FIG. 64. Chart of eastward migration of cod (Maslov). *1* Wintering areas of immature cod; *2* Migration of mature cod; *3* Migration of immature cod.

The seasonal change of cod diet (according to V. Zatzepin and N. Petrova) as a percentage of the index* of repletion is also given in *Table 71.*

Cod eats most intensively at depths of 50 to 100 m; lower down its food consumption declines sharply. Since the eastern part of the Sea is its main

Table 71. Autumn feeding of cod in eastern part (*winter lull*)

Periods	Food groups						
	Fish	Pelagic crustaceans	Other planktons	Benthos crustaceans	Other benthic animals	Index of repletion	Empty stomachs, per cent
›pring fishing in central fishery areas	84	10	3	1	2	175	25
’eriod of forced starvation	71	19	2	3	5	25	41
›ummer feeding in central fishery areas	30	61	1	3	5	30	26
Vhen migrating to the east	52	6	2	23	17	162	23
Vhen migrating to the west	78	7	12	1	2	171	24
mmature cod	61	13	19	1	6	50	44
Mature cod	37	15	—	22	26	7	80

* The index of repletion is the ratio of the contents of the intestines to the weight of fish, expressed as 1/100 of the percentage (*prodecimille*). There is a difference between the general index of repletion (for the whole contents of the intestines) and the particular indices (for the separate component groups).

feeding place, the highest indices of repletion of its intestines coincide with low temperatures (from $+1°$ to $-1°$) or almost zero.

The cod's characteristic range of feeding is already established when it is 25 cm long.

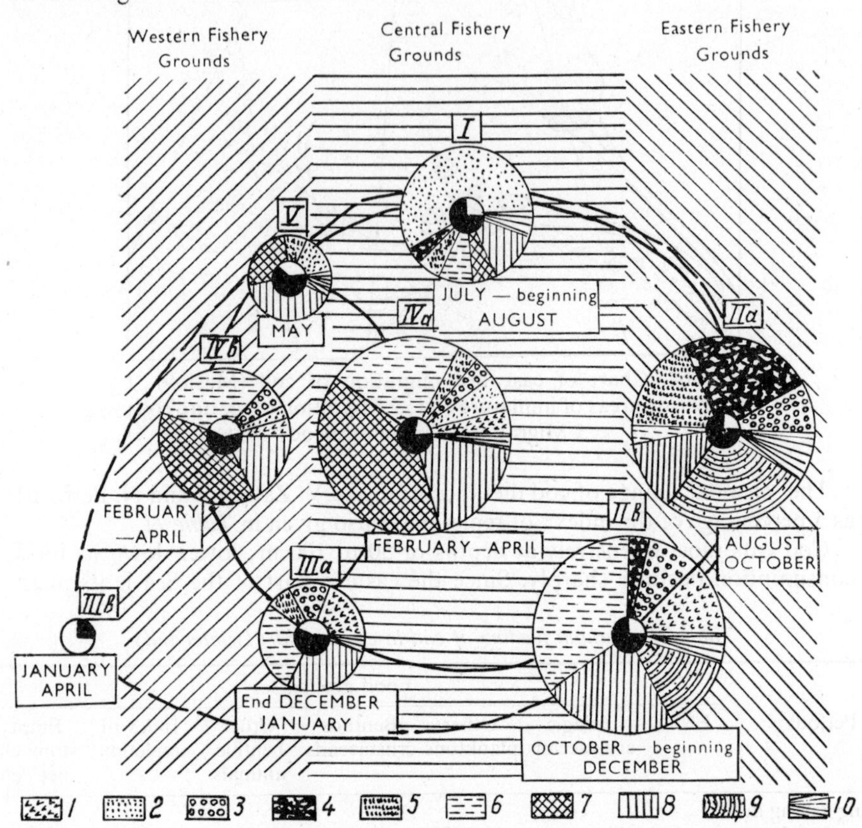

Fig. 65. Diagram of food cycle of Barents Sea cod (Zatzepin and Petrova, 1939). Continuous lines—immature cod; broken lines—mature cod; *I* Summer fattening; *II* Main autumn feeding; *IIIa* Period of lesser feeding during spawning migrations; *IIIb* During spawning; *IV* Spring fattening in (*a*) central and (*b*) western fishing regions; *V* Period of forced starvation. Areas of circles correspond to repletion indices. *1* Plankton organisms; *2* Euphausiaceae; *3* Prawns; *4* Bottom-living crustaceans; *5* Other bottom-living animals; *6* Herring; *7* Caplin; *8* Cod and haddock young; *9* Arctic cod; *10* Other fish.

For some sea areas, where cod gathers in dense shoals, migrating from one region to another, an inverse ratio has been recorded between the index of repletion of its intestines and its likelihood of being caught. In other areas, however, abundant cod yields were taken during its periods of intensive feeding. The cod's daily feeding routine of the Barents Sea is not expressed precisely (E. Zadulskaya and K. Smirnov, 1939). The hours of greatest repletion of the stomach differ with the seasons: in the summer and autumn they are from 8 a.m. to noon, in the spring from noon to 4 p.m., in winter from 4 to 8 p.m. The greatest repletion of the stomach seems to be linked with definite tidal phases (half flood and half ebb). Since there is no coincidence between the time of day and the tidal phase accurate dependence of the feeding rhythm on these two factors is destroyed.

The feeding of haddock. In contrast to cod, haddock feeds mainly on benthos (Fig. 67). Two hundred various forms of benthos have been found in haddock

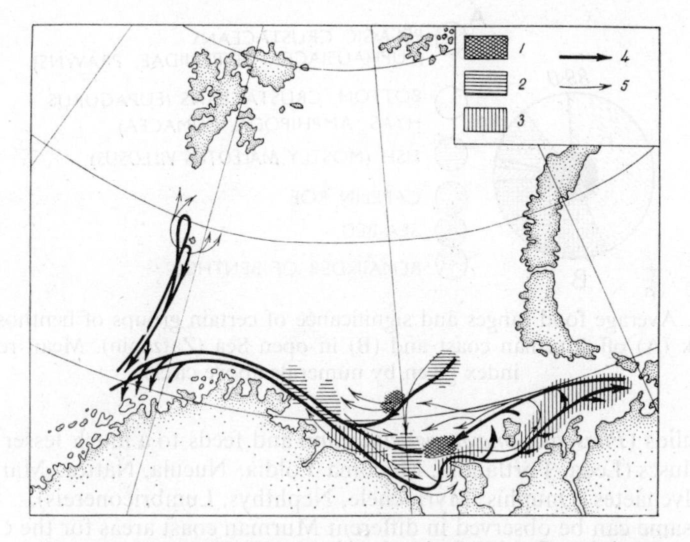

FIG. 66. Chart of haddock migration in Barents Sea. *1* Areas of pre-spawning migrations of mature haddock; *2* Winter shoaling areas of haddock; *3* Areas of summer and autumn shoaling; *4* Migration of mature haddock; *5* Migration of immature haddock (Maslov, 1944).

intestines, with a preponderance of brittle stars, bivalves, polychaetes and sipunculids. Ordinarily a large amount of the material of the sea bottom is found in the haddock's stomach. Off the Murman coast, in spring and at the beginning of summer, haddock feeds intensively on caplin, which approaches the shores for spawning, and on its spawn (Fig. 66).

The importance of the separate components of the haddock's food as a percentage of the total repletion index is shown in *Table 72* (according to V. Zatzepin, 1939 and A. Dekhtereva, 1931.)

V. Zatzepin drew an interesting comparison for the western Murman between the quantity of food consumed by haddock and the amount of benthos. This gives a definite estimate of the selective capacity of fish for its food *Table 73*).

Haddock prefers echinoderms (brittle stars and little sea-urchins) and

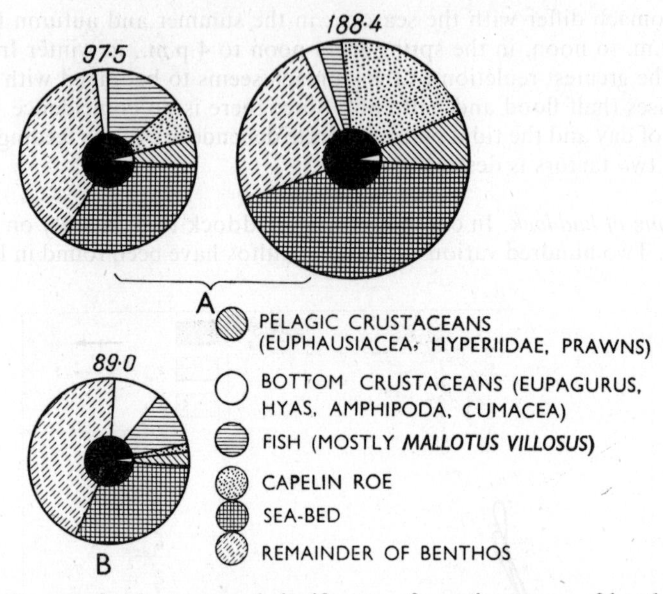

FIG. 67. Average food ranges and significance of certain groups of benthos-eating haddock (A) off Murman coast and (B) in open Sea (Zatzepin). Mean repletion index given by numerals above circles.

sipunculids (*Phascolosoma margaritaceum*) and feeds to a much lesser extent on molluscs (Leda, Portlandia, Macoma Yoldia, Nucula, Natica, Margarita) and polychaetes (Onuphis, Myriochele, Nephthys, Lumbriconereis).

The same can be observed in different Murman coast areas for the *Cyprina islandica* community (*Table 74*).

Here too the haddock's preference for some types of food is fairly evident. It is not clear whether the sea-bottom material gets into the haddock's intestines from the animals on which it feeds and thrives (brittle stars and Phascolosoma feed on the sea bottom), or is seized with the animals consumed, or is swallowed as such. Echinoderms become less and less important in haddocks' nutrition as they proceed to the east; they are replaced by small molluscs and polychaetes.

Table 72. Composition of haddock's diet

Food group	Murman coast	Open sea
Pelagic crustaceans (Euphausiaceae)	3·6	2·2
Bottom crustaceans (Amphipoda)	1·5	9·1
Remaining benthos	39·0	44·1
Fish	13·0	12·1
Sea-bottom material	35·3	31·4
General repletion index	97·5	89·0

Table 73. Selection of food by haddock

Food groups	Intestine content		Bottom fauna. Maldane–Astarte biocoenosis. Northern part of Kola Inlet	
	Percentage of total repletion index	Percentage of benthos repletion index	Percentage of food benthos	Percentage of total benthos
Fish ova	0·1	—	—	—
Fish	1·1	—	—	—
Pelagic crustaceans	9·5	—	—	—
Bottom crustaceans	1·4	—	0·5	0·2
Remaining benthos	54·0	—	—	—
Echinodermata	—	58·7	9·3	6·6
Sipunculida	—	17·0	15·0	7·1
Lamellibranchiata	—	9·5	18·0	56·3
Polychaeta	—	7·7	52·0	24·6
Gastropoda and others	—	5·7	1·9	0·9
Brachiopoda, Bryozoa, etc.	—	1·2	3·3	3·6
Varia	—	0·2	—	0·7
Sea-bottom material	33·9	—	—	—

Table 74

Food groups	Intestine content		Bottom fauna. *Cyprina islandica* off western Murman coast	
	Percentage of total index of repletion	Benthos content index of repletion per cent	Percentage of nutrient benthos	Percentage of total benthos
Fish ova	17·5	—	—	—
Fish (caplin)	15·4	—	—	—
Pelagic crustaceans	0·1	—	—	—
Bottom crustaceans	1·0	—	0·9	0·4
Other benthos	27·0	—	—	—
Lamellibranchiata	—	49·7	71·0	77·9
Polychaeta	—	22·6	15·0	8·2
Gastropoda and others	—	10·4	3·5	5·6
Echinodermata	—	9·5	2·5	1·3
Gephyrea	—	3·8	1·0	0·6
Tunicata	—	3·6	5·0	3·2
Varia	—	0·4	1·1	2·8
Sea-bottom material	39·0	—	—	—

There are two annual maxima in the feeding of the haddock (Fig. 68): the larger one in spring at the expense of caplin, which approach the coast for spawning, and its ova (index of repletion 256), and the autumn one, at the expense of benthos (the repletion index in the open sea is 180). In the intervals between the two maxima the repletion index of the stomach decreases to 40 to 45. The 'infauna-bottom feeders' are the best food for haddock; 'epifauna-seston feeding' (Zatzepin's terms) biocoenoses are of secondary importance in the haddock's nutrition (Fig. 69).

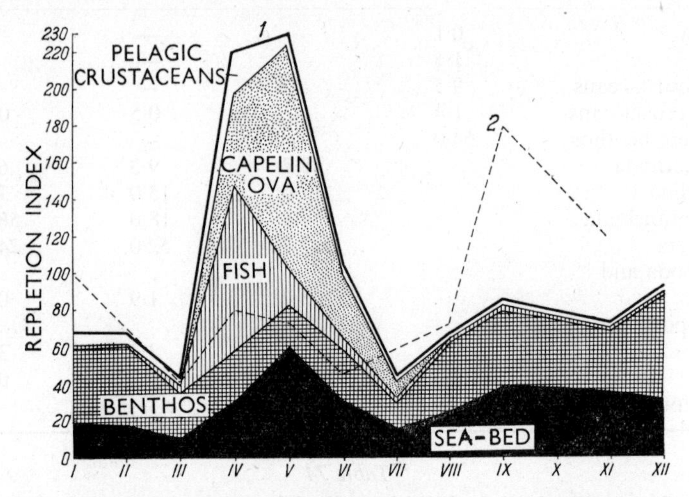

FIG. 68. Annual course of feeding of haddock in the Barents Sea (Zatzepin, 1939). *1* Mean repletion index in coastal area of Murman Peninsula. *2* Same for open Sea.

Nutrition of other benthophages. As regards the other benthos feeders the diet of the long rough dab (*Hippoglossoides platessoides*) (V. Brotzkaya and I. Komarova), the only flat-fish species, was examined most thoroughly. It is a typical inhabitant of the lower Arctic sub-region, widely distributed in enormous numbers throughout the Sea. *Hippoglossoides platessoides* feeds mostly on ophiura (*Ophiura sarsi*, *O. robusta*, *Ophiocten sericeum*, *Ophiopholis aculeata*) and the mollusc *Pecten groenlandicus*. Fifty-three per cent of the contents of the stomach of the dab consists of benthos (except crustaceans). Fish is also very important in its diet (35·4 per cent); *Triglops pingeli*, cod, haddock, *Boreogadus saida*, caplin and herring are most commonly found in its stomach. Pelagic forms (7·5 per cent) *Pandalus borealis* and bottom crustaceans (4 per cent) are of secondary importance in the diet of the dab. Benthos is markedly preponderant in the diet of a young dab (under 25 cm), while with the adult one fish and benthos are in the food in almost equal parts. The dab's food may change considerably in different areas, thus, on the Gusinaya bank it feeds almost exclusively on benthos, while in the Persey and Murman shallows fish forms 75 to 80 per cent of its diet and in the central shallow 60 per cent of its food consists of pelagic crustaceans (*Pandalus borealis*).

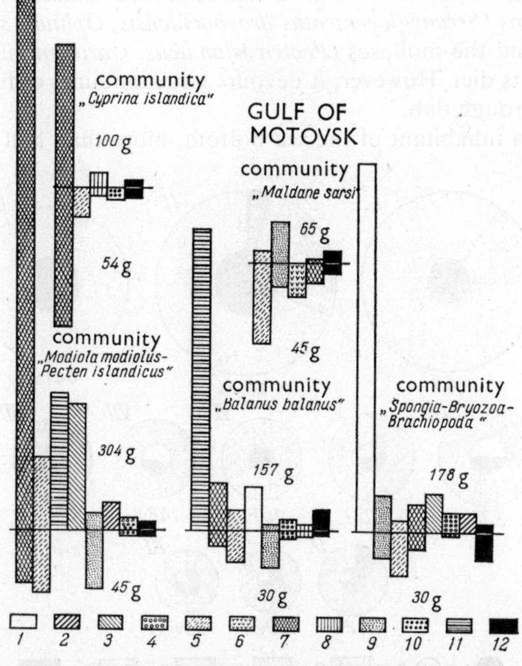

FIG. 69. Relationship of total (whole water column) and feeding (lower part) benthos for haddock on some typical biocoenoses of Murman coast (Zatzepin, 1939). *1* Porifera; *2* Coelenterata; *3* Bryozoa; *4* Brachiopoda; *5* Polychaeta; *6* Sipunculoidea; *7* Bivalves; *8* Gastropoda; *9* Echinodermata; *10* Tunicata; *11* Barnacles; *12* Others.

Definite seasonal cycles were observed in the feeding of long rough dab: it is low in winter and spring, especially in March–May, when the fish reaches its sexual maturity. The main feeding takes place in June–October. The annual change in the repletion index is given in *Table 75*.

The long rough dab's selective capacity is clearly shown by a comparison of its stomach-content with the fauna of the bottom areas inhabited by it.

The sea-dab (*Pleuronectes platessa*) differs greatly from the long rough dab. It feeds mainly on molluscs and polychaetes and, to a much lesser extent, on bottom crustaceans, sipunculids and brittle stars.

Table 75

Month	Feb	Mar	Apr	May	Jun	Jul	Aug	Sep
Index of repletion	41·0	10·25	43·18	18·0	78·8	88·8	87·6	102·7
No. with empty stomachs, per cent	38	72	68	80	3	11	20	7

Catfish (*Anarrhichas minor* and *A. lupus*) are also mainly benthos-eating; the echinoderms (*Stronyglocentrotus droebachiensis*, *Ophiura sarsi*, *Ophiopholis aculeata*) and the molluscs (*Pecten islandicus*, *Cardium ciliatum*) are preponderant in its diet. However, it devours large amounts of fish also, mainly cod and long rough dab.

Although an inhabitant of the sea bottom, more than half the diet of the

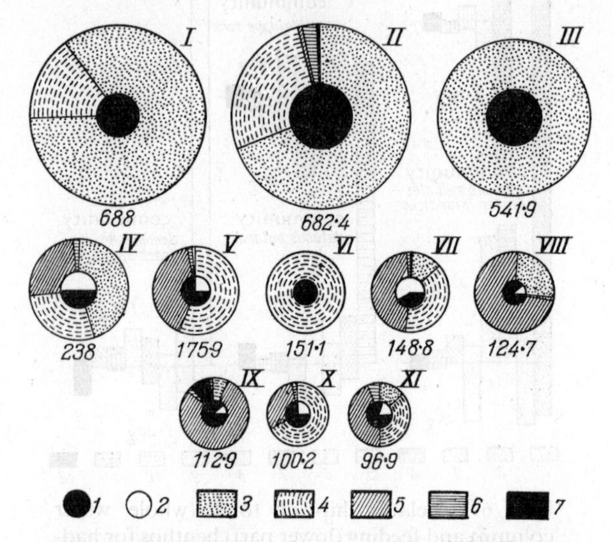

FIG. 70. Food ranges of various fish of the Barents Sea (Brotzky, Briskina, Bogorov, and others). I *Ammodytes tobianus*; II *Careproctus reinhardti*; III *Gadus poutassou*; IV *Liparis major*; V *Gymnacanthus tricuspis*; VI *Myoxocephalus quadricornis*; VII *Icelus bicornis*; VIII *Lycodes pallidus*; IX *Artediellus europeus*; X *Aspidophoroides olrickii*; XI *Triglops pingeli*. Repletion indices given by numerals under circles. White sectors inside circles denote percentages of empty stomachs. *1* Full stomachs; *2* Empty stomachs; *3* Pelagic crustaceans; *4* Bottom-living crustaceans; *5* Benthos; *6* Fish; *7* Sea-bed soil.

ray (*Raja radiata*) consists of pelagic organisms (60 per cent) with 20 per cen- fish and 20 per cent crustaceans and, to a lesser extent, benthos. Ray does not touch infauna at all, it chooses the mobile benthos forms such as bottom crust taceans and worms. Hence ray can be compared with cod as regards its feeding habits. Among fish it chooses caplin, cod, haddock and long rough dab, among the pelagic crustaceans *Pandalus borealis* and *Thysanoessa*.

Various non-commercial Barents Sea fish (M. Briskina, 1939) are typical benthophages (Fig. 70), which tear out the infauna from the bottom, as for example *Artediellus europeus*; others fatten on infauna, onfauna and on bottom crustaceans, as for example *Gymnacanthus tricuspis*, *Icelus bicornis*, *Aspidophoroides olriki*, *Triglops pingeli* and *Lycodes pallidus*. Still others thrive almost exclusively on bottom crustaceans, as *Myoxocephalus quadricornis*, *Lycodes seminudus* and *L. agnostus*; some feed equally on benthic and pelagic organisms (crustaceans) like *Careproctus reinhardti* and *Liparis major*; and finally a fifth group lives exclusively on pelagic crustaceans, as for example *Gadus poutassou* and *Ammodytes tobianus*.

Diet of herring and some other plankton-eating fish. Herring, caplin, *Boreogadus saida* and bass are the most characteristic plankton-eating fish of the Barents Sea. The southwestern parts of the Sea are the best feeding grounds for pelagic fish, and the eastern ones for benthos feeders. In the western part of the Sea even cod feeds mainly on pelagic organisms and in the eastern one on benthos.

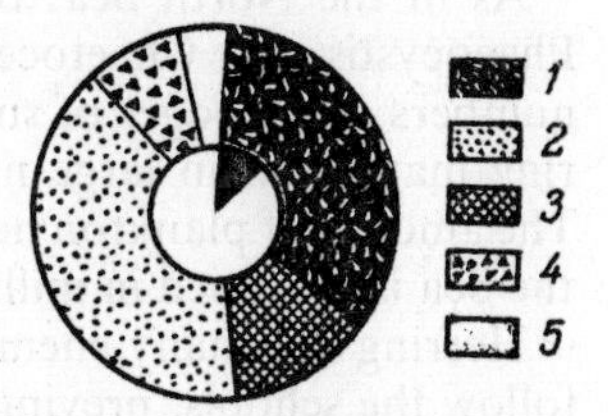

FIG. 71. Mean annual ranges of feeding of Murman herring in gubas of Murman Peninsula (Boldovsky). *1 Calanus finmarchicus*; *2* Cirripedia larvae; *3* Euphausiaceae; *4* Polychaete larvae; *5* Others.

During the summer (as was shown by Yu. Boldovsky, 1941) herring fattens on *Calanus finmarchicus*, *Thysanoessa inermis* and *Th. raschi*, which form no less than 90 per cent of the zooplankton consumed by it. Herring fry thrives on unicellular algae and on the larvae of various animals, but when a year old it begins to feed first on Calanus and then on Euphausiacea (Fig. 71).

The dependence of the rate of growth of a herring on the plankton (B. Manteufel, 1941) can be shown by comparing the amount of plankton with the growth of the herring during the first year of its life (*Table 76*).

Table 76

Year	1934	1935	1936	1937	1938
Average plankton biomass, mg/m^3 at the entrance to Motovsky Gulf in June	350	100	320	360	400
Increase in length of herring in the first year of life, mm	8·55	7·71	8·39	9·08	8·01

In the southwestern part of the Sea Ctenophora and Bolinopsis congregate at times in huge numbers of more than 200 mg/m^3; they may compete with the herring for food in summer. In such cases Calanus may all be consumed by ctenophores and herring would move into other areas. The feeding of herring proceeds most intensively in June, after which it decreases and then rises again in November. B. Manteufel (1941) has established a relationship similar to the one noted for cod, between the repletion of the herring and the ease with which it is caught. Herring are dispersed in places where *Calanus finmarchicus* shoals, and are not found there in commercial concentrations. In June and July the main mass of *Calanus finmarchicus* sinks down into the depths, the herring concentration increases, and the herring catch is larger. Once herring has eaten its fill it can thrive in shoals in zones of abundant plankton.

As in the North Sea, Barents Sea herring avoids places where the algae Phaeocystis and Chaetoceras bloom, but it may be present in commercial numbers at the edges of such zones. Descending to a depth of 100 m the herring may shoal in large numbers under the zone where these algae bloom. The amount of plankton needed for herring's food in the southwestern parts of the Sea is reckoned in millions of tons.

Herring has many enemies—cod, marine mammals, sea-gulls, which often follow the schools, preying on this tasty fish. Caplin (*Mallotus villosus*) is the herring's most dangerous rival as regards food; it is a comparatively small pelagic fish of the Osmeridae family, which thrives in the Barents Sea in huge numbers and comes up to the Murman coast to spawn. Polar cod (*Boreogadus saida*), a small pelagic fish also found in exceptionally large numbers in the Barents Sea, is not so dangerous a rival.

Their rivalry is weakened by the fact that they live in different parts of the Sea. Herring's main habitat lies in the southwestern part of the Sea, caplin's in the northern and eastern ones, while polar cod keeps mostly near the ice, thriving in cold water with a temperature below zero; it is the only pelagic fish closely connected with ice. On the other hand these three fishes are all devoured in huge numbers by other fish, mammals and birds.

The links between the food of polar cod and that of the other inhabitants of the sea are particularly curious. The distribution of this high Arctic fish links it with many floating-ice animals. In S. Klumov's opinion (1935) polar cod feeds on phytoplankton in the summer and zooplankton in the winter.

The predominant role of phytoplankton in the polar cod diet is, in Klumov's opinion, illustrated and confirmed by its love of ice since diatoms typically representative of the ice phytoplankton are predominant in its stomach. The polar cod food links are illustrated graphically by Klumov in Fig. 72.

History of fishing and hunting trades. Fishing and hunting trades have existed in the Barents Sea since the fifteenth century. They covered a large area from Finmark to the Pechora River in the east and as far as Spitsbergen to the north. In the sixteenth century some tens of thousands of fishermen, inhabiting the White Sea region, came to the Murman coast in the summer. At the end of the eighteenth century up to 270 craft would in some years appear off Spitsbergen coming from the White Sea. Up till the end of the last century the fishing industry of the Barents Sea was haphazard in character. It was run mainly by small commercial guilds in off-shore waters, in shallow, hardly seaworthy ships equipped with very primitive gear. N. Knipovitch, the head of the scientific and industrial expedition off the Murman coast, discovered that trawling is possible in the open Barents Sea. Foreign trawlers were the first to make use of this discovery at the turn of the century. Only in the last few years before 1914 did an Archangel tradesman, Spade, buy four trawlers abroad; his venture proved to be a success. Under the Soviet government trawling in the Barents Sea began to develop rapidly. The trawler fleet of the U.S.S.R. in the Barents Sea comprised 300 craft by the beginning of 1958

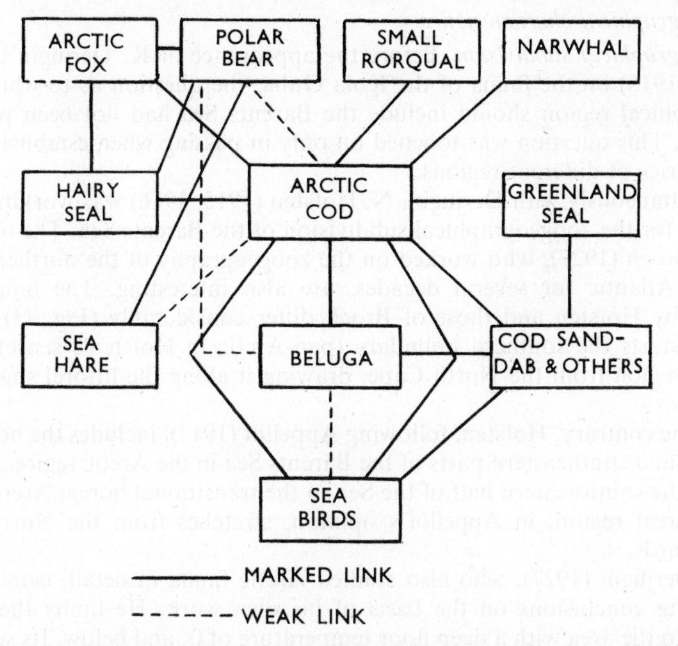

FIG. 72. Diagram of food correlations of Arctic cod (Klumov, 1935).

(counting only ships of more than 42 m length and including a powerful fleet of refrigerated trawler factory ships with a stern trawl sweep). In Soviet times the herring fishery has developed rapidly on the Murman coast. The hunting of marine animals—the Greenland seal—is a trade which has existed since time immemorial in the Gorlo of the White Sea.

Acclimatization prospects in the Barents Sea. The Barents Sea may turn out to be the most suitable region for the acclimatization of commercial fish and of the forms it feeds on, of all the northern parts of the Pacific Ocean.

There is no doubt that several members of the Pacific Ocean fauna of the lower Arctic and north-boreal aspects, for which the way through the Arctic Ocean is now closed, could thrive successfully in the Barents Sea, since its salinity and temperature conditions (potentially amphiboreal forms) are the same as those of their main habitats. Attempts have been made to bring into the White Sea the far eastern salmon (*Oncorhynchus gorbuscha*); Kamchatka crab was also prepared for transportation into the Barents Sea, but as yet no further ventures have been undertaken. No comprehensive study of the Pacific Ocean fauna as an acclimatization stock for the Barents Sea has so far been carried out. Neither should the idea of collecting stock for acclimatization in the Barents Sea among the low Arctic and sub-Arctic fauna (bipolar forms) be abandoned. It can be maintained with confidence that the acclimatization possibilities along these two lines merit further study.

Zoogeographical characteristics

Zoogeographical subdivision. Before the appearance of K. Derjugin's monograph (1915) on the fauna of the Kola Guba, the question as to which zoogeographical region should include the Barents Sea had not been properly studied. This question was touched on only in passing when establishing the boundaries of different regions.

Simultaneously with Derjugin, N. Hofsten (1915, 1916) was working out a scheme for the zoogeographical subdivision of the Barents Sea. The opinions of G. Broch (1927), who worked on the zoogeography of the northern parts of the Atlantic for several decades, are also interesting. The boundaries drawn by Hofsten and those of Broch differ considerably (Fig. 73). Broch (1927) starts the southern boundary (pan-Arctic in Hofsten's sense) of the Arctic region from the North Cape, drawing it along the littoral shallow of Norway.

On the contrary, Hofsten, following Appellöf (1912), includes the northern, eastern and southeastern parts of the Barents Sea in the Arctic region, assigning all the southwestern half of the Sea to the transitional boreal Arctic zone. The boreal region, in Appellöf's opinion, stretches from the North Cape southwards.

K. Derjugin (1927), who also studied Arctic fauna in detail, came to the following conclusions on the basis of his own work. He limits the Arctic region to the area with a deep floor temperature of 0° and below. Its southern boundary begins at the eastern Murman Peninsula near the entrance to the White Sea and extends to the northeast, north and northwest to Bear Island. This boundary almost coincides with the limit of the greatest southward movement of floating polar ice in winter. Derjugin considers the transitional region of mixed waters and fauna as much more significant than Appellöf and Hofsten, ascribing to it the importance of a separate zoogeographical region (the boreo-Arctic region of the two investigators mentioned). In Derjugin's opinion 0° to 5° or 6° is the typical temperature of this region; moreover, as a rule, no ice cover is formed there. Hence Derjugin includes about one-third of the whole of the Barents Sea in this region, which he calls the sub-Arctic.

Since Derjugin's investigations A. Schorygin (1928) was the first to survey the problem of the zoogeographical subdivision of the Barents Sea for the echinoderm group. This investigator has based his scheme on a statistical count of the frequency of occurrence of certain individual forms. Derjugin's boundaries between the Arctic and sub-Arctic benthos were corrected by this indirect but quantitative method. The boundary had to be moved 200 to 300 km to the west. Schorygin also drew a more accurate boundary between the low Arctic and high Arctic sub-regions in the northern and southeastern parts of the Barents Sea. His conclusions were later confirmed by a comprehensive quantitative analysis of the bottom fauna carried out by V. Brotzkaya and L. Zenkevitch in 1939 for the whole Sea and by Z. Filatova (1938) for the southwestern part of it (Fig. 73). Derjugin had drawn the boundary between the Arctic and sub-Arctic benthos so far to the east as a result of his observation of the occurrence of some individual boreal forms far to the east. However, this drift of the boreal forms, under continuous pressure of warm waters

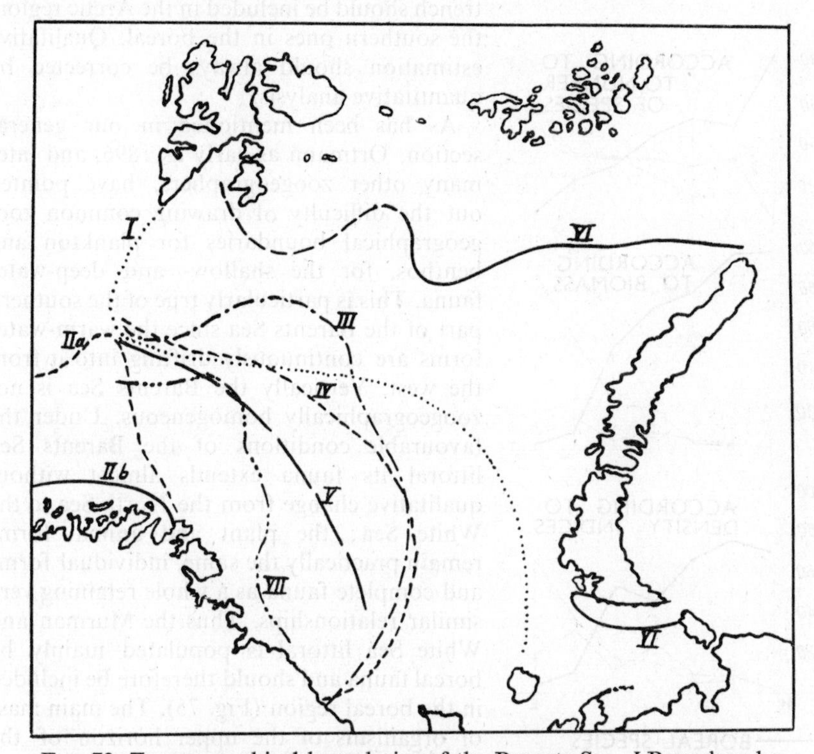

FIG. 73. Zoogeographical boundaries of the Barents Sea. *I* Boundary between Arctic and Atlantic-boreal sub-regions (Ortmann); *II* Limit of Arctic region (Broch): *a* for plankton, *b* for benthos; *III* Boundary between Arctic and sub-Arctic regions (Derjugin); *IV* Boundary between Arctic and boreo-Arctic regions (Hofsten); *V* Boundary between Arctic and transitional Atlantic region (Hentschel); *VI* Boundary between high Arctic and low Arctic sub-regions (Brotzky and Zenkevitch) identical with Schorygin's boundary; *VII* Boundary between Arctic and boreal benthos (Filatova), almost the same line as corresponding boundaries of Schorygin, Brotzky and Zenkevitch.

from the west, has little quantitative effect. The main mass of the fauna remains the same. A sharp numerical change of the fauna from the Arctic to boreal forms takes place much farther to the west. Z. Filatova's (1934) quantitative zoogeographical analysis of the fauna of the southwestern parts of the Barents Sea is very interesting. A count of the ratios of the boreal, Arctic and Arctic-boreal forms of the bottom communities makes it possible to draw a fairly clear boundary between the Arctic and boreal regions. (Fig. 74). This study brought Filatova to the conclusion that the introduction of a transitional region (boreo-Arctic according to Appellöf and Hofsten, or sub-Arctic according to K. Derjugin) is unnecessary. It is evident from Fig. 74 that the clearest picture is given by the biomass. The northern parts of the Atlantic trench should be included in the Arctic region, the southern ones in the boreal. Qualitative estimation should always be corrected by quantitative analysis.

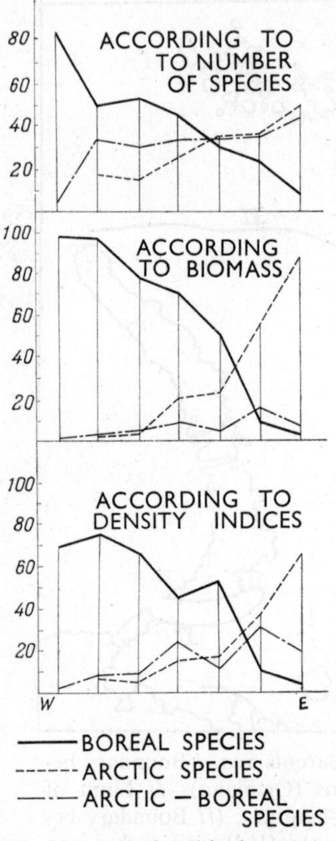

Fig. 74. Relationship between Arctic, boreal and Arctic-boreal species per cent in bottom fauna biocoenoses of southwestern part of Barents Sea from west to east (Filatova, 1934).

As has been mentioned in our general section, Ortmann as early as 1896, and later many other zoogeographers, have pointed out the difficulty of drawing common zoogeographical boundaries for plankton and benthos, for the shallow- and deep-water fauna. This is particularly true of the southern part of the Barents Sea since the warm-water forms are continuously drifting into it from the west. Vertically the Barents Sea is not zoogeographically homogeneous. Under the favourable conditions of the Barents Sea littoral its fauna extends almost without qualitative change from the North Sea to the White Sea; the plant and animal forms remain practically the same, individual forms and complete fauna as a whole retaining very similar relationships. Thus the Murman and White Sea littoral is populated mainly by boreal fauna and should therefore be included in the boreal region (Fig. 75). The main mass of organisms of the upper horizon of the sublittoral is also boreal in its characteristics. In the opinion of V. Zatzepin (1939), who made a special study of the Murman coastal fauna, the latter retains its boreal character up to the Gavrilov Islands. As one goes deeper, the boreal forms become less important, while the Arctic ones become predominant. However, owing to a warm, so-called Ruppin, branch of the Atlantic current, in the coastal region the boundary of the Arctic fauna recedes along the coast far to the east. Finally, as has been mentioned above, high Arctic fauna concentrate in the cold bottom water of some stagnant hollows of some sections of inlets on the Murman coast, even in its western parts. Thus a vertical change of the fauna from boreal to high Arctic may be observed within the same region as we proceed from the littoral to the depths.

The Barents Sea fauna thriving in an area where the warm Atlantic waters meet the local cold ones goes through continuous and fairly substantial changes, with warm-water forms now advancing, now receding, and being replaced by the cold-water ones. These migrations depend directly on the climatic changes, primarily on the greater or smaller thrust of the warm Atlantic waters.

History of fauna development. As yet the palaeogeographical changes of the Barents Sea during the Tertiary and Quaternary periods have not been sufficiently investigated. As has been said above, a rise in temperature of the

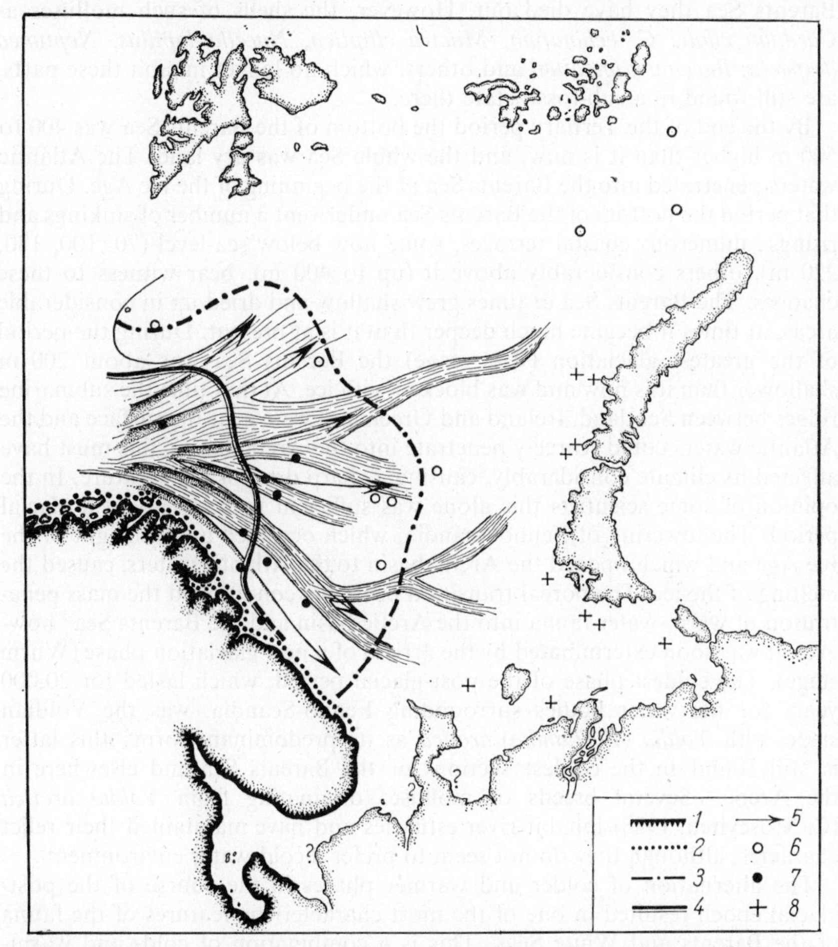

FIG. 75. Penetration of boreal forms into Barents Sea. *1* Littoral fauna; *2* Fauna of upper horizon of sublittoral; *3* Boreal pelagic fauna (Derjugin's boundary); *4* Boundary of boreal and Arctic faunas (Filatova); *5* Direction of migration. Places where cold-loving bottom-living fish *Lycodes agnostus* (*6*) and *Lycodes vahli* v. *septentrionalis* (*8*) and the thermophilic *Lycodes seminudus* (*7*) (Knipovitch) are found.

Arctic and a migration of numerous representatives of the boreal fauna into the Barents Sea have been observed during recent decades. It may be assumed that similar climatic ameliorations occurred in former times, when warm periods alternated with the cold ones. In the post-glacial epoch the highest rise of temperature occurred during the Littorina stage, that is 5,000 years ago. This considerable climatic amelioration (a rise in temperature of a few degrees) left a definite trace in the eastern part of the Barents Sea in the form of residual warm-water forms, which penetrated into the Barents Sea and the White Sea. Part of them are still living in the White Sea; in the eastern part of the Barents Sea they have died out. However, the shells of such molluscs as *Cardium edule, C. echinatum, Mactra elliptica, Nucella lapillus, Neptunea despecta, Buccinum undatum* and others, which no longer inhabit these parts, are still found in a sub-fossil state there.

By the end of the Tertiary period the bottom of the Barents Sea was 400 to 500 m higher than it is now, and the whole Sea was dry land. The Atlantic waters penetrated into the Barents Sea at the beginning of the Ice Age. During that period the bottom of the Barents Sea underwent a number of sinkings and risings; numerous coastal terraces, some now below sea-level (70, 100, 180, 220 m), others considerably above it (up to 400 m), bear witness to these changes. The Barents Sea at times grew shallow and dried up in considerable areas, at times it became much deeper than it is at present. During the period of the greatest glaciation (Riss stage) the Barents Sea was about 200 m shallower than it is now and was blocked with ice. At that time the submarine ridges between Scotland, Ireland and Greenland were near the surface and the Atlantic waters could scarcely penetrate into the Arctic basin; this must have affected its climate considerably, causing a sharp drop of temperature. In the opinion of some scientists this alone was sufficient to bring about a glacial period. The lowering of Fenno-Scandia, which occurred at the height of the Ice Age and which opened the Arctic basin to the Atlantic waters, caused the melting of the ice. The boreal transition probably conditioned the mass penetration of warm-water fauna into the Arctic basin and the Barents Sea; however, it was soon exterminated by the arrival of a new glaciation phase (Wurm stage). The coldest phase of the post-glacial period, which lasted for 20,000 years for the water bodies surrounding Fenno-Scandia, was the Yoldian stage with *Yoldia* (*Portlandia*) *arctica* as its predominant form; this latter is still found in the coldest sections of the Barents Sea and elsewhere in the Arctic. Several breeds of molluscs originating from *Yoldia arctica* (C. Mosevitch, 1928) inhabit river estuaries and have maintained their relict character, although they do not seem to prefer a cold-water environment.

The alternation of colder and warmer phases in the course of the post-glacial epoch resulted in one of the most characteristic features of the fauna of the Barents and White Seas. This is a combination of cold- and warm-water relicts which is frequently encountered even within small habitat areas. The White Sea fauna displays this most clearly.

The post-glacial climatic changes of the Arctic basin are due not only to the fluctuations of its sea-level and its temperature. As has been mentioned above, the changes of salinity must have been just as pronounced.

3

The White Sea

I. GENERAL CHARACTERISTICS

The White Sea is a comparatively small Arctic body of water communicating with the Barents Sea by a broad rather shallow channel. Compared with the Barents Sea, the White Sea has a more continental climate—a warmer summer, and a harsher winter in which, for not less than half the year, the Sea is covered along its shores by a broad continuous unmoving belt of ice, and out at sea by floating ice-floes.

A large inflow of river water and the restricted exchange of water with the open sea are causes of the reduced salinity of the Sea and of the considerable difference in salinity between the surface layer (25 to 40 m) and the deeper masses of the water which in summer, in some areas, reach a salinity of almost 10‰ (it is usually 4 to 5‰).

In winter, when huge masses of ice form on the surface of the Sea, of which a considerable part is carried out into the Barents Sea, and the surface layer of water becomes brackish, there may set in a vertical homohalinity and an intermingling of the whole column of water. In summer, when there is sharply differentiated saline and thermal stratification in two layers, the phenomena of stagnation and accumulation of carbon dioxide must take place in the deep layer of the bathymetric part of the Sea. The poverty of the bottom fauna and the predominance of brown mud point to this fact; however, so far there is no experimental evidence in favour of this view.

The instability of conditions of salinity, especially in the surface layer of the White Sea, is characteristic also for different seasons of the year and for different years.

The flora and fauna of the White Sea, in consequence of its low salinity and of the harshness of its winter, present, in the main, an impoverished Barents Sea population, with weakly expressed endemic features and a certain number of relicts, both warm-water and cold-water.

The summer rise and winter fall in temperature, more considerable than those in the Barents Sea, and the persistent low temperature in the bathymetric part of the Sea cause a zoogeographic polarization of the Sea. In different parts of it there exist simultaneously both warm-water and cold-water relicts, absent from the adjacent parts of the Barents Sea. At the same time the White Sea is the western limit of distribution of a series of Pacific Ocean forms. At great depths high Arctic animal forms are predominant; on the other hand low Arctic forms are principally characteristic of the upper levels of the Sea (down to 30 or 40 m and the littoral is inhabited by a north-boreal community of forms typical also of the Murman coast and the shores of Norway and the North Sea.

Not only in qualitative variety, but also by all indices of its biological productivity, the White Sea falls considerably below the Barents Sea (biomass, number of specimens, size, time of growth).

The fact that the productive capacities of the White Sea are several times lower than those of the Barents Sea is caused by its shorter period of vegetation and by a series of other physico-geographical factors and explains, in its turn, the relatively small commercial productivity of the Sea.

The only commercial fish present in quantity in the open sea are herring and pollack; in the Gorlo area, the Greenland seal is abundant.

II. HISTORY OF EXPLORATION

The first period

Interest in the study of the fauna of the White Sea arose at first in connection with the journey of K. Baer to Novaya Zemlya in 1837. Baer, who also visited the White Sea, drew attention to the richness of its fauna, especially in the Gulf of Kandalaksha. In 1864 the Moscow zoologist, A. Kroneberg, went to the White Sea and brought back a rich collection of marine animals. After that the initiative in the study of White Sea fauna passed to the Petersburg Society of Naturalists, which sent to the White Sea the zoologists F. Jarzhinsky and L. Iversen in 1869, and N. Wagner, C. Mereschkowsky and S. Herzenstein in 1876, 1877 and 1880. In 1870 a large-scale expedition to the White Sea and the Barents Sea was likewise carried out from Moscow by V. Uljanin. We are indebted to all these persons for the earliest information about the fauna of the White Sea.

The second period

A closer investigation of the fauna of the White Sea began, however, in 1881, when the above Society opened a biological station on Great Solovetsky Island, which existed there for 18 years and was transferred in 1899 to Aleksandrovsk on the Murman Peninsula. Over a series of years the outstanding Russian zoologists V. M. Schimkevitch, N. M. Knipovitch, A. Birula, K. Saint-Hilaire and many others worked at the Solovetsky biological station.

During the first 20 years of this century the work of K. Saint-Hilaire in the Kovda Guba region, and of N. Livanov in the Solovetsky Islands, was particularly notable.

The third period

From 1920 onwards there began a period of more intensive study of the White Sea by workers from the Hydrological Institute, the Northern Scientific and Fishery Expedition, and the State Oceanographic Institute. At the same time K. Derjugin also began work on the White Sea; he published a voluminous monograph devoted to it in 1928. In addition, several permanent establishments arose on the shores of the White Sea. The first of these, after the transfer of the Solovetsky station to the Murman Peninsula, was the summer biological laboratory founded by Saint-Hilaire at Kovda in 1908. In 1931 the Hydrological Institute set up its White Sea station at Piryu Guba (Umba) and the State Oceanographic Institute opened its branches at Archangel and Kandalaksha. Finally, in 1939, the White Sea Biological Station of Moscow University started functioning on the southern shore of the Gulf of

Kandalaksha (Rugozerskaya Guba); since 1945 the Biological Station of the Petrozavodsk University has been working at Gridin, and since 1957 the Biological Station of the Karelian Associate Branch of the Academy of Sciences of the U.S.S.R. at Chupa Guba.

III. PHYSICAL GEOGRAPHY, HYDROLOGY, HYDROCHEMISTRY AND GEOLOGY

Situation and size

The White Sea (Fig. 76) is an accessory body of water of the Barents Sea, to which it is connected by a broad sound, projecting far into the mainland. It is bounded by the coordinates 63° 48′ to 68° 40′ of north latitude and 32° 00′ to 44° 40′ of east longitude. The northern limit of the Sea is taken as being a line joining Sviatoi Nos and Cape Kanin.

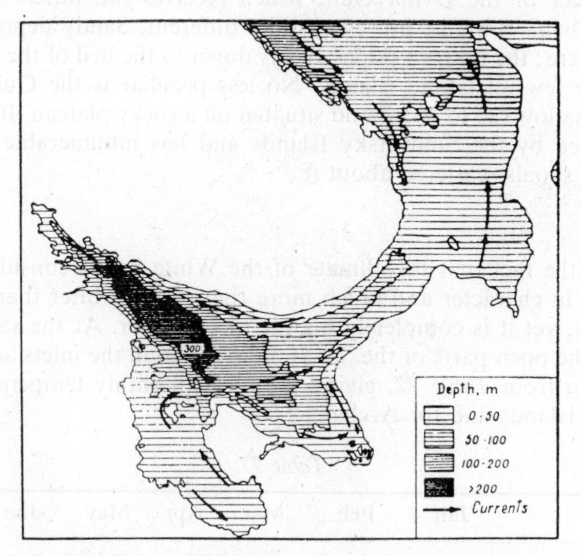

FIG. 76. Chart of White Sea with depths and currents.

The White Sea is subdivided into: (*1*) the funnel-shaped broad (100 to 170 km) shallow (20 to 40 to 80 m) outer part of the sound (to the northward of a line from Danilov Island to Voronov Island); (*2*) the Gorlo, the narrow (45 to 60 km), deeper (40 to 100 m) inner part of the sound, running southward as far as a line joining Cape Nicodiemsky and Cape Veprevsky; and (*3*) the White Sea proper (the basin), consisting of a central part, open sea, and three inlets, the Kandalaksha, Dvina and Onega Gulfs. The area of the whole sea is approximately 90,000 km^2, with a mean depth of 89 m. On a line from the Gulf of Kandalaksha to the Dvina Gulf the Sea extends for 480 km. The considerable freshness of the water of the White Sea is determined by its positive fresh-water balance (V. Timonov, 1950). The annual influx from the land composes 185 km^3, with 19 km^3 of sediment; evaporation accounts for 13 km³. So that inflow exceeds discharge by 191 km³. If this excess were distributed over the whole surface of the Sea, it would form a 2·2 m layer of fresh water, or one-fortieth part of the volume of the Sea.

Bottom topography

The greatest depth in the White Sea is about 330 m (off Cape Tury), and its central part is occupied by depths greater than 100 km, separated by the wide ridge of the Voronka and the Gorlo from the deep parts of the Barents Sea. The average depth of the basin is 110 m.

The deep bottom of the Gulf of Kandalaksha, which represents what in the Ice Age was the bed of a great glacier, is covered with moraine deposits and forms a series of depressions, which are separated on the seaward side by banks (end moraine). Along its shores are a great number of inlets and islands. The character of the Dvina Gulf, which receives the waters of the great Northern Dvina river, is, however, quite different. Sandy deposits are predominant here; the bottom slopes evenly down to the bed of the Sea, and the shores have few inlets and islands. No less peculiar is the Gulf of Onega, relatively shallow (20 to 40 m) and situated on a rocky plateau. It is separated from the Sea by the Solovetsky Islands and has innumerable islands and underwater shoals scattered about it.

Climate

In spite of the fact that the climate of the White Sea is considerably more continental in character and much more rigorous in winter than that of the Barents Sea, yet it is completely marine in character. At the same time the climate in the open parts of the Sea is milder than in the inlets and bights, as may be seen from *Table 77*, giving the mean monthly temperature for the Solovetsky Islands and for Archangel.

Table 77

Month	Jan	Feb	Mar	Apr	May	Jun	Jul
Solovetsky	− 9·6	−11·2	−8·7	−2·1	+3·7	+ 7·7	+12·2
Archangel	−13·5	−12·7	−7·8	−1·2	+5·0	+11·9	+15·7

Month	Aug	Sept	Oct	Nov	Dec	Mean Annual
Solovetsky	+11·2	+8·0	+2·6	+1·9	− 6·3	+0·5
Archangel	+13·5	+8·0	+5·7	+5·7	−11·3	+0·3

Ice cover

In consequence of its climate, which is harsher than that of the Barents Sea, considerable masses of ice are formed in the White Sea in winter and persist for about half the year, sometimes for seven months (in the region of Mudyug Lighthouse)—from the second half, or from the end, of October till the middle or end of May. Only at the shore does the ice form a continuous covering to the water, the coast ice as it is called, which is sometimes several kilometres wide. A continuous covering is also formed in the inlets and gubas and between the islands, where the ice may be as much as a metre thick. The open parts of the Sea are covered with floating ice of every kind.

Currents

The fresher surface waters of the White Sea flow out through the Gorlo into the Barents Sea along its eastern shore (the 'Winter Shore'). Along the western side (the Tersky Shore) more saline water flows into the Sea from the Barents Sea, as may be clearly seen from the sketch (Fig. 77).

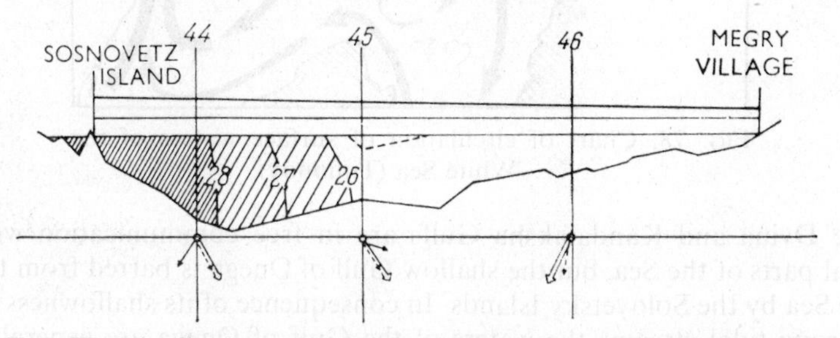

FIG. 77. Distribution of salinity on the cross section through the Gorlo of the White Sea along the line Sosnovetz Island to Megry village (Timonov, 1950).

Across the Gorlo (from Sosnovetz Island) very strong tidal streams in the Voronka, and especially in the Gorlo, check the perpetual currents and create a movement of the whole mass of water in the Gorlo first towards the Barents Sea, and then towards the White Sea. While the speed of a permanent outflow current will hardly exceed 20 cm/sec, the speed of the tidal shift may attain 7 to 8 km/h, or exceed 200 cm/sec. These streams and currents cause the most violent, turbulent confusion of the whole column of water in the Voronka and the Gorlo, and as a consequence their bed is covered with an extremely hard sediment.

As was shown by V. Shulejkin (1925), these tidal oscillations do not bring the waters of the Barents Sea into the White Sea, but only shift the masses of water in the Gorlo first in one direction and then in the other, for no more than ten miles on one flood tide. An excellent illustration of this system of currents and streams (Fig. 79) is given by Derjugin (1928, from the data of M. Virketis) from the pattern of the distribution of certain plankton organisms. V. Timonov (1947) presents the system of certain cyclonic and anticyclonic rotations of the surface waters of the White Sea (Fig. 78).

Calanus finmarchicus is not found in either the Voronka or the Gorlo, and is abundantly represented in both the Barents and White Seas. The infusoria *Tintinnopsis campanula* is carried into the Gorlo along with the outflow current; contrariwise, the typical Barents Sea infusoria *Cyttarocyllis denticulata* is carried along the Tersky shore into the White Sea.

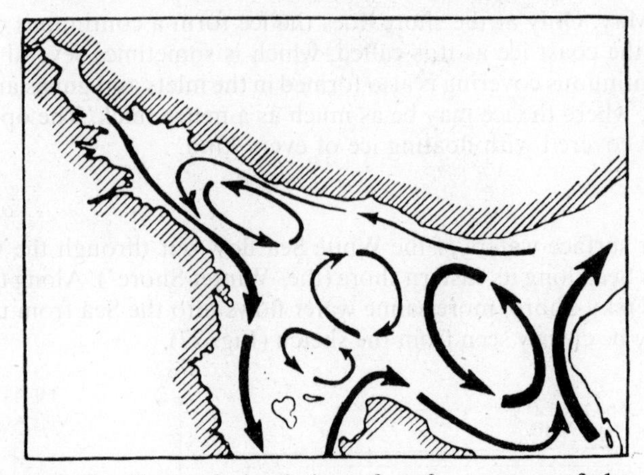

FIG. 78. Chart of circulation of surface waters of the White Sea (Timonov).

The Dvina and Kandalaksha Gulfs are in free communication with the central parts of the Sea, but the shallow Gulf of Onega is barred from the rest of the Sea by the Solovetsky Islands. In consequence of its shallowness and of the strong tidal streams the waters of the Gulf of Onega are generally well mixed from top to bottom, and are homothermic and homohaline. The Gulf of Onega is the part of the Sea which is best warmed in summer and best aerated, by virtue of which animal forms find here for themselves the most favourable conditions of existence.

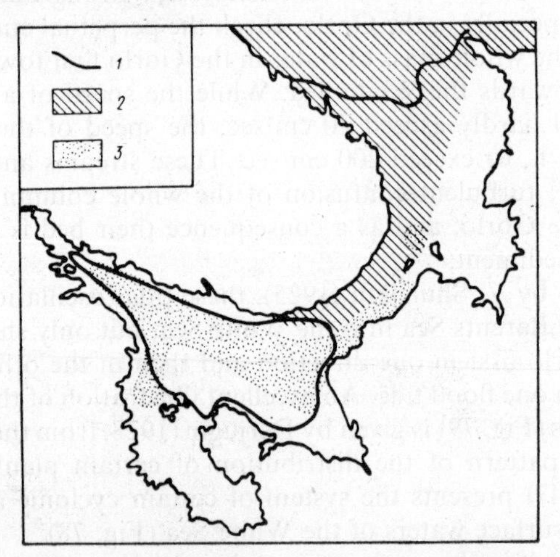

FIG. 79. Distribution of the Crustacea *Calanus finmarchicus* (*1*), plankton ciliates *Cyttarocyllis denticulata* (*2*) and *Tintinnopsis campanula* (*3*) in the White Sea (Derjugin from Virketis, 1928).

Temperature and salinity

The vertical distribution of salinity and temperature in summertime in the main basin of the White Sea is shown in Fig. 80. As may be seen, the temperature on the surface of the open sea at the warmest time of the year reaches 14° to 16°. With depth the temperature falls quickly and at 35 to 44 m it already equals zero. In the Dvina Gulf there is a dome-shaped rise of isotherms and isohalines, and the 0° isotherm is found at a depth of only 12 m. Derjugin suggests that this is the centre of the halistatic region formed by the circular rotation of the waters, and calls it the 'cold pole' of the White Sea. Farther down the temperature decreases still more, to $-1{\cdot}4°$ at approximately the

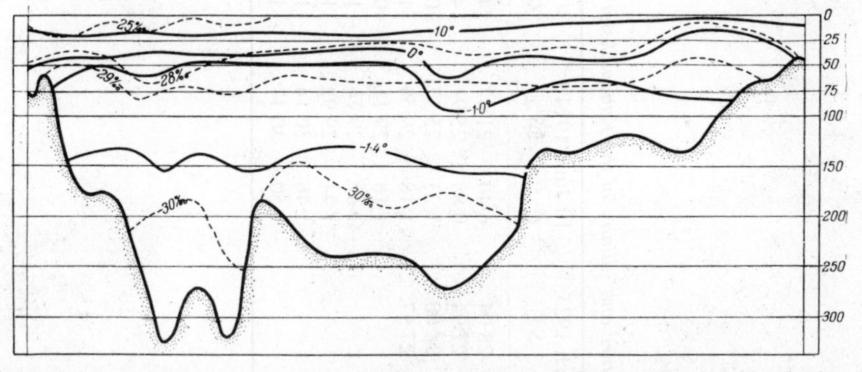

FIG. 80. Vertical ranges of salinity and temperature in the White Sea at the beginning of August 1922 on the cross section from Kandalaksha Bay to the Bay of Dvina (Derjugin, 1928).

150 m level, and in places drops even to $-1{\cdot}5°$. Such clearly expressed stratification is characteristic for salinity in summer as well. At the surface it is equal to 25 to 26‰ and in the depths it reaches 30 to 34‰.

In winter the picture is sharply changed. A condition is established very close to homothermic and the salinity of the surface layer rises considerably, as may be seen from *Table 78*, borrowed from Derjugin.

While in the open parts of the Sea (the Gulf of Kandalaksha) the summer temperature reaches 15° (Fig. 81), along the shoreline far up the inlets and bights this maximum is still higher and may exceed 20°. In this way the White Sea, in consequence of its small size and of the depth of its extension into the mainland, has much harsher winter climatic conditions than the Barents Sea. On the other hand, opposite correlation is set up in summer, and the surface layer of the White Sea, especially in the inlets, is much more strongly warmed than that of the Barents Sea, and the deep layers maintain a very low temperature all the year round.

This explains a series of biological phenomena. The depths of the Sea maintain a high Arctic fauna, while in the surface layer both Arctic and boreal forms may exist. Some of them are absent either in the Barents Sea or in those parts of pit adjacent to the White Sea.

Table 78. Annual variation of temperature and salinity in the Kandalaksha Gulf area

Depth	6 August 1922		29 October 1925		30 March 1923		10 June 1924		Range	
m	t°	S‰	t°	S‰	t°	S‰	t°	S‰	t°	S‰
0	14·65	23·80	3·00	25·44	−1·4	28·04	6·40	21·47	14·65 to −1·80	21·47 to 28·04
10	14·60	24·78	3·16	25·39	−1·5	27·94	0·88	25·91	14·60 to −1·52	24·78 to 27·94
25	10·40	26·04	3·17	25·72	1·5	28·00	−1·23	25·57	10·40 to −1·50	25·72 to 24·00
50	−0·95	28·37	1·21	27·47	−1·1	27·97	−1·18	29·59	1·21 to −1·40	27·47 to 28·59
100	−1·10	29·36	−0·92	28·62	—	—	−1·16	29·11	−0·92 to −1·10	28·62 to 29·36
150	−1·30	29·90	—	—	—	—	−1·47	29·76	−1·10 to −1·47	29·76 to 29·90
200	−1·40	30·00	−1·38	29·96	—	—	−1·44	29·92	−1·38 to −1·47	29·92 to 30·00
250	−1·40	30·10	—	—	—	—	−1·46	30·14	−1·40 to −1·46	30·10 to 30·14
300	−1·40	30·34	—	—	—	—	−1·50	30·17	−1·40 to −1·50	30·17 to 30·34

On the other hand the lowered salinity of the White Sea hinders the penetration of many forms, both Arctic and boreal, which are common in the Barents Sea, and even in those parts of it immediately adjacent to the Gorlo of the White Sea.

In spring and at the beginning of summer the surface water is less saline in

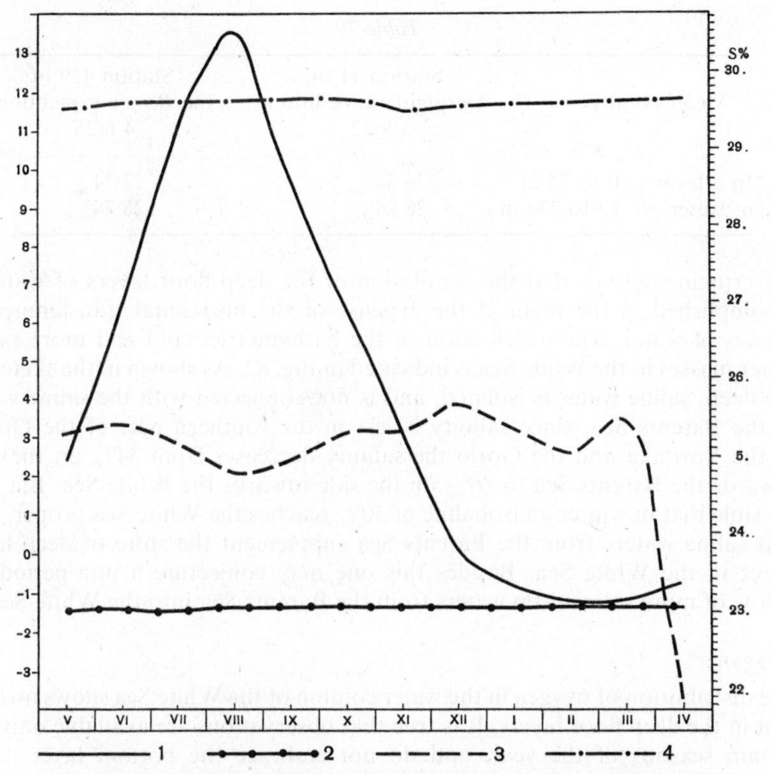

FIG. 81. Seasonal fluctuations of mean monthly surface salinity (3) and temperature (1), and of the bottom salinity (4) and temperature (2) in the open parts of the Kandalaksha Guba of the White Sea (Voronkov, Uralov and Chernovskaya).

consequence of the melting of ice and of the inflow off the land of water from melted ice. In winter it becomes more saline in consequence of the lessened inflow off the land and of the formation of sea-ice, and the difference in salinity at that season between the surface and the deep layers is only 2‰. In places where there is formation of ice on a large scale the water may become still more saline and may slide down submerged slopes into the depths. It is most probable that this is the way that partial aeration of the deep layer takes place in winter.

In consequence of the big inflow of river water into the White Sea, and of the difficulty of exchange of water with the Barents Sea, the salinity of the

White Sea is considerably less than that of the Barents Sea and, besides this, it may experience considerable variation from year to year. Thus a comparison of conditions of salinity in the central part of the Sea in 1922 and 1926 shows that during these four years the salinity of the upper layer of water increased considerably, while the lower layer maintained the same salinity (*Table 79*).

Table 79

Mean salinity		Station 11 of Derjugin's expedition 3/8/22	Station 429 of the *Persey* expedition 4/6/26
In a layer of water	0 to 75 m	26·34‰	27·74‰
	75 to 274 m	28·84‰	28·74‰

Derjugin suggests that the ventilation of the deep floor layers of water is accomplished in the main at the expense of the horizontal transference of masses of water. The distribution of the bathymetric, cold and more saline water masses in the White Sea is indicated in Fig. 82. As shown in the sketches, the deep, saline water is isolated, and is not connected with the saline water of the Barents Sea, since salinity is less in the southern part of the Gorlo. In the Voronka and the Gorlo the salinity decreases from 34‰ on the side towards the Barents Sea to 26‰ on the side towards the White Sea. But it is possible that in winter an isohaline of 30‰ reaches the White Sea proper, and that saline waters from the Barents Sea supplement the store of deep layer water in the White Sea. Besides this one may conjecture a non-periodical inflow of more saline deep waters from the Barents Sea into the White Sea.

Oxygen

The distribution of oxygen in the water column of the White Sea shows no lack of it in the deep floor layers. It is true that observations are available only for certain seasons of the year, and do not embrace the bottom layer itself. Nevertheless one must suppose that the bathymetric layers of water of the White Sea are sufficiently aerated. It has not yet been established how this is ensured, if, as Derjugin suggests, the convectional currents affect only the surface layers of water (not deeper than 50 to 60 m). Derjugin speaks of deep horizontal currents; but the nature of the latter remains uncertain, as well as the extent to which they ensure the aeration of the water near the bottom.

Oxygen in the White Sea is present in fairly large quantity throughout the water column. It has not been possible to establish stagnation phenomena, although the oxygen conditions of the true near-bottom layer still remain obscure. It is agreed that the White Sea presents a rare example of a body of water with a deep basin, separated by a high ridge from the open sea, and without the presence of pronounced stagnation.

The annual course of oxygen content in the Gulf of Kandalaksha has been given by E. Sokolova (1939) (Fig. 83). Some decrease of oxygen in the deep layer is observed in July and August. In the surface layer oxygen saturation is observed in April to July, caused by the activity of phytoplankton. Sometimes the saturation zone descends to a considerable depth. Thus at the end of June 1933 oxygen at one of the stations at the same cross section of the Gulf of Kandalaksha was distributed in the manner shown in *Table 80*.

It is possible that the passage of oxygen into the depths of the White Sea occurs together with the slipping of masses of water down slopes into the depths at the time of the winter rise of salinity of the surface water as a result

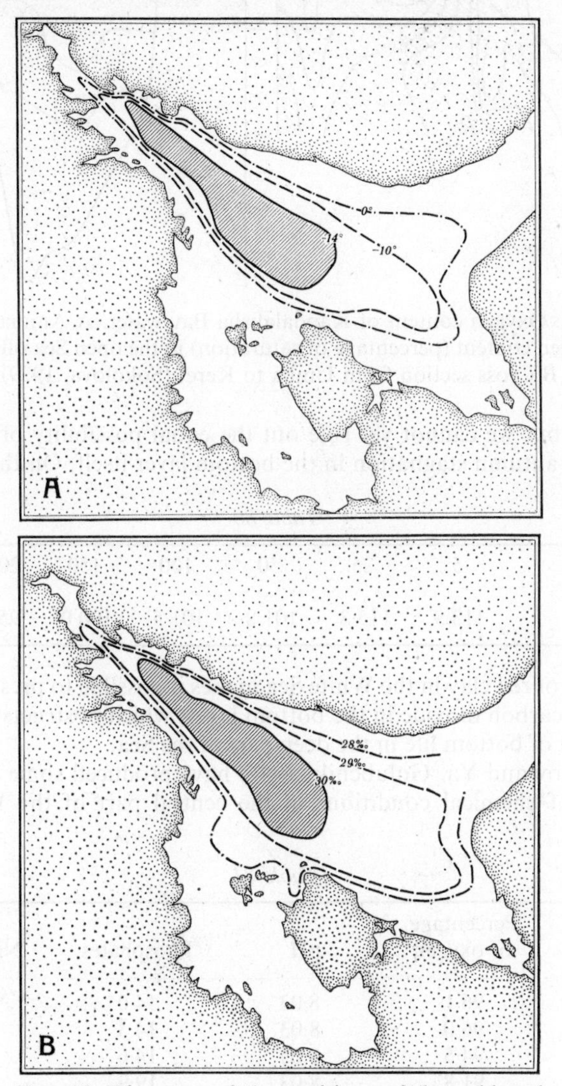

FIG. 82. Diagrams of the positions of the cold and saline deep waters of the White Sea in August 1922 (Derjugin, 1928): A—temperature, B—salinity.

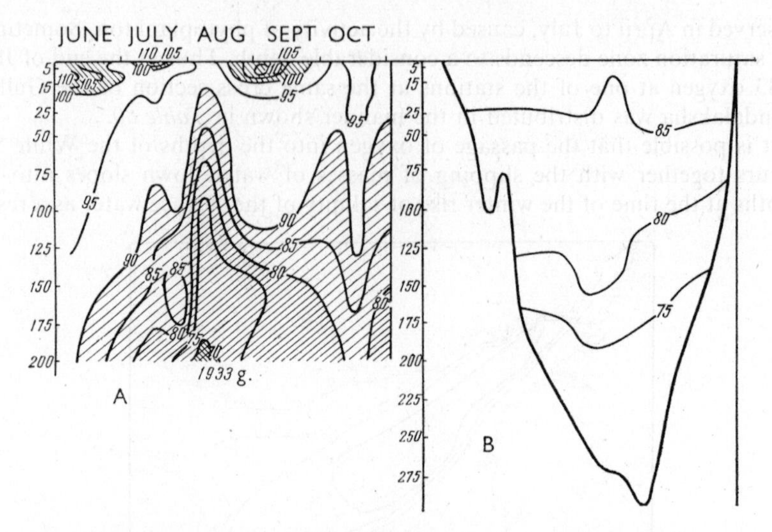

FIG. 83. Oxygen content of Kandalaksha Bay water. A Annual course of oxygen content (percentage of saturation) in the open Sea off Umba; B Cross section from Umba to Keret (Sokolova, 1939).

of freezing; but we cannot yet rule out the equal possibility of the onset of the summer–autumn stagnation in the bottom layer itself. On the other hand

Table 80

Depth, m	5	25	50	100	150	200	250
Percentage of oxygen	113·9	115·3	101·8	101·5	100·0	95·0	88·1

the presence of red clay in the White Sea makes it possible to presume an accumulation of carbon dioxide in the bottom layer, which obstructs an abundant development of bottom life in the deep part of the Sea.

A. Trofimov and Ya. Golubchik (1947) have produced some mean indices (*Table 81*) of chemical conditions in the central part of the White Sea in springtime.

Table 81

Depth m	Percentage of oxygen	pH	Phosphates	Nitrates
0	96·1	8·03	14·0	52
10	96·0	8·03	14·3	51
25	94·5	8·05	14·6	55
50	91·8	8·03	19·9	63
100	87·0	8·03	—	—
200	82·0	8·03	22·0	70

The sea-bed

The soils of the White Sea floor present every stage from cliff- and rock-bed along the shore and in the Gorlo to red clay in the central part (Fig. 84). In the Voronka and the Gorlo of the White Sea the sea-bed is covered with sand, shell gravel and stones, and in the Gorlo also with outcrops of cliff. The basin of the White Sea is mainly covered with very soft soils. Sand and silty sand run in a comparatively narrow strip along the shore.

Hard floors are widely distributed only in the Dvina Gulf, and especially in the Gulf of Onega. In the Gulf of Kandalaksha a very large number of

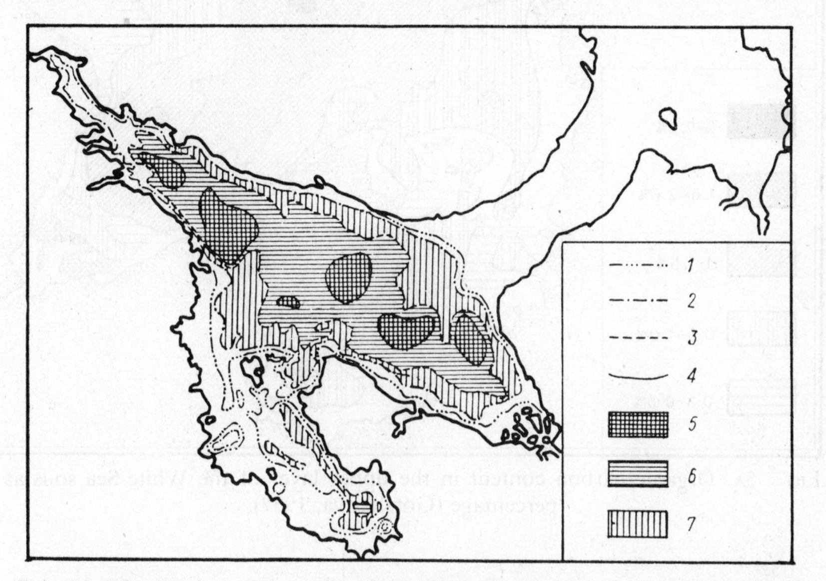

FIG. 84. Distribution of the soils of the White Sea (Gorshkova, 1957): *1* Less than 5% fine-grain fraction (<0·01 mm); *2* From 5 to 10% fine-grain fraction; *3* 10 to 30%; *4* 30 to 50%; *5* Clayey mud; *6* Mud; *7* Sandy silt.

rocks is observed, obviously of moraine origin; in the Gulf of Onega there is much variegation of the soils, which is dependent on the complicated system of currents. Outcrops of cliff are encountered here, and soft muds.

According to the data of T. Gorshkova (1957) the content of organic carbon in the sediments of the open parts of the White Sea (Fig. 85A) varies from 0·09 to 2·2 per cent, and for the whole of the White Sea the average is 1·14 per cent. In the enclosed parts of the inlets and gubas the highest percentage of organic carbon reaches 4·37 at the expense of enrichment by vegetable remains. These data are a good illustration of the direct interdependence of the quantity of organic matter and the mechanical composition of the sea-bed —chiefly of organic matter and muddy sediments (Fig. 85B).

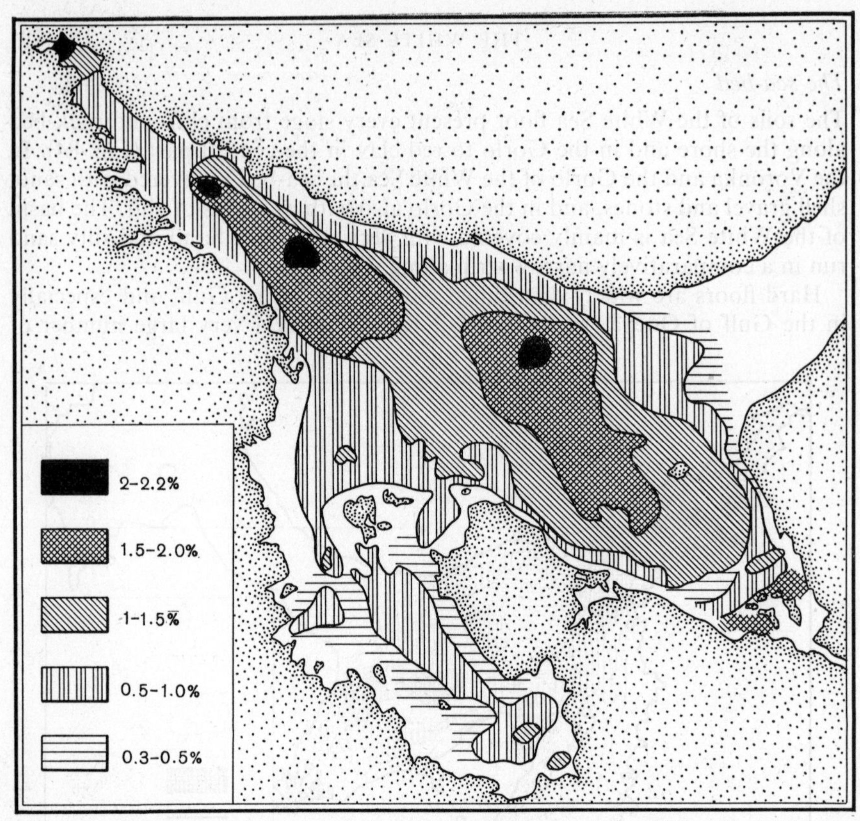

FIG 5A. Organic carbon content in the upper layer of the White Sea soils as a percentage (Gorshkova, 1957).

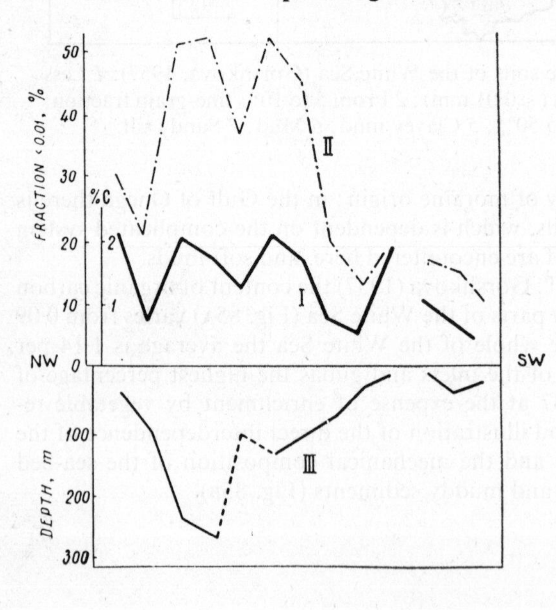

FIG. 85B. Average amount of organic carbon (I), and the $< 0{\cdot}01$ mm. fraction of the White Sea soils (II), along a cross section from Gulf of Kandalaksha to the Dvina Guba (Gorshkova, 1957). The lowest curve (III) is the bottom.

IV. FLORA AND FAUNA

Plankton

Qualitative composition. The plankton of the White Sea has up to now been very insufficiently studied. Its qualitative composition is given in *Table 82.*

Table 82

Plankton groups	No. of species and varieties	Plankton groups	No. of species and varieties	Plankton groups	No. of species and varieties
Flagellata	2	Protozoa	27	Pteropoda	2
Silicoflagellata	5	Hydrozoa	16	Cladocera	2
Chlorophyceae	9	Scyphozoa	3	Copepoda	13
Diatomacea	61	Ctenophora	3	Amphipoda	5
Peridinea	29	Chaetognatha	1	Schizopoda	7
		Rotatoria	2	Appendicularia	2
		Polychaeta	1		
Phytoplankton total	106*			Zooplankton total	84
				Plankton total	190

* The composition of phytoplankton according to P. Usachev.

In connection with the fact that the surface layers of the White Sea are warmed more in summer than those of the Barents Sea, and the deeper ones are warmed less, the thermophilic forms are concentrated in the surface layers and the cold-living forms in the deeper layers.

Of the former one should distinguish the ciliates *Amphorella subulata*, the peridineans *Ceratium fusus*, *Peridinium conicum*, the copepods *Calanus finmarchicus*, *Oithora similis*, *Microsetella atlantica*, *Centropages hamatus* and *Temora longicornis*, the Cladocera *Evadne nordmanni*, the appendicularian *Fritillaria borealis* and some others. Correspondingly considerable predominance in the deep layers pertains to, for instance, the cold-water crustaceans *Metridia longa*, and the ciliates *Tintinnopsis campanula* and *T. ventricosa*. Finally, the third group of forms is distributed evenly throughout the whole column. To these should be related the medusa *Aglantha digitalis*, the rotifer *Anuraea cruciformis* and the crustacean *Pseudocalanus elongatus*. In the plankton the predominant forms are the Arctic and Arctic-boreal, but also in the plankton there are true boreal elements which are partly relict already. Thus the Cadocera *Oothrix bidentata*, for instance, which is encountered in the northern part of the Atlantic Ocean, is absent from the Barents Sea, but has been established in the White Sea. The ciliate *Tintinnopsis campanula*, which is known from the Mediterranean, Black and North Seas and from the Gulf of Finland, has likewise been discovered in the White Sea. It has not been found in the Barents Sea. In the parts of the Barents Sea adjacent to the White Sea many plankton forms are not encountered which are common in the White Sea. Of these one may name the ciliate *Amphorella subulata*, the crustaceans

Centropages hamatus and *Temora longicornis*, and some species of diatom of the genus Chaetoceros (*Ch. danicum*, common in the Baltic Sea, *Ch. curvisetum*, *Ch. constrictum*, *Ch. scolopendra*).

Negative characteristics of the plankton of the White Sea. On the other hand more than 50 Barents Sea phytoplankton forms and about 50 zooplankton forms are absent from the White Sea. As M. Virketis has shown (1926), a series of boreal forms of copepods, *Rhinocalanus nasutus*, for instance, and *Metridia lucens*, *Oithona plumifera* and *Acartia clausi*, and equally typical Arctic forms *Ptychogastria polaris*, *Tiara conifera*, *Calanus hyperboreus*, *Euchaeta norvegica*, *Krohnia hamata*, *Oikopleura labradoriensis*, common in the Barents Sea, are absent from the White Sea. No less interesting also is the fact that 'certain species, common with Barents Sea species, exist in the White Sea in entirely different conditions'.

Quantitative distribution of zooplankton. As V. Jashnov has shown (1940), in the White Sea zooplankton *Calanus finmarchicus*, *Metridia longa* and *Pseudocalanus elongatus* are predominant in the spring, and, in contrast with the Barents Sea, only 38 per cent of the total biomass of zooplankton falls to the share of *Calanus finmarchicus*, to *Metridia longa* 23 per cent, to Chaetognatha 13 per cent, and to Euphausiaceae 1·1 per cent. At the same time *Calanus finmarchicus* (49·2 per cent) is dominant in the surface layer (down to 25 m), and *Metridia longa* (42·2 m) in the depths.

Nevertheless in the more thoroughly warmed areas of the Sea, in the Gulf of Onega, for example (L. Epstein, 1957), the main representatives of zooplankton are species of the genus Acartia with an admixture in time of warmth of *Centropages hamatus*, *Temora longicornis*, Cladocera and others, and in time of cold of *Calanus finmarchicus* and *Metridia longa*.

The greatest average density of zooplankton in the 25 m surface layer is 200 mg/m^3 (Fig. 86A). At a depth of 200 to 300 m the zooplankton biomass amounts to 50 mg/m^3. The mean spring biomass for the whole Sea is 100 mg/m^3. Jashnov (1940) suggests that the maximum zooplankton biomass of the White Sea must be approximately equal to the biomass of the southwestern part of the Barents Sea, and notices likewise a very great poverty in numbers of plankton in the Gulf of Onega and the Gorlo of the White Sea. V. Jashnov (1940) takes the maximum total zooplankton biomass of the White Sea as equal to 1½ to 2 million tons.

But L. Epstein (1957), for the more productive Gulf of Onega, points for 1951 to a mean plankton biomass in the open part of the Gulf of 157 mg/m^3 in the summer period and 37 mg/m^3 in the autumn; and, in the gubas of the White Sea coastline, to 210 mg/m^3 in summer and 11 mg/m^3 in winter. Epstein's data and certain other material give reason for suggesting that the biomass indicated by Jashnov is somewhat overestimated. Moreover, in the White Sea the phytoplankton sometimes gives a very great density (V. Khmisnikova, 1947) which in some areas is as high as 10 mg/m^3. The quantitative distribution of phyto- and zoo-plankton in August 1932 is shown in Fig. 86, A and B.

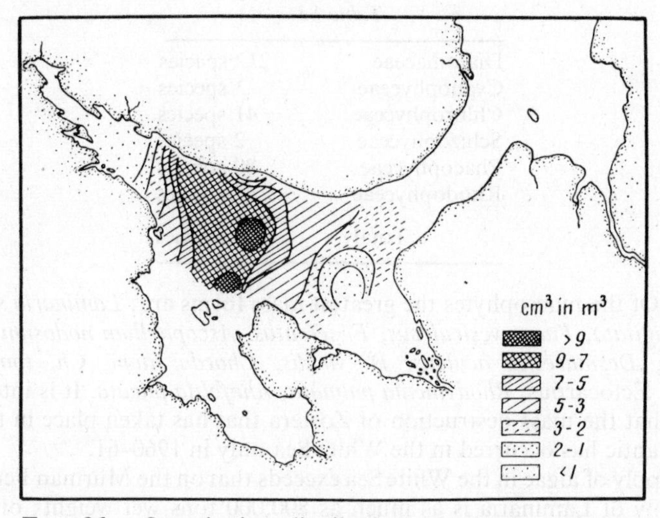

FIG. 86A. Quantitative distribution of phyto- and zooplankton in the 0 to 10 m layer of the White Sea (cm³/m³) (Khmisnikova, 1947).

Benthos

Phytobenthos. The qualitative variety of the White Sea flora is only slightly less than that of the Murman Peninsula. According to the data of E. S. Zinova (1928), A. D. Zinova (1950), K. I. Meyer (1933), and A. Kalugina (1958) the composition of the bottom algae in the White Sea is as set out in *Table 83*.

The flowering plants *Zostera marina* and *Z. nana*, the most interesting warm-living relicts in the White Sea, have a very great importance for life in this Sea. Zostera attains a specially large size in the White Sea (up to 2½ m), and on the other hand forms, as in the North Sea, a littoral dwarf variety

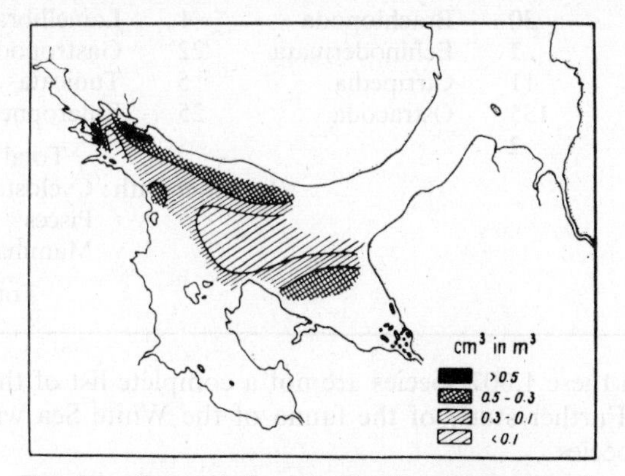

FIG. 86B. Quantitative distribution of plankton in the 50 to 100 m layer of the White Sea (cm³/m³) (Khmisnikova)

Table 83

Diatomaceae	212 species
Cyanophyceae	3 species
Chlorophyceae	41 species
Schizophyceae	2 species
Phaeophyceae	80 species
Rhodophyceae	67 species
Total	405 species

Z. nana. Of the macrophytes the greatest mass forms are: *Laminaria saccharina*, *L. digitata*, *Fucus vesiculosus*, *F. serratus*, *Ascophyllum nodosum*, *Alaria esculenta*, *Desmarestia aculeus*, *D. viridis*, *Chorda filum*, *Ch. tomentosa*, Pilayella, Ectocarpus, *Rhodymenia palmata*, *Ahnfeltia plicata*. It is interesting to note that the mass destruction of Zostera that has taken place in the northern Atlantic has occurred in the White Sea only in 1960–61.

The supply of algae in the White Sea exceeds that on the Murman Peninsula. The supply of Laminaria is as much as 800,000 tons wet weight; of Fucus, 250,000 tons, and of Zostera, which is absent from the Murman Peninsula, 400,000 tons. The total supply of algae in the White Sea—macrophytes and Zostera—is as much as 1·5 million tons wet weight.

Zoobenthos. The White Sea zoobenthos, from data that are not yet complete, comprises, according to Derjugin, more than 1,000 species (*Table 84*):

Table 84

Foraminifera	21	Cumacea	12	Harpacticoida	48
Cornacuspongia	32	Isopoda	9	Isopoda	92
Hydroidea	8	Hirudinea	2	Decapoda	13
Anthozoa	1	Gephyrea	4	Pantopoda	18
Turbellaria	25	Bryozoa	132	Amphineura	4
Nemertini	30	Brachiopoda	1	Lamellibranchiata	38
Priapuloidea	2	Echinodermata	22	Gastropoda	86
Oligochaeta	11	Cirripedia	5	Tunicata	28
Polychaeta	135	Ostracoda	25	Enteropneusta	2
Sipunculoidea	2			Total	948
			Together with:	Cyclostomata	1
				Pisces	51
				Mammalia	6
				Total	1,007

Clearly even these 1,007 species are not a complete list of the components of the fauna. Further study of the fauna of the White Sea will add several hundreds of species.

Zoogeographical characteristics. As has been said above, the fauna of the White Sea is not homogeneous from the zoogeographical standpoint. On the

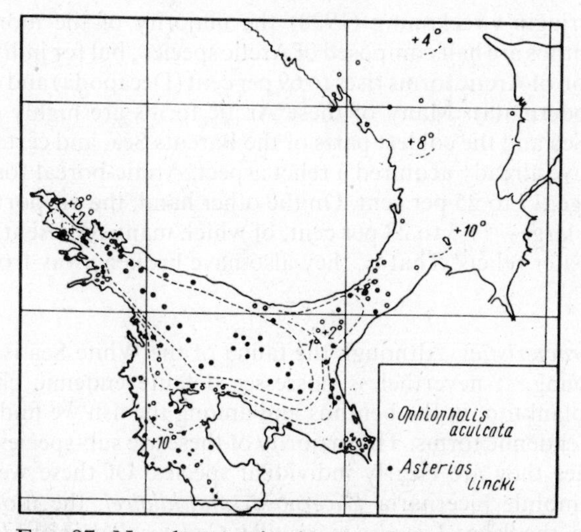

FIG. 87. Near-bottom isotherms of the White Sea and the distribution in it of the starfish *Asterias lincki* and ophiure *Ophiopholis aculeata* (Schorygin, 1926).

littoral, boreal forms predominate markedly. With increase of depth the number of Arctic forms becomes greater and greater, and finally the deep parts of the Sea are inhabited by fauna of a pronounced high Arctic character (*Table 85*).

As we have shown, the mass form of zooplankton in the surface layer is *Calanus finmarchicus*, while *Metridia longa* lives in masses in the depths. A comparison of the distribution of two echinoderms, the Arctic-boreal *Ophiopholis aculeata* and the cold-living starfish *Asterias lincki*, is even more significant (Fig. 87).

Table 85. Relationship of different zoogeographical groups in the bottom fauna of the White Sea as percentages of the total fauna

Zoogeographical groups	Littoral		Pseudo-abyssal	
Total number of species	43		52	
Boreal	23·25	41·53	0·0	0·0
Chiefly boreal	18·28		0·0	
Arctic boreal	22·93		15·3	
Chiefly Arctic	13·95		13·3	
Arctic	6·97	6·97	25·0	54·0
High Arctic	0·0		29·0	
Endemic	0·0		5·7	
Cosmopolitan species	6·97		7·7	
Bipolar	7·65		4·0	
		100·0		100·0

By K. Derjugin's reckoning (1928) the majority of the more substantial groups of benthos are half composed of Arctic species; but for individual groups the proportion of Arctic forms rises to 69 per cent (Decapoda) and even to 86 per cent (Echinodermata). Many of these Arctic forms are highly characteristic of the Kara Sea and the coldest parts of the Barents Sea, and certain ones in the White Sea have already acquired a relict aspect. Arctic-boreal forms compose, on the average, 17 to 25 per cent. On the other hand, the proportion of boreal forms is also large—11·5 to 23 per cent, of which many represent, in the White Sea, warm-water relicts. That is, they also have broken away from their main habitat.

Endemic characteristics. Although the fauna of the White Sea is, geologically speaking, young, it nevertheless possesses definite endemic characteristics. Both in the plankton, in the benthos and among the fish we find more or less pronounced endemic forms. The majority of these are sub-species and variants but sometimes they are clearly individual species. Of these we indicate the remarkably mobile lucernaria *Lucernosa saint-hilairei*, the mollusc *Lyonsia schimkevitchi*, the fishes *Lycodes maris-albi*, *Gadus callarias maris-albi*, *Clupea harengus pallasi maris-albi* and others. There is also a genus endemic in the White Sea, namely the Porifera *Crellomima imparidens*. As regards this last Derjugin suggests that either it is a fragment of a more ancient group, or its related forms will be found somewhere in the neighbouring seas.

Link with Pacific Ocean fauna. There are likewise in the White Sea a series of forms which establish a link between its fauna and the fauna of the seas of the Far East. The White Sea is the extreme western outpost of this fauna. Of this latter group one may point to one of the White Sea herring, *Clupea harengus pallasi maris-albi*, the lamprey *Lampetra japonica septentrionalis*, and the polychaete *Scalibregma robusta* which inhabits the Sea of Okhotsk and the White Sea.

Link with Baltic Sea fauna. Finally, the last group characteristic of the White Sea, which indicates the existence in the Yoldian stage of a link between the White and Baltic Seas. A series of forms both plant and animal are common to both Seas and are absent from the Barents Sea and even from the waters of the Norwegian coast. Among them are forms of both thermophilic and cold-living character. As indicated in the chapter devoted to the Baltic Sea, some geologists and zoogeographers deny the existence of a bygone link between these Seas in the post-glacial period; but the majority recognize it. The most interesting of the forms that inhabit both Seas is the marine grass *Zostera marina*, which in the Barents Sea is encountered in the most western part of the Murman Peninsula (beginning at Vayda Guba and farther to the west. The peridinean *Pyrophacus horologicum* and the diatom *Chaetoceros danicum*, which are common in the Baltic Sea, are likewise not encountered in the Barents Sea. In 1944 Z. Palenichko (1947) discovered in the Gulf of Onega a boreal polychaete which was new for the White Sea, *Nereis virens*. This is one of the most numerous representatives of the polychaete worms.

In its chief habitats *N. virens* attains 1 m in length. White Sea specimens are 20 to 30 cm long. According to fishermen, in spring the heteronereis stages of this polychaete, as big as snakes, sometimes appear in numbers on the surface of the water. On the Murman Peninsula individual specimens of *N. virens* have been found only in its most western part. They have not been caught farther east. It is possible that *N. virens* in the White Sea is a thermophilic relict; but it is more probable that it has penetrated here recently in consequence of the general rise in temperature of the Arctic. In late years *N. virens* has appeared also on the coast of Iceland, and it apparently ought to have been discovered throughout the Murman coast.

Other forms inhabit the White, Barents and Baltic Seas, but are wholly or partly absent from the coast of Norway and the North Sea. Examples are the Arctic littoral Priapuloidea *Halicryptus spinulosus*, the polychaete *Rhodine gracilior* and others.

The peculiar distribution of these forms might have been explained even without a direct link between both Seas in the past. When the climate was colder than it is today, many Arctic forms moved far to the south, and may have penetrated into the Baltic Sea through the North Sea. In a later phase, warmer than at present (the Littorina stage), the Arctic forms were shifted far to the north, and more thermophilic forms moved up after them and penetrated into Cheshskaya Inlet and through the Gorlo into the White Sea. The Baltic Sea, in consequence of the rigorous climatic conditions in its northern and deeper part, preserved Arctic relicts; the White Sea, because of the peculiarity of its thermal conditions, preserved both cold-water and warm-water relicts. But the existence of a direct link between the White and Baltic Seas is not based solely upon zoogeographical data, but also on geological investigations in regions lying between the two Seas. If the direct link has been established then the merging of the fauna of both may have occurred on a large scale. Thus we find in the White Sea fauna the following elements:

(*1*) Forms which also inhabit adjacent parts of the Barents Sea
(*2*) Warm-water relicts
(*3*) Cold-water relicts
(*4*) Forms common to the Baltic Sea
(*5*) Forms common to Far Eastern seas
(*6*) Endemic forms.

Thus the White Sea, like the Baltic Sea, and to some extent like the Barents Sea also, is not homogeneous from a zoogeographical point of view. The littoral fauna, as in the Barents Sea, bears a pronounced boreal character, the sublittoral has an Arctic character, and the pseudo-abyssal a pronounced high Arctic aspect.

History of the fauna. As the result of a detailed analysis of the fauna of the White Sea K. Derjugin (1928) came to the conclusion that 'the whole of it was formed during the period after the last glaciation and the freezing of the White Sea basin in the post-glacial epoch; that is, its age amounts to about 13,500 years'.

In the glacial period, as Derjugin suggests, the fauna of the White Sea must have been destroyed, since the basin of the sea was blocked with glacier ice. From the latest post-glacial phase to the present time a large number of high Arctic forms have been preserved in the White Sea, the most typical of them being the mollusc *Portlandia arctica*. Many of these forms possess a definitely relict character; they are not encountered in the adjacent parts of the Barents Sea, and are common in the Kara Sea and farther east. Such, for instance, besides *P. arctica*, are the polychaetes *Harmothoe badia*, *Melaenis loveni*, the holothurian *Cucumaria calcigera*, the crustaceans *Paroediceros intermedius* and *Acanthostepheia malmgreni*, the molluscs *Cylichna densistriata* and *Bela novaja-zemljensis*, the ascidians *Eugyra pedunculata* and *Rhizomilguta globularis*, the fishes *Lycodes agnostus* and *Liparis major* and others. At the same time, possibly there was also a link with the Baltic Sea.

In the warm Littorina stage the Arctic elements were shifted far to the eastward and remained in the shape of relicts in the coldest corners of the White Sea. A mass of thermophilic forms settled in the White Sea. Most probably in the period of this same post-glacial rise of temperature there also penetrated into the White Sea some Pacific Ocean forms such as the herring, the lamprey and others.

The colder temperature of modern times destroyed some of these forms, and some it transformed in the White Sea into thermophilic relicts. Examples of these forms we have already adduced. The period which has passed since the Ice Age has been shown to be sufficient for the creation of a whole series of endemic forms chiefly variants and sub-species and, only to a small extent, of new species.

Negative features in the fauna of the White Sea. Derjugin likewise subjected to analysis another interesting phenomenon in the fauna of the White Sea, which he called the negative features of the White Sea fauna. A whole series of forms which are most common in the Barents Sea are absent from the White Sea, as has been pointed out above in the description of the plankton. Of these common forms of benthos alone there may be reckoned no fewer than 125, which includes 45 molluscs, more than 25 crustaceans, 8 echinoderms, 7 polychaetes, 6 coelenterates, 5 poriferae and only 3 species of fish.

Derjugin explains this phenomenon by the entirely unfavourable hydrological conditions of the Voronka and the Gorlo. The turbulent mixing of the whole mass of water which takes place at flood-tide and ebb-tide, the considerable warming of the water in summer and its severe chilling in winter, the absence of soft sea-bed—all this makes extremely hard the transfer of tender pelagic forms and stages of development through the 200 to 300 km of the Voronka and Gorlo. In addition, the whole base mass of water in the Voronka and Gorlo is shifted by the tide alternately in one direction and then in the other, and the forward motion of permanent currents here is relatively feeble. Derjugin calls the conditions of the Gorlo 'a biological plug'. One cannot help agreeing with the correctness of this explanation for certain forms; but for the majority it is more probable to conjecture the destructive influence of a considerable fall in salinity—to 7 to 8‰—within a comparatively short distance.

If we set side by side the poverty of the Barents Sea fauna, against its transit into the White Sea, and the analogous impoverishment in the Baltic Sea, the coincidence, quantitatively, is most graphic; and in the flood-tides which lead into the Baltic Sea, the hydrological factor is absent by which Derjugin explains the poverty of the fauna of the White Sea.

With the passage from the North Sea at flood-tide, and with a fall in salinity from 35 to 27 or even 23‰, there occurs a sharp decrease in fauna from 1,500 species to nearly 1,000. Thus 'negative features' in the fauna of the central part of the Skagerrak are defined as approximately 500 animal species. A fall of salinity even to 32‰ causes a loss of 350 forms. It is likewise possible that the qualitative impoverishment of the fauna, with the transit from the open coasts of the ocean into a system of inlets and sounds jutting deeply into the land has, besides the loss of salinity and the powerful circulatory currents, yet other causes which have not yet been taken into account. It is known, for instance, that there is a general qualitative impoverishment of flora and fauna in seas that are smaller in dimensions.

In any case, it is impossible to explain this complicated phenomenon simply by the unfavourable hydrological conditions in the Gorlo. This is one of many causes, and very likely the least important.

Vertical displacement of zones. Likewise far from being fully understood by us are the phenomena of the vertical displacement ('the displacement of zones' in the earlier terminology) of groups and of individual forms, which are so pronounced in the fauna of the White Sea. On the one hand it is as if a general tendency to rise to lesser depths occurs, which may be conditioned in the first place by the low temperature of the depths and the lower transparency of the water; and on the other hand a series of littoral forms moves into the sublittoral and some forms from upper layers of the sublittoral into lower layers. The only explanation so far for these displacements is seen in the unfavourable influence of the piling up of ice on the shore in the course of a long harsh winter. For a series of forms, a part is probably also played by the considerable warming up of the surface waters at the shores in summer, which drives the cold-loving forms down into the depths.

Very significant data were produced by M. Gostilovskaya (1957) in a comparative study of the vertical distribution of bryozoans in the Barents and White Seas (*Table 86*).

Population of the supralittoral. Everywhere in the supralittoral of the White Sea, especially where there are accumulations of sea-weed cast up by the breakers, an abundant supralittoral fauna is found.

On the supralittoral, partly moving into the littoral, and even mingling with certain typically marine forms (*Balanus balanoides*, *Littorina rudis* and others), usually on the more sloping shores that are not subject to considerable surf, there settle in large numbers the flowering plants, *Plantago maritima*, *Triglochin maritimus*, *Aster trifolium* and *Salicornia herbacea*, which descend lowest of all on the littoral and mingle there with the fucoids.

Table 86

Species	Depth, m	
	White Sea	Barents Sea
Crisia producta	0–20	9–288
Tegella nigrans	15–40	14–230
Cribralina spitzbergense	9–50	30–320
Escharella dymphnae	7–45	12–170
Smittina majuscula	2–78	27–315
Porella fragilis	35–60	23–235
Umbonula arctica	2–91	5–297
Escharopsis rosacea	4–80	12–324

One of the areas of the sublittoral where there are accumulations of sea-wrack, along the northern shore of the Kandalaksha Bay, has been the subject of minute analysis by G. Gurvich and T. Matveeva (1939). 'The facies of this biotope', they write, 'is sufficiently varied even at first glance. Numbers of spiders run over the surface of the wrack, deeper down there crawl different Apterygota and mites, more rarely quick-moving beetles (Carabidae) and also myriapods can be seen. Still deeper Oligochaeta creep about in huge numbers, sometimes huddling together in whole bunches. At the very bottom of the layer of wrack amphipods are met with and in particles of cortex saturated with moisture, and in humus, live little characteristic Harpacticoida.' An account of the number of animals in the heaps of sea-wrack, which are often several metres wide and as much as half a metre thick, is given in *Table 87* and Fig. 88.

As may be judged from the data of the table, Oligochaeta constitute 96·05 per cent of the whole population of the heaps of sea-weed. Arachnoidea predominate in the top layer, Apterygota in the middle, and Oligochaeta in

Table 87

Groups	Quantity of organisms	
	No. of specimens per m²	Biomass, g/m²
Oligochaeta	480,400	237·60
Nematoda	5,200	—
Acarina	29,900	2·30
Araneina	1,300	0·72
Apterygota	72,900	1·46
Coleoptera larvae	3,700	4·78
Coleoptera imagines	1,400	5·52
Total	594,800	352·38

the lowest. The biomass also increases with depth. Among all this fauna there are only two species of crustaceans living in the lowest layer of the wrack, which are properly marine forms—the Amphipoda *Gammarus obtusatus* and the Copepoda *Itunella mülleri*. Newly formed heaps of sea-weed are soon

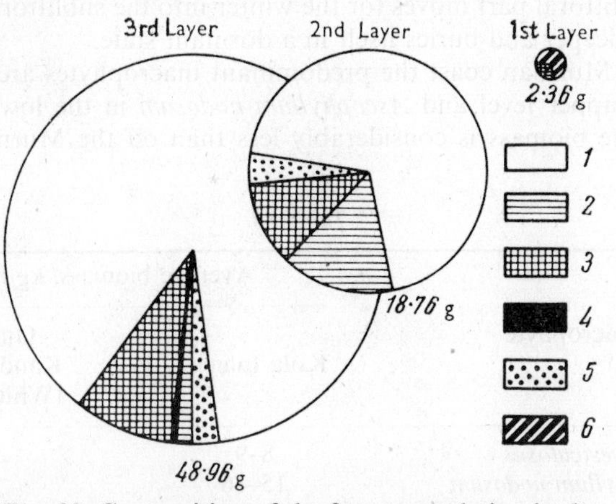

FIG. 88. Composition of the fauna population in the debris of the White Sea sublittoral (Gurvich and Matveeva). The biomass in g/m² is given below the circles. *1* Oligochaeta; *2* Apterygota; *3* Coleoptera larvae; *4* Coleoptera imagines; *5* Acarina; *6* Arachnoidea.

populated by specific fauna from the bottom floor. By autumn the fauna in the weed-heaps suffers a sharp impoverishment.

Among the Oligochaeta the highest significance pertains to the Enchytraeidae family (*Lumbricillus lineatus*, *Enchitraeus albidus* and others). Among the Tubificidae, *Clitellio arenaria* and *Tubifex costatus* have the greatest development. These are joined also by some species of the Naididae family (*Amphicteis leydigi*, *Paranais litoralis* and others).

Population of the littoral. The amplitude of the tidal range in the main basin of the White Sea usually reaches 1·5 to 2 m, and, as distinct from the Murman coast, sand-mud beaches extend here along nearly the whole shoreline, being only rarely interrupted by outcrops of cliff. Thus, although the foreshore in the White Sea is not particularly broad (usually some tens and rarely some hundreds of metres) yet on the whole its relative significance is much greater than on the Murman Peninsula, since in the larger part of the Sea it girdles the whole shore line. In the White Sea we find on the littoral all the same environment and biological phyla as on the Murman Peninsula, only somewhat less pronounced, with a slightly smaller qualitative variety and lower quantitative indices of flora and fauna. The whole basic selection of forms of the western Murman littoral is included here almost in its entirety. Of the predominant forms only *Nucella lapillus* and *Cardium edule* are absent.

If in summer the temperature of the air and water is higher in the White Sea than on the Murman coast, yet in winter the fauna of the littoral finds itself in much less favourable conditions. For many months the top layer of the littoral of the White Sea freezes, and is covered with a thick crust of ice. The fauna of the littoral part moves for the winter into the sublittoral, and part of it digs itself deeper and buries itself in a dormant state.

As on the Murman coast the predominant macrophytes are *Fucus vesiculosus* in the upper level and *Ascophyllum nodosum* in the lower. But in the White Sea the biomass is considerably less than off the Murman Peninsula (*Table 88*).

Table 88

Macrophyte	Average biomass, kg/m²	
	Kola Inlet	Gulf of Kandalaksha (White Sea)
Fucus vesiculosus	8–9	2–4
Ascophyllum nodosum	15–16	8–9

The White Sea sea-weeds are also smaller in size than those of the Murman Peninsula. In the Kola Inlet the length of individual strands of *Ascophyllum nodosum* reaches 1 m, but in the Gulf of Kandalaksha only 0·5 m.

Of the other macrophytes on the littoral one may point out *Pelvetia canaliculata*, *Fucus inflatus* and *F. serratus*. Great peculiarity is given to the White Sea littoral by patches of dwarf *Zostera nana* which settle on the lowest and moistest parts of the littoral, which are usually left covered with water even at low tide.

The zonation of the main fucoids of the foreshore—*F. vesiculosus*, *Asc. nodosum* and *F. inflatus*—is not so distinct in the White Sea as off the Murman Peninsula: all three species are mingled to a considerable degree.

E. F. Gurjanova and P. Ushakov (1929) give the following scheme for the vertical distribution of organisms in the littoral zone of the Terskiy coast:

Horizon I: Dead, owing to the grinding effect of ice.

Horizon II: Sandy beach	Scattered boulders
Zone I—Sand with biocoenosis: *Arenicola marina–Mya arenaria*, *Littorina rudis*.	*Littorina rudis*, *Balanus balanoides*.
Zone II—Silty sand with biocoenosis: *Zostera marina*, *Eteone arctica*, *Aricia quadricuspida*, *Pygospio elegans*, *Lineus gesserensis*, *Amphiporus lactifloreus*, *Macoma baltica*, *Littorina littorea*, *L. rudis*.	Fucoids with their biocoenosis: *Gonothirea loveni*, *Membranipora pilosa*, *Jaera marina*, *Gammarus* spp., *Littorina palliata*, *L. rudis*, *Hydrobia ulvae*, *Mytilus edulis*, *Pholis gunellus*, *Enchelíopus viviparus*.
On bare patches: *Arenicola marina*, *Fabricia sabella*, *Mya arenaria*.	Usually under stones: *Lineus gesserensis*, *Cephalothrix linearis*, *Halicryptus spinulosus*. Between stones: *Macoma baltica*, *Pygospio elegans*, Oligochaeta. Larvae Chironomidae.

Abrikosov Sokolova (1948) gives a subdivision of the littoral of the Gulf of Kandalaksha somewhat different from the above:

Upper horizon
On rocks—*Littinora rudis, Mytilus edulis*
Between rocks, frequently, the flowering plant *Aster trifolium*
Under rocks—pupae Insecta, Oligochaeta, Nematoda

Middle horizon
Balanus balanoides, Littorina rudis, Hydrobia, Rissoa, *Mytilus edulis*

Lower horizon
Littorina littorea, L. palliata, Buccinum groenlandicum, Natica clausa, Margarita helicina, Asterias rubens

Actinia equina is common on the undersides of rocks. Under the rocks *Gammarus* spp. is found in masses. In the White Sea many of the most typical littoral forms descend in considerable numbers into the sublittoral, as, for instance, *Mytilus edulis, Balanus balanoides, Gammarus obtusatus,* the *Littorina* species and others. On the other hand, as was established for the littoral of the Solovetsky Islands (A. Fedorov, 1928), many sublittoral forms (*Asterias rubens*, for instance) rise to the lower level of the littoral. But even on the very littoral of the White Sea the forms that inhabit it avoid, as it were, getting into the upper levels, and strain downwards, nearer the water. Sokolova has produced *Table 89* showing the quantitative ratio of the different forms inhabiting

Table 89

Form	Karlov Islands (eastern Murman coast) as a percentage of total biomass	Rugozerskaya Guba (Gulf of Kandalaksha) as a percentage of total biomass
Epifauna of scattered boulders		
Balanus balanoides	58·7	19·4
Mytilus edulis	28·5	33·2
Littorina rudis, L. palliata	12·4	24·2
Oligochaeta	0·06	16·6
Remainder	0·34	6·6
Total biomass	692·7	313·5
Flora of scattered boulders		
Fucus vesiculosus	40·4	34·5
F. inflatus	40·3	—
F. serratus	—	0·91
Ascophyllum nodosum	13·9	59·5
Rhodymenia palmata	4·5	2·2
Ahnfeltia	—	0·91
Remainder	0·9	1·98
Total biomass	5,754	3,103

the rocky littoral of the Kharlov Islands (eastern Murman coast) and of the southern shores of the Gulf of Kandalaksha.

On the sandy and silty-sand areas of the White Sea littoral among the infauna forms, the predominant ones are *Macoma baltica*, *Arenicola marina* and *Mya arenaria*. Quite characteristic, but of small significance in the biomass, are *Halicryptus spinulosus* and *Priapulus caudatus*. Of epifauna forms *Mytilus edulis*, *Littorina rudis*, *Hydrobia ulvae*, *Rissoa aculeus* are noted in considerable quantity.

As may be judged from *Table 90* (according to Z. Zavistovich and K. Voskresenski—unpublished material), the quantitative ratios between individual forms among the constituents of the littoral fauna are subject to considerable variations.

A comparison of the quantitative indices of the Murman and White Sea littoral fauna shows that the former is more plentiful in quantity, but that in quality the difference is insignificant.

The less favourable conditions for the development of littoral fauna in the White Sea, as compared with the Murman coast, are reflected not only in a decrease in the total biomass of plant and animal forms, but also in a decrease in the size of the body in a series of typical forms. Mytilus, Littorina, Balanus and Macoma have, in the White Sea, considerably smaller average dimensions. Thus *Macoma baltica*, for instance, has at one of the low tides in the Kola Inlet an average weight of 240 mg, but in the Gulf of Kandalaksha only 112 mg; the Kola Inlet *Littorina rudis* weighs 109 mg, but the White Sea one weighs 70 mg. Sea mussel similarly gives an average weight of 1,711 and 719 mg, and so on. Moreover a smaller size is characteristic of many representatives of the White Sea fauna. The White Sea cod and herring are considerably smaller than those of the Barents Sea. *Portlandia arctica* of the deeper parts of the White Sea is considerably smaller than the same form taken in the Novya Zemlya trough of the Barents Sea.

Thorough study of the microbenthos of the White Sea littoral has been carried out (1951) by V. Brotzkaya at the White Sea biological station of Moscow University. On the sandy littoral there have been discovered no fewer than 80 species of small invertebrates, mainly: Harpacticoida (24 species), Turbellaria (more than 20 species), Ciliata, Rotatoria, Nematoda, and several other groups. Some forms give very high density of population. In one cubic centimetre of bottom soil Nematoda yield up to 1,000 specimens, Harpacticoida up to 200, and Ciliata more than 1,000. Brotzkaya shares A. Remane's opinion (1933) that the microbenthos of the sandy sea-bed is the basic source of nourishment for the remainder of the bottom-feeding fauna.

At the White Sea biological station there has likewise been produced most useful work on the calculation of the relative sizes of body and the weight of different invertebrates of the littoral (N. Pertsov, 1952). This material gives easy means for the calculation of size from weight, which is essential in research into the feeding of fish, from the contents of their intestines.

Population of the sublittoral. As Derjugin indicates, the sublittoral zone, which in the Kola Inlet extends to 200 to 250 m, extends in the White Sea

Table 90. Quantitative composition of the fauna of the silty-sand littoral along the southern shore of the Gulf of Kandalaksha

Form	Rugozerskaya Inlet				Koneva Inlet silty-sand		Koneva Inlet silty drain-off from Zostera	
	Velikaya Salma No. of specimens	Velikaya Salma Biomass g/m²	Velikaya Salma No. of specimens	Velikaya Salma Biomass g/m²	No. of specimens	Biomass g/m²	No. of specimens	Biomass g/m²
Arenicola marina	8	28·400	29	34·420	176	54·930	—	—
Mya arenaria	1·4	26·375	0·6	9·160	18·5	49·845	—	—
Mytilus edulis	119	85·540	46	58·020	33	12·355	180	108·350
Macoma baltica	591	68·040	650	93·300	775	110·480	560	36·400
Littorina rudis	122	8·500	53	1·480	—	—	60	2·400
Littorina littorea	—	—	25	1·970	—	—	—	—
Littorina palliata	—	—	85	8·980	—	—	—	—
Hydrobia ulvae	496	—	1,866	6·660	—	—	—	—
Rissoa aculeus	340	4·550	—	—	—	—	—	—
Priapulus caudatus	0·5	0·330	—	—	—	—	200	26·000
Halicryptus spinulosus	0·4	0·220	0·3	0·230	—	—	—	—
Scoloplos armiger	8	0·243	—	—	50	2·250	—	—
Oligochaeta	570	0·770	6,933	9·33	—	—	—	—
Remainder (Jaera, Pygospio, Fabricia, Nereis)	—	0·080	131	3·704	25	0·250	40	0·200
Total	2,256·3	223·048	9,818·9	227·290	1,077·5	230·110	1,040	173·350
Minus sea mussel	2,137·3	137·508	9,772	169·270	1,044	217,755	860	55·000

only to 40 to 50 m. Accordingly the upper layer of this zone (the former 'litoral' of Derjugin) is also raised from 60 to 70 m to 12 to 16 m. *Mytilus edulis* and *Fucus serratus* descend from the littoral into the upper layers of the sublittoral; in the White Sea the holothurian *Chiridota laevis* descends from the upper layer of the sublittoral to great depths; and there rise upwards from below the red sea-weeds, poriferae, the hydroids and bryozoans, so characteristic on the Murman coast of the lower horizons of the sublittoral.

The vertical distribution of the bottom fauna of the White Sea makes it

*Table 91. Comparison of littoral fauna of western Murman Peninsula and White Sea**

Form	One of the big foreshore zones in the Kola Inlet			Gulf of Kandalaksha		
	No. of specimens per m²	Biomass g/m²	As a percentage minus sea mussel	No. of specimens per m²	Biomass g/m²	As a percentage minus sea mussel
Mytilus edulis	823	1,409·00	—	126	90·57	—
Macoma baltica	750	167·86	81·4	610	68·04	50·5
Arenicola marina	11	16·10	7·8	9	29·71	22·0
Cardium edule	1	8·92	4·3	—	—	—
Mya arenaria	—	—	—	1·5	21·65	16·1
Littorina rudis	44	4·80	2·3	122	8·50	6·3
Gammarus spp.	39	1·50	4·2 (Gammarus–Varia)	—	—	5·1 (Gammarus–Varia)
Priapulus caudatus	7	1·20		0·5	0·34	
Halicryptus spinulosus	24	1·20		0·5	0·23	
Hydrobia, Rissoa	—	—		791	5·19	
Varia	56	4·60		365	0·97	
Total	1,755	1,615·18		2,025·5	225·20	
Minus sea mussel	932	206·18	100·0	1,899·5	134·63	100·0

* The absence from the table of *Hydrobia ulvae* and *Rissoa aculeus* from the Kola Inlet and of the gammarids from the White Sea is explained by a deficiency in the collection of material.

possible to distinguish here the same zones and horizons as in the Barents Sea.

Derjugin takes as the lowest limit of the sublittoral a depth of 150 m, although usually vegetation disappears by a depth of 40 to 56 m. The littoral flora and fauna of the White Sea moves, without any sudden leap (as happens on the Murman coast), into the sublittoral; and most characteristic of the upper horizon of the sublittoral are *Fucus inflatus*, and *F. serratus* on rocky bottoms, and *Chorda filum* and *Zostera marina* on soft ones. Lower still there extends a great belt of *Laminaria saccharina*, *L. digitata*, Alaria, Ahnfeltia and others.

The upper division of the sublittoral, extending to 40 to 45 m, begins on soft bottoms with Zostera growths which here attain luxuriant bloom (individual stems are as much as 3 m long), or *Chorda filum*, which attracted to itself partly littoral fauna (*Mytilus edulis*, *Littorina rudis*, *L. palliata*, *Rissoa aculeus*, *Hydrobia ulvae*, *Skenea planorbis*, *Macoma baltica*, *Priapulus caudatus*, *Halicryptus spinulosus*, *Arenicola marina*, *Lineus gesserensis* and others) and partly sublittoral (*Ophelia limacina*, *Asterias rubens*, *Polydora quadrilobata*, *Chiridota laevis* and others). Zostera extends as far as 5 to 6 m in depth. The belt of Laminaria may, on scattered boulders, reach the lower edge of the littoral, and at spring tides is partly exposed. Besides the Laminaria, which compose the main mass of vegetation, there are here always many other different brown and red algae, partly epiphytes. Corallina and cork Lithothamnion may likewise attain a high stage of development here. At a depth

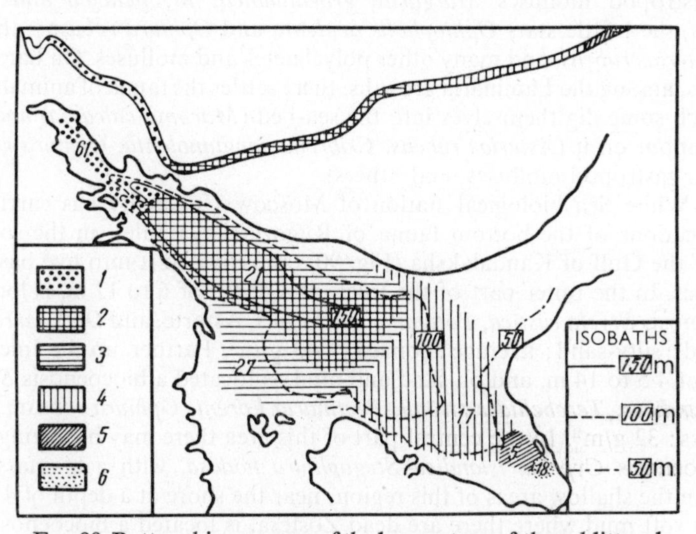

FIG. 89. Bottom biocoenoses of the lower stage of the sublittoral and pseudolittoral of the White Sea (Zenkevitch, 1927). Boxed numerals refer to the isobaths; the other numerals denote biomass (g/m^2) (61, 21, 17, 5 and 18). Different shading indicates the various bottom biocoenoses: 1 *Leda pernula*, *Yoldia hyperborea*, *Astarte montagui*; 2 *Portlandia arctica*, *Leda pernula*, *Asterias lincki*; 3 *Astarte montagui*, *Leda pernula*, *Ophiocantha bidentata*; 4 *Astarte borealis*, *Yoldia hyperborea*, *Leda pernula*; 5 *Portlandia arctica*, *Yoldia hyperborea*, *Pectinaria hyperborea*; 6 *Mesidothea entomon*, *Macoma baltica*.

of approximately 10 m the belt of Laminaria comes to an end (on the Murman coast it goes down to 15 m and more, the biomass of sea-weeds falls sharply, and the red algae become predominant: Prilota, Phyllophora, Odonthalia and others).

As on the Murman coast, so here also thallus and rhizome Laminaria give shelter to a luxuriant and quite analogous fauna. On the thallus Laminaria there settle in quantities the gasteropod molluscs *Margarita helicina* and *Lacuna divaricata*; *Lucernaria quadricornis*, and *Haliclystus octoradiatus* which give special peculiarity to the sublittoral of the White Sea; the bryozoans

Lichenopora verrucaria, *Crisia eburnea*, the polychaete *Spirorbis borealis* and the crustacean *Caprella septentionalis*. Certain littoral forms come down from above, such as *Mytilus edulis*, *Littorina rudis*, *Rissoa aculeus* and others. To the dominant forms mentioned there are added numerous hydroids, bryozoans, molluscs, nemertineans, the characteristic sucking-fish *Cyclopterus lumpus* and others. Rhizoid Laminaria, which attach themselves to rocks, forming a tent-like structure, give shelter to a rich fauna, and chiefly to the polychaetes *Nereis pelagica*, *Phyllodoce maculata*, *Castalia punctata*, *Harmothoë imbricata*, *Pholoë minuta*, and amphipods *Amphitaë rubricata* and *Jscheroceros anguipes*, the gastropod molluscs *Margarita groenlandica*, *M. helicina* and *Rissoa aculeus*, the brittle stars *Ophiopholis aculeata* and *Ophiura robusta*; the star-fish *Asterias rubens*, and many other polychaetes and molluscs. On bare sandy patches, among the Laminaria growths, there settles the fauna of animal forms, of which some dig themselves into the sea-bed (*Macoma calcarea*) and some crawl about on it (*Asterias rubens*, *Cribrella sanguinolenta*, *Ophiura robusta*, various gastropod molluscs, and others).

The White Sea biological station of Moscow University has carried out investigations of the bottom fauna of Rugozerskaya Inlet, in the southern part of the Gulf of Kandalaksha (Fig. 90), and divided it into five basic bio-coenoses. In the outer part of the Inlet, at a depth of 6 to 12 m, is located a biocoenosis *Styela rustica*, *Potamilla reniformis*, Astarte, and *Ophiura robusta*. Sea-bed: silty-sand; average biomass: 243 g/m^2. Farther up the Inlet, at a depth of 4·5 to 14 m, and on sand and mud, is located a biocoenosis *Serripes groenlandicus*, *Terebellides strömi*, *Pectinaria koreni*, *Ophiura robusta*; mean biomass: 32 g/m^2. In the central part of this area there may be distinguished a biocoenosis *Cyprina islandica–Stegophiura nodosa*, with a biomass of 96 g/m^2. In the shallow areas of this region, near the shore at a depth of 4 to 5 m and on soft mud where there are dead Zostera, is located a biocoenosis with a considerable intermingling of relict brackish-water forms: *Pontoporeia femorata*, *Nephthys paradoxa*, *Mysis oculata*, and Cumacea. The mean bio-mass of this is 25 g/m^2. In that part of the Inlet, where there is soft mud with dead Zostera at a depth of 3·5 to 6 m, is located a biocoenosis *Macoma baltica–Nephthys paradoxa–Scoloplos armiger*, with a biomass of 30 g/m^2. In the inner part of the Inlet salinity falls at ebb-tide to 3 to 4 per cent, and at flood-tide it rises to 21 to 22 per cent in the surface layer and to 22·5 per cent in the bottom layer.

G. Gurvich and I. Ivanov (1939) give a description of several benthic com-munities in the upper level of the sublittoral on soft bottoms in the area of Umba (Gulf of Kandalaksha). At a depth of 4 to 6 m they distinguish a com-munity with the following predominant forms: polychaetes, *Terebellides strömi* and *Scoloplos armiger*; echinoderms, *Ophiura robusta* and *Asterias rubens*; the bivalve *Astarte montagui*; and the small Cumacea *Brachydia-stylis resime*; the biomass of this community is 89 g/m^2.

Below the Laminaria zone (10 to 45 m) extends the level of the red algae: Phyllophora, Rhodophyllis, Delesseria, Polysiphonia and others.

As Derjugin points out (1928): 'This level is rich in life, and in it one may evidently distinguish certain groups which have not yet been studied in detail.

Here there are many different representatives of the poriferae, bryozoans, polychaetes, crustaceans, echinoderms, ascidians and molluscs, some living on the sea-weeds themselves, some on the rocks, some on the sea-bed which here is usually mud.'

In the inner parts of the Inlet the red algae Phyllophora flourishes luxuriantly, at a depth of 6 to 22 m on the muddy sea-bed, and is accompanied by its community of animal forms with average biomass of 29 g/m². The predominant form is *Ophiura robusta*. Of the polychaetes *Scoloplos armiger*, *Nephthys minuta* and *Myriochele oculata* predominate; sometimes ascidians

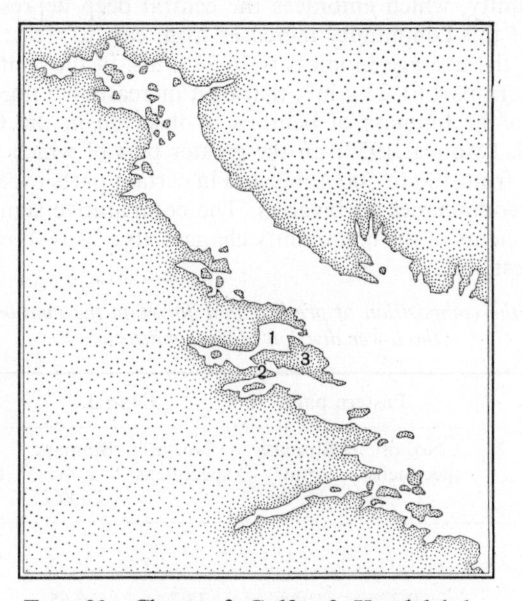

FIG. 90. Chart of Gulf of Kandalaksha including Rugozerskaya Inlet. *1* Bab'e More; *2* Site of White Sea Biological Station of Moscow University; *3* Velikiye Is.

are found in great numbers; most characteristic among the molluscs are *Astarte elliptica*, *Cardium ciliatum* and *Axinus flexuosus*. Rather deeper (20 to 30 m) colonies of *Portlandia arctica* are encountered in combination with *Leda pernula*, *Myriochele oculata*, *Yoldia hyperborea*, *Pectinaria hyperborea* and Maldanidae. This community, which has a biomass of 25 g/m², is in composition very like the communities on mud bottoms of the lower level of the sublittoral, but it is characteristic of it that Portlandia exists here for a considerable period of the year at a temperature above zero, and is separated from the population which inhabits the deep part of the White Sea.

The lower division of the sublittoral (45 to 150 m) is characterized by the great predominance of spacious areas of mud bottom, with only an occasional rock, which are inhabited by red algae of various forms (Ptilota, Odonthalia, Delesseria, Ahnfeltia, Polysiphonia and others). On these last there develops a luxuriant population of poriferae, hydroids and bryozoans (about 160 species, according to Derjugin). On the chief areas of soft mud bottom a clear predominance pertains to infauna consisting of comparatively few forms of bivalves (*Astarte borealis, A. elliptica, Yoldia hyperborea, Leda pernula, Macoma calcarea, Dacrydium vitreum, Cardium ciliatum*), polychaetes (*Pectinaria hyperborea, Maldane sarsi*) and echinoderms (*Asterias lincki, Ophiocantha bidentata*).

The census of the bottom fauna, carried out with the help of the Petersen bottom-dredge, makes it possible to note the exact limits of this soft-mud-bottom community, which embraces the central deep depression (Fig. 89). The biomass of this community increases from east to west; in the eastern part of the sea the average biomass is 16·78 g/m², in the central part 26·86, and in the western part 61·23 g/m²; that is, it increases 3·5 times. A considerable increase in the biomass of benthos is observed in the Gulf of Onega (according to S. Ivanova, 1957), in the greater part of which the biomass of benthos ranges from 100 to 500 g/m², and in certain parts exceeds this range, with a clear predominance of bivalves. The comparative significance of the separate components of the community changes also, as is shown in *Table 92*, from east to west.

Table 92. Change in the composition of predominant forms in the mud-bottom community of the lower division of the sublittoral

Mean total biomass	Eastern part		Central		West part	
	No. of specimens	Biomass g/m² 16,766	No. of specimens	Biomass g/m² 26,862	No. of specimens	Biomass g/m² 61,230
Dominant forms:						
Astarte elliptica, A. montagui	9·3	4·68	33·7	6·65	34	16·01
Dacrydium vitreum	2	0·02	61·5	0·67	22	0·22
Yoldia hyperborea	2·2	0·26	—	—	8	5·87
Leda pernula	13·9	2·16	18	1·39	72	7·75
Macoma calcarea	1	0·03	—	—	7	5·12
Asterias lincki	—	—	0·38	0·02	—	—
Ophiocantha bidentata	1·8	0·23	7·3	1·86	—	—
Pectinaria hyperborea	5	0·58	1·15	0·55	4	0·78
Maldane sarsi	52	0·85	0·3	0·01	3	0·15

The basic role in this community belongs to the bivalves (34 to 64 per cent of the biomass); the polychaetes are considerably less numerous (11 to 39 per cent) and the echinoderms rank third (up to 20 per cent).

The population of the pseudo-abyssal. The pseudo-abyssal zone, which occupies the bathymetric part of the Sea (150 m), is characterized by its small amount of light, absence of vegetation and feeble fluctuations of temperature (about −1·4°) and salinity (about 30 per cent) and finally by its brown soils formed of soft silty clay. The average biomass of this community is 20·6 g/m², and its dominant forms are the two molluscs *Portlandia arctica* and *Leda pernula* and the two echinoderms *Asterias lincki* and *Ophiocantha bidentata*.

Derjugin considers the crawling transparent jellyfish *Lucernosa saint-hilairei*, the pink transparent actinian (not yet identified), the molluscs *Modiolaria nigra* var. *bullata*, *Chaetoderma nitidulum* var. *intermedia*, the polychaetes *Myriochele heeri* and *Maldane sarsi*, the crustacean *Acanthostepheia malmgreni* and *Rozinante fragilis*, the asterid *Poraniomorpha tumida*, the transparent ascidian *Eugyra pedunculata*, the small fish *Liparis major*, as equally characteristic for this peculiar community.

The qualitative indices for this pseudo-abyssal community are given in *Table 93*.

Table 93. Constituents of the pseudo-abyssal community according to the data obtained by use of bottom-sampler

Form	No. of specimens per m²	Biomass g/m²	Biomass Total biomass per cent
Astarte elliptica, A. montagui	1·1	1·314	
Dacrydium vitreum	3·4	0·039	
Yoldia hyperborea	0·6	0·440	
Leda pernula	21·0	5·130	
Portlandia arctica	46·0	4·373	
Others		0·530	
Total Lamellibranchiata	—	11·823	57·75
Pectinaria hyperborea	0·3	0·070	
Maldane sarsi	5·0	0·085	
Others		1·220	
Total Polychaeta		1·375	6·35
Asterias lincki	1·1	4·350	
Ophiocantha bidentata	2·0	0·531	
Total Echinodermata		4·881	18·68
Crustacea		0·242	1·18
Coelenterata		0·995	4·83
Sipunculoidea		1·670	8·11
Others (Gastropoda and Nemertini)		0·637	3·10
Average total biomass		21·632	100·0

The population of the bays. The distribution and composition of the biocoenoses of the benthos of the Rugozerskaya Inlet (the southern side of the Gulf of Kandalaksha, see Fig. 90) are given in Fig. 89. The Inlet is adequately enclosed from the sea except for a narrow pass. The depth of its middle part reaches 25 m. G. Gurvich (1934) has given a description of the bottom communities of the Bab'e Sea, which is separated from the rest of the Sea by the western side of Velikiye Islands (Gulf of Kandalaksha). The fairly large (9×13 km) and comparatively shallow (down to 39 m) Bab'e Sea is connected with the White Sea by two narrow and very shallow passes (Fig. 90). Below 15 m the circulation is slack, the oxygen content is low (about 50 per cent), low temperature is permanent (below 20 m it is below zero), while its salinity is comparatively high (close to 27‰).

The whole of the shallow part of the Bab'e Sea down to 4 to 6 m is covered with Zostera fields. *Macoma baltica*, *Mya arenaria*, *Arenicola marina*, *Littorina littorea*, *L. rudis* and other typical inhabitants of the littoral come down here from it. *Asterias rubens* grows here in huge numbers. Sublittoral forms like

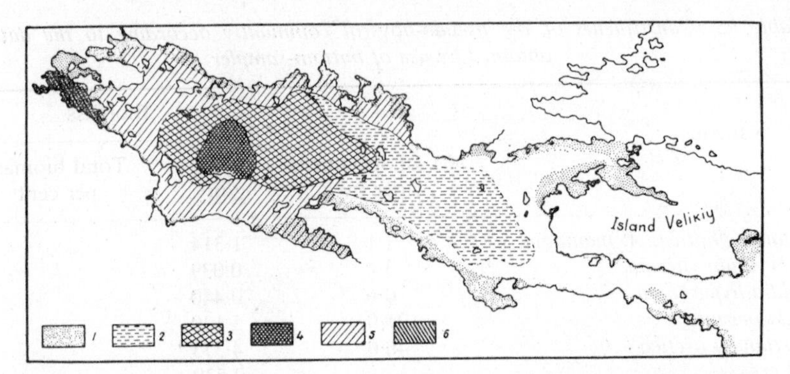

FIG. 91. Bottom biocoenoses of Rugozerskaya Inlet and their dominant forms (Brotzky and Zhdanova and Semenova): 1 *Leda pernula*, *Yoldia hyperborea*, *Astarte montagui*; 2 *Portlandia arctica*, *Leda pernula*, *Asterias lincki*; 3 *Astarte montagui*, *Leda pernula*, *Ophiocantha bidentata*; 4 *Astarte borealis*, *Yoldia hyperborea*, *Leda pernula*; 5 *Portlandia arctica*, *Yoldia hyperborea*, *Pectinaria hyperborea*; 6 *Mesidothea entomon*, *Macoma baltica*.

Macoma calcarea, *Ophiura robusta* etc. become predominant in the lower parts of this level.

From 7 m downwards Zostera is replaced by red algae, mainly Phyllophora, with a small admixture of Laminaria. Like the Zostera, Phyllophora encircles the whole of the Bab'e Sea, extending to a depth of 15 m. *Ophiura robusta* is a dominant animal form in this Sea, among the rest the following should be noted: the ascidian *Boltenia echinata*; the molluscs: *Astarte elliptica*, *Saxicava arctica*, *Macoma calcarea*; the echinoderms: *Ophiura nodosa*, *Ophiopholis aculeata*, *Asterias rubens*, *Cribrella sanguinolenta* etc.; the polychaetes: *Harmothoe imbricata* and *H. nodosa*; and the crustaceans.

This zone is the feeding ground of large numbers of cod.

Below 15 m the growth of red algae is cut off abruptly and the algae are replaced by a *Portlandia arctica* community; a definite impoverishment in forms takes place. The population consists of the following forms: the molluscs *Macoma calcarea*, *Astarte elliptica*, *Saxicava arctica Pandora glacialis*,

Cardium ciliatum, the echinoderms *Stegophiura nodosa* and *Ophiura robusta*, many polychaetes and a considerable number of amphipoda. The Arctic forms are predominant at this depth of the Bab'e Sea. *Mysis oculata typica* is abundant throughout. The deepest part of the Sea (below 25 m) is almost free of animal forms.

This impoverishment of fauna, common in such cases, and the rise of the boundaries of the vertical zones observed when passing from the Barents Sea to the White Sea is even more accentuated as one moves from the White Sea to the more or less isolated gubas, lagoons and pools. We have here a case of the changes repeating the zonalities characteristic for the whole of the White Sea as if in miniature.

Some original bottom communities of the Gulf of Dvinak may also be noted. Thus, for instance, large colonies of *Mesidothea entomon* and *Macoma baltica*, with a biomass of 18 g/m^2, consisting mostly (86 per cent) of Mesidothea, live at fairly high temperature in the fresh or almost fresh waters off the Northern Dvina estuary, on sandy bottoms at a depth of 5 to 10 m. A little farther down the Sea lives a community poor in numbers (about 5 g/m^2), but characterized by one of its constituents—*Portlandia arctica*. In some places the Sea is abundantly populated by Mytilus colonies. *Portlandia arctica*, a relict of the coldest phases of the post-glacial period, is characteristic of the coldest parts of the Arctic basin. It lives in large numbers in the central depression of the White Sea, in the Novaya Zemlya trench, in Sturfjord in eastern Spitsbergen, in the Kara Sea, etc. Special races of this mollusc, which can stand considerable water-dilution and, probably, periodically, a rise of temperature, inhabit the estuaries of the rivers flowing into the Arctic basin, such as the Dvina, Pechora, Ob, Yenisey and others.

It is remarkable that a deep-floor fauna like that of the White Sea, and in particular *Portlandia arctica*, has remained till this day in comparatively shallow, stagnant gubas along the White Sea shores, and in the never-warmed deep parts. One of these gubas—the Glubokaya Guba of the Great Solovestkiy Island—served as the object of N. Livanov's fundamental study (1912). Derjugin thinks that the bathymetric fauna must have remained in these gubas since the severe climate period, and that the cold-water fauna, which has now migrated to the depths, at that time populated the whole sea. 'Glubokaya Guba', says Derjugin, 'represents in miniature those properties which, on a larger scale, are found throughout the White Sea, as the relicts of a vast ancient basin.'

Productivity

The great poverty of White Sea bottom fauna is clearly shown by the quantitative data given above. This quantitative impoverishment increases gradually with depth, and in the lower sublittoral and the pseudo-abyssal zone the benthos biomass becomes 5–10–15 times smaller than that of the Barents Sea. The average benthos biomass of the White Sea is probably about 20 g/m^2, whereas in the Barents Sea it is 100 g/m^2. This quantitative impoverishment affects, as has been mentioned above, not only animal and vegetable organisms, not only the biomass as a bulk, but also the average weight and size of individual specimens of most of the characteristic forms. The population of individual forms of the White Sea, so far as we could observe, never reached a density characteristic of the other regions of the Arctic. This can be shown by a comparison of the quantitative data for a number of forms common to the Barents and White Seas (*Table 94*).

Table 94. The largest biomass determined for certain forms in the White and Barents Seas and in some other regions of the Arctic

Form	White Sea		Barents Sea		Other Arctic regions
	No. of specimens	Biomass g/m²	No. of specimens	Biomass g/m²	Biomass g/m²
Molluscs					
Astarte elliptica	55	39·1		173·0	307·0
Astarte montagui	105	20·1		80·0	
Axinus flexuosus	105	3·5		4·4	9·0
Cardium ciliatum	10	19·8		365·5	243·6
Serripes groenlandicus	3	6·2		308·0	
Macoma calcarea	20	23·6	186	243·0	941·0
Portlandia arctica	160	13·0		9·0	
Leda pernula	200	21·1	120	23·5	
Yoldia hyperborea	30	26·1	145	30·0	134·0
Nucula tenuis	210	15·2	190	18·0	
Saxicava arctica	35	1·2		600·0	291·5
Polychaetes					
Lumbriconereis fragilis	35	7·0		13·0	14·0
Maldane sarsi	400	5·2	7,710	95·0	
Myriochele	750	2·0	1,000	7·0	
Pectinaria hyperborea	22	6·0	500	63·7	

Only a few forms in the White and Barents Seas give similar biomass indices, although the living conditions in the White Sea are exceptionally favourable for a number of forms, such as *Zostera marina* among the plants and *Portlandia arctica*, *Leda pernula*, *Yoldia hyperborea*, *Asterias lincki* and others among the animals. Moreover both as regards the inflow of river water and the supply of vegetative detritus, the White Sea may be classed as a most favourable environment. In this respect there is some similarity between the White and Baltic Seas. The biomass indices of this latter are also comparatively very low. The scarcity of the Baltic Sea fauna is naturally related to the bad aeration of deep-floor layer and to a considerable dilution of the waters of the eastern and especially the northern parts of the Sea. In the White Sea this last factor is not of much importance for the quantitative development of its fauna; as regards the deep-floor layer aeration, most investigators consider it quite sufficient for the development of bottom life.

We think that the lowering of the indices of biological productivity of the White Sea is mainly due to two factors. For the littoral fauna and for that of the upper sublittoral, the determining factors are the very long, severe winter, the short vegetation period of the plant organisms and the ice conditions of the off-shore zone which are adverse for this latter. Life has no time to attain any great density during the four or five summer months, while the severe winter destroys a large number of organisms. In the lower sublittoral and the pseudo-abyssal the low temperature and the gas content constitute adverse factors for full development of life. Deep-sea layers and especially the true deep-floor layer have not yet been sufficiently studied, and the possibility of the periodical occurrence of shortage of oxygen cannot be denied. On the other hand, the wide distribution of brown muds in the White Sea depression, as in other bodies of water, may be an indication of unfavourable conditions of the vertical circulation, and probably of a considerable periodical concentration of carbon dioxide in the presence, apparently, of sufficient amounts of oxygen. Brown mud with its very poor life, always characteristic of depressions and hollows, and undoubtedly very badly aerated (for instance the deep depression of the Polar basin), still remains an enigma. Brown mud is undoubtedly unsuitable for the development of life owing either to some specific mechanical (considerable softness; porosity) or chemical (presence of carbon dioxide; abundance of ferric or manganic oxides) properties. The productivity of the flora and fauna is limited by the seven months of winter and the heavy ice cover. The sharp summer stratification, restricting vertical circulation, is also of great importance, since it causes the weak development of bottom life frequently from a depth of 15 to 25 m. Low temperature, characteristic of the whole depth of the White Sea, except for its thin uppermost layer, has a considerable effect on the growth of living forms. M. Kamshilov (1957), however, confirms V. Jashnov's (1940) opinion, by some data obtained much later, that as regards the plankton biomass the White Sea could rank side by side with the southwestern part of the Barents Sea (*Table 95*).

Table 95. Mean annual zooplankton biomass of the Barents and White Sea (M. Kamshilov, 1957)

Sea	Regions investigated	Biomass mg/m²
Barents Sea	Coastal regions (B. Manteufel)	44·2
	The regions of the Murman Biological Station investigation in 1952	61·8
	Open Sea (V. Jashnov's and B. Manteufel's data)	100·0
White Sea	Gulf of Kandalaksha (Murman Biological Station survey in 1952)	198·8

Food correlations

The diet of White Sea fish has not been properly studied. Only the feeding of herring has been comprehensively studied by L. Chayanova. Although in the White Sea *Calanus finmarchicus* is the most common component of the herring's food, its diet is most varied, however, consisting of Copepoda,

Cladocera, Chaetognatha, Euphausiacea, Mysidacea, Amphipoda and the eggs and larvae of different invertebrates and fish. Herring feeds also on fry, mainly its own. Its food varies greatly with the season (Fig. 92). The White Sea herring fattens up in May: during the rest of the year its feeding is not intensive. From September onwards herring practically stops eating, and the percentage of empty stomachs in October may reach 40. In the spring its main food is *Calanus finmarchicus*, in summer and autumn other Copepoda. Spawning herring do not stop eating, but eat less. The rapacity of herring is demonstrated not only by the fact that it prefers to devour great numbers of

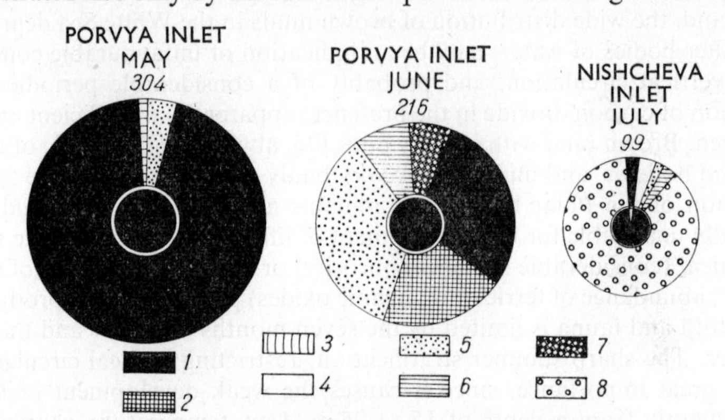

FIG. 92. Food ranges of the White Sea herring in different months (Chayanova, 1939). Repletion indices denoted by associated numerals. *1 Calanus finmarchicus*; *2* Small Crustacea; *3* Euphausiaceae; *4* Mysidacea; *5* Amphipoda; *6* Sagitta; *7* Pteropoda; *8* Fish larvae.

its own young, but also by its obvious preference for the larger forms of plankton.

The young navaga, like herring, feeds mostly on different small plankton crustaceans. The food of the adult navaga is also greatly varied; however, contrary to that of the herring, its main food consists of benthos, chiefly worms and crustaceans (up to 70 per cent of its food). One-fifth of navaga's food consists of fish-smelt, caplin, launce, *Boreogadus saida* and others, including navaga itself. Navaga grows more rapacious with age, often swallowing a prey almost as big as itself.

While spawning in January, navaga eats very little; once its spawning is over it once more falls greedily upon its food.

Seals and porpoises are the navaga's chief enemies.

Pollack or Polar cod also form an essential link in the food-chain of the White Sea. The Arctic seas conceal an inexhaustible store of the small Gadidae.

The young Polar cod, like navaga, feeds on crustaceans; when growing in size it changes to fish, and its predatory instincts and voracity are just as bad as those of navaga, enormous numbers of which it devours, and for which it itself also serves as food. The Greenland Sea, *Phoca hispida* and *Delphinapterus leucas* devour countless masses of Polar cod, navaga and herring.

Fishing

The total catch of the White Sea fisheries reaches 15,000 tons, which includes 2,500 tons of herring.

N. Dmitriev has pointed out (1957) that in the White Sea the chief quarry of fishery consists of herring, navaga, smelt, White Sea cod, dab, and white-fish. Owing to its delicious flavour, salmon is particularly important for trade. At times large shoals of the Arctic cod (*Boreogadus saida*) and caplin (*Mallosus villosus*) enter the White Sea. The bulk of the Sea herring trade consists of some endemic species of herring with few vertebra (*Clupea harengus pallasi*). Besides these species large numbers of multi-vertebrate Murman herring (*Clupea harengus harengus*) appear at times in the White Sea. Moreover the White Sea is the extreme western limit of the distribution of the Pacific Ocean herring (*Cl. har. pallasi*) of a later origin. There are two small-sized endemic forms of cod in the White Sea—*Gadus morhua* f. *hiemalis* Taliev and *G.m. maris albi* Derjugin. Moreover the large Barents Sea cod appears in the White Sea from time to time.

The hunting of marine animals, and primarily of the Greenland seal (*Histriophoca groenlandica*) which has for many centuries been intensively hunted by man, is of great importance in the White Sea. The Greenland seal, of which the greater number spend the summer on the floating ice of the Greenland, Barents and Kara Seas and northward of them, migrate far to the south during the winter while the breeding season is on. There are three main gatherings of breeding seals: Newfoundland, Jan Mayen and the White Sea. At the end of November and the beginning of December the rookeries of seal gather in the White Sea, in February and March the seals calve on the ice of the White Sea Gorlo, and at the end of March and the beginning of April rookeries of seal are carried out of the Gorlo with the ice northwards into the open sea. The hunting season of the Soviet and Norwegian vessels is timed to coincide with this period. Powerful icebreakers with slaughtering gangs set out to hunt seals in the early spring just when the ice begins to move out of the White Sea. They are escorted by reconnaissance aircraft and manned by crews of up to 1,500 men. The size of the total White Sea herd of 'skins' has been estimated at several million head with the help of aerial photographs (S. Freiman and S. Dorofeev). The Soviet and Norwegian annual catch is about 300,000 head. Small numbers of smaller seals, the 'nerpa' (*Phoca hispida*) and of the large bearded seals (*Erignathus barbatus*) are caught all along the shores of the White Sea. Beluga (*Delphinapterus leucus*) is very common in the White Sea, and is caught off some parts of the coast during the time when it approaches land. Of the marine animals mentioned the Greenland seal and beluga feed on navaga, herring and *Boreogadus saida* and the *Erignathus barbatus* on molluscs and crustaceans.

In view of the vast natural resources the collection of varec and sea-weed (Laminaria and Ahnfeltia) should be greatly developed in the White Sea.

E. Palenichko estimates the natural resources of sea mussels in the White Sea at 20 to 30 thousand tons (it can be assumed that the actual amount is considerably higher) so that its exploitation is still at an inconsiderable level.

4

The Kara Sea

I. GENERAL CHARACTERISTICS

The Kara Sea (Fig. 93) is the first of the series of high Arctic epicontinental seas lying along the northern shores of Siberia. With its western boundary at Novaya Zemlya and its eastern limit at the western shores of the Taimyr Peninsula and at the Severnaya Zemlya Archipelago, the Kara Sea is wide open to the waters of the central part of the Arctic basin through the sound between Franz Joseph Land and Severnaya Zemlya. Like other Siberian seas, the Kara Sea loses much of its salinity, especially in its upper layer, from the inflow of large rivers, and this leads to a fall in the salinity of the upper layer throughout the Arctic basin.

Favourable conditions for the penetration of fresh-water fauna, mainly plankton and fish, into the southern parts of the Siberian seas are created by their considerable dilution with river water. Abundant brackish areas at river mouths and estuaries give shelter to a varied, most original fauna which, in its aspect, is a high Arctic relict brackish-water fauna—a legacy of the Ice Age—consisting mainly of fish and crustaceans.

The Kara Sea may have been the centre of the evolution of this remarkable fauna which penetrated, as a set of forms, far to the south into the depth of Eurasia as far as the Caspian Sea and westward to the basin of the Baltic Sea.

Of all the Siberian seas the Kara Sea alone is exposed, in its western part, to the influence of the warmer and more saline waters of the Barents Sea with its characteristic flora and fauna. On the other hand, warmer and more saline Atlantic waters, of the intermediate layer of the central part of the Arctic basin, carrying a most original fauna rich in forms, penetrate from the north through the troughs into the deeper layers of all the four seas, but principally into the Kara Sea. The penetration of the boreal and abyssal fauna into the Kara Sea from the north with the deep cold waters is also characteristic.

The Siberian seas are paradoxical in their aspect owing to the above-mentioned hydrological characteristics: in their northern parts the deep-water layers of all of them are much warmer and have a qualitatively richer fauna. The endemic marine fauna of all the four Siberian seas, except perhaps the southern part of the Chukotsk Sea adjacent to the Bering Strait, has a definitely high-Arctic aspect.

The shallows off the shores of the Kara Sea differ greatly both in their conditions and fauna from those of the deep central part. The first are well aerated, better warmed, often considerably diluted, and populated by a fauna rich in variety and at times in numbers. The second, characterized by its low temperature and high salinity, has a thick brown mud floor and is populated by a fauna poor both in its numbers and its variety. Its characteristic features are a great preponderance of echinoderms, exceptionally

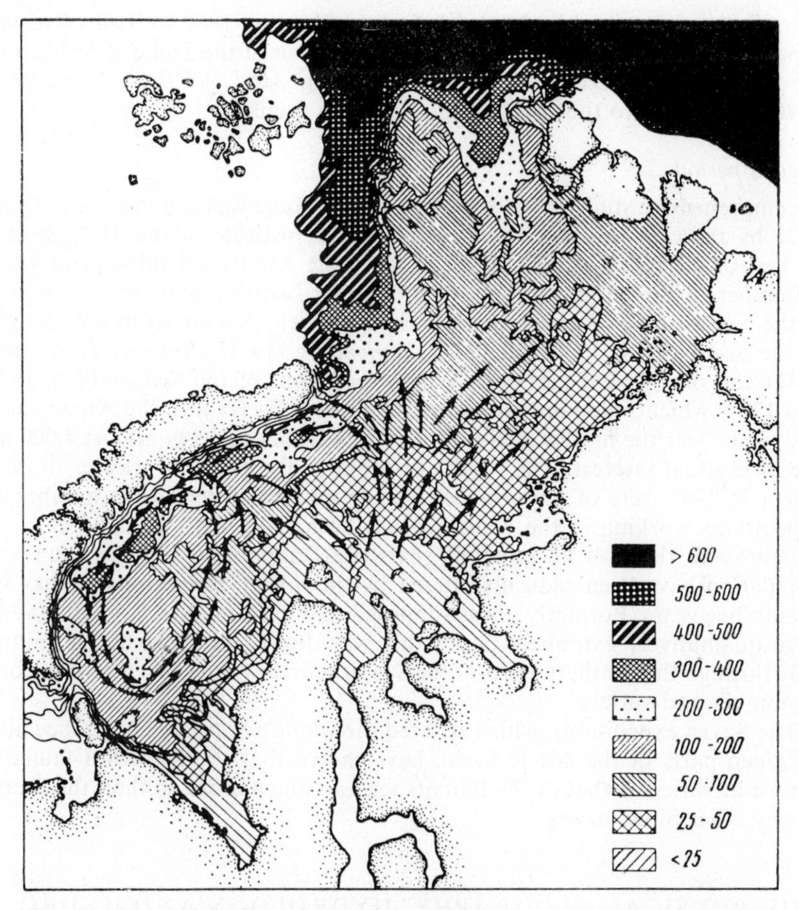

FIG. 93. Chart of the Kara Sea with depths and currents (according to data of Arctic Institute).

large sizes of invertebrates, very poor fish, and very low indices of biomass and productivity.

The Kara Sea is a true outpost of the high Arctic, since all the characteristic features of the endemic high Arctic conditions and all the attenuating influences of the foreign Atlantic waters are reflected in it with extreme clarity.

II. HISTORY OF EXPLORATION

First period

The first data on the Kara Sea were collected by the Swedish expeditions of O. Nordenskjöld in 1875 (in the *Pröven*), in 1876 (in the *Imer*) and in 1878 (in the *Vega*). In 1882 and 1883 biological work was carried out there by a Dutch expedition in the *Varna* and by a Danish one in the *Dymphna*. In 1893 the

Kara Sea was surveyed by Nansen's famous *Fram*, in 1900 by Toll's Russian expedition in the *Zarya*, in 1907 by the expedition of the Duke of Orleans in the *Belgica* and in 1918 by R. Amundsen in the *Mod*. All these expeditions have contributed to the study of the Kara Sea fauna.

Second period

A comprehensive study of the Kara Sea and its fauna was begun as recently as 1921 by the expedition of the Oceanographic Institute in the *Malygin* and by that of the Hydrographic Directorate in the *Taimyr*. In subsequent years a number of Soviet expeditions of the Arctic Institute and the Committee of the Northern Sea Route cruised in the Kara Sea. Among them the voyages of the *Sedov* (1929, 1930 and 1934), *Lomonosov* (1931), *Rusanov* (1931 and 1932) and others, and particularly the expeditions of the *Sadko* (1935, 1936 and 1937) which sailed to the north of the Kara Sea far into the Arctic basin and which was the first to haul bottom fauna from depths of almost 4,000 m, are of especial interest. The results of the expedition of the trawler *Maxim Gorky* in 1945 were of importance. During the Soviet period the number of expeditions working in the Kara Sea has been more than doubled in comparison with those of all previous years. Earlier opinions on the Kara Sea population have been radically altered by the Soviet expeditions of the last twenty-five years. Formerly it was supposed that the Kara Sea flora and fauna were qualitatively extremely poor; this was due to the expeditions sailing only through the southern parts of the Sea, where the fauna is in fact very poor in number and variety.

The Soviet expeditions, which covered the whole Sea up to its entrance into the open parts of the Arctic basin, have shown that the Kara Sea fauna is almost as varied as that of the Barents sea and much more so than the fauna of any other Siberian sea.

III. PHYSICAL GEOGRAPHY, HYDROLOGY AND HYDROCHEMISTRY

Boundaries

The Kara Sea is bounded on the west by Novaya Zemlya and on the east by Severnaya Zemlya (56° to 105° E longitude); it extends northwards from 68° to about 81° N latitude.

Bottom topography and size

A deep trench, with depths down to 200 m in the south and to 600 m in the north, stretches along the coast of Novaya Zemlya. East of this trench the bottom begins to rise to the extensive shallows of the Yamal and Taimyr peninsulas (Fig. 93), with depths of less than 50 m. The area of the Kara Sea is 883,000 km^2, and its volume 104,000 km^3. Its average depth is 118 m, and its greatest depth 620 m.

Another deep trench enters the northern part of the Kara Sea from the north to the west of Severnaya Zemlya; it may be connected with the deep

Schokalsky and Vilkitsky Straits, which separate the islands of Severnaya Zemlya.

In the northern part of the Sea (north of 80° N latitude) towards the Arctic basin there is an increase of depth. The middle zone of the sea, extending from southwest to northeast and in the northern part due north, forms a wide plateau, with depths of 50 to 200 m, which rises in two wide submarine terraces from the Novaya Zemlya trough to the Yamal and Taimyr shallows.

Currents

The Kara Sea is connected with the Laptev Sea through the deep Vilkitsky and Schokalsky Straits. Huge masses of river water, of the order of 1,500 km^3 annually, flow into it, forming a layer of fresh water about 2 m deep over the whole surface. The waters of the Ob and Yenisey rivers in their main mass are carried to the northeast, along the western coast of Taimyr. Part of these waters turn north and northwest to the northern end of Novaya Zemlya and then, partly swerving west and southwest, they create a cyclonic rotation of the waters of the southern part of the Sea between Yamal and Novaya Zemlya (Fig. 93). Skirting Novaya Zemlya, and also penetrating in smaller amounts through the straits of Novaya Zemlya, the 'Atlantic' waters of higher salinity enter the Kara Sea, and flow from the west, out of the Barents Sea, sinking down below the much less saline surface waters. Larger volumes of more saline and less cooled 'Atlantic' waters enter the Kara Sea from the north, in the depths, at some hundreds of metres, between Franz Joseph Land and Severnaya Zemlya and from the northeast out of the Laptev Sea through Vilkitsky and Schokalsky Straits.

Temperature and saline conditions

The surface waters of the Kara Sea in the region of the Ob–Yenisey shallows have a salinity of 7 to 10‰ and, in the warmest season, a temperature of 5° to 8°. As one moves westwards and northwards the salinity increases, reaching 32 to 34‰. The deeper layers are considerably more saline and colder. One of the *Malygin*'s stations in September 1921 opposite the Ob estuary (*Table 96*) may be given as an example. The ranges of temperature and salinity for the central part of the southern half of the Sea in the centre of the cyclonic rotation are given in *Table 97* for August 1921.

Table 96

Depth m	t° C	S‰	O_2/cm^3
0	4·32	5·07	7·62
5	4·19	4·33	7·62
7·5	1·17	15·48	7·31
10	0·16	24·30	6·83
15	−1·45	30·55	6·73
24	−1·54	31·04	6·76

Table 97

Depth m	$t°$ C	S‰	O_2/cm^3
0	2·70	29·42	—
10	2·40	29·88	8·0
25	—1·45	33·57	8·32
50	−1·65	34·49	—
120	−1·52	34·72	7·88

In the western part of the Sea, in the depths of the Novaya Zemlya trough, the salinity is 34·5 to 34·7‰ and the temperature is −1·6° to −1·75°. For example, the conditions at one of the *Persey* stations east of Matochkin Shar (September 1927) may be given (*Table 98*). Throughout the Kara Sea

Table 98

Depth m	$t°$ C	S‰
0	3·95	26·41
10	3·95	27·14
25	0·95	33·44
50	−0·80	34·02
100	−1·53	34·40
200	−1·66	34·47
360	−1·64	34·70

at a depth of 10 to 20 m a sharp fall of temperature and an increase in salinity are observed; at depths greater than 50 m salinity does not fall below 34‰, while the temperature remains below zero all the year round. The currents skirting Novaya Zemlya from the north have a salinity of 32 to 33‰ at the surface and a temperature of 0·5° to 1·0°.

Dilution of the surface layer by the Ob–Yenisey waters can be detected throughout hundreds of kilometres north of the river estuaries, even to the east of Cape Zhelaniye up to 77° N latitude (*Tables 97* and *99*).

Table 99

Depth m	$t°$ C	S‰
0	0·4	27·65
10	0·36	30·36
25	0·09	32·78
50	−1·11	34·16
218	−1·49	34·79

Side by side with the surface layer, with its considerable loss of salinity and its summer rise in temperature, and with the deep, highly saline waters of practically constant low temperature, there is in the Kara Sea in the summer a definite intermediate cold layer 50 to 100 m deep. This layer is formed by the sinking of the cold surface waters, which in the previous winter had been considerably cooled and have become much more saline as a result of the formation of an ice cover (Figs. 94 and 95). The presence of a thick cold intermediate layer is an indication of a comparatively weak vertical circulation.

Like all the marginal seas, more or less cut off from the open ocean, with a large inflow of river water, the Kara Sea is characterized in its surface layer by unstable saline conditions which depend on the amount of river water. As an example of this one may mention the differences in the temperature and saline conditions of the sea in 1927 and 1945, given in Figs. 94 and 95. In 1945 the inflow of river water into the Kara Sea was only about two thirds of the many years average amount and the salinity of the surface sea waters was found to be considerably higher. However, as can be seen from the cross sections, the deep water retained its salinity. A general warming up was equally clearly perceptible. Low temperature ($-1{\cdot}6°$ to $-1{\cdot}7°$) was retained only in the deepest layer. The surface layers were warmed most of all. In the summer of 1945 the Kara Sea was completely free of ice for several months.

In summer the dilution of the surface layer prevents vertical circulation; in winter, however, it causes a further increase of ice formation. As a result salt water, formed on the surface, sinks into the depths. In winter the temperature of the surface layers of the Kara Sea is mostly $-1{\cdot}6°$ to $-1{\cdot}8°$, while its salinity is 34‰ and higher. This feature of the hydrological conditions in the Kara Sea is similar to that of the White Sea.

Atlantic waters of the intermediate layer of the Arctic basin (salinity up to 35‰; temperature up to $2{\cdot}5°$) and the much colder waters of the same salinity lying beneath them, enter the northern part of the Sea at depths of 150 to 300 m.

Ice frequently begins to form in the Kara Sea as early as September, while proper melting only begins in June. The summer is short and cold. The central part of the Sea is not covered with solid ice, even in winter time, but wide firm ice belts and large stranded hummocks are formed at the shores.

The general character of the summer ranges of temperature and salinity throughout the Kara Sea waters in 1945 is given in the hydrological cross section in Fig. 96. As may be seen from the second diagram, the northern part of the Sea is warmed more than the central part, while the southern one is under the influence of the warmer waters entering it from the Barents Sea and of the local coastal ones.

The hydrological conditions of the Kara Sea are most complicated owing to the entrance of deep currents of warmer and more saline Atlantic waters into it from the north, partly from the Barents Sea and partly directly from the Arctic basin; to the exchange of water through the Kara Gates with the Pechora region of the Barents Sea, and with the Laptev Sea in the east; to the inflow of huge masses of river water from the south; and finally to sharply

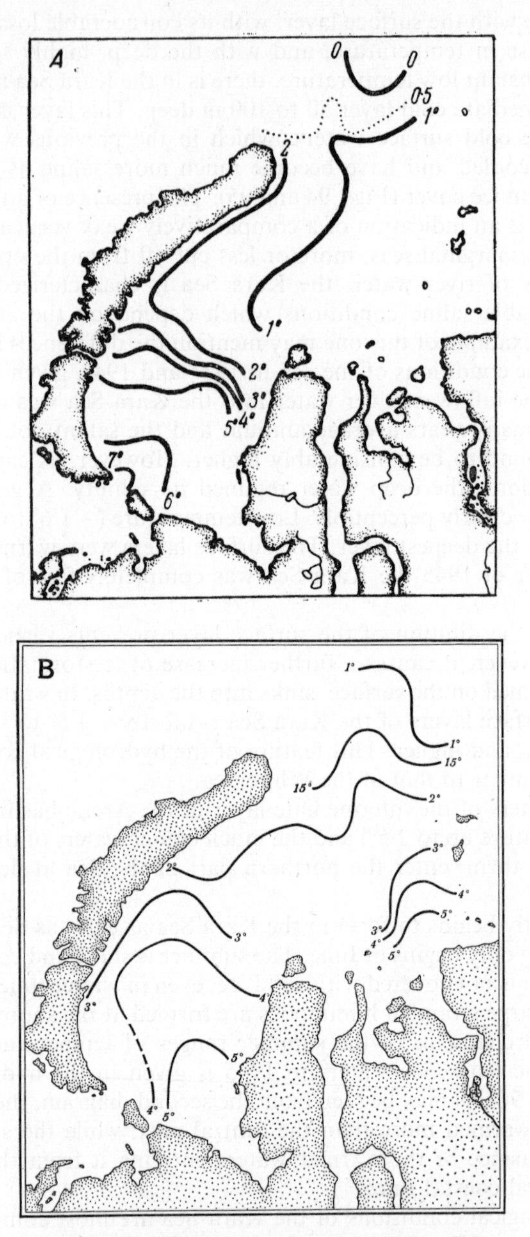

Fig. 94. Range of surface temperatures of the Kara Sea: A In September 1927 (Vasnetzov); B In September 1945 (Zenkevitch and Filatova).

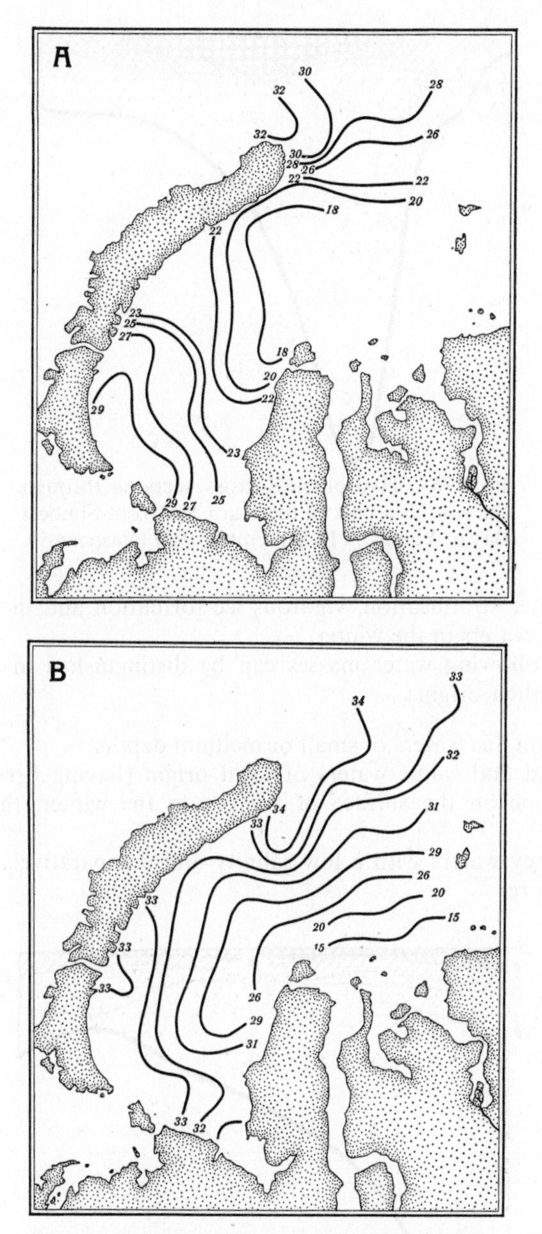

FIG. 95. Surface salinity range in the Kara Sea: A In September 1927 (Vasnetzov); B In September 1945 (Zenkevitch and Filatova).

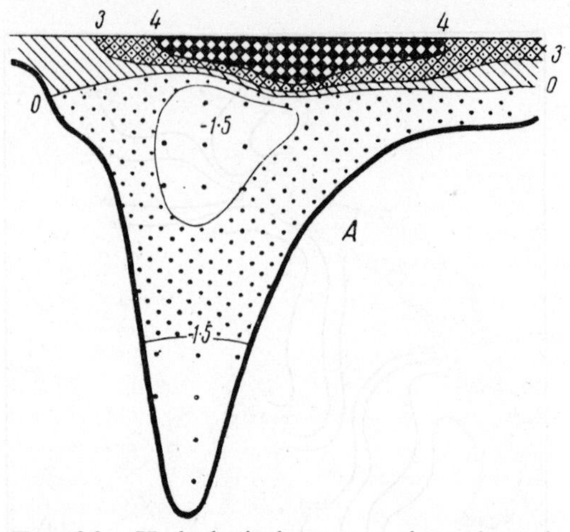

FIG. 96A. Hydrological cross sections through the southern part of the Kara Sea from Shubert Bay to Yamal. A In September 1927 (Vasnetzov).

defined summer stratification, vigorous ice formation and the formation of surface saline waters in the winter.

Thus the following water masses can be distinguished in the Kara Sea according to their origin:

(*1*) Local Kara Sea waters of small or medium depths.
(*2*) Deep cold and saline waters of local origin (having become cold and more saline on the surface of the sea in the winter, they have sunk down).
(*3*) Ob–Yenisey waters with a low salinity and comparatively high summer temperature.

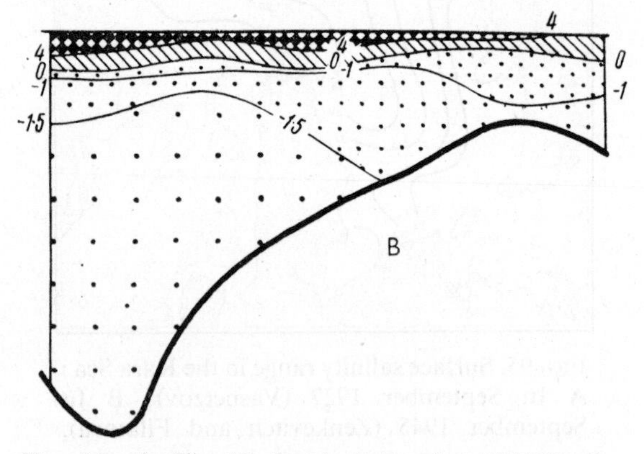

FIG. 96B. As Fig. 96A but in September 1945 (Zenkevitch and Filatova).

(*4*) Atlantic saline and relatively warmer waters which penetrate into the Kara Sea by three ways:
   (*a*) from the north from the central parts of the Arctic basin from its intermediate 'warm' layer,
   (*b*) from the northwest from the Barents Sea, between Franz Joseph Land and Novaya Zemlya, and
   (*c*) from the southwest through the Kara Gates.

(*5*) Cold and saline deep waters, which penetrate into the northern parts of the Sea from the lower layers of the central part of the Arctic basin.

Soils

Silts and clayey ooze are preponderant in the central, northern and northeastern deep parts of the Sea (Fig. 97). In its eastern part, mainly in the shallows opposite the Ob and the Yenisey estuaries, silty sand and sand floors are preponderant. The finer-grained bottoms of the Kara Sea are usually coloured brown in their upper layer; this is explained, as in other cases, by the presence of manganese and iron oxides. The boundaries of the brown mud distribution are given in Fig. 98. Brown muds and the ferromanganate concretions so characteristic of them are more widely distributed in the Kara Sea than in any other body of water in our Arctic. In the Kara Sea the brown mud attains a thickness of 18 cm, lying over the silts and grey-blue clays. In the deeper parts of the Sea the brown mud is usually thicker (Fig. 98). The deep-water troughs running out of the Arctic basin from the north are also covered with brown mud.

Manganese is particularly active in this process. Getting into the deeper layers of the silt (the reduction zone) manganic oxides are reduced to the manganous state. These soluble compounds are dissolved in deep water, get oxidized again and are precipitated on to the sea-bed, where reduction may occur again. Hence there is an active consumption of oxygen in the deep layer and brown mud is characterized by the presence of both managanese and iron in an oxidized state.

There is much that is still not clear about the zones of formation of brown muds, the chemical state of the overlying deep-water layer, and the effect of such a sea-bed on organisms. One might suppose that an accumulation of brown mud takes place where there is an inflow of river waters, which drain the marshland and carry out into the sea large amounts of iron and manganese. However, the northern part of the Barents Sea and the central part of the Arctic basin are too far removed from river estuaries for this. The brown muds are most widely developed in the deeper parts, more or less stagnant, of the water bodies; at the same time oxygen is required in sufficient amounts for the oxidation of the iron and manganese. A large number of ferromanaganese concretions, frequently of large size, are characteristic of the Kara Sea.

The intensity of the oxidation–reduction reactions in the deep-water layer above the brown mud is indicated by a high oxidation–reduction potential; the index of the active reaction, however, is lower, probably as a consequence of the presence of carbon dioxide. This is connected also with the small

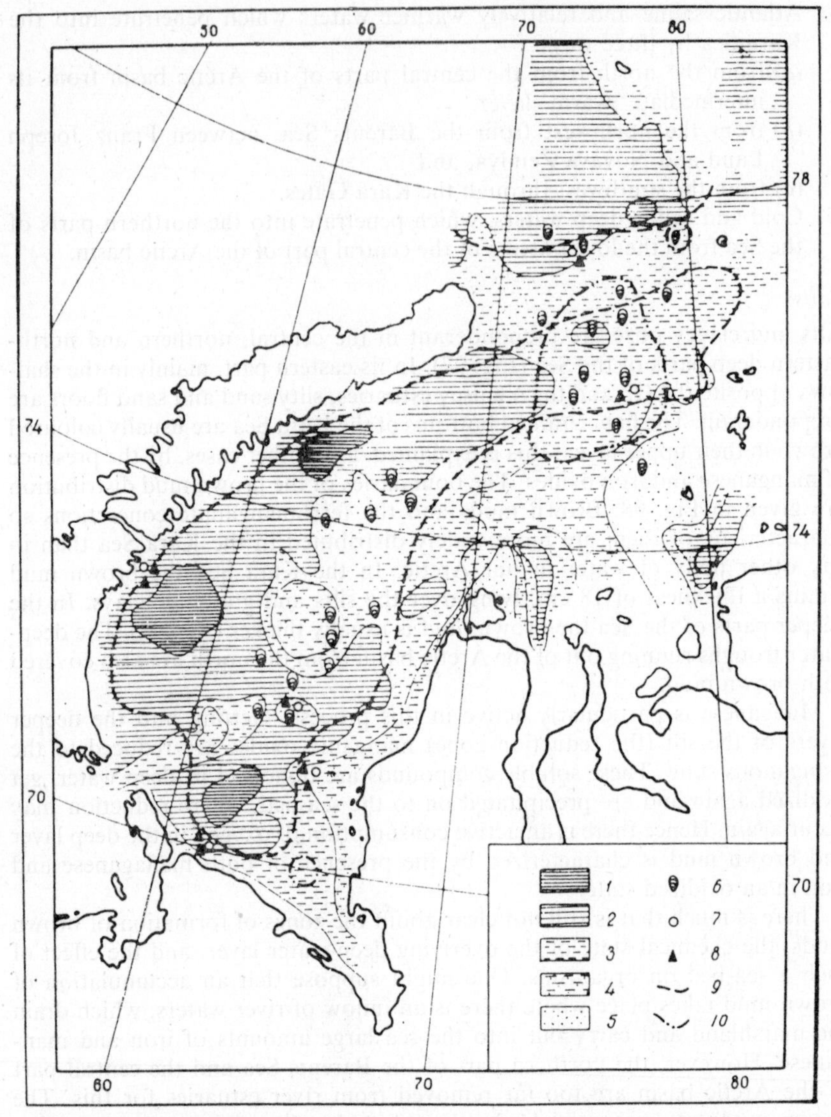

FIG. 97. Kara Sea sea-bed soils. *1* Clay and mud; *2* Silt; *3* Sand–mud; *4* Silty sand; *5* Sand; *6* No data; *7* Ferromanganate concretion; *8* Rock; *9* Gravel; *10* Limit of distribution of underlying clay (Gorshkova).

amount, and sometimes complete absence, of bicarbonates in the brown mud.

Life is always scarce in the brown mud, but it is not clear why this is so. It may be caused by a lack of free oxygen (taken up from the deep-water layer by manganese compounds), by an accumulation of carbon dioxide, or, as has been suggested by Hessle (1924) for the Baltic Sea, by the poisonous properties of manganese.

As has been pointed out by T. Gorshkova (1957), the percentage of organic carbon in the upper layer of the Kara Sea floor is comparatively small, varying between 0·27 and 1·99.

None of these three reasons explains the fact that some animal forms thrive

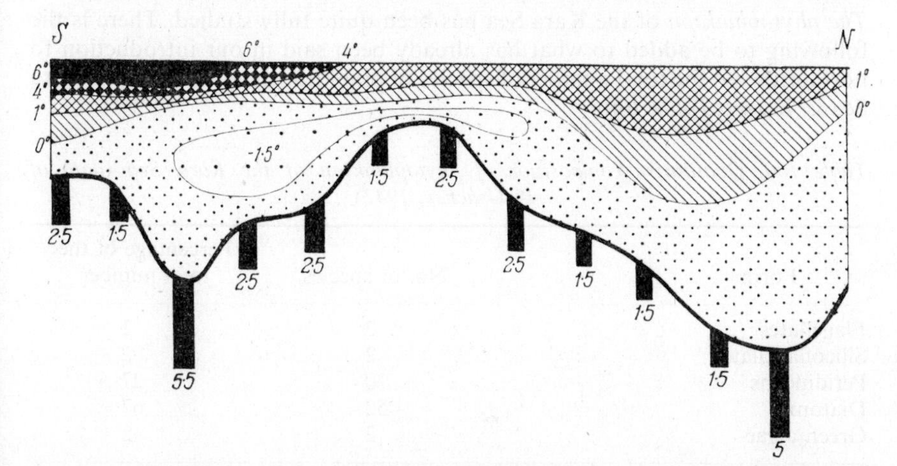

FIG. 98. Temperature cross section along the Kara Sea from the Karskie Vorota towards NNE to 81° N latitude in mid-September 1946 (Zenkevitch and Filatova). The thickness of the brown mud layer is given below in cm.

on brown mud, notably all echinoderms (especially the brittle stars, asterids and holothurians); some coelenterata (Metridium, Umbellula); some molluscs (Pecten) and crustaceans (Mesidothea, Sclerocrangon).

Lack of oxygen and high concentration of carbon dioxide are specially marked in the deep-water layer of the Ob–Yenisey region, where the difference in the salinity of the surface and deep-water layers is considerable (P. Lobza, 1945).

IV. FLORA AND FAUNA

General characteristics

The pelagic and bottom life of our northern seas situated east of Novaya Zemlya is several times poorer in numbers than that of the Barents Sea, but as to the qualitative variety of its benthos the fauna of the Kara Sea is not much inferior to that of the Barents Sea. This is all the more remarkable, considering the much more severe climate of the Kara Sea, its smaller size and its inferiority to the Barents Sea as regards the variety of its biotopes. For instance, all littoral fauna is absent from the Kara Sea, and since it does not contain the macrophyte growths so characteristic of the upper level of the Barents Sea sublittoral, very many forms peculiar to this level in the Barents Sea are absent from the Kara Sea.

The qualitative wealth of the Kara Sea fauna, and probably also of the northwestern part of the Laptev Sea, is explained by its being the meeting ground of fauna of different origins. This is connected with the different sources of the water masses noted above.

Plankton

The phytoplankton of the Kara Sea has been quite fully studied. There is the following to be added to what has already been said in our introduction to northern seas: the total number of species of plankton algae found in the Kara Sea is 78 (see *Table 100*).

Table 100. Qualitative composition of phytoplankton of the Kara Sea (data of P. Usachev, 1947)

Form	No. of species	Percentage of the total number
Flagellates	2	2
Silicoflagellates	2	2
Peridineans	20	27
Diatoms	52	67
Green algae	2	2
Total	78	100

According to P. Usachev (1947), two areas of increased phytoplankton biomass can be distinguished in the Kara Sea:* a northern one near Wiese Island with a biomass of 1 to 3 g/m³ and more, in the parts of the Sea warmed by the warmer Atlantic waters and near the edge of the melting ice; and a southern one, influenced by the inflow from the Ob and Yenisey, with a biomass of more than 1 g/m³ (Fig. 99). It is evident from the diagrams given that the main mass of plankton is adapted to the upper 25 m layer (more than 500 mg/m³).

Typical spring diatoms are preponderant in the northern region; in the southern one later forms and forms typical of the estuarial zones are found side by side with the former. In Usachev's opinion (1946) the productivity of Kara Sea phytoplankton is about equal to the indices for the northeast region of the Barents, Laptev and East Siberian Seas. The phytoplankton mass in some cases is as high as 6 to 8 g/m³.

Qualitative composition of zooplankton. V. Khmisnikova (1936) has recorded 169 forms of plankton for the whole Kara Sea, not counting larvae and

* It should be borne in mind that all data on Kara Sea phytoplankton refer to the short summer period of one to two months and are valid for one area and for one time of the year. No observations exist for different seasons of the year and for different parts of the Sea simultaneously.

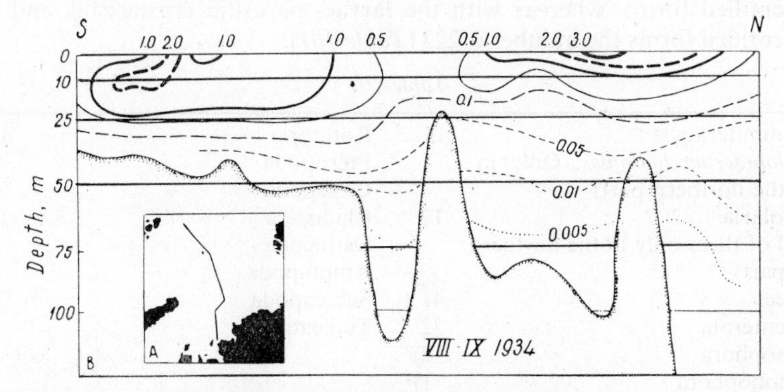

FIG. 99A, B. Quantitative distribution of phytoplankton (g/m³) in the Kara Sea, August–September 1934 (Usachev, 1946).

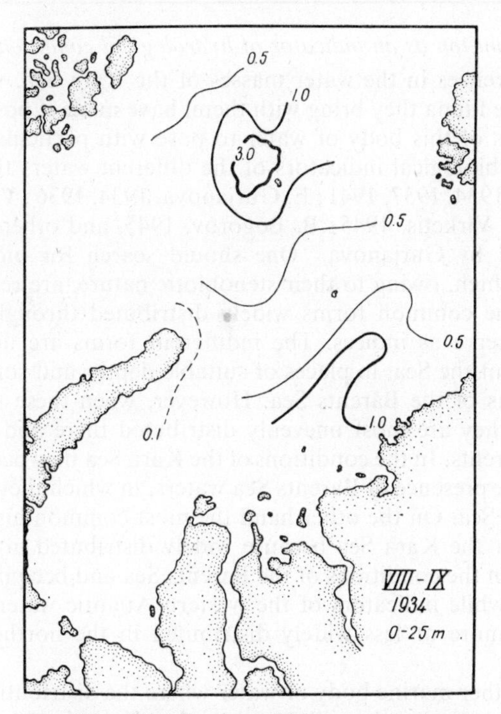

FIG. 99C. Distribution of biomass of phytoplankton in the Kara Sea according to the materials of the expedition of the icebreaker *Sedov* of the Arctic Institute (August–September, 1934. For the 0 to 25 m layer, g/m³) (Usachev, 1941).

unidentified forms, whereas with the larvae, parasitic crustaceans and the unidentified forms the number is 223 (*Table 101*).

Table 101

Foraminifera (*Globigerina bulloides.* Only in the northern part)	1	Rotatoria	11
		Pteropoda	2
		Copepoda	50
Radiolaria (10 of them only in the northern part)	12	Cladocera	11
		Ostracoda	3
		Amphipoda	4
Ciliates	41	Schizopoda	5
Coelenterata	22	Tunicata	5
(Ctenophora	2)		
(Siphonophora	1)		
Vermes	2		
		Total	169

Kara Sea zooplankton as an indicator of hydrological conditions

The sharp differences in the water masses of the Kara Sea, varying in their origin and in the fauna they bring with them, have made it possible for different investigators of this body of water to pose with particular precision the problem of the biological indicators of the different waters that compose it. (G. Gorbunov, 1934, 1937, 1941; E. Gurjanova, 1934, 1936; V. Khmisnikova, 1936, 1937; M. Virketis, 1945; B. Bogorov, 1945, and others). As has been justly remarked by Gurjanova, 'One should search for biological indices among forms which, owing to their stenobiotic nature, are restricted in their distribution. The common forms widely distributed throughout the whole Arctic cannot serve as indices. The indifferent forms are uniformly distributed throughout the Sea, in places of suitable depths and soils; they are the indifferent forms of the Barents Sea. However, when these species get into the Kara Sea, they are most unevenly distributed there and depend on the range of the currents. In the conditions of the Kara Sea they become biological indicators of the presence of Barents Sea waters, in which they are distributed about the Kara Sea. On the other hand the most common high Arctic forms —indifferent for the Kara Sea because widely distributed in it—are already becoming rare in the conditions of the Barents Sea and become indicators for Arctic waters, while indicators of the western Atlantic waters would be the boreal species more or less widely distributed in the northern part of the Atlantic Ocean.'

There is no other marine body of water where the distribution of the fauna gives such clear and abundant illustrations for the understanding of the origin of its masses of water as the Kara Sea. A very large number of plankton and benthos forms can serve as indicators of both fresh and brackish waters, and of waters penetrating from the west from the Barents Sea, and from the north from the central parts of the Arctic basin. Among these it is possible to distinguish the forms belonging to the warm Atlantic intermediate layer and those of the cold Arctic bathyal and abyssal waters.

The following biogeographic groups are commonly distinguished in the Kara Sea plankton:

(*1*) forms widely distributed throughout the Arctic
(*2*) forms of western origin (Atlantic–Barents Sea forms)
(*3*) forms belonging to the cold Arctic waters, which have come from the north
(*4*) forms of the warm Atlantic intermediate layer of the central part of the Arctic basin
(*5*) brackish-water forms
(*6*) fresh-water forms.

Khmisnikova distinguishes four main regions in the Kara Sea according to the distribution of these groups (Fig. 100).

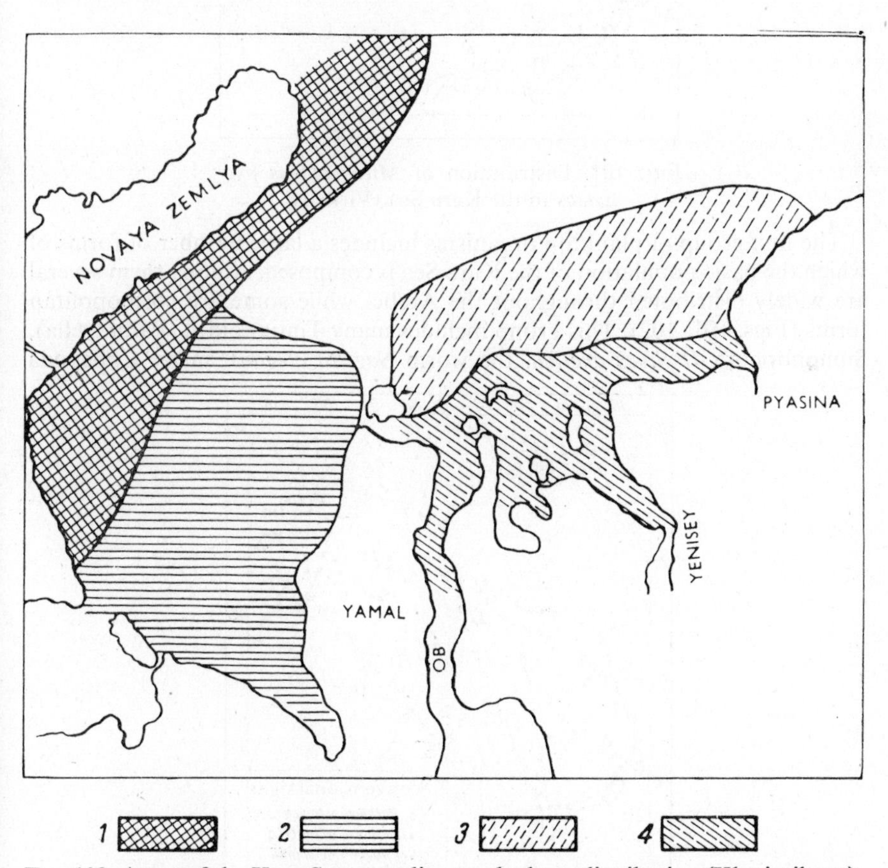

FIG. 100. Areas of the Kara Sea according to plankton distribution (Khmisnikova). *1* Area of penetration of Atlantic and Arctic forms from the north; *2* Area of penetration of Barents Sea forms from the south; *3* Area of predominance of brackish-water forms; *4* Area of predominance of fresh-water forms.

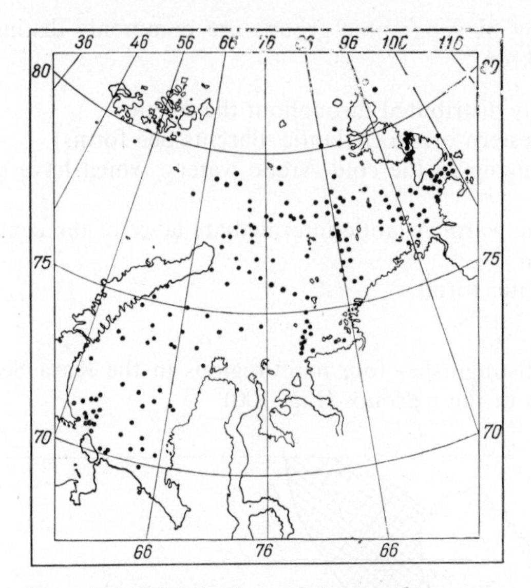

FIG. 101. Distribution of *Microcalanus pygmaeus* in the Kara Sea (Virketis).

The first group of plankton organisms includes a large number of forms of which the basic population of the Kara Sea is composed. Among them several are widely distributed throughout the Arctic, while some are cosmopolitan forms (Figs. 101, 102). This group includes many Tintinnoidea (Parafavella), Siphonophora *Diphyes arctica*, the worm *Sagitta elegans*, many Copepoda

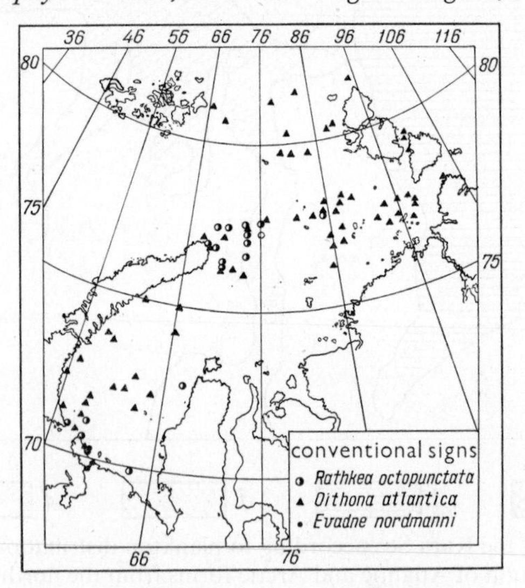

FIG. 102. Distribution of some Atlantic–Barents Sea forms in the Kara Sea (Virketis).

(*Calanus finmarchicus*, *C. hyperboreus*, *Pseudocalanus elongatus*, *Microcalanus parvus*, *Oithona similis*) and some salps (*Fritillaria borealis* and *Oikopleura vanhoeffeni* and others). The cold-water forms are characteristic of the deep water of the Kara Sea (below the 50 to 100 m layer)—*Calanus hyperboreus*, *Euchaeta glacialis*, *Metridia longa*, *Conchaecia borealis*, *Parathemisto oblivia*, *Euthemisto libellula*, *Diphyes arctica* and *Clione limacina*.

Of the upper layer of water the following are characteristic: *Pseudocalanus elongatus*, *Oithona similis*, *Centropages hamatus*, *Thysanoessa neglecta*, *Temora longicornis*, *Acartia longiremis*, *Oithona plumifera* var. *atlantica*, *Microsetella*

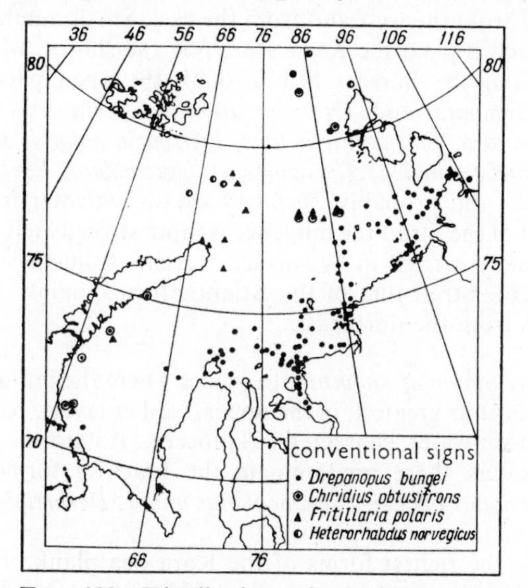

FIG. 103. Distribution of plankton forms which have penetrated from the north and forms from inland discharge in the Kara Sea (Virketis).

norvegica, *Oikopleura labradoriensis*; among the sea-weeds *Halosphaera viridis* is the most typical. Most of these forms have arrived from the west.

The quantittaively richest form, *Calanus finmarchicus*, in its mature state, lives in the deepest layers of water, but while young is adapted to the upper zones. The forms of western origin come into the Kara Sea from the Barents Sea, either skirting Novaya Zemlya from the north or through the southern passages. At times only a few penetrate into the Kara Sea (Fig. 103); sometimes, however, they go far to the eastward, as far as the passages into the Laptev Sea.

The ciliates *Salpingella acuminata*, *Acanthostomella norvegica*, *Evadne nordmanni*, *Podon leuckarti*, meduse—*Rathkea octopunctata*, crustacea—*Evadne nordmanni*, *Podon leuckarti*, *Centropages hamatus*, *C. typicus*, *Temora longicornis* and *Oithona atlantica* are included in this group of forms.

The third group of cold-water Polar forms, penetrating from the north, is similar in its distribution in the Kara Sea to the fourth, which comes also from the north, but from the warm Atlantic intermediate layer.

The former may be said to include *Amphimelissa setosa*, *Amallophora magna*, *Chiridius obtusifrons*, *Euchaeta glacialis*, *Fritillaria polaris*, the fourth group —the radiolarian *Pectacantha oikiskos*, the jelly-fish *Homoeonema platygonon*, the crustaceans *Euchaeta norvegica*, *Heterorhabdus norvegicus*, *Thysanoessa longicaudata*, *Themisto abyssorum* and others (Fig. 103).

A comprehensive study of the zooplankton of the Vilkitsky Strait led M. Virketis (1944) to the conclusion that members of the zooplankton penetrate this region both from the west and from the east. Small numbers of brackish-water forms reach it from the Kara Sea along the shores, while the Atlantic forms arrive from the Barents Sea through the open parts of the Strait (*Salpingella acuminata* and *Oithona atlantica*). The Arctic-basin forms (*Amphimelissa setosa*, *Euchaeta glacialis*, *Frittilaria polaris*) and the Atlantic forms (*Sticholonche zanglea*, *Thysanoessa longicaudata*, *Euchaeta norvegica*, *Aglantha digitalis* and probably *Themisto abyssorum* enter from the east. In the western part of the Strait the influence is more strongly felt of the brackish-water forms chiefly carried in by surface currents from the west, and in the eastern part of the Strait that of the Atlantic forms mainly brought in with the deep waters from the northeast.

Quantitative distribution of plankton. In places where the influence of the Ob–Yenisey waters is at its greatest, in the upper, fresher layers, plankton acquires a completely fresh-water character (Cladocera, Rotatoria, Copepoda). In the brackish waters there predominate the brackish forms *Limnocalanus grimaldii*, *Drepanopus bungei*, *Pseudocalanus major*, *Derjuginia tolli*, *Lenicella calanoides*.

Quantitatively the richest forms of the Kara Sea plankton are the Copepoda, namely *Calanus finmarchicus* (four-fifths of the total biomass) and *Oithona similis* and *Pseudocalanus elongatus* (one-fifth of the total biomass). Appendicularia (Fritillaria and Oikopleura) and Chaetognatha (*Sagitta elegans*) are also of great significance. At times they form the largest biomass. Sometimes the polychaete larvae acquire a very important place in the plankton biomass. In the most diluted southern parts of the Sea Copepoda biomass is inferior to that of the Rotifera (mainly Synchaeta) and Cladocera.

The average quantitative significance of the separate groups of the Kara Sea zooplankton is given in *Table 102*, due to V. Bogorov (1944, 1946).

Jashnov (1940) considers that the average plankton biomass of the western half of the Sea is 4·5 tons/km^2, and of the total Sea in summer it is 5 million tons.

Benthos

Bottom flora. The phytobenthos of the Kara Sea is represented by only 55 forms, which is less than a third of the specific composition of the Barents Sea algae (*Table 103*).

Thus, in contrast to the Barents Sea, the bottom flora of the Kara Sea is qualitatively much poorer than its bottom fauna. This results primarily from the peculiar conditions of the Kara Sea.

Table 102. Significance of Kara Sea zooplankton groups

Group	Eastern part	Ob–Yenisei region	South-western part	Gulf of Yenisei
Phytoplankton biomass, mg/m³	1,622	900	122	24
Zooplankton biomass, mg/m³	48	46	43 (34 according to Jashnov)	150
The significance of individual groups in relation to the total zooplankton biomass, per cent				
Copepoda	76·0	53·5	74·0	40·0
Appendicularia	19·0	—	2·8	—
Chaetognatha	0·1	—	2·2	—
Polychaeta larvae	0·7	0·4	12·0	—
Rotatoria (Synchaeta)	3·3	41·0	0·5	47·4
Cladocera	—	—	8·0	11·1
Mollusca larvae	0·4	—	8·0	—
Others	0·5	5·1	0·5	1·5

Adapted mainly to the upper levels of the sea bottom—the littoral and sub-littoral—the bottom algae do not find favourable conditions for existence in the Kara Sea, especially during harsher climatic periods. The penetration of the bottom algae into the Kara Sea from the north through the deep central parts of the Arctic basin, as with zoobenthos, is impossible.

Some members of the Barents Sea flora are at times found off the eastern shores of Novaya Zemlya, but these forms belong to the upper horizons of the sublittoral and they are represented by dwarf specimens of the genus Fucus. Farther east along the shores of the mainland and off the islands higher algae are absent; they have been observed in small quantities in western Taimyr only.

The problem of the origin of the Kara Sea bottom flora is easily solved; this cannot be said, however, of its fauna. The overwhelmingly predominant part of the flora consists of Barents Sea forms, which penetrate into the Kara Sea from

Table 103

Groups of phytobenthos	Number of species in Kara Sea	Barents Sea	White Sea
Green	7	32	33
Brown	22	69	48
Red	26	71	53
Total	55*	172	134

* According to A. D. Zinova's (1950) data there are 59 species of brown and red algae in the Kara Sea.

the west through the straits and round the northern island of Novaya Zemlya.

Of the 55 macrophytes inhabiting the Kara Sea, 49 species (89 per cent) are common to the western shores of Novaya Zemlya, and 46 species (82 per cent) to the Murman coast. However, the Kara Sea macroflora contains mostly cold-water forms, while the warm-water ones decrease. The following Arctic forms are characteristic of the Kara Sea: *Laminaria agardhii*, *L. solidungula*, *L. nigripes*, *Fucus evanescens*, *F. inflatus*, *Phyllaria dermatodea*, *Omphalophyllum ulvaceum*, *Turnerell septentrionalis* and *Sarcophyllis arctica*. Apart from these the following are the most widely distributed forms in the Kara Sea: *Chaetomorpha melagonium*, *Pylaiella litoralis*, *Chaetopteris plumosa*, *Desmarestia aculeata*, *Ptilota pectinata*, *Phyllophora brodiaei*, *Ph. interrupta*, *Rhodimenia palmata*, *Delesseria sinuosa*, *Odonthalia dentata*, *Rhodomela lycopodioides*, *Polysiphonia arctica* and *Eutora cristata*.

Qualitative composition of bottom fauna. At the present time it is still impossible to give a complete list of the Kara Sea bottom fauna since the identification of individual groups is neither uniform nor complete.

Some groups of Kara Sea benthos are as varied as those of the Barents Sea. According to G. Gorbunov's (1939) count 1,200 species of bottom-living animal forms have now been identified in the Kara Sea (*Table 104*).

It has to be kept in mind when considering this list that 91 forms given in it for the Kara Sea have so far been found only in the straits but not in the Sea itself. On the other hand, some benthos groups have not yet been properly studied. Taking this into account one may assume that the number of species of the bottom animal forms actually living in the Kara Sea is no fewer than 1,500 (about 60 per cent of the Barents Sea fauna).

Within the limits of the Sea itself the highest specific variety of the bottom fauna is found in two areas. First of all along the eastern shores of Novaya Zemlya and partly in the Baydaratskaya Guba and off the coast of Yamal, whither the Barents Sea waters carry its varied fauna. The fauna is brought largely by waters skirting Novaya Zemlya to the north and through the Kara Gates, and to a lesser extent through Matochkin Shar and Yugorsky Shar. This fauna is adapted mainly to the shallows of the Sea outside the zone of brown mud.

Secondly a varied fauna of the bathyal and abyssal layers of the north Atlantic and the central parts of the Arctic basin penetrates the Kara Sea from the north. This fauna is distributed mostly about the great depths of the Sea since it is very tolerant of the conditions of life of the brown mud. However, some individual members of this fauna move to places outside the limits of the brown mud, where the water is less deep.

G. Gorbunov (1946) notes that one of the *Sadko* stations recorded 200 species of different animal forms at 698 m near the northern end of the slope tending towards the greater depths, between Franz Joseph Land and Severnaya Zemlya.

As one moves from the northern parts of the Sea into the southern, and from the shores of Novaya Zemlya into the central part of the Sea, the qualitative variety of the fauna decreases, while the quantitative predominance of

*Table 104**

Benthos groups	Number of species in			
	Kara Sea	Barents Sea	White Sea	Laptev Sea
Foraminifera	135	190	(80?)	46
Porifera	61(37)	135	52	8
Coelenterata	86(62)	109	82	41
Nematoda	(41)	—	—	—
Polychaeta	148(151)	200	120	36
Gephyrea	8(8)	11	4	7
Bryozoa	172(151)	200	93	10
Brachiopoda	2(4)	4	1	?
Copepoda	(13)	—	—	?
Cirripedia	6(5)	6	6	?
Isopoda	49(46)	37	7	8
Cumacea	19(23)	9	4	?
Schizopoda	12	21	7	2
Tanaidacea	4	—	—	—
Amphipoda	225(221)	262	80	63
Decapoda	14(17)	25	13	5
Pantopoda	25(29)	24	18	7
Mollusca	138(157)	224	127	57
Echinodermata	47(55)	62	22	33
Tunicata	31(29)	50	28	26
Pisces	61(17)	174	53	39
Total	1,263(1,196)	—	—	—

* The numbers in parentheses are taken from the work of T. Pergament (1945).

some individual forms, so characteristic of the southern part of the Sea (Stuxberg, the zoologist of the O. Nordenskjöld expedition, drew attention to it as early as 1886), and of the central parts, with brown mud soils, becomes more and more evident.

The basic fauna of the Kara Sea consists of the high Arctic endemic fauna peculiar to the epicontinental seas of the Arctic basin. This high Arctic fauna consists of two quite different generic groups: one, typically marine, inhabits the more saline parts; the other, living in brackish water, is adapted to river mouths and estuaries, and to the inlets of the southern and southeastern parts of the Sea.

One may add to this high Arctic marine fauna some pan-Arctic forms, i.e. forms thriving in both the Arctic sub-regions—the low Arctic and the high Arctic, and the Arctic-boreal forms, with an even wider distribution, which are common to both the Arctic and the boreal regions. A few forms are distributed even more widely throughout the whole world ocean.

The following most common forms may be mentioned (G. Gorbunov, 1937) among this group of fauna typical of the Kara Sea: the molluscs *Portlandia lenticula*, *P. intermedia*, *P. fraterna*, *P. arctica*, *Leda pernula*, *Astarte acuticosta*, *A. crenata*, *A. borealis*, *A. montagui*, *Pecten* (*Propeamussium*) *groenlandicum, P. imbrifer, Lima hyperborea, Arca glacialis,* Axinus (*Thyasira flexuosus*), *Saxicava arctica,* crustaceans *Mesidothea sabini, M. sabini robusta, M. sibirica, Calathura robusta, Munnopsis typica, Anonyx nugax, Acanthostepheia malmgreni, Hetairus polaris, Eualus gaimardi, Sabinea septemcarinata, Hegocephalus inflatus, Haploops tubicola, Paroediceros lynceus, Arrhis phylonyx,* the worms *Onuphis conchilega, Pista maculata, Pectinaria hyperborea, Apomatus globifer, Nereis zonata, Nephthys malmgreni, Terebellides strömi,* and the pycnogenids *Nymphon robustum, N. spinosum* var. *hirtipes, N. sluiteri* and *N. strömi gracillipes,* the echinoderms *Ophioscoles glacialis, Ophiocantha bidentata, Ophiocten sericeum, Ophiopleura borealis, Stegophiura nodosa, Pontaster tenuispinus, Ctenodiscus crispatus, Myriotrochus rincki, Trochostoma arctica* and *Trochoderma elegans, Gorgonocephalus arcticus, Heliometra glacialis* and *Poliometra prolixa.*

Moreover in the off-shore, mainly southernly, more shallow part of the Sea the following are preponderant: *Portlandica arctica, P. fraterna, Macoma calcarea, M. baltica* and *M. moesta, Astarte borealis* and *A. montagui, Mesidothea sibirica,* while in the depths *Portlandia frigida, Astarte acuticosta* and *A. crenata, Pecten groenlandicus, Ophiopleura borealis* and *Poliometra prolixa* are more significant.

The bays and inlets of the southern part of the Sea, which receive the inflow of rivers from the mainland, give shelter to an abundant brackish-water fauna, which here represents the basic part of the community. Marine and fresh-water euryhaline forms are mingled with it. Thus, for example, according to A. Probatov's data (1934) from the Kara Inlet (southwestern shore of Baydaratskaya Inlet) the proportions of the 25 species of fish present are as given in *Table 105.*

Table 105

Group	No. of fish species	Percentage
Typically fresh-water fishes	2	8
Of a brackish relict aspect (Salmonidae, Coregonidae, Osmeridae, goby, Gadidae, stickleback)	16	64
Marine euryhaline fishes	7	28

Among the invertebrates a whole community of the brackish-water relicts is found here in large numbers, first of all the crustaceans *Limnocalanus grimaldi, Mysis oculata, M. relicta, Mesidothea entomon glacialis, Pontoporeia affinis, Pseudalibrotus birulai, Gammaracanthus loricatus lacustris, Oediceros minor, Monoculodes minutus, Acanthostepheia incarinata* and *Brandtia fasciatoides.*

All these relict crustaceans provide abundant food for fish, which are also relict. Whereas the Ob–Yenisey waters, spreading over the surface of the south of the Kara Sea, at times carry members of fresh-water plankton far to the north, and still farther north the brackish-water community (Fig. 100), so also the salty deep waters pulled by the undertow far up the estuarian zones draw with them more euryhaline bottom dwellers such as, for example, the polychaetes *Ampharete vegae*, *Marenzelleria wireni*, *Laonice annenkovae*, the molluscs *Portlandia arctica*, *P. aestuariorum*, and *Cyrtodaria kurriana* usually found only in fresh water, and with them the genuine marine forms: *Perigonimus yoldiae-arcticae*, *Nephthys malmgreni*, *Terebellides strömi*, *Mesidothea sibirica*, *M. sabini robusta*, *Diastylis sulcata stuxbergi*, *Paroediceros intermedius*, *Gammarus setosus*, *Lora novajya-zemlyensis*, *Rhizomolgula globularis* and others.

The last-mentioned marine bottom dwellers penetrate to the south of Cape Drovyanoy in Obskaya Inlet, and in the Gulf of Yenisey as far as the Shirokaya Bay.

There is a considerable quantitative preponderance of echinoderms in the Kara Sea benthos, and, in fact, this Sea may quite rightly be called the sea of echinoderms. In the deep western part of the sea no less than four-fifths of the benthos biomass consists of echinoderms. However, the echinoderms here are not as varied as in the Barents Sea. Gorbunov records only 47 species of echinoderms for the Kara Sea itself. Apparently, the molluscs too are not so strongly represented here as in the Barents Sea. Besides the echinoderms species of the genera Portlandia, Mesidothea and Synidothea stand out among the rest of the bottom fauna.

The zoobenthos of the Kara Sea as an indicator of its hydrological conditions. Several mass benthos forms of the Barents Sea penetrate into the Kara Sea either by skirting Novaya Zemlya or by entering through the southern passages, such as the Arctic-boreal, low Arctic, sub Arctic and to some extent boreal ones. Here they become indicators of the warmer and more saline Barents Sea waters (Fig. 104). This influence of the more warmth-loving Barents Sea fauna is plainly felt in the region between the islands of Wiese and Uyedineniye. Here in the region of Wiese Island, and to the east of it, approximately up to 87° E longitude there are found Arctic-boreal species foreign to the Kara Sea. All these forms are brought here by the terminal streams of the Novaya Zemlya branch of the North Cape current which enters the northern part of the Kara Sea from the west.

The heating of this part of the Kara Sea by the warm waters of the intermediate layer, which enters it from the north, furthers the penetration of the Barents Sea fauna into the central part of its northern half. The molluscs *Pecten islandicus*, the crustaceans *Epimeria loricata*, *Pleustes panoplus*, *Aristias tumidus*, *Centromedon pumilus*, *Eurysteus melanops*, *Calathura brachiata*, *Pandalus borealis*, *Spirontocaris turgida*, *S. spina*, the echinoderms *Ophiopholis aculeata*, *Henricia sanguinolenta*, *Stephanasterias albula*, *Strongylocentrotus droebachiensis*, *Psolus phantapus*, and the brachiopod *Rhynchonella psittacea* are most characteristic of this fauna. Some members of this fauna go down the Novaya Zemlya trough as far as Blagopoluchiya Bay and Pakhtusov Island.

Gorbunov's survey has shown that Matochkin Shar is of little importance for the immigration of the Barents Sea fauna to the east. The Kara Gates play a much greater role in this movement, and the influence of the flow of the

Barents Sea forms through that passage is felt even along the western shores of Yamal. Such warm-water forms as *Orchomenella nana*, *Tryphosa hoerringi*, *Hyas araneus*, *Eupagurus pubescens*, *Mytilus edulis*, *Solaster endeca*, *Cucumaria frondosa*, cod, haddock and others have been found on the Kara Sea

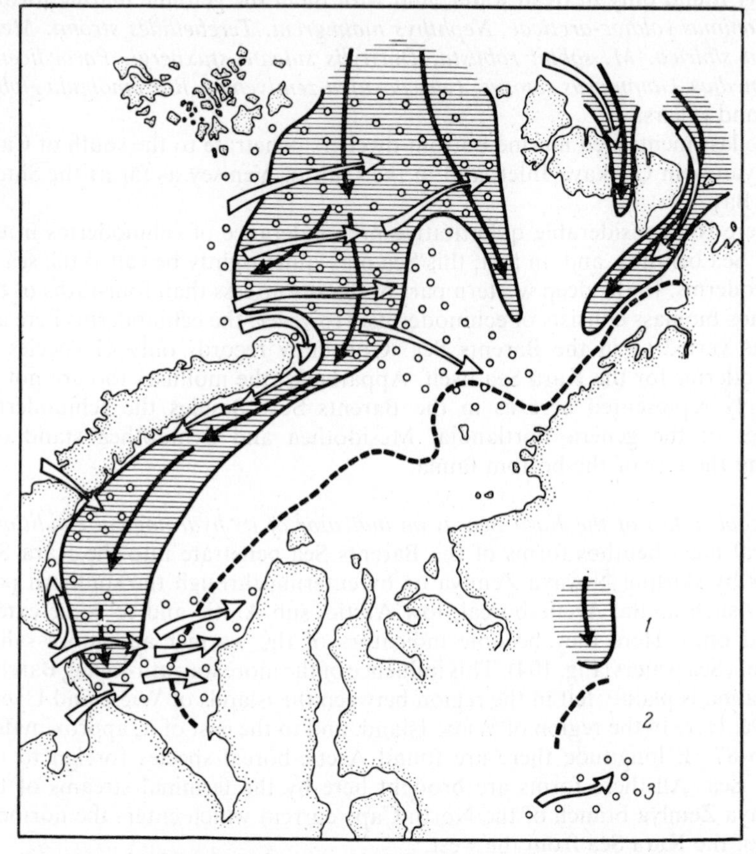

FIG. 104. Main ways of penetration into the Kara Sea of benthos of different biogeographical nature (according to different workers). *1* Forms of the intermediate warm layer and of the cold deep layers; *2* Northern boundary of forms brought down by the discharge from the mainland; *3* Sublittoral deep-water forms and those of the Barents Sea (marked by circles).

side in immediate proximity to the Kara Gates. The latter have a purely Barents Sea fauna.

Many typical members of the Kara Sea fauna such as *Synidothea bicuspida*, *S. nodulosa*, *Mesidothea sabini*, *M. sibirica*, *Lembos arcticus*, *Paramphithoe polyacantha*, *Melita formosa* and others penetrate through Yugor Shar from east to west into the Pechora region of the Barents Sea. No immigration to the west through the Kara Gates has been observed.

A large number of original forms, characteristic of the warmer waters of the northern Atlantic, immigrate from the great depths of the Arctic basin and from the intermediate 'warm' layer of the Atlantic waters from the north into the Kara Sea.

At the same time a strongly marked phenomenon 'of the displacement of zones' occurs in the Kara Sea. The bathypelagic fauna of the Arctic basin penetrating the Kara Sea from the north through the deep troughs, and the

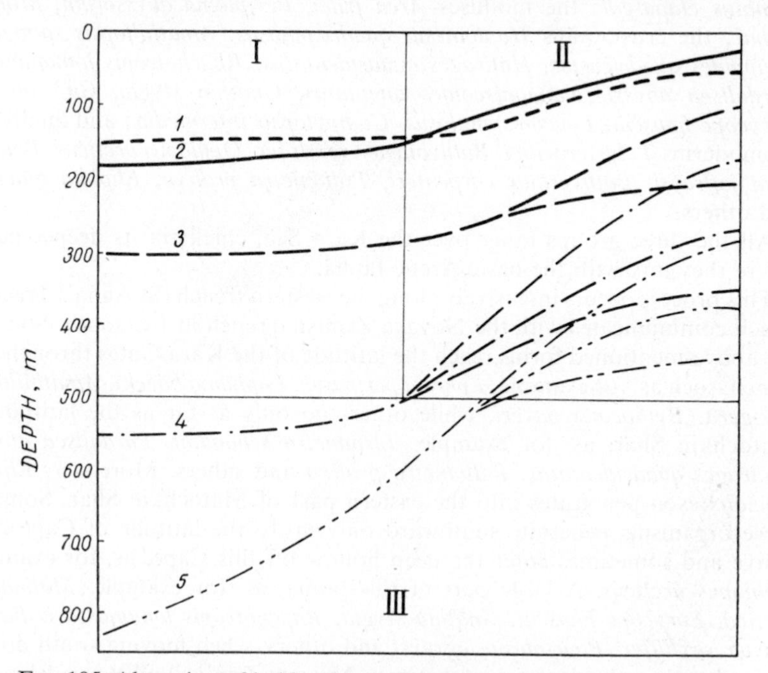

FIG. 105. Alteration of habitat-level of members of the bottom fauna in Kara Sea. *I* Barents Sea; *II* Kara Sea; *III* Arctic basin and its slopes; *1* and *2* Main biocoenoses of the Barents Sea; *3* Echinoderm community; *4* Deep-water Atlantic fauna; *5* Abyssal fauna of the Arctic basin (Filatova and Zenkevitch, 1957).

Barents Sea fauna immigrating to the Kara Sea, rise to some levels unusual for them (Fig. 105). This is often observed when passing from the oceans to the seas fringing them, and from the seas into their bays. *Portlandia arctica*, which lives at depths of 150 to 200 m in the Pechora trough of the Barents Sea and in the White Sea, is frequently found at depths of 17 to 35 m in the Kara Sea. Shell gravel horizon (IIIrd group in the Barents Sea communities), which occupies depths of 100 to 200 m and even 250 m of the Barents Sea, rises to 20 to 100 m in the Kara Sea. The echinoderm community including *Ophiopleura* and *Trochostoma* lives in the Barents Sea at a depth of 300 to 400 m and in the Kara Sea at 50 to 100 m.

It is interesting that certain bathyal and abyssal forms reach the Kara Sea after bypassing the Barents Sea altogether, and possibly do not meet in the Kara Sea. Owing to the bottom topography the bathypelagic forms of the Arctic basin can penetrate more easily into the Kara and Laptev Seas than into the Barents Sea, except, perhaps, at its most northeasterly corner.

Among these forms penetrating from the north the following may be noted: *Virgularia glacialis* and the huge *Umbellula ancrinus*, reaching 2·5 m in length; the polychaetes *Melinnexis arctica*, *Jasmineira schaudini* and *Hyalopomatus claparedi*; the molluscs *Arca frilei*, *Periploma abyssorum*, *Mohnia mohni*; the crustaceans *Haplomesus quadrispinosus*, *Amathillopsis spinigera*, *Cleippides quadricuspis*, *Halirages quadridentatus*, *Rhachotropis lomonossovi*, *Pardalisca abyssi*, *Nannoniscoides ungulatus*, *Gnathia stygia*, *Gn. robusta*, *Eurycope hanseni*, *Leucon spinulosus*, *Compylopsis intermedia*; and finally the echinoderms *Tylaster willei*, *Bathybiaster vexillifer*, *Ophiopus arcticus*, *Pourtalesia jeffreysi*, *Bathycrinus carpenteri*, *Poliometra prolixa*, *Elipidia glacialis* and others.

All the three groups range over the Kara Sea, chiefly in its deeper parts, where they mix with the basic Arctic fauna.

This process occurs intensively along the western trench (St Anna's Trench), which communicates with the Novaya Zemlya Trench at the south. Some of the above-mentioned forms reach the latitude of the Kara Gates through this trench, such as, for example, *Ephesia peripatus*, *Laphania boecki*, *Amathillopsis spirigera*, *Bythocaris payeri*, while others go only as far as the latitude of Matochkin Shar, as, for example, *Jasmineira schaudini*, *Pardalisca abyssi*, *Halirages quadridentatus*, *Poliometra prolixa* and others. Moreover, *Elpidia glacialis* even penetrates into the eastern part of Matochkin Shar. Some of these organisms penetrate southward only up to the latitude of Cape Zhelaniye and sometimes enter the deep hollow off this Cape, as, for example, *Ophiopus arcticus*. A large part of this fauna, as, for example, *Melinnexis arctica*, *Eurycope hanseni*, *Gnathia stygia*, *Rhachotropis lomonossovi*, *Bathybiaster vexillifer*, *Pourtalesia jeffreysi* and others, when moving south do not go farther than the deep trench between Novaya Zemlya and Wiese Island.

Gorbunov records a more intensive penetration into the Kara Sea through the western trench than through the eastern. As has been mentioned above, the Kara Sea fauna acquires an original aspect owing to the rising of boreal and abyssal forms—which penetrate the Kara Sea from the north—to shallow depths which are unusual for them. Such deep-water dwellers as *Eurycope hanseni*, *Pardalisca abyssi*, *Paralibrotus setosus*, *Erichtonius brasiliensis*, *Poliometra prolixa*, *Tylaster willei* and others are found here at comparatively shallow depths.

As we have pointed out, this phenomenon is observed not only with the alien fauna, but also with typical Kara Sea forms which live here at lesser depths than in the Barents Sea; as for example, *Hymenaster pellucidus*, *Ophiopleura borealis* and others (Fig. 106).

The second route for the penetration of fauna from the central part of the Arctic basin into the Kara Sea (the boreal and abyssal forms both of the Arctic basin itself and of the north Atlantic, and the moderate bathymetric Atlantic forms living at moderate depths), passes, as has been shown by

Gorbunov, through the northern deep part of the Laptev Sea and through the deep Schokalsky and Vilkitsky Straits. Such characteristics forms as *Melinnexis arctica*, *Eurycope hanseni*, *Gnathia stygia*, *Halirages quadridentatus*, *Rhachotropis lomonossovi*, *Poliometra prolixa Elipidia glacialis* and others

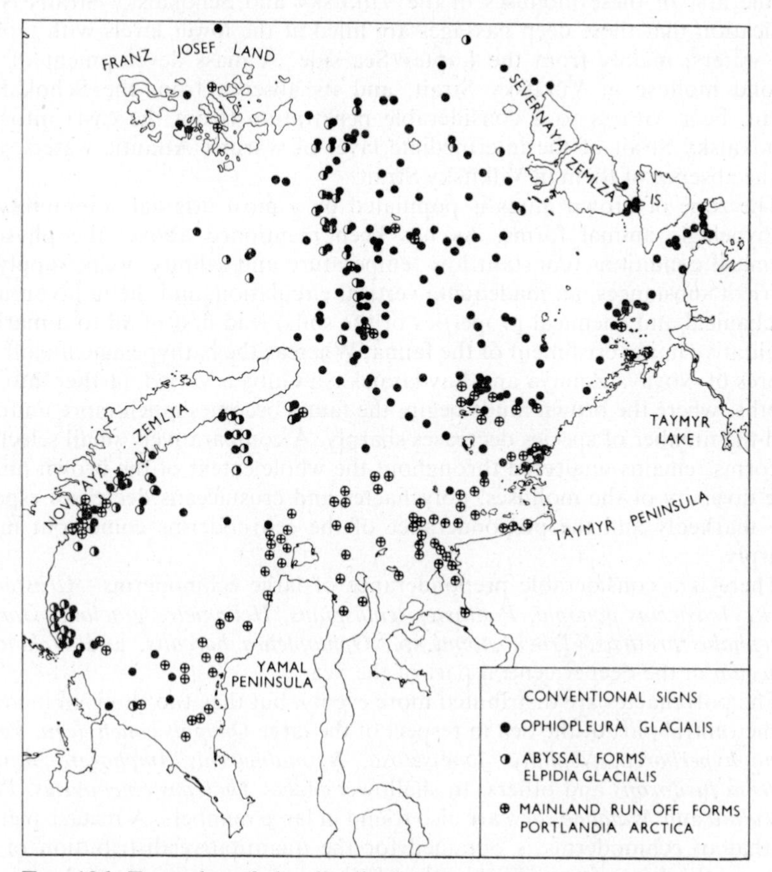

FIG. 106. Examples of the distribution in the Kara Sea of forms of different origin—lower Arctic (*Ophiopleura borealis*) from the west, bathyal and abyssal from the north and forms brought by the mainland discharge.

have likewise been found in these Straits (Fig. 106). It is not yet known how far this propagation spreads into the Kara Sea.

Shallow-water sub-Arctic, Arctic-boreal and even boreal forms, unknown in the other part of the Kara Sea and foreign to its endemic fauna, such as *Stylaroides hirsuta*, *Tryphosa hoerringi*, *Haliragoides inermis*, *Henricia sanguinolenta*, *Ophiopholis aculeata*, *Strongylocentrotus droebachiensis*, *Psolus phantapus* and others, penetrate through these Straits into the Kara Sea, by a route which so far is unknown.

The medium and shallow depths of the Kara Sea are populated mainly by a typical, sublittoral, Arctic circumpolar and east-Arctic fauna. In his analysis of the propagation of the molluscs *Portlandia arctica* and *Pecten groenlandicus* in the Siberian seas, G. Gorbunov (1941) suggests that the absence of the first of these molluscs in the Vilkitsky and Schokalsky Straits is an indication that these deep passages are filled at the lower levels with typical sea waters, mainly from the Laptev Sea side. A mass development of the second mollusc in Vilkitsky Strait, and its absence from the Schokalsky Strait, bear witness to a considerable penetration (from the east) into the Schokalsky Strait of the intermediate layer of warmer Atlantic waters, and of the absence of them in Vilkitsky Strait.

The zone of brown muds is populated by a most original community of bathypelagic animal forms. As has been mentioned above, the physico-chemical conditions (constant low temperature and salinity, weak supply of nutrient substances, an inadequate vertical circulation, and the unfavourable mechanical and chemical properties of the soils) lead first of all to a marked qualitative impoverishment of the fauna. Whereas the bathypelagic life off the shores of Novaya Zemlya and Baydaratskaya Guba is varied, farther into the depths, where the brown muds begin, the fauna becomes much more uniform and the number of species decreases sharply. A comparatively small selection of forms remains unaltered throughout the whole extent of the brown muds. The diversity of the molluscs, polychaetes and crustaceans decreases especially markedly and the preponderance of the echinoderms comes out more sharply.

There is a considerable preponderance of large echinoderms—*Urasterias lincki*, *Icasterias panopla*, *Pontaster tenuispinus*, *Heliometra glacialis*, *Gorgonocephalus arcticus*, *Trochostoma* sp., *Ophiopleura borealis*, and *Ophiocten sericeum* in the deeper central part of the Sea.

The polychaetes are distributed more evenly, but they too show an increase in the central part of the Sea in respect of the large *Onuphis conchylega*, *Pectinaria hyperborea*, *Nephthys longisetosa*, *N. malmgreni*, *Ampharete arctica*, *Owenia fusiformis* and others. In shallower places *Thelepus cincinnatus*, *Pista maculata* and *Maldane sarsi* are also found in large numbers. A reverse picture to that of echinoderms is obtained for the quantitative distribution of bivalves—the large forms live in the shallows on grey sandy mud: *Astarte borealis placenta*, *Serripes groenlandicum*, *Astarte montagui*, *Macoma calcarea*, *M. moesta* and *Portlandia arctica*. In the northern part of the Sea, the biomass increases to 100 to 200 and even to 300 g/m^2 in respect of *Astarte crenata crebricostata*, in the southern part—of *Cardium ciliatum*. In the area of the Novaya Zemlya Trench the bivalves form a biomass of about 1 g/m^2, mainly in respect of *Axinus orbiculatus*, *Thyasira ferruginosa*, *Dacridium vitreum*, *Yoldiella frigida*, *Y. fraterna*, *Y. lenticula* which are all of small size. Foraminifera are highly developed in the Kara Sea (Z. Shchedrina, 1938) and adapted mainly to the bathymetric part of the sea; hence the numbers of Foraminifera increase with the increase of the brown mud areas and decrease of benthos biomass. Sand Foraminifera are greatly predominant in the deeper parts occupied by brown mud, while the lime Foraminifera are so in the southeastern shallow parts; this stands in agreement with the suggestion of the increased amounts of carbon dioxide in the regions of brown mud. Z. Shchedrina (1938) and T. Gorshkova (1957) recorded *Ammobaculites cassis*, *Verneulina polystropha*, *Spiroplectammina biformis*, *Elphidium gorbunovi*, *Reophax curtus* and others in the shallow areas. Shchedrina relates *Trochommina turbinata*, *Nonion labradoricum*, *N. orbiculare*, *N. stelliger*, *Hormosina globulifera*, *H. ovicula*, *Saccoriza ramosa*, *Trochammina globuliformis*, *Elphidium incertum* and others to the group of the brown mud forms.

On the brown muds the main forms are the Foraminifera *Saccorhiza ramosa* and *Harmosina globulifera*, the sponge *Polymastia uberrima*, the coelenterate *Actinium metridium*, members of the Eunephthya genera and the very large coral *Umbellula encrinus*, the polychaetes *Nephthys ciliata*, *Nicomache lumbricalis*, and *Thelepus cincinnatus*, the Sipunculidae *Phascolosoma minuta*, the crustaceans *Mesidothea sabini*, *M. sibirica*, *Sabinea septemcarinata* and *Sclerocrangon ferox*, the pantopoda *Colossendeis proboscidea*, the gastropod mollusc *Neptunea curta*, the bivalves *Pecten groenlandicus* and *Astarte crebricostata* and especially various echinoderms, also the asteroids *Pontaster tenuispinus*, brittle stars *Ophiopleura borealis*, *Ophioscolex glacialis*, *Ophiocantha bidentata*, *Asterias panopfa*, *A. lincki*, *Hymenaster pellucidus*, the holothurians Molpadia and Trochostoma, and the lilies *Poliometra prolixa*.

A comparatively large number of forms which rise above the bottom, such as Metridium, Umbellula, Eunephtya, Colossendeis, Poliometra are characteristic of the whole of this fauna. The very large size of most of the abovementioned forms is remarkable; on the other hand the predominance of the 'parachute' type of forms—Polymastia, Mesidothea, Pecten, Pontaster, Hymenaster, Gorgonocephalus and others—is also interesting. These three factors are evidently the ways of adaptation to soft-floor conditions.

It is difficult to understand how the echinoderms with their solid calcareous skeletons can reach such a high level of well-being on the brown mud, since the carbonates are not retained in the floor itself, and we have never found any accumulation of shell gravel in the areas of the occurrence of brown mud; on the contrary a rapid process has been observed of the solution of the shells of dead molluscs and an evident shortage of calcium carbonate in the living ones.

The fish population of the brown mud, which is very small, is also remarkable. It consists usually of small-sized members of the Cyclopteridae, Zoarcidae and Cottidae families (the most common ones are *Liparis coefoedi*, *Icelus bicornis* and *Triglops pingelii*). However, even these small-sized fish are extremely rarely found. None of the rich selection of commercial fish of the Barents Sea are found on the brown mud. They are kept away also by the low temperature of the bathymetric layer all the year round (below zero). Only the long rough dab (*Hippoglossoides platessoides*) lives here in small numbers, as immature specimens or mature dwarfs.

The biocoenotic groups of the Kara Sea benthos were thoroughly studied by Z. Filatova and L. A. Zenkevtich (1957). These workers have distinguished seven basic biocoenoses (Fig. 107) which have been combined into four groups: (1) high Arctic, bathypelagic with a preponderance of echinoderms, Foraminifera, small-sized molluscs and polychaetes; (2) high Arctic shallow-water forms, also with a preponderance of echinoderms, mostly small brittle stars; (3) high Arctic forms from the littoral shallows with a preponderance of molluscs; and (4) low Arctic Barents Sea forms.

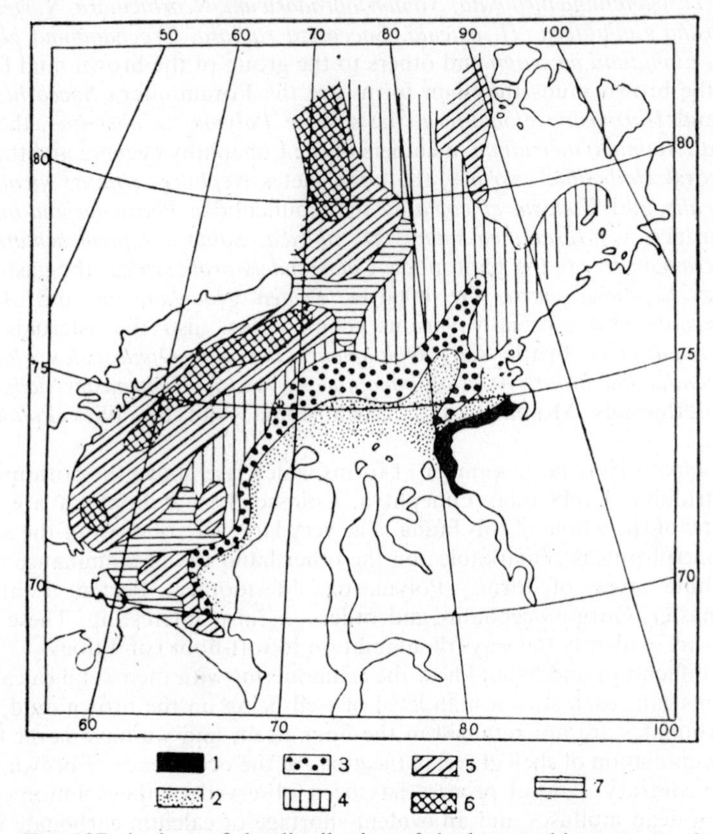

FIG. 107. A chart of the distribution of the bottom biocoenoses of the Kara Sea (Filatova and Zenkevitch, 1957). 1 *Portlandia aestuariarum*; 2 *Portlandia arctica*; 3 *Astarte borealis placenta*; 4 *Ophiocten sericeum*; 5 *Ophiopleura borealis*; 6 *Ophiopleura–Elpidia*; 7 *Spiochaetopterus typicus.*

Quantitative distribution of benthos. In spite of its great qualitative variety the bathypelagic fauna of the Kara Sea is much inferior in numbers to the benthos of the southern half of the Barents Sea (Fig. 109); however, in some regions of the Kara Sea it is higher than the benthos biomass of its northern part. The average benthos biomass of the western part of the Sea is 50 g/m².

As can be seen from the chart, the benthos biomass of the central part of the Sea, in the area of brown muds, is less than 5 g/m², and at times is no more

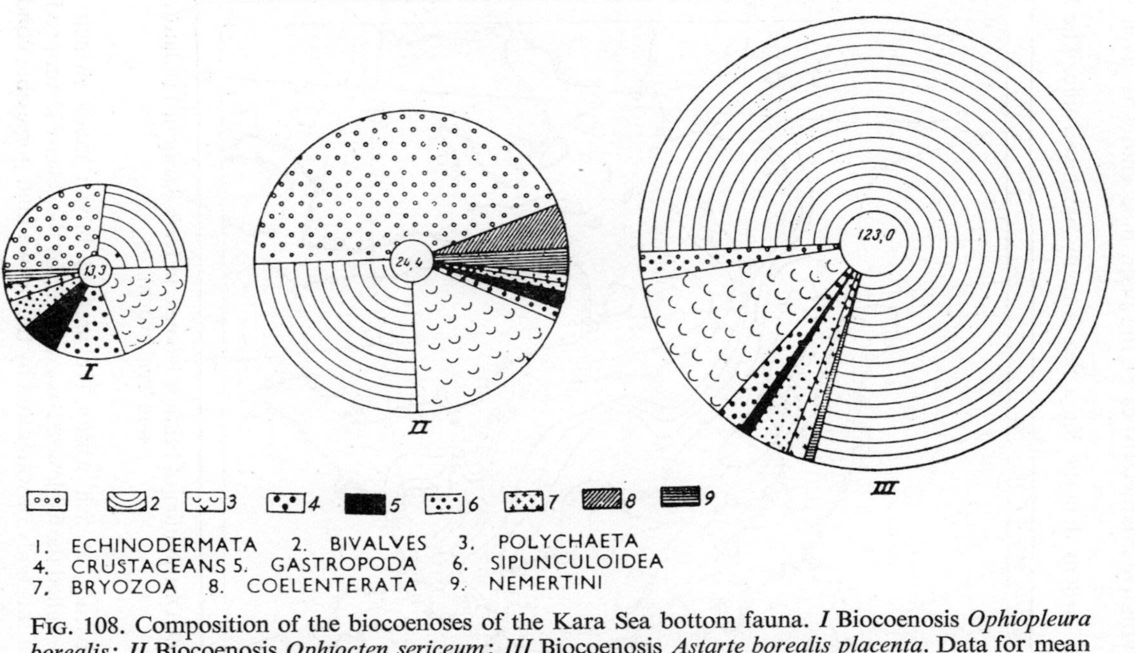

FIG. 108. Composition of the biocoenoses of the Kara Sea bottom fauna. *I* Biocoenosis *Ophiopleura borealis*; *II* Biocoenosis *Ophiocten sericeum*; *III* Biocoenosis *Astarte borealis placenta*. Data for mean biomass (g/m^3) inside the circles (Filatova and Zenkevitch, 1957).

than 1 to 3 g/m². The biomass increases at lesser depths, and on the shallows off the Yamal shores to 100 or 200 and at times even to 300 g/m².

The quantitative characteristics of the main biocoenoses is given in Fig. 108.

Thus it is evident that the Kara Sea is really bioanisotropic. The almost

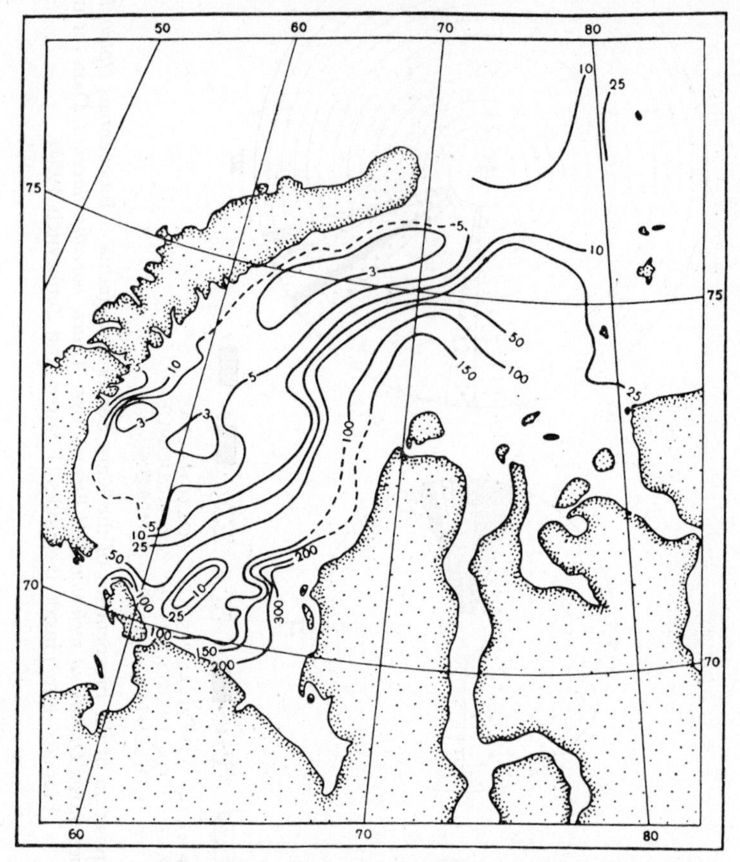

FIG. 109. Distribution of benthos biomass in Kara Sea (g/m³) (Filatova and Zenkevitch).

complete absence of fish within the area of brown muds (which might justifiably be called the fishless sea) is explained by the general lower productive properties of this body of water and by the brown mud possessing conditions unfavourable to fish-life.

The benthos biomass of the Kara Sea brown mud is twenty times lower than the average Barents Sea biomass; the productivity difference, however, is still more marked, since the processes of biological plankton production are almost suspended for 8 to 9 months and as a consequence all the links of the food chain are slackened. The lowering of productive properties of the Kara Sea becomes even more evident when benthos is estimated from the point of view of its nutrient significance.

A very great predominance of echinoderms and above-mentioned excessive size bring the amounts of edible benthos within the zone of brown muds to practically nothing.

Quite another picture is observed in the shallow coastal zone of the Kara Sea (on the average less than 50 m deep). Benthos is fairly abundant here and there is quite a large number of fish.

Fish

Kara Sea fish (according to A. P. Andriashev, 1954) include the 53 species listed in *Table 106*.

Table 106

Petromyzonidae	1	Scombresocidae	1	Ammodytidae	1
Squalidae	2	Gadidae	6	Scombridae	1
Rajidae	1	Gasterosteidae	2	Scorpaenidae	1
Clupeidae	2	Lampridae	1	Cottidae	6
Salmonidae	5	Anarhichaedidae	1	Agonidae	3
Osmeridae	2	Lumpenidae	3	Cyclopteridae	1
Anguillidae	1	Pholidae	1	Liparidae	2
Belonidae	1	Zoarcidae	4	Pleuronectidae	4
				Total	53

In respect of brackish-water forms, suitable conditions for developing local fisheries exist in the southern part of the Sea, off the mainland and along the coast of Novaya Zemlya. Raw material for this would come chiefly from Arctic Sea whitefish (coregonoids), frostfish (Osmeridae), navaga and arctic cod (Gadidae) and among the other families Polar dab and goby. Many other fish are caught there of the coregonoids and certain salmon (beardie, *Stenodus leucicthus nelma*, grayling and others) and herring. Cod is fairly frequently caught off the Novaya Zemlya coast, especially within the regions of the Kara Gates and Matochkin Shar.

The exceptional poverty of the fish population of the open parts of the Kara Sea is obvious from the following fact. In 1945 a trawler expedition worked in the Kara Sea. A commercial otter-trawl was in operation for 43 hours in different parts of the Sea. The total amount of fish caught was about 500 small-sized specimens, of a total weight of a few dozen kilogrammes.

Zoogeographical composition of the fauna. The nine following benthos groups may be distinguished in the Kara Sea fauna, according to the nature of their geographical range: (*1*) Arctic (mostly high Arctic) circumpolar forms; (*2*) Forms of the eastern sector of the Arctic. To these two groups, forming the nucleus of our Siberian Sea fauna, belong no less than 50 per cent of all the Kara Sea benthos. In the group of the Arctic forms of the Arctic eastern sector, the brackish-water community, living in large numbers in the diluted waters of the off-shore zones and the river mouths, is of importance. These are the relicts of former eras of more considerable water-dilution and of even more severe climate; (*3*) Arctic-boreal species; (*4*) Sub-Arctic Barents Sea forms; (*5*) The bathypelagic fauna of the central parts of the Arctic basin, which penetrates through the deep troughs on to the continental shelf of the marginal seas of the eastern part of the Arctic; (*6*) Warm-water north Atlantic forms, which penetrate into the Kara Sea either directly from the north from the warm intermediate layer of the central part of the Arctic basin, or from the west from the Barents Sea; (*7*) Fresh-water forms; (*8*) Endemic forms of the Kara Sea; (*9*) Cosmopolitan forms.

Except for the fourth group this division can be applied to the fauna of other seas situated to the east of the Kara Sea. Gorbunov gives the following zoogeographical characteristics for the 97 mass species of the Kara Sea in percentages:

High Arctic	15	52	Arctic-boreal	46
Pan-Arctic	37		Cosmopolitan	2

It should be noted that, among the mass benthos forms, the sub-Arctic and warm-water Atlantic species are not represented.

5

The Laptev Sea

I. HISTORY OF EXPLORATION

Nordenskjöld's expedition on the *Vega* (1878–79) marked the beginning of the exploration of the fauna and flora of the Laptev Sea, which was continued by the Russian expeditions of Toll on the *Zarya* (1900–03) and Vilkitsky on the *Taimyr* and *Vaigach* (1913). In the Soviet era the Norwegian expeditions on the ship *Mod* (1918–20 and 1921–24), and the Soviet expeditions of Khmisnikov (1926) and of Yu. Tchirikhin (1927) on the icebreakers *Lithke* (1934) and *Sadko* (1937), have worked in the Laptev Sea.

II. PHYSICAL GEOGRAPHY

Situation, bottom topography and size

The Laptev Sea lies to the east of the Taymyr Peninsula and Severnaya Zemlya, extending to the Novosibirsk Islands. The Laptev and East Siberian Seas have the most severe climate and the lowest salinity of all the seas off the northern coast of Asia.

As in the Kara Sea, a deep gully enters the western part of the Sea from the north; saline and somewhat warmer waters flow into the Laptev Sea through it. To the east of the northern end of Taymyr the great depths of the Arctic basin approach nearest to the Asian coast, lying only 100 to 200 km off the Severnaya Zemlya and Taymyr shores. The area of the Sea is 650,000 km^2; its volume is 338,000 km^3, its average depth is 519 m and its greatest depth is 2,980 m.

Temperature and salinity

The eastern part of the Sea with depths no greater than 60 to 80 m is considerably diluted, and in summer warmed by the abundant waters of the great Siberian rivers: Khatanga, Lena, and Yana. At a distance of 100 km and more to the northeast of the Lena estuary the salinity is 5 to 6‰ down to a depth of 20 to 25 m (Fig. 110). The fresh Lena waters, carried out far to the north, dilute the surface layers of the Sea. In 1893 the *Fram* recorded a salinity of 14·9‰ in latitude 75° 32′ and a salinity of 18‰ at 76° 21′, northwest of the Novosibirsk Islands, 500 km from the Lena estuary. The highest salinity is observed in the northwestern part of the Sea, whence more saline waters enter from the north; a salinity of more than 28‰ was observed there even on the surface.

In the northwestern part the surface temperature, even in the summer, may be about zero. Ranges of temperature and salinity taken north of the Khatanga river near the Taymyr Peninsula (76° 04′ N latitude) during the *Vega* voyage, in August, are given in *Table 107*.

In the southeastern part of the Sea the highest surface salinity is 17·0‰ and the deep-water salinity is 30·5‰. The salinity is commonly much lower,

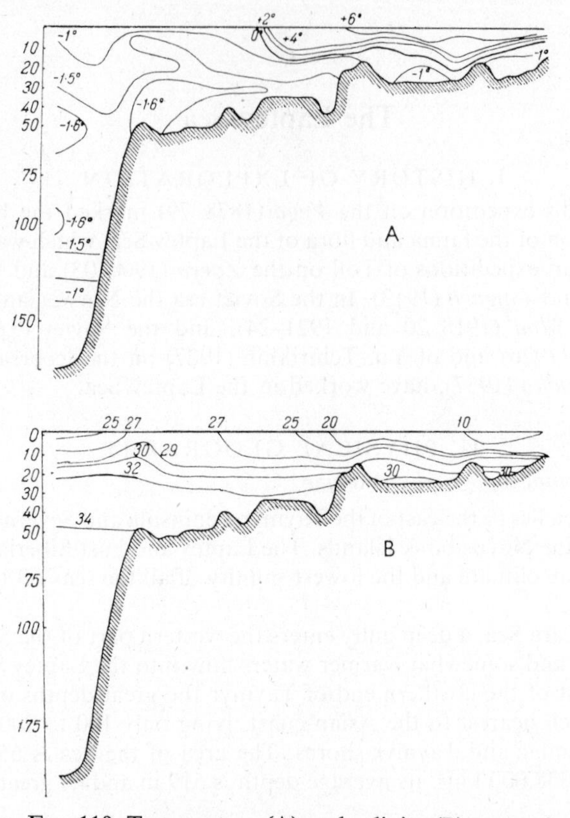

FIG. 110. Temperature (A) and salinity (B) ranges in the cross section of Laptev Sea from its southeastern part (on right of graph) to northwest (Wiese).

decreasing more and more as one approaches the rivers. In the southeastern part the temperature rises in the summer and on the surface it may reach 5° to 8°. The ranges of temperature and salinity observed by Yu. Tchirikhin

Table 107

Depth, m	t°	S‰
0	−0·5	27·4
10	−1·0	28·2
20	−1·1	29·8
30	−1·2	31·9
40	−1·3	33·5
50	−1·4	33·6
59	−1·4	34·4

northward from the Lena estuary in 71° 43′ N latitude are given in *Table 108*.

Table 108

Depth, m	$t°$	$S‰$
0	8·12	Insignificant
8	−0·43	19·04
15	−0·75	23·33

Evidently the fauna of the upper and lower layers of water would differ greatly. The diluted surface layers of the western part of the Sea spread northwards for hundreds of miles from the river estuaries and the salinity at that distance is at times 15–18–25‰. On the other hand the saline waters travel southwards along the bottom troughs.

After a long, harsh winter, when the waters are almost at freezing temperature, there comes a short summer, and the surface waters of the parts of the Sea freed from ice are warmed partly by the river waters, partly by the sun, to a few degrees (up to 4°) above zero. But the polar ice limit is not far away even in the summer.

III. FLORA AND FAUNA

According to the investigations of K. Derjugin (1932), M. Virketis (1932), I. Kisselev (1932) and A. Popov (1932) the Laptev Sea plankton and benthos have the composition given below.

Table 109

Flagellata	6	Conjugatae	4
Peridineae	28	Diatomaceae	61
Chlorophyceae	25	Cyanophyceae	24
		Total	148

Qualitative composition of phytoplankton

According to Usachev, the species and forms which have been found in the southern part of the Sea, which is exposed to the strong influence of the Lena waters, are those listed in *Table 109*.

In this fairly large selection of forms Kisselev distinguishes first of all the groups of brackish-fresh-water forms (23 per cent), most common within the off-shore, highly diluted region: *Aphanizomenon flos-aquae*, the species Anabaena, *Melosira italica*, *M. islandica*, *M. granulata*, *Asterionella gracillima* and some others.

The author includes a number of species Diploneis and Navicula in the group of the brackish-water forms (4 per cent). And finally to the group of marine forms (5 per cent) there belong: *Thalassiosira baltica*, *Coscinodiscus*, *marginatus*, *Chaetoceros gracile* and *Ch. Wighami*, *Caloneis brevis*, *Navicula* sp., *Dinophysus arctica*, *Peridinium breve*, *P. pellucidum* and others.

Qualitative composition of zooplankton

Virketis gives the composition (species and forms) for the zooplankton of the same part of the Sea in the form shown in *Table 110*.

Table 110

Tintinnoidea	5	Rotatoria	27
Scyphomedusae	1	Cladocera	5
Ctenophora	1	Copepoda	10
		Total	49

Seasonal phenomena in plankton development

Bogorov who collected plankton in the western part of the Laptev Sea in 1934 during the period of plankton 'spring' found in the surface layer (0 to 10 m) some algae in bloom (average 3,400 mg/m³); the zooplankton, however, had not yet reached its maximum (the average biomass was 110 mg/m³). On the other hand in the eastern part of the Sea the plankton development had already reached its summer phase—phytoplankton decreased (average 500 mg/m³) while the amount of zooplankton had risen to 313 mg/m³. At places of maximum bloom the phytoplankton biomass had in the western part of the Sea reached 14,132 mg/m³.

Quantitative distribution of zooplankton

In his quantitative analysis of the plankton of the Laptev and East Siberian Seas, V. Jashnov (1940) compares the data for: (*1*) the middle part of the Laptev Sea (depth 50 to 80 m); (*2*) a number of stations to the north and northeast of Novosibirsk Islands, and (*3*) the cross section from Kotelni Island to the Gulf of Tiksi (*Table 111*).

In some cases Appendicularia, mollusc and polychaete larvae and the pteropoda molluscs are of importance in the plankton.

It is evident from *Table 111* that Copepoda form not less than a third of the total plankton, frequently reaching 98 to 99 per cent of the whole biomass in the surface layer. Here the plankton still retains its Kara Sea character, changing its composition sharply as one moves eastward: *Calanus finmarchicus* practically disappears and is replaced first by *Pseudocalanus elongatus* and then by the inhabitants of brackish waters—*Pseudocalanus major*, *Limnocalanus grimaldi*, and *Drepanopus bungei*.

'Thus', says Jashnov, 'three concentric zones running along the Siberian coast may be distinguished. The first zone, situated in close proximity to the shore, is inhabited by a typical brackish-water fauna; the second, farther away from the shore, is characterized by the presence of marine, mainly euryhaline, species which penetrate here through the lower water layers; the third zone is a transitional one between the second and the true marine one. The width

Table 111

	Central part of Laptev Sea per cent		Stations to north and northeast of Novosibirsk Islands per cent		Section from Kotelni Island to the Gulf of Tiksi (eastern part of the Laptev Sea) per cent	
Calanus finmarchicus	52·3		3·5		1·7	
Pseudocalanus elongatus	11·1		43·1		27·7	
Limnocalanus grimaldi	—	71·3	0·2	58·2	23·3	82·6
Drepanopus bungei	—		—		21·0	
Pseudocalanus major	2·6		7·2		7·3	
Other Copepoda	5·3		4·2		1·6	
Mollusca (Pteropoda)	12·3		3·1		—	
Chaetognatha	13·7		21·8		10·0	
Coelenterata	0·7		7·2		6·6	
Others	2·0		8·3		0·8	

and distance from the shore of these zones depend primarily on the quantity of fresh water brought in by the rivers.' Jashnov (1940) points out the very interesting fact that the brackish-water community is the only endemic and autochthonous community of plankton in the Arctic basin. The western limit of its distribution is the Kara Sea. 'All the other plankton forms belong either to the number of widely distributed species or to forms whose existence is conditioned by the penetration of the Atlantic and Pacific waters into the Arctic zone.' Jashnov adds *Halitholus cirratus* and *Calycopsis birulai* to the few crustaceans of this community.

The mean biomass of the summer zooplankton of the Laptev and East Siberian Seas, according to Jashnov (1940), is 72 mg/m³, with fluctuations from 24 to 200 mg/m³ (about 3 tons beneath each 1 km²). The total biomass of summer zooplankton in the Laptev Sea is about 3 million tons, and in the East Siberian Sea about 2 million tons.

Qualitative composition of zoobenthos

So far 405 benthos forms are known for the Laptev Sea (*Table 112*).

Table 112

Foraminifera	46	Echinodermata	33	Pantopoda	7
Porifera	8	Cirripedia	4	Lamellibranchiata	23
Hydrozoa	36	Isopoda	8	Gastropoda	32
Anthozoa	3	Amphipoda	87	Cephalopoda	1
Polychaeta	36	Schizopoda	2	Tunicata	24
Bryozoa	10	Decapoda	5	Pisces	40
				Total	405

In the diluted southeastern part of the Laptev Sea only 73 species of even this meagre fauna have been encountered (Coelenterata 5, Porifera 4, Polychaeta 8, Bryozoa 7, Mollusca 19, Crustacea 17, Pantopoda 2, Echinodermata 2, Tunicata 7, and Pisces 5).

The high Arctic forms are overwhelmingly predominant in this fauna.

Near the river estuaries either brackish-water or the most euryhaline marine forms are predominant: the crustaceans *Gammaracanthus loricatus*, *Gammarus wilkitzkii*, *Mesidothea entomon*, *Mysis oculata* var. *relicta*, the polychaetes *Polydora quadrilobata* and *Euchone papillosa*, the molluscs *Portlandia arctica*, the fish *Myoxocephalus quadricornis*. Farther out to sea *Mesidothea sabini*, *M. sibirica*, *Acanthostepheia malmgreni* and others become gradually predominant.

Popov notes a remarkable similarity between the fauna of the southeastern part of the Laptev Sea and that of the Ob–Yenisei Bay of the Kara Sea: in both cases the main part of the benthos consists of *Mesidothea sibirica*, *M. sabini* var. *robusta*, *Onisimus botkini*, *Portlandia arctica siliqua*, *Gammarus wilkitzkii*, and *Pseudalibrotis birulai*.

Qualitative composition of fish fauna

The composition of fish according to their families also deserves our attention (*Table 113*).

Table 113

	No. of species	Percentage			No. of species
Salmonidae	7	18	77	Agonidae	2
Cottidae	9	23		Osmeridae	2
Zoarcidae	7	18		Cyclopteridae	1
Liparidae	5	13		Pleuronectidae	1
Gadidae	2	5		Clupeidae	1
Acipenseridae	1			Gasterosteidae	1
				Total	39

The high Arctic and brackish-water forms are even more prevalent here than in the Kara Sea.

The fauna of the deep-water northwestern part of the Laptev Sea and that of the passages between the Severnaya Zemlya Islands must be even greater in variety. As in the Kara Sea large numbers of Arctic deep-water and intermediate warm-layer fauna of the deep trench rise to lesser depths. Some Barents Sea forms in small numbers reach the western part of the Laptev Sea.

6

The Chukotsk Sea

I. SITUATION AND HISTORY OF EXPLORATION

The Chukotsk Sea lies to the east of Wrangel Island as far as Cape Barrow and is connected with the Pacific Ocean by the shallow, narrow Bering Strait. For this reason its fauna is of special interest.

The study of the fauna of the Chukotsk Sea began with the collections made by A. Stuxberg, of the O. Nordenskjöld expedition on the *Vega* (1878–79). The Soviet period—especially the expedition of the icebreaker *F. Lithke* (1929, 1934), the Pacific Ocean expedition of the State Hydrological Institute (1932–33), the expeditions of the *Chelyuskin* (1933, 1934) and finally in 1935 that of the icebreaker *Krassin**—has been most fruitful as regards the exploration of the Chukotsk Sea.

II. PHYSICAL GEOGRAPHY

Size and bottom topography

The Chukotsk Sea (Fig. 111) is fairly large (582,000 km^2), but very shallow, being for the most part less than 50 m deep. Its volume is 51,000 km^3, its average depth 86 m, and its greatest depth 180 m.

A trench with depths of more than 50 m (the average depth of the Sea being about 45 m) enters the Chukotsk Sea to the east of Wrangel Island. This trench at first runs towards the Chukotsk Peninsula and then eastwards along it. North of 73° 30′ N latitude the bottom begins to slope down steeply into the greater depths of the Arctic basin. The floor of the Bering Strait and of the Herald Shoal is hard (sand, gravel, pebble, rock); the rest of the bottom consists of silty sands and clayey mud.

Currents

A fairly warm, strong current (Fig. 111) enters the Chukotsk Sea through the Bering Strait, travelling north along the eastern boundaries of the Sea; north of Cape Hope it divides into two branches—a northeastern and a northwestern. A cold current leaving De Long Sound moves southeast along the coast of the Chukotsk Peninsula, part of it entering the Bering Strait, but its main mass turning back into the southern part of the Sea. In general the movement through the Bering Strait is that of the Pacific Ocean waters into the Chukotsk Sea, and only to a very small extent a flow of the Chukotsk waters to the south.

Temperature and salinity

It is evident from the range of the bottom temperatures in August (Fig. 112) that the Chukotsk Sea waters are only very slightly warmed. The sea conditions

* In our further exposition we shall use the detailed summary of P. Ushakov (1945).

are very severe. For seven months (November to May) the temperature of even the surface waters remains below −1·5° (−1·6° to −1·8°); in June, September and October it keeps at about 0°, and only in July and August, off the coast, does it rise to 3°, 5° or 7° (monthly average). Only in the south-western part of the Sea, in the region of the Bering Strait, does the temperature at times rise to 12° to 14° in the summer. The deeper layers of water (except

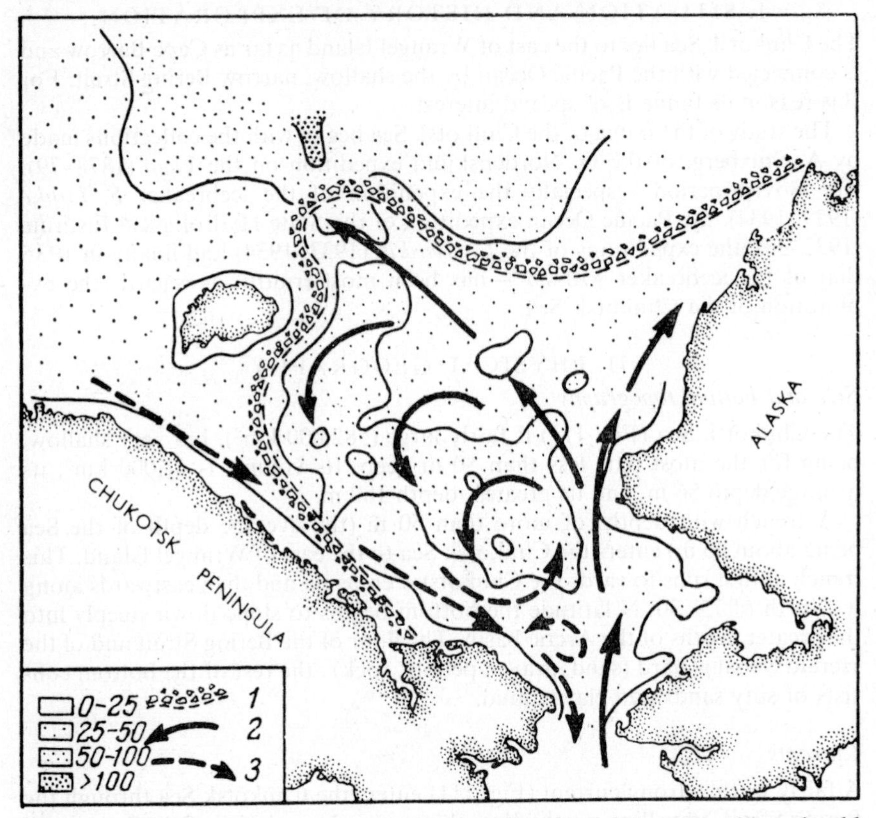

FIG. 111. The Chukotsk Sea showing depths, direction of the warm (*2*) and cold (*3*) currents and the summer boundary of the ice (*1*) (Ushakov).

for the eastern part of the Sea) have a temperature of almost 0° even in the summer (Fig. 112). In the northern parts of the Sea, near the open, deep parts of the Arctic basin, a curious temperature range is observed in the summer: 'the influence of the warm waters of the Bering Strait is still felt in the surface layer down to 20 m. The temperature reaches 2° to 3°; lower down, at a depth of 100 m, there are Arctic waters with a temperature of up to −1·7°; still lower a heating effect is observed and at a depth of 150 m the temperature is 0°' (Ratmanov, 1939). This is as far as the influence of the intermediate warm layer extends to the east.

The salinity range of the Chukotsk Sea shows a good many variations.

Waters flowing into it from the East Siberian Sea through De Long Sound have, in their deeper part, a salinity of 31·7 to 32·6‰. To the north their salinity increases, reaching 34·8‰. The salinity of the surface layers varies greatly. In summer time in the parts adjacent to the Chukotsk Peninsula the

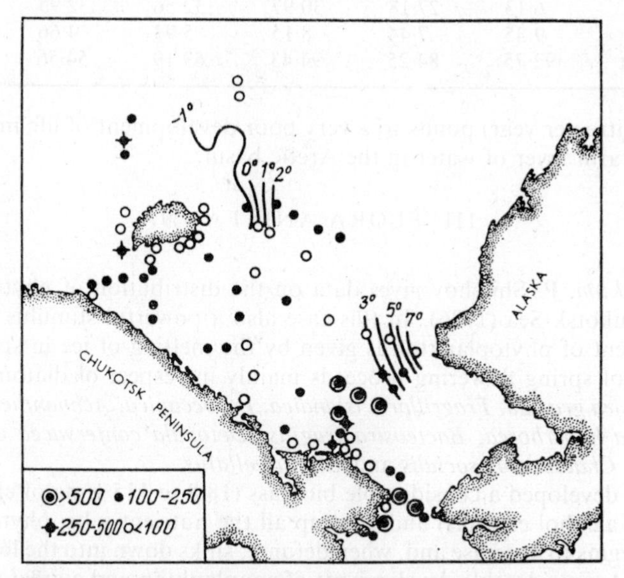

FIG. 112. Quantitative benthos distribution in the Chukotsk Sea, g/m³ (Ushakov, 1952). Summer bottom isotherms are also marked.

surface layers have a salinity of only 3–5–8‰ and sometimes even less. In the rest of the Sea it usually remains at 29 to 32·5‰ in the surface layers, but often it decreases in the regions of the melting ice by a few parts per thousand. In winter time the surface layers must acquire a considerably higher salinity owing to freezing of the water. The ice content of the Chukotsk Sea changes from year to year, and the mean ice limit in August and September, i.e. the warmest season of the year, can be indicated only approximately (Fig. 110).

Oxygen content

It is of great interest that the oxygen content in the warmed deep layer of 'Atlantic' waters, entering the Chukotsk Sea from the north, is greatly reduced, in some cases down to 20·47 per cent of saturation. The 1935 data of one of the *Krassin* stations for the northern part of the Chukotsk Sea are given in *Table 114*.

Deep 'Atlantic' water lost 5 or 6 cm³ of its oxygen per litre, receiving no fresh supply, since the time [in N. Zubov's opinion (1944) no less than four or five years] of its sinking beneath the upper diluted layer of water in the region of Spitsbergen. Such a small oxygen consumption (approximately

Table 114

Depth, m	0	10	25	50	100	154
$t°$	−0·60	−1·25	−1·46	−1·70	−1·66	−0·04
S‰	6·13	27·18	30·97	32·56	32·95	34·47
O_2 cm³	9·35	7·44	8·15	5·93	4·66	2·43
O_2 per cent	92·75	84·25	94·43	69·19	54·56	30·07

1 m³ per litre per year) points to a very poor development of life in the intermediate warm layer of water in the Arctic basin.

III. FLORA AND FAUNA

Plankton

Phytoplankton. P. Shirshov gives data on the distribution of phytoplankton in the Chukotsk Sea (1936). In this case also a powerful stimulus to a mass development of phytoplankton is given by the melting of ice in spring. This outbreak of spring flowering proceeds mainly in respect of diatoms such as *Thalassiosira gravida*, *Fragrillaria islandica*, *Fr. oceanica*, *Achnanthes taeniata*, *Amphipora hyperborea*, *Bacteosira fragilis*, *Detonula confervacea* and a few species of *Chaetoceros socialis* and *Ch. furcellatus.*

Having developed a considerable biomass (18·8 to 115·1 mg of chlorophyll per m³ in alcohol extracts) and used up all the nutrient salts, phytoplankton rapidly begins to decrease and, when defunct, sinks down into the lower layers of water. A considerable development of zooplankton and a great scarcity of phytoplankton are characteristic of the summer period of plankton life in the Chukotsk Sea. The amount of chlorophyll is usually expressed in fractions of a milligramme and rarely a few milligrammes (up to 5 or 6) per m³. In better heated sea waters the predominance of the peridineans and in the colder water of the Chaetoceros diatom genus are characteristic of 'summer' plankton.

Zooplankton. The Pacific Ocean forms have an influence on the Chukotsk Sea zooplankton. Jashnov notes the presence here of such forms as *Calanus cristatus*, *C. tonsus*, *Eucalanus bungei*, *Acartia tumida* and others, pointing out the small role played by these foreign forms which are present in restricted numbers.

According to M. Virketis (1952) the Chukotsk Sea zooplankton consists of 93 species (not counting the larvae and the doubtful forms), the Copepoda, Protozoa and Coelenterata (74 species) forming the main mass of the species. The Arctic-boreal species are the most important in respect of mass (17 per cent). The Arctic and boreal forms are equally represented. The following forms can serve as indicators of the presence of Pacific Ocean waters: among the Protozoa: *Acanthostemella norvegica*, *Tintinnopsis japonica*, *T. Kofoidi*, *Tintinnus rectus*; among the jellyfish: *Rathkea octopunctata*; among the Cladocera: *Evadne nordmanni* and *Podon leuckarti*; and among the Copepoda *Calanus cristatus*, *C. tonsus*, *Eucalanus bungei*, *Acartia clausi*, *Epilabidocera amphitrites* and others. The most typical Arctic forms are the Infusoria *Metacylis vitroides*, the jellyfish: *Euphysa flammea* and *Aeginopsis laurentis*; the Copepoda *Calanus hyperboreus*, *Euchaeta glacialis* and *Metridia longa*, and the Appendicularia *Oikopleura vanhoeffeni*.

V. Bogorov (1939) and V. Jashnov (1940) give a quantitative percentage ratio of various plankton groups of the Chukotsk Sea, set out in *Table 115*.

Table 115

Form	Plankton composition in the second half of July 1934 (Bogorov's data)		Plankton composition, August–September 1929 (Jashnov's data)
	Throughout whole water column	Surface layer (10 m deep)	
Calanus finmarchicus	—	—	44·8
Pseudocalanus elongatus	—	—	25·2
Other Copepoda	15·5	33·3	73·0
Chaetognatha	13·6	1·0	14·0
Coelenterata	—	—	5·0
Appendicularia	36·7	33·6	—
Larvae of Decapoda	25·0 } 27·6	7·5 } 32·6	—
Larvae of Polychaeta	1·3	14·0	—
Larvae of Mollusca	—	7·4	—
Larvae of Cirripedia	1·3	2·7	—
Others	6·6	0·5	8·0

The difference in the plankton composition as given by these two authors depends on the fact that Jashnov collected his data in the western and north-western parts of the Sea, often far removed from the coast, whereas Bogorov collected his data close to the Siberian shores. The relative decrease of Copepoda near the shores and the large admixture of larval forms is striking. Data on the phyto- and zoo-plankton biomass are given in *Table 116*.

The reduction of the open sea biomass to almost one-third (right-hand column) must be attributed to the season: the collection was made in the second half of July, when zooplankton had not yet reached its full development. The low indices of both parts of plankton for the Cape Angueme region (second column) are explained by the accumulation of solid ice. The eastern and western parts of the Sea were already clear of ice and phytoplankton was in a state of vigorous bloom. According to V. Jashnov's calculation the largest total biomass is almost 1 million tons; this is apparently a considerable underestimate.

Benthos

Qualitative composition. The qualitative composition of the flora and fauna of the Chukotsk Sea reveals a complex mixture of an Arctic fauna of Pacific and Atlantic origin. According to data compiled by A. D. Zinova (1952) 70 species of green, brown and red algae—29 brown and 31 red—have been

Table 116

Characteristic	Biomass of zoo- and phyto-plankton in central areas of Chukotsk Sea, mg/m³ (Bogorov's data)				Zooplankton biomass in open parts of Chukotsk Sea (Jashnov's data)
	Upper water layer down to 10 m			Through-out water column	Throughout water column
	Eastern part of Sea to Cape Angueme	Cape Angueme area among heavy ice	Western part of Sea	Whole Sea	Northwestern part of Sea
Zooplankton	232·2	100·0	139·5	160·0	64·0
Range	38 762	10 304	71 208	56 465	The greatest 177
Phytoplankton	1,510·0	379·1	2,760·0	—	—
Total biomass	1,742·2	479·1	2,899·5	—	—

found in the Chukotsk Sea. The following numbers of animal species and variants found in the Chukotsk Sea (*Table 117*) have so far been published.

As yet this list is very incomplete. Many groups have not yet been examined (Turbellaria, Nemertini, Nematoda) and others not sufficiently analysed. However, the considerably greater poverty of the Chukotsk Sea fauna compared with that of the varied fauna of the Barents Sea is revealed by a comparison of the wealth of species of its groups already studied in detail.

P. Ushakov (1952) supposes that the shallow depths, the preponderance of hard bottoms, the lowered salinity and the severe temperature conditions of the Chukotsk Sea should be considered the causes of this poverty.

Distribution. The littoral zone of the Chukotsk Sea is not populated. Only at a depth of 5 to 8 m do macrophytes live (*Entermorpha crinita*, *Dichyosiphon*

Table 117

Foraminifera	43	Cumacea	7
Porifera	8 (no less than 25)	Mysidacea	2
Hydrozoa	41	Euphausiacea	2
Alcyoniaria	2	Amphipoda	103
Actiniaria	12	Isopoda	12
Polychaeta	176	Decapoda	22
Sipunculoidea	3	Pantopoda	9
Priapuloidea	1	Mollusca	106
Echiuroidea	1	Echinodermata	31
Bryozoa	113	Enteropneusta	2
Cirripedia	7	Tunicata	28
		Pisces	37
		Total	755

faeniculaceus, *Desmarestia aculeata*, *Laminaria saccharina*, *L. bongardiana*, *Antithamnion borealis* and others).

The fauna populating the shallow sand floor (7 or 8 m) off Wrangel Island is similar in its composition to that inhabiting similar floors and depths off Novaya Zemlya. The benthos biomass in this zone is a few dozen grammes per m^3.

The population of the chief, mud-covered areas, 30 to 50 m deep, is very similar to that of the southeastern parts of the Barents Sea, and apparently to that of all the shallow Siberian seas. The basic forms here are *Macoma calcarea*, *Nucula tenuis* and *Terebellides strömi*. Apart from them the most usual among the polychaetes are: *Lysippe labiata*, *Nephthys ciliata*, *Chaetozone setosa*, *Scoloplos armiger*, *Capitella capitata*, *Scalibregma inflata* and *Sc. robusta*; among the molluscs: *Yoldia* sp. and *Axinus flexuosus* var. *gouldi*; among the crustaceans: *Ampelisca eschrichti*, *Amp. macrocephala*, *Acanthostepheia malmgreni*, *Byblis gaimordi*; and among the echinoderms: *Ophiura sarsi*, *Myriotrochus rinkii*, *Ctenodiscus crispatus* and *Ophiocten sericeum*. The ratio between the individual biomass groups is also similar to that of the southeastern part of the Barents Sea (*Table 118*).

Table 118

Vermes	35·2 g/m²	Gastropoda	2·0 g/m²
Crustacea	31·8 g/m²	Lamellibranchiata	114·6 g/m²
Echinodermata	16·2 g/m²	Varia	14·4 g/m²
		Mean biomass	214·2 g/m³

Cirripedia, hardly represented in the Kara Sea, and so far not discovered in the Laptev Sea, appear again after a long break in the Chukotsk Sea.

Benthos biomass (Fig. 112) varies usually from a few dozen grammes to 100 to 200 g/m^2, increasing only at the most southern part of the Sea and in the Bering Strait, mainly in respect of the epifauna (up to 500 g/m^2 and more). The numerical distribution of the bottom fauna in the Bering Strait and the Chukotsk Sea is given by groups in Fig. 112.

As has been pointed out by Ushakov, the main part of the bottom fauna of the Chukotsk Sea consists of Arctic-boreal, eurybiotic, widely distributed forms, as for instance, the amphipods *Ampelisca macrocephala*, *A. eschrichti*, *Pontoporeia femorata*, the polychaetes *Chaetozone setosa* and others. However, a boundary can be drawn between the areas characterized by a preponderance of typically Arctic forms, which are peculiar for all parts of the Arctic basin, and those with a preponderance of Pacific Ocean boreal forms, which penetrate through the Bering Strait. The influence of the Pacific Ocean waters on the local Arctic ones is clearly indicated by these two groups of forms (Fig. 113).

Ushakov specifies the following forms as the most characteristic Arctic and high Arctic forms—Foraminifera: *Elphidium gorbunovi*; hydroids: *Perigonimus yoldiae arcticae*; polychaetes: *Melaenis loveni*, *Gattyana amundseni*; bryozoans: *Eucratea loricata* var. *cornuta*, *Notoplites sibirica*; amphipods:

Onisimus genus and also *Haploops laevis*, *Ampelisca birulai*, *Priscillina armata*, *Acanthostepheia malmgreni*; isopods: *Mesidothea sibirica*, *M. sabini robusta*; decapods: *Spirontocaris phippsti*, *Antinoella badia*, *Castalia aphroditoides*, *Lumbriconereis algida*, *A. beringiensis*, *Arrhis phylonyx*, *Rozinante fragilis*, *Sabinea septemcarinata*, *Eualus gaimardi belhcheri*; echinoderms: *Urasterias linki*, *Heliometria glacialis*, *Ophiocten sericeum*, *Eupirgus scaber*; molluscs: *Portlandia arctica*, *Montacuta spitzbergensis*, *Periploma fragilis* and others.

In the southwestern part of the Chukotsk Sea the boreal Pacific Ocean

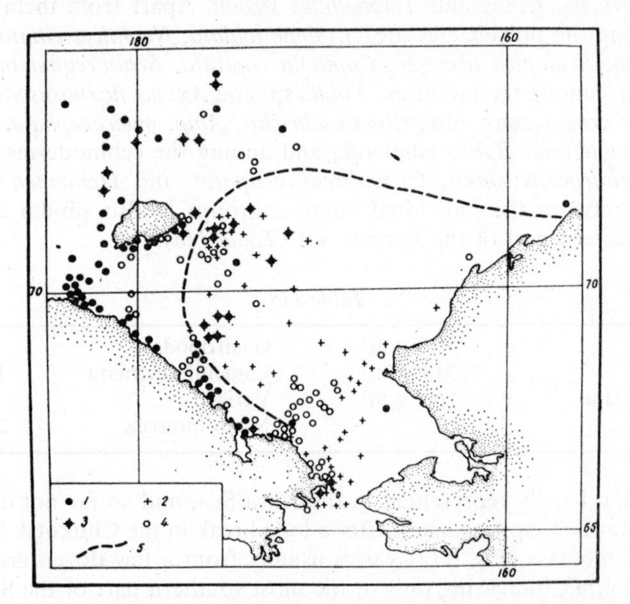

FIG. 113. Distribution of (*1*) high Arctic and (*2*) boreal Pacific forms in Chukotsk Sea; (*3*) Station with both groups; (*4*) Stations with low Arctic fauna (Ushakov).

forms are widely distributed; 50 per cent of the species consist of these groups of fauna, especially of the Decapoda, Echinodermata and Tunicata. Among the hydroids the following should be mentioned: *Halecium ochotense*, *Abietinaria variabilis*, *A. turgida*, *Sertularia similis*; among the polychaetes: *Eunoe spinicirrus*, *E. barbata*, *E. depressa*, *Gattyana ciliata*, *Spinter vegae*; among the bryozoans: *Eucratea loricata* var. *macrostoma*, *Dondrobeania pseudolevenseni*, *Leischara orientalis*; among the Cirripedia: *Balanus hesperius*, *Mesostylis dalli*, *M. bidentata*; among the amphipods: *Ampelisca derjugini*, *Harpinia gurjanovae*, *Pontharpinia nasuta*, *Metopa submajuscula*, *M. robusta*; the isopod *Janiria alascensis*; the decapods: *Pandalus goniurus*, *Eualus suckleyi*, *E. flexa*, *E. camtchatica*, *Crangon dalli*, *Pagurus rathbuni*, *Paralithodes platypus*, *Myas coarctatus alutaceus*, *Chionoecetes opilio*; the molluscs: *Yoldia scissurata*, *Venericardia crebricostata*, *V. crassidens*, *V. paucicostata*,

Cardium californiensis, *Serripes laperousii*; the echinoderms: *Solaster dawsonia arcticus*, *Asterias rathbuni anomala*, *Ophiura maculata*, *Gorgonocephalus caryi* typ. et f. *stimpsoni*, *Echinarachnius parma*, *Psolus peronii*, and others.

The Chukotsk Sea fish fauna includes 37 species, distributed as shown in *Table 119*.

Table 119

Cottidae	9	Lumpenidae	2
Salmonidae	7	Gasterosteidae	1
Zoarcidae	5	Sticheidae	1
Pleuronectidae	4	Ammodytidae	1
Osmeridae	3	Agonidae	1
Gadidae	2	Liparidae	1

Seventy-five per cent of all the fish of the Chukotsk Sea consists of the five first-mentioned families. High Arctic forms of the Arctic Ocean occur mainly in waters adjacent to the western side of Wrangel Island and to the north of it along the northern coast of Chukotsk almost up to the Bering Strait. The Pacific Ocean forms are found in masses in the Bering Strait, penetrating the Chukotsk Sea in two prongs: a northwestern one towards Herald Island and a northeastern one along the shores of Alaska (Fig. 111).

This distribution stands in complete agreement with the main currents of the Chukotsk Sea (Fig. 111).

In the northern part of the Chukotsk Sea, at the edge of the continental shelf, Ushakov has found some typical Atlantic forms (*Portlandia lenticula*, *P. fraterna*), which, along with Atlantic waters, have penetrated the regions of the Arctic basin so far removed from the Atlantic.

7
The Baltic Sea

I. GENERAL CHARACTERISTICS

The Baltic is a shallow (usually with depths no greater than 100 m), semi-enclosed, epicontinental sea of the temperate zone which is considerably diluted with fresh water. Closely embraced by the mainland, it is connected with the open sea by a complex system of shallow straits (Fig. 114).

The unstable salinity conditions of the surface layer and sharply defined saline stratification which are features of the Baltic Sea stamp the whole set of its conditions on the distribution of life in it. A relatively feeble exchange of water with the North Sea, the formation of considerable stagnant biologically poor zones in places where there are deep depressions, the distinctive set of conditions of the Gulf of Bothnia and the general low level of biological productivity are conditioned by these factors.

In the post-glacial era the Baltic Sea was changing shape, acquiring and losing outlets to the open sea both to the west and to the northeast, its water becoming first more and then less saline. This complex geological history has also brought about the genetically complex composition of its population. Ice relicts of the Yoldian period, true brackish-water fauna, and euryhaline immigrants from the North Sea and from fresh waters, may be distinguished in it. The first and second of these groups are fragments of the fauna now populating the Arctic basin in its least saline waters.

The Baltic Sea and its least saline areas are the most southern part of the habitat of these two groups, which now are in the main separated from their habitat. The forms which had migrated from the North Sea in later periods (the third group) inhabit mostly the upper, better heated, layers; they include in their number forms typical of the north European littoral.

Thus the Baltic Sea, as regards its zoological geography, is divided into two: the shallower southern and southwestern parts of the Sea are populated mainly by boreal fauna, while the deeper northern and northeastern parts of the Sea are populated by a fauna of Arctic aspect. The Baltic Sea communities are characterized by their oligomixed nature which is particularly marked within the more dilute part of the sea.

The productivity of the Baltic Sea is low. Its benthos biomass decreases rapidly as it passes from the Belts and Oresund to the farther parts of the Baltic, from hundreds of grammes to a few dozen per m^2, and even to a few grammes in the eastern inlets. In the north of the Gulf of Bothnia the benthos biomass is only a fraction of a gramme.

II. HISTORY OF EXPLORATION

The Baltic Sea, its fauna and its flora have been very fully studied by the combined efforts of the scientists of Denmark, Sweden, Finland, Russia, Poland and Germany.

The Swedish zoologist S. Loven (1864) laid the foundation of the study of the fauna of the western part of the Baltic Sea.

A number of comprehensive works on the fauna of the Baltic Sea appeared in the second half of the last century, among which the following should be noted: the researches of K. Möbius (1873) on invertebrates and, in collaboration with Fr. Heinke (1883), on fish; the work of K. Brandt on Kiel Bay fauna (1897), and that of O. Nordquist on the fauna of the invertebrates of the north of the Baltic Sea and of the Gulf of Bothnia. In the 'nineties Danish and Finnish scientists began their study of the Baltic Sea. From 1913 onwards a whole series of papers was published by the Swedish zoologist Sv. Ekman.

The first quantitative survey of this fauna was carried out by the Dane, C. G. Joh. Petersen (1913, 1914, etc.) and by the Swede, G. Thulin (1922).

The extensive series *Die Tierwelt der Nord- und Ost-see*, which first appeared in 1927 is the most comprehensive summary of work on fauna of the Baltic Sea. A number of significant studies have been carried out by K. Demel, A. Remane, K. Shliper, Sv. Sägerstråle, I. Valinkangas and others during recent decades.

III. PHYSICAL GEOGRAPHY, HYDROLOGY, HYDROCHEMISTRY AND GEOLOGY

Size and subdivisions

A characteristic feature of the orography of the Baltic Sea is its considerable extent from south to north (more than 1,200 km); from Copenhagen to the end of the Gulf of Bothnia is about 1,500 km. This causes great climatic differences between the southern and northern parts of the Sea.

In Spethmann's opinion (1912) the area of the Baltic Sea is equal to 385,000 km^2 (Sägerstråle suggests that it is 420,000 km^2), while its volume is 21,700 km^3. The greatest width of the Sea is approximately 300 km.

The annual inflow of fresh water is 630 km^3, or 1/34 of the total volume of the Sea. Four hundred and sixty-five km^3 of water is brought into the Baltic Sea by the 250 rivers which flow into it.

The Baltic Sea, with its large number of islands and bays and its somewhat varied bottom topography, is subdivided into several natural areas. The system of subdivision accepted by Sv. Ekman (1931) is set out below, although other investigators prefer other subdivisions:

A. Belts (transitional area)	Called also West Baltic Sea	1. Danish belt 2. German belt
B. Oresund (transitional area)		
C. Baltic Sea proper	I. South Swedish–Pomeranian Baltic	3. Arcona or Rügen region 4. Bornholm region
	II. Central part of Baltic Sea	5. West Baltic central part 6. East Baltic central part
D. Gulf of Riga (marginal area)		
E. Gulf of Finland (marginal area)		

F. Åland Sea (transitional area)
G. Southwest Finnish Quarken Sea (transitional area)
H. Gulf of Bothnia (marginal area) { III. Outer part of Gulf: Bothnia Sea (Bottensee)
IV. Inner part of Gulf (Bottenwiek)

The Belts are also known as the West Baltic Sea. The southern strait of Oresund and the Darss Ridge, i.e. the eastern boundary of the German Belt, form the western boundary of the Baltic Sea proper. The most westerly part of the Baltic Sea proper, the Arcona or Rügen region (Arcona or Rügen Sea), lies to the west of Bornholm Island; to the east is the Bornholm region with its deep Bornholm depression. These two areas are sometimes called the South Baltic Sea or the South Swedish–Pomeranian Baltic Sea. Farther east and north is the central area of the Baltic Sea, divided into eastern and western parts by the island of Gotland. The transitional area between the Baltic Sea proper and the Gulf of Bothnia is occupied by the Åland Sea west of the Åland Islands and by the Quarken Sea, or the Southwest Finnish Quarken Sea, to the east of them.

Bottom topography

The southern part of the Kattegat is nowhere more than 40 m deep. The three narrow straits which connect the Kattegat with the Baltic Sea—the Great and Little Belts and Oresund—are even shallower. Oresund, in the latitude of Copenhagen, is only 7 m deep. The Little Belt is a little deeper, and in its shallowest part is 10·5 m deep. In the Great Belt and its continuation in the direction of the Baltic—the Langeland Belt—there is a continuous trench with a depth of at least 30 m. However, farther to the east and before entering the Baltic proper this system of straits becomes even shallower. Still farther to the east depths begin to increase. Before the island of Bornholm is reached there is the Arcona depression with depths down to 53 m. The next significant hollow is situated east of Bornholm Island (the Bornholm depression) with a maximum depth of 105 m (see Fig. 114). Farther north the floor rises again slightly and then north of Gotland it goes down sharply; the 80 m contour line encloses a large area between the Gulf of Riga and Stockholm, which stretches southwards with a tongue each side of Gotland (Gotland depression) and contains some exceptionally deep areas. Among them is the greatest depth in the Baltic Sea—the Lansort depression, 459 m. deep. The Gotland depressions extend even to the Gulf of Finland, becoming progressively shallower as one moves east (40 m and less).

The Gulf of Bothnia, on the contrary, is separated from the Gotland depression by shoals (30 to 50 m) off the Åland Islands (Åland Ridge). The Gulf of Bothnia itself is also divided by a shallow ridge off the Quarken into two deeper parts: the southern one, the Bothnian Sea (Bottensee) with a maximum depth of 294 m, and the northern one—Bottenwiek—with a maximum depth of 140 m. Finally a closed hollow with depths down to 301 m lies to the west of the Åland Islands.

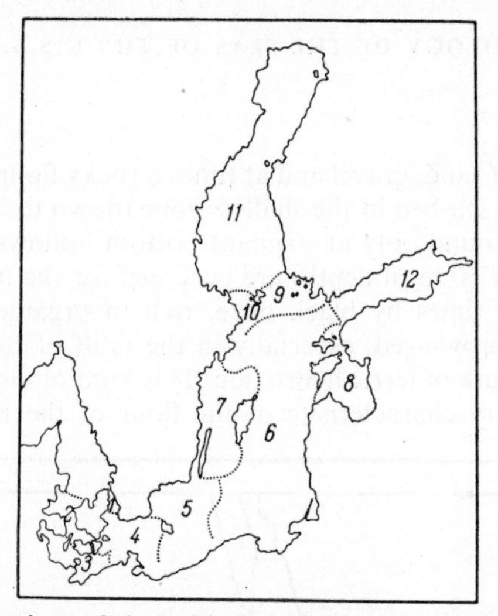

FIG. 114A. Regions of the Baltic Sea (Ekman). *1* Oresund; *2* Danish Belt; *3* German Belt; *4* Arcona depression; *5* Bornholm depression; *6* Eastern part of central depression; *7* Western part of central depression; *8* Gulf of Riga; *9* S. Quarken; *10* Åland Sea; *11* Gulf of Bothnia; *12* Gulf of Finland.

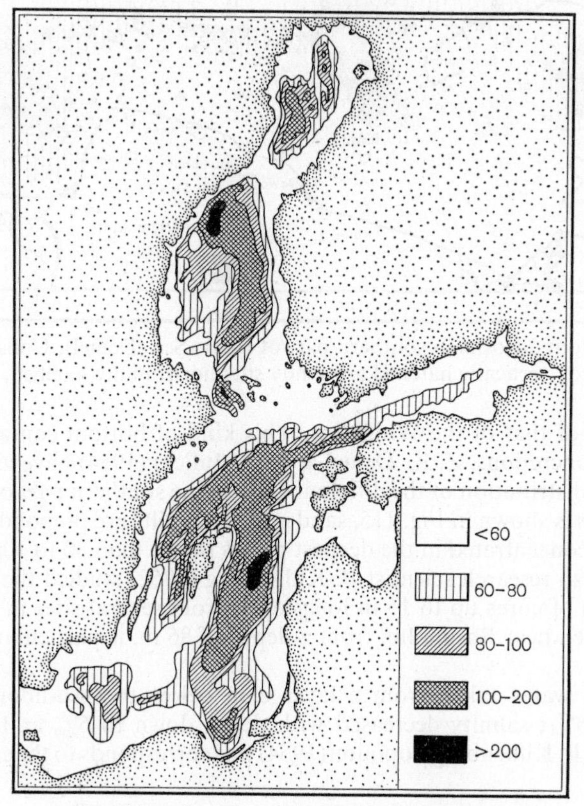

FIG. 114B. Depths of the Baltic Sea (Ekman).

The sea-bed

A preponderance of sand, gravel and at times a rocky floor, are the characteristic features of the sea-bed in the shallow zone (down to 50 m) of the Baltic. Ooze bottoms are found only in stagnant bottom hollows. The deeper parts of the bottom (over 50 m in depth) are occupied for the most part by clayey mud with sand, at times by black ooze, rich in organic detritus. The sea bottom is usually brown-red, especially in the Gulf of Bothnia; this colour is due to an admixture of ferric hydroxide. This kind of distribution of brown mud deposits is very characteristic of the floor of the Kara Sea and to a

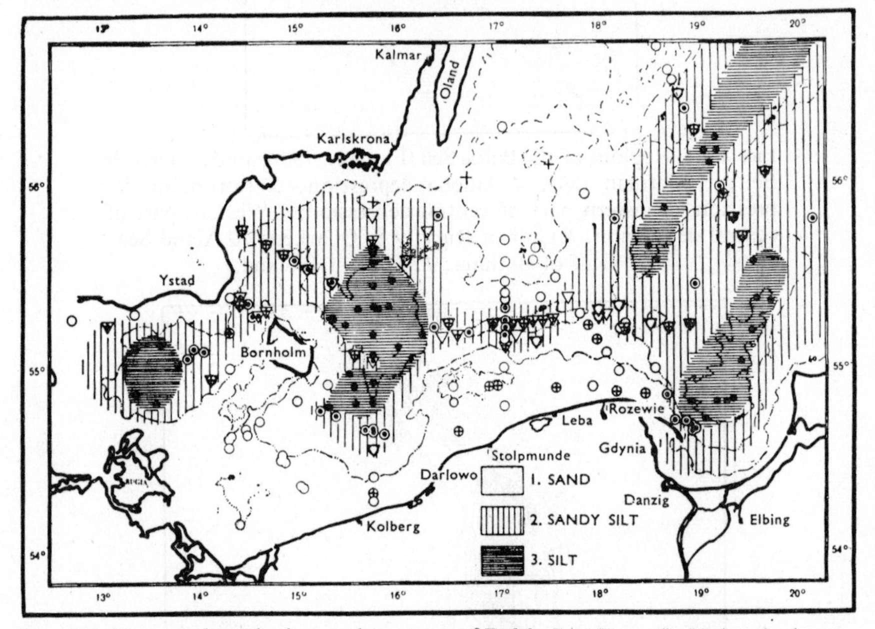

FIG. 115. Bottom deposits in southern part of Baltic Sea (Demel). Unhatched areas are sand; vertically hatched are sandy silt; horizontally hatched, silts.

lesser extent of that of the White Sea. This kind of bottom contains a large amount of concretions. Z. K. Demel and Z. Mulicki (1954) have given a map showing the distribution of the different soils of the southern part of the Baltic (Fig. 115). As is shown in Fig. 115, sand and sandy silts are preponderant here. Soft ooze is concentrated in the deepest places (more than 80 to 100 m).

The Swedish research scientist B. Kullenberg (1952) studied the salinity of the solutions of cores up to 15 m long taken from several sites in the Baltic. The core taken near Bornholm, from a depth of 86 m, is particularly demonstrative.

Interstitial water taken from a layer 2 m below the sea-floor indicated salinity of 15‰; salinity decreased with depth down to 6‰ at 12 to 15 m (Fig. 116). In B. Kullenberg's opinion (1954) this corresponds to the early period of the ice lake-sea (12,000 to 13,000 years ago). The great variety and contrasts displayed by the different parts of the Baltic Sea shores are connected with the difference of its geological structure and with the history of its development in the Quaternary Period. The boundary of the crystalline rocks of the Baltic icefoot is adjacent to the top end of the Gulf of Finland. The coastline of the northern and western parts of the Sea is formed of granites and gneisses (Finland and Sweden). The Quarken shapes of the southern shores of Finland, the Åland Archipelago and Sweden were formed when this area was submerged. The shores of Sweden belong to the fjord type. All these shores are rising at a high rate, especially at the head of the Gulf of Bothnia (up to 1·2 cm annually). Palaeozoic deposits of the Russian shelf are laid bare at the southern shores of the Gulf of Finland; farther south they drop below sea-level. The whole coast from the Gulf of Riga to Jutland consists mainly of loose Quaternary deposits exposed to considerable destruction by the sea. Large masses of alluvium formed during this process are transported from west to east, and then from south to north. As a result, large sand wash forms are created—the characteristic peninsulas and shoal heads of the southern coast. Wind action leading to the formation of powerful dune belts, at times up to 60 m high, is a feature of the southern and eastern shores of the Baltic Sea.

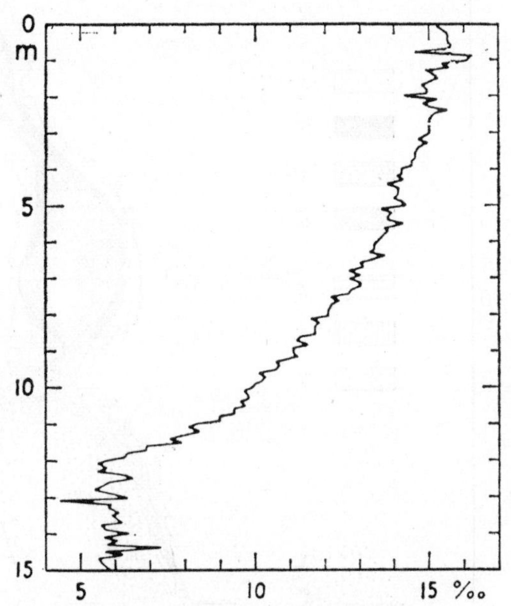

FIG. 116. Change of salinity with depth at the seafloor of the Baltic Sea (Küllenberg).

Temperature

The bottom topography described above, together with the contour of the coastline, exerts a very strong influence on the hydrological conditions of the Baltic Sea. It brings about a relatively small water-exchange with the North Sea, the formation of considerable stagnant zones with poor development of life in the deep hollows and, finally, the distinctive set of conditions in the Gulf of Bothnia. In the first place temperature conditions are affected. During the season of the year when the water column has its lowest temperatures (February), the surface waters of the northern parts of the Baltic (Gulfs of Bothnia and Finland) are below 0°. In the warmer southern parts, the temperature is slightly above 2°. The two northern gulfs have an ice cover over most

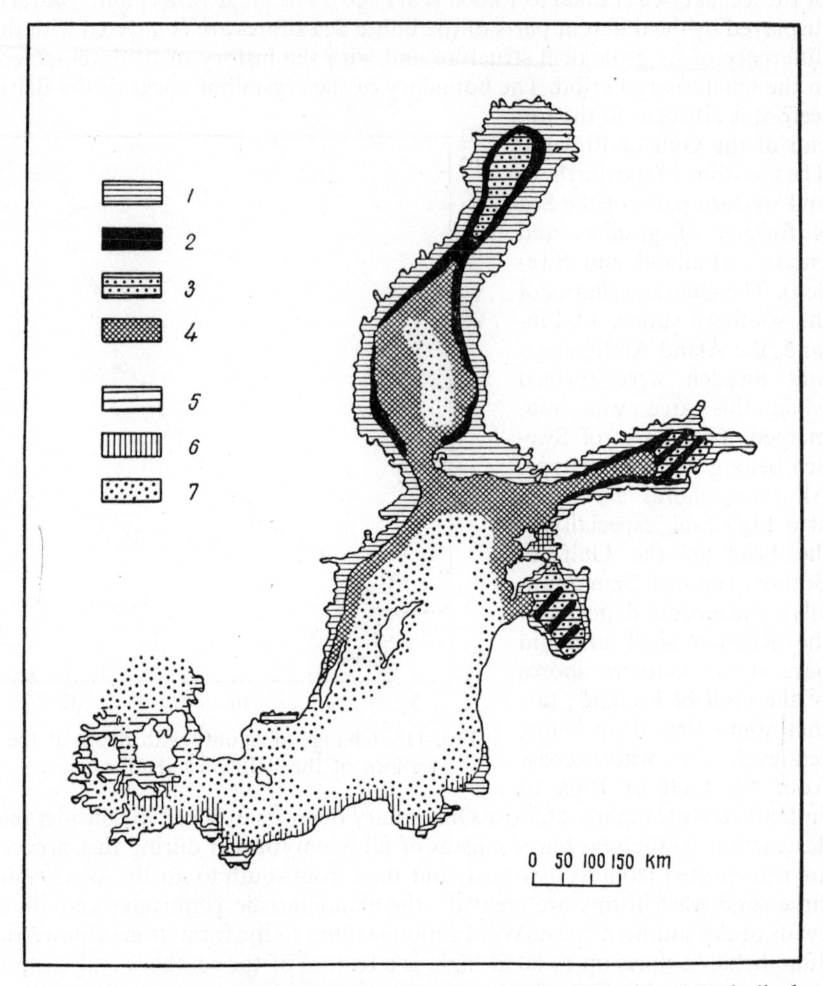

FIG. 117. Ice chart of the Baltic Sea (Blütgen, 1938). *1* Fast ice; *2* Periodical drift pack ice; *3* Periodical floes; *4* Periodical drift ice; *5* Episodical fast ice; *6* Episodical pack ice; *7* Episodical drift ice.

of their surface: in the inner parts for 2 to 5 months and more, at the inner end of the Gulf of Finland for 3 to 6 months and at the top of the Gulf of Bothnia for as much as 5 to 7 months. The ice conditions of the Baltic Sea are shown in Fig. 117.

Such temperatures are unknown in the North Sea, which lies alongside the Baltic and in the same latitude (Fig. 118). During the warmest time of the year (August) the surface temperatures of both Seas are practically the same. The heat conditions of the deepest parts of the sea undergo slight variations in temperature in the course of the year. Below 50 m and down to the bottom the temperature usually ranges between 3° and 5° in the southern parts of the Sea, and between 1° and 5° in the northern ones (Åland depression).

The phenomenon of dichothermia is very common in the Baltic Sea; the coldest layer of water (intermediate cold layer) lies usually not at the bottom

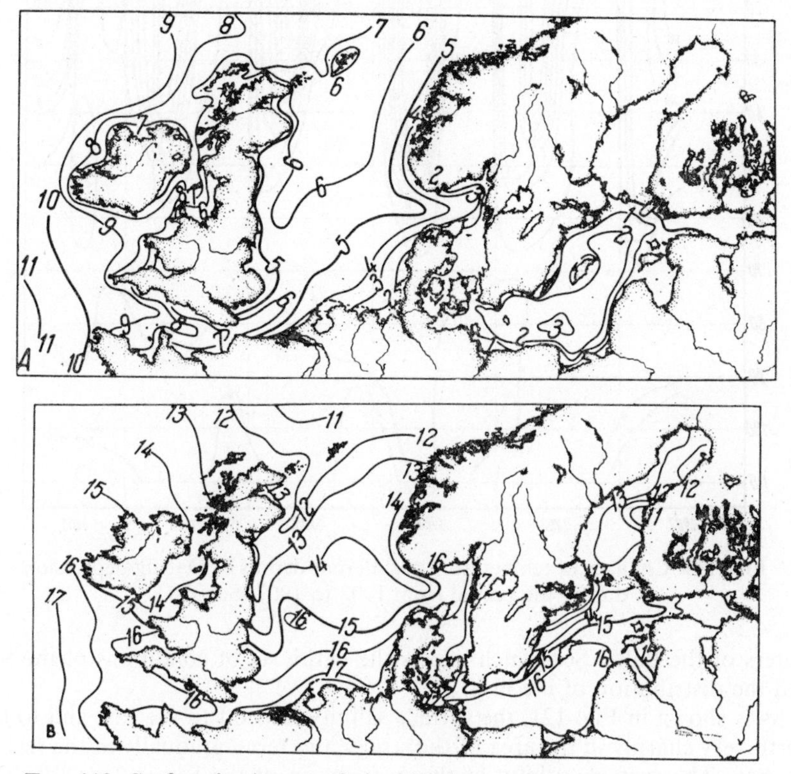

FIG. 118. Surface isotherms of the North and Baltic Seas in February (A) and August (B) (Schulz).

but at a depth of 60 to 100 m. At the bottom the temperature rises again from 3° to 5° (Gotland and Danzig depressions). In this respect the diagram in Fig. 119 is most instructive; it gives the changes of temperature at different depths in the depression situated at the entrance to Danzig Bay, which has a maximum depth of 113 m. The range of July temperatures in the area of the Island of Gotland is given in Fig. 120.

Salinity

The most characteristic features of the hydrology of the Baltic Sea comprise the instability of its saline conditions, especially in its transitional areas, the movement of the more saline near-bottom water from west to east along the deep troughs with a simultaneous surface discharge current in the opposite direction and, in consequence, a sharp division of salinity in two layers of the

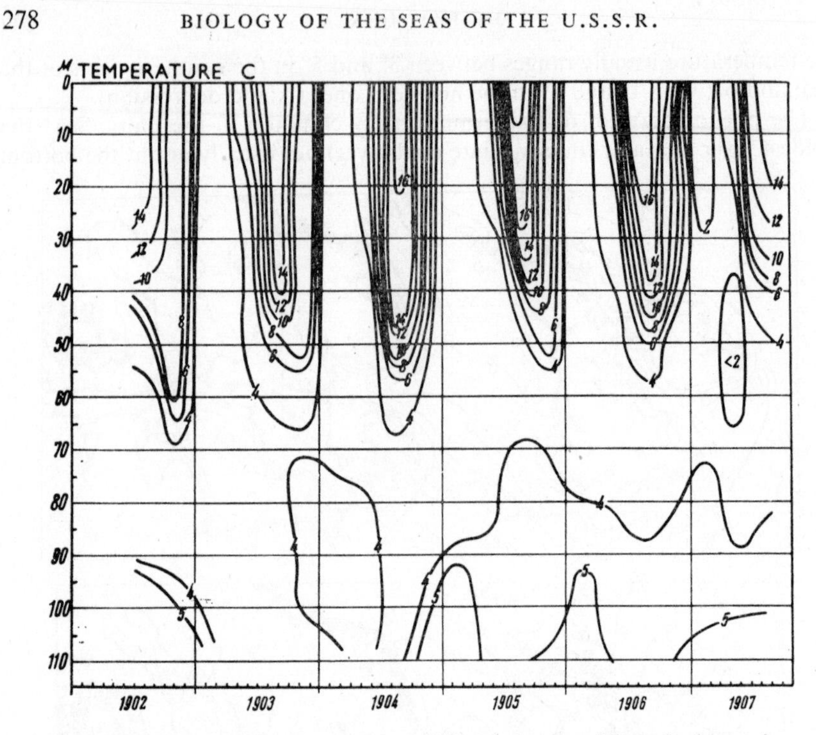

FIG. 119. Changes of temperature at different depths of Danzig depression during the period from 1902 to 1907 (Schulz).

waters of the Baltic Sea which affects the entire set of conditions of the Sea and the distribution of life in it.

As is shown in Fig. 121, the surface salinity falls off to the east and to the north very sharply in the area of the straits and more gradually in the rest of the Sea. The surface salinity of the main basin of the Sea is 2 to 8‰. The salinity conditions of the deep layers of the Baltic Sea (Fig. 122) result primarily from its bottom topography and from its water-exchange with the North Sea through the straits. A great difference in the salinity of surface water—discharge Baltic current—and that of the lower layers—the deep compensating current from the North Sea to the Baltic—is observed all the year round in the straits connecting these two Seas. The salinity changes are

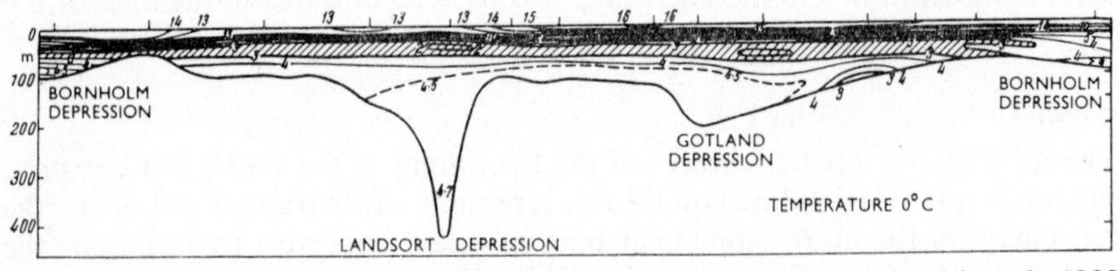

FIG. 120. Temperature range at different depths round Gotland Island in July 1922 (Schulz).

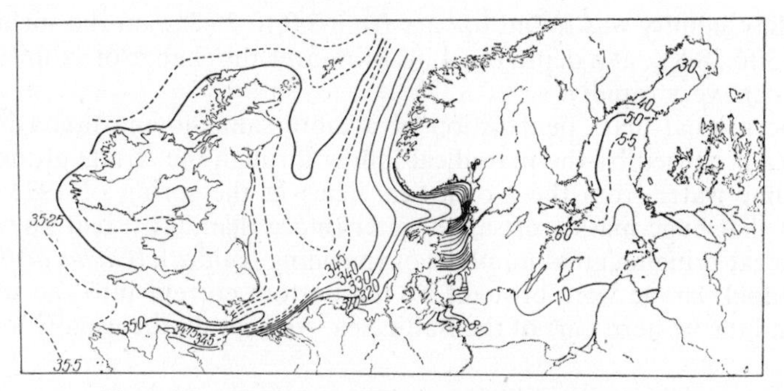

FIG. 121. Surface salinity of the Northern and Baltic Seas in August (Schulz).

especially abrupt in the straits, in relation to both space and time, depending on the season, and above all on the direction and force of the wind. Thus at one and the same spot, in Oresund, the fluctuations of salinity observed on the surface ranged from 7·2 to 22·4‰ and at a depth of 17 m from 11·7 to 22·5‰. The magnitude of the variations in the area of the Darss ridge is about the same.

At another point in Oresund, within a period of six months salinity on the surface ranged from 6·8 to 25·7‰ and at a depth of 8 m from 8·2 to 25·7‰.

FIG. 122. Near-bottom November isohalines (‰) of the Baltic Sea. Broken lines are May surface isohalines (Ekman).

In Kiel Bay salinity was found to vary from 3·9 to 26·3‰ on the surface and from 10·3 to 28·8‰ at a depth of 14 m. Moreover the change of salinity sometimes occurs very rapidly.

The occasional mass penetration of a more saline-loving fauna into the Baltic Sea is caused by the periodical inflow through the straits of masses of more saline water from the North Sea. Thus in the spring of 1923 Schulz reported that huge masses of saline water (more than 34‰) had flowed into the Kattegat bringing great numbers of spawning haddock (*Gadus aeglefinus*). The haddock larvae were brought by the bottom current into the southern straits and the western part of the Baltic Sea. As a result, the usually low yield

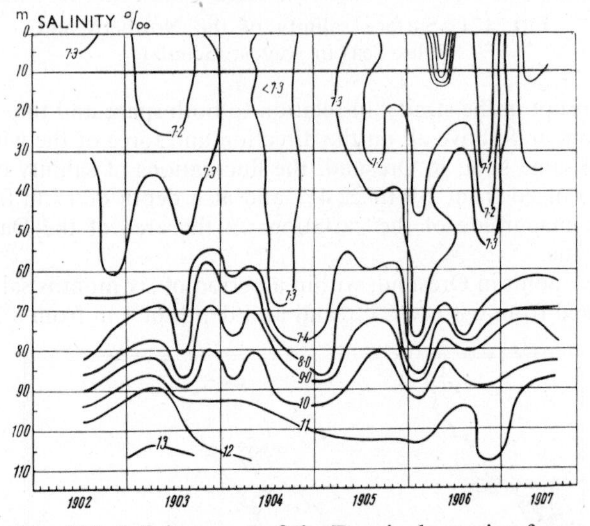

FIG. 123. Salinity range of the Danzig depression from 1902 to 1907 (Schulz).

of haddock rose in 1925 to 50,000 kg, and in January and February 1926 to 500,000 kg, but the catch fell off sharply in March as the haddock migrated back to the Skagerrak to spawn.

Deep saline waters, penetrating periodically through the deep troughs into the Bornholm depression, frequently form there a very complex system of overlapping, accompanied by the usual phenomena of stagnation. The highest salinity observed there was 18·93‰, the lowest—14·87‰ (September 1921), with an oxygen content of 0·7 per cent. However, at other times and at precisely the same depths an oxygen content of 80 per cent has been recorded. It has been noted that a layer of water of the same thickness as that over the shallows situated to the west—approximately 40 m—is homohaline; in winter it is also homothermic and is well mixed.

The diagram of the Danzig depression in Fig. 123 is a clear illustration of this. The deep waters of the Bornholm depression (105 m) may partly penetrate even farther into the deeper Gotland depression (249 m). The salinity of the Danzig depression (113 m) varies, however, from 10·01 to 13·5‰, that of the Gotland one from 11·49 to 12·65‰, and that of the Landsort one (427 m, north of Gotland Island) from 9·83 to 11·08‰. The amplitude of the salinity fluctuations decreases from 4 (Bornholm depression) to 1·15‰ as one moves east.

The instability of the saline conditions is very marked not only in the western part of the Baltic Sea but also in the eastern. This is well illustrated by Sv. Sägerstråle (1951 a) for the Gulf of Finland. In the western part of the Gulf in 1927–49, at a depth of 5 m, the salinity varied from 4·29 to 6·80‰, and in its eastern part from 0·07 to 4·96‰.

Salinity fluctuations affect the distribution and biology of organic life. Sv. Sägerstråle (1951 a) gives a number of interesting examples, among them the differences in the time taken by the medusa, *Aurelia aurita*, to reach maturity.

Gas conditions

Saline and gas conditions off Gotland Island, shown on the diagrams (Figs. 124, 125), are most significant. The deep saline water is poor in oxygen and

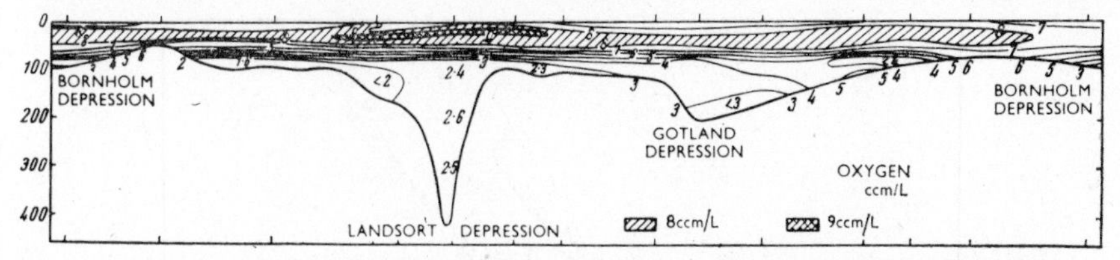

FIG. 124. Oxygen distribution in waters round Gotland Island in June 1922 (Schulz).

rich in carbon dioxide. In the autumn there is a vigorous vertical circulation which continues even in the winter; but it embraces only the upper 60 or 70 m layer. The summer warming which follows penetrates deeper still but

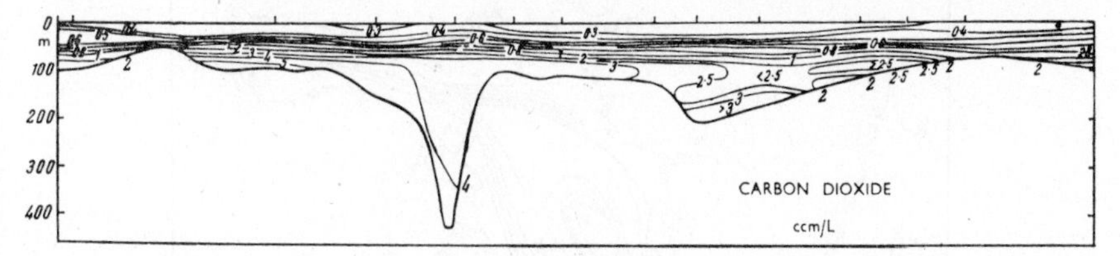

FIG. 125. Distribution of carbon dioxide in waters round Gotland Island in July 1922 (Schulz).

does not last long enough to warm the whole layer cooled during the winter. This is the reason for the existence of an intermediate cold layer, between the two warmer layers, at a depth of 40 to 60 m. The hydrological and hydrochemical conditions of Baltic waters in summer time off Gotland Island may be illustrated by the data given in *Table 120* (15 July 1922, west of Gotland Island).

Table 120

Depth m	Temperature $t°$	Salinity $S‰$	Nitrogen cm³/l.	Oxygen cm³/l.	Carbon dioxide cm³/l.	Total gas content cm³/l.	Oxygen per cent of total	Carbon dioxide per cent of total	pH
0	12·4	7·0	13·8	7·4	0·4	21·6	34	1·8	8·08
20	8·8	7·0	14·8	8·2	0·4	23·4	35	1·7	8·05
40	2·3	7·3	16·8	8·6	0·7	26·2	33	2·6	7·76
60	3·5	8·68	16·3	4·3	2·8	23·4	18	12·0	7·27
80	4·3	9·52	15·9	2·1	4·5	22·5	9	20·0	6·95
97	4·3	9·85	15·9	1·6	5·7	23·2	7	25·0	6·87

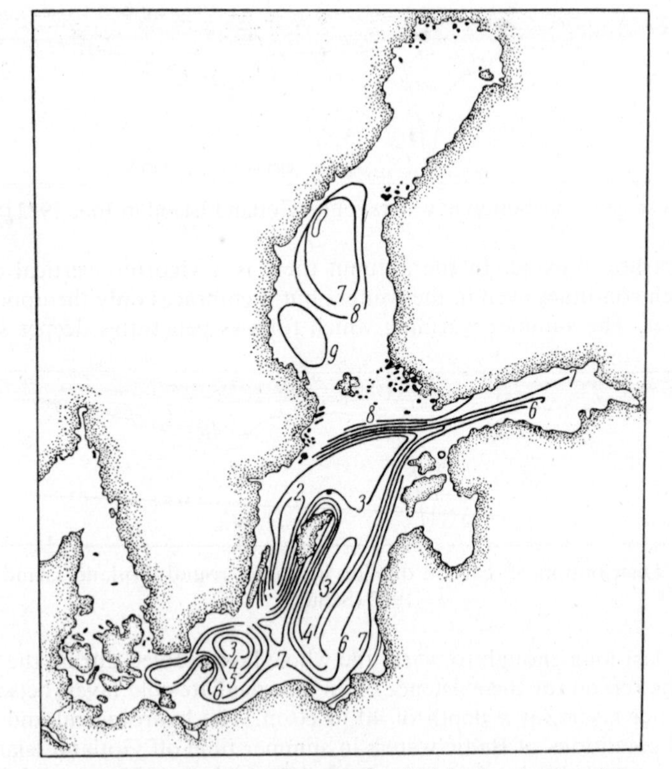

FIG. 126. Distribution of oxygen (cm³/l.) in the depths of the Baltic Sea in May 1922 (Schulz).

It is interesting to note that the ratio of the amount of carbon dioxide formed at this depth to the oxygen consumed is about 0·9, which corresponds to the respiratory coefficient of the organisms inhabiting the depths of the Baltic Sea; this has been confirmed by experiments with fish.

The acid conditions of the deep Baltic waters have a characteristic effect on the process of the decomposition of mollusc shells (Grippenberg, 1934).

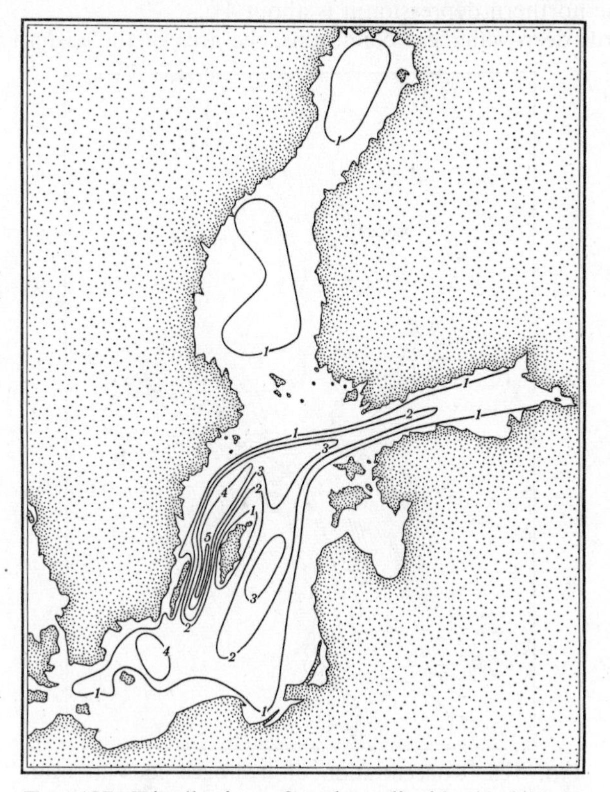

FIG. 127. Distribution of carbon dioxide (cm^3/l.) in near-bottom waters of Baltic Sea, May to July 1922 (Schulz, 1935).

This process has also been observed to be strongly developed in the deep part of the Kara Sea.

The summer distribution of oxygen and carbon dioxide, and the concentration of hydrogen ions in the bottom layer of the Baltic Sea, are shown in Figs. 126, 127 and 128.

The Gulf of Bothnia is separated from the rest of the Sea by a shallow ridge, which does not let through the deep saline waters from the west; this affects its hydrological conditions.

As shown in the three figures given, the gas conditions in the deep layers of both Bothnian depressions are much more favourable than in the southern part of the Sea. Thus in the deep layers of the Åland depression at a much lower temperature (1·18° to 3·81°) and a lesser salinity (6·8 to 7·02‰), the deep-water salinity is only 1‰ higher than that of the surface water, the vertical circulation reaches the bottom and the amount of oxygen at 300 m is still 6·5 to 8·7 cm³/l. at 73 to 93 per cent of saturation. In the southern depression of the Gulf of Bothnia the deep-water salinity varies between 6 and 6·5‰, while in the northern depression it is about 4‰.

As regards deep-water gas conditions, the area of the eastern part of the

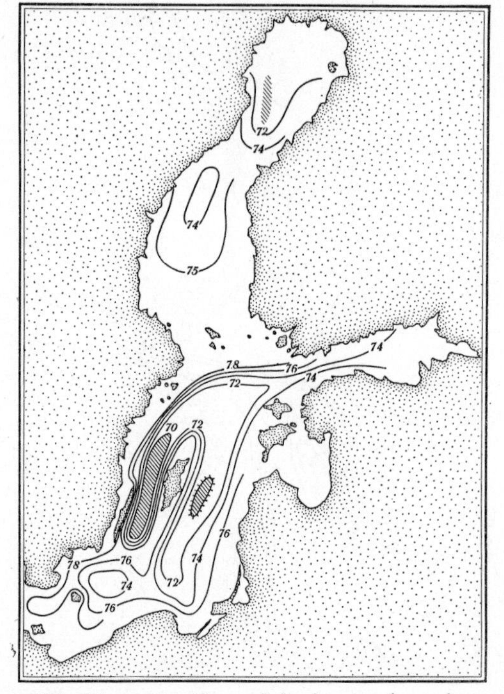

FIG. 128. Concentration of hydrogen ions in near-bottom waters of Baltic in May to July 1922 (Schulz).

deep trough, which extends from the Gotland depression to the entrance to the Gulf of Finland, is most interesting. Deep saline waters from the Gotland depression penetrate into this area, while the surface waters, by contrast, are considerably diluted; so that conditions are created which are extremely unfavourable for vertical circulation. The following phenomena have been observed in the area to the north of Dagö Island at a depth of 180 m (Bogskar depression): marked salinity fluctuations (9·20 to 10·14‰), increased temperature (3·71° to 4·96°) and changes in oxygen content from 0 to 2·49 cm³/l. (0 to 29 per cent of saturation).

The range of deep-water salinity of the Gulf of Finland is shown in Fig. 129, while the hydrological conditions of the most eastern part of the Gulf up to Neva Guba are given in Fig. 130.

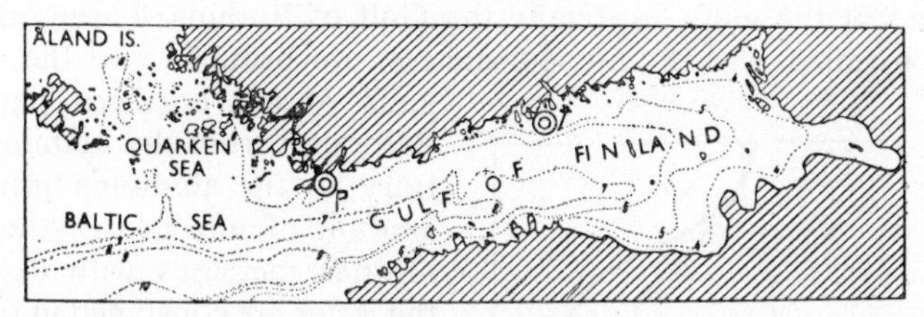

FIG. 129. Range of near-bottom salinity (‰) in the Gulf of Finland (Sägerstråle). The populated points at Twerminn (T) and Pelling (P) are marked on the chart.

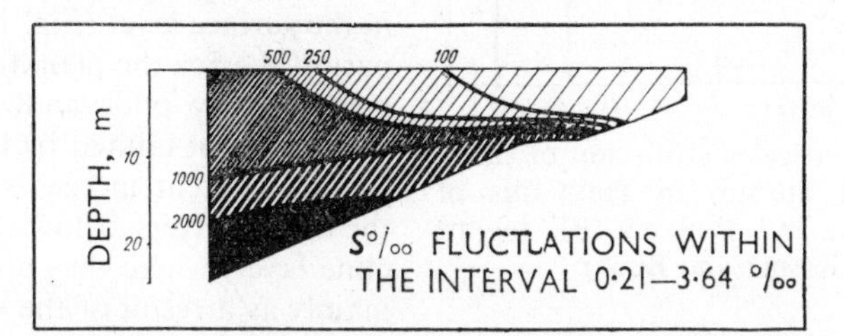

FIG. 130. Hydrological cross section from the Neva Guba westwards to the south from Kotlin Island (Derjugin). Chlorine content in mg/l. is shown by the numerals.

Distribution of nutrient salts

We have not yet got a sufficiently full picture of the distribution of nitrogen and phosphorus compounds in the Baltic (Fig. 131). The conditions of the northern and eastern parts of tne Sea and some points of the most western part of it (Kiel Bay) have been best investigated. The amount of ammonia varies from 0 to 50 mg/m³. Its content is somewhat higher in surface waters

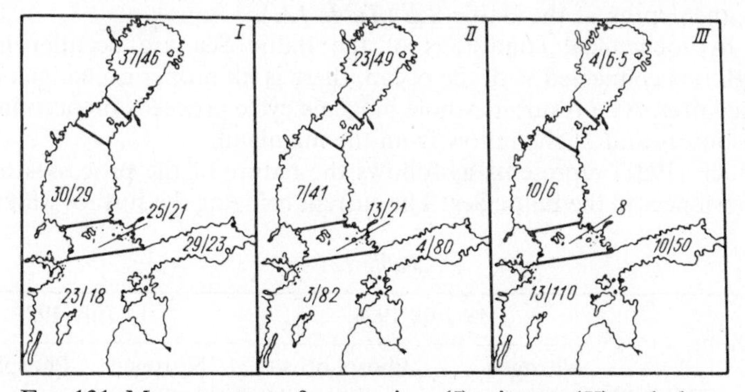

FIG. 131. Mean content of ammonium (*I*), nitrates (*II*) and phosphates (*III*) in the Baltic Sea. Numerator corresponds to their content in the surface layer, denominator in the depth. The natural regions are divided by lines (Buch).

at the head of the gulfs, especially the Gulf of Bothnia. Large amounts of nitrogen, together with humus substances, are brought into the two large gulfs of the northern part of the Baltic Sea from the mainland. Contrary to the ammonia nitrogen the amount of nitrogen in the form of nitrates increases with depth, since the latter are consumed in the surface layer by phytoplankton. Only in the inner part of the Gulf of Bothnia is there a fairly high content of nitrates in the surface layer (Fig. 132). In this part of the Sea the plankton development is very poor and, clearly, its growth is not limited by the nitrates. Nitrate content increases sharply in the deeper layers below the thermocline layer, where they are produced mainly as a result of the nitrification of organic matter. The reduced content of nitrate in the deep parts of the Gulf of Bothnia is due to a very restricted inflow of deep waters from the main basin of the Sea, owing to a shallow ridge which bars their entrance. In the Gulf of Finland, which has no such ridge at its entrance, nitrate content is the same as in the open parts of the Sea. The data on plankton distribution accord fully with such a distribution of nitrates.

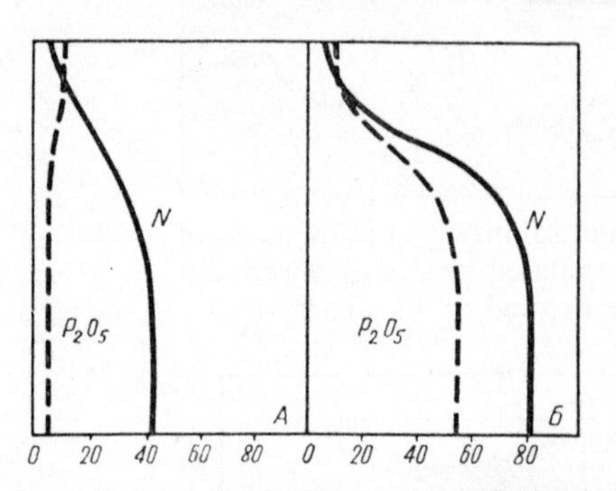

FIG. 132. Vertical distribution of phosphates and nitrates in the Gulfs of Bothnia (A) and Finland (B), mg/m³ (Gessner and Buch).

The distribution of phosphates is somewhat similar to that of nitrates: they are scarce on the surface, their number increases considerably in the depths. Here too, however, the Gulf of Bothnia stands apart: its deep waters are poor in phosphates; this is, perhaps, the main factor limiting plankton development. The difference between the two Gulfs is illustrated in Fig. 132.

There are some considerable annual variations in the content of nutrient salts in the depths of the Baltic Sea (*Table 121*).

The hydrochemical conditions of the Baltic Sea are peculiar in that, although it is connected with the ocean, there is no proper exchange of water with the latter. As a result its whole biogenic cycle proceeds on account of its own resources and of the inflow from the mainland.

K. Buch (1931) represents as follows the nature of the processes of plant food substances in the Baltic Sea. The current bringing the surface waters from

Table 121

Depth, m	19 July 1928		14 July 1929	
	Nitrogen	Phosphorus	Nitrogen	Phosphorus
0	0	0	0	8·7
70	65	13	300	8·7
198–220	70	87	175	98

the inner parts of the Sea towards the straits carries with it the living matter produced in those inner parts. As they die off, the organisms must sooner or later sink into the depths; the organic matter oxidizes, turns into mineral matter and is accumulated on the bottom. The deep current moving in the

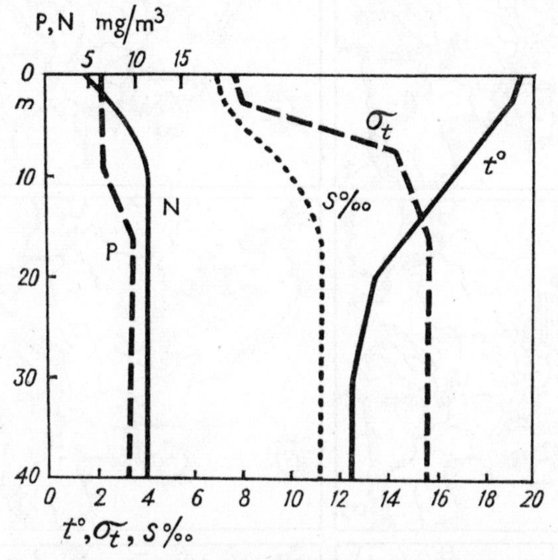

FIG. 133. Vertical distributions of phosphorus, nitrogen, density, temperature and salinity in the Arcona depression in August 1932 (Buch from Gessner). σ_t indicates density at any given temperature.

opposite direction carries back into the inner parts of the Sea the decomposed nutritive substances.

The Gulf of Bothnia, however, has its own independent hydrochemical life. As a result of this isolation of the separate parts of the Sea, and the obstacles to the movements of organic substances to the southwestern part of the Sea, these areas are poorer in nutritive matter than the northern ones; this is confirmed by the data given by Buch for the Arcona depression (Fig. 133).

IV. THE GEOLOGICAL PAST

The composition of the fauna of the Baltic Sea, its ecological characteristics and its distribution—more so than in the case of any other sea—cannot be properly understood without taking account of its geological past. In that respect the Baltic Sea is undoubtedly the best-studied Sea in the world (Fig. 134). From its last glaciation period, i.e. for the last 15,000 years, the history of the Baltic Sea has been thoroughly studied. A sufficiently complete and reliable history of this period and even its chronology can be found in the works of the geologists, botanists and zoologists of primarily Sweden, Norway and Finland. The study of this history of the Baltic Sea is linked with the

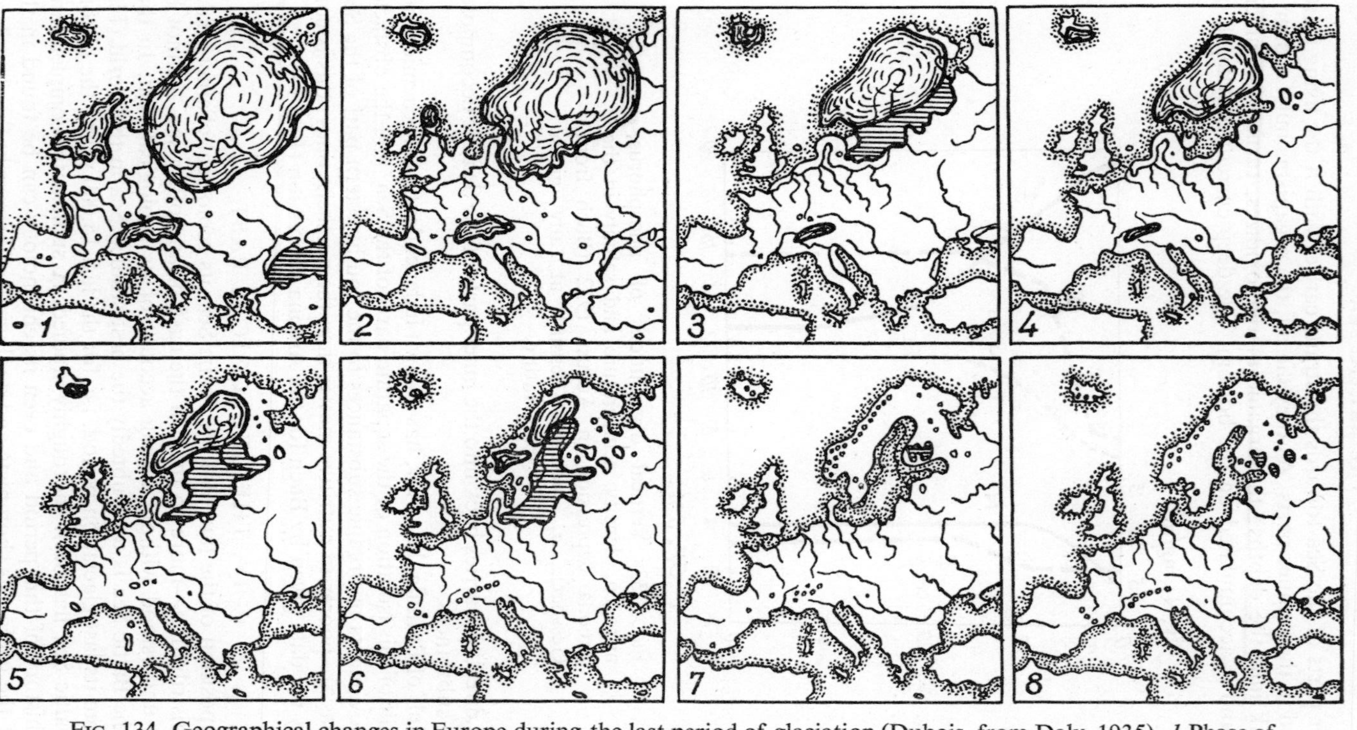

FIG. 134. Geographical changes in Europe during the last period of glaciation (Dubois, from Daly, 1935). *1* Phase of the maximum of the last glaciation; *2* Danish glaciation; *3* Baltic Ice Lake; *4* Yoldic Sea; *5* Ancyl Sea; *6* Last phase of Ancyl Lake; *7* Littorina Sea; *8* Contemporary phase.

names of the zoologists S. Loven, M. Sars and S. Ekman, the botanists Sernander and L. Post, the geologists G. De-Geer, A. Högbom, G. Munthe, V. Ramsay, M. Sauramo, N. Jakovlev and others. The first ideas on this subject were due to the Swedish zoologist S. Loven (1839 and 1864) and to the Norwegian zoologist M. Sars (1865).

Evolution of the Baltic Sea

According to the latest data the history of the Baltic Sea can be set down in the form of *Table 122*.

Table 122

Chronology	Glacial periods	Stages of the Baltic Sea	Climatic periods of southern Sweden
– 1,000		Modern stage	Sub-Atlantic period
Beginning of New Era	Post-glacial period	(Sea of Mya and Limnae)	(cold and wet)
1,000			
2,000		Littorina Sea	Sub-Boreal period (warm and dry)
3,000			
4,000			
5,000		Ancyl lake	Altantic period (warm and wet)
6,000			Boreal period (warm and dry)
7,000	Finnish glaciation		Sub-Arctic period
8,000			
9,000		Yoldian Sea	
10,000			
11,000	Gothland glaciation		
12,000		Baltic ice lake (Rybnoe Lake)	Arctic period
13,000	Danish glaciation		

Fluctuations of sea-level and alterations of climate

Marked climatic fluctuations correspond to considerable changes both in the sea-level and in the location of the dry land. In southern Finland traces of the level of the Baltic ice lake (also known as Rybnoe Lake) are found at 150 m, and of the Yoldian Sea at 90 m above the present sea-level (Sauramo). The curves for the eustatic fluctuations of the sea-level (according to Antew) are given in Fig. 135 (these fluctuations are caused by the change in the volume of water in the ocean, as a result, for instance, of the accumulation or melting of ice on the mainland or islands during the Ice Age at the time of climatic changes). It is apparent that the accumulation of continental ice in the Polar regions may cause considerable fluctuations of the ocean's level either by their melting or by their massing. During the last Glaciation Period (*Wechseleiszeit*), the ice masses of the northern hemisphere exceeded those of the present day by 32,800,000 km³; for the southern hemisphere the difference is 4,100,000 km³. The level of the ocean must have been 93 m lower than it is

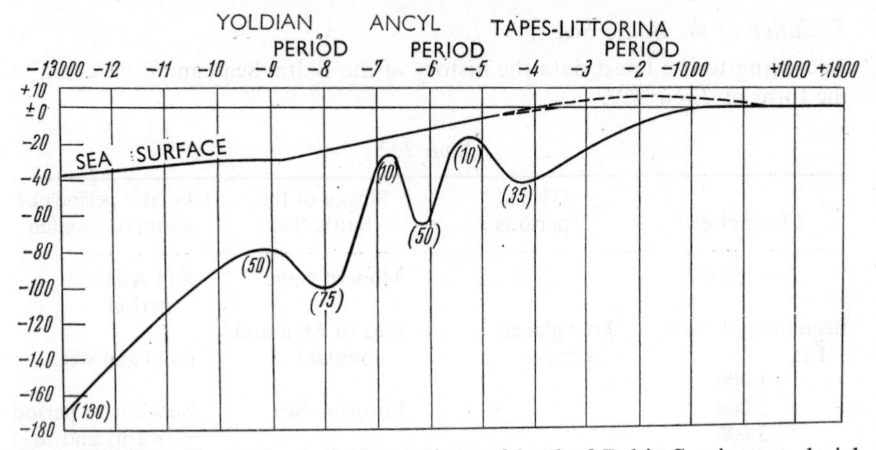

FIG. 135. Eustatic and isostatic fluctuations of level of Baltic Sea in post-glacial period at Lysekil (Antew).

now on account of the increase of the Polar ice (corresponding approximately to 34,000,000 km³ of water). Northern glaciation alone must have resulted in a lowering of the sea-level by 88 m (Antew, 1928). It has been established that some thousands of years ago the ocean level was 5 to 6 m higher than it is at present; this might be related to intensive melting of the Polar ice during the warm phases of the post-glacial period (Boreal, Atlantic and sub-Boreal periods 3,000 to 9,000 years ago) and to the isostatic* variations of the level of the mainland at some point of the Swedish coast of the Skagerrak.

The Ice Lake Sea

As a result of the violent melting of ice, which took place fifteen or twenty thousand years ago, the Baltic depression was filled with huge masses of melted ice water. The level of the Ice Lake Sea which had formed in this way and spread widely was considerably higher than that of the ocean. This body of water had an outflow to the ocean in the west; on the east it was connected with Lake Ladoga; it existed 13,000 years ago.

The Yoldian Sea

As the masses of continental ice which had supported the level of the Baltic Ice Lake receded, the level fell, until at last masses of cold saline ocean waters rushed into the Baltic Sea through the broad passage which was formed

* Caused by the lowering or rising of land.

linking it with the North Sea. The Yoldian Sea was created with its *Yoldia* (*Portlandia*) *arctica*, *Arca borealis*, *Mya truncata* and other members of cold-water Arctic fauna.

So far it has not been finally determined whether the Yoldian Sea was connected in the northeast with the White Sea through Lakes Ladoga and Onega. Several authors (G. De-Geer, 1910 and more recently N. Jakovlev, 1926, A. Arkhangelsky and others) considered that during the Yoldian Period there was a wide connection between the Baltic and White Seas. Lately, however, a number of authors (Munthe, Sauramo, Ekman and others) have denied such a connection, considering that the Yoldian Sea did not extend eastwards beyond Lake Ladoga. The salinity of the Yoldian Sea fell far short of the salinity of the ocean, and the Sea existed for a very short time (according to Munthe for no more than 700 years, according to Sauramo for 500).

Ancylus Lake Sea

The rising of the dry land in the area of southern Sweden again separated the Yoldian Sea from the ocean. For a second time the Baltic waters underwent a loss of salinity, which turned the sea into the cold, strongly diluted Ancyl Lake Sea (Fig. 134). This was populated by, among others, the fresh-water molluscs *Ancylus fluviatilis*, Lymnaea, Unio and others, and had a strong outflow to the west. G. De-Geer estimates the length of this phase to be 2,200 years.

The Littorina Sea

As a result of the subsidence of the bottom of the southwestern part of the Baltic and a eustatic rise of the level of the ocean (Ramsay) a link was again established with the ocean at the end of the Ancylus Period. Once more the Baltic waters began to be more saline, and their salinity reached higher than the present level (Fig. 136). This Littorina phase of increased salinity (Littorina

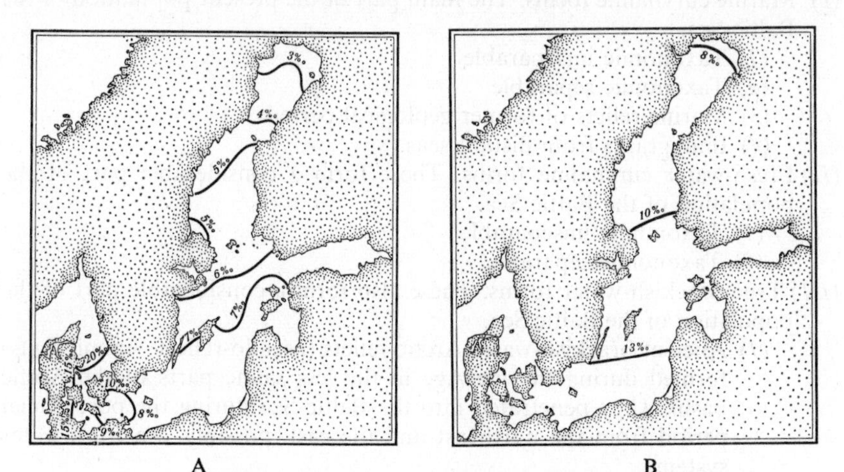

FIG. 136. Surface salinity of the contemporary Baltic Sea (A) and of the Littorina Sea (B) (Petterson).

Sea) and slightly higher temperature (the air temperature in southern Sweden was 2° to 2·25° higher than at present) lasted for about 4,000 years. A new fauna appeared, with *Littorina littorea*, *Cardium edule*, *Mytilus edulis*, etc. Subsequently, as a result of the rising of the sea-floor in the region of the straits during the last 4,000 years, the inflow of the ocean waters slackened and the Baltic Sea acquired a salinity approaching that of today. In the following period further distinction has been made between the Limnae Sea (*Lymnaea peregra*) and the Mya Sea (*Mya arenaria*); the difference between these two phases and the present phase is small as regards hydrology, and it consists mainly of a change of fauna.

V. FLORA AND FAUNA

The present population of the Baltic Sea was evolved during the post-glacial period and is very varied in its composition. It consists of three main components—marine, fresh-water and brackish-water (in the narrow sense of this word). In so far as the Baltic Sea has a low salinity all its population can be considered as brackish in the broad sense of the word; however, brackish-water fauna in the narrow sense—the population of the Ice Age and the Arctic basin—are also included in its composition.

It is essential, therefore, to make a distinction between the population of a brackish body of water and a brackish fauna, retaining this term only for the fauna which is brackish in the narrow sense of the word, i.e. fauna which is the result of a (geologically) prolonged development of a fauna which is marine in origin and partly also fresh-water under conditions of considerably lowered salinity. The population of the Baltic Sea consists of the following groups (Fig. 137):

(*I*) Marine euryhaline forms. The main part of the present population of the Baltic Sea.
- (*1*) Taxonomic unseparable
- (*2*) Taxonomic separable
- (*3*) Marine relicts of former geological periods
- (*4*) Immigrants from distant seas.

(*II*) Fresh-water euryhaline forms. These form a considerable part of the population of the Baltic Sea.
- (*1*) Taxonomic unseparable
- (*2*) Taxonomic separable.

(*III*) True brackish-water forms. These also form a considerable part of the population of the Baltic Sea.
- (*1*) Ancient brackish-water Arctic relicts (pseudo-relicts—immigrants) formed during the Ice Age in the less saline parts of the Arctic basin. They penetrated into the Baltic Sea during the post-glacial period from the northeast and the east, possibly, via fresh-water systems.
- (*2*) Brackish-water forms which had originated from the fresh-water ones.

As in other brackish-water bodies the qualitative variety of the flora and fauna of the Baltic Sea is not large; nor are the indices of biological productivity high. Some individual, mostly euryhaline, members of the fauna of the adjacent fully saline sea basins frequently become very numerous. Biocoenoses with a few (mesomixed) or with very few (oligomixed) species are characteristic of such bodies.

Many of the forms of the Baltic Sea sink to great depths, penetrating into the areas with a salinity lower than that of the North Sea, and the fresh-water forms move into areas of higher salinity. Sägerstråle has pointed out (1957) that *Macoma baltica* and *Scoloplos armiger* are encountered in the Baltic Sea down to 100 to 140 m (Hessle, 1924). *Fucus vesiculosus*, which does not go more than 5 m deep into the Kattegat, descends in the Baltic Sea to 10 to 12 m (Waern, 1952). *Idothea baltica* in the Gulf of Finland reaches a salinity of 3 to 4‰, but ceases at a salinity of 10 to 15‰ near the coast of Jutland (Johansen, 1918). Fresh-water forms, on the contrary, enter much farther into the saline waters of the Baltic Sea. For example, *Lymnaea peregra* goes up to 10 to 11‰, while in Jutland it does not enter more than 5 to 7‰ (Jaeckel, 1950; Johansen, 1918).

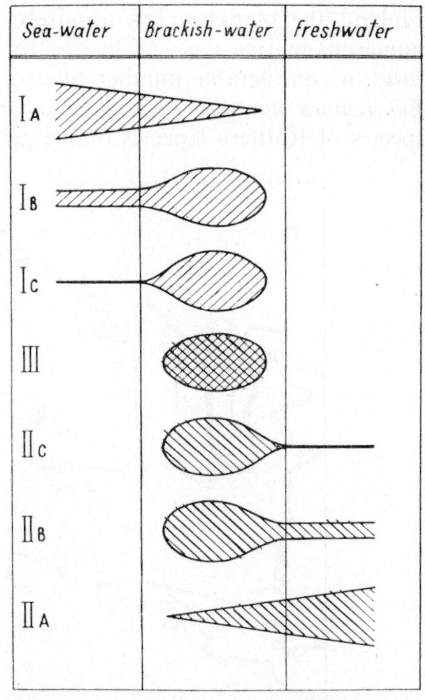

FIG. 137. Composition of barckish-water population. *I* Marine, euryhaline fauna; *IA* Typical marine forms d veloping only slightly in brackish waters; *IB* Marine forms of greater mass development in brackish water; *IC* Marine forms weakly connected with marine habitats, living mostly in brackish waters; *IIA* Typical fresh-water forms, which penetrate into brackish water; *IIB* Fresh-water forms of greater mass development in brackish waters; *IIC* Fresh-water forms weakly linked with fresh-water habitats, living mostly in brackish water; *III* Typical brackish-water forms alien to marine and fresh-water forms.

Many marine groups do not penetrate, or only penetrate in small numbers, into the Baltic Sea: Porifera, Actiniaria, Madreporaria, Octocorallia, Solenogastres, Scaphopoda, Pteropoda, Cephalopoda, Echinodermata and others.

Plankton

Qualitative changes of plankton from west to east. Plankton suffers a marked qualitative change as one leaves the Belt and Oresund and enters the Baltic Sea (Fig. 138).

While plankton in the straits leading to the Baltic Sea does not differ much from that of the North Sea, in the upper parts of the Gulfs of Bothnia and Finland the plankton has a purely fresh-water character. Instead of the numerous marine species Chaetoceros, Rhizosolenia, *Ceratium tripos* and *C. fusus*, a considerable number of hydro-medusae, Copepoda (*Oithona nana*, *Eurytemora hirundo*, *Paracalanus parvus*, *Acartia longiremis*), the marine species of Rotifera (species of the genus *Synchaeta mastigocera*), numerous

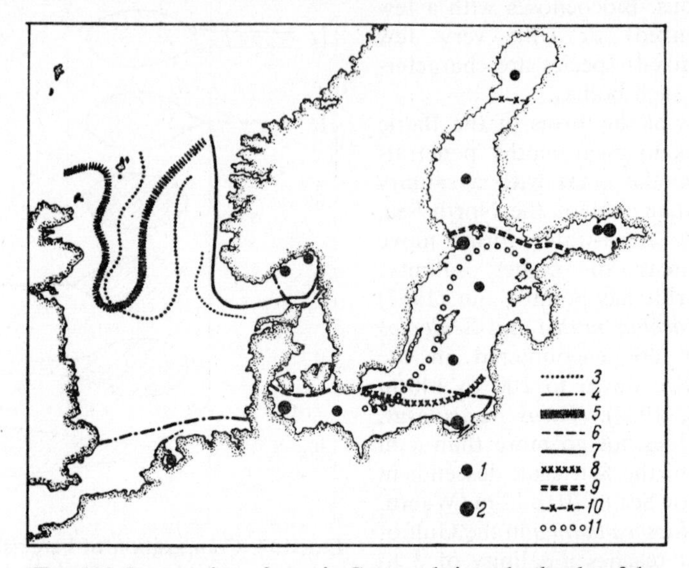

FIG. 138. Penetration of certain Copepoda into the depths of the North Sea and into the Baltic Sea (Pesta). *1 Eurytemora hirundoides typicus*; *2 E. hirundo*; *3* Oithona; *4* Southern boundary of *Oithona similis* (northeastern in the Baltic Sea); *5* Northern boundary of *Oithona mana*; *6* Eastern boundary of Centropages; *7 Metridia longa*; *8* Northern boundary of *Paracalanus parvus*; *9* Northern boundary of *Pseudocalanus elongatus*; *10* Northern boundary of *Acartia bifilosa*; *11* Southern boundary of *Limnocalanus grimaldi*.

Tintinnoidea (Parafavella, Tintinnopsis), a series of the species Sagita, the pteropod mollusc *Limacina retroversa* and others, we have east of the Darss ridge throughout the Baltic the blue-green algae *Aphanizomenon flos-aquae*, *Nodularia spumigena* and *Anabaena baltica*; the diatoms *Chaetoceros wighami*, *Thalassiosira baltica* and *Ch. danicum*, which sometimes bring about a summer and autumn flowering of the peridineans *P. depressum* and *P. pellucidum*, *Prorocentrum micans*, *Dinophysis baltica*, *Goniaulax catenata* and others, some Infusoria, for instance *Tintinnopsis campanula*, *Helicostomella subulata*, among the Rotifera a preponderance of Brachionidae, and the species *Collotheca pelagica*. Most of the Rotifera belong to euryhaline fresh-water forms (*Brachionus angularis*, *B. pala*, *B. bakeri*, *Anuraea aculeata*,

A. cochlearis, *A. eichwaldi*, *A. tecta*, *A. quadrata*, *Collotheca pelagica*, *C. mutabilis*, *Notolca striata*, *Triarthra longiseta*, *Polyarthra trigla*, *Asplanchna brightwellii*) or the brackish-water ones (*Anurea cruciformis* var. *eichwaldi*, *Synchaeta baltica*, *S. monopus*, *S. fennica* and *S. littoralis*).

The copepod crustaceans are presented mainly by *Eurytemora hirundoides*, *E. affinis*, *E. hirundo*, *Acartia bifilosa* (on some sites *A. tonsa*), *Pseudocalanus elongatus*, *Temora longicornis* and *Eurytemora hirundoides*, and in the coldest parts of the Sea *Limnocalanus grimaldi* (Fig. 138), among the daphnid *Bosmina maritima*, *Evadne nordmanni* and some species of Podon, and in the parts of the Gulf with the lowest salinity *Daphnia cucullata*, *Chidorus sphaericus*, *Leptodora kindti* and other fresh-water forms. In the deeper layers of the western part of the Sea *Calanus finmarchicus*, *Oithona similis* and *Sagitta elegans* f. *baltica* are frequently encountered. The mysid *M. oculata* is widely distributed throughout the Baltic Sea. The other mysids—*Gastrosaccus spinifer*, *Praunus inermis* and *P. flexuosus*—are found in the Baltic Sea in smaller numbers. The larvae of the bottom-living animals and especially Macoma, Hydrobia, Balanus, Membranipora and the polychaetes form a considerable constituent of the plankton. Among the tunicates *Oikopleura dioica* and Fritillaria are encountered. Among the large plankton forms the medusa *Aurelia aurita* is found at times in large numbers throughout the Sea, and in the southern part of the Sea *Cyanea capillata*, *Pleurobrachia pileus*, *Hyperia galla*, *Sagitta elegans baltica* (I. Markovsky, 1950).

An interesting phenomenon was noted by J. Välikangas (1926) for the Baltic Sea, namely that a large number of fresh-water forms develop most rapidly not in fresh water but at a salinity of 3·45 to 5·4‰. Examples are *Tintinnidium fluviatile*, *Floscularia* sp., *Asplanchna brightwellii*, *Triarthra longiseta*, *T. brachiata* and others.

C. Brandes (1939) distinguishes three groups of forms in the plankton of the Baltic Sea: the 'marine', the brackish-water and the fresh-water. Although many of the marine forms penetrate deep into the Sea, they are fairly rare there and do not have a mass development.

The Darss ridge forms a marked boundary as regards both hydrography and biology. This is particularly clear in the case of plankton. Brandes has noted that the 'marine' forms are preponderant to the west and the brackish-water ones to the east. At a salinity of more than 9‰ the marine *Ceratium tripos*, Melosira, Rhizosolenia and the ciliates Parafavella are markedly preponderant. With further loss of salinity the brackish-water form *Chaetoceros danicus* and the ciliates Helicostomella and Aphanizomenon are no less markedly preponderant. At a salinity below 6·5‰ the fresh-water forms Chlorophyceae, Chroococcacea and some Rotifera (Brachionus, Ratulus and others) become abundant. The change of some plankton in a cross section from the Fehmarn Belt to deep inside the Baltic Sea is shown in Fig. 139.

Two biogeographical communities stand out clearly in the Baltic Sea phytoplankton (I. Nikolaev, 1951): the Arctic and the Boreal Arctic of the spring period (*Table 123*).

The two communities partly overlap one another, but broadly speaking the Arctic community is more marked in the spring at a temperature of

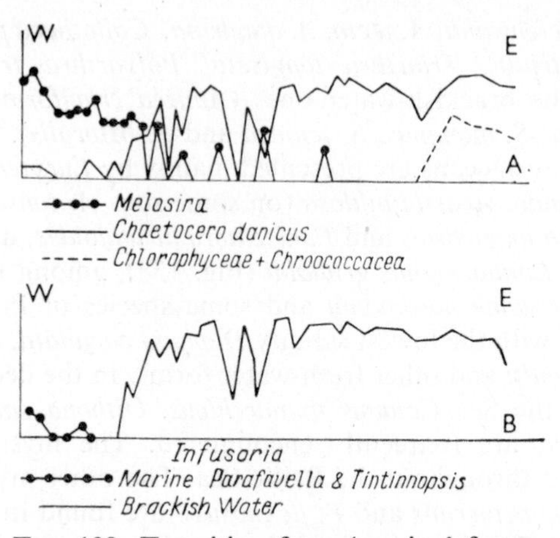

FIG. 139. Transition from 'marine' forms of plankton to 'brackish-water' forms as one passes from the Belt into the Baltic. A Seaweeds; B Infusora (Brandes, 1939).

2° to 5° and in the northern part of the Sea. The Boreal Arctic community develops most at temperatures from 3° to 4° to 8° to 10°, both in the spring and in the autumn. The two communities are characterized by their broad euryhalinity. I. Nikolaev (1951) has pointed out that 'there is a break between the Arctic region of distribution and the Baltic Sea in the case of these forms'.

Table 123

Arctic forms	Boreal Arctic forms
Melocira arctica	*Chaetoceras gracilis*
Achnanthes taeniata	*Chaetoceras holsaticus*
Fragilaria cylindricus	*Chaetoceras wighami*
Navicula granii	*Sceletonema costatum*
Navicula Vanhöffeni	*Thalassiosira baltica*
Nitzschia frigida	*Nitzschia longissima*
Goniaulax catenata	*Paridinium achromaticum*
	Dinobryon pellucidum

Plankton development in various parts of the Sea. The Baltic Sea plankton is poorer both qualitatively and quantitatively than that of the North Sea and the parts of the Atlantic Ocean adjacent to it. As has been pointed out by F. Gessner, this results in the greater transparency of the Baltic Sea waters as compared with those of the North Sea. Organic matter is accumulated in the deep depressions of the Baltic, which are poor in oxygen and rich in carbon dioxide. The occurrence of such deep depressions in a body of water causes a more or less inadequate development of its plankton life, especially as geologically the Baltic basin was fed by melt waters, poor in nutritive substances (Ice and Ancylus Lakes). At the same time in some sections of the Baltic Sea, in bays and gulfs well supplied with organic matter from the mainland, plankton development is vigorous.

I. Nikolaev (1957) notes that the seasonal changes in the qualitative composition of the plankton are very marked owing to the fact that what he terms the 'marine cold-water (Arctic) communities' and the 'fresh-water brackish (warm-water) ones' change places during the cold and warm periods in the year. The accumulation of nutritive matter in the upper layers of the Sea and the arrival of the sunny period result in a springtime 'blacking' of diatomous phytoplankton in April. Intensive flowering is at that time observed in the inlets. During the blooming the following forms develop in specially large masses: the diatoms *Sceletonema costatum*, *Achnanthes taeniata*, *Thalassiosira baltica*, *Chaetoceras holsaticus*, and *Melosira arctica*; and among the peridineans: *Dinobryon pellucidum*. Among the zooplankton the following take part in the spring blooming: the ciliates *Mesodinium rubrum*, 3 or 4 species of Strombidium, *Tintinnopsis tubulosa*, *T. brandti*, *Cothurnia maritima* and others; the Rotifera *Synchaeta monopus* and *S. baltica*; the Copepoda Pseudocalanus, *Acartia longiremis*, *A. bifilosa*, *Temora longicornis*, *Eurytemora hirundoides*; and in the inlets *Limnocalanus grimaldi*, *Acartia bifilosa*, *Eurytemora hirundoides*, *Sagitta elegans baltica*, *Fritillaria borealis*; the mysids *Mysis oculata* var. *relicta* and *M. mixta*.

In summer these forms disappear gradually and the dominant position is occupied by the blue-green algae *Aphanizomenon flos-aquae* and *Nodularia spigena*; the diatoms *Chaetoceras wighami*, *Actinocyclus ehrenbergi*, *Thalassiosira nana*, *T. baltica*; and among the peridians *Peridimum pellucumid*, *Dinophysis baltica*. In July and August the blue-green algae are in full bloom everywhere. By the end of the summer period the following animal forms reach their maximum mass development: among the ciliates *Helicostomella subulata*; the Rotifera *Keratella cochlearis*, *K. aculeata*; the Copepoda *Acartis bifilosa* and *Eurytemora hirundoides*; and in huge numbers the Cladocera *Bosmina coregoni* f. *maritima* and *Evadne nordmanni*. The fresh-water aspect of the summer plankton is infringed only by the Medusa *Cyanea capillata*, *Aurelia aurita*, and the Ctenophore *Pleurobrachius pileus*. The larvae of the bottom-dwelling invertebrates are also mixed with plankton in large masses at this time of the year.

In autumn (November, December) the plankton loses its summer forms. The diatom *Coscinodiscus grani* begins to grow in large masses: the seasonal changes described are clearly shown in Fig. 140.

All plankton species are very poorly represented in the Gulf of Bothnia, especially in the central parts of its northern half, which K. Levander called in 1900 'practically sterile'. The plankton there does not bloom even at the beginning of the summer when sunlight is abundant.

Indices of plankton productivity. In the Arcona depression the very small possibility of plankton development is evident from the vertical distribution of the basic factors of the medium. The marked differences in the temperature and salinity of the surface and deep-water layers, which restrict vertical circulation, and the poor supply of nutrient salts do not provide favourable conditions for plankton growth. Feeble development of plankton leads to an almost complete disappearance of phosphates and nitrates in the surface layer. The course of this process is shown in Fig. 141. The phosphates and

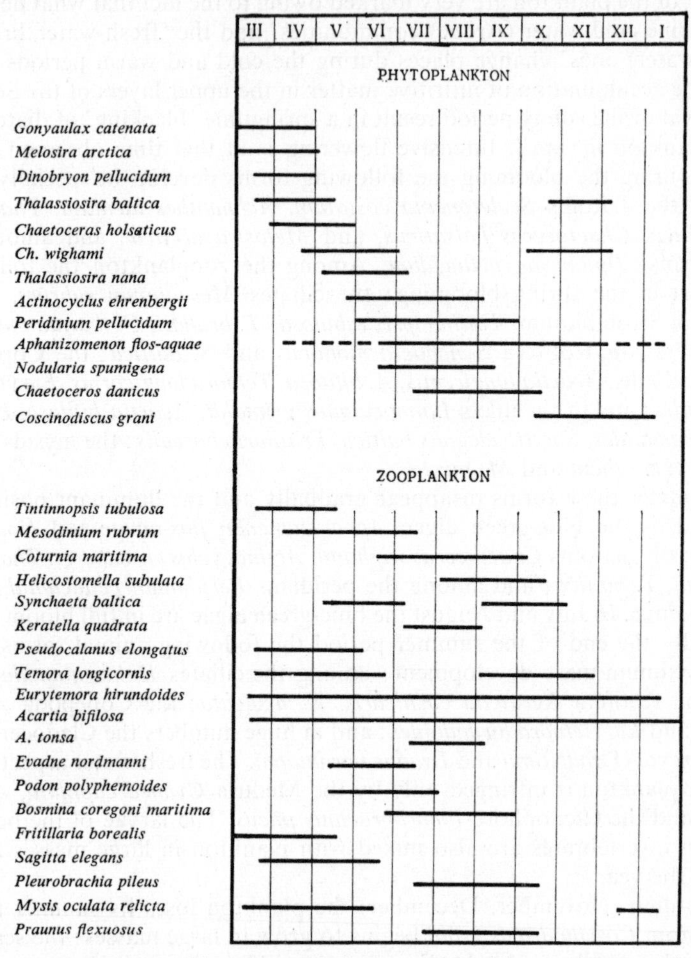

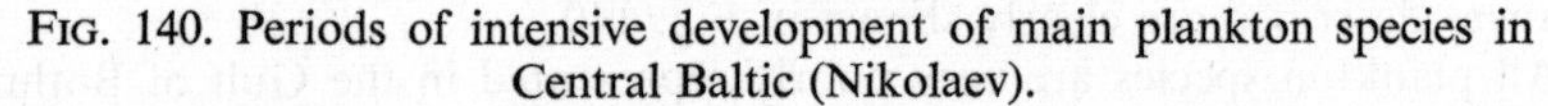

FIG. 140. Periods of intensive development of main plankton species in Central Baltic (Nikolaev).

nitrates are removed in March and April by an increase in the growth of plankton (diatom). In May the dying plankton carries them to great depths; thus the surface layer of water loses both its plankton and its nutrient salts. A partial regeneration of the phosphates and nitrates in June, July and August results in a small new increase of plankton, when Cladocera is predominant in the zooplankton. Plankton does not develop in winter when the temperature is low and sunlight scarce, although the nutrient salts are more concentrated as a result of winter vertical circulation. At that time Copepoda is the dominant form. Phytoplankton begins to develop rapidly with the first

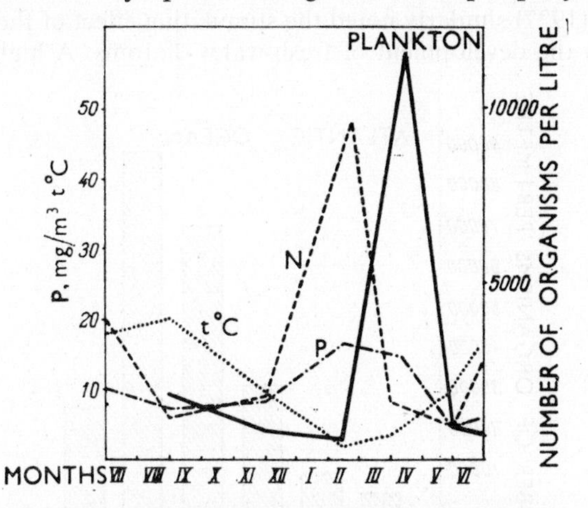

FIG. 141. Alterations in the quantity of plankton and nutrient substances with the months in the surface layer of the Arcona depression (Gessner, 1940).

rays of spring sunshine, using all the nutrient salts and thus killing off the plankton. As early as 1908 C. Apstein, working on the quantitative data of

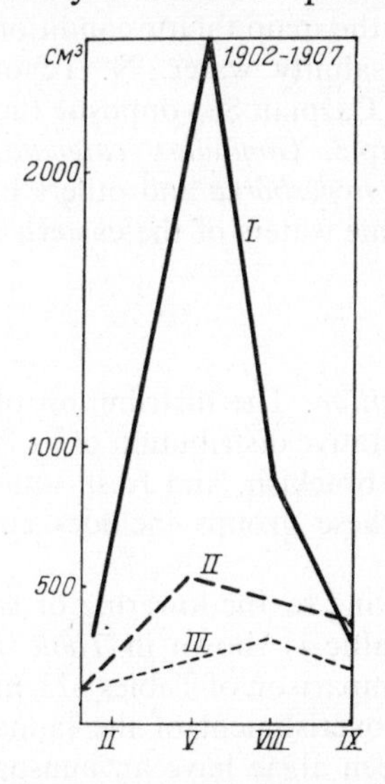

FIG. 142. Plankton biomass in the Northern (*II*) and Baltic (*III*) Seas and in the straits (*I*), in cc in the water column of 1 m² section (Apstein).

Baltic Sea plankton, noted its huge development in May in the Beltsee, the straits between the North and Baltic Seas (Fig. 142). Moreover he had found that plankton growth in the Baltic is considerably poorer than in the North Sea. The quantitative indices of plankton even in the most productive southern part of the Sea are much lower than those of the corresponding parts of the Atlantic (Fig. 143).

R. Kolbe (1927) similarly noted the stimulating effect of the slightly brackish water on the development of fresh-water diatoms. A high concentration

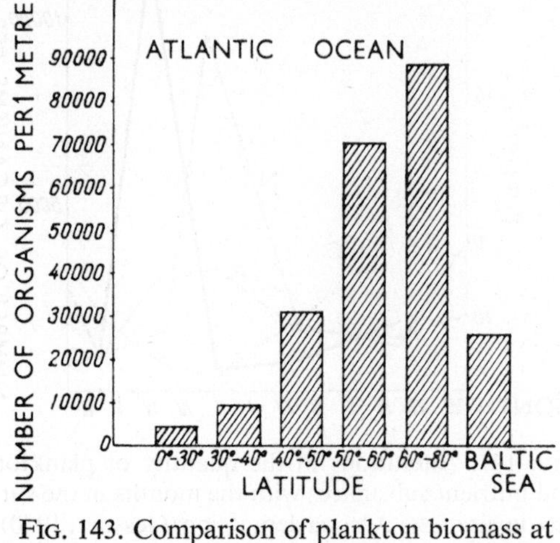

FIG. 143. Comparison of plankton biomass at different latitudes in the Baltic Sea and the Atlantic (Gessner).

of nutrient matter must be considered the main factor conditioning the mass development of these forms in low-salinity water. N. Tchougounov has observed a similar phenomenon in the Caspian Sea opposite the Volga delta.

Some Arctic species as, for example, *Goniaulax catenata*, *Achnanthes taeniata*, *Fragilaria cylindrus*, *Melosira hyperborea* and others break out into intensive flowering in the cold springtime waters of the eastern and northern parts of the Baltic Sea.

Benthos

Bottom vegetation—qualitative composition. The distribution of flora in the Baltic Sea is wholly similar to the qualitative distribution of its fauna. Among the vegetable organisms marine, true brackish, and fresh-water forms may also be distinguished, and each of these groups includes euryhaline and stenohaline representatives.

The impoverishment of the flora owing to the lowering of salinity as one moves from the North Sea to the Baltic is shown in *Table 124*, which is copied from K. Hofmann (1940). A comparison of Tables 123 and 124 reveals a much more intense qualitative impoverishment of the fauna than of the flora. Many representatives of the green algae have an unusually luxuriant group in the Baltic Sea. Among the brown algae some, like *Pylaiella rupincola*, develop intensively there also. As a rule, however, sea algae do not grow properly in the Baltic Sea; thus, for example, the large marine algae *Laminaria saccharina* in the Arctic region grows to a size of only a few centimetres. The

Table 124

Group of algae	Off Boguslen, salinity of 27–33‰	Off Sud Halland and Schonen, salinity of 17–24‰	Baltic Sea proper (according to Svidelius)
Green	68	29	15
Brown	102	45	20
Red	99	56	16
Total	269	130	51

plants decrease in size the farther they penetrate into the diluted waters of the Baltic, and this is accompanied, as in the case of the zooplankton, by sterility. Thus, for example, the small forms *Polysiphonia nigrescens* and *Rhodomela subfusca*, inhabiting the inner parts of the Baltic, multiply very rarely (S. Sägerstråle, 1957).

Propagation to the east. Just as with the fauna the Darss ridge sets a definite limit to the propagation of marine algae to the east. To the west of the ridge there is an abundance of such forms as *Chaetopteris plumosa*, *Stylophora tuberculosa*, *Spermatochnus paradoxus*, *Laminaria flexicaulis*, *Fucus ceranoides*, *Ascophyllus nodosum* among the Phaeophycae and different species of Porphyra, *Chondrus crispus*, *Cystoclonium purpurescens*, *Rhodimenia palmata*, *Delesseria sanguinea*, *Polysiphonia urceolata* and other red algae. None of this luxuriant marine flora extends eastward of the Darss ridge, and the flora of the Baltic Sea east of the ridge contains such brown algae as *Fucus vesiculosus*, *Chorda filium*, *Ch. tomentosum*, *Elachista fucicola*, *Dictyosiphon foeniculaceus*, *Gobia baltica*, *Strichtyosiphon* (*Phlocospora*) *tortilis*, *Sphacelaria racemosa*, *Ectocarpus siliculosus*, *E. confervoides*, *Pylaiella litoralis*. *Limnaria saccharina* reaches the shores of Bornholm, and *Fucus serratus*—Gotland; among the red algae are *Asterocystis ramosa*, *Phyllophora brodiaei*, *Polysiphonia violacea*, *P. nigrescens*, *Rhodomela subfusca*, *Ceramium diaphanum*, *Furcellaria fastigiata* and others. As for the green algae, various species of Ulva, Monostroma, Enteromorpha and Chaetomorpha may be added.

This composition of the flora is typical for the areas with a surface summer salinity of about 8‰. A sharp decrease of marine forms is encountered again at the entrance to the Gulf of Bothnia and at the transition from its outer to its inner part.

Floral plants occupy a significant place in the coastal vegetation of the Baltic Sea; their distribution according to salinity is given in Fig. 144A.

The algae of the Baltic Sea extend to a depth of 25 m; the number of species according to Hessner is given in *Table 125*. The red and brown algae descend deeper than the others.

Only the most hardy forms reach the northern parts of the Gulf of Bothnia (Fig. 144), namely: *Fucus vesiculosus*, *Chorda filum*, *Elachista fucicola*,

Table 125

Depth, m	Red algae	Brown algae	Green algae	Blue-green algae
0–2	4	11	39	15
2–4	14	14	16	5
4–8	18	15	10	2
8–12	11	9	3	—
12–18	9	6	2	—
18–25	7	5	—	—

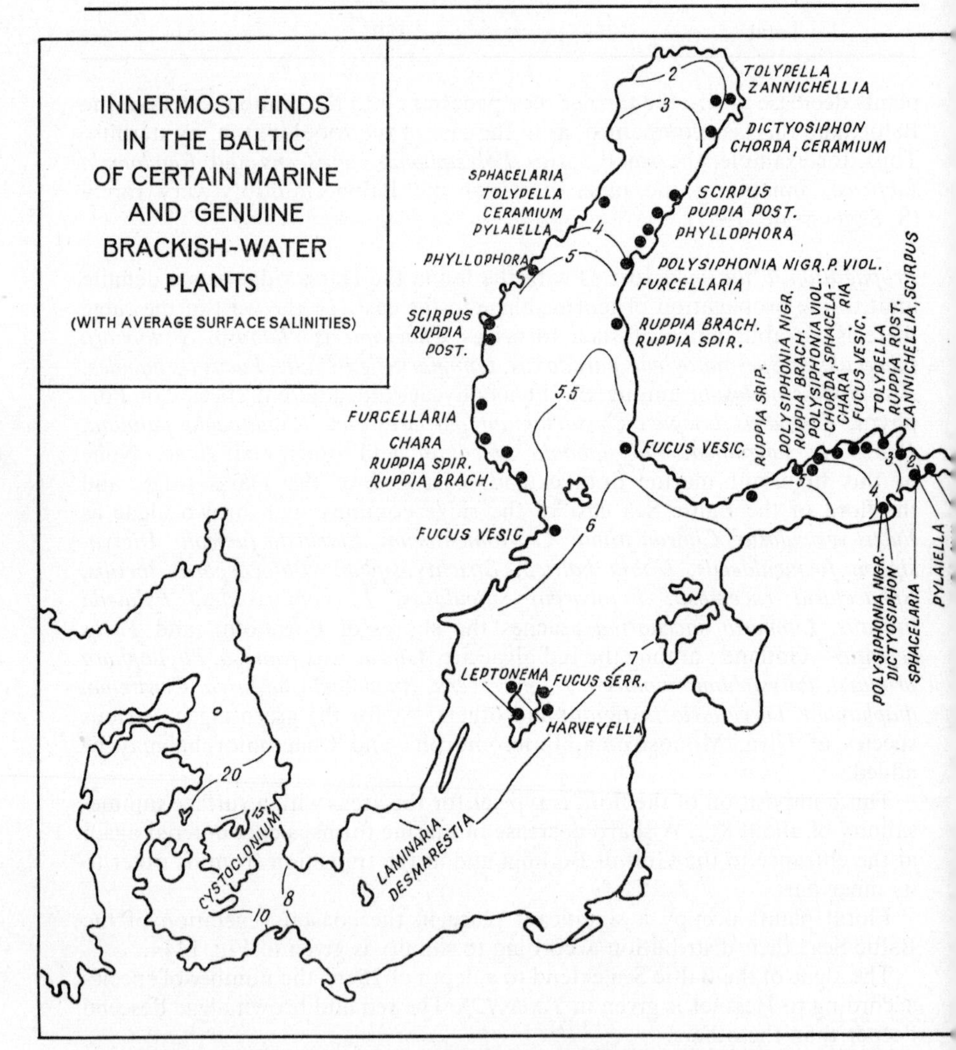

FIG. 144A. Penetration of some marine and brackish-water plants far into the Baltic Sea (Sägerstråle).

Dictyosiphon foeniculaceus, *Gobia baltica*, *Strichtyosiphon tortilis*, *Ceramium diaphanum* and *Asterocystis ramosa*; moreover, here they are greatly reduced in size.

There are no tides in the Baltic Sea; however, considerable changes in the level of the Sea have been observed under the effect of the wind and of differences in pressure. These fluctuations are at times as large as 1 to 1·3 m. This

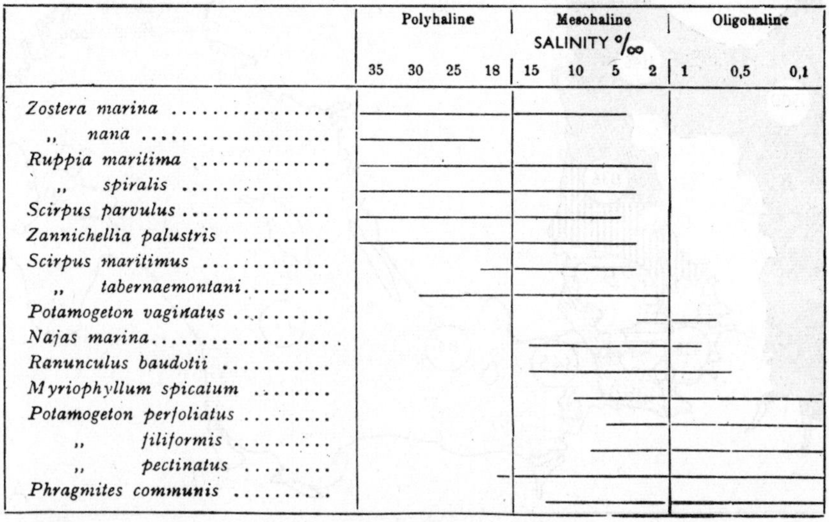

SALINITY ‰	Polyhaline	Mesohaline	Oligohaline
	35 30 25 18	15 10 5 2	1 0,5 0,1
Zostera marina			
,, *nana*			
Ruppia maritima			
,, *spiralis*			
Scirpus parvulus			
Zannichellia palustris			
Scirpus maritimus			
,, *tabernaemontani*			
Potamogeton vaginatus			
Najas marina			
Ranunculus baudotii			
Myriophyllum spicatum			
Potamogeton perfoliatus			
,, *filiformis*			
,, *pectinatus*			
Phragmites communis			

FIG. 144B. Correlation between salinity and the distribution of flowering marine plants (Gessner).

is reflected in the zonal distribution of the coastal vegetation and can be expressed in the following pattern (M. Waern, 1952; F. Du Rietz, 1950):

(*1*) The geolittoral or geo-amphibiotic belt. Covered with water either when the sea-level rises, or by waves and the swell. The upper limit of summer growth of algae.
(*2*) The hydrolittoral or hydro-amphibiotic belt. Exposed at a low level of water, thickly covered by threadlike sea-weeds (*Cladophora glomerata*). The lower limit of summer growth of algae.
(*3*) Sublittoral. Always covered with water.

Zoobenthos

Qualitative composition. One of the three main components of Baltic Sea fauna is the greatly impoverished North Sea fauna (Atlantic fauna), which penetrates into the body of water through the straits and undergoes, with the fall in salinity, a marked loss in the number of species (Fig. 145), and the degeneration of individuals. K. Brandt was the first to estimate the Atlantic fauna in the Baltic Sea (1897). Ekman revised Brandt's data in 1935 from data published in the series *Die Tierwelt der Nord- und Ostsee*. We give below

Ekman's table with some additions from Brandt's table, from Remane (1940), and new additions (marked by asterisks in *Table 126*) according to S. Sägerstråle (1957).

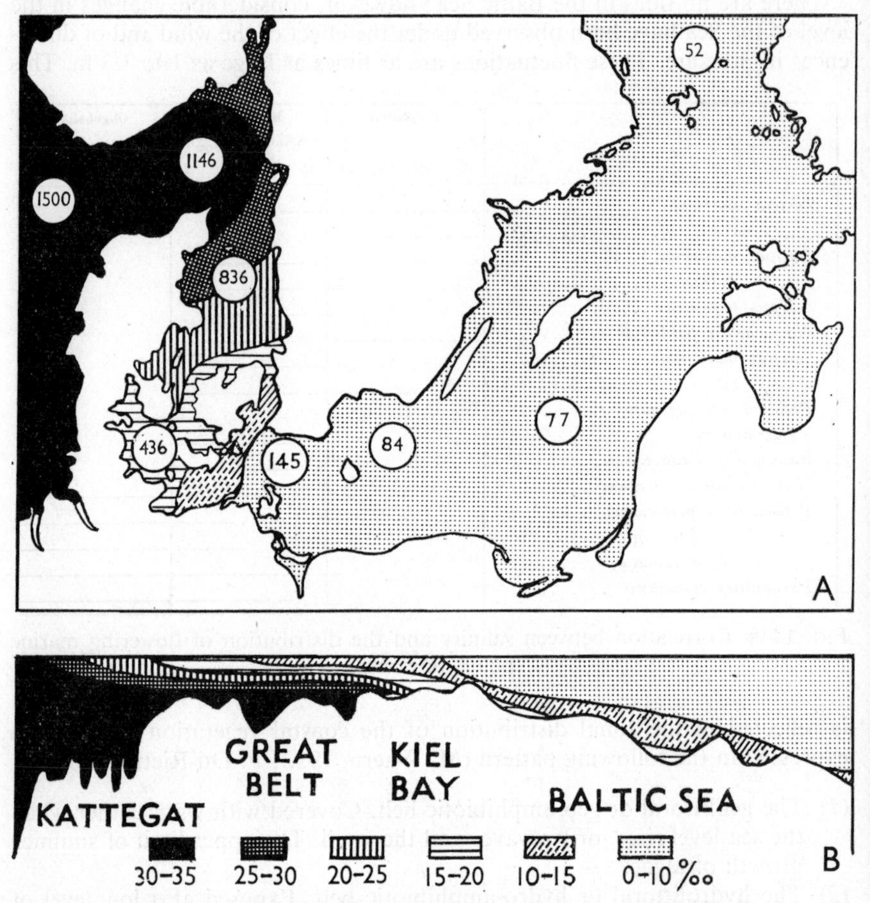

FIG. 145A. Alteration of salinity from the passage from the North Sea far into the Baltic. A Surface salinity in February; B Change of salinity along the vertical cross section in August (Remane and Wattenberg). Numbers of animal species are encircled in A.

There is an excellent summary of present knowledge concerning the distribution of Baltic Sea fauna in the works of the Finnish investigators J. Välikangas (1933) and S. Sägerstråle (1957), and the Swedish zoologist Ekman (1933 and 1935).

Propagation to the east. The most common Baltic hydroids—*Clava squamata*, *Sertularia pumila*, *Obelia geniculata* and *Campanularia flexuosa*—are characteristic only of the western part of the Sea. Of the two Medusa known to exist in the Baltic Sea—*Cyanea capillata* and *Aurelia aurita*—the second penetrates farther to the east and north, reaching the shores of Finland; it is encountered in areas with 5·75 to 6·0‰ salinity at the surface and 7‰ at the bottom. Four actinians penetrate as far as Kiel Bay—*Helcampa duodecimcirrata, Urticina felina, Metridium dianthus* and *Sagartia viduata*; but they do not go farther east than Kiel Bay.

There is a marked decrease in the number of polychaete species in the Belt; even in the southern part of the Baltic Sea only 25 species of them are known including: *Travisia forbesi, Syllis armillaris, Nereis pelagica, Fabricia sabella, Arenicola marina, Nephthys ciliata, N. coeca, Scoloplos armiger, Terebellides*

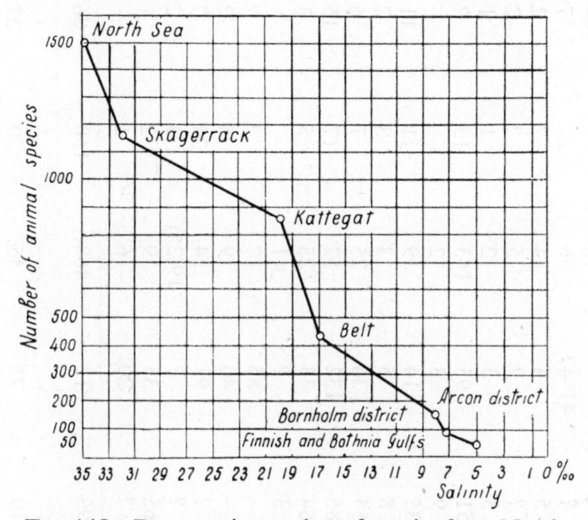

FIG. 145C. Decrease in number of species from North Sea to Baltic compared with the decrease in salinity (Zenkevitch).

strömii, Pygospio elegans, Harmothoe sarsi and *Nereis diversicolor*. In the Belt and the Sound about 143 species of polychaetes have been identified (Eliasson, 1920). *Pygospio elegans* and Terebellides reach the entrance of the Gulfs of Finland and Bothnia (Fig. 146). *Nereis diversicolor* and *Harmothoe sarsi* penetrate into the Gulfs (a little farther into the Gulf of Finland) and there survive a lowering of salinity in the surface layers to 5·25‰.

Among the Gephyrea only *Priapulus caudatus* penetrates into the Baltic Sea, remaining in the most westerly parts of it, while *Halicryptus spinulosus*, which thrives in great numbers at the bottom of the Baltic Sea, reaches halfway up the Gulf of Finland and to the Åland Islands and the Quarken of Finland (Fig. 146).

Bryozoa are represented in the Baltic Sea proper by only four forms; among these only *Membranipora pilosa* f. *membranacea* is still found at a salinity of 4‰ (Fig. 146).

According to the summary due to Haas (1926), only five of the 87 species

Table 126

Group	North Sea	Skagerrak	Kattegat	Belt	Arcona area	Bornholm area	Central Baltic area	Gulfs of Finland and Bothnia
Porifera	15	—	—	13	3	—	—	—
Hydroid polyps	96	?	41–47	36	21	7	1	1†
Scyphozoa	9	5	4	4	2	2	2	1‡
Actinaria	15	?	?	5	?	2	1	—
Ctenophora	3	3	3	2	1	1	1	—
Polychaeta*	271	251	193	143	15	?	12	3§
Sipunculoidea	15	9	3	2	—	—	—	—
Copepoda calanoida	70	35	14	19	11	11	11	9
Cirripedia (non-parasitica)	8	8	5	3	3	2	1	1
Isipoda	80	55	36	25	7	6	5	4¶
Amphipoda	330	285	132	52	17	15	12	5**
Decapoda	90	64	33	25	5	3	3	2‖
Amphineura	—	3	?	1	—	—	—	—
Prosobranchia	—	—	85	17	?	?	3	1
Opisthobranchia	—	—	40	19	5	?	2	—
Lamellibranchiata	170	?	92	34	24	7	5	4††
Bryozoa	70	?	?	19(25)	3	2	2	1
Echinodermata	70	65	35	9	2	1	—	—
Ascidia	?	?	20	6	1	—	—	—
Total	1,432	893	812	468	150	86	87	55
Fresh-water fish	—	—	—	—	—	—	6	20
Fish	120	105–110	75	55	30	27	26	23

* For the Danzig region K. Demel notes also *Polynoe cirrata*.
† *Laomedea loveni*.
‡ *Aurelia aurita*.
§ *Harmothoe sarsi, Nereis diversicolor, Pygospio elegans*.
‖ *Leander adspersus fabricii, Crangon vulgaris*.
¶ *Idothea baltica, I. granulosa, Jaera marina* (*albifrons*).
** *Gammarus locusta, G.* (*saddachi*) *oceanicus, Calliopius laeviusculus, Pontoporeia femorata, Corophium volutator*.
†† *Cardium edule, Macoma baltica, Mya arenaria, Mytilus edulis*.

of bivalves found in the Kattegat exist in the central part of the Baltic Sea, and each of these forms a dense population in separate areas of the Sea. These forms are, in order of decreasing importance: *Macoma baltica*, *Mya arenaria*,

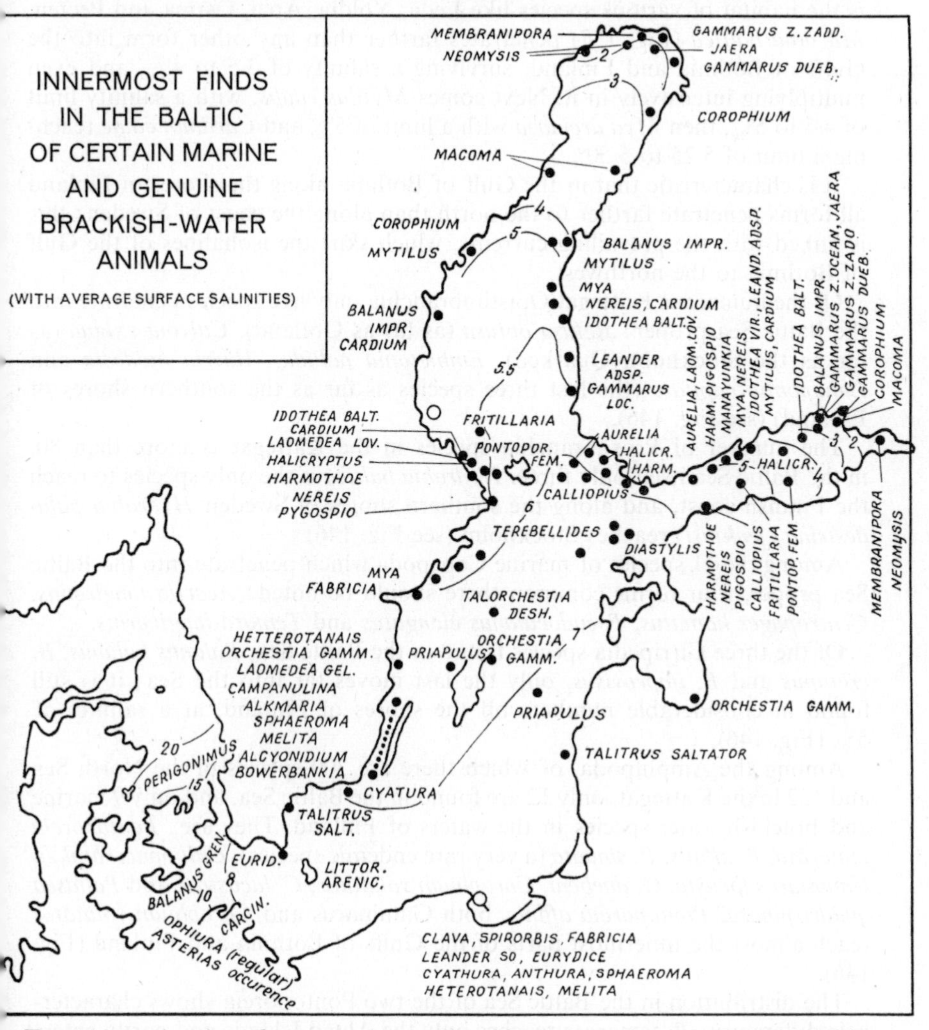

FIG. 146. Penetration of some marine and brackish-water animals far into the Baltic Sea (Sägerstråle, 1957).

Cardium edule, *Mytilus edulus* and *Macoma calcarea*. *Macoma baltica*, far and away the most dominant form not only among the molluscs but among the whole fauna, has found in the Baltic Sea exceptionally favourable conditions for existence. In the Bornholm area two more bivalves—*Astarte elliptica* (synonym: *A. compressa*) and *A. borealis* (a cold-water relict)—should be added to the five given above. Farther to the west, within the transitional region, the number of molluscs increases markedly, and such typical North Sea forms as *Nucula nucleus*, *Mya truncata*, *Corbula gibba*, *Saxicava rugosa*, *Teredo navalis*, the species Syndesmya and Venus appear, while the Kattegat is the habitat of various species like Leda, Yoldia, Arca, Ostrea and Pecten. *Macoma baltica* (Fig. 137) penetrates farther than any other form into the Gulfs of Bothnia and Finland, surviving a salinity of 3·5 to 4‰, and even multiplying intensively in it. Next comes *Mytilus edulis*, with a salinity limit of 4·5 to 5‰, then *Mya arenaria* with a limit of 5‰ and *Cardium edule* reaching a limit of 5·25 to 5·50‰.

It is characteristic that in the Gulf of Bothnia along the shores of Finland all forms penetrate farther to the north than along the coast of Sweden; this is linked with the prevailing currents, which skirt the isohalines of the Gulf of Bothnia to the northwest.

Of the numerous Kattegat Opisthobranchia only five species penetrate into the Baltic Sea proper: *Retusa obtusa* (as far as Gotland), *Calvina exigua* (as far as the Stockholm Quarken), *Embletonia pallida*, *Alderia modesta* and *Limapontia capitata* (the last three species as far as the southern shores of Finland) (see Fig. 146).

The number of Prosobranchia species in the Kattegat is more than 80, in the Baltic Sea itself only three. *Hydrobia baltica* is the only species to reach the Finnish coast, and along the southern shores of Sweden *Hydrobia paludestrina* (*jenkinsi*) reaches Stockholm (see Fig. 146).

Among the 11 species of marine Copepoda which penetrate into the Baltic Sea proper, four forms common there should be noted: *Acartia longiremis*, *Centropages hamatus*, *Pseudocalanus elongatus* and *Temora longicornis*.

Of the three Cirripedia species found in the Baltic Sea, *Balanus balanus*, *B. cretanus* and *B. improvisus*, only the last moves far into the Sea; it is still found in considerable numbers off the shores of Finland, at a salinity of 5‰ (Fig. 146).

Among the Amphipoda, of which there are 300 species in the North Sea and 132 in the Kattegat, only 12 are found in the Baltic Sea, and only 9 marine and brackish-water species in the waters of Finland. They are: *Pontoporeia femorata*, *P. affinis*, *P. sinuata* (a very rare endemic species), *Calliopius rathkei*, *Gammarus locusta*, *G. duebeni*, *Corophium volutator*, *C. lacustrae* and *Pallasea quadrispinosa*. *Pontoporeia affinis*, both Gammarus and *Corophium volutator* reach almost the innermost parts of the Gulfs of Bothnia and Finland (Fig. 146).

The distribution in the Baltic Sea of the two Pontoporeia shows characteristic differences. *P. femorata* reaches only the Åland Islands and partly enters the Gulf of Finland. *P. affinis* is an Arctic brackish-water form. The density of its population increases gradually as one moves north and east, as also happens with *Pallasea quadrispinosa* and *Limnocalanus grimaldi* (Fig. 146). *P. affinis* lives in many lakes of Northern Europe and Northern America as a relict. *Pallasea quadrispinosa* is found in water with a salinity of up to 5 to 6‰ off the Swedish shores of the Central Baltic and the Gulf of Bothnia and in the Gulf of Finland.

Among the Isopoda, *Mesidothea entomon* and *Iaera albifrons* enter farther into the zones of lower salinity than the other forms; *Idothea baltica* enters both Gulfs, while *Idothea granulosa* and *I. viridis* do not go beyond the entrances of the two Gulfs.

Decapoda of marine origin are very poorly represented in the central area of the Baltic Sea. There are 64 species of decapod crustaceans in the Swedish waters of the Skaggerak and Kattegat; in Oresund there are 24, and in Kiel Bay 10. Only two species—*Crangon crangon* and *Leander adspersus* var. *fabricii* —inhabit the central basin.

Apart from *Mysis oculata*, which densely populates this Sea, *Mysis vulgaris* and *M. flexuosa* among the Mysidacea penetrate far into the Sea.

Of the echinoderms only the most euryhaline, *Asterias rubens* and *Ophiura albida*, are found in the Baltic Sea itself.

Finally the sea fish most common in the Baltic Sea are: the brackish-water race of herring, which occupies first place in the fishing industry; *Clupea harengus membras* (the so-called Baltic herring), and then the following: *Cl. sprattus, Gadus morrhua, Lumpenus lampetriformis, Cottus scorpius quadricornis, Liparis liparis, Cyclopterus lumpus, Pholis gunellis, Zoarces viviparus, Spinachia spinachia, Nerophis ophidion, Siphostoma typhle, Ammodytes lanceolatus, A. tobianus, Pleuronectes flesus* and *Bothus maximus.*

Decrease in size. Like many other groups of organisms with a calcareous skeleton, the molluscs diminish in size with decreasing salinity as one moves eastwards (Fig. 147). *Mytilus edulis*, which is up to 150 mm long off the shores of Great Britain, is no more than 110 mm long in Kiel Bay, no more than 40 mm off the Finnish coast, and only 20 to 25 mm at the far end of the Gulfs of Bothnia and Finland. Off the Åland Islands Mytilus is no more than 37·5 mm long, while off Liban it is 38·5 mm. West of Bornholm it reaches 55·5 mm. The fluctuations in the maximum size within the limits of the Baltic Sea proper are small, and a marked increase occurs only in the transitional region of the Belts and Oresund, this being related to changes in salinity. The same is observed with Cardium and Mya. The maximum size of *Cardium edule* at the northern boundary of its distribution is 18·5 mm; northwest of the Åland Islands it is 23·7 mm, while in the North Sea its average size is 45 mm. In the North Sea and Kiel Bay the largest *Mya arenaria* is about 100 mm long; off Gotland it is 58 mm, and at the eastern boundary of its distribution in the Gulf of Finland it is 36·5 mm. In the case of many forms the decrease in their size at the limits of their habitat, in the less saline sectors of the Baltic Sea, is linked with the loss of reproductive power. The adult forms exist, but either multiply very rarely or not at all. At a salinity below 6‰ the normal sexual cells are formed in *Aurelia aurita*, but the scyphistomae are not developed (Sägerstråle, 1951).

At the same time it is interesting to note that this rule of a decrease in size associated with a fall in salinity does not hold good with certain forms. *Macoma baltica*, for example, is 22 mm long in the North Sea and retains this length in the Baltic Sea. It is true there are some indications that at the extreme limits of its distribution in the Gulfs of Bothnia and Finland the size of *M. baltica* falls to 15 to 18 mm. According to K. Levander (1899), however,

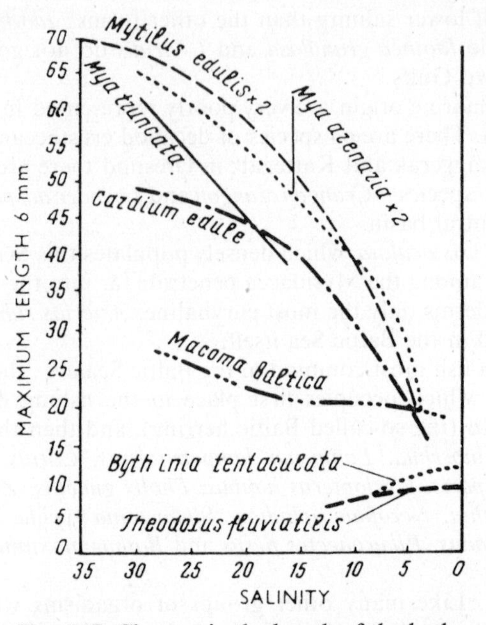

FIG. 147. Changes in the length of the body of marine bivalves and fresh-water Gastropoda with change in the salinity of the medium (Remane, 1934).

Macoma reaches 21 to 24 mm in the areas west of Helsingfors, which are most favourable for its existence (as regards its feeding). For the rest, both Cardium and Mytilus are larger in this area. Unlike Mytilus, Mya and Cardium mentioned above, the size of Macoma is clearly only slightly affected by changes of salinity. *Macoma baltica* becomes smaller with the depth of its habitat (*Table 127*).

According to H. Luther's data (1908) *Macoma baltica* from the inner bays of the Gulf of Finland is larger in size than the samples from the Littorina Sea deposits.

At the same time, marine forms without a calcareous skeleton often do not undergo a decrease in size, as for example the amphipods *Gammarus zaddachi oceanicus* and *Corophium volutator*, and the shrimp *Leander adspersus fabricii*, which are the same size in Danish waters as in the Gulf of Finland.

Table 127

Depth, m	Sedimentation	Longest shell, mm
1–5	Gyttja	21–24
1·2–2·5	Sand	16
35–36	Gyttja	15

Many fresh-water forms decrease in size when they penetrate into brackish water as, for example, *Theodoxus fluviatilis* or *Bithynia tentaculata*.

The change in the size of the body with the passage from one medium to another is illustrated in Fig. 147.

A. Remane (1935) has observed that alongside the decrease in size there is a reduction of the calcareous skeleton as one moves into less saline areas.

Brackish-water forms are also reduced in size as they move into fresh water, but they do not become smaller when they move into more saline waters; examples are *Gasterosteus aculeatus*, *Pleuronectes flesus*, *Hydrobia ulvae*, etc.

Preponderance of North Atlantic littoral species. One of the most remarkable features of Baltic Sea fauna is the huge preponderance of typical littoral forms belonging to the North Atlantic. Almost all the main forms of the littoral of the North Sea, Scandinavia, the Murman Peninsula and the White Sea are encountered here: among the polychaetes: *Fabricia sabella*, *Arenicola marina*, *Pygospio elegans*, *Nereis diversicolor*, *Nephthys coeca*; among the Gephyrea: *Priapulus caudatus* and *Halicryptus spinulosus*; among the molluscs: *Macoma baltica Mya arenaria*, *Cardium edule*, *Mytilus edulis* and some species of Hydrobia and *Limapontia capitata*; among the crustacea: *Gammarus locusta*, *G. duebeni*, *Jaera albifrons*, *Balanus improvisus*; among the echinoderms: *Asterias rubens*; and even the common littoral fishes: *Pholis gunellus* and *Zoarces viviparus*. This phenomenon, wholly exceptional in its scale, of almost all the littoral fauna migrating into the sublittoral, deserves the closest attention of biologists.

Presumably the colonization of the sublittoral in the Baltic Sea by the biocoenosis *Macoma baltica* could have taken place only in circumstances under which this horizon was poorly colonized by other organisms. The phenomenon of competition or, so to speak, the biological resistance offered to the colonization of the sublittoral by the fauna already existing there, was either very weak or non-existent.

Probably during the Littorina Period the littoral biocoenosis of Macoma—highly eurybiotic as regards salinity, temperature and oxygen—penetrated without difficulty into the Baltic Sea. Meeting no serious competitors, it populated densely the upper levels of the sublittoral. Eurytopic to a high degree, these littoral forms penetrated farther into the Baltic Sea to waters which are less saline. The Baltic Sea is tideless and their allied biotope is absent there but, owing to their euryhalinity and the absence of competition, they took almost complete possession of the upper level of the sublittoral. The Arctic relict cold-water community is predominant at the lower horizon but it too moved to much lower levels: it is related to the zone of the shore off Greenland, while in the Baltic Sea it is concentrated in the deep-water zone.

Fresh-water forms. As one moves farther into the Sea the marine forms become less numerous at the same time as the fresh-water forms come more and more into evidence; in the least saline parts of the Sea they form a considerable, and at times the predominant, part of the population. They penetrate into Baltic Sea waters with a salinity of 4 to 6‰, while some forms are found even at a salinity of 7‰. Among the fresh-water plants which penetrate the saline Baltic waters we can point out the water moss: *Fontinalis dolecorlica*, *Phragmites communis*, several species of Scirpus, Potamogeton, Myriophyllum, Ranunculus, Chara, Enteromorpha, Cladophora and Ulotrix.

The larvae of insects (chironomid, dragonflies, mayfly, etc.) form a highly characteristic part of the population of the considerably diluted waters of the Sea.

In the least saline parts of the Sea the following fresh-water molluscs are strongly represented: *Neritina* (*Neritella*) *fluviatilis*, *Bythinia tentaculata*, *Physa fontinalis*, *Paludina contecta*, *Limnaea stagnalis* var. *livonica*, *L. ovata* var. *baltica*, *L. peregra*, *L. palustris* var. *litoralis*, *Planorbis vortex*, Anodonta and Unio. Among the fresh-water crustaceans, *Asellus aquaticus* is common in the off-shore waters (up to 6·13‰). In the plankton, even in the open sea, such forms of Rotifera as *Anuraea cochlearis*, *Notholca longispina* and *Asplanchna priodonta* are common.

Among the fresh-water fish, *Coregonus lavaretus*, *C. albula*, *Abramis brama*, *Esox lucius*, *Lota lota*, *Perca fluviatilis* and *Thymallus thymallus* are widely distributed and are of commercial importance.

A certain number of plant and animal forms—emigrants from fresh waters and now living in the less saline parts of the Baltic Sea—are either very rare or completely absent from the adjacent fresh-water lakes. Among the plants one may name: *Najas marina*, *Zannichella repens*, *Z. pedunculata*, *Potamogeton panormitonus*, *Myriophyllum spicatum* and *Utricularia neglecta*; and among the animals: the Porifera *Ephydatia fluviatilis*, the mollusc *Theodoxus fluviatilis*, together with some species of water bugs and water beetles.

Penetration into the Baltic Sea of new species from the Atlantic. The Baltic is a young sea, but it may be assumed that the relationships of the components of its fauna are fairly stable, and that the population of it by marine forms, and the distribution of different inhabitants throughout the Sea, are in the main a complete process. Some forms, however, are still penetrating it, either actively or passively, and migrating from west to east.

Among new, contemporary immigrants the following groups may be distinguished: (*1*) immigrants from distant seas; (*2*) new immigrants from the North Sea; (*3*) forms migrating from the western parts of the Sea to the central and eastern parts.

To the first group belongs the diatom algae *Biddulphia sinensis*, the gastropod mollusc *Potamopygus jenkinisi*, the copepod *Acartia tonsa* and the bryozoan *Alcyonidium palyonum*, two crabs—*Rhitzopanopeus harrisi* spp. *tridentata* (Birstein, 1952) and *Eriocheir sinensis*, perhaps the most interesting representative of this group, is also called the Chinese hairy-legged crab; it has rapidly populated the shores of the North and Baltic Seas, as if it had found its second home there. Some earlier immigrants should be included in this group, such as *Mya arenaria*, found off the shores of Europe since the sixteenth and seventeenth centuries (I. Hessle, 1946), and some Caspian elements which have penetrated from the south through river systems: *Cordylophora caspia*, *Dreissena polymorpha* and *Corophium curvispinum*. I. Nikolaev (1951) points out that brackish-water forms are the most significant in this group. Evidently they were chiefly transported across the oceans by ships which remained for a long time in harbours, where the salinity of the water is usually low and various brackish-water forms are numbered among the inhabitants.

The Chinese crab was first discovered in the lower waters of the Elbe and Weser. It has been suggested that it was brought from China around 1912 by ships, possibly in their water tanks or in the growths which covered the sides of the ship. During the last twenty-five years the crab has migrated along the southern shores of the North Sea, the straits and the shores of the Baltic Sea,

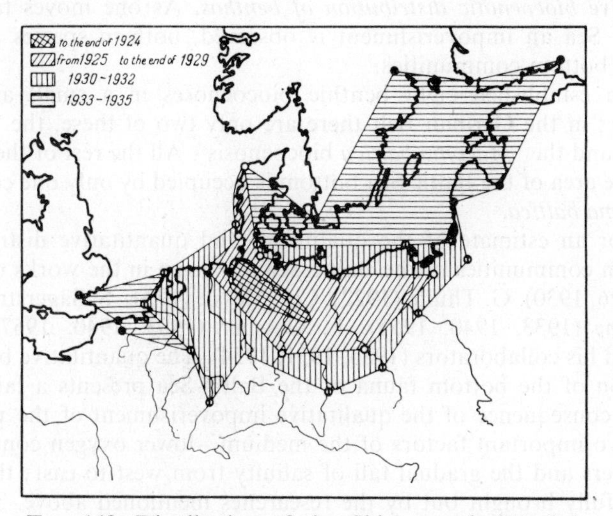

FIG. 148. Distribution of the Chinese crab *Eriocheir sinensis* in the Baltic basin (Peters and Panning, 1933). Penetration up the rivers is shown by ○ and ●.

and up the river systems. Its migration in the last fifteen years is shown on the chart (Fig. 148). The fact that in new places the crab appears first of all near large ports is evidence of its being brought by ships. Now it has settled over an area of no less than 1,000,000 km². This crab is a small, very active animal (the largest are 7 cm long) which in unfavourable conditions is capable of coming out on land and traversing it for quite considerable distances. In some areas, especially in Germany, the Chinese crab has multiplied greatly and become a very serious pest. It damages fishing nets, but the greatest harm it does is through the destruction of the shore by its innumerable burrows. A persistent campaign is waged against it. In some places as many as 50,000 crabs are caught in a day. In the Elbe alone the catch (1935) was more than 500 tons a year, i.e. no less than ten million specimens. The crab cannot breed in fresh water; it comes down to the estuaries for this purpose.

I. Nikolaev has assembled the data on the second and third groups of forms

(1949). He points out that in the changes of Baltic Sea flora and fauna account should be taken not only of the qualitative factors—the appearance of a formerly unknown form, but also the quantitative ones—a rare form can become predominant.

Among the species formerly unknown in the Baltic Nikolaev notes the diatom algae *Coscinodiscus granii* and the mullet *Mugil capito*, and among the forms which have migrated into the eastern and northern areas of the Sea: *Sagitta elegans baltica*; the amphipod *Bathyporeia pilosa*; and among the fish: anchovy (*Engraulis encrassicholus*), marine pike (*Belone belone*), mackerel (*Scomber scomber*) and the marine turbot (*Onos cimbrius*).

Quantitative biocoenotic distribution of benthos. As one moves farther into the Baltic Sea an impoverishment is observed, both in species and in the variety of bottom communities.

Petersen established eight benthic biocoenoses in a small area of the Skagerrak; in the German Belt there are only two of these, the 'Abra biocoenosis' and the '*Macoma baltica* biocoenosis'. All the rest of the comparatively huge area of the Baltic Sea bottom is occupied by only one community, the *Macoma baltica.*

Data for an estimate of the qualitative and quantitative distribution of the bottom communities of the Baltic Sea are given in the works of A. Hagmeier (1926, 1930), G. Thulin (1922), Chr. Hessle (1924), S. Sägerstråle (1923), A. Remane (1933, 1940, 1955), F. Gessner (1933, 1940, 1957), and K. Demel and his collaborators (1935, 1951, 1954). The quantitative biocoenotic distribution of the bottom fauna of the Baltic Sea presents a fairly simple picture in consequence of the qualitative impoverishment of the population and the two important factors of the medium—lower oxygen content in the deeper layers and the gradual fall of salinity from west to east; this general picture is fully brought out by the researches mentioned above. The distribution of the main bottom communities throughout the Baltic Sea is given in Fig. 149. The data refer to the average benthos biomass in g/m³.

In general, moving from west to east, we can distinguish in the Baltic Sea four main biocoenoses: (*1*) Cyprina+Astarte (a modification of Petersen's 'Abra biocoenosis') in the German Belt (Kiel and Mecklenburg Bays and the adjacent sea areas); (*2*) *Macoma calcarea* (Arcona and Bornholm depressions and the adjacent sea areas); (*3*) *Macoma baltica* and *Astarte borealis* (most of the Baltic Sea and the Gulfs of Bothnia and Finland); and (*4*) Pontoporeia+Mesidothea (the northern part of the Gulf of Bothnia).

(1) *Cyprina+Astarte biocoenosis.* According to the results of Petersen's work in the deeper parts of the southern Kattegat, the dominant forms are *Abra alba*, *Macoma calcarea*, and *Cyprina islandica*, while in the shallower Kiel and Mecklenburg Bays *Cyprina islandica* and *Astarte borealis* become markedly preponderant; they provide, at some stations, a biomass of up to 450 g/m² in the first of these bays, and 190 g/m² in the second. The average biomass of the whole of this area is 176·6 g/m². 110·2 g of this consists of *Cyprina islandica* and 32 g of *Astarte borealis*. All the rest provides only 34·4 g/m² (see Fig. 150).

In these areas west of the Darss ridge, a still considerable qualitative variety of benthos is observed; there are a large number of worms: *Nephthys ciliata*, *N. coeca*, *Terebellides strömi*, *Pectinaria koreni*, *Scoloplos armiger* and

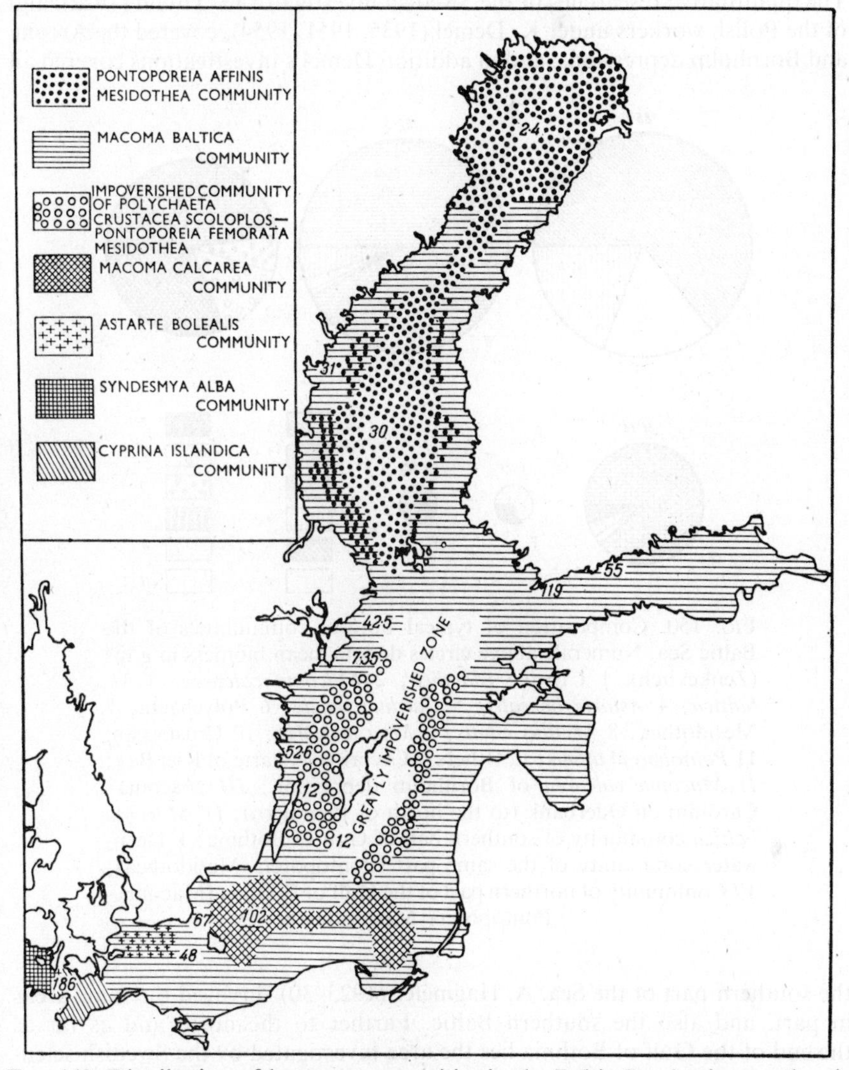

FIG. 149. Distribution of bottom communities in the Baltic Sea (various authors)

Rhodine loveni are especially frequent; among the molluscs: *Macoma calcarea* and *M. baltica*; *Syndesmya alba*, which is already found in large numbers in the western part of the Northern Belt; *Modiolaria nigra*; among the crustaceans: *Diastylis rathkei*, *Pontoporeia femorata*; and among the echinoderms: *Ophiura albida*.

The region of the typical Baltic mesomixed and oligomixed communities only begins, however, east of the Darss ridge (Fig. 151). This ridge may in fact be called a distinct quantitative-biocoenotic boundary (I. Välikangas, 1933). The quantitative researches of the Swedish investigator G. Thulin (1922), and of the Polish workers under K. Demel (1935, 1951, 1954), covered the Arcona and Bornholm depressions, and in addition Demel's investigations covered all

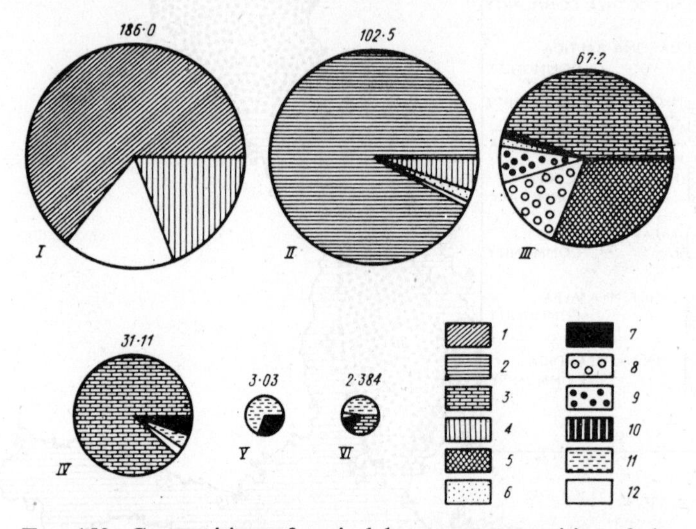

FIG. 150. Composition of typical bottom communities of the Baltic Sea. Numerals above circles denote mean biomass in g/m² (Zenkevitch). 1 *Cyprina islandica*; 2 *Macoma calcarea*; 3 *M. baltica*; 4 *Astarte borealis*; 5 *Cardium edule*; 6 Polychaeta; 7 Mesidothea; 8 *Mytilus edulis*; 9 *Mya arenaria*; 10 Crustacean, 11 *Pontoporeia affinis*; 12 Others. *I* Cryprina–Astarte of Kiel Bay; *II Macoma calcarea* of Bornholm depression; *III* Macoma–Cardium on Oderbank (to the north of Pommern); *IV Macoma baltica* community of southern half of Gulf of Bothnia; *V* Deep-water community of the same part (Pontoporeia–Mesidothea); *VI* Community of northern part of the Gulf of Bothnia (Macoma–Pontoporeia–Mesidothea).

the southern part of the Sea. A. Hagmeier (1923–30) surveyed the same areas in part, and also the southern Baltic. Farther to the north and as far as the end of the Gulf of Bothnia lies the area investigated by the Swedish scientist Chr. Hessle (1924). Along the Finnish shores of the Gulf of Finland the Finnish investigator S. Sägerstråle conducted research (1933). A. Schurin has described the distribution of benthos in the Bay of Riga (1957). The researches of these investigators make it possible to give a quantitative biocoenotic estimate of the Baltic Sea benthos.

On the whole it can be assumed that to the east of the Darss ridge there is a single bottom biocoenosis, *Macoma baltica*; this form, however, develops especially in the shallower parts of the Sea and, in general, as depth increases it gradually disappears.

(2) *Macoma calcarea+Astarte borealis biocoenosis.* In the deeper northern half of the southwestern part of the Baltic Sea (below 40 m) the benthos composition undergoes a change—*Macoma baltica* decreases markedly in numbers, or disappears altogether, and is replaced by *Macoma calcarea* and *Astarte borealis*, the former being more abundant in the Bornholm depression and the latter in the Arcona depression (Fig. 150).

In some places in the Arcona depression *Astarte borealis* forms very dense

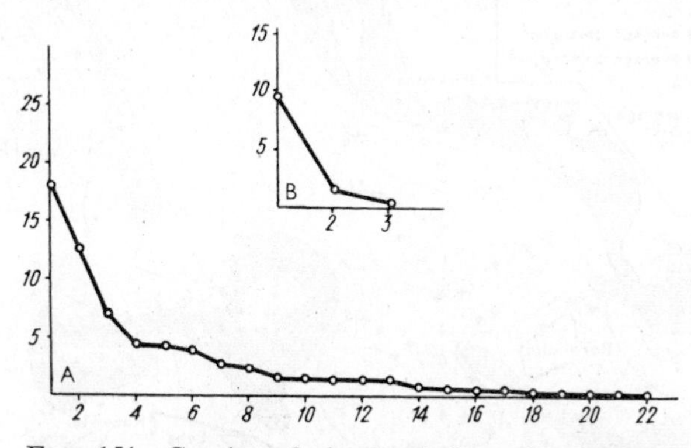

FIG. 151. Graphs of density indices (Zenkevitch). A For the mesomixed community of the Arcona depression; B For the oligomixed community of the inside part of the Gulf of Bothnia. For A: *Macoma baltica, Terebellides strömi, Halicryptus spinulosus, Astarte borealis,* etc.; for B: *Pontoporeia affinis, Macoma baltica, Mesidothea entomon.*

populations with a biomass of 177 g/m² and 346 specimens per 1 m². Besides the two mollusc forms, crustaceans are represented there at depths of 100 to 150 m by *Pontoporeia femorata, Diastylis rathkei* and the worms by *Harmothoe sarsi, Scoloplos armiger, Aricidea suecica, Terebellides strömi, Priapulus caudatus* and *Halicryptus spinulosus.* The *Astarte borealis* community occupied the Arcona and Bornholm depressions, extending to the east right up to the entrance of the Bay of Danzig. The average benthos biomass for the Bornholm region is about 102·5 g/m².

(3) *Macoma baltica biocoenosis.* A little to the east of Mecklenburg Bay the typical *Macoma baltica* biocoenosis begins; it remains almost unchanged right up to the Bay of Danzig through the southern, shallower parts of the Sea. The average biomass of this whole area may be taken as about 48·15 g/m² (see Fig. 150). *Macoma baltica* begins here to become the dominant benthos form. Some other forms, however, are well represented still: *Cardium edule, Mytilus edulis* and *Mya arenaria, Macoma calcarea, Astarte borealis* and

Syndesmya alba are poorly represented here. Among the worms the following may be noted: *Nephthys ciliata, Scoloplos armiger, Nereis diversicolor, Pygospio elegans, Terebellides strömi, Harmothoe sarsi, Halicryptus spinulosus*; among the crustaceans: *Diastylis rathkei, Pontoporeia femorata, Bathyporeia pilosa* and, in altogether negligible numbers, *Mesidothea entomon.* The last named, like *Pontoporeia affinis*, has its western limit of distribution east of Mecklenburg Bay, becoming a mass form to the east and north. On the other

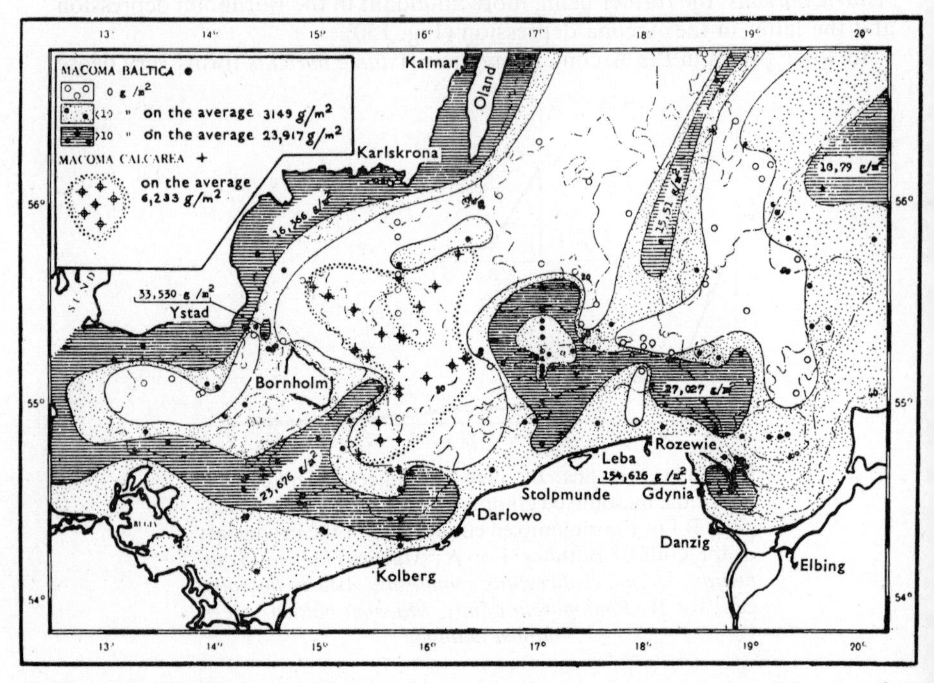

FIG. 152. Distribution of *Macoma biocoenosis* in southern Baltic Sea (Demel and others, 1954).

hand such forms as Mya, Cardium and Mytilus gradually disappear as one moves eastward.

K. Demel and his collaborators W. Mankowski and Z. Mulicki (1951, 1954) as a result of comprehensive investigations over a number of years, were able to draw a very interesting picture of the qualitative and quantitative distribution of the bottom fauna of the southern part of the Baltic Sea (south of 56° 45′). Demel reports that the *Macoma baltica* biocoenosis covers the whole of the shallow zone of the southern part of the Baltic Sea (Fig. 152). In deeper places *Macoma baltica* gradually disappears and is replaced by the biocoenosis of worms (*Scoloplos armiger, Halicryptus spinulosus, Priapulus caudatus*) and crustaceans (*Pontoporeia femorata* and *Diastylis rathkei*) (Fig. 153). Demel thinks that the propagation of *Macoma baltica* into the depths is limited by the lack of oxygen. In the greatest depths of the Gotland depression colonies of *Scoloplos armiger* alone have been discovered. The region inhabited by

Astarte borealis extends through the Arcona depression and the Slypsk trough and farther to the east; the Bornholm depression is inhabited by *Macome calcarea* (Fig. 154). In the Slypsk trough *Terebellides strömi* appears in great masses, and Demel thinks it possible to distinguish in this area an Astarte–Terebellides biocoenosis.

At lesser depths in the southern part of the Baltic Sea *Mytilus edulis* is numerically a markedly preponderant form (Fig. 155), accompanied by *Cardium edule*, *Mya arenaria*, *Macoma baltica* and others.

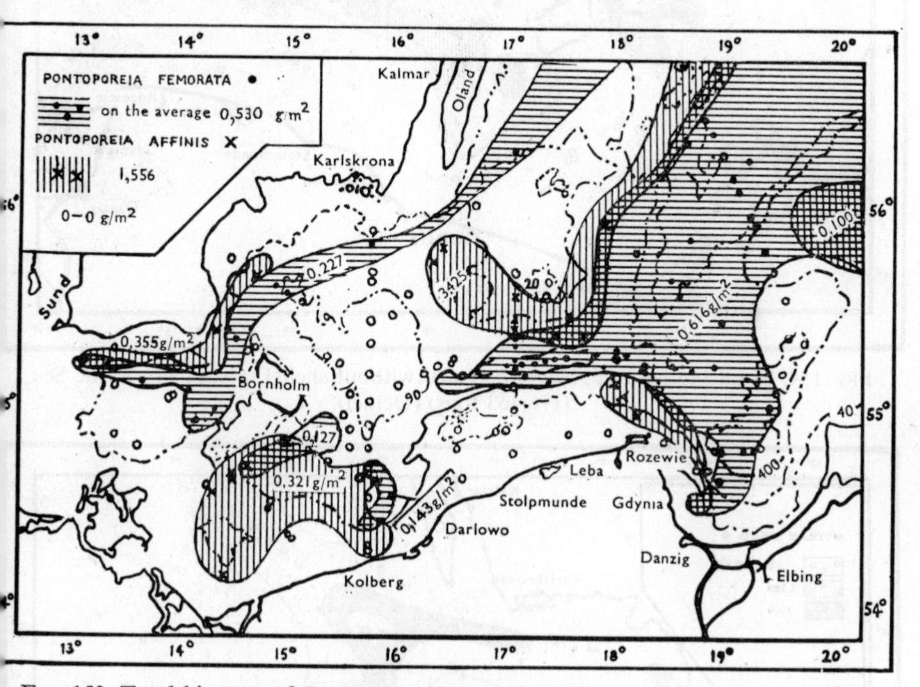

FIG. 153. Total biomass of *Pontoporeia femorata* (20,460 tons) and of *Pontoporeia affinis* (29,533 tons) (Demel).

The mass forms of the fauna at times provide a great density of population as regards number of specimens (*Table 128*).

In comparison with the middle and northern parts of the Baltic Sea, the large number of Mytilus, Astarte and *Macoma calcarea* is conspicuous. K. Demel and Z. Mulicki (1954) have also drawn a chart of the distribution of the benthos biomass in the southern part of the Baltic Sea (Fig. 156) and its contents by separate components (*Table 129*).

Thus 90 per cent of the total biomass of bottom fauna consists of bivalves.

Some visual outlines of the distribution of bottom fauna are also given by Demel and Mulicki; the meridional cross section through the Bornholm depression is given in Fig. 157.

The same picture, as for all the southern part of the Sea, is repeated on a

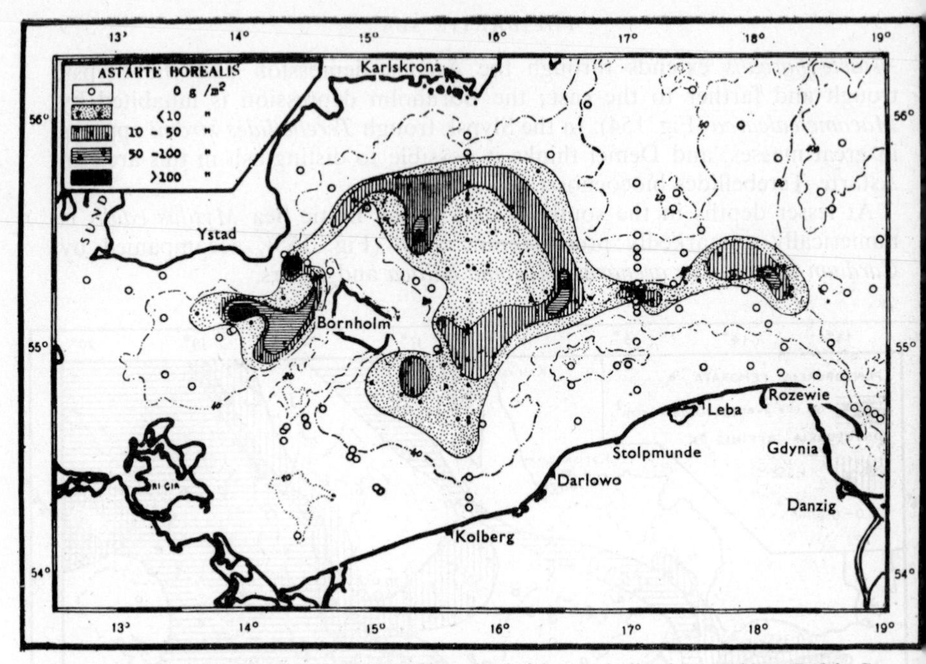

FIG. 154. Total biomass of *Astarte borealis* (without shells) in southern Baltic Sea (176,463 tons) (Demel).

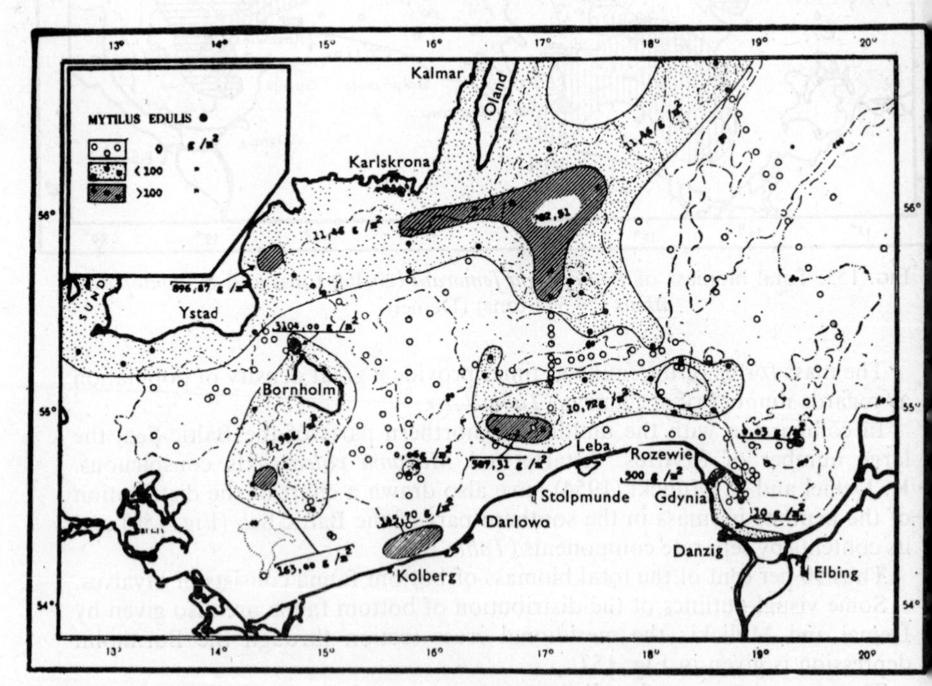

FIG. 155. Total biomass of *Mytilus edulis* (without shells) in southern Baltic Sea (3,407,263 tons) (Demel).

Table 128

Forms	Max. no of specimens per 1 m²	Max. biomass, g/m²
Macoma baltica	2,455	76
Astarte borealis	2,065	126
Macoma calcarea	110	64·68
Terebellides strömii	333	3·38
Pontoporeia femorata	900	4·39
P. affinis	1,779	18·55
Diastylis rathkei	115	
Scoloplos armiger	515	7·5
Halicryptus spinulosus	92·4	6·4
Mytilus edulis	7,010	31·0
Mesidothea entomon	60	7·8

small scale in the Bay of Danzig. At a depth of less than 100 m *Macoma baltica* biocoenosis is preponderant; deeper down it gives way to *Scoloplos armiger*, *Mesidothea entomon* and *Pontoporeia femorata*.

Demel distinguishes two main groups of bottom biocoenoses: the deeper and colder-water biocoenosis consisting exclusively of stenothermic cold-water species, and the biocoenoses of shallower and warmer coastal waters

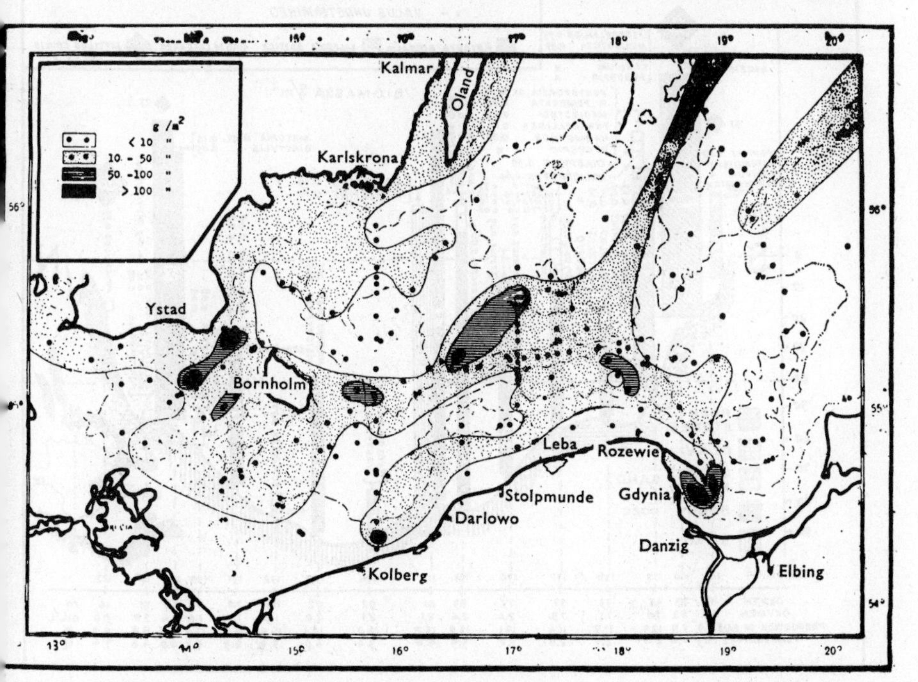

FIG. 156. Zoobenthos total biomass in southern Baltic Sea without *Mytilus edulis* (Demel and Mulicki, 1954).

Table 129

Species	Average biomass, g/m²	Total biomass for southern part of Baltic Sea, tons
Mytilus edulis	0·03–3,104	3,407,263*
Macoma baltica	3·1–23·9	837,008
Astarte borealis	10–100	176,463
Mesidothea entomon	0·7–28·6	48,560
Macoma calcarea	6·2	46,614
Pontoporeia affinis	1·5	29,533
P. femorata	0·5	20,460
Diastylis rathkei	0·5–2·0	6,756
Others	—	190,740
	Total	4,763,397

* All molluscs given in wet weight without shells.

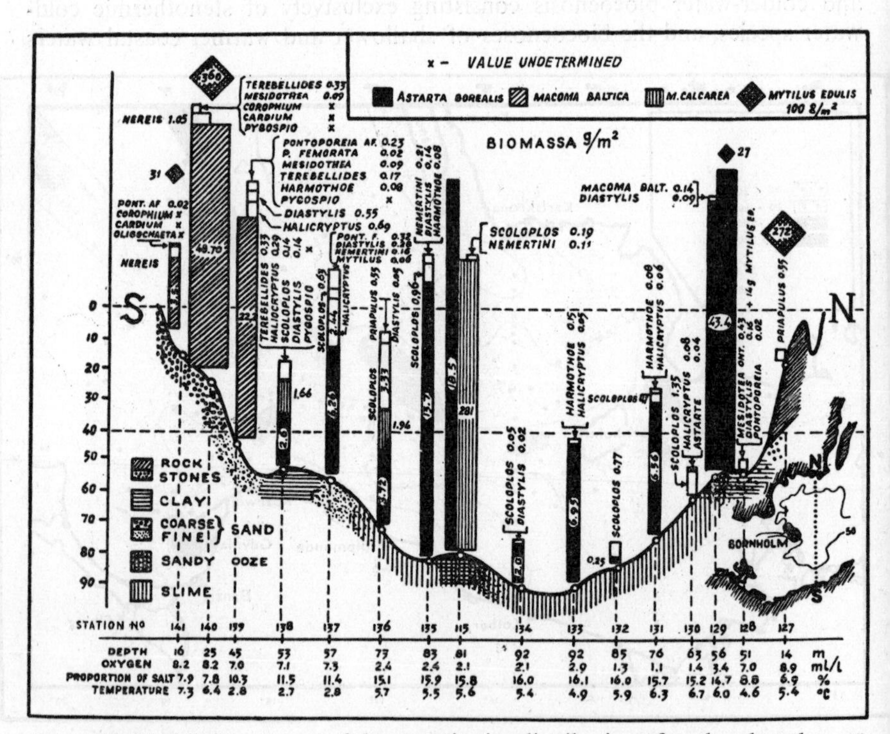

FIG. 157. Meridinial contour of the quantitative distribution of zoobenthos through the Bornholm region of the Baltic Sea (Demel and Mulicki, 1954).

comprising mainly eurythermic species. The first group is qualitatively poor and uniform, consisting almost exclusively of such Arctic species as *Mesidothea entomon*, *Polynoe cirrata*, *Mysis mixta*, *Halicryptus spinulosus*, *Pontoporeia femorata*. Demel likewise includes the relict forms *Terebellides strömii*, *Macoma baltica* and *Diastylis rathkei*. The shallower zone is inhabited by a fairly varied fauna; its most characteristic forms are: *Cardium edule*, *Mya arenaria*, *Nereis diversicolor*, *Macoma baltica*, *Mytilus edulis*, *Gammarus locusta* and *Balanus improvisus*. The boundary of the two groups of fauna (the surface and the bathypelagic) lies at a depth of 25 to 40 m.

As regards the fate of the *Macoma baltica* biocoenosis farther north, it should be pointed out that the area of Gotland Island serves as a kind of boundary dividing this biocoenosis into two parts. South of Gotland the benthos has not yet the distinct oligomixed nature characteristic of the more northerly regions. Mytilus, Mya and Cardium do not yet lose their importance completely; on the other hand such forms as *Pontoporeia affinis* and *Mesidothea entomon* are still not yet developed to a significant extent. *Pontoporeia femorata* still supplants its kindred species *P. affinis*. These two characteristic biocoenoses of the Baltic fauna are adapted to two different biotopes. *P. affinis* inhabits the less saline, shallower parts of the Sea and is often preponderant on sand bottoms. *P. femorata* keeps to more saline, deeper layers and is frequently found in large numbers on mud bottoms.

The benthos composition in the area of Gotland and the Åland Islands is set out in *Table 130*.

Table 130

Depth, m	*Mesidothea entomon*		*Pontoporeia femorata*		*Macoma baltica*		Chironomidae		Total weight, g/m²
	No. of specimens per m²	Wt, g/m²	No. of specimens per m²	Wt, g/m²	No. of specimens per m²	Wt, g/m²	No. of specimens per m²	Wt, g/m²	
0–10	—	—	2	—	180	14·21	—	—	19·28
11–50	6	1·85	208	0·69	49	7·17	22·67	0·52	11·78
>50	3	2·80	66	0·40	24	0·05	—	—	11·96

Encircling Gotland Island at depths below 80 m lives an impoverished benthic community. As the depth increases, firstly the molluscs disappear, then the worms and finally the crustaceans. Only the polychaete *Scoloplos armiger* can live on mud bottoms infected with hydrogen sulphide. The last representatives of the remaining animal population—*Pontoporeia femorata* and *Terebellides strömii*—disappear a little earlier.

Another very characteristic Baltic Sea form, *Mesidothea entomon*, which is abundant in the western and northern parts of the Sea, gradually disappears south of the latitude of Åland Island.

As one moves farther to the north into the Åland Islands area the selection of saline-loving forms (*Cardium edule*, *Nereis diversicolor*, *Terebellides strömii*,

Harmothoe sarsi, *Halicryptus spinulosus*, *Pontoporeia femorata*, *Idothea granulosa* and *I. viridis*) becomes poorer still; there is a further drop of salinity to 1‰; this is the extreme northern limit of its distribution. It is practically never found north of the Åland Islands, where *Pontoporeia affinis*, Mesidothea and Chironomidae begin to appear in considerable numbers.

The quantitative relationship of the main forms of benthos given in *Table 131* is characteristic of the area of the Åland Islands.

Table 131

Depth, m	Mesidothea		Pontoporeia		Macoma		Chironomidae		Total weight, g/m²
	No. of specimens per m²	Wt, g/m²	No. of specimens per m²	Wt, g/m²	No. of specimens per m²	Wt, g/m²	No. of specimens per m²	Wt, g/m²	
0–10	8·30	2·88	627	2·33	228	55·10	19	0·35	65·31
11–50	6·65	2·57	1,344	3·02	93	19·45	—	—	25·62
>50	7·15	1·60	1,705	4·90	—	—	—	—	6·57

In the open sea to the west of the Åland Islands, at depths greater than 40 m, the benthos biomass reaches 44·36 g/m² and 91 per cent of the benthos consists of *Macoma baltica*. Deeper down a picture typical of the whole of the Gulf of Bothnia is established: the biomass is reduced to 10 g/m² owing to the decrease of *M. baltica* (23 per cent); *Pontoporeia affinis* becomes the dominant form, comprising half of this fauna. Chr. Hessle (1924) suggests that these two forms (*M. baltica* and *P. affinis*) are either competitors for food, or that crayfish destroys the Macoma larvae. Hessle tries in this way to find an explanation for the peculiar bathymetric distribution of both forms and, chiefly, for the fact that *Macoma baltica* disappears with increasing depth in the areas north of Gotland Island, that is, in the areas of mass development of *Pontoporeia affinis* in the deeper layers. Off Åland Island, and to some extent off Gotland, the populations of *Macoma baltica* are very abundant at depths of 100 to 140 m (i.e. in water which is very poor in oxygen); but *Pontoporeia affinis* does not grow in large numbers there. Its place is taken by *P. femorata*, with which *M. baltica* can exist without harm to itself. *Mesidothea entomon* chiefly inhabits the deep waters of the Åland Sea and of the Gulfs of Bothnia and Finland, existing at the expense of *Pontoporeia affinis*, which is its basic food.

On the soft soils of the northern part of the central area the polychaetes *Nereis diversicolor* in shallower places, and *Harmothoe sarsi* in deeper ones (down to 200 m), are added to the three main fauna forms—Mesidothea and the two species of Pontoporeia, which form the basic food of fish in the area.

Towards the south *Harmothoe sarsi* increases in numbers at lesser depths, limited by a salinity of about 7‰; simultaneously it becomes more important as fish food. *Pygospio elegans* and *Halicryptus spinulosus*, though not as important, are also significant on the sandy bottoms of the central area.

The same benthic biocoenoses which were already formed in the area of

Gotland Island, Pontoporeia–Mesidothea–Macoma, is very clearly represented in the Gulf of Bothnia, with a tendency for the biomass to be considerably less.

The benthos biomass decreases markedly as one moves northwards (except along the very shores of the bays). In the south of the Gulf of Bothnia (Bottensee) in the shallow zone of the open sea the biomass is 30 to 40 g/m² down to a depth of 40 m; but with increasing depth it is reduced to a few grammes on account of the decrease of the number of specimens and the reduced size of *Macoma baltica* and *Mesidothea entomon.* The benthos composition at depths above and below 40 m is given in Fig. 150. For the southern part of the Gulf of Bothnia the same decrease with depth is given in *Table 132.*

Table 132

Depth m	*Mesidothea entomon*		*Pontoporeia affinis*		*Macoma baltica*		Total weight, g/m²
	No. of specimens	Wt, g/m²	No. of specimens	Wt, g/m²	No. of specimens	Wt, g/m²	
0–10	12	2·99	466	1·43	211	35·67	40·24
11–50	6·35	1·15	617	1·24	13·90	13·90	16·70
>50	5·4	0·80	1,158	2·35	—	—	3·15

The northern part of the Gulf of Bothnia with a salinity of no more than 4‰, with the latter falling as one moves northwards, has an extremely impoverished benthos with an average yield of 2·384 g/m². *Pontoporeia affinis* is the dominant form here; it is followed by *Mesidothea entomon, Macoma baltica* and finally by the oligochaetes (see Fig. 151). *M. baltica* moves northwards only up to a salinity of 3·5‰, disappearing when the water is less saline than this. The graph of the indices of the community density is given in Fig. 151. Of the 22 stations surveyed by Hessle in the northern part of the Gulf of Bothnia, Macoma was found at only two, Pontoporeia at 19. The highest quantitative indices for the latter are 2,160 specimens per m² at a weight of 4·3 g. The average for all the Bottenwiek stations is 505 specimens and 1·32 g/m². The corresponding data for Mesidothea are 2·7 specimens and 0·32 g/m², and for Macoma 15 specimens and 0·80 g/m². The biomass decrasese somewhat with depth. For depths of less than 10 m it equals, on an average, 3·32 g/m², while at 11 to 50 m it is 2·44 g/m². In the bays of the off-shore zone of the Gulf of Bothnia the fauna is undoubtedly much richer in numbers, primarily on account of Chironomidae and Oligochaete larvae.

However, there are so far no quantitative data on this part of the Gulf. On the basis of his own researches Hessle comes to the conclusion that Bottenwiek is very poor in benthos biomass, mainly as a result of a considerable admixture of iron oxides in the sea-bed. A considerable area of the floor of the Gulf is covered with these non-productive red sands. As for the number of specimens, here too it is at times high—up to 1,000 specimens of *Pontoporeia affinis* per 1 m².

(*4*) *Pontoporeia+Mesidothea biocoenosis*. In the most northern part of the Gulf of Bothnia, at a salinity of 3·5‰, Macoma disappears and is replaced by the Pontoporeia+Mesidothea biocoenosis in its pure form. This in its turn passes at the shore-line into a mixed biocoenosis of Chironomidae and Oligochaeta.

In the Gulf of Finland we find a similar but somewhat different picture. As has been mentioned above, this Gulf is not separated from the central part of the Sea either by islands or a submarine ridge; hence the way is open for both more saline waters and their characteristic fauna to enter through the deep channel.

We shall consider the bottom fauna of the Gulf of Finland in greater detail, from east to west, beginning at the Nevskaya Guba.

Research organized by the State Hydrological Institute in 1923–24 and 1934–35 under the direction of Derjugin has shown that the so-called Nevskaya Guba, i.e. the area separated from the open sea by Kotlin Island and the Oranienbaum shoal, has completely fresh-water conditions. A small amount of salinity, evident in the western part of the Nevskaya Guba, has no substantial influence on the fauna, which there has a true fresh-water character with a preponderance of molluscs, oligochaetes and insect larvae. To the west of the Oranienbaum shoal the typical Baltic relict community mentioned above comes in full strength with a preponderance of *Mesidothea entomon*, *Pallasea quadrispinosa*, *Pontoporeia affinis*, *Mysis oculata* and the addition of some extremely euryhaline forms such as *Gammarus zaddachi*, *G. locusta* f. *reducta*, *G. duebeni*, *Neomysis vulgaris* f. *baltica*, *Zoarces viviparus*, and the fresh-water chironomids. In this area, to the south and west of Kotlin Island, the deep-water layer has an unstable salinity with marked fluctuations. Saline water frequently flows in at a lower layer from the west (the phenomenon of internal waves). Thus the distribution of salinity given in *Table 133* was once observed in March 25 km west of Kotlin Island.

Table 133

Depth m	Temperature t° C	S‰
0	14·8	1·52
3	14·7	1·52
10	14·6	1·63
23	4·5	5·01

In February the saline stratification somewhat to the east of this station was even more strongly marked (*Table 134*).

According to different observations, the deep-water salinity south of Kotlin Island was at one time 3·44‰, at another 0·52‰. Without doubt the magnitude of these fluctuations may be even greater. If the surface salinity fluctuations west of Kotlin Island can reach a magnitude of from 0·03 to 1·28‰ and probably more, then in the deep-water layer they may be from 0·5 to 5·00‰.

Table 134

Depth m	Temperature $t°$ C	$S‰$
0	0·0	0·03
3	0·0	0·07
5	0·0	0·49
10	0·8	3·56
16	1·1	3·96

It must be perfectly clear from the above why in winter this saline, deep water has a higher temperature than the surface layers, and why it retains its reduced amount of oxygen, thereby destroying its winter homohalinity and homothermia. The arrival of this water in summer also destroys the summer homothermia and homohalinity.

Moving from the Nevskaya Guba to the west, we observe a gradual change in the composition of the mass forms. According to the researches of S. Sägerstråle (1923), in the Pellinge area (coast of Finland, marked approximately centrally on the chart—Fig. 121—of the Gulf of Finland) at a salinity of 5 to 6‰ the main components of the benthos are again *Macoma baltica*, *Mesidothea entomon*, *Pontoporeia affinis* and Chironomidae, with the addition of *Cardium edule*. In other words we already have here the *Macoma baltica* biocoenosis.

Farther to the west, where the Gulf of Finland opens into the Sea, in the Twerminn area (see Fig. 129), with the deep-water salinity slightly above 6‰ and the annual variations of salinity of not more than 1·7‰, the dominant form is again *Macoma baltica*; it is followed by Chironomidae, *Pontoporeia affinis*, *Cardium edule*, *Mesidothea entomon*, with the addition of *Halicryptus spinulosus* and *Mytilus edulis*. The biomass of the Gulf of Finland increases considerably from 25–75 to 60–206 g/m² (the average for Pellinge is 55 and for Twerminn 119 g/m²) as one moves from the centre of it to its exit.

The first area of S. Sägerstråle's work (Pellinge, 1932) has a soft mud bottom rich in organic matter, the so-called gyttja or sapropel. The composition of the bottom communities of this area are illustrated in Fig. 158. The first is at a

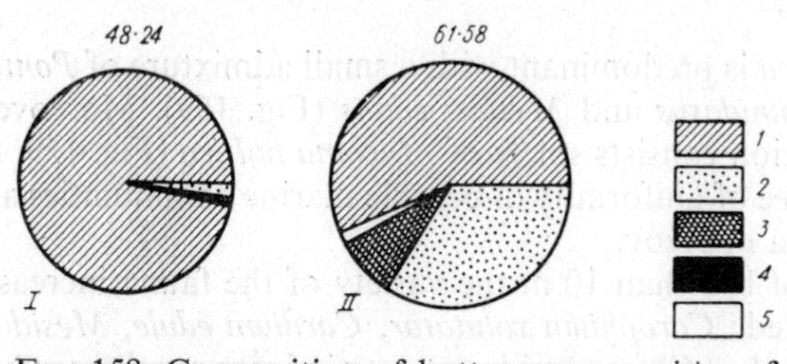

FIG. 158. Composition of bottom communities of shores of Finland (Pellinge) (Sägerstråle, 1932). Mean biomass, g/m², is shown above the circles. 1 *Macoma baltica*; 2 *Mesidothea entomon*; 3 *Pontoporeia femorata*; 4 Chironomidae; 5 Others.

depth of 14 to 17 m, the second at 9 to 10 m. To the west, in the Twerminn area, there are at certain stations communities identical with these. At other stations a number of new forms are found; and if, off Pellinge, we find the Macoma–Pontoporeia–Mesidothea biocoenosis, here at deeper places (25 to 37 m) on the same gyttja, we find Macoma–Pontoporeia–Halicryptus (Fig. 159). At lesser depths (10 to 25 m) there is an extreme paucity of forms;

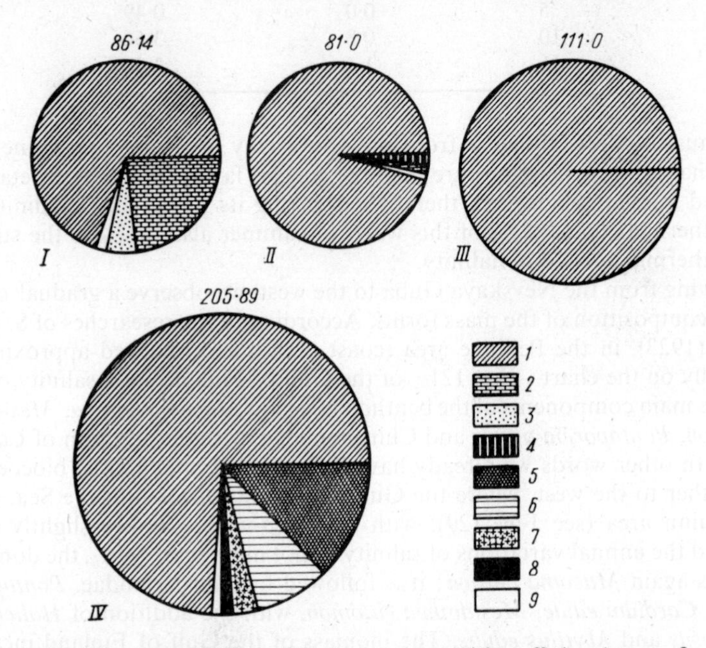

FIG. 159. Composition of bottom communities off the shores of Finland (Twerminn) (Sägerstråle, 1932). Mean biomass, g/m², is shown above the circles. 1 *Macoma baltica*; 2 *Pontoporeia affinis*; 3 *Halicryptus spinulosus*; 4 *Mytilus edulis*; 5 Chironomidae; 6 *Cardium edule*; 7 *Corophium volutator*; 8 *Mesidothea entomon*; 9 Others.

Macoma baltica is predominant with a small admixture of *Pontoporeia affinis*, *Halicryptus spinulosus* and *Mytilus edulis* (Fig. 159). Moreover at times the whole population consists solely of *Macoma baltica* (Fig. 159, *III*). Examples of such a degree of uniformity of benthic marine communities are found again only in the Sea of Azov.

At depths of less than 10 m the variety of the fauna increases and several forms are added: *Corophium volutator*, *Cardium edule*, *Mesidothea entomon*, *Nereis diversicolor*; Chironomidae appear in large numbers, while *Halicryptus spinulosus* disappears (Fig. 159).

However, as had been shown by Sägerstråle, Chironomidae in the Baltic Sea are adapted only to the shallows and disappear with increasing depth (*Table 135*).

Table 135

Depth, m	No. of Chironomid specimens per m²		
	Twerminn		Pellinge
	June–July 1926	September 1928	September 1922
1–3	200–487	942	54
9–11	408	—	18·84
14–20	3	10	11

Maximum numbers of specimens and biomass. In conclusion we give the data for the maximum indices of the biomass, and the numbers of specimens of various bottom forms off the Finnish shore of the Gulf of Finland according to Sägerstråle (*Table 136*).

Table 136

Forms	No. of specimens per m²	Weight, g/m²
Tetrastemma obscurum	13	0·22
Nereis diversicolor	44	7·4
Harmothoe sarsi	145	0·79
Tubifex tubifex	217	0·84
Halicryptus spinulosus	75	4·93
Cardium edule	14	16·84
Macoma baltica	1,407	152·14
Mytilus edulis	188	15·77
Neritina fluviatilis	10	0·28
Bythinia tentaculata	3	0·67
Hydrobia baltica	120	0·43
Pontoporeia affinis	7,006	27·68
Pontoporeia femorata	128	0·73
Gammarus locusta	110	1·39
Corophium volutator	2,433	5·70
Mesidothea entomon	44	20·69
Asellus aquaticus	93	0·64
Chironomidae	1,662	32·96

S. Sägerstråle (1944, 1957) distinguishes as an individual biocoenosis the overgrowth of *Fucus vesiculosus*. It consists in a high proportion of the crustaceans *Gammarus* (*zaddachi*) *oceanicus*, *G. zaddachi salinus*, *G. zaddachi*, *Idotea granulosa*, *I. baltica*, *I. viridis*, *Taera albifrons* (*marina*), *Praunus flexuosus*, *P. inermis*, *Leander adspersus fabricii*, *Mytilus edulis*, the *Cardium edule* fry, *Balanus improvious*, *Laomedea loveni*, *Membranipora crustulenta* and *Pelmatohydra oligactis*, which attach themselves to the algae. The fresh-water elements are represented by *Theodoxus fluviatilis*, *Limnaea peregra* (*ovata*) and by chironomid larvae. In more enclosed places there are also the larvae of Tcrihoptera, Turbellaria, *Planaria lacustria*, *Polycelis nigra*, the oligochaetes *Stylaria lacustris*, *Nais elinguis*, and the Porifera *Ephydatia fluviatilis*.

For the first time the microfauna of the coastal sands has been subjected to examination on the model of the Baltic Sea (Remane, 1933, 1952). The original interstitial fauna (Mesopsammon) was found to be abundant in the following species: Turbellaria, Gastrotricha, Archiannelida, Tardigrada, Ostracoda, Harpacticoida and Nematoda. Near Twerminn (southern Finland) the number of microbenthos organisms in some cases is more than 100,000 specimens per 1 m^2, mainly on account of nematodes and ostracodes.

A. Schurin has carried out a comprehensive survey of the bottom fauna of the Gulf of Riga (1961). Three characteristic features may be noted for bottom fauna of the Gulf of Riga: (*1*) a general qualitative impoverishment, (*2*) decrease in size of all the main components, probably as a result of lower salinity which makes this fauna completely accessible to local fish as food, and (*3*) a rise in the levels of vertical distribution of biocoenoses and of individual forms. Whereas in the open parts of the Sea the replacement of the shallow-water mollusc benthos by the deep-water one, with a preponderance of crustaceans, takes place at depths of 50 to 100 m, in the Gulf of Riga this change occurs at 10 to 20 m (Fig. 160).

On the actual shores of the Gulf of Riga the biocoenosis of the macrophyte overgrowth is well represented, with abundant settlements of small amphipods (*Leptocheirus pilosus*, *Gammarus locusta*, and others) and mysids (*Praunus inermis* and *P. flexuosus*). In the sublittoral zone (2 to 20 m) there is a very marked preponderance of bivalves (over 95 per cent) and especially *Macoma baltica*, *Mya arenaria* and *Cardium edule*, but at a depth of 10 to 20 m the molluscs are greatly reduced in numbers, while the crustaceans and worms increase; the latter, and above all *Pontoporeia affinis*, are markedly dominant at 20 to 40 m. The number of *Pontoporeia affinis* may reach 7,000 specimens per 1 m^2. Among the other organisms the most significant are *Mesidothea entomon*, *Pontoporeia femorata*, *Halicryptus spinulosus* and *Mysis mixta*. *Macoma baltica* is still found in small numbers. Below 40 m (and down to 60 m) in the stagnant zone of the central depression five species in all have been found: *Pontoporeia femorata*, *Pont. affinis*, *Mesidothea entomon*, *Mysis mixta* and *M. oculata* f. *relicta*. The molluscs and worms are entirely absent. Total biomass of benthos in the Bay of Riga is about 670,000 tons (Shurin, 1961).

General characteristics of productivity. The data on the qualitative distribution of the Baltic Sea (Fig. 161) can therefore be summarized as follows. At the start there are the biocoenoses of the Danish Belt and Oresund which are diversified and rich in biomass (200 to 300 g, sometimes kilogrammes, in the case of Modiolaria and Mytilus). Then, as one moves to the east and north, an ever greater impoverishment is observed, both in quality and quantity; this continues until it finds its extreme expression in the uniformity of the inner parts of the Gulfs of Bothnia and Finland, where at every step one finds almost pure populations of *Macoma baltica* on the gyttja in the bays. Starting from the Darss ridge itself we find, in effect, only one biocoenosis—*Macoma*

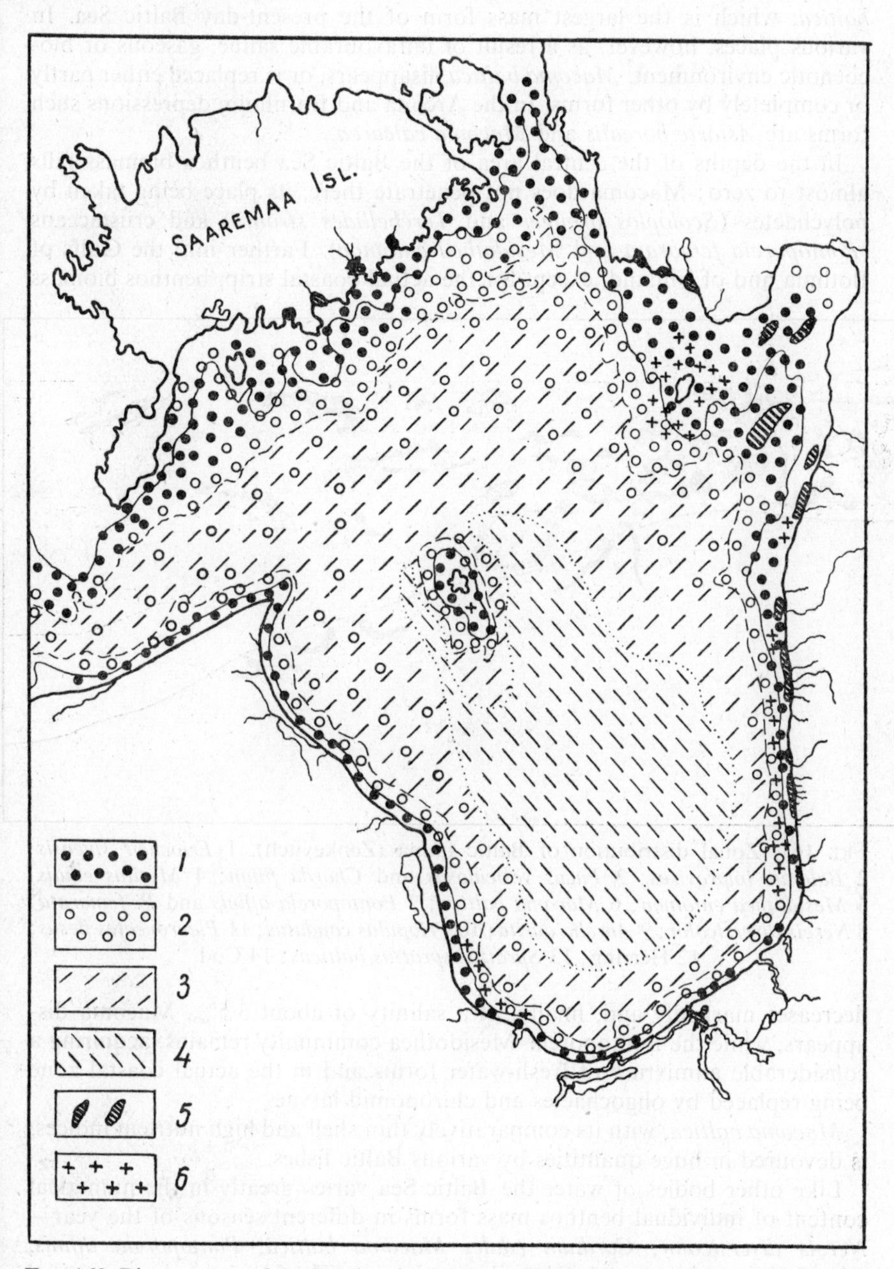

FIG. 160. Biocoenoses of the benthos in the Bay of Riga (Shurin, 1961). 1 *Cardium–Mya–Macoma*; 2 *Macoma baltica*; 3 *Pontoporeia affinis*; 4 *Pontoporeia femorata*; 5 *Dreissena polimorpha*; 6 *Mytilus–Balanus*.

baltica, which is the largest mass form of the present-day Baltic Sea. In various places, however, as a result of unfavourable saline, gaseous or biocoenotic environment, *Macoma baltica* disappears, or is replaced either partly or completely by other forms. In the Arcona and Bornholm depressions such forms are *Astarte borealis* and *Macoma calcarea*.

In the depths of the central area of the Baltic Sea benthos biomass falls almost to zero; Macoma does not penetrate there, its place being taken by polychaetes (*Scoloplos armiger* and *Terebellides strömii*) and crustaceans (*Pontoporeia femorata* and *Mesidothea entomon*). Farther into the Gulfs of Bothnia and of Finland, except for the actual coastal strip, benthos biomass

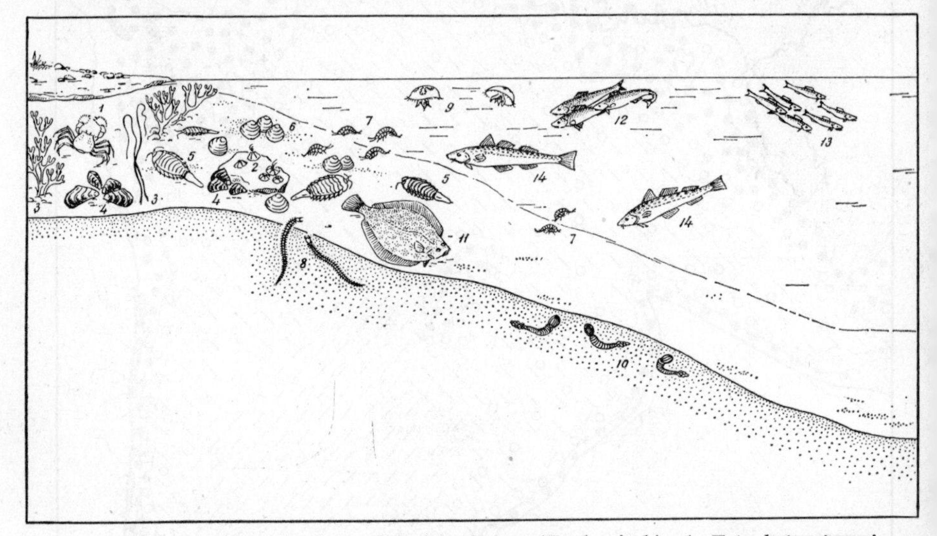

FIG. 161. Zonal distribution of Baltic fauna (Zenkevitch). 1 *Eriocheir sinensis*; 2 *Balanus improvisus*; 3 *Fucus vesiculosus* and *Chorda filum*; 4 *Mytilus edulis*; 5 *Mesidothea entomon*; 6 *Macoma baltica*; 7 *Pontoporeia affinis* and *P. femorata*; 8 *Nereis diversicolor*; 9 *Aurelia aurita*; 10 *Priapulus caudatus*; 11 *Pleuronectes flesus*; 12 Herring; 13 *Sprattus sprattus balticus*; 14 Cod.

decreases markedly and, finally, at a salinity of about 3·5‰, Macoma disappears, while the Pontoporeia–Mesidothea community remains, acquiring a considerable admixture of fresh-water forms and in the actual coastal zone being replaced by oligochaetes and chironomid larvae.

Macoma baltica, with its comparatively thin shell and high nutrient indices, is devoured in huge quantities by various Baltic fishes.

Like other bodies of water the Baltic Sea varies greatly in the numerical content of individual benthos mass forms in different seasons of the year—*Nereis diversicolor*, *Cardium edule*, *Macoma baltica*, *Pontoporeia affinis*, *Mesidothea entomon* and *Corophium volutator*. The last-named, an original member of the Amphipoda group which lives in U-shaped tubes in the bottom, also provides an example of sharp fluctuations in numbers from year to year. The observations of S. Sägerstråle of Twerminn (Finland), carried out during 1928–31, have shown that *Corophium volutator* lives for only one year. Over this period the fluctuations in the number of specimens of this crayfish per 1 m^2, all collected in the same place, are given in *Table 137*.

Table 137

1928				1929				1930					1931		
y	Jul	Sep	Nov	May	Jun	Jul	Nov	Apr	May	Jun	Oct	Nov	Apr	Oct	Nov
[illegible]	184	5,429	4,210	3,151	1,712	105	1,774	338	188	4	81	124	56	1,992	1,834

The same type of fluctuations were observed by Sägerstråle in the case of another amphipod, *Pontoporei aaffinis*. These fluctuations are of special interest since both crayfish are important items in the diet of fish.

A very approximate estimate, probably with considerable errors, can be made for the benthos biomass of the whole Baltic Sea and its separate regions for the summer season (*Table 138*).

Table 138

Area	Total benthos biomass, tons	Average benthos biomass, g/m^2
Northern part of the Gulf of Bothnia with reduced biomass	9,000	0·2
Southern part of Gulf of Bothnia	1,200,000	12·4
Gulf of Finland	1,200,000	57·0
Gulf of Riga	658,000	38·5
Baltic Sea proper (north of 56° N latitude)	3,500,000	25·0
Southern part of Sea (south of 56° N latitude)	4,763,000	60·0
Belts and Oresund	2,170,000	186·0
For the whole Sea	13,500,000	33·0

VI. ORIGIN OF THE FAUNA

The main components

Four main components can be distinguished in the Baltic Sea fauna: (*1*) marine cold-water relicts of the post-glacial period; (*2*) true brackish-water fauna, consisting mainly of Arctic brackish-water relicts of the Ice Age; (*3*) marine fauna, representing a greatly impoverished Atlantic fauna; and (*4*) fresh-water fauna (its most euryhaline representatives). The first group, and to some extent the second, form groups of relicts of cold-water European boreal and Arctic fauna.

The marine cold-water relicts of the Ice Age

According to Ekman's determination, a form may be considered a relict for a given area if its habitat is cut off from its main habitat and if it or its original form evolved in an environment different from that in which the relict form exists today. Ekman calls a relict form pseudorelict if it has penetrated by a second stage into its present environment from some other body of water. As regards the Baltic Sea fauna it is often difficult to decide whether some form is a relict or a pseudorelict, especially if one takes account of the fact that during the colder phases of the post-glacial period some of those forms may have had a continuous habitat across the North Sea. Thus the mark of a relict is its isolation from its main habitat either in space or in time. Many forms which are abundant in the central and northern parts of the Baltic Sea (Figs. 162 and 163) are either entirely absent from, or rare off, the western and northern coasts of Scandinavia (Figs. 164, 165 and 166), their main habitat being the Arctic Ocean.

All these forms in the Baltic Sea may be considered as marine ice relicts of the Yoldian stage, which in an earlier, colder period had a continuous habitat including the Arctic basin. The following are such relicts: among Hydrozoa: *Halitholus cirratus*; among molluscs: *Astarte borealis* (Fig. 167); among worms: *Halicryptus spinulosus* (Fig. 166); among crustaceans: *Mesidothea entomon*, *Pontoporeia affinis* and *P. femorata* (Fig. 163); *Pallasea quadrispinosa*, *Mysis oculata*, *M. mixta*, *Limnocalanus grimaldi* (Fig. 162); among fish: *Myoxocephalus quadricornis* (Fig. 164); and among mammals: *Phoca hispida* (*Ph. foetida*).

S. Ekman (1935) has subdivided all these Ice Age marine relicts into three groups. In the first group he includes the forms which at the present time also live in their main habitat, the Arctic basin, only in greatly diluted or fresh water. They are usually called true brackish-water forms or, strictly speaking, Arctic brackish-water relict fauna. This group includes: *Mesidothea entomon*, *Pontoporeia affinis*, *Limnocalanus grimaldi*, *Pallasea quadrispinosa*.* The second group consists of the extremely euryhaline forms *Phoca hispida*, *Myoxocephalus quadricornis* and *Mysis oculata*, which can thrive equally well in sea and fresh water. Euryhaline marine and brackish forms, of less euryhalinity than the previous group, belong to the third group, namely: *Pontoporeia femorata*, *Mysis mixta*, *Halicryptus spinulosus*, *Astarte borealis* and the hydroid *Halitholus cirratus*.

It is clear from the charts that the representatives of this last group avoid the least saline parts of the Baltic Sea. Ekman suggests that during the Ancylus stage these forms must have disappeared from the Baltic Sea; he admits that they may have found a refuge in the western part of the Sea within the region of the present-day straits. These forms populated the Baltic Sea again during the Littorina period.

Some of these relicts are found in the Baltic Sea in greater numbers than anywhere in the Arctic region. Moreover the fauna of the Baltic Sea contains a number of forms which are, as it were, intermediate between relicts and the forms with a continuous distribution. These latter are abundantly represented in the Baltic and the Arctic basin but are not found in large amounts in the intervening areas. Such forms include the polychaetes *Artacama proboscidea* and *Harmothoe sarsi*, and the molluscs *Macoma* (*Tellina*) *baltica* amd others.

* S. Sägerstråle explains the genesis of *P. quadrispinosa* in a different manner (see la ter)

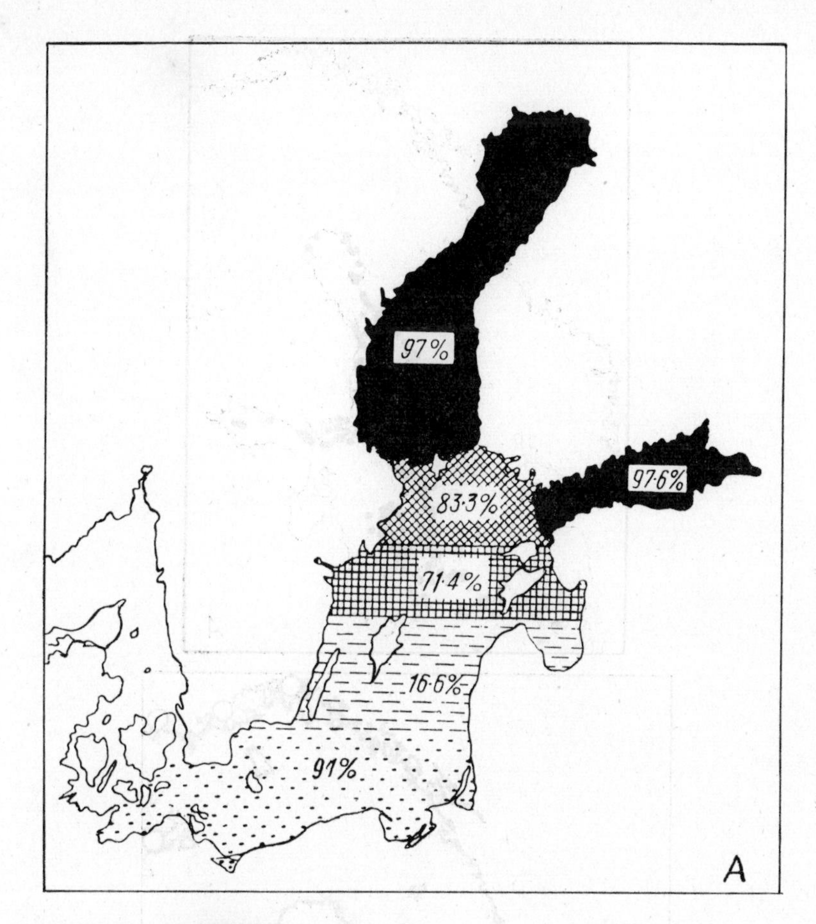

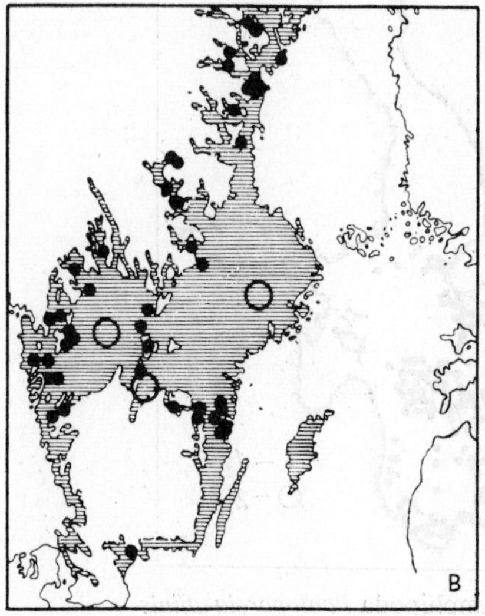

FIG. 162. Distribution of the copepods *Limnocalanus grimaldi* in the Sea (A) and *L. macrurus* in the lakes of Sweden (B) (Ekman, 1937). The hatched part of the territory of Sweden was submerged during the Yoldic period (same on Figs. 148 and 149).

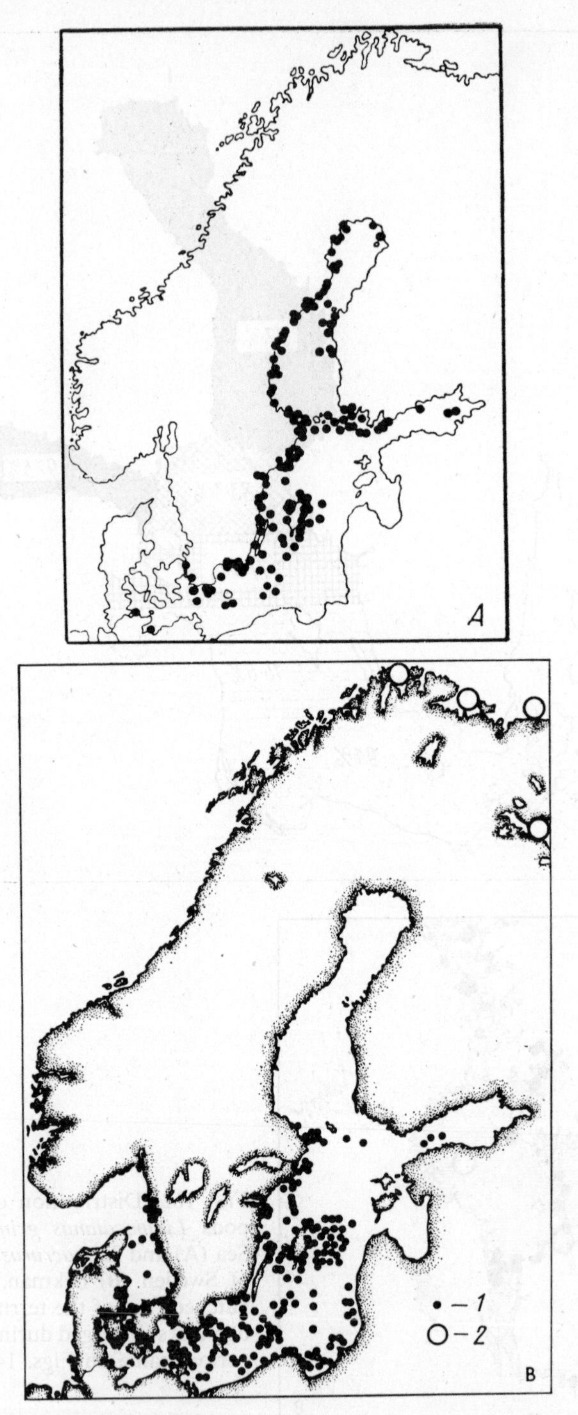

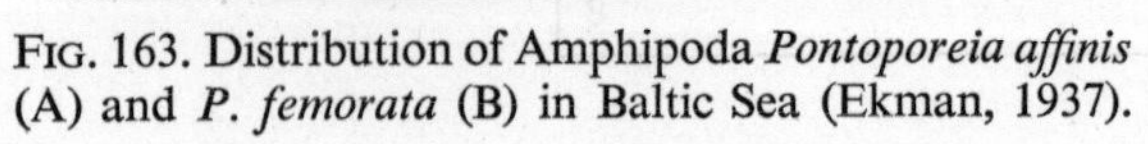

FIG. 163. Distribution of Amphipoda *Pontoporeia affinis* (A) and *P. femorata* (B) in Baltic Sea (Ekman, 1937).

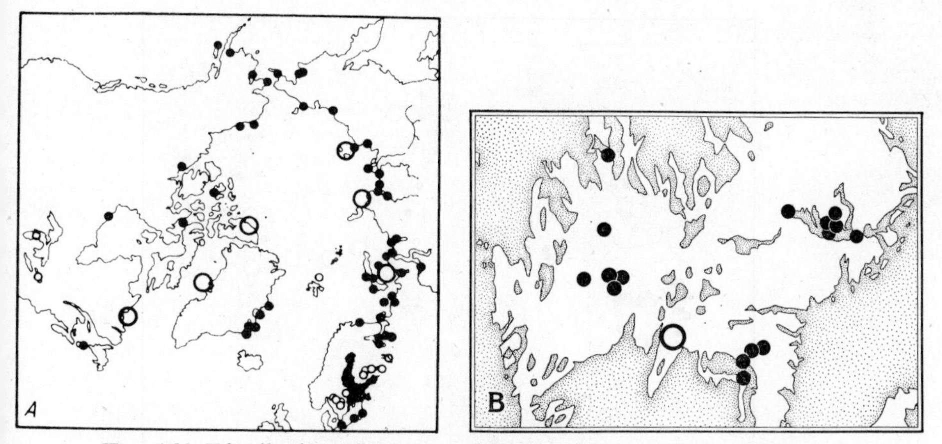

FIG. 164. Distribution of *Myoxocephalus quadricornis* (A) in the Sea and the lakes (B) of Sweden (Ekman).

Several such forms are found in the southeastern part of the North Sea. The Baltic Sea, stretching far from south to north, and with a very severe climate in the north, provides a most favourable environment for the preservation of cold-water relicts. It is possible that low temperature, rather than salinity, promotes the existence of Arctic brackish-water relicts in the northern part of the Baltic.

The same can be seen in the case of polychaetes. It follows from the zoogeographical analysis of this group given by A. Friedrich (1938) that, whereas for the North Sea and the Baltic together the boreal, Lusitanean and Lusitanean–boreal species form 53·2 per cent, and the Arctic, Arctic–boreal and

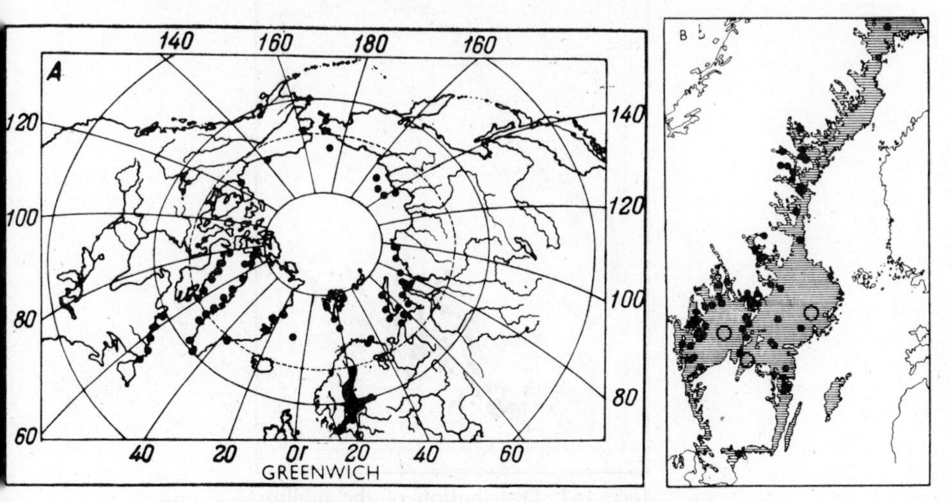

FIG. 165. Distribution of *Mysis oculata* in the Sea (A) and *M. o. relicta* in the lakes of Sweden (B) (Ekman).

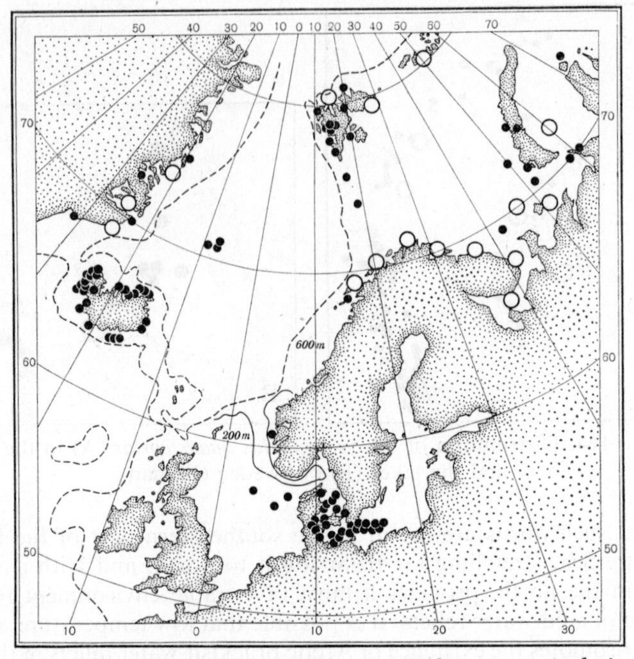

FIG. 166. Distribution of the worm *Halicryptus spinulosis* (Ekman).

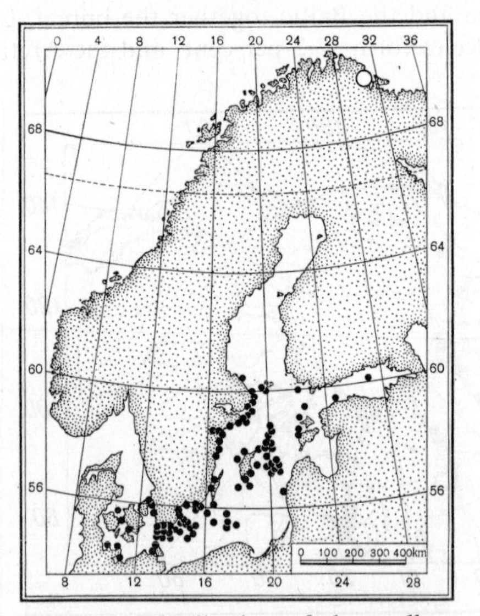

FIG. 167. Distribution of the mollusc *Astarte borealis* (Ekman and Johansen).

Arctic–Mediterranean 42 per cent, for the Baltic Sea alone the first group comprises only 22 per cent and the second 70 per cent.

Comparing the Baltic Sea fauna with that of the east Greenland fjords G. Torhson (1934) makes a good appreciation of the Arctic nature of the former. He points out that the similarity between the Greenland biocoenosis *Astarte borealis* and the corresponding one from the Belt and the Baltic Sea is remarkable. In the latter we again find: *Macoma calcarea, Astarte borealis, A. banksi, A. elliptica, Modiolaria nigra, Priapulus caudatus, Scoloplos armiger*

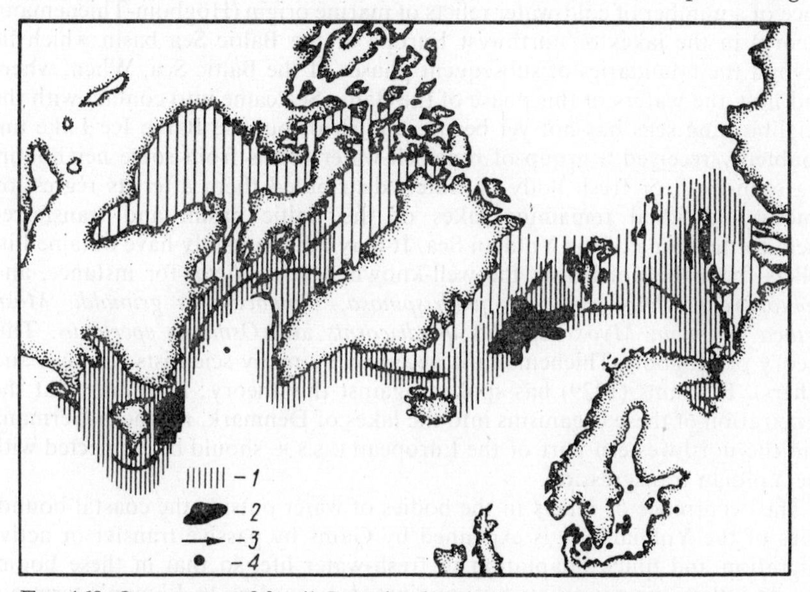

FIG. 168. Occurrence of fossil Greenland seal on the shores of the Baltic and its contemporary habitat in the Arctic basin (Ekman, 1930). *1* Sites of feeding migrations; *2* Breeding areas; *3* Routes of migration; *4* Occurrence in fossil state.

(in eastern Greenland *Sc. cuvieri*) and some other polychaetes. In the shallower places of the Baltic Sea *Macoma calcarea* is replaced by *M. baltica*, remaining, however, in deeper patches. Torhson thinks that the fauna of the deep-water zone of the Baltic Sea and the Belt corresponds to that of the coastal zone of the eastern shores of Greenland and represents the Arctic relict biocoenosis in the Baltic.

Many Arctic forms have moved their habitat to the north, leaving only their fossil remains in the Baltic Sea area (Fig. 168). Thus *Phoca groenlandica* was common in the Baltic even during the Littorina period, and was abundantly used in the food of primitive man. It is not clear how the Greenland seal could survive the fresh-water phase of the Ancylus Lake and the warm Littorina phase. Ekman considers this seal a Yoldian Sea relict in the Littorina Sea.

When and in what way did the Ice Age marine ancestors of the present-day relicts penetrate into the Baltic Sea? The answer to this must be sought first of all in the questions touched on above concerning the role of the Ice Lake Sea and the joining of the Yoldian Lake and White Sea.

The so-called 'ribbon' clays are thought to be the characteristic type of the deposits of the Ice Lake Sea. They have been discovered in a number of places between the Baltic and White Seas at heights of up to 180 m (on the shore of Lake Onega). The Baltic Ice Lake Sea covered a considerable area of north and northwest Europe, leaving in the south large inlets which became lakes. Some scientists connect with the waters of this Ice Lake Sea the appearance of a number of cold-water relicts of marine origin (Högbom-Thienemann theory) in the lakes of northwest Europe of the Baltic Sea basin which lie beyond the boundaries of subsequent phases of the Baltic Sea. When, where and how the waters of this phase of the Baltic Sea came into contact with the neighbouring seas has not yet been established, but the Baltic Ice Lake undoubtedly received a group of brackish-water forms from some neighbouring semi-fresh or fresh body of water, distributed them after its regression among individual remaining lakes of the Baltic basin, and transferred them to the fauna of the Yoldian Sea. It may quite possibly have obtained its relicts from the northeast; the well-known *Mysis relicta*, for instance, and *Pontoporeia affinis*, *Pallasea quadrispinosa*, *Limnocalanus grimaldi*, *Mesidothea entomon*, *Myoxocephalus quadricornis* and *Osmerus eperlanus*. This theory of Högbom-Thienemann is accepted by many scientists (Ekman and others). E. Gams (1929) has spoken against this theory; he thinks that the penetration of these organisms into the lakes of Denmark, northern Germany and the northwestern part of the European U.S.S.R. should be connected with the Yoldian transgression.

The occurrence of relicts in the bodies of water outside the coastal boundaries of the Yoldian Sea is explained by Gams by passive transfer or active migration and quick adaptation to fresh-water life, so that in these bodies of water they are not relicts but immigrants according to Ekman's terminology (relicts for the areas into which they were transferred or penetrated at a second stage). Gams rejects any link between the history of these relicts and the Ice Lake Sea. Many hydrobiologists, however, do not admit the possibility of passive transfer or active migration of these animals from one body of water to another, or against the current of a river. The migration capabilities of such crayfish as Limnocalanus, Mysis, Pontoporeia, and of Pallasea almost to the same extent, are very weak. Thus among the large number of Scandinavian bodies of water investigated there is not a single one situated above the mean boundaries of the Yoldian Sea which contains even one of the four crustaceans mentioned. Their occurrence as a result of transfer by birds or flying insects is, obviously, quite impossible. Therefore the passive or active penetration of these crayfish into lakes which do not belong to the Baltic Sea basin, as for example the Seliger Lake, is thus even more improbable.

Högbom's theory of ice lakes of large area and high level extending south much farther than the boundaries of the Yoldian Sea, can be used to explain problems of a biological nature which arise if the possibility of passive transfer or active migration of relict crayfish from one body of water to another is accepted.

As for the glacial marine relicts inhabiting saline-brackish waters which could not have populated the fresh-water ice lakes, Ekman, sharing the point of view of Münthe and Sauramo, thinks that they arrived in the Yoldian basin from the west.

The climatic conditions of the North Sea and the adjacent parts of the Atlantic at the time were so severe that the Arctic fauna may have migrated far to the south and lived in the North Sea. However, this fauna may have come from the northeast, if we assume that the Yoldian Sea was connected with the White Sea, or if this connection existed at later periods.

Sägerstråle (1957) likewise accepts this route of the penetration into the Baltic Sea of a part of the brackish-water Arctic relicts; he divides them into several groups according to the time and route of their penetration into the Baltic Sea.

(*1*) *Limnocalanus macrurus* (according to Sägerstråle the Baltic form *L. grimaldii* evolved from it), *Pontoporeia affinis*, *Pallasea quadrispinosa* and *Mysis relicta* were the first immigrants from the fresh waters in the north to the Baltic Sea. Sägerstråle thinks that the isopod Pallasea came from the fresh waters of Siberia.

(*2*) The second group of relicts, *Mesidothea entomon*, *Gammaracanthus lacustris*, *Cottus quadricornis* and *Phoca hispida*, penetrated into the Baltic Sea during the period of ice-recession, when the Gulf of Finland was freed of ice. They may have migrated from the northeast from an ice lake in the area of the White Sea, perhaps during the Littorina period when the water was not yet saline.

(*3*) During the Littorina stage all these relicts were pushed into the least saline areas and the penetration of Atlantic fauna and flora from the south-west began; for example: *Littorina littorea*, *Pontoporeia femorata*, *Mysis mixta*, *Halicryptus spinulosus*, and other remains of the cold-water fauna of the Ice Age. In the case of some forms—*Pallasea quadrispinosa* is given as an example—S. Sägerstråle (1957) accepts the view of P. Pirozhnikov (1937) and E. Gurjanova (1946, 1951) regarding the west Siberian (Kara Sea) centre of the evolution of a number of forms, and of their migration south down to the Caspian Sea west of the Ural mountains via the Ob basin; this theory is based on the fact that the Kara Sea is now inhabited by a community of brackish-water forms nearest to the Caspian immigrants (Fig. 169). For the rest, Sägerstråle is inclined to consider *P. quadrispinosa* as genetically related to the Lake Baikal *P. kessleri*. The fresh-water bodies of water of the Ice Lake period may have served as further routes of migration (Fig. 170). Following the opinion of Soviet authors (N. Lomakin, 1952), Sägerstråle is inclined to connect the migration of the Caspian Pontoporeia (*P. affinis microphthalma*), Gammaracanthus (*G. loricatus caspius*) and *Mesidothea entomon* with the fate of the Siberian ice lakes.

In whatever way these forms penetrated into the basin of the Baltic Sea, as a result of a subsequent change in the coastal contour and the rise of temperature in the adjacent areas of the Atlantic, a discontinuous habitat was created, the conditions of the Baltic were altered, and forms became partly extinct, partly relicts.

The cold-water mollusc *Yoldia* (*Portlandia*) *arctica* is the most characteristic form of the Yoldian Sea fauna known to us. Some other forms are, however, equally characteristic, for example the diatom *Campylodiscus clypeus*. *Yoldia arctica*, however, could have lived only in the most saline western parts of the Sea. *Myoxocephalus quadricornis* and *Phoca foetida* in the large Finnish lakes are probably remnants of this fauna, since these lakes had been cut off from the Baltic Sea as early as the Littorina stage. The Yoldian

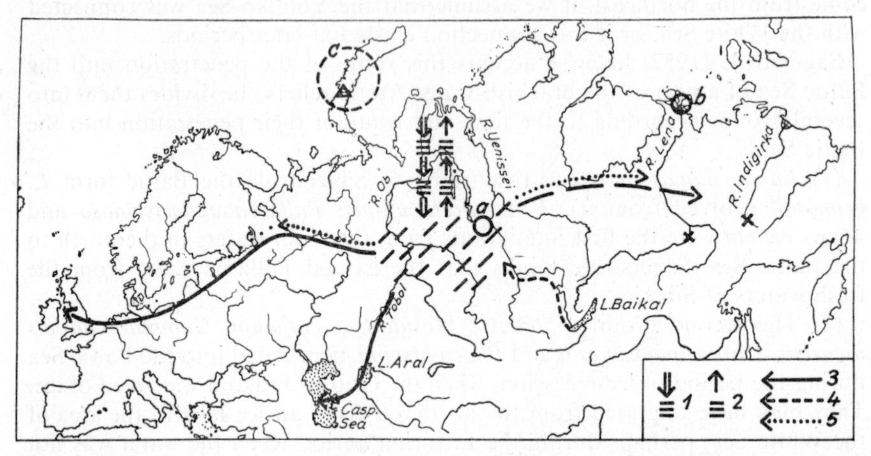

FIG. 169. Conjectured role of Siberian Ice Lake at period of its greatest glaciation, in evolution and distribution of glacial relicts. The lake is marked by cross-hatching: *1* and *2*: routes of exchange of glacial forms; *3* and 5: migration of forms of marine origin; *4*: migration of the ancestor of *Pallasea quadrispinosa* (possibly *P. kessleri*) from Lake Baikal. Places of occurrence of *P. quadrispinosa* are marked by a circle: *a*, in Nalim's Lake; *b*, in river Lena estuary; *c*, in Novaya Zemlya. Occurrence of *P. laevis* (possibly descended from *P. quadrispinosa*) is indicated by a triangle. Occurrence of *Mesidothea entomon* in eastern Siberia is marked by crosses (Sägerstråle).

Lake phase did not last long (barely 700 years according to Münthe; only for 500 years according to Sauramo, 1953).

A rise of land in the western part of the Yoldian Lake cut it off from the ocean; it lost much of its salinity and turned into the low-salinity, closed Ancylus Lake Sea with a powerful flow of water to the west into the North Sea. This phase, according to De-Geer, lasted for 2,200 years. When this body of water lost its salinity it became densely populated with fresh-water forms, among them the molluscs *Ancylus fluviatilis* and various species of crustaceans and molluscs (Limnaea, Planorbis).

Penetration of Atlantic fauna

During the Littorina stage salinity off Gotland reached 12‰ (Fig. 136); now this salinity is found only in the Belt. The Baltic Sea again became connected with Lake Ladoga. For this phase the mollusc *Tapes decussatus* is most characteristic. *Mytilus edulis*, *Cardium edule*, *Hydrobia baltica*, *Neritella fluviatilis* appeared, and also *Littorina littorea* and *L. rudis*, both now absent from the Baltic Sea. At that time *L. littorea* reached 62° 20′ N, while now it

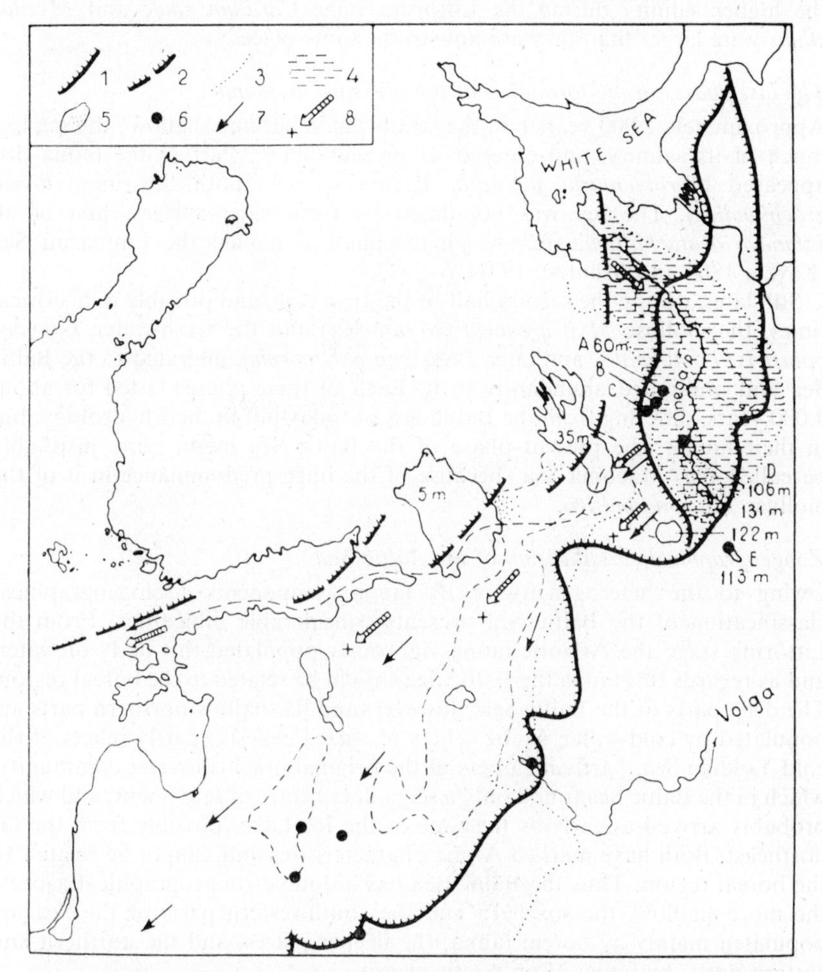

FIG. 170. Ice Lake and its role in the distribution of relicts (Sägerstråle, 1957). *1* Limit of ice cover (in the northern part, according to various authorities); *2* Tentative location of ice cover; *3* Watershed; *4* Onega Ice Lake; *5* Lake deposits; *6* Distribution of relicts (associated numerals denote altitude above sea-level, m); A Lake Kenozero; B Lake Pochozero; C Lake Terekhovo; D Latsha Lake; E Kubensk Lake; *7* Route of migrations of relicts; *8* Cross-distribution impossible for ecological reasons.

does not go farther than Malmö, Warnemünde and Rügen. *Rissoa membranacea* lived round the Åland Islands during the Littorina stage, while now it does not east of Oresund. *Phoca vitulina*, which now does not go farther north than Gotland, in the Littorina Sea reached 64° N in the Gulf of Bothnia.

Besides *Phoca groenlandica* and *Ph. vitulina* other seals—*Phoca hispida, Ph. foetida, Halichaerus gryphes*—lived in the Littorina Sea. In keeping with the higher salinity during the Littorina stage *Cardium edule* and *Mytilus edulis* were larger than they are now in the same places.

The last phases in the formation of the present-day fauna

Approximately 2,000 years B.C. the straits again became shallow; the sea lost much of its salinity, and entered its present phase. Part of the fauna disappeared (*Scrobicularia piperata*, Rissoa species, both littorines, *Phoca groenlandica*). The sea was populated by fresh-water species, first of all *Limnaea ovata baltica*, after which the phase is named the Limnaean Sea (Loven, 1864 and Münthe, 1931).

Still later, during the second half of the Iron Age, and possibly in historical times, the mollusc *Mya arenaria* (Myan Sea) and the fresh-water *Limnaea palustris, L. stagnalis*, and later *Dreissena polymorpha*, migrated to the Baltic Sea and multiplied abundantly in it. Each of these phases lasted for about 4,000 years, differing from the Baltic Sea of today not in their hydrology, but in their fauna. The present phase of the Baltic Sea might quite justifiably be called the 'Macoma Sea' because of the huge predominance in it of the mollusc *Macoma baltica*.

Zoogeographical classification of the Baltic Sea

Owing to the heterogeneity of its fauna components a biogeographical classification of the Baltic Sea presents considerable difficulties. From the Littorina stage the Atlantic fauna vigorously populated this body of water, and as regards this fauna the Baltic Sea should be related to the boreal region. The deep parts of the Baltic Sea, however, and its shallow northern parts are populated by cold-water Arctic relicts of varied genesis: partly relicts of the cold Yoldian Sea, partly members of the original brackish-water community, which in the Baltic Sea found only a secondary centre of settlement, and which probably arrived as early as the time of the Ice Lake, possibly from the far northeast. Both have marked Arctic characteristics and cannot be related to the boreal region. Thus the Baltic Sea has a double zoogeographical aspect: the more shallow, the southern and the southwestern parts of the Sea are populated mainly by boreal fauna, the deeper places, and the northern and eastern parts, by fauna of an Arctic aspect.

Zonation

We have had to point out several times that it is impossible to create a single system of division of marine and brackish-water fauna according to the salinity of the water, and that the zonation of each low-salinity body of water must have its own special features.

The first schemes for the classification of waters according to their salinity were worked out for the Baltic Sea. The problems of brackish waters were also first studied in the Baltic Sea. The scheme of the German hydrobiologist H. Redeke (1922), worked out for the Zuyderzee, was used as the basis of these classifications.

Three investigators, I. Välikangas (1933), A. Remane (1935) and S. Sägerstråle (1957), have given a more detailed estimate of the brackish waters of the Baltic Sea. The first of them has established three marked limits of qualitative change of Baltic Sea fauna as we move from west to east: (*1*) the area lying between the Kattegat on one side and the Belt and Oresund on the other, with salinity fluctuations of 15 to 20‰; (*2*) the outlets from these straits into the Baltic Sea with a salinity of 8 to 10‰; and (*3*) a zone of much reduced salinity, which differs somewhat for various groups: 3 to 3·5‰ salinity for the brown and red algae and a little higher for the molluscs.

Välikangas, on the basis of Redeke's scheme, divides the marine waters into the oligohaline (0·2 to 2·0‰), mesohaline (2·0 to 16·5‰) and polyhaline (>16·5‰) as in *Table 139.*

Table 139

Zone	Salinity ‰
Fresh waters	<0·5
Oligohaline brackish waters	0·5 to 3
Meiomesohaline waters	3 to 8 (10)
Pleiomesohaline waters	8 (10) to 16·5
Polyhaline brackish waters	16·5 to 30
Sea-waters	>30

Remane approached this problem in a rather different way. He took as a basis the natural distribution of organisms and counted the number of species of different genesis in waters of varying salinity. Thus Remane was the first to apply, in the classification of the brackish zone, an indirect quantitative method. He established that in the Baltic Sea marine forms more than 50 per cent were at a salinity of 30 to 17‰, while in the range 17 to 8‰ the proportion fell from 50 to 30 per cent. As a result Remane gives the following subdivisions for the Baltic Sea according to its salinity:

I. Purely marine zone — 35 to 15‰
II. Brackish-water zone — 15 to 3‰
- (*1*) Brackish-marine mixed zone with a preponderance of marine forms — 15 to 10‰
- (*2*) True brackish-water zone with a maximum development of specific brackish-water fauna — 10 to 5‰
- (*3*) Brackish–fresh-water mixed region with a preponderance of fresh-water elements — 5 to 3‰

III. Fresh-water zone — <3‰

Moreover the limits for various groups of organisms may be different. Remane's system is applicable to benthos; for plankton the fresh-water elements are already dominant at a salinity of 5 to 7‰. Remane distinguished the four following groups of organisms:

(*1*) Euryhaline fresh-water forms
(*2*) Euryhaline marine forms

(*3*) Steno- and eury-haline brackish-water forms
(*4*) Highly euryhaline organisms, the distribution of which does not depend on water salinity.

Finally the following classification of brackish water was accepted by the Venetian symposium in 1958 as the most suitable for the Baltic Sea:

Zone	Salinity, ‰
Hyperhaline	>40
Euryhaline	40 to 30
Mixohaline	30 to 0·5
Mixoeuhaline	>30 (less than the adjacent euhaline waters)
(mixo) polyhaline	30 to 18
(mixo) mesohaline	18 to 5
(mixo) olyghohaline	5 to 0·5
Fresh water	<0·5

and further subdivisions for the (mixo) mesohaline and (mixo) oligohaline zones:

(mixo) mesohaline	
α-meshohaline	18 to 10
β-mesohaline	10 to 5
(mixo) oligohaline	
α-oligohaline	5 to 3
β-oligohaline	3 to 0·5

However, this scheme is too detailed and therefore difficult to apply in practice. For that reason Remane's classification, given above, is preferable.

The brackish-water relicts in the Baltic Sea which have retained their Arctic aspect most are: *Mesidothea entomon*, *Limnocalanus grimaldii*, *Pontoporeia affinis*, *Myoxocephalus quadricornis* and *Phoca hispida*.

However, *Mysis mixta*, *M. relicta*, *Astarte borealis*, *Pontoporeia femorata* and *Halitholus cirratus* are very closely akin to them, although in the Arctic regions they do not belong, as the others do, to the preponderant brackish-water forms. The third group—steno- and eury-haline brackish-water animals in the Baltic Sea—comprises a fairly considerable group.

S. Sägerstråle (1957) includes in the group of true brackish-water organisms of the Baltic Sea (except for the Ice Age relicts and the immigrants from other seas) 15 species of plants and 43 species of animals:

Cyanophyceae	*Anabaena baltica*
Diatomaceae	*Thalassiosira baltica*, *Chaetoceros subtilis*, *Ch. wighami*, *Synedra tabulata*, *S. pulchella*
Rhodophyceae	*Ceramium tenuicorne*
Phaeophyceae	*Ectocarpus confervoides fluviatilis*, *Portoeirema fluviatile*

Characeae	*Tolypella nidifica, Chara baltica, Ch. canescenes (Ch. crinita)*
Phanerogamae	*Scirpus parvulus, Zannichellia pedunculata, Najas marina*
Ciliata	*Tintinnopsis tubulosa, T. brandti, Leprotintinnus bottnicus*
Cnidaria	*Protohydra leuckarti, Pelmatohydra oligactis*
Turbellaria	*Promesostoma baltica, P. cochlearis, P. lugubra, Koinocystis twaerminnensis*
Rotatoria	*Synchaeta fennica, S. monopus, Anuraea cruciformis eichwaldi, A. quadrata platei, A. cochlearis recurvispina*
Nemertini	*Prostoma obscurum*
Polychaeta	*Streblospio dekhuyzeni, Alkmaria romijni*
Ostracoda	*Cytherura gibba, Cytheromorpha fuscata*
Copepoda	*Eurytemora affinis, E. hirundoides, Acartia bifilosa*
Cladocera	*Bosmina coregoni maritima*
Decapoda	*Palaemonetes varians*
Isopoda	*Sphaeroma hookeri, Cyathura carinata, Idothea viridis*
Tanaidacea	*Heterotanais oerstedi*
Amphipoda	*Bathyporeia pilosa, Melita palmata, Gammarus zaddachi zaddachi, G. z. salinus, G. duebeni, Leptocheirus pilosus, Corophium lacustre*
Coleoptera	*Ochtebius marinus, Laccobius decorus, Haemonia mutica, H. pubipennis*
Gastropoda	*Hydrobia ventrosa, Alderia modesta*
Bryozoa	*Membranipora crustulenta, Victorella pavida.*

However, this group can be considerably reduced since some of the animal forms included (possibly as many as 15) are not endemic to the Baltic Sea. Some of the forms enumerated have possibly not been adequately identified.

Even if these endemic forms exist, their endemism is evidently very recent and probably not sufficient to relate them to true brackish-water organisms. Relict forms of much more ancient origin, which penetrated into the Baltic Sea at a second stage, are much more deserving of this name. Remane increases this list considerably, including 68 denominations of animals alone (adding the Ice Age relicts and immigrants from other bodies of water). The following forms from his list are not included in that of Sägerstråle given above:

Coelenterata	*Cordylophora caspia*
Turbellaria	*Procerodes ulvae*
	Acrorhynchus robustus
	Macrostomum hystrix
Rotatoria	*Proales similis, Linasia tecusa, Eucentrum evistes, E. rousseleti, Erignatha thienemanni, Aspelta baltica, Colurella dicentra, Notholca striata, N. bipalium, Brachionus plicatilis, Euchlanis plicata, Synchaeta lavina, S. littoralis, Testudinella clypeata, Pedalia fennica*
Polychaeta	*Manayunkia aestuarina, Polydora redekei*

Copepoda	*Acartia tonsa, Eurytemora hirundo, Limnocalanus grimaldii, Nitocra lacustris, N. spinipes, Ectinosoma curticorne, Mesochra rapiens, M. liljeborgi, Laophonte mohammedi, Schizopera clandestina, Cletocamptus confluens, Horsiella brevicornis, Idunella muelleri*
Ostracoda	*Cyprideis littoralis, Loxoconcha gauthieri, Leptocytere castanea, Cypridopsis aculeata, Heterocypris salina, Candona angulata*
Isopoda	*Tanaidacea, Mesidothea entomon, Sphaeroma rudicaudum*
Mollusca	*Hydrobia jenkinsi, Congeria cochleata.*

A list of 15 plant and 87 animal forms is obtained from both investigators taken together.

What prevents this fauna from leaving the limits of the brackish-water zone and from becoming euryhaline forms in the broadest sense of the word? After all they are all descendants of either marine or fresh-water forms. This is a complex phenomenon, which cannot be explained by a single cause. First one must point out that the brackish-water fauna of the Baltic Sea consists basically of three groups—crustaceans, fish and Rotifera. Hence not all the animal groups constitute equal parts in the population of the brackish-water zones.

The origin of the local brackish-water fauna can most probably be explained by the centuries-long fluctuations of salinity suffered by a zone of transitional salinity. The aquatoria, which contain the most typical brackish-water community, are known to have passed through continuous changes of salinity (named by L. Zenkevitch (1933) 'salinity pulsations') during previous geological periods (the Quaternary and to some extent the Tertiary too), and at the present day a typical instability of saline conditions is characteristic of them. Salinity fluctuations in one direction or the other must inevitably have attracted certain forms from both the marine and fresh-water fauna; and after that, in the order of species formation, the salinity fluctuations must have strengthened in a hereditary way the adaptation of an organism to varying salinity. In this process the biocoenotic factor no doubt played a significant role.

Remane accepts the possibility of specific action of brackish water on organisms. However this is only a surmise; there are no precise data about it. For the rest, if the explanation given above is accepted, there is no need of any further explanation. It is of interest to note that forms of marine origin are preponderant in the brackish-water fauna, comprising about 60 per cent.

Other zonal classifications according to salinity have been used for particular areas of the Baltic Sea. Thus A. Willer (1925), in his magnificent survey of Frishhaff, used the generally accepted terminology of the classification of bodies of water according to salinity (eury–poly–meso–oligo–steno-halinity), but he attached to it a purely local meaning, as if Frishhaff had been a marine body of water of full value as regards salinity.

He distinguishes inside Frishhaff, for example, stenohaline brackish-water organisms, typical of a 'polyhaline' zone, and 'euryhaline brackish-water organisms', typical of a mesohaline zone. The 'euryhaline fresh-water organisms', according to Willer, are those which are met throughout Frishhaff. In actual fact Willer's highest salinity, his 'polyhaline' zone, corresponds only to the lower part of Redek's mesohaline zone. The typical, widely distributed euryhaline Medusa, *Aurelia aurita*, becomes with Willer a stenohaline brackish-water form.

F. Riech (1926), also for Frishhaff, and L. Szidat (1926) for Kurishhaff followed practically in the path of Willer. It is entirely understandable that the whole classification is confused by the introduction of such schemes. The problem becomes more controversial in the case of an independent and even enclosed sea like the Caspian. In his quantitative survey of benthos in the northern part of the Caspian Sea N. Tchougounov (1923) distinguishes the 'marine', the 'brackish-water' and other zones. The maximum salinity of the Caspian Sea, except the highly saline inlets of the eastern shores, is no more than 14‰; hence Tchougounov's marine zone has a salinity which is in practice never found in seas. There are sufficient reasons to regard the Caspian Sea as a whole as a brackish-water basin, but according to Tchougounov 'the brackish-water zone' is a narrow band close to the Volga delta. Thus, when drawing separate local schemes of zonation according to salinity, the subdivisions used must be introduced as small units, after the determination of the place of a given body of water in the general scheme for the seas.

Fish

Among the fish population of the Baltic Sea (it is poor in species), *Myoxocephalus quadricornis*, salmon (*Salmo salar*) and representatives of coregonids (*Coredonus laveretus* and *C. albula*) can be ascribed to the brackish-water Arctic relicts. The most important from the commercial aspect are Baltic herring (*Clupea harengus membras*), sprat (*Sprattus sprattus balticus*), and cod (*G. morrhua*). Flatfish (*Pleuronectes platessa* and *P. limanna* in the southern part of the Sea and *P. flesus* in the eastern) are of some importance in fisheries. Fresh-water fish which are of significance for the industry are pike (*Esox lucius*), golden shiner (*Abramis brama*), perch (*Perca fluviatilis*) and some others; river eel (*Anguilla vulgaris*) should be added to these fish. The fisheries of the Baltic Sea outside the straits have a yield of about 3 million centners of fish, which gives about 80 kg/hectare, while the Gulf of Riga has an annual yield of 500 to 600 thousand centners, or 30 to 36 kg/hectare (1 hectare= 1,000 m^2).

The following are most important as food: among the molluscs: Macoma, Mytilus and Lymnaea; among the crustaceans: Pontoporeia, Mesidothea, Corophium, Gammarus, Idothea and Mysis, and among the insect larvae: Chironomidae and Trichoptera.

THE SOUTHERN SEAS OF THE U.S.S.R.

8

General Characteristics and Geological History

I. GENERAL CHARACTERISTICS

The Black, Azov, Caspian and Aral Seas, and to some extent the Mediterranean and even the Red Sea, for all the differences in their physical geography, have a number of important features in common. All these Seas possess a salinity of their own, different from that of the ocean; this was particularly so in the historical past, when at times it exceeded the normal salinity of the ocean in areas with a negative balance of fresh-water inflow (throughout the Mediterranean and Red Seas, in many gulfs, inlets and the Sivash of the Black, Azov and Caspian Seas). At times it decreased below that of the ocean (the Black, Azov, Caspian and Aral Seas).

Equally characteristic of all these bodies of water, which are isolated from the open ocean, is the temperature of their deep layers; excluding the Azov and Aral Seas, this temperature is high in comparison with the open ocean —about 9° in the Black Sea, 5° to 6° in the Caspian, 13·5° to 13·7° in the Mediterranean and 21·5° in the Red Sea. Their temperatures correspond, to some extent, to the lower average temperature of their upper layers in winter.

These common features of the system of seas from the Black Sea to the Aral Sea are chiefly due to their common origin, which is linked with the geological past of the so-called South Russian geosyncline. This, it is assumed, constitutes a remnant of the ancient Tethys geosyncline, which underwent a complex process of the isolation of sea-basins during almost the whole Neogenic Period.

A considerably lower salinity (10 to 22·5‰), as compared with the normal marine salinity, and a significant difference between the surface and deep-layer salinities, are also very characteristic of the South Russian bodies of water. The marked saline stratification is accentuated by an abrupt temperature stratification which appears in the warm season of the year, when surface water is at times warmed to 27° to 30°. In winter, on the other hand, the surface layer of water becomes very much cooled, and a larger or smaller ice-cover is formed. Saline, and sometimes temperature, stratification causes the formation of hydrogen sulphide on the bottom, when, either at certain seasons or throughout the year, deep waters in the more or less thick layers are contaminated. A. Archangelsky (1938) thinks that the contamination of the Black Sea with hydrogen sulphide is not peculiar to its present phase, but is a characteristic phenomenon common to all the bodies of water of the South Russian geosyncline of the Neogene system.

Lastly, the historical basis of the fauna of the Southern Seas of the U.S.S.R. is a peculiar relict fauna which is itself, in the final analysis, a remnant of the Tethys fauna (Sarmatian, Pontic and Caspian fauna) formed by a complicated succession of lower and higher salinity phases. To this fauna are added in greater or lesser numbers immigrants from fresh waters and far-travelled immigrants (pseudorelicts) from the Arctic basin (chiefly in the Caspian). Atlantic (Mediterranean) fauna comes in vigorously from the west, individual forms penetrating as far as the Aral Sea.

The difference between all these seas in respect of their fauna is most marked. The Red Sea is populated by the tropical fauna of the Indian Ocean. The Mediterranean fauna is a descendant of the south boreal fauna of the Atlantic Ocean; the Caspian Sea preserves in its fullest form the remarkable relict 'Caspian' fauna; the least saline parts of the Black and Azov Seas are inhabited by the 'Caspian' fauna, while the Mediterranean (Atlantic) fauna populates the main basin.

II. THE GEOLOGICAL PAST

Evolution of the Seas of the Neogene System

The geological history of our South Russian Seas has been traced in its main features by the work of a number of investigators. Special credit in this field is due to Andrussov and, lately, Archangelsky.

N. Andrussov (1918) writes: 'the main characteristic of the history of the Neogene . . . of the Ponto-Caspian regions is their continuous and ever increasing isolation from the ocean, leading to a change in the salt content of the inland water basins which were being formed there, mainly in the direction of lesser salinity, although at times an increase of salinity has also been observed. . . . Owing to this isolation and the change in the salinity of the waters covering different parts of the regions, the history of the fauna of these waters affords a series of most interesting and instructive phenomena. The marine fauna which originally inhabited them during the middle Miocene era underwent a number of changes under the influence of changes in the composition of the water. On the one hand it is simply a gradual disappearance of the stenohaline forms; on the other it is a survival of forms less sensitive to fluctuations in salinity (euryhaline forms), which is accompanied by considerable morphological and anatomical changes, by great mutability of species and the evolution of numerous new species and even genera . . .'

Lower and Middle Miocene Periods

During the Lower and Middle Miocene Periods a fully saline sea, with a typically marine fauna of Mediterranean type and wide connections with the ocean, stretched throughout the south of the European part of the U.S.S.R., extending far to both the west and east (Fig. 171).* The process of the separation of this huge sea, part of the disappearing Tethys, from the ocean may already have begun by the end of the Middle Miocene, individual parts of the Sea losing some of their salinity. The rise of the mountains and the formation of watersheds broke up the Middle Miocene Sea into more or less isolated parts, which collected masses of river water and lost some of their salinity.

* B. Zhizhchenko (1940) thinks that in the southern part of the U.S.S.R. there was a much diluted basin (Aral Stage) by the end of the Oligocene and the beginning of the Miocene Period, after which normal oceanic conditions were restored.

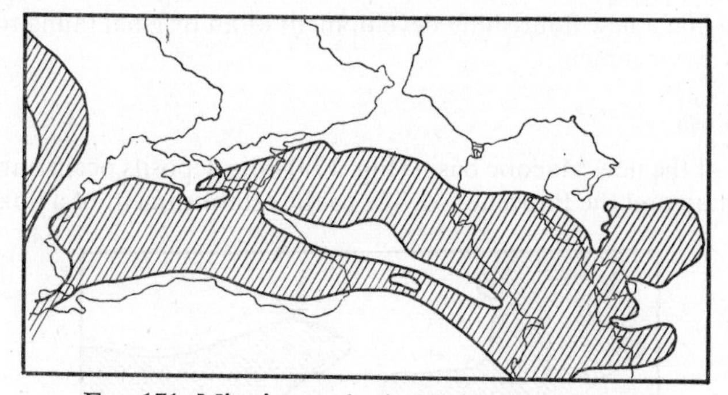

FIG. 171. Mitmiocene basin (Zhizhchenko, 1940).

Sarmatian basin

During the Upper Miocene a Sarmatian basin, cut off from the open seas, was formed in the place of the Middle Miocene basin (Fig. 172).

A number of the most typical members of the Mediterranean fauna disappeared in the Sarmatian basin as, for example, the sea urchins, the bivalves Arca, Pectunculus, Leda and its most typical representatives Cardium, Pecten, Venus, Corbula, Conus, Natica, Turitella and others. Pleurotoma, Murex, Lucina, Loripes, Corbula and others continued to exist there for some time. The hardiest forms survived: the gastropods Cerithium, Trochus, Buccinum, Nassa and the bivalves Cardium (small size), Modiola, Tapes, Mactra, Syndesmya, Donax, Ervilia. As has been pointed out by V. Bogachev (1933) a peculiar vertebrate fauna was also associated with the Sarmatian basin: among fish: grey mullet, gadidae, Clupea, dolphins and other Cetotheria, and seals (very similar to the present Caspian seal). Later the Sarmatian basin lost much of its salinity, becoming possibly much less saline than the present Black Sea. Conditions favourable for the development of a hydrogen sulphide zone were created by the existence of a considerable difference in the salinity of the surface and deep layers of the sea. Almost the whole Sarmatian basin fauna rapidly died off under the effect of considerable general loss of salinity and the contamination of the deep layers by hydrogen

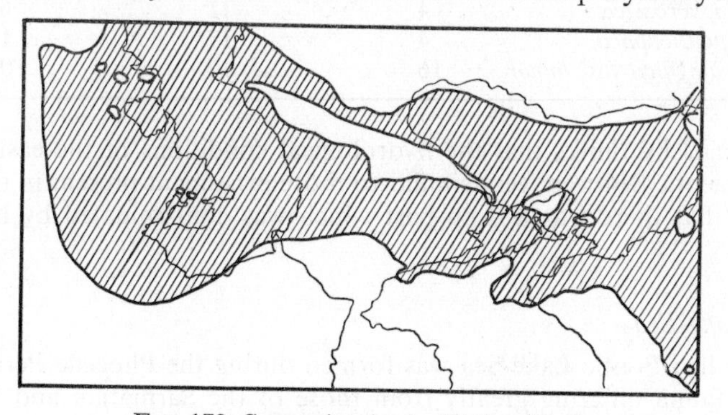

FIG. 172. Sarmatian basin (Kolesnikov).

sulphide, while a new flourishing development of an original fauna took place in the new environment.

Maeotic basin

The fauna of the new Maeotic basin (Fig. 173)—its deposits occurring between the Sarmatian and the Pliocene—owing to the establishment of a link with the

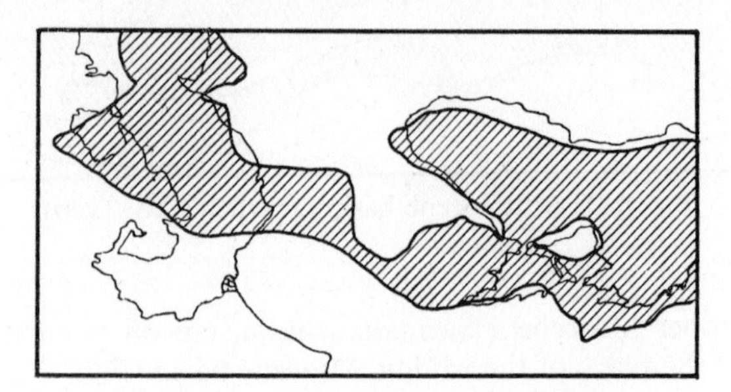

FIG. 173. Maeotic basin (Kolesnikov).

ocean again received a number of typical Mediterranean forms alien to the Sarmatian period (Ostrea, Venerupis, Lucina, Dosinia, Cerithium, Arca), retaining only a few of the Sarmatian ones. The composition of the fauna in the upper deposits of the Maeotic basin changed sharply again and, displacing the Mediterranean forms, species of the genus Congeria and the gastropods Neritina, Hydrobia and Micromelania appeared.

The process of loss of salinity in the Maeotic basin in the vicinity of the Kerch peninsula is well illustrated by Andrussov's table (1926) of the number of species in the three overlapping layers of deposits (*Table 140*).

Table 140

Layers with:	Marine species	Brackish-water species	Fresh-water species
Congeria novorossica	4	11	6
Congeria panticapaea	4	17	1
Modiola volhynica var. *minor*	16	10	0

Archangelsky thinks that the hydrological conditions of the eastern part of the Maeotic Sea were very similar to those existing at present in the Black Sea and that there was a deep part which was contaminated by hydrogen sulphide.

Pontic Lake-Sea

The so-called Pontic Lake-Sea was formed during the Pliocene Period (Fig. 174), its fauna differing greatly from those of the Sarmatian and Mediterranean. The huge inland brackish-water lake-sea (similar to the present-day

Caspian Sea) had a fauna characterized by a marked predominance of Dreissensiidae and Cardidae which retained a certain successive link with the Maeotic basin fauna.

'Any geosyncline,' writes A. Archangelsky (1927), 'situated between two platforms, at certain stages of its development is bound to undergo a stage of dismemberment into a system of basins similar to that of the Caspian–Mediterranean Sea. . . . The rise of some parts of the geosyncline and the lowering of others can break up the geosyncline basin into a complex system of deep bodies of water, some connected with the open sea, some entirely cut off from it.'

'The development of the Pontic basin', write M. Gerasimov and K. Markov (1939), 'is closely connected with the considerable loss of salinity of

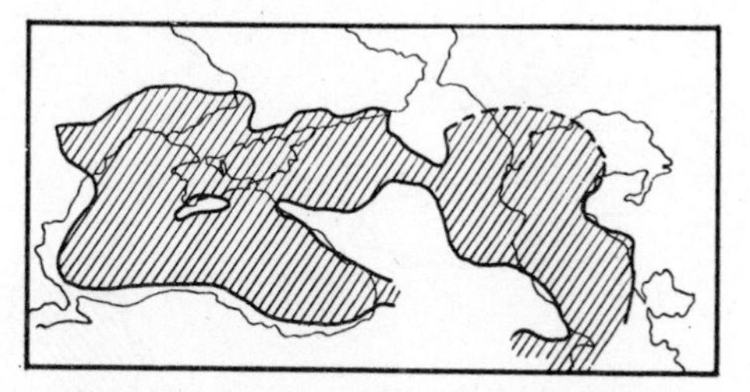

FIG. 174. Pontic Lake–Sea (Andrussov).

the Maeotic basin with the replacement of the "semi-marine" "Euxine" conditions by those of a greatly diluted inland lake-sea of the "Caspian" type. Only the Cardidae, some Gastropoda and Dreissensiidae of the Maeotic fauna passed over into the Pontic basin; the numerous forms of the Melanopsidae, Paludinidae and Limnaeidae families were added to it in great numbers from the rivers and lakes. The true Cardium are no longer there, only the Limnocardium; but Didacna, Monodacna and Prosodacna are numerous.' N. Andrussov (1918) assumes that this Pontic community was formed in the west in the Middle-Danube lake-sea and was then propagated to the east.

According to A. Archangelsky (1934) the basin of the Caspian Sea was separated, either at the end of the Pontic Period or after it, by the rise of its floor from the Black Sea part of the Pontic Lake-Sea, and since then the development of the fauna of both parts proceeded independently (Fig. 175).

The Black Sea basin during the Middle and Upper Pliocene

In the western half, in the Cimmerian basin, the Pontic type of the fauna was further developed. The Pontic fauna became considerably impoverished in the subsequently somewhat less saline and warm Kuyalnits basin.

The fauna of the last of the Pliocene basins, in the area of the present Black Sea—the Chaudinsk Lake-Sea—differs greatly from that of the Kuyalnits one; according to Andrussov it is a derivative of the Pontic fauna, although it has a great similarity with that of the present Caspian Sea.

The history of the fauna of the Caspian part of the Pontic basin is different.

The deposition of productive sediments

Thicks layers of productive formation covered with deposits lie in Azerbaijan on the Pontic layers; these layers are found on other parts of the Caspian shores, being made up of sand, clayey sand and clay. Their fauna is very poor, consisting of either purely fresh-water or land molluscs. During the period of the accumulation of the productive deposits the body of water was considerably reduced in size and, in the opinion of V. Baturin (1931), it was limited to a southern basin with the waters of Volga, Samur, Kura, Uzboi

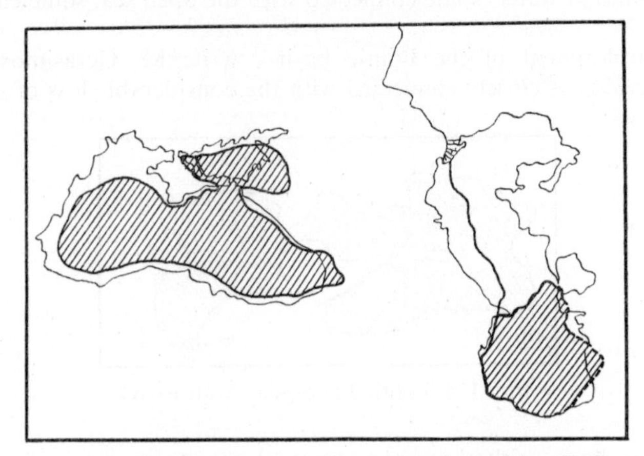

FIG. 175. Basins of Cimmerian era (Archangelsky, 1927), and of the productive zone era (Baturin, 1931).

(from the east) and other rivers flowing into it, and its water then became almost fresh (Fig. 175). The productive formation, apparently connected by its deposits with the river deltas, contains in its layers huge accumulations of petroleum, the origin of which may be due to vigorous delta growths, whereas the North Caucasian petroleum beds, as has been pointed out by A. Archangelsky (1927), belong to the deep-water environment of the Middle-Maeotic basin in the depths of the Chokraksky and Karagatsky Seas contaminated with hydrogen sulphide.

Akchagyl basin

The next deposits of Precaspian marine sediments (after the Pontic ones) were those of the Akchagyl basin, when the waters of the Caspian basin moved north on a wide front and, to a lesser degree, spread east and west (Fig. 176) as the result of the submersion of the Precaspian region.

The fauna of the Akchagyl basin, characterized by its considerable salinity, differs fairly sharply from that of the Pontic basin. It includes numerous species of Mactra, Cardium, calcareous sea-weed, Avicularia and other marine forms, which suggests that the salinity of the Akchagyl basin was quite high. No explanation has yet been put forward for the high salinity of the Akchagyl waters and the marine aspect of its fauna, in spite of the fact that the preceding basin had very small quantities of productive deposit and its waters were almost completely fresh. The Akchagyl basin must have received, from somewhere, both the main mass of the saline water filling it and the corresponding fauna, which had a clearly expressed Sarmatian aspect* (Andrussov, 1902). Although the existence of a link in the west between the Akchagyl and Kuyalnits basins has lately been established, the former could not have obtained its marine forms from the latter, which was

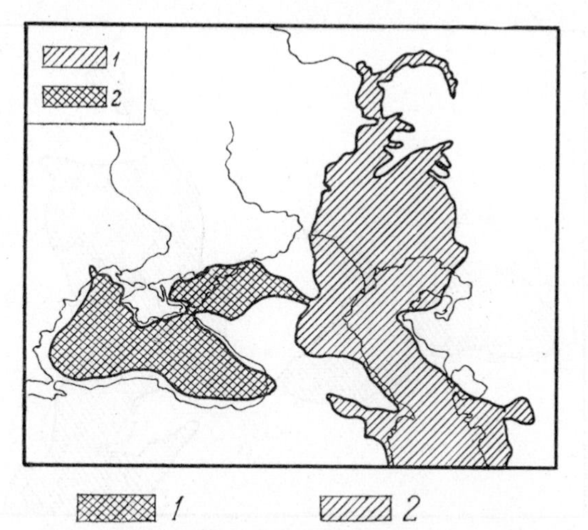

FIG. 176. Kuyalnits (*1*) and Akchagyl (*2*) basins (Archangelsky).

at that time a brackish-water basin of the Caspian or Pontic type, and itself could rather have obtained a part of its forms from the east, from the Akchagyl basin. A. Archangelsky (1934) admits only 'one single possible route for the fauna from the southeast, from Persia, perhaps from the region of the Persian Gulf'. The originally poor Akchagyl fauna became very rich in species at the middle of the existence of this basin. During its last phase the Akchagyl Sea was connected with the Black Sea region through the discharge of its waters to the west, south of Manych. At that time a certain number of Ackhagyl forms penetrated to the west. Later the Akchagyl Sea began to contract rapidly, its waters lost their salinity, and the rich Akchagyl fauna died out almost completely except for some gastropods—Cardidae. Many of the Dreissensiidae appeared simultaneously.

The Apsheron and Baku basins

The size of the Caspian basin became greatly reduced during the Apsheron period (Fig. 177). The Apsheron basin, and the Baku basin which followed it,

* V. Kolesnikov (1940), however, considers the similarity between the Akchagyl and Sarmatian faunas as purely extraneous. In his opinion this fauna has no connection with the south-Russian Miocene or Pliocene.

had a salinity similar to that of the present Caspian Sea. Their population, consisting of numerous species of Didacna, Adacna, Dreissensia, Neritina and Micromelania, was close to the present-day Caspian fauna. I. Gerasimov and K. Markov (1939) suppose that 'as a result of the loss of salinity of the Apsheron basin immigrants from the west, from the Black Sea (Kuyal'nik–Chauda) appeared in it. In the Baku basin era the flow of immigrants (from Chauda) had evidently increased still further. Forms of the Pontic fauna

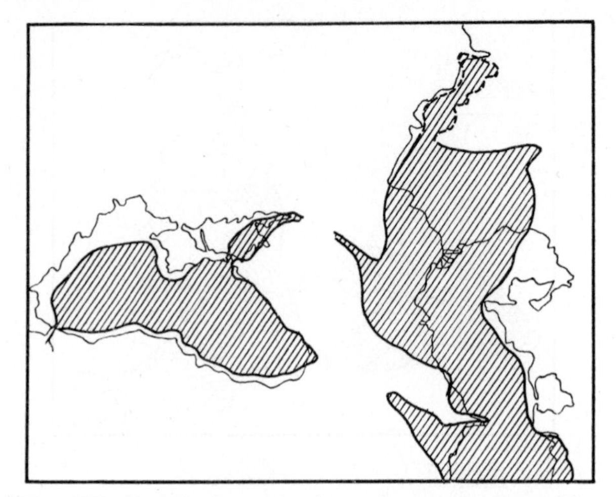

FIG. 177. Chaudinsk and Apsheron basins (Archangelsky and Kolesnikov).

which had evolved in the Black Sea began to immigrate into the Caspian Sea.'

The closed brackish Apsheron lake-sea obtained its fauna from three sources: (*1*) from Akchagyl (Clessinia, Apscheronia), (*2*) from some fresh-water source (Neritina, Melania, Melanopsis), and (*3*) in great quantity from the Euxine region of the Chauda basin, probably through its connection along the Manych depression (Dreissensia, Didacna, Monodacna). The modern Caspian fauna is the result of a further, but now independent, evolution of this fauna in the basin of the Caspian Sea.

History of the Tertiary fauna of the Caspian Sea

Reviewing the history of the Caspian Sea fauna during the Tertiary period, V. Bogachev (1932) lays stress on the numerous marked changes of fauna, which seem to break the genetic link of the fauna of one era with that of the subsequent one. He discerns such interruptions in the transition from the Sarmatian fauna to the Maeotic, from the latter to the Pontic, and from the Pontic to the Akchagyl. Bogachev explains these changes by assuming, in accordance with the views of E. Suess (1888), the existence of 'refuge' bodies of water ('caspians' as Suess called them) in which one or other fauna could survive

Bogachev (1932) thinks that for the Middle-Miocene fauna such a 'refuge' was preserved in Asia (in Turkestan) and from it the fauna penetrated first into the Maeotic basin and later into the Akchagyl. Other 'refuges' may have existed for the Sarmatian and Pontic faunas. Other investigators assume a repeated penetration of Mediterranean forms from the west, from the Mediterranean Sea. If one takes into account the fact, for example, that in the present-day Gulf of Taganrog there exist side by side the completely different Mediterranean and Caspian faunas which have occupied this body of water in turn during the post-Tertiary changes of salinity, the Suess conception of a 'refuge' becomes wholly realistic. *Table 141* sets out the history, described above, of the Black and Caspian Seas and their faunas.

Table 141

Middle Miocene	Middle Miocene basin of full salinity (Remains of Tethys)	
Upper Miocene	Brackish-water Sarmatian basin (to the east beyond the Aral Sea, to the west up to the middle Danube lowland)	
	Towards the end a great reduction in size, then again an enlargement and transition	
	Maeotic basin; semi-marine 'Euxine' conditions [A. Derzhavin (1928) thinks that the Black Sea was connected with the Sea of Marmora]	
Pliocene	Pontic basin, considerable loss of salinity of the Maeotic basin. 'Caspian' conditions with a lowered salinity	
	Towards the end the Black, Caspian and Aral Seas are separated from each other	
	Cimmerian basin	The basin of productive deposits.
	Kuyalnits basin	Akchagyl basin (was for a time connected with the Kuyalnits basin)
	Chaudin basin (was connected through the Bosphorus with the low-salinity Sea of Marmora, had no connection with the Mediterranean)	Apsheron basin (was temporarily connected with the Chaudin basin) Baku stage
	Ancient Euxine basin (Caspian type of fauna)	Ancient Caspian basin (with a temporary link through a flow into the Black Sea along the Kumo–Manych depression)
	A connection is established with the Mediterranean (Karangatsky Sea)	
Post-Tertiary Period	Novo–Euxine basin Contemporary phase	Post-glacial transgression. Contemporary basin

The Black Sea during the Quaternary Period

During the Quaternary Period the salinity changes of the Black Sea were caused, on the one hand, by the existence or the absence of a connection with the Mediterranean, on the other by the general climatic conditions of the glacial and post-glacial periods and, in the first place, by the inflow of river-waters, mainly from melting ice.

At the beginning of the Quaternary Period the Black Sea had a low salinity and was populated by a Pontic fauna differing but little from that of the Pontic basin; its boundaries, moreover, have hardly changed at all up to the present. Only along the Kumo–Manych depression is the Black Sea fauna found, in deposits lying far outside its present boundaries. However, the Black Sea salinity and its fauna underwent several substantial changes as time went on.

The so-called Ancient Euxine basin with a Caspian type of fauna was connected with the Sea of Marmora; the latter, however, had no link with the Aegean Sea and the Mediterranean and had the same Caspian fauna. After the formation of the Dardanelles, the Black Sea was filled with Mediterranean water and the Mediterranean fauna, while the Caspian fauna was pushed far into the corners of the sea, which had lost some of their salinity. Later the entry of the Mediterranean waters into the Black Sea was interrupted by new risings of the bottom, and the body of water again lost some of its salinity, its Mediterranean fauna died out, and it was occupied by Caspian fauna. The latest subsidences of the shores again caused an inflow of Mediterranean waters and the arrival of its fauna, while the Caspian autochthonous forms were pushed away into the river mouths and inlets. The salinity of the water column increased from 7 to 22‰ from the time when a connection between the Black Sea and the Mediterranean was established; at present, however, the salinity balance of the Black Sea is near the equilibrium point (S. P. Brujevitch, 1952). The alternations of the south-Russian basins during the Quaternary Period, according to A. Archangelsky (1932), are given in *Table 142*.

A. Archangelsky and N. Strahov (1938) suggest that the glaciation periods correspond to the low-salinity phases, and the interglacial periods to the phases of increasing salinity.

The Caspian Sea during the Quaternary Period

The history of the Caspian Sea in the Quaternary Period begins in the Baku basin with a fauna similar in its general features to the present one. This fauna passes over into the subsequent post-Baku basins. Adacna, Monodacna and Dreissensia are the most characteristic among the molluscs. The fluctuations of salinity during the Ice Age and post-glacial period are mainly reflected in a greater or smaller admixture of brackish- and fresh-water forms (Neritina, Corbicula, Clessinia, Micromelania, Paludina, Unio, Valvata, Anodonta and others). In the Caspian Sea, however, salinity did not reach the high level of the Karangat basin during its high-salinity periods, but instead its waters became more fresh than those of the Black Sea basin during the periods of decreasing salinity. As a result the marked changes of fauna characteristic of the Black Sea are absent in the Quaternary history of the Caspian Sea.

The main difficulty in the Quaternary history of the Caspian Sea is the

Table 142

Basin	Salinity	Rise or subsidence of littoral	Conformity with the Ice Age phases (Gerasimov and Markov, 1939)
Chaudin lake-sea	Greatly lowered	Rise	
Ancient Euxine lake-sea	Greatly lowered		Mindel glaciation
Uzunlar basin (connected with Mediterranean)	Low	Subsidence	Mindel–Riss interglacial era
Karangat Sea (by the end the link with the Mediterranean is broken)	Saline		Riss–Würm interglacial era. Riss glaciation
Novo–Euxine lake-sea	Semi-fresh	Rise	Würm glaciation
Ancient Black Sea basin (new connection with the Mediterranean)	Slightly saline	Subsidence	
Contemporary Black Sea	Saline		

synchronization of its separate phases with the general climatic changes and the explanation of the occurrence of changes of sea-level.

The Baku basin covered a larger area than the present Caspian Sea, and large parts of the northern Precaspian lowland were covered with its waters. Evidently at that time there was an outflow to the west into the Ancient Euxine basin. The succeeding Khazara basin was less saline but was of the same size. As time went on the size of the basin gradually decreased, its level fell and its salinity increased somewhat. I. Gerasimov and K. Markov (1939) consider that 'there are no indications of any considerable change in the salinity conditions of the Caspian Sea during the Quaternary Period'. However it is difficult to agree with their opinion. The historical period covered by them appears as *Table 143*.

The Kumo–Manych depression several times served as a channel linking the two seas and making possible either one-way or two-way penetration of the fauna. The two above-mentioned authors provide the following scheme:

1. Pontic	The Manych region is submerged by the waters of the Pontic Sea
2. Akchagyl	Ingression of the Akchagyl waters. Migration of fauna from the east
3. Kuyalnits–Chauda Apsheron–Baku period	Ingression of Chauda water Migration of fauna from the west

Table 143

Era	Basin	Salinity	Level	Connection with Black Sea	Connection with Turan basin	Comparison
Baku	Baku	Average	Average, more or less stable	Linked with Ancient Euxine basin	Outflow of fresh water	Ice Age
Lower Caspian	Khazar	Very low	Fluctuating, rise and fall	Interrupted	Outflow ceased	
Upper Caspian	Khvalynsk	Slight salinity	Rise	Connected with Novo–Euxine basin	Outflow along Uzboi	
Con-temporary	Con-temporary			Interruption	Outflow stopped	Post-glacial period

4. Ancient Euxine period, Lower Caspian era (Khazar basin)	Sea strait. Free exchange of faunas
5. Upper Euxine period, Upper Caspian era (Khvalynsk basin)	Sea strait. Probable migration of fauna from the east
6. Contemporary era	Drying up. Erosion by river waters

History of the Aral Sea

Contrary to the earlier view regarding the expansion of the Sea during the greatest Caspian transgression, in one of the interglacial eras (Khvalynsk era) through the Uzboi into the Sarakamysh hollow and the Aral Sea, A. Archangelsky considers (1915) that the body of water occupying this area had no connection with the Caspian Sea and was a huge completely fresh-water lake with an outflow through the Uzboi (thick deposits of clay and sand with Dreissensia, Limnaea, Unio and others). Later on this lake became much smaller in size, and subsequently it was again filled with water as a result of the climate becoming damper; a system of brackish lakes was formed in the depressions of the Sarakamysh hollow and along the Uzboi, and at this time *Cardium edule* penetrated into the Aral Sea. With the transition to the present era the climate again became dry and the Aral Sea acquired its present outline.

A. Behning (1938) discovered a whole series of forms of the Caspian fauna in the lakes of the old bed of the Uzboi (Yaskhan, Karatogelek, Topiatan). Besides several fish, among which the later Mediterranean immigrant *Atherina mochon pontica caspia* is of particular importance, he listed for those bodies of water the molluscs *Dreissensia polymorpha*, *Theodoxus pallasi*, *Th. danubialis*, the crustaceans *Dikerogammarus haemobaphes*, *Pontogammarus crassus*, *Corophium curvispinum* and the little fish *Proterorhinus marmoratus*. Behning thinks that the Caspian transgression reached Lake Yaskhan and there left all these relicts.

Archangelsky's opinion, that there was no direct link between the Caspian and Aral Seas, and his assumption of a complete loss of salinity by the latter at the beginning of the Quaternary era, does not explain its genetic link with the Caspian, which is indubitable in spite of all the poverty of its fauna. Taking this into consideration V. Beklemishev (1922) relates the penetration of the Caspian elements into the Aral Sea to the Maeotic period, assuming, as did L. Berg (1908), the possibility of the survival of the most euryhaline Caspian forms in the Aral Sea in the post-Tertiary period. C. Grimm (1877) gave a different explanation for the impoverishment of the Aral fauna: he thought that the salinity of the Aral Sea had at one time increased greatly, causing the extinction of most forms of the Caspian fauna.

Differences in the history of the southern seas

Thus each of our four southern seas had a separate history in the late Tertiary and Quaternary Periods. The Black Sea underwent the greatest fluctuations in temperature, salinity and fauna and the smallest in its water-level. The Caspian Sea underwent much greater fluctuations in its level, but its salinity changes were much less.

The simplest history is that of the Aral Sea, which was only formed in the middle or second half of the Quaternary Period.

In general (I. Gerasimov and K. Markov, 1939) the history of these seas can be presented in the form of *Table 144*.

Table 144

Black Sea	Caspian Sea	Aral Sea	Comparison with glaciation phases
Freshened Chaudin basin	Brackish Baku basin	Aral–Sarakamysh alluvium plain	
Freshened Ancient Euxine basin	Freshened Khazar basin		Riss glaciation
Brackish Uzunlar basin. Saline Karangat Sea (connected with Mediterranean)		Formation of Aral Sea	Tirrene period
Slightly brackish Novo–Euxine basin	Brackish water Khavalyn basin	Outflow of part of Amu-Darya waters (through Uzboi)	Würm glaciation
Brackish Ancient Black Sea (connected with Mediterranean)	Gradual lowering of its level	Drying up of Uzboi	Monastyr period

As one moves eastward the waters of the Black, Caspian and Aral Seas undergo a lowering of their saline composition relative to that of the ocean (*Table 145*).

Table 145. Comparative saline composition of waters of ocean and Black, Caspian and Aral Seas, expressed in percentages of the total (L. Berg from L. Blinov)

Salt components	Ocean	Black Sea	Caspian Sea	Aral Sea
$CaSO_4$	3·94	2·58	6·92	14·98
$MgSO_4$	6·40	7·11	23·56	25·87
KCL	1·69	2·99	1·21	2·05
NaCl	78·32	79·72	62·15	56·07
$MgCl_2$ $MgBr_2$	9·44	9·07	4·54	0·82
$CaCO_3$ CO_2	0·21	1·59	1·24	0·21
Total salinity	34·30	18·60	12·86	10·61

The increase of sulphates from 10·34 to 40·85 per cent and the decrease of chlorides from 89·45 to 58·94 per cent are the most characteristic features of these changes. The change of the salt content of the water of the south-Russian seas is not a simple derivative of the river discharge, although it is controlled by it. Whereas the saline composition of the Caspian Sea salt content can be considered as the 'chemical legacy' of the ocean, exposed for some time to the influence of river discharge and subjected to a complex conversion, the Aral Sea water is by origin metamorphized water of the coastal drainage. This can be shown by a comparison of the salt composition of the water of the Caspian Sea and that of the Volga, in percentages (*Table 146*) (S. Brujevitch, 1937, 1941).

Table 146

Salts	Ocean	Caspian Sea	Volga, off Astrakhan
Na	30·593	24·82	6·67 (Na + K)
K	1·106	0·66	
Ca	1·197	2·70	23·34
Mg	3·725	5·70	4·47
Cl	55·292	41·73	5·46
Br	0·188	0·06	
SO_4	7·692	23·49	25·63
CO_3	0·207	0·84	34·43

This fact comes out even more clearly in a comparison of the salt composition of the Aral Sea water with the average ionic discharge over many years of the rivers Amu-Darya and Syr-Darya (*Table 147*) (O. Alekin, 1947).

Table 147

River	Ca^{2+}	in%	Mg^{2+}	in%	$Na^{+}+K^{+}$	in%
Amu-Darya	83·1	17·6	11·12	2·4	43·4	9·2
Syr-Darya	87·6	16·1	20·6	3·8	43·8	8·0

River	HCO_3^-	in%	SO_4^{2}	in%	Cl^-	in%	Sum of ions
Amu-Darya	153·5	32·6	104·9	22·3	74·1	15·7	470·8
Syr-Darya	186·1	35·1	164·4	30·2	40·3	7·4	543·8

III. SOME PECULIARITIES OF THE DEVELOPMENT OF FAUNA AND FLORA

General features

The palaeogeographic changes discussed above in the seas which covered the southern part of Europe and Asia during the Tertiary and Quaternary Periods influenced their fauna in a radical way, primarily through loss of salinity which was at times very considerable.

The genetic heterogeneity of the fauna of our southern seas is the result of their history.

Relict community

The so-called ancient autochthonous community—the originally marine Tertiary fauna elaborated by the fresher-water phases—may perhaps have had a variety of origins. The marine fauna had several opportunities of breaking into the bodies of water which occupied the area of the Black and Caspian Seas. Most characteristic of the Caspian autochthonous fauna are the families and genera of the Porifera Mecznikowiidae, the hydroids Cordylophora, the jelly-fish Caspionema and Ostroumovia, the molluscs Cardiidae (Adacna, Monodacna, Didacna), Dreissensiidae, Hydrobiidae (Micromelania, Caspia, Clessiniola, Hydrobia, Theodoxus), the polychaetes Hypania, Hypaniola, Parhypania, the crustaceans Pontogammarus, Corophium, Gmelina, Amathillina, Pseudocuma, Mesomysis, Paramysis, Metamysis, Astacus, the bryozoans Victorella, the fish Acipenseridae,* Caspialosa, Clupeonella and Gobiidae. This autochthonous community in the main evolved from the marine fauna of the Tethys, which had spread its relicts throughout the brackish and fresh bodies of water of southeastern Europe and central Asia (including the Baikal and Okhrida lakes, the fauna of which is akin to that of the Caspian Sea). This autochthonous community, dominant in the Caspian Sea, is concentrated in the least saline parts of the more saline Black–Azov Sea basin in the firths, river-mouths and the eastern part of the Gulf of Taganrog, while the open parts of the Black and Azov Seas are

* The weight of evidence, however, suggests the derivation of Acipenseridae from fresh water.

populated by Mediterranean fauna which penetrated into it after breaking through the Dardanelles.

Table 148, drawn from the data of A. Derzhavin (1925), F. Mordukhai-Boltovskoy (1939) and M. Bacesko (1940), is a good illustration of this.

Table 148

	Order				
	Mysidacea	Cumacea	Amphipoda	Total	Percentage
Black Sea:					
Mediterranean	8	6	41	55	62·5
Caspian	9	1	19	28	31·8
Endemic	5	—	—	5	5·7
Total	21	7	60	88	100
Azov Sea:					
Mediterranean	2	1	13	16	33·3
Caspian	6	8	15	29	60·4
Endemic	2	—	1	3	6·3
Total	10	9	29	48	100
Lower Volga:					
Mediterranean	—	—	2	2	5·7
Caspian	9	10	14	33	94·3
Endemic	—	—	—	—	—
Total	9	10	16	35	100

When investigating the fauna of the Dnieper delta, F. Mordukhai-Boltovskoy (1948) found that on the sands and clayey-sand bottoms of the arms of the delta 'the fauna has on the whole a clearly expressed Caspian character. Fresh-water species are generally of secondary importance, and in the main arms, where there is a bottom of pure sand . . . the predominance of the Caspian crustaceans, especially the mysids, becomes even more evident. At some stations Caspian species were found exclusively.' On rock bottoms the Dreissensia biomass may amount to 3·6 kg/m^3, an amount which has not been found even in the Caspian Sea (see below). On the contrary, in the macrophyte growths of the littoral zone and in the lakes of the delta typical fresh-water fauna is markedly predominant, while the Caspian elements are either secondary or absent. Subsequently more light has been thrown on this phenomenon through research carried out by Yu. Markovsky (1953–55).

The fauna of the deltas of the Dnieper and Don are very similar: in both cases 'the significance of the Caspian fauna decreases with a fall in the speed of the current and with the transition to bodies of water of the lake type'.

Distribution of relicts in the Azov and Caspian basins

Latterly J. Birstein (1946) and F. Mordukhai-Boltovskoy (1946, 1960) have approached from a new standpoint the problem of the time of penetration into the Azov–Black Sea basin of the forms of the Caspian fauna living there at present.

The Azov–Black Sea basin is almost free of the endemic forms of the Caspian fauna (except for *Moerisia maeotica* (Ostroumovia) among the coelenterata, *Corophium maeoticum*, *Hemimysis serrata*, *Astacus colchicus*, *Gammarus shablensis*, *Niphargoides intermedius*, *Stenogammarus compresso-similis* among the crustaceans, Percarina among the fishes and *Clupenella abrau* and *Monodacna colorata* and *M. pontica* among the molluscs); this is an indication, contrary to widespread opinion, of a very recent penetration of Caspian fauna into the Sea of Azov followed by its settlement in the Black Sea. In the opinion of these workers, this penetration through the Manych Strait should be related to the post-glacial period. P. Dvoichenko (1925), however, had earlier expressed the same point of view for the whole of the Caspian fauna of the Azov–Black Sea basin (migration during the Novo–Euxine period).

Mordukhai-Boltovskoy relates this migration to the period of the Khvalynsk transgression. Both authors accept the possibility of the mass extinction of Pontic fauna in the Azov–Black Sea basin during the period of greatly increased salinity in the Karangat era.

Taking issue with the two above-mentioned authorities, A. Derzhavin (1951) has noted that 95 species and 50 genera of Ponto–Caspian autochthonous forms live in the lower reaches of rivers and in inlets in the northwest part of the Black Sea (from the Danube to the Dnieper), correspondingly 54 species and 32 genera live in the rivers and inlets of the Sea of Azov, and 64 species (34 genera) in the northern Caspian river basins. Moreover, a large number of autochthonous relict Pontic forms absent from the Volga are found in the rivers and inlets of the Black and Azov Seas. Derzhavin reckons among such forms five genera and seventeen species of fish, six genera and fourteen species of molluscs, two genera and three species of mysids, one genus and ten species of amphipods and one species of decapods. According to Derzhavin in all 46 species (15 genera) absent from the basin of the river Volga, and 43 species (18 genera) absent from the Sea of of Azov live in the river basins of the northwest part of the Black Sea. Moreover, Derzhavin points out the fact that these forms thrive in fresh water and their colonization of saline water would inevitably have been difficult. If the colonization of the Caspian fauna had proceeded through the Sea of Azov and in a comparatively recent period, the picture would have been just the opposite.

Thus, without denying that an exchange of fauna took place in a recent geological period between the Black and Caspian Seas, Derzhavin considers that an autochthonous fauna of the Pontic type existed in the Black Sea in the pre-Khvalyn period. V. Pauli (1957) supports Derzhavin's opinion on the basis of his examination of the distribution of the mysids of the Black Sea and the Sea of Azov. Seven species of mysids live in the Black Sea and only five in the Sea of Azov. Yu. Markovsky (1953), who considers the 'Caspian' fauna in the inlets of the northwest part of the Black Sea to be a legacy of the Pontic period, is of the same opinion. The facts quoted by Mordukhai-Boltovskoy himself (1958) to some extent contradict his own opinion on the

Khvalyn age of the 'Caspian' fauna in the Azov–Black Sea basin. 'The comparative richness of the Caspian fauna in the northern approaches to the Black Sea', he writes, 'is apparent not only in its high biomass, but also in the considerably greater number of its species (as compared with the Sea of Azov basin—L.Z.). Whereas we used to reckon 49 species of (Caspian—L.Z.) invertebrates for the river Don, and only 23 for the River Kuban, for the rivers Dnieper and Bug we have no less than 69 (Markovsky), and 64 for the Danube.'

A very curious phenomenon comes to light in a comparison of the distribution of the autochthonous relict community in the Azov and Caspian Seas (V. Beklemishev, 1922; later developed by J. Birstein, 1946, F. Mordukhai-Boltovskoy, 1953 and Yu. Markovksy, 1953–56). In the Sea of Azov basin the relicts are in the main concentrated in the area of the river mouths in fresh water. In the Caspian Sea, however, most of them live in the saline waters of the Sea itself.

Mordukhai-Boltovskoy points out, for example, that the mollusc *Caspia gmelini*, which he found in the delta of the Don, in the Caspian lives only in the Sea itself. The Don delta is in fact the main place where the relicts in the Sea of Azov accumulate; some of them are found there in large numbers (*Mesomysis kowalewskyi* up to a few g/m², Hypania and Hypaniola at times up to 10 g/m², and large quantities of Monodacna and Dreissensia). Only six or seven species of these relicts are found in the Sea of Azov itself, while in the Gulf of Taganrog their number rises to 25 forms in the less saline parts (counting not only the peracarids, but also the molluscs, polychaetes and coelenterates) *Table 149*).

Table 149. Distribution of autochthonous relict forms in the Sea of Azov and the River Don

	Open parts of Sea of Azov	Middle part of Gulf of Taganrog	Estuary (part) of Don	Lower Don	Don upper course	Voronez river
Total number of relict forms	7	About 12	25	46	9	3
As percentage of total fauna	14·3	24·5	51·0	93·9	16·3	6·1
S‰	11	5–7	0–2	Fresh water		

The fact that the main mass of the relicts is adapted to the Don delta is particularly interesting, since the pre-delta zone of the Gulf of Taganrog is abundantly populated by fresh-water forms, which are often accumulated there in very considerable numbers. Thus the Caspian relicts in the basin of the Sea of Azov cannot endure a rise of salinity as well as the fresh-water forms; in other words they are more 'fresh water' than the fresh-water organisms themselves.

It has been shown, by the research done in the lower reaches of the rivers and in the inlets of the northwestern part of the Black Sea by Markovsky and some Bulgarian investigators, that in this area the aspect of the 'Caspian' Sea fauna is even more a 'fresh water' one than it is in the Sea of Azov.

The same fauna, or fauna very nearly the same from a taxonomic standpoint, exists in the Caspian Sea at a much higher salinity (up to 12 or 13‰). Some species, which in the conditions of the Caspian Sea must be considered comparatively stenohaline and avoiding fresh water, enter the rivers in the Azov–Black Sea basin (*Table 150*). Among such forms the following may be mentioned: *Pandorites podoceroides*, *Pontogammarus maeoticus*, *Caspia gmelini*, *Clesissiola variabilis* (Dnieper inlet), *Dreissensia rostriformis* (Bug inlet) and others. M. Bacesko (1948) discovered the polychaete *Manayunkis caspia*, which lives in saline water in the Caspian Sea, in the Danube. Lateolabrax has a fresh-water habitat in the Bug inlet and a marine one in the Caspian Sea. Birstein pointed out that the Azov *Monodacna colorata* and *Dreissensia polymorpha* perish very rapidly in the Azov and Caspian waters at a salinity of 5‰ (by chlorine).

The following relicts, among others, live in the Don; two species of coelenterates, two bivalves and one gastropod mollusc, two polychaetes, one species of leech and 38 species of higher crustaceans. Only three species of relict forms living in the Sea of Azov are absent from the Don delta.

Among relicts, apart from Malacostraca, only one polychaete was encountered in the Volga and Ural rivers. In addition, all the relict forms live in the open parts of the Sea.

The most natural explanation of this remarkable difference in the distribution of the autochthonous fauna in two seas situated side by side seems to lie in the difference of their historical past and their salinity, and finally in the influence on the autochthonous fauna of a stronger rival—the Mediterranean fauna. A stronger fauna displaces the weaker one from all regions where it can live itself. This proposition can only have a most general character. Some of the forms of Caspian fauna in other bodies of water are very powerful competitors of the local fauna, as are, for example, the Caspian immigrants into the Baltic Sea, and still more, into fresh water. According to Mordukhai-Boltovskoy (1960) some Caspian forms attain greater numbers and biomass in the Black and Azov Seas than in the Caspian Sea. Thus, for example, in the Azov–Black Sea basin *Dreissensia polymorpha* yields a biomass of up to 4·7

Table 150. Distribution of autochthonous relict forms in the Caspian Sea, Volga and Ural

	Throughout Caspian Sea	Northern Caspian	Volga Delta	Middle Volga	Upper Volga
Total number of relict higher crustaceans	98	62	35	9	4
			38·8%	9·2%	4·0%
			Ural Delta	Up to Libshchensk	Up to Uralsk
	(100%)	(63·3%)	13	8	2
			13·3%	8·2%	2·0%
S‰	Up to 13	<10		Fresh water	

kg/m² with 92,000 specimens, *Pontogammarus maeoticus*—1·38 kg/m² with 90,000 specimens, *Hypania invalida*—5,500 and 15·4 g/m², *Monodacna colorata*—9,000 and 1·35 kg/m², *Corophium maeoticum*—39,780 and 158·7 g/m², and so on. It is most characteristic that in relation to salinity the autochthonous and Mediterranean forms are distinct from each other; this is clearly seen even in the case of the mysids (Fig. 178).

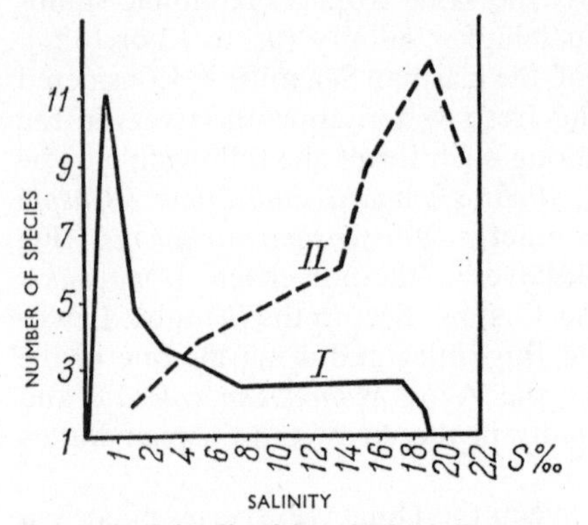

FIG. 178. Distribution of Black Sea mysids according to salinity: *I* Relicts (endemic forms); and *II* Mediterranean forms (Bacesko).

Penetration of the relict community into fresh water

The autochthonous relict community penetrated into fresh water during the phases of greatest loss of salinity and the subsequent increase of salinity. The migration into fresh water was easiest for the crustaceans and fishes and for some individual species of coelenterates, molluscs, bryozoans and polychaetes. Like the fresh waters of the Arctic basin those of the basins of our southern seas give shelter to an abundant relict fauna (*Table 150*).

Fresh-water immigrants

The low salinity of the bodies of water situated where the Black and Caspian Seas now lie opened them to immigrants from fresh water. In this case too, fish yield the greatest number of species, mainly the cyprinoid and Percidae families, and, to a lesser extent, next come the lower crustaceans, molluscs, oligochaetes and insect larvae (Chironomidae).

The Arctic community

The Arctic relict (or rather pseudo-relict) community which penetrated into the south-Russian bodies of water from the north in the post-glacial period, consisting mainly of crustaceans, is most original. It includes also some fish, seal and, possibly, the polychaete Manayunkia. The Arctic immigrants are very scarce in the Black Sea and are absent from the Aral Sea.

The Mediterranean community

The Mediterranean flora and fauna which filled the Black and Azov Seas penetrated as far as the Aral Sea, although the connection between the Black and Caspian Seas through the Kuma–Manych system and farther east through the Uzboi was poor. Some thousands of years ago the mollusc *Cardium edule* penetrated in this manner into the Aral Sea and Lake Charkhal, the fish Atherina and the sea-weed *Zostera nana* (the latter also into the Aral Sea) also migrated there at some unknown time. In recent decades the eastward penetration of Mediterranean immigrants has continued, either with the passive participation of man (Rhizosolenia, Mytilaster and two species of shrimps Leander and two species of Balanus), or through measures being taken for acclimatization (two species of the grey mullet Mugil, the polychaete Nereis and the mollusc Syndesmya and some others). This enormous activity of some forms of Mediterranean fauna, and their indubitable advantages over the Caspian and Aral forms in the struggle for existence, is a clear indication of the wide possibilities of acclimatization farther east of the euryhaline Mediterranean fauna, inhabiting the Black Sea and the Sea of Azov. The migration of the two brackish-water forms—the medusa Blackfordia and the crab *Rithropanopeus harrisi tridentatus*—from the northwestern part of the Atlantic Ocean to the Caspian Sea is also most curious.

Impoverishment of the Mediterranean fauna

For the reasons enumerated above the qualitative differentiation of the Mediterranean fauna decreases with its movement to the east (Fig. 179).

The Mediterranean flora and fauna become four times poorer by the time they reach the Black Sea, while in the Sea of Azov only 2·5 per cent remains.

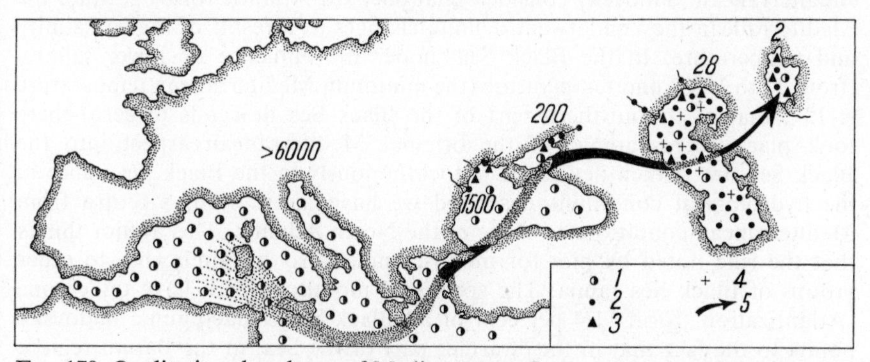

FIG. 179. Qualitative abundance of Mediterranean flora and fauna and its impoverishment with its movement eastward. Total number of animal species is denoted by the numerals (Zenkevitch). *1* Mediterranean fauna; *2* Caspian fauna; *3* Freshwater fauna; *4* Arctic immigrants; *5* Direction of migration.

The qualitative impoverishment in the Black Sea affects primarily the most stenohaline part of the population—Radiolaria, Siphonophora, Ctenophora, corals, many groups of crustaceans and especially decapods, all the molluscs and especially cephalopods and gastropods, the echinoderms, the tunicates and fish.

In the Sea of Azov, of the 200* Mediterranean coelenterates only three species are found, of the 1,457 species of molluscs only 12, of the 51 species of crabs only one, of the 300 species of pelagic copepods only 8, and so on.

Another characteristic factor in the qualitative impoverishment of the

* The number of species of Mediterranean animals, according to Gr. Antipa (1941).

Black Sea fauna is the absence of deeper-water fauna or a fauna connected in its development with great depths (below 125 to 150 m).

The 'Atlantization' of the Mediterranean fauna in the Black Sea

The characteristic differences between the fauna of the Black and Azov Seas and that of the Mediterranean had already been observed by the first investigators of the fauna of our southern seas. K. Kessler (1860) pointed out that fish in the Black Sea are often smaller than in the Mediterranean, 'which is the result, probably, of lower temperature and less salinity'. This was also noted by H. Ratke as early as 1837. V. Sovinsky too dwelt on this phenomena (1902). S. Zernov (1913) pointed to the fact that the Mediterranean crab *Carcinus maenas* is considerably smaller in size than those in the Black Sea and off the shores of Great Britain. Zernov expressed the opinion that 'once in the Mediterranean the crab became smaller, and when passing into the colder water of the Black Sea it grew again in size'.

A. Sadovsky (1934) approached this problem on a wider front. He established for 14 species of Black Sea molluscs (including sea mussel, oysters, Patella, Syndesmya and others) a closer relationship in the shell structure (size, shape, thickness, sculpturing, colouring) with Atlantic species than with Mediterranean. Sadovsky considers that once the Atlantic forms got into the Mediterranean they underwent definite changes as a result of higher salinity and temperature. In the Black Sea, under the influence of lower salinity (from 37 to 18‰) and temperature (the minimum Mediterranean temperature is 13°; that of the northern part of the Black Sea descends to zero) there took place a 'reshaping' of the original Mediterranean aspect into the Black Sea one, which developed autochthonously in the Black Sea, since in the hydrological conditions described we have, as it were, a return from Mediterranean conditions to those of the North Atlantic. This author thinks that the rule noted by him for molluscs must also be applicable to other groups of Black Sea fauna. The species of molluscs which have undergone 'Atlantization' form 11·4 per cent of all Black Sea malacofauna. Sadovsky points to the fact that in the 'warmer part of the Sea, in the Batum region, one observes a greater similarity between some of the molluscs and the Mediterranean ones than one sees in the northern part of the Sea'. Finally, Sadovsky observes another interesting phenomenon in the case of Patella and Mytilus: when young they resemble the Mediterranean forms more closely, in maturity this resemblance is lost.

The affinity between the Black Sea fauna and that of the northern parts of the Atlantic Ocean lies first in the selection of genera and species, and secondly in the above-mentioned morphological resemblance between the Black Sea and the Atlantic Ocean forms. As regards the former feature of resemblance, Sovinsky says that in the Black Sea a selection was made of the northern forms which had remained there since the Ice Age, and which had died out or were poorly represented in the Mediterranean. Thus the Black Sea fauna is a selection of cold-water relict species. To what extent can the morphological peculiarities mentioned above also be explained by their relict character, i.e. did these forms get into the Black Sea as 'northern' forms during the Ice Age, as suggested by Sadovsky, or did they go through the process of 'Atlantization' in the Black Sea for a second time under the effect of more stringent conditions of life? It is quite evident that both possibilities must be considered. If the appearance of some characteristics can be easily explained by the effect of Black Sea climatic conditions (size of the body, thickness of the shell), others are easier to understand from the standpoint of their relict origin (shape of the shell, sculpturing).

Among the group variations through which different Black Sea species may have gone besides the change of size, one may note, for example, the solidity of the mollusc shells. G. Afanas'ev has shown (1938) that the Black Sea molluscs have a lighter shell than those of the fully saline seas. The ratio of

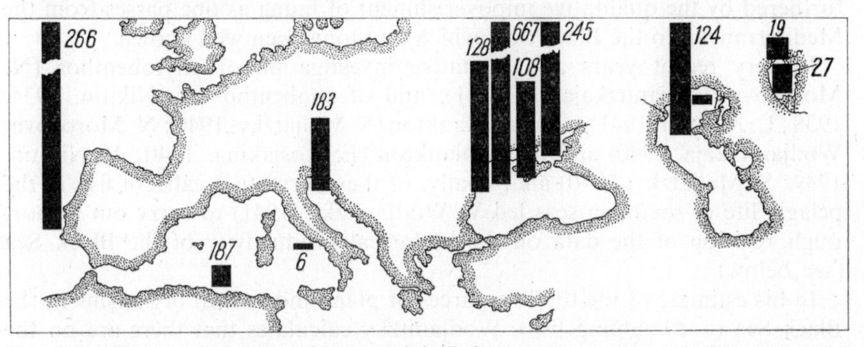

FIG. 180. Changes in benthos biomass (g/m²) from west to east along the system of southern bodies of water (Zenkevitch, 1947).

the weight of the shells to that of the body for the Black Sea bivalves varies from 0·95 to 4·5 per cent (average 1·8 per cent), while for molluscs of fully saline seas it varies from 1·25 to 10·8 per cent (average 3·5 per cent).

Changes of biomass from west to east

The regular change in the intensity of the processes of biological productivity from west to east is closely linked with the hydrological and hydrochemical conditions of the southern European seas. A marked decrease of benthos biomass, from a few hundred g/m² to some tens, is observed as we pass from the Atlantic Ocean to the Mediterranean Sea through the Straits of Gibraltar; it reaches its minimum in the eastern part of the Mediterranean Sea (a few g/m²). Only in some places off the coast and at the mouths of rivers does the biomass increase. In the Sea of Marmora the biomass is already greater; it reaches fairly high indices in the Black Sea (100 to 200 g/m² and more). In the Sea of Azov the processes of biological production reach their maximum. Farther east a decrease of productive capacities is again observed, less significant in the Caspian Sea and more marked in the Aral Sea (Fig. 180).

The Mediterranean Sea can be cited as an example of the least biologically productive sea in the world; the Sea of Azov, on the contrary, is the most productive.

The decrease of biomass in the Mediterranean Sea and its subsequent increase in the Black and Azov Seas must be explained first by the changes in the quantity of nutrient salts in the zone of photosynthesis. The subsequent decrease in the Caspian and especially in the Aral Sea should be accounted for by the qualitative changes in the flora and fauna composition and some peculiarities of the hydrological conditions in these seas.

As a result of the absence until very recently of any data on the quantitative distribution of life in the Black Sea, owing to the hydrogen sulphide contamination of its depths and the shortage of information on its very rich pelagic life, and owing to the proximity of the Sea of Azov which is exceptionally abundant in life, a false picture of the poverty of life in the Black Sea was gradually built up, beginning with Ratke and Nordmann. This was furthered by the qualitative impoverishment of fauna as one passes from the Mediterranean to the Black Sea, which had long been well known.

In very recent years a quantitative investigation of phytobenthos (N. Morozova-Wodjanitzkaja, 1936–41), and of zoobenthos (V. Nikitin, 1934, 1938; L. Arnoldi, 1941), of phytoplankton (S. Maljatzky, 1940; N. Morozova-Wodjanitzkaja, 1940) and of zooplankton (E. Kosjakina, 1940; V. Nikitin, 1939; S. Maljatzky, 1940) and, finally, of the enormous wealth of fish in the pelagic life of the open seas led V. Wodjanitzky (1941) to carry out a thorough revision of the data on the biological productivity of the Black Sea (see below).

In his estimate of the total resources of plant and animal organisms in the Black Sea (not counting fish), Wodjanitzky calculates that there are on the average about 150 g of organisms per 1 m^2 of sea surface, i.e. approximately the same as in the Barents Sea. The productivity of the Black Sea, however, must be several times higher than that of the Barents Sea owing to its much higher temperature.

Thus as regards its biological productivity the Black Sea should almost occupy the second place in the system of the Mediterranean–Black–Azov–Caspian and Aral Seas.

Fish migrations

This gradual increase of biological productivity from west to east in the Mediterranean–Sea of Azov system has produced a peculiar pattern of spawning and feeding migrations of the fish population; it seems, as it were, to consist of three main links, besides a series of secondary ones. This pattern of migration was brought into being largely through the effect of the temperature–salinity range within the limits of the whole basin—in summer time the temperature of the upper layers of water remains almost the same throughout the whole basin, but in the winter the amplitude of its fluctuations is more than 15°; moreover the eastern part of the basin remains covered by ice for a long time.

The range of salinity, which is maintained naturally throughout the whole year, is even more marked: from 37 to 38‰ in the Mediterranean Sea to 9 to 10‰ in the Sea of Azov.

All these spawning–feeding migrations have a single general direction—eastward for feeding, westward for spawning (Fig. 181). It is possible to distinguish among them two large groups, connected with the thermopathy and halopathy of the corresponding race of fish. Some fish move between zones of small salinity range, keeping always within zones of similar salinities (stenohaline) and during their whole existence living within the boundaries of one body of water; others can survive during their travels considerable changes of salinity (euryhaline) and can pass from one body of water to another. The same can be said about temperature conditions—some can only survive limited changes of temperature during the year (stenothermic); others can live through considerable temperature fluctuations (eurythermic). This is illustrated by the diagram in Fig. 182.

It is remarkable that Sarda, which populates the eastern part of the Mediterranean, moves in the summer to the Black Sea for feeding and spawning.

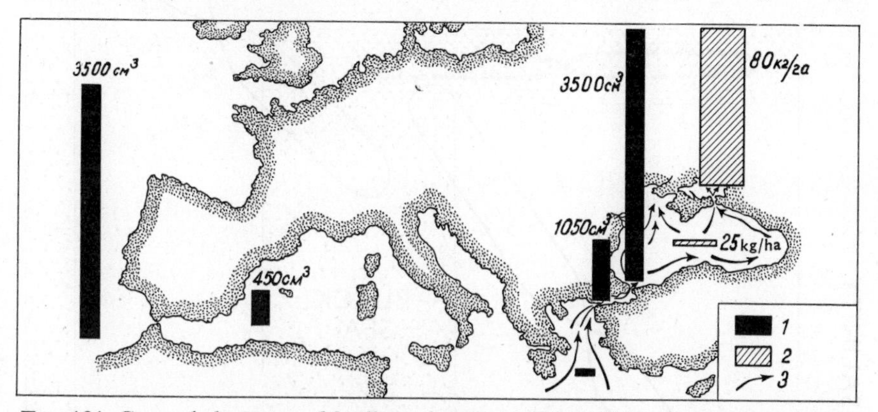

FIG. 181. General character of feeding migrations of fish (*3*) in eastern part of Mediterranean, Black and Azov Seas, contrasted with abundance of plankton (*1*) (see explanation in text) and with commercial productivity (*2*) (kg/ha) (Zenkevitch, 1947).

This is possibly evidence that the past history of the eastern Mediterranean shoal of Sarda was somewhat exceptional—maybe that its fate was linked during some periods of the Quaternary Period with life in bodies of water of low salinity. A series of most interesting regularities was established by A. Svetovidov (1943, 1948, 1957) in his comparison of the taxonomic composition, distribution, biology and size of fish in the Azov–Black Sea and Caspian basins. First of all, Caspian pelagic fish are larger than those in the Black and Azov Seas. *Caspiolosa brashnikovi*, with a length of 20 to 35 cm (*C. br. brashnikovi*) in the Caspian Sea and 16 to 20 cm (*C. br. maeotica*) in the Black Sea, can be taken as an example. The longest specimens of these two forms of herrings ever found were 49 and 31 cm; *C. caspia caspia* is usually 18 to 22 cm long, its greatest length being 28 cm, while *C. caspia tanaica* is 14 to 16 cm long, with a maximum length of 20 cm. This holds true for all the members of the Caspialosa and Clupeonella genera. The same was observed with grey mullet—the largest size of the Black Sea *M. saliens* is 34 cm, while that of the Caspian *M. saliens* is 39 cm; *M. auratus* has corresponding lengths of 42 and 54 cm; *Atherina mochon pontica* reaches a length of 12·5 cm, while the Caspian *A. m. p.* form reaches 14·0 cm. The Black Sea pipefish (*Syngnatus nigrolineatus*) reaches 21·5 cm in length, and the Caspian (*S. n. caspius*)—23·0 cm. The fact that the Baltic herring, acclimatized in the Aral Sea, is much larger in size than that in the Baltic Sea (more than 20 cm) is most interesting. According to some data, Nereis and some

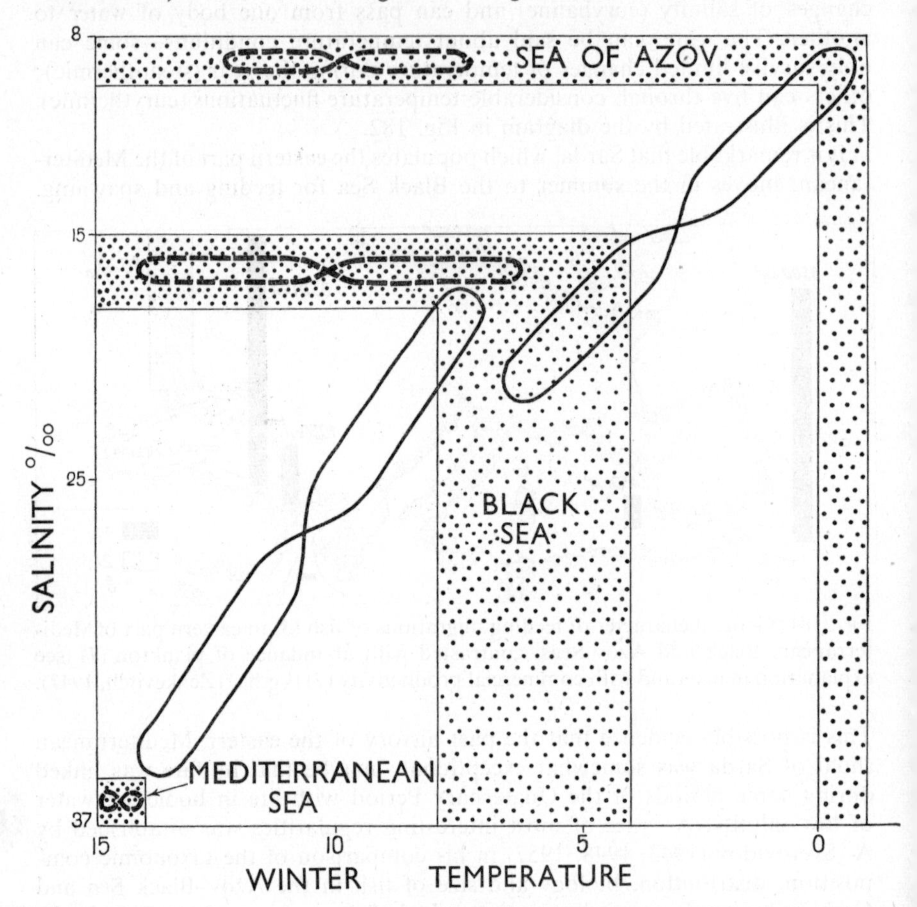

FIG. 182. Two types of fish migrations in the Mediterranean, Black and Azov Seas (Zenkevitch).

prawns transplanted from the Sea of Azov into the Caspian are also larger in size.

It is very curious that a reverse relationship is apparent in the case of bullheads (Gobiidae)—the majority of them are much smaller in the Caspian Sea. Thus, for example, in the Sea of Azov the largest size of *Gobius melanostomus* is 23·5 cm, and in the Caspian Sea (*affinis* form) only 19·6 cm; *Proterorhinus marmoratus* in the Sea of Azov and *Pr. m. nasalis* in the Caspian Sea are respectively 11·5 and 7·0 cm in length, etc. Svetovidov explains this difference by the fact that pelagic fish in the Caspian Sea, in contrast to those of the Black and Azov Seas, have no powerful competitors; it might also be the effect of higher temperature. The other peculiarity to which Svetovidov drew attention lies in the fact that in the Caspian Sea they form a larger number of species and a considerably larger number of smaller taxonomic subdivisions. Six species of herring and one species of the Clupeonella genera live in the Black Sea; in the Caspian there are eight species and sixteen smaller subdivisions of herring of the genera Caspiolosa. This difference is also explained by Svetovidov by the absence from the Caspian Sea of competitive members of pelagic herring and other genera (in the Black Sea there are Spratella, Sardina, Sardinella and Alosa), which has furthered the evolution of the species. However, this might be rather more due to changes of salinity which repeatedly occurred in the Caspian basin during the Tertiary and Quaternary periods, during which a part of the Clupeidae must have died out and the remainder have gone through a period of vigorous development of forms.

Finally Svetovidov also notes a third very characteristic feature of the Caspian Clupeidae—a large number of purely 'marine' species and forms which do not enter fresh waters, but which migrate great distances within the sea and multiply in sea water. This relates both to the three Caspian species of the genus Clupeonella and to the species of the genus Caspialosa (*C. brashnikovi*, *C. saposhnikovi*, *C. sphaerocephala*). Svetovidov thinks that in the Black Sea such forms were 'pushed into the least saline parts of the Black and Azov Seas by more vitally active Mediterranean immigrants'. Both Caspian Clupeidae forms, which make long migrations, and the purely 'marine' forms are absent from the Black and Azov Seas. These most curious facts and the explanations given for the phenomena discussed above require further research and additional speculation.

Zoogeographical affinity

The marked differences between the fauna of the Mediterranean and Caspian Seas makes it impossible to include both in the same zoogeographical unit. The Black Sea and the Sea of Azov must be included, as the Black Sea–Azov province, in the Mediterranean–Lusitanian subregion of the boreal region; as for the Caspian Sea it should not be included as part of a Pontic–Caspian–Aral province of the Mediterranean subregion as was done by V. Sovinsky (1902), neither should it be considered as the Caspian province, as was done by A. Derzhavin (1925). The Caspian fauna is too original and has little in common with the Mediterranean fauna. Therefore it is more correct to give to the Caspian Sea a separate zoographical place of its own as the Caspian relict region.

9

The Black Sea

I. GENERAL CHARACTERISTICS

The Black Sea may be considered as a tributary of the Mediterranean of a markedly anomalous character which penetrates deep inland. It is connected with the Mediterranean Sea through the Bosporus and the Dardanelles; it is 3,000 km away from the Atlantic Ocean. Its considerable depth, its great reduction in salinity by the inflow of river water, and an influx of bathymetric saline waters from the Sea of Marmora create a sharp saline stratification of the Black Sea waters into an upper layer, inhabited by a rich flora and fauna, and deep masses of water contaminated by hydrogen sulphide. There is very little exchange of water between the two layers. The fauna of the Black Sea consists of three genetically different elements.

The sections of the Sea with the lowest salinity—inlets and river mouths and the rivers themselves—are inhabited by Caspian relict fauna. Members of the fresh-water fauna move into these parts of the Sea from the rivers and at times become abundant there.

The Sea, however, is inhabited by the most euryhaline forms of the Mediterranean flora and fauna; the number of species is about four times smaller than that in the Mediterranean. The Black Sea fauna is numerically inferior to that of the Sea of Azov and considerably superior to that of the Mediterranean.

A luxuriant development of the pelagic fauna, enormous growths of red algae, phyllophora and a marked display of filter-feeders (Mytilus, Modiola and others): such are the biological characteristics of the Black Sea. It is a feeding ground for many Mediterranean fish, while a number of Black Sea fish leavit in summer time, moving to the Sea of A zov to feed.

II. HISTORY OF THE STUDY OF THE BLACK SEA

First period

The exploration of the Black Sea was begun by the voyages of P. Pallas (1793–94) who devoted the third volume of his work *Zoographia Rosso-Asiatica* (1811) to the genetic link between the Black and Caspian Sea fauna.

In 1858 the Russian ichthyologist K. Kessler worked on the shores of the Black Sea; he expressed, with remarkable precision, a correct opinion on the geological part of the Black Sea (1874). Kessler arrived at the following conclusions: (*1*) at one time the Black, Azov and Caspian Seas formed one single body of brackish water; (*2*) the Caspian Sea was separated from the Black Sea before the latter was connected with the Mediterranean; (*3*) the migration of Mediterranean fauna into the Black Sea is continuing; (*4*) the last phase of the rise in salinity of the Black Sea caused its original fauna to move into the less saline parts of the Sea and into the Sea of Azov.

A more profound study of the invertebrate fauna of the Black Sea was begun by the end of the 'sixties with the investigations of V. Tchernjavsky (mainly of the crustaceans).

In 1868 V. Uljanin, who later became the first director of the Sevastopol Biological Station founded in Odessa in 1871–72 and was transferred to Sevastopol in 1879, began his investigations of the Black Sea. As a result of his work Uljanin produced for the Black Sea a list containing 380 species of animals and proceeded to a zoogeographical appraisal of the Black Sea fauna which remains basically correct to this day. The Black Sea fauna is mainly a greatly impoverished Mediterranean fauna which has acquired only a feebly marked independent character, and which shares some unimportant features with the Aral–Caspian fauna.

On the initiative of our greatest geologist, N. Andrussov, a composite sounding expedition worked in the Black Sea, which included Andrussov and O. Ostroumov, with the hydrologist I. Spindler as its director. During this expedition the contamination of the deep layers of the Sea by hydrogen sulphide and the absence of life there was discovered for the first time. Later the work of Ostroumov in 1892–94 in the Bosporus, the Sea of Marmora and in some parts of the Black Sea and the Sea of Azov was of great importance. Westward of the Bosporus were found shells of Caspian molluscs in a semi-fossil state, an indication that the Sea of Marmora had formed part of the Pontic basin. On the other hand, Ostroumov showed that the fauna of the eastern part of the Sea of Azov and of the river mouths and inlets of the Black Sea bore the greatest resemblance to that of the Caspian Sea.

Thus the main ideas on the Black Sea fauna, its relation to the Caspian and Mediterranean faunas, the history of its origin and development, were formed by the beginning of the present century. The work of V. Sovinsky (1902) who summed up all the information collected earlier on the Black Sea, is an excellent conclusion to this stage of the investigation of its fauna and zoogeography.

Second period

In the year of the publication of Sovinsky's monograph, S. Zernov began his work on the Black Sea as the Director of the Sevastopol Biological Station; the second period of the investigation of the Black Sea fauna is linked with his name. This ecological qualitative biocoenotic stage is characterized by a comprehensive investigation of the distribution of life in the coastal zone and of the main factors determining it (sea-bed, temperature, swell, etc.). Zernov's ten years of work were concluded by the writing of his widely known monograph *On the Study of Life in the Black Sea* (1913).

Third period

The great development of oceanographic investigation during the Soviet epoch has also had its effect on the study of the Black Sea. Several research institutes have been created and a series of expeditions has worked in the Sea. Among the expeditions the most important were: the Azov and Black Seas

Scientific Industrial Expedition, under the leadership of N. M. Knipovitch, which worked for six years (1922–28), the expedition of the Hydrographic Directorate, of the Sevastopol Biological Station and the Hydrological Institute, under the leadership of Yu. M. Schokalsky and, finally, the expeditions of the Hydrographic Directorate in the ship *Hydrograph* in 1932 and 1935.

At present hydrological investigations of the Black Sea are being carried out by the Sevastopol Biological Station of the Academy of Sciences of the U.S.S.R., by the Karadag Biological Station of the Ukrainian Academy of Sciences, by the Novorossiysk Biological Station of Rostov University, by the Scientific Fisheries and Biological Station of Georgia, and by the Azov–Black Sea Scientific Investigation Institute of Fisheries and Oceanography.

III. PHYSICAL GEOGRAPHY AND HYDROLOGY

Situation and size

The Black Sea is situated between 46° 32·5′ and 40° 55·5′ N latitude and between 27° 27′ and 41° 42′ E longitude. To the northeast the Black Sea is connected with the Sea of Azov by the Kerch Strait and to the southwest with the Sea of Marmora through the Bosporus. The greatest length of the Sea is 1,149 km. Its greatest width is 611 km. The Black Sea is characterized by the

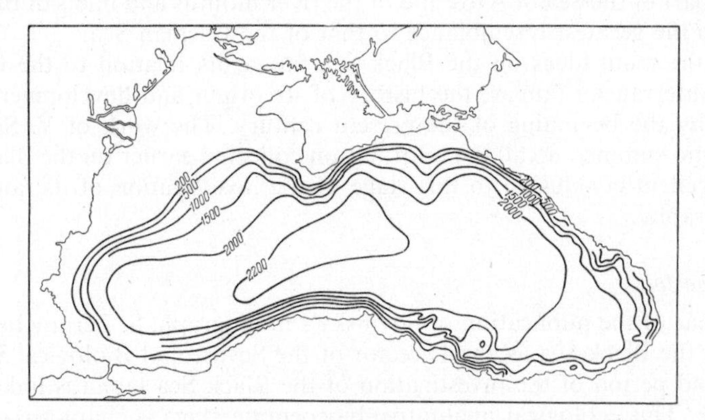

FIG. 183. Bottom topography of Black Sea (Archangelsky and Strahov).

absence of coastal features, by its small number of bays and inlets, by the almost complete absence of islands and by its very steep shores (Fig. 183), except for the northwestern part of the Sea (Karkinitsk Bay). The surface of the Black Sea is 423,488 km², its volume 537,000 km³, its greatest depth 2,245 m, its average depth 1,271 m. The 100 m isobath approaches the coast almost everywhere, moving away from it only in the western, northeastern and mainly in the northwestern part of the Sea. The angle of the floor dip is usually 4° to 6°, but it often reaches 12° and even 14°.

Water balance

The Black Sea total water balance comprises the following elements: the annual river inflow of fresh water is 400 km^3, most of this being Danube water (203 km^3); the Dnieper and Bug inflow is only 54·7 km^3 and that of the Dniester 8·4 km^3. A surface current of Azov waters of lesser salinity runs into the Black Sea through the Kerch Strait diluting the northeastern corner of the Sea, while the more saline Black Sea waters (17 to 17·5‰) enter as a deep current the area of the Sea of Azov off Kerch. Black Sea waters of about 13‰ salinity enter the Sea of Marmora as a surface current through the Bosporus (348 km^3 annually), while a deep reciprocal current of saline Sea of Marmora water enters the Black Sea (202 km^3 per year), running down the slope of the floor off the Bosporus.

Currents

As in every other sea the main current of the Black Sea has a counter-clockwise circular motion (Fig. 184). In the narrowest part of the Sea, between the Crimean Peninsula and a spit running out from the Anatolian coast, part of the waters moving from the west go north and the Sea is thus divided as it were into two parts, each with its own circular motion. In each of these circular currents is formed its own halistatic area. In the course of the current all the isolines go down while in the halistatic areas, in contrast, they rise in a cupola-shaped pattern.

Important additions to this system were introduced by N. Knipovitch (1932), E. Skvortzov (1929), V. Nikitin (1929), A. Dobrovolsky (1933) and G. Neumann (1942). In the eastern part of the Sea there is not one but two halistatic areas, divided by a current running approximately in the direction Samsun–Tuapse. In the most eastern part of the Sea, in the Batum area, there is another circular current, but here, contrary to the three previous halistatic areas, the circulation of the water has an anticyclonic character, and therefore the iso-surfaces are not cupola-shaped, but form cup-shaped depressions. Moreover, the existence of certain more or less important anticyclonic and cyclonic rotations of waters in different parts of the Sea has been established. As will be shown below, the character of the movement of water masses in the Black Sea is well reflected by the lower limit of plankton distribution.

The general course of the iso-surfaces is given in Fig. 185, which is a diagram of a cross section of the halistatic area of the Black Sea from coast to coast. It is evident from this diagram that the isoline goes down most steeply not off the coast itself, but at some distance from it; the current too usually does not run near the coast itself. The upper limit of hydrogen sulphide in the centre of the halistatic area rises to 100 m, while in the area of the current itself it goes down to 155 m. As has been suggested by V. Nikitin and E. Skvortzov (1926) the descent of the isolines off the coast may also be furthered by the water being driven off and on by winds, which causes considerable vertical mixing. The fact that the hydrological conditions of the Black Sea are undergoing substantial secular changes, as a result of the alterations of climate, of the mainland run-off and of the water exchange through the Bosporus and the

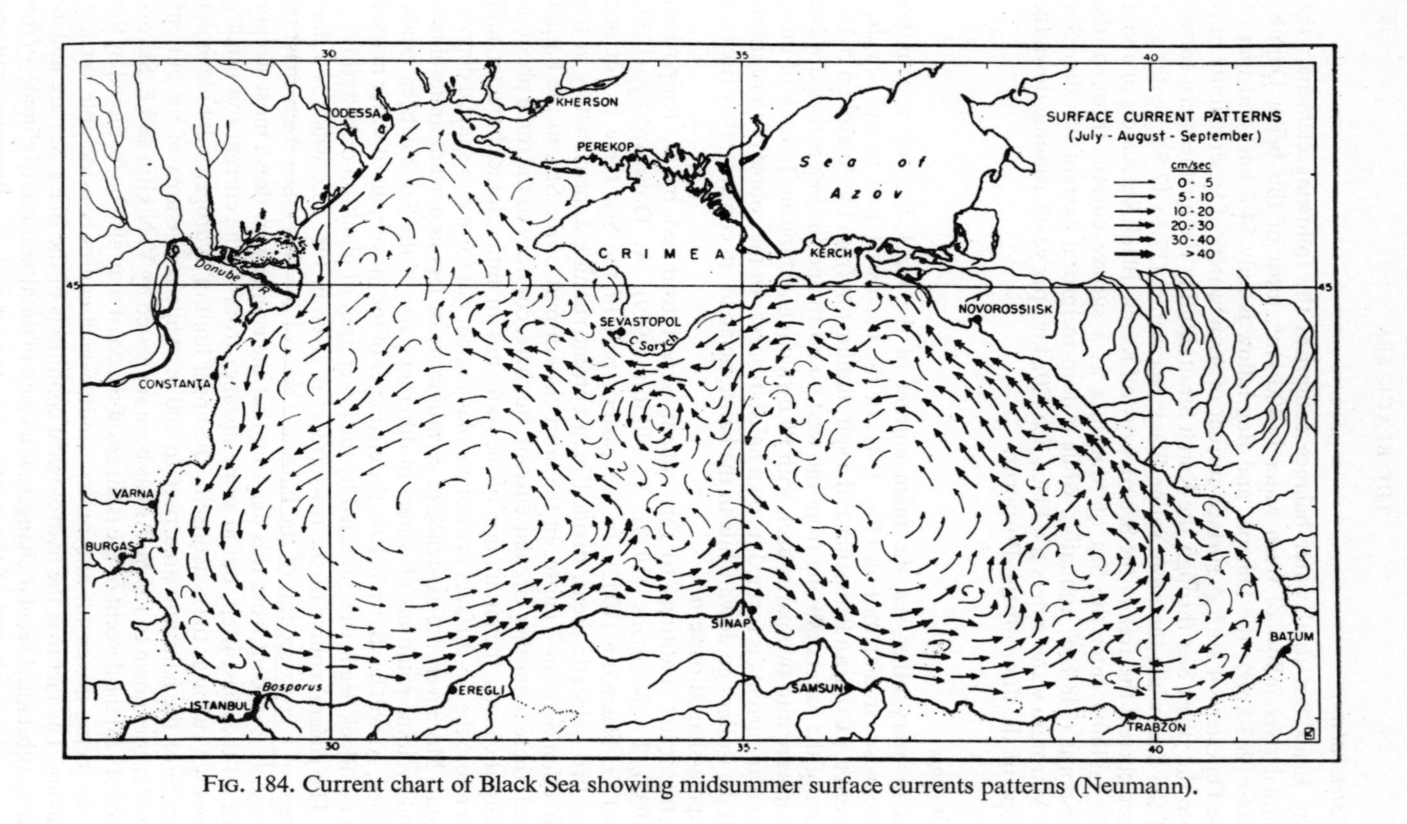

FIG. 184. Current chart of Black Sea showing midsummer surface currents patterns (Neumann).

Kerch Strait, is noted in recent literature (S. P. Brujevitch, 1953; A. Bogdanova, 1959). A certain rise in salinity in the upper layer and a fall in salinity throughout the water-column have been observed in the Black Sea for a period of 25 years (1924–51). The decrease of salt content through that period for the whole Sea was determined as 2 milliards of tons (A. Bogdanova, 1959). This is caused primarily by the loss of salts through the Bosporus being greater than the supply, a fact which is linked in its turn with a 19‰ rise in salinity in the upper layer of the sea as a result of a decrease of the mainland run-off.

In Bogdanova's opinion the decrease in salinity of the deep layers is connected with the slackening of the deep Bosporus current. The change in salinity of the upper layer and the main column of water should have improved vertical circulation. In addition, cooling of the intermediate layer (75 to 300 m) and some warming up of the deeper layers were recorded.

In the off-shore zone animals were found at depths of a little more than 200 m; on the other hand in the halistatic area patches were found where plankton animals disappeared at a depth of no more than 87·5 m. Hence the length of the Black Sea water column populated by animals varies greatly in different parts of the Sea.

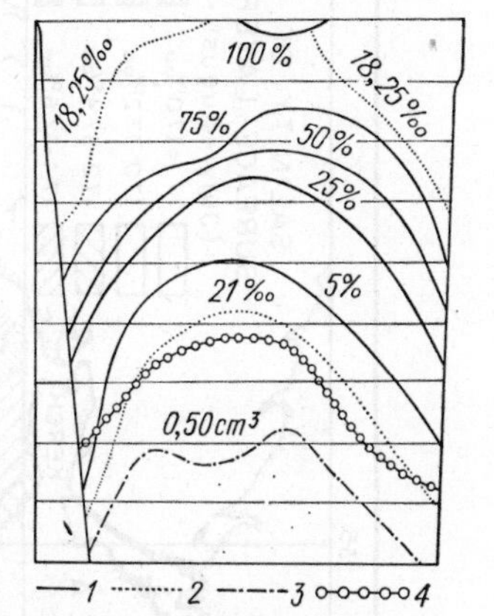

FIG. 185. Hydrological cross section from southern coast of Crimea southwards to Anatolian shore in February 1925 (Nikitin, 1930). *1* Isoxygen, % saturation; *2* Isohaline, ‰; *3* Lines of equal content of hydrogen sulphide, cm³/l. (its upper limit); *4* Lower limit of plankton.

Fluctuations of water level

The fluctuations in the amount of water coming from the mainland, or from rainfall, evaporated from the sea surface, entering the Sea as a result of water exchange with the neighbouring seas through the straits may affect the volume of sea-water. During recent decades changes in the Black Sea level, with an amplitude of about 32·5 cm, have been observed. Seasonal changes in the sea-level have been observed with ranges of 15 to 27·5 cm. Finally, the changes of sea-level may be due to the wind and tides. The latter during the spring tide reach an amplitude of about 8 cm.

Salinity

As in any other inland sea having impeded water exchange with a fully saline sea, the salinity of the upper layer may undergo considerable fluctuations depending on climatic changes, which, as we shall see below, is of some significance to the development of life. The upper layers of the Black Sea, except for areas adjacent to the river mouths and some parts of the coast subject to salinity fluctuations, have a salinity of 17 or 18‰ (Fig. 186). The

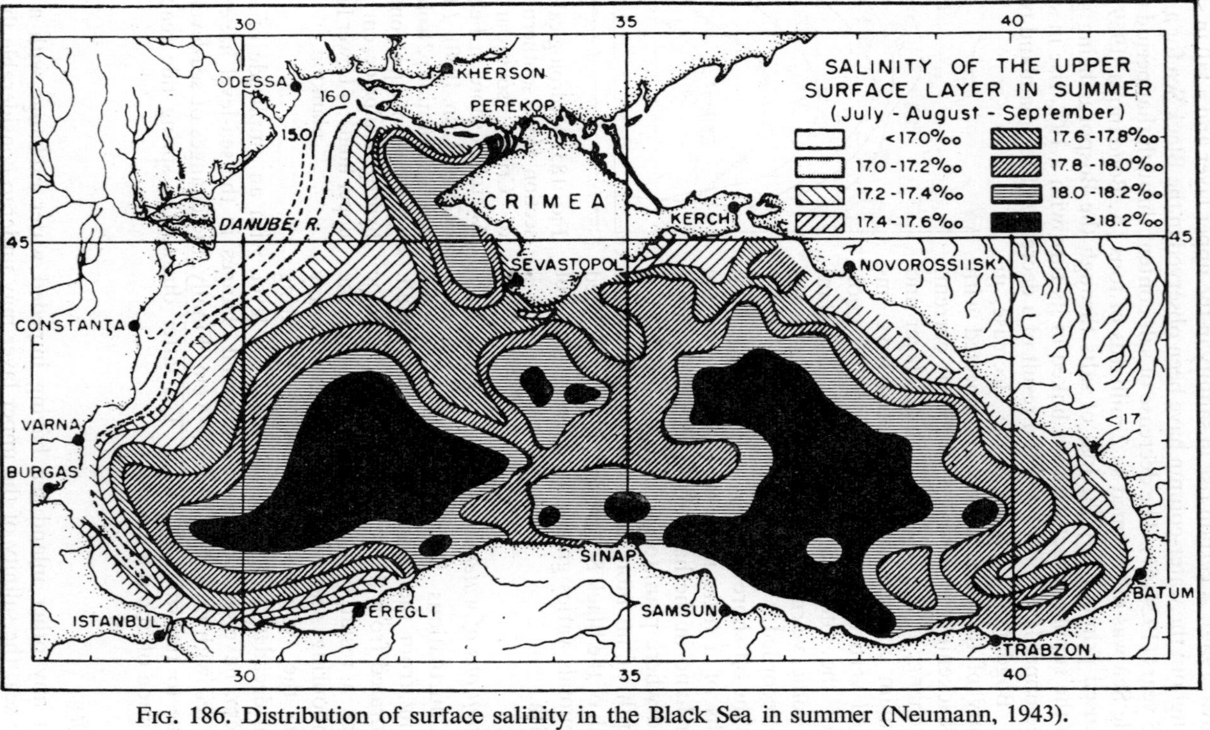

FIG. 186. Distribution of surface salinity in the Black Sea in summer (Neumann, 1943).

lowest salinity is found in the northern part of the western half of the Sea and in the region adjacent to the Kerch Strait. The salinity of the deep layers of water, except for the area near the Bosporus, reaches 22·5 to 22·6‰.

Temperature

At the coldest time of the year (January and February) the surface waters of the northwestern, and at times of the northeastern, corners of the Sea are considerably cooled, down to and below zero Centigrade (in some cases down to −1·4°), whereas the southern parts of the Sea maintain a temperature of 8 or 9°, and at times higher. The river mouths and inlets of the northern part

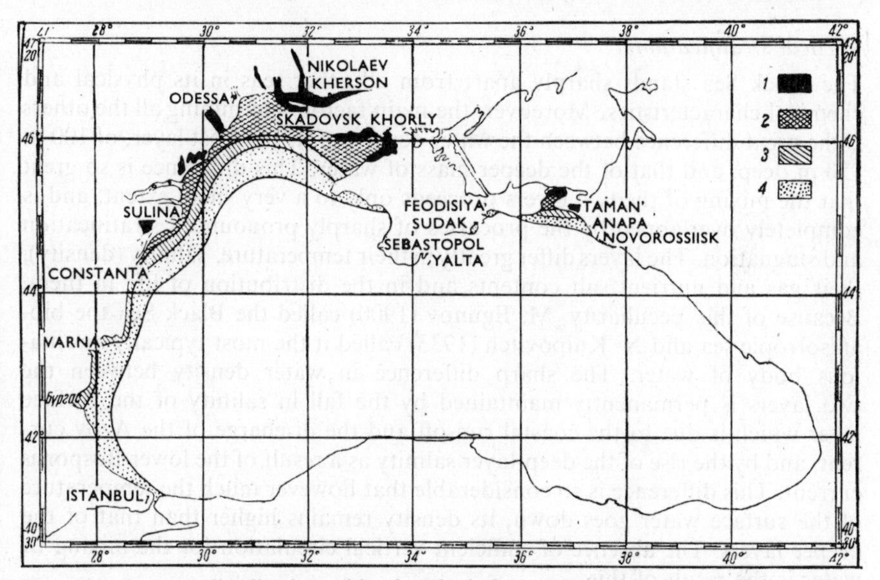

FIG. 187. Largest distribution of ice in Black Sea: *1* In mild winters; *2* In normal winters; *3* In severe winters; *4* Maximum distribution in exceptionally severe winters (Velokurova and Starov, 1946).

of the Sea have an ice cover every year. The open northwestern regions of the Sea are also covered with ice when the winter is severe. The Dzharylgatch and Karkinitsk inlets are frequently covered with an ice sheet (Fig. 187). The same phenomenon, but to a lesser extent, is observed in the northeastern corner of the Sea: the formation of coastal ice off Anapa is of frequent occurrence. Large masses of floating ice may be formed during an exceptionally severe winter off the Crimea and along the northwestern coast of the Black Sea; bays and inlets may be covered with ice. At the hottest time of the year (usually in August) the temperature of the surface waters off the shores is 27° to 28° and sometimes even 29° (or slightly higher); in contrast with the winter season, its fluctuations in different parts of the Sea are comparatively small (3° or 4°). The fluctuations of the average annual temperature of the Black Sea surface waters off the shores are 11·0° to 11·4° near Odessa, and

16·5° to 17·9° near Batumi. The range of temperature changes in the open sea is considerably less than off the shores: according to the data available the winter minimum is 6·6°, while the summer maximum is 27° with an amplitude of more than 20°, while the annual range off the shores is 31°, i.e. 11° more.

Transparency

In the open parts of the Black Sea, with depths over 200 m, the water transparency (the depth for the disappearance of a white disc) varies usually from 18 to 21 m. Transparency decreases near the coast. The highest transparency observed in the Black Sea was 30 m.

Vertical stratification

The Black Sea stands sharply apart from all other seas in its physical and chemical characteristics. Moreover, the main factor determining all the others is the great difference between the water density of its topmost layer, of 100 to 150 m deep, and that of the deeper mass of water. This difference is so great that the mixing of the two layers proceeds only to a very small extent, and is completely overlapped by the processes of sharply pronounced stratification and stagnation. The layers differ greatly in their temperature, salinity (density), their gas and nutrient salt contents and in the distribution of life in them. Because of this peculiarity, M. Egunov (1900) called the Black Sea the bio-anisotropic sea and N. Knipovitch (1933) called it the most typically anomalous body of water. The sharp difference in water density between the two layers is permanently maintained by the fall in salinity of the surface layer which is due to the coastal run-off and the discharge of the Azov current, and by the rise of the deep-layer salinity as a result of the lower Bosporus current. This difference is so considerable that however much the temperature of the surface water goes down, its density remains higher than that of the deeper layers. The absence of sufficient vertical circulation for the mixing of water is the result of this.

A picture of the distribution of the surface salinity is given in Fig. 186, and that of the vertical changes of salinity and temperature during the warmest and coldest seasons of the year in the middle part of the Sea is given in *Table 151*, taken from Nikitin's work.

Table 151

Depth,	Temperature, °C			Salinity ‰	
m	Summer	Winter	Amplitude	Summer	Winter
1	22·11	7·15	20·1	18·24	17·44
25	14·07	6·76	16·25	—	17·97
50	8·40	7·70	5·04	19·80	18·40
100	8·55	8·14	1·14	20·63	20·28
150	8·67		0·48	21·01	
500	8·90		0·21	22·01	
2,000	8·94		0·25	22·23	

As is shown in *Table 151*, containing data at great depths taken at one of the stations, the annual fluctuations of temperature and salinity affect only the 150 m upper layer, while deeper down they remain practically constant throughout the year, the temperature being between 8° and 9° and the salinity a little above 22‰. The difference in salinity between the surface and deep waters reaches 4 or 5‰.

Oxygen and hydrogen sulphide

In the Black Sea the amount of oxygen decreases sharply with the depth, while that of hydrogen sulphide increases starting at 150 m; this is shown in *Table 152*.

Table 152

Depth, m	Observed fluctuations of oxygen content, cm^3/l	Average content of hydrogen sulphide cm^3/l
0	4·57–7·62	—
25	2·51–8·64	—
50	1·05–7·76	—
100	0·12–7·16	—
125	0·00–3·16	—
150	0·00–2·71	0·088
200	0·00–1·88	0·470
300	0·00–1·93	1·480
500	0·00	3·779
1,000	0·00	5·637
2,000	0·00	5·796

As in other seas, the maximum oxygen content is at a depth of 25 m (up to 124–133 per cent). Moreover, its supersaturation is regularly observed; this is the result of phytoplankton activity.

One of the most striking peculiarities of the Black Sea is the very great amount of hydrogen sulphide which contaminates its depths. As early as 1892 the chemist A. Lebedintzev, a member of Andrussov's expeditions, the first to investigate the phenomenon of hydrogen sulphide fermentation in the depths of the Black Sea, expressed an opinion on the existence of two sources of hydrogen sulphide, in both cases formed as a result of intensive bacterial activity.

B. Issatchenko, during his microbiological investigations of the Black Sea (1924), discovered bacteria responsible for the formation of hydrogen sulphide in both ways. The bottom dwelling bacteria of the genus Microspira (mainly *M. aestuarii*) are the main source of hydrogen sulphide; as a result of their vital activity sulphates are reduced, carbonates are formed, and hydrogen sulphide is liberated. According to P. Danilchenko and N. Chigirin (1926) 99·4 to 99·6 per cent of the whole of the hydrogen sulphide in the

Black Sea is the result of this process, which was first discovered for the open seas by Murray.

The hydrogen sulphide formation proceeds in two phases: the sulphate is first reduced to sulphide with the evolution of carbon dioxide, according to the equation:

$$CaSO_4+2C \rightarrow CaS+CO_2$$

During the second phase the sulphide is decomposed by carbon dioxide, hydrogen sulphide is evolved and a carbonate is formed

$$CaS+2CO_2+2H_2O \rightarrow Ca(HCO_3)_2+H_2S$$
$$Ca(HCO_3)_2 \rightarrow CaCO_3+CO_2+H_2O$$

Moreover, some intermediate products are also formed

$$R2^-S_2O_3 \text{ and } R2^-SO_3$$

In other words, the whole process can be expressed as

$$SO_4^{2-} \rightarrow SO_3^{2-} \rightarrow S_2O_3^{2-} \rightarrow S^{2-}$$

As has been shown by P. Danilchenko and N. Chigirin (1929), in the Black Sea the carbonate content increases while there is a certain decrease of sulphates with depth (*Table 153*).

Table 153

Depth, m	Carbonate content g/l.	Sulphate content g/l.	$S_2O_3+SO_3$	Relative amounts of sulphates
200	0·1040	1·477	1·15	1·502
300	0·1052	1·486	1·44	1·498
500	0·1155	1·518	1·58	1·497
1,000	0·1259	1·515	1·77	1·485
2,000	0·1304	1·506	2·83	1·474

The intermediate products of the reduction of sulphates, the amounts of which increase with depth, were also found.

Anaerobic bacteria, which take part in the putrefaction of albuminous substances in the absence of oxygen, are the second source of the hydrogen sulphide formed. Anaerobic sulphide is oxidized by oxygen penetrating from above: these two gases are as it were antagonists, however, since both may occur simultaneously (in small amounts) on the boundary of the oxidation–reduction zones. Hydrogen sulphide can be oxidized by ozygen in the absence of bacteria, but in the Black Sea hydrogen sulphide oxidizing bacteria were recorded everywhere.

The upper limit of hydrogen sulphide gives a very clear picture of the horizontal course of the iso-surfaces (G. Neumann, 1953). In the centres of anticyclonic rotation the iso-surfaces are raised while in centres of cyclonic ones they are lowered (Fig. 188). As we have seen before, the contamination of the

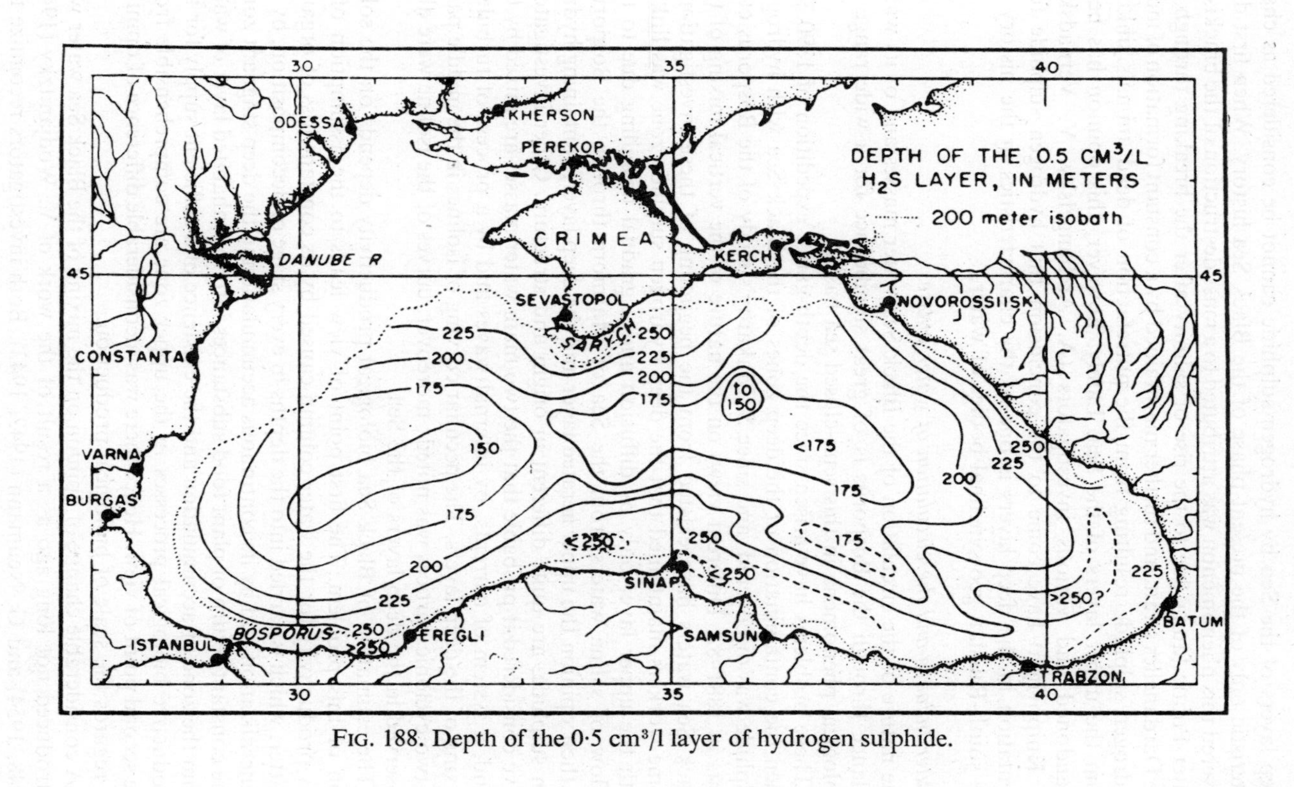

FIG. 188. Depth of the 0·5 cm³/l layer of hydrogen sulphide.

deep layers of the Sea by hydrogen sulphide cannot be considered as characteristic only of the present phase of the Black Sea history. When first discovered this phenomenon was attributed to a mass destruction of the brackish-water Pontic fauna due to the rise of salinity after the breaking through of the Dardanelles strait, and further maintained by a constant formation of more hydrogen sulphide resulting from the putrefaction of dead animals sinking from the upper layers of the Sea. Lately, however, this opinion has been abandoned and various investigators (A. Archangelsky, V. Vernadsky, N. Knipovitch) have come to the conclusion that hydrogen sulphide fermentation in the deep layers is one of the characteristics in the history of the south-Russian geo-synclinal bodies of water.

Water balance and the circulation of water masses

The nature of the circulation of the Black Sea water masses and of its water balance through the Bosporus is of great significance for a wide range of biological phenomena in this semi-closed sea basin.

These problems have arisen since the depth-gauge expedition of 1890–91, when the contamination of the deep zones of the Black Sea with hydrogen sulphide was discovered, and since S. Makarov's study of the Bosporus currents in 1881–82. Different views on the nature of the vertical mixing of the Black Sea waters have existed from the beginning of these investigations. Some workers maintained that the deep hydrogen sulphide zone was linked with the upper layer only by diffusion and a gradual upwelling due to the inflow of saline waters from the Sea of Marmora through the Bosporus. In their opinion the upper aerated layer and the deep layer, containing hydrogen sulphide, are quite different in origin and structure. Other investigators have considered it probable that the two main water masses are mixed by the wind, a system of currents, by internal waves and by a process of turbulent mixing of the deep layers. The peculiar curving of isolines in the middle parts of two cyclonic vortices was noted; moreover, curves of the isoline were also observed in the deep layers of the Sea.

The estimation of Black Sea biological productivity depends on the solution of this problem. The first point of view leads to the assumption of a low productivity for the water column caused by its constant loss of organic matter, which is carried into the depths in every stage of decomposition, by its mineralization and by its continuous accumulation in the deep stagnant zone. The constant return of plant food substances into the inhabited layer of water from the zone of accumulation and the existence of a sufficient supply for the productive biological processes in the upper zone are comprehensible from the second point of view. Hence there was a considerable difference of opinion as regards the scale of biological production.

A considerable change of opinion on the mixing of the Black Sea water was introduced not long ago as a result of the work of V. Wodjanitzky (1941, 1948, 1954) and G. Neumann (1942, 1943). Both investigators recognize the presence of an exchange between the inhabited and hydrogen sulphide layers.

The former proposed the following scheme of water circulation for the Black Sea, based on the analysis of hydrological data (*Table 154*) and the

Table 154. Mean values of hydrological data for the deep waters of the Black Sea (Wodjanitzky)

Depth, m	Actual temp., °C	Potential temp., °C	Salinity $S‰$	Specific volume, V^t	Stability $E \times 10^8$
200	8·60	8·67	21·33	0·98374	—
500	8·87	8·82	21·95	329	109
1,000	8·96	8·86	22·20	313	20
1,500	9·04	8·89	22·23	309	6
2,000	9·11	8·90	22·27	308	2

distribution of iso-surfaces, while taking into consideration the water balance through the Bosporus.

According to Wodjanitzky the path of the water masses in a cyclonic circular current is not rectilinear, but spirals towards the outer sides of the current, i.e. from the central halistatic zone to the periphery (Fig. 189). Moreover, the vertical mixing of water between the separate zones proceeds differently at various depths.

In Wodjanitzky's opinion: 'The moving forces causing vertical water exchange are: (*1*) the wind creating a system of surface currents, (*2*) the earth's rotation, throwing the currents to the right hand side and causing a spiral

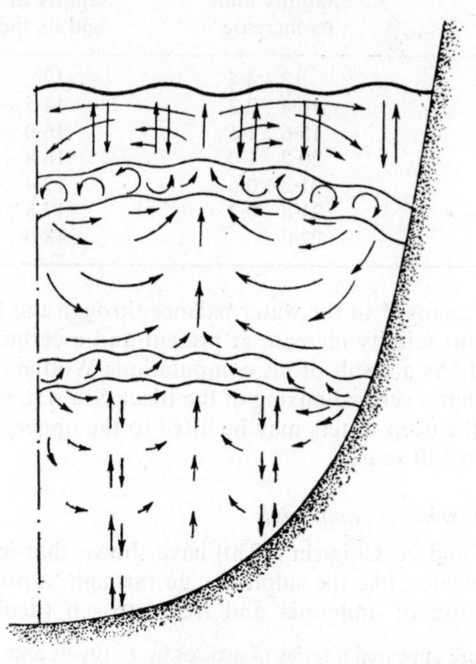

FIG. 189. Operational diagram of vertical water exchange in the Black Sea (Wodjanitzky).

rotation of the current, (*3*) the cooling of the surface layers, (*4*) the warming up of the deep layers, (*5*) the internal waves, (*6*) turbulence and diffusion.' Wodjanitzky thinks it possible, as a first approximation, to divide the Black Sea water vertically into five zones—three main and two intermediate ones (Fig. 189). 'In the first zone,' he writes, 'the water rises in the centre, there is a horizontal movement towards the periphery, and a sinking down there—a thermal convection. A turbulent mixing (internal waves) takes place in the second zone. In the third there is a rise in the centre, a horizontal movement away from the centre and a sinking down at the periphery. There is some turbulent mixing with internal waves in the fourth zone. There is some thermal convection and a feeble movement away from the periphery in the fifth zone.'

This problem cannot be solved without taking into consideration the water balance through the Bosporus, and Wodjanitzky makes the following computation: if the annual inflow of Sea of Marmora waters is 200 km³ (*S* 36‰) and the outflow is 360 km³ (*S* 12‰) and if the salinity is taken into consideration in both cases (the salinity of the Sea before it became connected with the Dardanelles being 12‰, and the period lasting 6,000 years), the salinity balance of the basin can be represented in the manner indicated in *Table 155* and Fig. 190.

Table 155

Time years	Salinity and its increase	Salinity at surface and its increase
0	12+4·4	12
1,000	16·4+2·2	14·5+2·5
2,000	18·6+1·6	16·0+1·5
3,000	20·2+1·0	16·8+0·8
4,000	21·2+0·6	17·4+0·4
5,000	21·8+0·2	17·8+0·2
6,000	22·0	18·0

If this rate of change* in the water balance through the Bosporus is maintained, there is no salinity increase at present and a certain equilibrium has been established. As a result of his computations Wodjanitzky (1948) draws the conclusion that a vertical mixing of the Black Sea waters takes place at all levels and that the deep waters may be lifted to the upper, inhabited layer of the Sea in 100 to 130 years.

Nitrogen and phosphorus compounds

P. Danilchenko and N. Chigirin (1930) have shown that in the depth of the Black Sea the nitrates, like the sulphates, go through 'a process of reduction with the formation of ammonia and free nitrogen (denitrification.) 'The

* In 1942–46 there appeared a series of articles by F. Illyott and O. Ilgaz, attempting to prove that the Bosporus discharge current takes with it the reverse current waters, and that this current does not actually reach the Black Sea. The opinions of these authors were not accepted.

amount of nitrogen in the photosynthetic zone of the ordinary sea is either zero or very small; it increases, however, with depth.

In the depths of the oceans the amount of nitrogen in the form of nitrates usually does not exceed 0·06 to 0·07 mg/lb; at the surface it may rise to 0·11 to 0·16 mg/lb. The amount of nitrate nitrogen in the seas is usually expressed in microgrammes per pound.

The ammonia content of the upper layer of the Black Sea is also practically the same as that of the open seas and oceans; it increases, however, with depth,

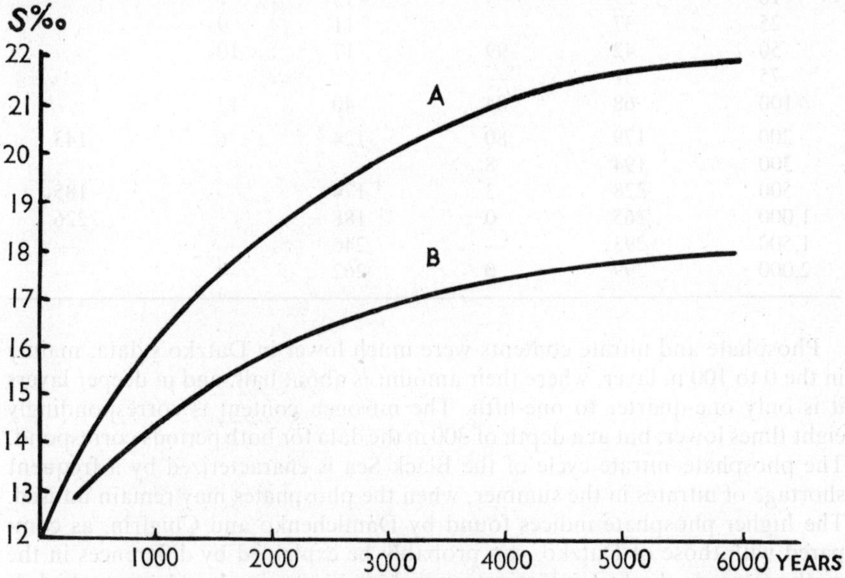

FIG. 190. Reconstructed course of the alteration of salinity in the Black Sea after the break-through of the Bosporus waters (Wodjanitzky, 1948): A Salinity at surface; B Mean salinity.

and at 1,500 to 2,000 m the amount of ammonia nitrogen is 1·10 to 1·46 mg/lb.

The content and distribution of nitrates and phosphates in the Black Sea were first investigated by Danilchenko and Chigirin in 1929 and 1930. Twenty years later their work was repeated by V. Datzko, and considerable deviations from the earlier data were found. Lately M. Dobrzanskaja (1958) has investigated the distribution and changes of phosphates throughout the Black Sea column of water. This author notes the frequent absence of phosphates from the upper region of the water (50 to 60 m) in spring and summer, although in some years phosphates are present throughout the year in the upper layer of the whole Sea during the periods of marked deficiency of nitrates. In some areas of the Sea there is a pronounced increase in phosphate content as a result of the off- and on-shore winds and the phenomena resulting from them. Within the halistatic areas the phosphate iso-surfaces rise, and off-shore they sink, with fluctuations of 50 to 100 m (*Table 156*).

Table 156. The mean content of phosphate phosphorus and of nitrates in Black Sea

	Danilchenko and Chigirin (1930)		Datzko (1950)		Dobrzanskaja (1958)
Depth, m	Phosphate phosphorus	Nitrates	Phosphate phosphorus	Nitrates	Phosphate phosphorus
0	29	71	12	13	
10	29	—	13	7	
25	37	—	11	9	
50	42	99	17	10	
75	51	—			
100	68	84	40	13	
200	179	80	124	6	143
300	194	8			
500	228	3	174	—	185
1,000	265	0	188	—	226
1,500	293	—	240	—	—
2,000	299	0	262	—	—

Phosphate and nitrate contents were much lower in Datzko's data, mainly in the 0 to 100 m layer, where their amount is about half, and in deeper layers it is only one-quarter to one-fifth. The nitrogen content is correspondingly eight times lower, but at a depth of 300 m the data for both periods correspond. The phosphate–nitrate cycle of the Black Sea is characterized by a frequent shortage of nitrates in the summer, when the phosphates may remain unused. The higher phosphate indices found by Danilchenko and Chigirin, as compared with those of Datzko, can probably be explained by differences in the methods used; the first investigators included organic phosphorus, which is scarcer in the deep-water layers than at the surface. Generally speaking the amount of biogenic matter (phosphates and nitrates) in the inhabited deep regions of the Black Sea 'is approximately of the same order as its content in the waters of Central and Southern Caspian' (V. Datzko, 1954) and somewhat lower than in the Sea of Azov.

Datzko has also determined the carbon content of the Black Sea water, both in solution and in precipitate (*Table 157*); it was found to be of the same order at various depths of the Sea and similar to that of other seas.

Thus the data given are lower than those for the Sea of Azov where the average carbon content of dissolved substances was, according to the same author in 1949–50, 5·44 mg/l; in suspension 0·82 mg/l; the total being 6·26 mg/l.

A. Kriss (1958), examining the data on the sulphate and hydrogen sulphide contents of the depths of the Black Sea, does not see any inverse correlation between them, and therefore throws some doubt on the ideas of previous investigators as to the formation of hydrogen sulphide from decomposed sulphates; he gives as an example one of the stations (*Table 158*) from the paper of B. Skopintsev and F. Gubin (1955).

Table 157

Depth, m	Mean carbon content in solution	precipitated	Total
0	3·11	0·19	3·30
10	3·24	0·24	3·60
50	3·26	0·34	3·60
100	3·15	0·51	3·66
200	3·23	0·30	3·53
500	3·13	0·36	3·49
1,000	3·03	0·31	3·34
1,500	2·98	0·28	3·26
2,000	2·83	0·27	3·10

Kriss does not share the opinion of P. Danilchenko and N. Chigirin (1926) that a reduction of sulphates by organic carbon is also indicated by a comparison of the distribution of calcium and carbonates with that of hydrogen sulphide. Thus Kriss has reason to doubt Danilchenko and Chigirin's suggestion that 'hydrogen sulphide in the Black Sea results from the reduction of sulphates by the carbon of organic substances through the formation of intermediate products down to sulphides, and the decomposition of the latter by carbonic acid and bicarbonates with the evolution of hydrogen sulphide'. Without questioning this idea Kriss agrees with the opinion of Andrussov, expressed earlier, that the hydrogen sulphide in the Black Sea 'is the sum total of hydrogen sulphide developed during the putrefaction of organic matter . . . plus the hydrogen sulphide formed as a final result of the reduction of sulphates'.

Moreover S. Brujevitch (1953), the authority on this question, says that an examination of all the data on hydrogen sulphide fermentation in the Black Sea 'leaves no doubt that in the main mass hydrogen sulphide is the result of sulphate reduction, and not of the decomposition of albuminous compounds'.

Table 158. Vertical distribution of hydrogen sulphide and of sulphates at Station 3 (1955)

Depth, m	Hydrogen sulphide mg/l	Sulphates g/kg
146	0·32	1·6330
194	0·52	1·6521
285	1·74	1·6643
290	3·64	1·6812
729	5·50	1·6739
976	6·40	1·6759
1,226	7·03	1·6823
1,475	6·64	1·7088
1,725	7·34	1·6777
1,975	7·27	1·6793

N. Chigirin (1930), the first worker to investigate the distribution of phosphates in the Black Sea, came to a number of interesting conclusions: phosphorus of dead plants remains mostly in the oxidation zone, while that of most dead animals is driven into the reduction zone and accumulates there. Sixty per cent of the total plankton phosphorus may consist of the latter; the annual amount of phosphorus brought in with river water forms about 1 per cent of the total amount of phosphates dissolved in the oxidation zone. Hence some definite amounts of phosphorus compounds are brought in from the reduction to the oxidation zone. An alkalinity two to three times higher than that of the open seas and considerably greater fluctuations in hydrogen ion concentration are also most characteristic of the waters of the Black Sea.

Dynamics of organic matter

All life in the Black Sea is concentrated in the upper layer, owing to its oxygen and hydrogen sulphide distribution; this layer is 150 to 200 m thick, forming only 10 to 15 per cent of the volume of the Sea. The immense volume of the deeper layers (85 to 90 per cent) is inhabited only by anaerobic bacteria. Organic substances which reach the depths from the upper layer return to a small extent and accumulate at the bottom. The feeble vertical circulation, resulting in the accumulation of large amounts of organic matter in the depths, also decreases the productive capacity of the Sea. As has been shown by Danilchenko and Chigirin, the oxidation of nitrogen, ammonia and nitrites to nitric acid; of sulphur, sulphides, bisulphites, sulphites and hydrogen sulphide to sulphuric acid; and the oxidation of ferrous and manganous compounds into the ferric and manganic ones, takes place in the oxidation zone; there are no nitrites or nitrates in the reduction zone, which contains comparatively large amounts of ammonia and nitrogen, a smaller amount of sulphates, and a larger one of carbonates and bicarbonates. Since hydrogen sulphide is formed by the reduction of sulphates, in the deep layers of the reduction zone their content is greatly reduced. In the hydrogen sulphide zone of the Black Sea carbon, hydrogen, sulphur, phosphorus and silicon accumulate, as well as nitrogen compounds. The combination of these conditions with the existence of the hydrogen sulphide zone leads to a comparatively low general and industrial productivity of the Black Sea in comparison with the Sea of Azov.

Sediments

The sediments of the Black Sea can be divided into two groups: those of the oxidation zone (continental shelf) and those of the reduction zone (continental slope and central depression). The shallow-water sediments were comprehensively investigated by S. Zernov in the first decade of the present century. Deep-water sediments were thoroughly studied in the Soviet era (1924–33) mainly by A. Archangelsky* (Fig. 191). The floor topography of the Black

* In this work Archangelsky succeeded in obtaining, by means of so-called core tubes, a bottom core in 4 m in length, and deep-water sediments of various parts of the Sea were synchronized by them. On the other hand, the micro-lamination of these sediments, which in Archangelsky's opinion is annual, gave him the possibility of expressing in chronological order the duration of the deposition periods of each sediment.

Sea reflects the chart of water circulation: in the off-shore sand zone, shell gravel and shallow-water muds are preponderant; in the area of the currents crossing the Sea in the direction of the Crimea and of the northern part of the Caucasian coast the bottom becomes more coarse-grained; the halistatic areas have the softest bottom. The amount of the fine fraction increases with depth (up to 96·5 per cent); so does the amount of organic matter, and the

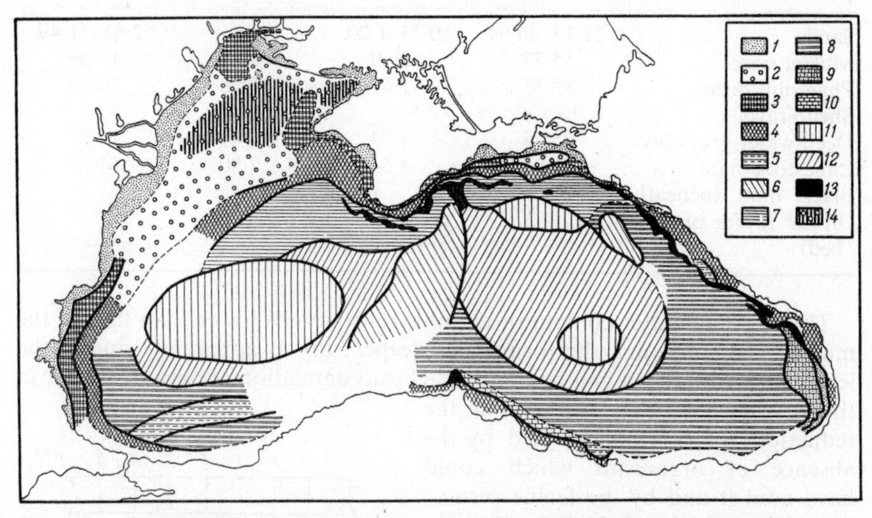

FIG. 191. Distribution of contemporary deposits of Black Sea (Archangelsky and Strahov, 1938, with the addition of Phyllophora beds). *1* Sand; *2* Shell gravel; *3* Mussel ground; *4* Phaseolin mud; *5* Grey deep-sea clay; *6* Grey clay with calcareous mud interlays; *7* Transitory mud; *8* Same with grey mud interlays; *9* Same with grey mud and sand interlays; *10* Same with several grey mud interlays; *11* Calcareous mud; *12* Calcareous mud with grey clay interlays; *13* Site free of contemporary deposits; *14* Phyllophora beds.

increase of its carbonate content with depth is, perhaps, the most characteristic feature of the Black Sea. The mean values of these changes are given in *Table 159*.

The remarkable fact that the content of organic carbon in the present-day Black Sea sediments of the hydrogen sulphide zone is practically the same, down to the greatest depths, as that in 'normal' water basins was recorded by N. Strahov (1941). This can be explained by the energetic decomposition processes of organic residues and the return of the decomposition products into the water column. A considerable amount of calcium carbonate in the shallow-water muds is due to the presence of shell gravel. The calcium carbonate of the deep-water oozes of the Black Sea is also of organic origin, but both in its structure (a fine powder) and in the mode of its formation it differs from that of the oxidation zone. It is mainly the product of the vital activities of the desulphating and denitrifying bacteria which take part in the reduction of sulphates (with the formation of hydrogen sulphide) and nitrates.

Table 159

Sediment	Fine fraction (0·01) in insoluble (in HCl) residue (percentage)	Organic carbon, dry weight of soil (percentage)	Organic non-carbonate substances (percentage)	Calcium carbonate as carbon dioxide (percentage)
Sands	21·13–46·94	0·73–1·20	—	2·63–11·49
Mussel ooze	55·77	2·60	4·92	17·69
Phaseolin ooze	82·53	1·61	3·20	20·59
Shell gravel	—	—	—	53
Deep-water grey clay	95·23	1·74	3·43	15·81
Limestone mud	91·95	4·54	7·80	61·87
Black mud (beneath upper layers of sea-bed)	—	8·65–20·32	35	—

The organic matter content of the phaseolin ooze is lower than that of the mussel ooze, although the former lies deeper; this is apparently due to the lesser density of its animal population. The accumulation of organic matter in the still deeper oozes, already in the reduction zone, is conditioned by the absence of organisms which could have used it and by the feeble vertical circulation which would have brought it up into the upper layers of the Sea.

The first to make a comparison of the salinity of the bottom water with that of the main masses of sea water in former geological periods was S. P. Brujevitch (1952). A sharp decrease in salinity, down to 4‰ (in chlorine) at a depth of 6 m, was recorded by the examination of cores from the deeper parts of the Black Sea. This, according to Brujevitch, is the salinity of the Novo-Euxine basin of brackish water; he points out that in the open sea there is no change of salinity with depth (Fig. 192). The same method was later used by B. Kullenberg (1954) in the Baltic Sea with the same result.

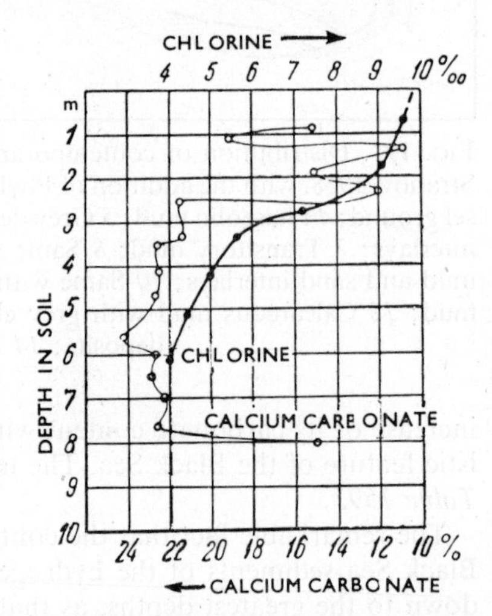

FIG. 192. Alterations in chlorine and calcium carbonate content with the depth in the sea-bed (Brujevitch).

Benthos remains are almost absent while plankton remains are predominant on the floor of the reduction zone in the deep-water sediments of the Black Sea. The predominant part played by plankton organisms in the formation of organic matter on the deep floor of the Black Sea is also shown by the carbon/nitrogen ratio. While on the shallow floor this ratio is about 4 to 4·5 (below the plankton one), it is 6 to 8 in the deep-water grey clay, i.e. almost a typical plankton ratio.

By calculating the number of thin layers in the grey clay cores, Archangelsky has determined that (assuming that the layers are annual) the 1 m sedimentation of grey clay took 5,000 years to accumulate. From the organic matter content of the grey clay it is possible to calculate that 6 tons of organic carbon accumulated on 1 km^2 in a year during the deposition period. In a similar manner, Archangelsky has calculated that 4·2 tons of organic carbon were accumulated per 1 km^2 of the floor annually during the period of deposition of the Maikop Oligocene clays. The magnitude of these deposits of organic matter, accumulated on the bottom of the Black Sea, can be assessed by the fact that the amount of organic carbon contained in the column of Oligocene and Miocene deposits in the Sulak and Yaryk-Su area (near the Caspian Sea) over about 500 km^2 is approximately equal to the total amount of coal in the Donets basin ($67{,}170 \times 10^6$ tons).

IV. FLORA AND FAUNA

Plankton

The qualitative composition of phytoplankton. According to the latest data of N. Morozova-Wodjanitzkaja (1954) the phytoplankton of the Black Sea comprises 350 species (*Table 160*).

Table 160

Group	No. of genera	No. of species	No. of species (percentage)
Diatomeae	48	150	42·9
Peridineae	23	146	41·7
Coccolithineae	7	18	5·1
Cyanophyceae	5	6	1·7
Silicoflagellata	5	6	1·7
Pterospermaceae	2	6	1·7
Heterocontae	2	2	0·6
Cystoflagellatae	1	1	0·3
Volvocaceae	6	11	3·1
Euglenaceae	2	3	0·9
Chytysomonadineae	1	1	0·3
Total	102	350	100

N. Morozova-Wodjanitzkaja and E. Belogorskaya (1957) have recorded 18 species of coccolithophorides, which had been thought to be absent from the Black Sea.* Some members of this group are abundantly developed in the Black Sea. Morozova-Wodjanitzkaja found up to 850,000 specimens of *Pontosphaera huxleyi* in the Bay of Sevastopol during her March and April

* P. Usachev (1947) was the first to record the coccolithophorides in the Black Sea.

sampling in one litre of water with a biomass of about 300 mg/m^3. Pontosphaera is just as abundant in the plankton of other areas of the Black Sea, especially just off-shore.

This author sees a similarity between the phytoplankton of the Black Sea and that of the North Sea, the Norwegian fjords, and the bays of sub-Arctic and Arctic seas, as well as that of the Caspian and Aral Seas.

Among the diatoms the following genera are richest in species: Chaetoceros, Coscinodiscus, Rhizosolenia and Melosira, and among the Dinoflagellata–Peridinium, Dinophysis, Gonyaulax and Ceratium.

Of the individual species the most significant among the diatoms are *Skeletonema costatum*, *Chaetoceros radians*, *Cerataulina bergonii*, *Leptocylindrus danicus*, *Thalassionema nitzschioides*, *Rhizosolenia calcar-avis*, *Rh. fragilissima*. Among the Dinoflagellata the most important are *Prorocentrum micans*, *Gonyaulax cordata*, the species Glenodinium, *Exuviella cordata* and some species of Peridinium, *Ceratium tripos*, *C. furca* and *C. fusus*. The presence of a large number of fungi, at various stages of development, throughout the upper (down to 300 m) layer of the Black Sea has been discovered during the study of its phytoplankton by N. Morozova-Wodjanitzkaja (1957).

Qualitative composition of zooplankton. The zooplankton of the Black Sea is poorer in species and has the composition given in *Table 161*.

Table 161

Group	No. of species	Percentage
Tintinnoidea	16*	21·2
Hydromedusae	7	9·2
Scyphomedusae	2	2·8
Ctenophora	1 (16)†	1·4
Rotatoria	14‡	18·6
Polychaeta	1	1·4
Cladocera	12 (5)	16·0
Copepoda	17 (304)	22·6
Isopoda	2	1·4
Chaetognatha	3 (6)	4·0
Appendicularia	1	1·4
Total	75	100

* L. Rossolimo (1922) gives 25 species and varieties of Tintinnoidea for the Black Sea

† The data in brackets are the numbers of species in the Mediterranean fauna.

‡ For the open sea and its parts of lower salinity M. Galadzhiev (1948) records 22 species of Rotifera.

Apart from the forms mentioned, a large number of eggs and larvae of various pelagic and bottom invertebrates and fish are found among the Black Sea plankton during certain periods of the year. The difference between the Mediterranean plankton and that of the Black Sea lies in the absence of radiolarians, siphonophores, pteropods, molluscs and salps, and, of some typical larvae of bottom-living organisms.

The researches of V. Nikitin (1926, 1928, 1929, 1930, 1939, 1941), A. Kusmorskaya (1950, 1954, 1955) and I. Galadzhiev (1948) on the Karkinit Bay are the most comprehensive investigations of the zooplankton of the open parts of the Black Sea.

The main forms of zooplankton of the open parts of the Black Sea comprise *Noctiluca miliaris* among the Cystoflagellata; *Cyttarocylis helix*, *C. ehrenbergi*, *Tintinnopsis campanula*. *T. ventricosa*, *T. tubulosa*, *Tintinnus mediterranea* and *T. subulatus* among the Tintinnoidea; *Aurelia aurita* and *Pilema pulmo* among the true Medusae; the ctenophore *Pleurobrachia pileus*; the following Copepoda: *Oithona nana*, *O. similus*, *Paracalanus parvus*, *Acartia clausi*, *Calanus helgolandicus*, *Pseudocalanus elongatus*, *Centropages kroeyeri*; the Cladocerans *Evadne nordmanni*, *E. spinifera*, *Podon polyphemoides*; *Sagitta euxina* among the Chaetognatha and *Oikopleura dioica* among the Appendicularia. Moreover, in the off-shore regions the Hydromedusae *Rathkea octopunctata* and *Sarsia tubulosa*, the Copepoda *Pontella mediterranea*, *Anomalocera patersoni*, the *Penilla avirostris* and the Chaetognath *Sagitta setosa* are just as abundant. The relatively large isopod crustacean *Idothea algirica* is found everywhere in the plankton, at times in large numbers.

Apart from the above-mentioned forms, eggs and larvae of various pelagic and botton invertebrates and fish are mixed with the coastal plankton, especially in the summer. Among them the most abundant are anchovy ova, the larvae of Lamellibranchiata and the eggs and larvae of various Copepoda.

Vertical distribution of plankton. Several groups can be distinguished in the Black Sea plankton by the character of their vertical distribution.

Some forms are distributed alike in winter and summer. The greatest mass of them is usually adapted to a depth of 15 to 50 m. Their vertical distribution is only slightly affected by variations of temperature and light, observed throughout the seasons. These forms include *Oithona nana*, the most abundant Copepoda, *Acartia clausi*, *Paracalanus parvus* and *Oikopleura dioica*. *Idothea algirica* and *Noctiluca miliaris* are similar in distribution but the numbers of the latter fluctuate considerably during the year; it is very scarce in the winter and multiplies intensively in summer.

The next group is represented by cold water stenothermal forms found in winter at all depths; in summer they sink to the greater depths. This group includes *Calanus helgolandicus*, *Pseudocalanus elongatus*, *Oithona similis*, *Sagitta euxina* and *Pleurobrachia pileus*. Throughout the whole of the cold period of the year (December to April) they are found from the surface to the lower limit of plankton distribution. With the spring warming up of the upper layer of water they sink down, disappearing gradually from the uppermost 50 m layer. At the end of November, with the autumn fall in temperature, they move into the upper waters, remaining there until the beginning of May. This migration takes place only in the uppermost 50 to 60 m layer, since below this the hydrological conditions are comparatively constant and there is little change in the distribution of the cold water forms throughout the year.

The upper temperature limit for Sagitta is 10° or 11°, for Pleurobrachia—12° or 13°, for Calanus and Pseudocalanus—13°, and for Oithona—14°.

Finally, a third group develops only in summer, keeping to the upper, warm layer of water. During the summer warming-up these forms occupy a greater and greater depth of water. When cooling begins they become gradually scarcer, disappearing completely from the plankton in the winter. This group includes *Centropages kroeyeri*, *Evadne nordmanni*, *Evadne spinifera* and *Podon polyphaemoides*.

The lower temperature limit for these species frequently coincides with the upper temperature limit of the previous groups of forms.

Hence in different inhabited zones of the Black Sea both constant and temporary plankton species can be observed, the temporary ones appearing either as a result of migration from the deeper layers, or developing in the upper, warm layer in summer only. This is shown by V. Nikitin (1929) in a clear diagram reproduced by us in an abbreviated form (*Table 162*).

Vertical migrations. Thus some plankton species have seasonal vertical migrations. V. Nikitin thinks (1929) that under Black Sea conditions the main factor causing these migrations is temperature, which masks the effect of light.

The plankton forms inhabiting layers below 50 m must have the capacity to exist, under Black Sea conditions, with little oxygen. In the deepest inhabited layers, where the amount of oxygen is no more than 4 per cent and may be less, five or six species are still found, among them *Calanus helgolandicus* and *Pseudocalanus elongatus*. Their high eurybiotic form was proved experimentally by V. Nikitin and E. Malm (1927).

Apart from the seasonal migrations, daily migrations have been observed for a number of species, conditioned primarily by variations in light. The most pronounced daily migrations are those of *Calanus helgolandicus* and *Sagitta euxina*.

The lower limit of distribution. Owing to the hydrological and hydrochemical conditions of the Black Sea, both plankton and benthos exist only in the upper layer of the Sea. In the central parts the plankton is concentrated in the upper layer at 100 to 150 m, and in the littoral areas and in those of the middle of the Sea between the shores of the Crimea and Anatolia, in the 150 to 175 m layer. In the littoral areas of the western part of the Sea the lower boundary of the inhabited zone lies a little higher (125 to 150 m) and in the eastern area a little lower (175 to 200 m) than the average position. Thus the lower boundary of the Black Sea inhabited zone is not horizontal, but slopes from west to east with about 50 m difference in level. This sloping of the lower boundary of the inhabited zone is conditioned by the greater decrease in salinity in the western part of the Sea, which hinders vertical circulation. We shall see below that the same phenomenon is found for the lower boundary of benthos distribution.

As is shown by a closer examination of the distribution limit of the Black Sea pelagic plankton (Fig. 193), this is mostly in accordance with the general

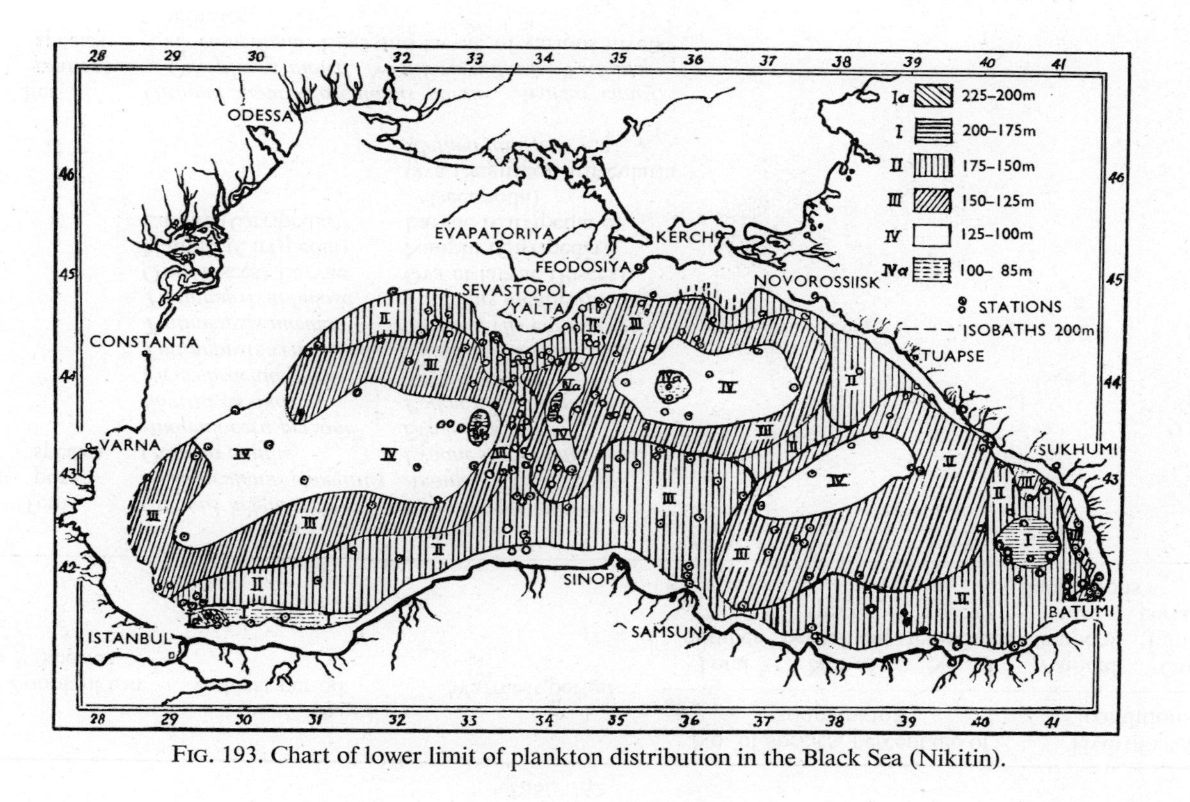

FIG. 193. Chart of lower limit of plankton distribution in the Black Sea (Nikitin).

Table 162

Depth, m	Zooplankton species	Coldest period	Warmest period	No. of species, percentage of zooplankton: Total number	No. of species, percentage of zooplankton: No. of permanent species	No. of species, percentage of zooplankton: No. of temporary species	Hydrological conditions: Annual temperature fluctuations	Hydrological conditions: Oxygen minimum percentage
0–3				100	23	77	17°	90
	Temporary species	*Calanus helgolandicus*	*Centropages kroyeri*					
		Pseudocalanus elongatus	*Anomalocera patersoni*					
		Oithona similis	*Evadne nordmanni*					
		Anomalocera personi	*Evadne spinifera*					
		Sagitta euxina	*Podon polyphaemoides*					
		Pleurobrachia pileus	*Sagitta setosa*					
		Tintinnopsis ventricosa	*Cyttarocylis helix*					
3–15		*Tintinnopsis nucula*	*Cyttarocylis ehrenbergi*	86·5	26·5	73	15·5°	93
		Tintinnopsis tubulosa	*Tintinnus mediterraneus*					
		Ova (Pisces) Larvae	Ova et larvae (Pisces)					
		Nauplii (Cirripedia)	Nauplii (Cirripedia)					
		Larvae (Cirripedia)	Larvae (Cirripedia et Decapoda)					
			Ova (Sagittae) Auricularia					
			Idothea algirica					
	Permanent species	*Oithona nana*, *Parcalanus parvus*, *Acartia clausi*, *Oikopleura dioica*, *Noctiluca miliaris*, *Tintinnopsis campanula*. Eggs and larvae of various invertebrates						

15–25	Temporary species	*Calanus helgolandicus* *Pseudocalanus elongatus* *Oithona similis* *Anomalocera patersoni* *Sagitta euxina* *Pleurobrachia pileus* *Tintinnopsis ventricosa* *Tintinnopsis nucula* *Tintinnopsis tubulosa* Ova (Pisces) Larvae (Pisces) Nauplii (Cirripedia) Larvae (Cirripedia)	*Calanus helgolandicus* *Pseudocalanus elongatus* *Centropages kroyeri* *Evadne nordmanni* *Podon polyphaemoides* *Sagitta setosa* *Pleurobrachia pileus* *Cyttarocylis helix* *Cyttarocylis ehrenbergi* *Tintinnopsis campanula* *Tintinnus mediterraneus* *Tintinnus subulatus* Ova et larvae (Pisces) Larvae (Cirripedia et Decapoda) Pilidium *Idothea algirica*	82·5	30	70	8·0°	95
	Permanent species	*Oithona similis, O. nana, Paracalanus parvus, Acartia clausi, Oikopleura dioica, Noctiluca miliaris.* Eggs and larvae of various invertebrates						
25–50	Temporary species	*Tintinnopsis campanula* *Tintinnopsis ventricosa* *Tintinnopsis nucula* *Tintinnopsis tubulosa* Ova et larvae (Pisces) Larvae (Cirripedia)	*Sagitta setosa* *Cyttarocylis ehrenbergi* *Tintinnopsis campanula* *Tintinnopsis ventricosa* *Tintinnopsis davidoffi* *Tintinnus mediterraneus* *Tintinnus subulatus* Ova et larvae (Pisces) Larvae (Cirripedia) *Idothea algirica* Larvae (Decapoda)	71	47	53	5·0°	90

Table 162—continued

Depth, m	Zooplankton species	Coldest period	Warmest period	No. of species, percentage of zooplankton			Hydrological conditions	
				Total number	No. of permanent species	No. of temporary species	Annual temperature fluctuations	Oxygen minimum percentage
	Permanent species	*Calanus helgolandicus, Pseudocalanus elongatus, Oithona similis, O. nana, Paracalanus parvus, Acartia clausi, Oikopleura dioica, Sagitta euxinna, Pleurobrachia pileus, Noctiluca miliaris, Cyttarocylis helix.* Sagitta and Copepoda eggs, mollusc and polychaete larvae						
50–75	Temporary species	*Tintinnopsis ventricosa* *Tintinnopsis tubulosa* Ova et larvae (Pisces)	*Sagitta setosa* *Cyttarocylis helix* *Cyttarocylis ehrenbergi* *Tintinnopsis ventricosa* *Tintinnus mediterraneus* *Tintinnus subulatus* Ova et larvae (Pisces) Larvae (Cirripedia) *Idothea algirica*	50	61·5	38	1·0°	30
	Permanent species	*Calanus helgolandicus, Pseudocalanus elongatus. Oithona similis, O. nana, Parcalanus parvus, Acartia clausi, Oikopleura dioica, Sagitta euxina, Pleurobrachia pileus, Noctiluca miliaris.* Sagitta and Copepoda eggs, mollusc and polychaete larvae						

75–100	*Calanus helgolandicus, Pseudocalanus elongatus, Oithona similis, O. nana, Parcalanus parvus, Acartia clausi, Oikopleura dioica, Sagitta euxina, Pleurobrachia pileus, Noctiluca miliaris*	29	100	0	0·25°	8
100–125	Same except *Acartia clausi*	27	100	0	0·10°	5
125–150	Same except *Oithona nana*	21	100	0	0·50°	3
150–200	*Calanus helgolandicus, Pseudocalanus elongatus, Oithona similis, Oikopleura dioica, Sagitta euxina.* Polychaete larvae					

Footnote to page 410.

* Recently the results of A. Kriss' microbiological investigations were strongly criticized (A. Bogoyavlensky, 1962, Y. Sorokin, 1962). The criticism is based upon the fact that microbiological water sampling with the aid of metallic (brass) water bottles proved to lack adequate sterility. This statement refers to the fact that water bottles act as a source for a plentiful supply of water samples with micro-organisms. According to the view of the above-mentioned authors the water bottles as a rule break through the water surface next to the board of the ship and hence are profusely stuffed with micro-organisms which do not tear away from the water bottles. The results of the investigations carried out by Y. Sorokin both in the Black Sea and in the Pacific Ocean with the aid of an originally developed method for sterile water sampling radically differ from the data collected by A. Kriss. According to Y. Sorokin the number of micro-organisms in the abyssal area of the ocean as well as in the grounds situated at great depths far flung from the coastal areas is negligible. The same authors maintain that A. Kriss' data fail to show a numeric increase of micro-organisms as one moves from the higher latitudes to the lower ones. Y. Sorokin observed quite a contrary picture. The micro-zonation of the oceanic waters including the abyssal waters established by A. Kriss is also subjected to total doubt. In other words A. Bogoyavlensky and Y. Sorokin disprove all the quantitative data of A. Kriss, excluding the data from the surface layers and epicontinental coast regions. The main fault of the latter's concept lies in the erroneous method used by the author.

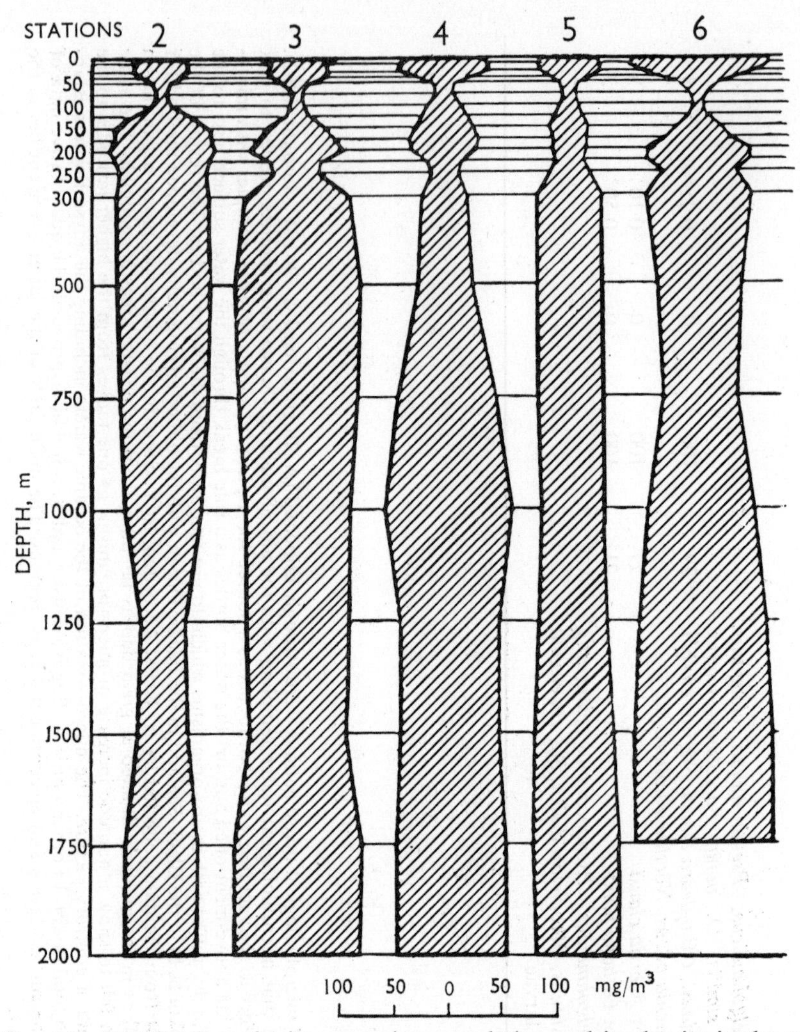

FIG. 194. Distribution of micro-organism population and its density in the water column of the Black Sea (Kriss, 1958).

scheme for the horizontal circulation of the upper layer of water, determining equally the position of the lower limit of oxygen and the upper limit of hydrogen sulphide.

Black Sea micro-organisms and their quantitative distribution. In his monograph A. Kriss (1958) gives some data on the total number and the biomass of the Black Sea bacteria population, determined by the method of membrane ultra-filters (Figs. 194 and 195).* The number of micro-organisms decreases from one or two hundred thousand specimens per 1 ml of water to a few tens of thousands as one moves away from the coast, and especially in zones with strong influence of coastal run-off. The largest number of micro-organisms is found at depths of 10 to 75 m.

Bacteria biomass changes with the same regularity. The minimum number of micro-organisms is found at depths of 75 to 150 m, where the bacterial population of the upper layer is replaced by the community of the hydrogen sulphide zone (mainly by a particular group of filamentary micro-organisms). The number of micro-organisms in the hydrogen sulphide zone is considerably

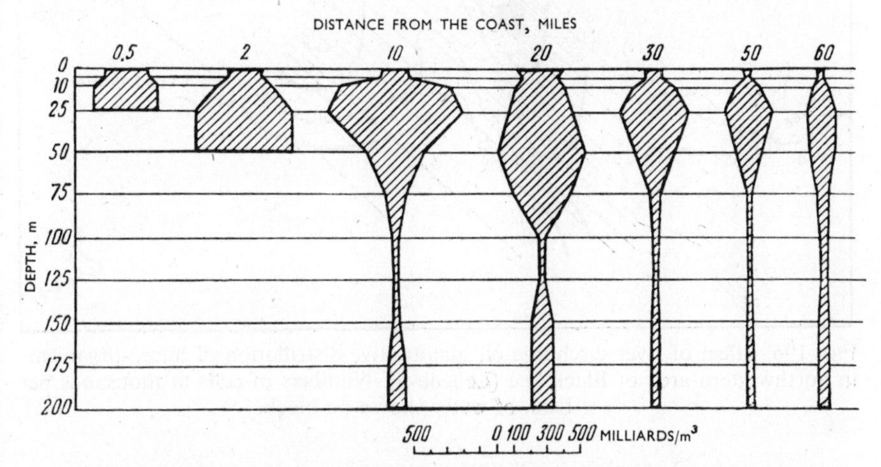

FIG. 195. Distribution of micro-organism population in Black Sea and the alteration of its density with the distance from the coast (Kriss).

higher than that of the surface oxygenated zone. Another sharp rise in the number of micro-organisms is observed in the upper layer of the sea-bed, where it reaches $1\frac{1}{2}$ to 3 milliards per 1 g of the wet weight with a biomass of 3 to 6 g/m^2. The effect of river discharge on the number of micro-organisms in the water is clearly shown by M. Lebedeva (Fig. 196). The quantitative range of micro-organisms changes in winter, owing to a considerable fall in temperature: their main mass is then concentrated in the 0 to 50 m layer. The number of bacteria decreases sharply deeper down, only increasing again in the hydrogen sulphide zone (Fig. 197). Kriss gives comparative values of phyto- and zoo-plankton biomass as an illustration to his data (*Table 163*). According to these data the biomass of bacteria is considerably higher than the quantity of plant and animal plankton, and if we take into consideration a much greater biological activity of the micro-organisms, their immense importance will become evident both for the phytoplankton and zooplankton of the surface zone and for the biochemical processes in the hydrogen sulphide zone. In the oxygenated zone a direct connection can be observed between the quantity of micro-organisms and the plant and animal population, both in the main mass of water and in the sea-bed.

Kriss determined the rates of multiplication of micro-organisms by a direct

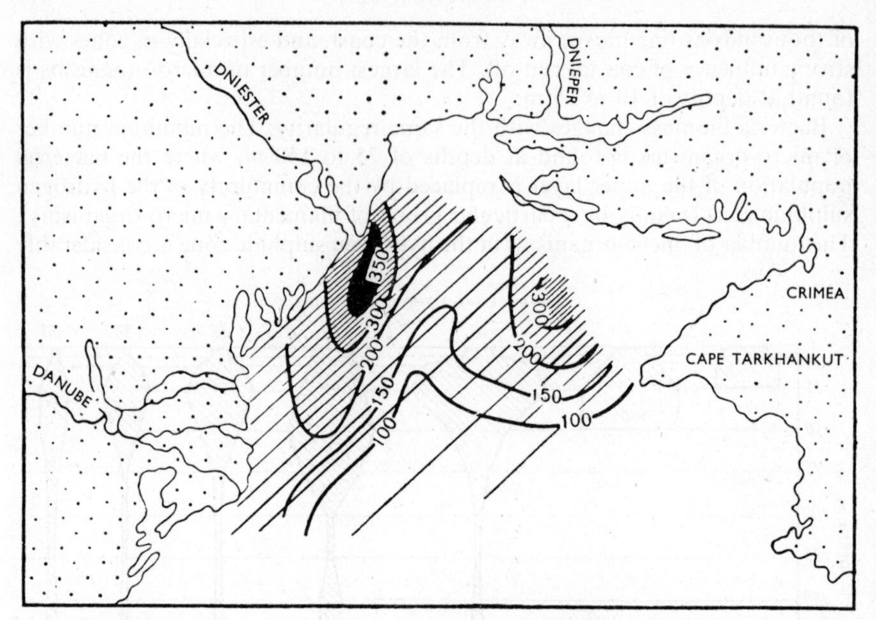

FIG. 196. Effect of river discharge on quantitative distribution of micro-organisms in northwestern area of Black Sea (Lebedeva). Numbers of cells in thousands per 1 ml. of water shown on block.

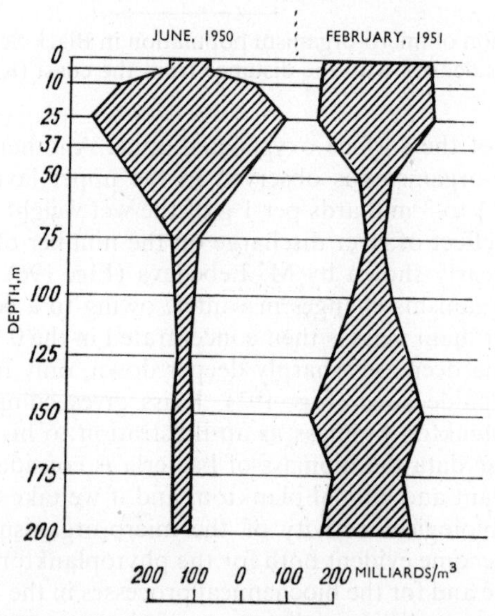

FIG. 197. Vertical distribution of micro-organism population on the coastal and sea stations in Black Sea in summer and winter (Lebedeva).

Table 163. Biomass of micro-organisms, phytoplankton and zooplankton in the eastern part of the Black Sea

Location	Mean biomass throughout the Sea, mg
Mean biomass per 1 m^3 in the 0 to 200 m layer	20
Mean biomass per 1 m^3 in the 200 to 2,000 m layer	40
Total biomass of micro-organisms beneath 1 m^2 of the sea surface	74,050
Same for phytoplankton	11,600
Same for zooplankton	36,800

method of lowering glass slides to different depths and counting the number of bacterial cells at definite time intervals. The average daily *P/B* coefficient (ratio of production to biomass daily) is determined on the basis of these observations. For the daily exposure of slides in the open part of the Sea an average *P/B* coefficient of 0·2 to 0·7 was obtained. Similar indices have been found for the Caspian Sea and the Arctic Ocean. The highest average daily *P/B* coefficients have been recorded in the Pacific Ocean (the daily gain in weight being about 80 per cent). Kriss gives the annual *P/B* ratio for the active photosynthetic layer (0 to 50 m) in the Black Sea as 58·4, and for the hydrogen sulphide zone—29·2.

A. Kriss (1958) has also attempted to determine the total mass of micro-organisms in the water of the Black Sea and the order of magnitude for the mineralization of the organic matter resulting from their activity. For the active photosynthetic layer (0 to 50 m) this value is 6·5 mg/m^3, approximately 0·1 per cent of the average content of organic matter in the Black Sea waters. Deeper down, at 50 to 125 m, the concentration of micro-organisms is more or less constant and equal to about 7 mg/m^3, while the value for organic matter mineralization at this depth is about 1 mg/m^3.

A. Kriss (1958) comes to the following conclusion as a result of his comprehensive analysis: 'The synthesis of organic matter in the form of microbial cells proceeds on a large scale in the Black Sea at the price of carbon dioxide assimilation; the amount of organic matter formed as a result of autotrophic nutrition of micro-organisms is greater than that produced through photosynthesis by the organisms of the oxygen zone. If the amount of organic matter produced by phytoplankton throughout the whole Black Sea comprises 4,000,000 tons (59 mg/$m^3 \times$ 67,594 km^3 of the oxygenated zone), then the total mass of organic matter in the form of autotrophic (filamentary) micro-organisms is more than 15 million tons (33 mg/$m^3 \times$ 462,360 km^3 of water in the hydrogen sulphide zone). Thus, the complete mineralization of dead organic matter, the regeneration of biogenic compounds in the form required for aquatic plant nutrition, the synthesis of organic matter from inorganic compounds and direct participation in nutrient chains constitute the manifold activities of micro-organisms in the creation of biological and in particular commercial productivity of seas and oceans.'

But Y. Sorokin, criticizing Kriss' method of water sampling, has recently argued against the supposedly huge productivity of autotrophic sulphur bacteria and protein origin of hydrogen sulphide. In his opinion nitrificators and denitrificators, practically absent from the Black Sea depths, play only a minor role, and autotrophic production does not exceed that of photosynthetic activity.

Quantitative distribution of phytoplankton. P. Usatchev (1926, 1928) laid the foundation of the quantitative study of the Black Sea phytoplankton in his survey of the northwestern part of the Sea. Later some data were collected by N. Morozova-Wodjanitzkaja for the shores of the Crimea (1940), by G. Konoplev (1937–38) for the Bay of Odessa, by V. Nikitin (1939) for the Batum area and by S. Maljatzky (1940) for the open part of the Sea.

The diatoms are of preponderant significance in the Black Sea phytoplankton, the second place is occupied by Dinoflagellata. The number of plant specimens in the plankton is exceeded by that of the animals (Fig. 198A, B). As in the open seas there are in the Black Sea two main bloom periods: the autumn–winter–spring one linked mainly with a mass development of diatoms, and a much weaker summer one, controlled by the multiplication of Dinoflagellata. An increase of the diatoms is again observed in the autumn (Fig. 199). In the winter there is a sharp preponderance in the phytoplankton of *Skeletonema costatum* (up to 4 million cells per litre), *Chaetoceros radians* and *Ch. socialis* (up to 31 million cells), *Thalassionema nitzschioides* and *Thalassiosira nana* (up to 30,000 specimens) and *Cerataulina bergoni* (up to 1·7 million specimens).

From May onwards, and especially in the hot months (July and August), the development of Dinoflagellata proceeds vigorously: *Exuviella cordata* (up to 18,000 per litre), *Prorocentrum micans* (up to 72,000 specimens), *Goniaulax polyedra* (up to 66,000 specimens), some species of *Glenodinium apiculata* (up to 39,000 specimens) and *Peridinium triquetrum* (up to 43,000 specimens). Among the diatoms *Thalassionema nitzschioides* also grows in large numbers in the summer. A second autumn maximum of diatoms is observed in November, when the phytoplankton passes into its winter state (*Table 164*).

The spring outburst of phytoplankton is four or five times greater in its number of cells than the winter maximum and 2,000 times greater than the autumn maximum. A comprehensive picture of the quantitative sequence of phytoplankton during the year in the circumlittoral parts of the Bay of Sevastopol is given in *Table 165* (according to Morozova-Wodjanitzkaja's data in the year 1938–39).

Marked changes, not only seasonal but annual, are observed in the composition and quantity of phytoplankton in the Black Sea. The average annual number of Dinoflagellata in the plankton of the Bay of Sevastopol was 31,000 specimens in 1938, and of diatoms 19,000 specimens per litre, with an average annual total amount of phytoplankton 52,000 cells per litre; while in 1939 the corresponding data were: 14,000, 3,240,000 and 3,257,000 per litre. Thus the average annual number of Dinoflagellata in 1939 was half that in 1938, while the number of diatoms in 1939 was, on the contrary, so much

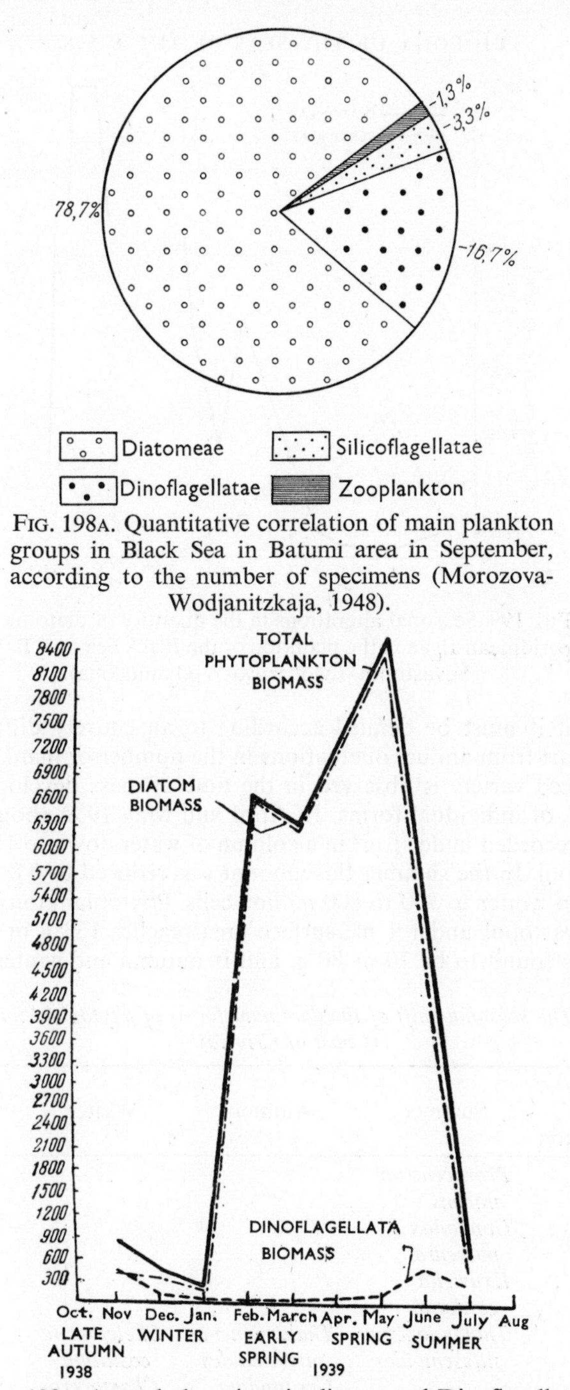

FIG. 198A. Quantitative correlation of main plankton groups in Black Sea in Batumi area in September, according to the number of specimens (Morozova-Wodjanitzkaja, 1948).

FIG. 198B. Annual alterations in diatom and Dinoflagellata biomass in Sevastopol area (Morozova-Wodjanitzkaja, 1948).

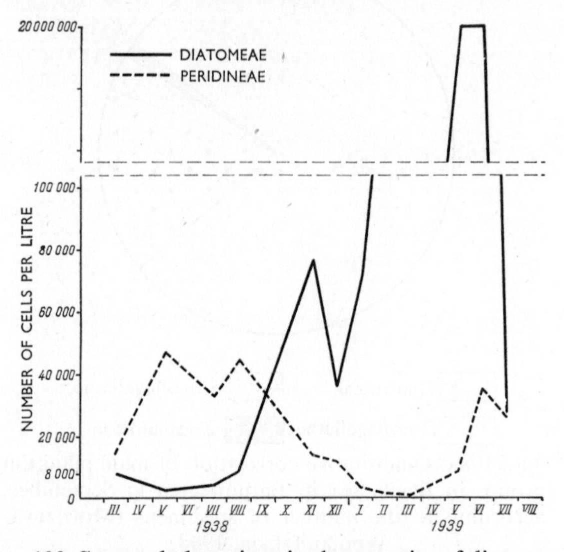

FIG. 199. Seasonal alterations in the quantity of diatoms and peridinean algae in the plankton of the Black Sea and Bay of Sevastopol (Morozova-Wodjanitzkaja).

greater that it must be defined according to an entirely different order of values. Apart from annual fluctuations in the number of plankton specimens a pronounced variety is observed in the time of mass development and the significance of individual forms. In April and May 1939 about 300 milliard cells were recorded under 1 m² in a column of water down to 15 m in the Bay of Sevastopol. In the summer this amount was reduced to 0·8 to 1·5 milliard cells, and in winter to 700 to 800 million cells. Phytoplankton biomass in the Bay of Sevastopol under 1 m² surface area reaches 133 g in the spring. In June it was found to be 70 or 80 g, and in autumn and winter it dropped to

Table 164. The seasonal shift of the dominant forms of phytoplankton in Black Sea (Coast of Crimea)

Groups of phytoplankton	Summer	Autumn	Winter	Spring
Peridineae	*Prorocentrum micans* *Goniaulax polyedra* *Exuviella cordata*			
Diatomeae	*Thalassionema nitzschioides*	*Thalassionema nitzschioides* *Cerataulina bergonii*	*Skeletonema costatum* *Chaetoceros radians*	*Cerataulina bergonii* *Chaetoceros radians*

Table 165

Group	August	November	January	March	May	July
iatomeae	8,665	77,077	93,235	2,141,783	20,204,560	27,000
inoflagellata	45,405	16,325	3,213	332	8,440	25,800
licoflagellata	583	1,340	465	130	100	100
thers	1,667	1,110	1,550	600	500	2,600
Total	56,320	95,852	98,463	2,142,845	20,213,600	55,500

6 to 10 g (at a depth of 15 m). During its spring bloom the amount of phytoplankton increases as one moves from the open sea to the coast, bays and inlets (according to Morozova-Wodjanitzkaja (1948), 250 to 300 times). Thus, in July 1938, 25 miles away from the Crimean shore there were, at a depth of 0 to 25 m, on the average 11,000 cells per litre, and in the Bay of Sevastopol 37,000; the respective data for October were 17,000 and 107,000. During the spring bloom up to 31 million cells per litre were recorded in the Bay of Sevastopol.

Phytoplankton density decreases with depth, but it is still high at a depth of 100 m; in depths below 50 m phytoplankton cells probably sink down and phytosynthesis is no longer possible.

Whereas in its open parts the Black Sea is considerably inferior to the Sea of Azov as regards its quantity of phytoplankton, in its bays and inlets the amount of phytoplankton approximates to that of the Sea of Azov.

A comparison of the quantitative data on the Black Sea phytoplankton with those of different areas of the Atlantic Ocean (the off-shore zones) leads Morozova-Wodjanitzkaja to the conclusion that 'as regards its quantitative phytoplankton development the Black Sea is not inferior to the North Sea . . . or the Atlantic Ocean near the North American coast. . . . In the Antarctic the amount of phytoplankton (number of cells) is ten times higher than in the open parts of the Black Sea, but it is much lower than that of its bays and inlets.'

S. Maljatzky (1940) gives the quantitative data on the average content of phytoplankton in the photosynthetic zone (a 75 m layer of water) in the open parts of the northeastern half of the Sea. At the beginning of the summer (Fig. 200A) phytoplankton is particularly abundant in the part of the Sea adjacent to the Kerch Strait and in the circumlittoral zone south of Novorossiysk: in the second half of the summer high indices of phytoplankton biomass were found also in the central parts of the Sea (Fig. 200B). In the first case the biomass in some areas was more than 200 mg/m³; in the second more than 400 mg/m³: i.e. it was found to be close to the phytoplankton biomass of the Central Caspian.

S. Maljatzky (1940) and N. Morozova-Wodjanitzkaja have given a description of the phytoplankton of the eastern half of the Sea. The phytoplankton of the western half of the Black Sea and of the northwestern area was comprehensively studied by P. Usachev (1928) and G. Pitzik (1950, 1954).

Both investigators have recorded high productivity indices for this area of the Sea. The number of phytoplankton in the Odessa area reaches 5 milliard cells per 1 m³ (G. Pitzik, 1950), and in the Bay of Sevastopol 30 milliard cells (up to 12 g/m³: N. Morozova-Wodjanitzkaja, 1940, 1948). These data are commensurable with those for the Sea of Azov. In the open part of the Black Sea, in summer, the amount of phytoplankton is estimated as 5–10–15 million cells per 1 m³, and its biomass in tens of mg/m³; however, it is many times less than in the bays and inlets and in the shallows of the Sea, and hundreds of thousands of times less than in the Sea of Azov, although in some places in the open sea and in some samplings the amount of phytoplankton was of the order of hundreds of milligrammes and even up to 1,700 g/m³.

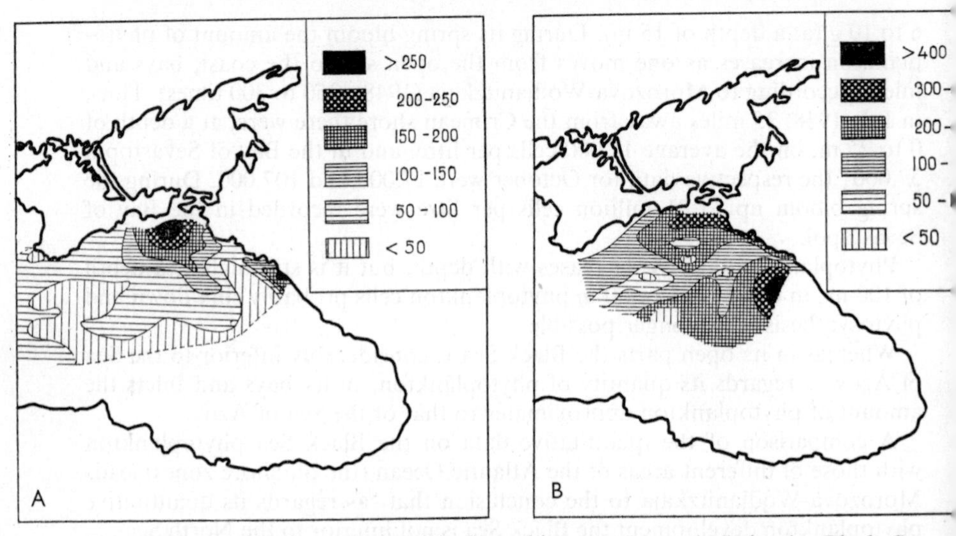

FIG. 200. Distribution of phytoplankton biomass (in mg/m³) in the Black Sea (Maljatzky, 1940). A 21 May to 5 June 1939; B 2 to 7 August 1939.

Phytoplankton biomass throughout the Black Sea was estimated by G. Pitzik (1954) in a number of years as about 2·8 to 6·2 million tons. N. Morozova-Wodjanitzkaja (1957) has tried to compute some general indices of Black Sea plankton productivity. She thought that the daily production of phytoplankton in the open part of the Sea was 9·5 g in autumn and winter, and at the beginning of the summer about 11·3 g under 1 m² of surface. The daily *P/B* ratio (the ratio of the daily gain of production to biomass) was 1·7 in February, 2·2 in June and 1·2 in September. Moreover, she has determined the daily coefficient (the ratio of daily consumption to the original biomass, *C/B*) as 1·2 to 1·7, and the daily coefficient (ratio of production to consumption, *P/C*) in the spring and early summer as 1 to 1·2, i.e. at that time of the year consumption is completely compensated for by new growth (production). By the end of the summer and in the autumn (September to November) this last coefficient is equal to 0·9, i.e. consumption exceeds new growth.

Quantitative distribution of zooplankton in the open parts of the Sea. Nikitin (1945) has given a general picture of the quantitative distribution of plankton (both animal and plant) in the open part of the Sea. He has determined the total plankton biomass as approximately 7 million tons (6,937,714 t), half of the plankton being contained in the upper 50 m layer, while the lower 150 to 175 m layer contains only 1 per cent of its bulk (Fig. 201). The Sea of Azov is a body of water attached to the Black Sea which is remarkable in many respects.

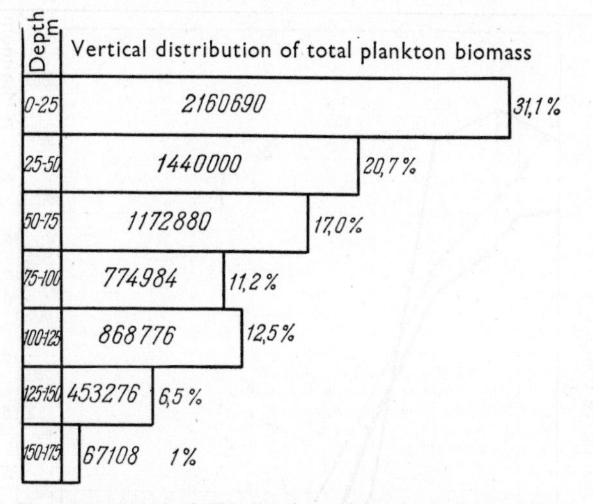

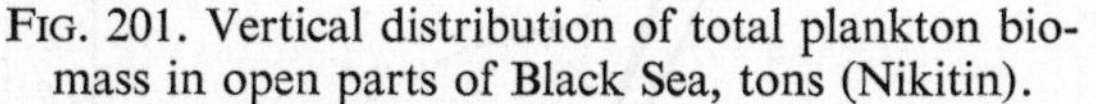
FIG. 201. Vertical distribution of total plankton biomass in open parts of Black Sea, tons (Nikitin).

It is essentially a broad, very shallow inlet of the Don, with water only slightly saline. Owing to a number of circumstances it is supplied with abundant mineral substances.

Investigations made in recent years have led to a situation where the Sea of Azov can now perhaps be placed among those seas of the U.S.S.R. which have been most comprehensively studied.

The average plankton biomass decreases steadily from top to bottom (*Table 166*).

Table 166

Depth, m	0–25	25–50	50–75	75–100
Biomass, mg/m³	210	147	121	84

Depth, m	100–125	125–150	150–175 (150–225)
Biomass, mg/m³	90	54	38

The increase of biomass in the 100–125 m layer as compared to the layer above it, is explained by the accumulation in it of such cold water forms as *Calanus helgolandicus* and *Pseudocalanus elongatus* throughout the greater part of the year.

The decrease in plankton numbers with depth is accompanied by its qualitative impoverishment (Fig. 202). Below 50 m there is a considerable decrease in the amount of oxygen and in the pH value, indicating increasing amounts of free carbon dioxide. The average plankton biomass throughout the inhabited zone is 118 mg/m³ (according to Maljatzky, 100 to 130 mg/m³).

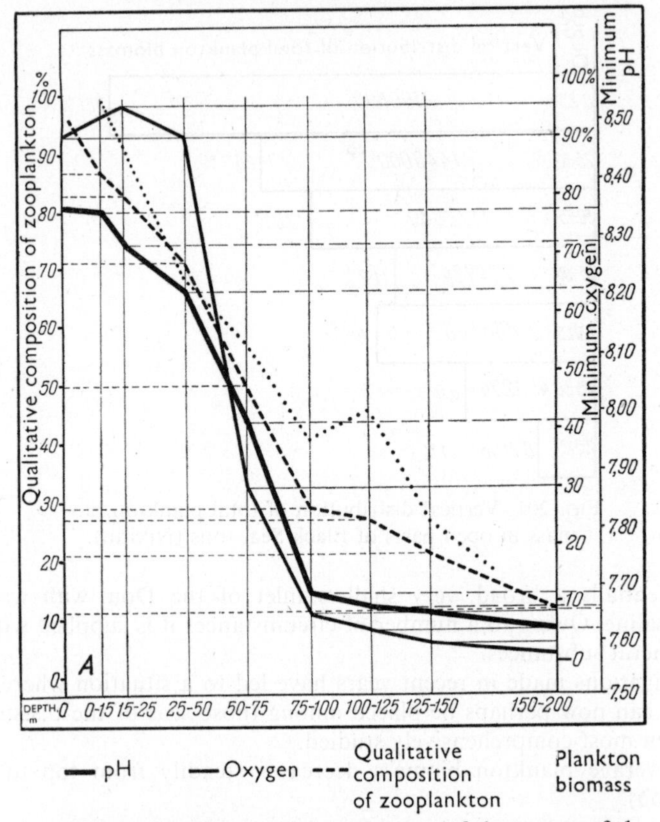

FIG. 202. Vertical distribution of oxygen, of the course of the active reaction, and of the qualitative and quantitative distribution of plankton in Black Sea (Nikitin). Biomass and number of plankton species of the upper horizon are taken as 100 per cent.

A. Kusmorskaya (1950, 1954, 1955) has carefully studied the zooplankton of the Black Sea, chiefly as food for fish, and the life cycles of mass forms. She notes among the fish-food organisms the preponderance of the following forms: *Calanus helgolandicus*, *Pseudocalanus elongatus*, *Acartia clausi*, *Penilla avirostris*, predatory and voracious forms of Medusa, *Pilemo pulmo* and *Aurelia aurita*, *Pleurobrachia pileus* and *Sagitta setosa* are usually larger in mass than food plankton, which they devour in huge amounts. Among them *S. setosa* only is eaten by some fish (sprat and hardtail).

C. helgolandicus breeds throughout the year, apparently producing five or six generations (N. Klucharev, 1948; L. Chayanova, 1950). Its average amount, in all its stages, under 1 m² of surface is about 1,000 specimens.

During the cold season of the year *C. helgolandicus* keeps mostly to the upper layers of the Sea and in the summer to the lower ones, but in summer also Calanus travels vertically to the depth each day. During daylight its mass is concentrated at a depth of 75 to 100 m, and during darkness in the 0 to 10 m layer (*Table 167*). *Pseudocalanus elongatus* behaves in a similar manner.

Table 167. Vertical distribution of edible zooplankton biomass in April 1949, percentage of total biomass in open part of Sea. (*A. Kusmorskaya*)

Level, m	6 a.m. to 10 a.m. Total mass of plankton	6 a.m. to 10 a.m. Calanus	9 p.m. to 11 p.m. Total mass of plankton	9 p.m. to 11 p.m. Calanus	2 a.m. to 3 a.m. Total mass of plankton	2 a.m. to 3 a.m. Calanus
0–10	4·3	2·0	80·7	91·5	18·5	13·4
10–25	36·0	15·0	17·3	6·5	29·0	40·3
25–50	11·4	10·0	1·6	1·8	38·0	37·3
50–75	3·0	3·0	0·4	0	4·0	9·0
75–100	45·3	70·0	0	0	0·5	0
00–150	0	0	0	0	0	0

In contrast to *C. helgolandicus*, the development of *Acartia clausi* proceeds throughout the year in the upper layer (0 to 50 m), and in the warm period of the year the upper maximum of plankton development depends on the growth of *A. clausi* and *Penilla avirostris*. As regards numbers Penilla occupies the first place, Acartia the second and Calanus the third (*Table 168*).

Table 168. The numbers of Calanus, Acartia and Penilla, April to August, in the 0 to 150 m layer of the open Sea under 1 m² (*A. Kusmorskaya*)

Species	April	July	August	October
C. helgolandicus 1949	4,330	3,760	3,920 (1948)	127
A. clausi	7,950	12,210	39,980 (1948)	2,850
P. avirostris	—	—	56,250 (1951)	—

Acartia clausi (L. Chayanova, 1950) produces nine generations in one year. The numbers of *Noctiluca miliaris* reach 2,000 to 6,000, sometimes even 9,000, specimens per 1 m³ (in one case 80,000 specimens/m³ were recorded) and *Pleurobrachia pileus* gives in the 50 to 100 m layer 2–5–6 and up to 15,000 specimens per 1 m³. At times they form a fairly considerable supplement to food-plankton (*Table 169*).

An approximate distribution of food-zooplankton for August 1950 is given in Fig. 203 (except the Medusa, Pleurobrachia and Noctiluca). The total

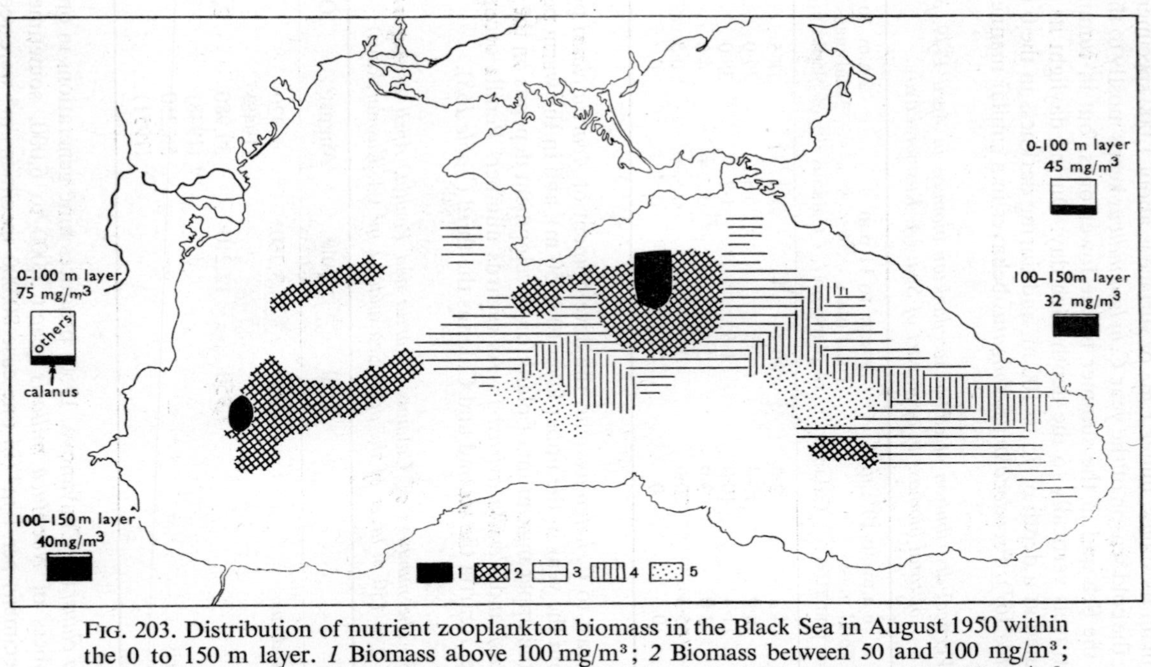

FIG. 203. Distribution of nutrient zooplankton biomass in the Black Sea in August 1950 within the 0 to 150 m layer. *1* Biomass above 100 mg/m^3; *2* Biomass between 50 and 100 mg/m^3; *3* Between 30 and 50 mg/m^3; *4* Between 20 and 30 mg/m^3 *5* Biomass less than 20 mg/m^3.

Table 169. Role of inedible forms of zooplankton in the Black Sea, according to 1948–49 data (A. Kusmorskaya)

Biomass, mg/m^3	Western half April	Western half August	Eastern half September
Plankton composition			
Edible zooplankton	68	200	100
Noctiluca miliaris	68	200	168
Pleurobrachia pileus	46	144	73
Total	179	484	341

amount of zooplankton and its separate components may undergo considerable annual and seasonal fluctuations, like those mentioned above for phytoplankton, as is evident from a comparison of Figs. 199 and 201. In the northwestern part of the Sea, in bays and inlets, the amount of plankton is always greater than in the open sea; in all these fluctuations, however, it is on a fairly high level in the open sea too, as compared with other seas. An increased amount of plankton is always observed in the western part of the Sea, which is due to the proximity of the highly productive, northwestern, shallow area and to an abundant river-discharge. A second highly productive Sea area lies off the southeastern coast of the Crimea, this peculiarity being due to the outflow of highly productive waters from the Sea of Azov. Generally speaking the fluctuations in Black Sea plankton productivity display a definite dependence (Fig. 204) on the variations of river-discharge (A. Kusmorskaya, 1955). The mean biomass of food plankton in the Black Sea varies between the limits 175 and 930 mg/m^3 (A. Kusmorskaya, 1955) (*Table 170*). *Pseudocalanus elongatus* and *Acartia clausi* are the main zooplankton forms of the shallows of the northwestern area of the Black Sea (0 to 10 m). *Calanus helgolandicus* becomes a mass form in the deeper part. There is a considerable admixture of Penilla, Evadne and Podon in the shallows in summer (Fig. 205).

The nature of the zooplankton biomass distribution in the lower level of the inhabited zone is different, where it corresponds well with the general character of the circulation of the Black Sea water masses (Fig. 206).

The changes in the biomass and composition of the summer food-zooplankton of the northwestern area shallows are given in *Table 171*.

Similar data are obtained from a comparison of the Black and Caspian Seas zooplankton biomass (A. Kusmorskaya, 1950) (*Table 172*).

However, substantial additions should be made to this table. The predatory plankton forms (Medusa, Ctenophora, Sagittae, Flagellata, *Noctiluca miliaris*), which probably devour zooplankton like the Ctenophora of the Barents Sea and thus decrease its significance as nutrient for fish, are absent from the Caspian Sea.

The shallow northwestern part of the Black Sea, distinguished by its high indices of plankton and benthos biomass, serves in summer as feeding ground for many fish and their young. In some years, however, the picture is quite

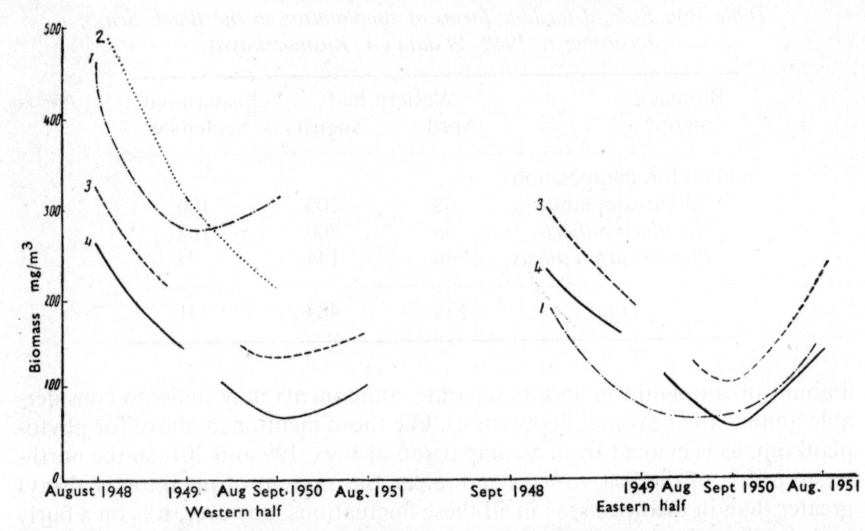

FIG. 204. Annual fluctuations in the volume of river-discharge and in the biomass of nutrient zooplankton in the 0 to 25 m layer of the Black Sea. *1* Total discharge; *2* Summer floods; *3* Nutrient zooplankton biomass; *4 Penilia avirostris* biomass (Kusmorskaya).

different. Thus in 1955 a sharp decrease of food zooplankton and a mass development of the diatoms *Rhizosolenia calcar-avis* were observed. They may be the link in an inverse relationship. The same picture was observed in the Sea of Azov in the summer of 1955 (25 to 50 mg/m³ in July and August). A considerable mass of fish, chiefly anchovy, moved away from the northwestern part of the Sea. The feeding conditions began to deteriorate in the northwestern part of the Black Sea after 1952. In 1954 the amount of food-plankton decreased by several times (E. Yablonskaya, 1957). In 1955 the

Table 170. Annual and seasonal fluctuations in the biomass of food zooplankton in different parts of the Black Sea (A. Kusmorskaya, 1954)

Month	Open sea western half, 1949 mg/m³	0–100 m layer eastern half, 1951 mg/m³	Northwestern part 0–10 m layer, 1951 mg/m³
February	60 (1951)	51	18
April	65	—	42
May	—	25	—
June	—	—	599
July	60	—	930
August	140	79	417
September	—	—	384
October	46	—	323
December	—	—	—

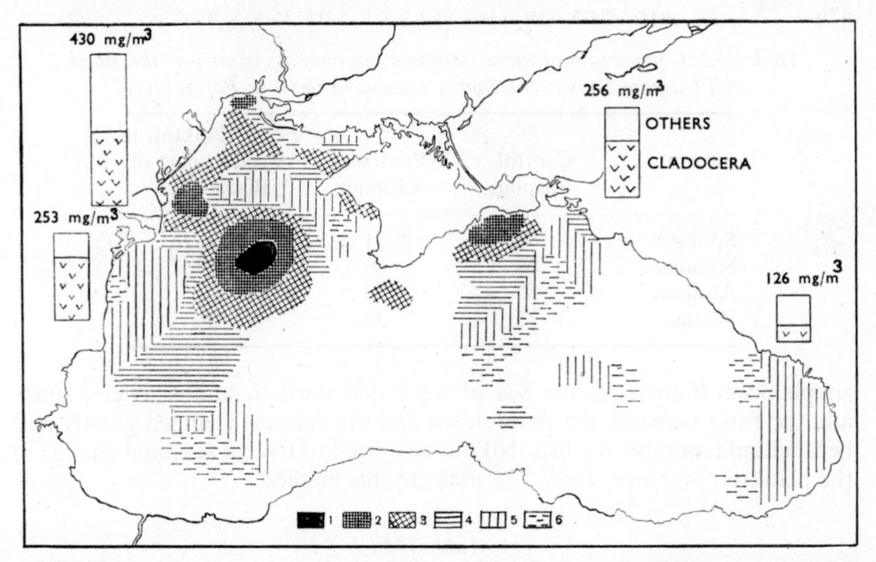

FIG. 205. Distribution of nutrient zooplankton biomass in the Black Sea in August 1951 in the 0 to 25 m layer (Kusmorskaya, 1950). *1* Biomass above 1,000 mg/m³; *2* Biomass between 500 and 1,000 mg/m³; *3* Between 300 and 500 mg/m³; *4* Between 200 and 300 mg/m³; *5* Between 100 and 200 mg/m³; *6* Between 50 and 100 mg/m³.

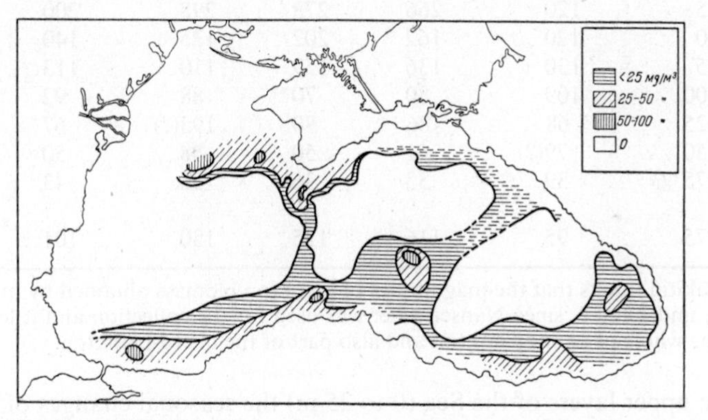

FIG. 206. Horizontal distribution of plankton biomass in Black Sea in the 150 to 175 m layer (Nikitin).

Table 171. Changes (mg/m³) in the food-zooplankton biomass in the 0 to 10 m layer (A. Kusmorskaya, 1950)

Month	Mean biomass, mg/m³	Acartia	Penilla	*Evadne podon*	Pseudo-calanus	Sagitta	Remainder
July	175	101	7	24	4	—	39
August	852	330	188	78	—	—	256
October	385	51	—	—	27	237	65

Table 172. Comparison of mean zooplankton biomass (g/m^3) of the Black and Caspian Seas according to seasons in the 0 to 100 m layer

Season	Central Caspian	Southern Caspian	Food-plankton in western part of Black Sea
Spring	86	21	65
Summer	96	60	140
Autumn	55	30	—
Winter	33	34	—

zooplankton biomass in the Sea of Azov decreased by almost twelve times and the ratio between the peridineans and the diatoms changed greatly and became unfavourable for fish. Nikitin also tried to trace a seasonal change in the plankton biomass. *Table 173* indicates his method.

Table 173

Depth m	Average plankton biomass,* mg/m^3					
	May	June	July	Aug–Sep	Oct–Nov	Feb
0–25	120	266	278	298	200	95
25–50	120	162	202	125	140	133
50–75	130	136	159	110	113	80
75–100	109	80	70	88	92	64
100–125	68	86	80	193(?)	67	48
125–150	79(?)	51	50	58	50	34
150–175	39	33	36	36	43	40
0–175	95	116	125	130	101	71

* V. Nikitin thinks that the magnitudes of plankton biomass obtained by him are considerably understated, since Nansen's net was used for the collection and it lets through almost the whole of nannoplankton and also part of the micro-plankton.

In the upper layers of the Sea (0 to 25 m) the seasonal changes of plankton biomass are marked, but they are already attenuated at depths of 25 to 50 m, while below 50 m they are practically absent. This is in complete conformity with the course of the annual fluctuations of various factors of the environment, primarily with temperature. Moreover, it is to be borne in mind that the main mass of phytoplankton is concentrated in the upper 25 m layer

V. Wodjanitzky estimates the total Black Sea plankton biomass as 12 to 18 million tons (1941), and its annual productivity as no less than 225 million tons.*

* In V. Nikitin's book *The Feeding of Anchovy* (Engraulis encrasicholus *L.) in the Black Sea off the Shores of Georgia* the total plankton biomass is given as 7 million tons, and the annual production as 105 million tons. All these data should at present be considered as provisional.

In our general estimation of the biomass and productivity of the Black Sea plankton we have to accept that these data are high and of the same order as those of the Caspian Sea, which is completely confirmed by V. Wodjanitzky's (1941) opinion on the high biological productivity of the Black Sea.

Pelagic community. Some regions of the Sea, remote from the shores and mainly within the convergence zones, are inhabited by an original pelagic biocoenosis described by B. Iljin (1933) and somewhat resembling the Sargasso Sea fauna, since it consists of large gatherings of floating plants, but, in contrast to the Sargasso Sea, these are dying eel-grass leaves brought out by currents from the shores. As has been described by Iljin, among the mass of floating material live many animal-forms, which have specially adapted themselves to this environment. Among them the more common ones are: pipefish (*Syngnathus schmidti*); stickleback (*Gasterosteus aculeatus*); the isopod (*Idothea algirica*), and large crab megalops (probably *Liocarcinus holsatus* and *Portunus arcuatus*); and at times in large numbers grey mullet larvae, young fry, and the young of the year; anchovy (*Engraulis encrasicholus*), sprat (*Spratella sprattus phalerica*); pipefish (*Syngnathus schmidti*) and the predators feeding on it; mackerel (*Scomber scombrus*); Sarda (*Pelamys sarda*); Tuna (*Thynnus thynnus*), and dolphin (*Delphinus delphis*). All these forms have typical characteristics of pelagic organisms; it is, however, unknown whether stickleback can spawn away from the shores, while grey mullet forms part of this biocoenosis only when young. Among the birds the stormy petrel is always present.

S. Maljatzky has established (1940) the existence of several areas of abundant gatherings of living organisms in the northern part of the eastern half of the Sea; he thinks that these areas are connected with the areas of increased vertical circulation.

Not only an increase in the amount of zooplankton but a huge shoaling of pelagic fish—anchovy, sarda and also dolphins—is observed in these areas. This is also the spawning ground of both these fish (Fig. 207). The fact that the spawning grounds of anchovy and sarda are always separate may be due, Maljatzky thinks, to a mass devouring of anchovy by sarda.

Benthos and Nekton

The qualitative composition of phytobenthos. The qualitative composition of Black Sea macrophytes was investigated by N. Voronichin (1908) and E. S. Zinova (1936); N. Morozova-Wodjanitzkaja (1927–41) has done much comprehensive research on its ecology and chiefly on its quantitative distribution.

At present there are 236 known species of green, brown and red algae. With the passage from the Mediterranean Sea to the Black Sea the macroflora is much less impoverished than the animal forms; only with the passage into the saline waters of the Sea of Azov does the number of species of the bottom-living algae drop markedly, as is shown in *Table 174*.

Apart from the algae two species of flowering plants—*Zostera marina* and

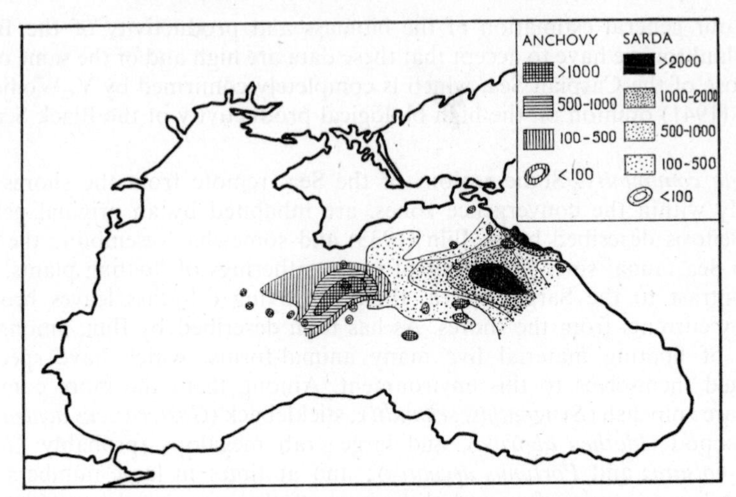

FIG. 207. Distribution of anchovy and Sarda roe in northeastern corner of Black Sea in May 1939 (Maljatzky).

Z. nana (*Z. minor*)—are of importance in the vegetation of the Black Sea. Among the Black Sea sea-weeds the dominant forms are: *Phyllophora nervosa*, *Cystoseira barbata* and *C.b.* var. *placida*.

Among the green algae the most important are *Chaetomorpha chlorotica*, *Enteromorpha intestinalis*, some species of Cladophora and *Ulva lactuca*; among the brown ones *Cystoseira barbata* with its variant *placida* and *Scytosiphon lamentarius* (in winter); and among the red ones *Phyllophora rubens* var. *nervosa*, *Ceramium rubrum* and *C. diaphanum*, *Polysiphonia subulifera*, *P. variegata*, *P. elongata*, *P. opaca* and *Laurencia obtusa*.

It is quite remarkable that in contrast to the animals, the bottom-living algae of the Black Sea have not evolved a single endemic autochthonous form:

Table 174

Group	Mediterranean Sea: Bay of Naples (Funck)		Black Sea (Voronichin and Zinova, from Morozova-Wodjanitzkaja)			Sea of Azov, excluding the Kerch Strait (L. Volkov)		
	No. of genera	No. of species	No. of genera	No. of species	No. of species, per cent of Mediterranean	No. of genera	No. of species	No. of species, per cent of Mediterranean
Green algae	27	63	23	92	58	7	19	30
Brown algae	56	93	41	51	55	3	4	4
Red algae	126	267	43	127	47·5	5	10	4
Total	209	423	107	270	56	15	33	38

they are simply an impoverished flora of the Mediterranean Sea. N. Morozova-Wodjanitzkaja points out also the small size of the Black Sea algae—on the average 10 to 30 cm. The largest, Cystozera, is not longer than 1.2 m.

Quantitative distribution of phytobenthos. In examining the quantitative distribution of macrophytes in the Black Sea it is necessary first of all to distinguish the marine flowering plant eel-grass which, as has been mentioned above, is represented in the Black Sea by two species. The main mass of eel-grass is found in the northeastern part of Karkinitsk Bay (Fig. 208), where it forms wide submarine meadows at depths of 0·5 to 6 m on sandy mud, at times

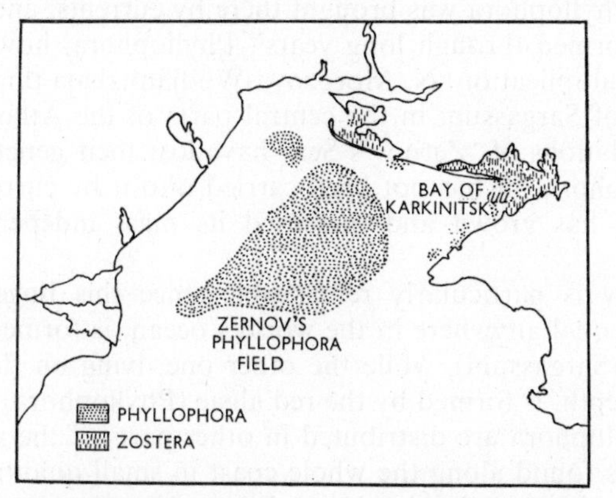

FIG. 208. Distribution of Phyllophora and Zostera growths in northwestern corner of Black Sea (Morozova-Wodjanitzkaja).

together with Ruppia and Potamogeton; it is found even deeper (down to15 or 20 m), but only in small amounts. It is found in small amounts along the whole coast of the Black Sea in its inlets and bays. In the most favourable environment the eel-grass biomass reaches 5 kg/m² (on the average 1·5 kg/m²). The abundant growths of eel-grass are concentrated off the Black Sea shores; in the shallows of Karkinitsk Bay they form a mass of no less than 200,000 tons, while V. Wodjanitzky has determined the total amount in the Black Sea as 1 million tons (1941). The epidemic caused by the fungus Labirintula, which afflicted the north Atlantic Zostera in the 'thirties, spread to the Black Sea and destroyed *Zostera marina* wholesale. Besides Zostera the eel-grass *Phyllophora rubens* var. *nervosa* should also be discussed separately. Phyllophora, probably a special ecological form, is found along the whole shore of the Black Sea, but 95 per cent of its total mass is concentrated in the northwestern part of the Sea (Fig. 208). This accumulation of algae, reckoned as not less than 5 to 6 million tons,* covers the mud–shell gravel floor in one huge mass over an area of about 15,000 km² in the region called 'Zernov's Phyllophora Sea' in honour of Academician S. Zernov, who discovered it

* V. Wodjanitzky (1941) determines the bulk of Phyllophora in the northwestern part of the Black Sea as 17 million tons, which is obviously an exaggeration.

in 1908. The magnitude of these accumulations is obvious from the fact that they are of the same order as those of the Sargassum weed in the Sargasso Sea. The accumulation of Phyllophora in the Black Sea is, possibly, the mightiest accumulation of red algae throughout the whole world ocean. The bulk of all the other macrophytes throughout the Black Sea is no more than 500,000 tons. Phyllophora occurs at a depth of 30 to 60 m, i.e. at places where macrophytes are not usually found in large numbers. On the average the density of Phyllophora is 1·7 kg/m^3, but in individual cases it reaches 13 kg/m^2. K. Meyer (1937) came to the conclusion 'that in the Phyllophora Sea we find a layer of Phyllophora which appears to have been torn from its original habitat in the littoral zone. Phyllophora was brought there by currents, and huge stocks of it have been formed through long years'. Phyllophora, however, retains its capacity for multiplication. N. Morozova-Wodjanitzkaja thinks that, like the accumulation of Sargassum in the central parts of the Atlantic, the Phyllophora accumulations of 'Zernov's Sea' have lost their genetic link with the coastal Phyllophora—it has not been carried into it by currents throughout the years, but has grown and increased its mass independently through vegetation.

This analogy is particularly remarkable since this huge accumulation, which has no equal anywhere in the world's ocean, is formed by the brown, drifting algae (Sargassum), while the other one, lying on the sea-floor at a considerable depth, is formed by the red algae (Phyllophora). Small accumulations of Phyllophora are distributed in other parts of the northwest of the Black Sea; it is found along the whole coast in small quantities. The occurrence of Phyllophora in the depths of the northwestern part of the Sea disturbs the general course of the decrease of macrophyte biomass with depth. Without Phyllophora this general course of decrease has the aspect shown in *Table 175*.

Table 175

Depth, m	Mean biomass of macrophytes in g/m^2
0–10 (coastal cliffs)	>1,000
10–20 (sand and shell gravel)	20
20–30	5
30–50	1
50–90	0·1

The algae biomass is usually no higher than 2·5 kg/m^2, rising rarely to 8 to 13 kg/m^2.

The specific composition of the predominant forms changes also with depth; however, the general order of the vertical change of algae remains: green—brown—red (*Table 176*).

Owing to the steep slope of the shores of the Black Sea the width of the littoral zone occupied by macrophytes is not great, usually 3 to 6 km, and at times only 1 km. It extends to 150 km only in the Odessa and Kirkinitsk Bays.

Table 176

Depth, m	Most common associations of macrophytes (N. Morozova–Wodjanitzkaja)	Mean biomass, kg/m²	Highest biomass, kg/m²
0–2	Conferva (Cladophora and Chaetomorpha) in bays	—	—
0–15	*Zostera marina* and *Z. minor*	1–1·5	4
0–23	*Cystoseira barbata*	1	6–7
4–35	Gracillaria, *Polysiphonia elongata*, Zanardinia		
25–35	*Phyllophora rubens*		

The macrophyte biomass of the littoral zone of the Black Sea (without the Phyllophora Sea vegetation) is only 0·5 million tons; moreover, the second place after Phyllophora is occupied by the brown alga *Cystoseira barbata*. The Cystoseira association produces at depths of 0·5 to 23–28 m a biomass of an average of 3 kg/m² (at times up to 6 or 7 kg/m²).

If 90 per cent of the total mass of the Black Sea macrophytes consists of Phyllophora, then about 9 per cent of it is Cystoseira, whereas all the other macrophytes form not more than about 0·7 per cent. Thus only two species of benthos bottom-living algae are markedly predominant in the Black Sea.

Whereas the littoral zone of the Black Sea is not as rich in macrophytes as the northern part of the Atlantic, its annual productivity is very near to that of the latter, and is even somewhat higher.

According to N. Morozova-Wodjanitzkaja (1941) the highest annual macrophyte productivity is observed in bays, inlets and lagoons (up to 17 kg/m², and 7 to 8 kg/m² in the open sea) (*Table 177*).

The qualitative composition of zoobenthos and fish fauna. The Black Sea fauna is on the average four or five times poorer than that of the Mediterranean; moreover, different groups vary in the degree of their impoverishment. Some groups could not penetrate into the Black Sea at all: such were Siphonophora, Gephyrea, Brachipoda, Scaphopoda and Cephalopoda, Enteropneusta and Salpae. Other groups became much poorer in the Black Sea, as for example Ctenophorae, corals, Amphineura, Echinodermata and Tunicata (*Table 178*).

The number of species of macrophytes and animals decreases greatly from the Black Sea to the Sea of Azov; this can be seen by the example of the polychaetes (according to V. Vorobieff, 1932) (*Table 179*). Evidently in the case of polychaetes the number of genera decreases more rapidly than that of the families, and that of the species more rapidly than that of the genera.

Lowered salinity (to 19‰) and the comparatively narrow habitable upper layer were the main factors preventing the Mediterranean fauna from settling in the Black Sea. V. Wodjanitzky (1936) has brought out this last factor as affecting the life of fish when writing 'that members of the Mediterranean ichthyofauna could settle in the Black Sea only when in all stages of their development they kept to the upper layers of water (or off the shores)'. In

Table 177

Group	Quantitative indices of some macrophytes in Novorossiysk region Mean biomass g/m²	Annual productivity g/m²	Ratio of productivity to biomass (*P*/*B*)
Brown algae			
Cystoseira barbata	2,348·9	4,605·0	1·96
Dilophus repens	39·7	201·5	5·08
Scytosiphon lamentarius	9·8	51·8	5·29
Cladostephus verticillatus	3·9	23·3	5·97
Green algae			
Chaetomorpha chlorotica	167·8	1,041·3	6·21
Enteromorpha intestinalis	71·6	290·5	4·06
Cladophora spp.	69·7	275·1	3·95
Ulva lactuca	93·6	314·1	3·36
Red algae			
Ceramium rubrum	34·8	197·0	5·66
Gelidum crinale	27·0	134·9	5·00
Polysiphonia subulifera	61·2	19·7	3·59
Flowering plants			
Zostera marina	19·4	64·1	3·30

his opinion, in discussing the colonization of the Black Sea by the Mediterranean fauna its most characteristic feature—the development of hydrogen sulphide in its deeper layers—should be kept in mind. Lowered salinity, however, is much more important as a limiting factor. As we have seen, a considerable number of animal groups living in the Mediterranean are either absent from the Black Sea, or represented there by some individual species.

A. Valkanov published in 1957 a list of fauna of the Bulgarian shore of the Black Sea. The list contains 343 species of four variants of Protozoa and 1,005 species and 23 variants of multicellular organisms. M. Bacesco's mentioning of the occurrence of the polychaetes *Monayunkia caspica* ssp. *fluviatilis* (*danubicus*), an evidently Pontic relic, in the lower reaches of river Danube is most interesting.

The process of the formation of Black Sea fauna is, possibly, incomplete as yet and new forms may continue to penetrate into the Black Sea from the Mediterranean. Two species of acorn barnacle (*Balanus amphitrite communis* and *B. perforatus* var. *angustus*), discovered by G. Zevina and N. Tarasov (1954) in the fouling of ships, may be included among the new immigrants from the Mediterranean to the Black Sea. Continuous migration of new flora and fauna forms from the Mediterranean may be seen from the example of phytoplankton. Some species of Mediterranean diatoms, recent arrivals from the Mediterranean (*Rhizosolenia calcar-avis*, *Örataulina bergoni* and *Leptocylindricus danicus*), have now become mass forms in the Black Sea.

Table 178

Group	Number of species* Mediterranean Sea	Black Sea	Black Sea species per cent of Mediterranean
Porifera	110	42	38
Coelenterata	208	44	21
including			
Scyphozoa	36	3	8·3
Ctenophora	16	1	6
Anthozoa	47	5	10·6
Mesozoa	10	?	
Plathelminthes	279	152	54·5
Nemertini	65	18	28
Nematoda	156	84 (15 parasites)	54
Kinorhyncha	17	9	53
Chaetognatha	6	3	3·3
Acantocephala	25	5	20
Gephyrea	29	1	3·4
Phoronoidea	1	1	100
Polychaeta	516	153	29·7
Pantopoda	37	5	14
Copepoda	304	77	25·3
Ostracoda	125	25	20
Cirripedia	43	4	9·3
Cladocera	5	6	120
Leptostraca	2	0	0
Amphipoda	223	70	31·4
Isopoda	159	32	20
Cumacea	22	12	55
Schizopoda	40	22	55
Decapoda	251	35	14
Amphineura	22	2	9
Lamellibranchiata	358	49	14
Gastropoda	965	74	7·7
Scaphopoda	14	0	0
Cephalopoda	72	0	0
Pteropoda	26	0	0
Bryozoa	306	12	4
Kamptozoa	11	1	9
Brachiopoda	23	0	0
Echinodermata	53	5	9·4
Tunicata	200	16	8
Enteropneusta	3	0	0
Branchiostomata	1	1	100
Pisces	549	180 (Mediterranean) 112)	
Reptilia	3	0	0
Mammalia	5	4	80
Total	5,244	1,145	21·8

* The number of species of the Mediterranean fauna apart from protozoa are taken from the book of Gr. Antipa (*Marea Neagra*), 1941.

Table 179. Number of polychaete families, genera and species

Sea	Families		Genera		Species	
	Total number	Per cent	Total number	Per cent	Total number	Per cent
Mediterranean	36	—	214	—	433	—
Black	24	66·6	77	36·0	123	28·4
Azov (except inlets and Sivash)	7	19·4	7	3·2	9	2·1

The Bosporus region, the most saline sector of the Black Sea, gives shelter to immigrants from the Mediterranean, which are not found anywhere else in the Black Sea. Twenty forms of this type, including anthozoa echinoderms, molluscs, polychaetes and others have been found there.

The heterogeneity of the Black Sea fauna is conditioned, like that of the Caspian Sea, by its past history and its lowered salinity. Its fauna comprises three main components: (*1*) relict autochthonous fauna (commonly called Pontic or Caspian); (*2*) Mediterranean immigrants, and (*3*) fresh-water forms. These three elements are partly territorially separated, partly mixed; this provided N. Knipovitch (1933) with an opportunity of giving a more detailed classification of the Black Sea fauna according to its habitat. Knipovitch distinguishes the following groups mostly from the instances of fish (see also *Table 180*).

1. Pontic relicts, which have survived only in the parts of the Black Sea with very much lowered salinity, especially in its inlets, and the fresh waters of the lower reaches of its rivers.

2. Pontic relicts inhabiting the Black Sea generally, but not met in the Sea of Azov; for example, some herrings: *Caspialosa nordmanni*, *C. pontica* and others.

3. Pontic relicts inhabiting both the Black Sea and the Sea of Azov. To this group belong the sturgeon family, some herrings, for example, the Azov herring (*Caspialosa maeotica*), and *C. tanaica* etc.

4. Mediterranean immigrants forming part of the settled population of the Black Sea. This includes the main mass of organisms living in the Black Sea.

5. Mediterranean immigrants, which appear in the Black Sea temporarily, and do not multiply in it.

Table 180. Composition of the Black Sea fish

	Total number of species and sub-species	Number of Pontic relicts	Number of Mediterranean immigrants	Number of fresh-water forms
According to Knipovitch (1932)	159	28	97	34
According to Slastenenko (1938)	180	31	112	37

6. Mediterranean immigrants, which feed and spawn in the summer in the Sea of Azov and come back to the Black Sea in winter; such as, for instance, the Azov form of anchovy.

7. Fresh-water forms.

As regards the wealth of species the following forms are notable: the autochthonous Acipenseridae (6 species), the mixed Clupeidae (9 species), the fresh-water Cyprinidae (23 species), the Mediterranean Mugilidae (5 species), partly the fresh-water Percidae (8 species), the Mediterranean Sparidae (8 species), Labridae (8 species), the mixed Gobiidae (22 species), the Mediterranean Blenniidae (8 species) and Syngnathidae (7 species).

Moreover, some forms, which penetrated into the Black Sea even earlier but do not multiply there, are growing acclimatized, forming some separate Black Sea colonies. Lobster, mackerel, Sarda, tuna and others can be included among these forms. Finally, there are some forms which used to spawn very rarely in the Black Sea before, but which within recent years have multiplied there annually in large numbers.

The Black Sea is supplemented also by occasional immigrants from more distant countries. V. Makarov (1941) has lately found in the Bug and Dnieper inlets a mass settlement of the crab *Rithropanopeus*, carried there on ships from the Zuyder Zee (Holland), which had come even earlier to the European shores from the coast of Northern America. The gastropod mollusc *Rapana bezoar* which has done incalculable harm to the oyster and Mytilus colonies, mainly off the Caucasian shores, came to the Black Sea from the Sea of Japan in a similar manner. Some Mediterranean forms, settled in the Black Sea, have found here particularly favourable conditions for development, and, although small in size, they form a very dense population. Thus there are the algae Phyllophora and Cystoseira; the molluscs *Teredo navalis*, *Cardium edule* and *Syndesmya ovata*; the polychaetes *Nereis diversicolor*, *N. cultrifera*, *N. succinea*, *Nephthys hombergii* and *Melinna palmata*, and a number of others.

The fauna which penetrated into the Black Sea has not yet had time to change much and to deviate from the original Mediterranean species. This demonstrates the youth of this fauna. Thus E. Slastenenko records (1938, a, b) only nine Black Sea endemic forms among 105 species and sub-species of fish of Mediterranean origin living in the Black Sea.* As early as 1902 Sovinsky pointed out that among the 680 Mediterranean immigrants only 194 (28 per cent) had evolved taxonomically separate forms. Frequently this evolution of the Black Sea forms into species and sub-species is temporary in character. Thus, for example, until lately anchovy inhabiting the Black Sea were divided into two sub-species: the Azov *Engraulis encrasicholus maeoticus* (I. Puzanov, 1936) and the Black Sea *E. e. ponticus* (I. Aleksandrov, 1927); moreover, it was proposed (A. Mayorova, 1934) to divide the latter into two regions—an eastern and a western. Moreover, there was a tendency to consider anchovy as a relict of the Tertiary Period. S. Maljatzky (1939), having reconsidered the whole of this problem, came to the conclusion that the anchovy

* A tenth—the pipefish *Syngnathus phlegon longicephalus*—described by V. Nikitin (*Transactions* of the Zoological Institute of the Georgian Academy of Sciences, 1946), may be added to them.

populations of the Mediterranean, Black and Azov Seas are not isolated from each other, but to a certain extent are constantly mingling with each other, forming only local ecological varieties. Maljatzky does not consider anchovy as a relict in the Black Sea. In exactly the same manner V. Zalkin (1938) does not consider the Black Sea dolphin *Phocaena relicta* as an individual species. It is only a sub-species, and is likewise not a Tertiary relict but a form which arrived in the Black Sea recently.

The characteristic features of the distribution of fauna in the Bosporus and the Sea of Marmora, conditioned by a gradual general decrease of salinity from the Dardanelles to the Bosporus and by the existence of two currents in the Bosporus and the region round it—the upper Black Sea current and the deep, much more saline one—were established by the researches of Ostroumov in the nineties of the last century. The boundary between the two currents sinks gradually as one approaches the Black Sea. Off Constantinople it lies at a depth of 20 m, and at the entrance into the Bosporus at 50 m. As a result the upper-layer fauna has a Black Sea character, and that of the deeper layer a Mediterranean one. A. Ostroumov (1893–6) has recorded 60 forms, also found in the Black Sea, in his collection of the coastal fauna in the Bosporus area. On the other hand, in deeper layers the fauna has a markedly Mediterranean character. Already at a distance of 18 km from the entrance into the Black Sea, 49 per cent of the molluscs and more than 50 per cent of the amphipods were found to be extraneous to the Black Sea. Sea lilies, sea urchins, sea stars, the Siphonophora Dimophyes, and eight-rayed corals were found here. Off the Prinkipo Islands 70 per cent of molluscs did not belong to the Black Sea.

The surface plankton of the Sea of Marmora is also under considerable influence from the dominant Black Sea forms, but below 20 to 30 m it has a typically Mediterranean character.

Qualitative-biocoenotic characteristics of zoobenthos. More than 50 years ago S. Zernov, in his work 'On the study of the life of the Black Sea' (1912), gave a very full picture of the qualitative-biocoenotic distribution of the Black Sea bottom-living fauna. The scheme given by Zernov has been neither changed nor substantially supplemented by further researches. It appear ass *Table 181*, and Figs. 209, 210 and 211.

Biocoenoses of supralittoral and pseudolittoral. Having reconsidered the question of the existence of a 'littoral' zone in the Black Sea, L. Arnoldi (1948) came to the conclusion that 'from the biological point of view there is no theoretical difference between the flood- and ebb-tide phenomena as such, and the fluctuations of the sea-level, which depend equally on the flood-tides of cosmic origin and on the seiche (wind-induced tides)'. Confirming the existence of a littoral zone in the Black Sea, Arnoldi distinguishes a Black Sea type of littoral, using the word 'pseudolittoral' for it. A supralittoral (a zone washed only by the surf) lies above the pseudolittoral.

O. Mokievsky, having very carefully studied the littoral fauna of the western shores of the Crimea (1949), within the zone of distribution of marine organisms above sea-level, also distinguishes two separate zones of amphibiotic life—the supralittoral and pseudolittoral. In his view the first 'corresponds completely to the supralittoral of the open seas, the second—the overwash zone or pseudolittoral—is analogous to the true littoral . . . the pseudolittoral, like the true littoral, is subject to periodic drainage and flooding, since it is

FIG. 209. General picture of distribution of Black Sea bottom fauna (Zernov's data slightly altered). *1* Crab Pachygrapsus; *2* Barnacle Balanus; *3* Mollusc Patella; *4* Brown alga Cystoseira; *5* Green alga Ulva and Enteromorpha; *6* Sea mussel (Mytilus); *7* Actinia; *8* Sea-urchin; *9* Nemertines Lineus; *10* Lower worms Saccocirrus; *11* Amphipoda (scuds); *12* Mollusc Venus; *13* Red mullet; *14* Flat fish Rhombus; *15* Crab-hermet Diogenes; *16* Zostera; *17* Pipe fish; *18* Crenilabrus; *19* Sea-horse; *20* Shrimp Leander; *21* Oysters; *22* Sea-robin Pecten; *23* Mussel; *24* Red Porifera Phyllophora; *25* Red Porifera Suberites; *26* Ascidian Ciona; *27* Phaseolin mollusc (*Modiola phaseolina*); *28* Brittle star Amphiura; *29* Mollusc Throphonopsis; *30* Medusa *Pilema pulmo*; *31* Ctenophora Pleurobrachia; Hydrogen sulphide.

situated within the limits of the fluctuation of deep-water waves'. In Mokievsky's opinion the supralittoral lies above the limit of overwash, and the water impregnating it enters the beach owing to its capillarity.

The bivalves *Donacilla cornea* and the polychaete *Ophelia bicornia* (*Oph. taurica* ?) are the mass forms of the pseudolittoral of the Crimean coast. In some cases Donacilla gives a biomass of up to 689 g/m^2 and 3,100 specimens per m^2, and Ophelia yields 394 g/m^2 and 400 specimens per m^2. Apart from these two dominant forms the following are fairly common: the amphipod *Pontogammarus maeoticus*, with a maximum biomass of 83 g/m^2 and greatest number of specimens of 11,800 per m^2; *Mytilus mysid*, *Gastrosaccus sanctus*, the isopod *Euridice pulchra*, and the polychaetes (Spionidae) *Nerine cirratus* and *Nerinides cantabra*. *Sphaeroma serratum* and *Idothea baltica* are much

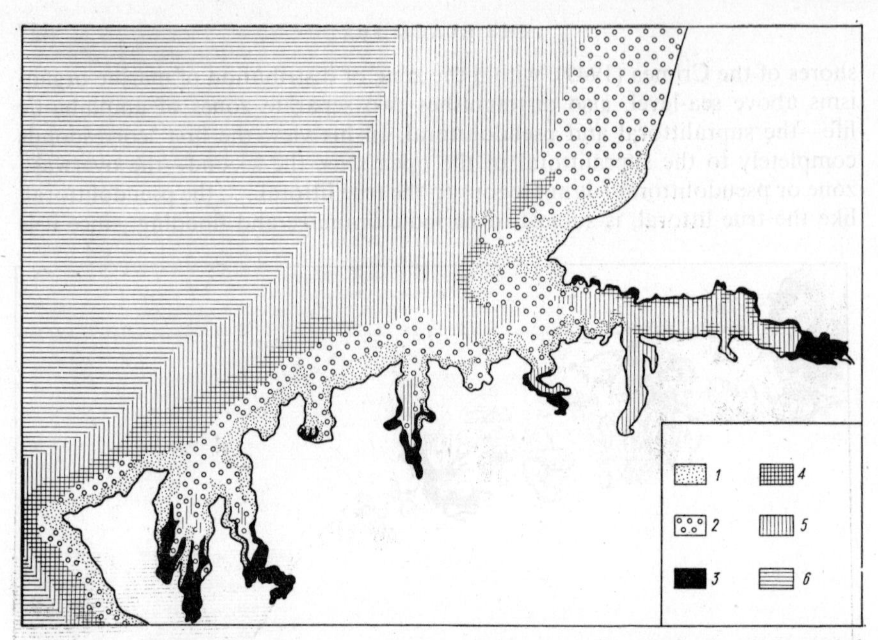

FIG. 210. Chart of distribution of bottom biocoenoses in Black Sea, Sebastopol region (Zernov, 1912). *1* Biocoenosis populating cliffs overgrown with Cystoseira, with some patches of sand; *2* Biocoenosis populating cliff sand and gravel and very fine shell gravel; *3* Biocoenosis populating Zostera and water-weed beds; *4* Biocoenosis living on oyster banks; *5* Mussel mud biocoenosis; *6* Phaseolin ooze biocoenosis.

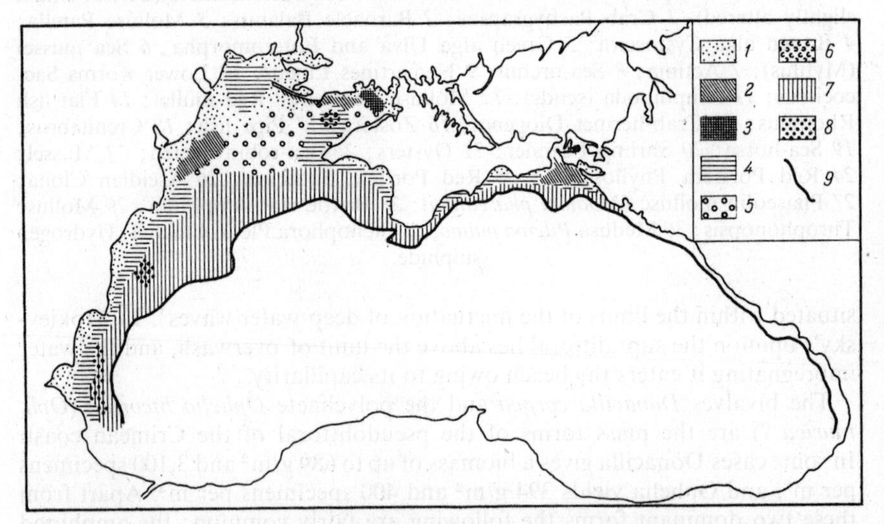

FIG. 211. Distribution of bottom biocoenoses in the northern part of Black Sea. *1* Coastal sand and cliff biocoenoses; *2* Shell gravel biocoenoses; *3* Biocoenosis of Zostera growths; *4* Mussel mud biocoenosis; *5* Phyllophora growth biocoenosis; *6* Biocoenosis of dead Zostera out by the Sea; *7* Phaseolin ooze biocoenosis; *8* Biocoenosis of Terebellide ooze; *9* Limit of life (Zernov, 1912).

rarer crustaceans of the pseudolittoral. In Mokievsky's opinion the population of the supralittoral is characterized by the amphipod *Talorchestia deshayesei* with a maximum biomass of 121 g/m^2 and a maximum number of specimens of up to 48,400 per m^2, and by the isopod *Tylos latrelei* var. *pontica* with a high population-density (up to 129 g/m^2 and 11,800 specimens per m^2) and also, among specimens washed ashore, some insects, arachnids and oligochaetes, and the amphipods *Orchestia gamarellus* and *Orchestia montagui.*

The biocoenosis of the inhabitants of the coastal cliffs and immobile rocks sinks at times in the open parts of the Sea to a depth of 28 m; more usually, however, to 15 m, and inside inlets to a few metres only. Above sea-level a true littoral fauna finds shelter on the cliffs, although there are no tides in the Black Sea. 'Together with the algae (Scythosiphon, Ceramium, Enteromorpha, Corallina) some molluscs, *Littorina neritoides* and *Patella pontica*; the barnacles *Chthamalus stellatus*; the crabs *Pachygrapsus marmoratus* and *Eriphia spinifrons*; the isopod *Lygia brandtii* (which lives only above sea-level), and the land snail *Aplexia myosothis* (under the rocks) come out of the water, sometimes to a height of two or three metres above it.

On the more sloping shores, at the very edge of the water and slightly above it, dead eel-grass, Cystoseira, Phyllophora and other algae are commonly washed ashore. A specific refuse fauna washed up by the Sea settles down on these heaps of dead plants, and especially under them, a mass of oligochaetes, amphipods and isopods.

Just below sea-level thick growths of Cystoseira invest all the cliffs with a dense covering; there are also some *Mytilus galloprovincialis*. In more polluted places Cystoseira is replaced by green algae, sea lettuce and sea grass. Apart from Cystoseira the cliffs are overgrown, to a much lesser extent, by other seaweeds. These sea-weed beds are inhabited, besides the forms mentioned, by a large number of gastropods: Rissoa, *Nassa reticulata*, Trochus; the cliff oyster; the crab *Xantho rivulosus*; the shrimps *Hippolyte varians* and *Leander squilla*; many Porifera, hydroids, bryozoans (especially Membranipora) and polychaetes, often with lime tubes, amphipods and isopods. Rock-burrowing molluscs, commonly *Petricola lithophaga*, bore passages through the cliffs.

Sand and mud shore biocoenoses. These produce a whole number of modifications depending on the depth of their occurrence and on the structure of the floor; they sometimes spread down to 18 to 27 m. The coarser sand stretching directly from the water's edge, called by Zernov 'Saccocirrus sand', gives shelter to an original fauna of worms. It is inhabited by a number of Turbelaria, *Procerodes lobata* and *Cercyra papillosa*; by the archiannelides *Saccocirrus papillocercus* and *Protodrilus flavocapitatus*; the polychaetes Nerine and *Spio ornatus*; by nemerteans, *Lineus lacteus*, *Eunemertes gracilis*, *Borlasia vivipara*; various amphipods and nematodes; the gastropods *Nassa reticulata* and Rissoa; hermit crabs (*Diogenes varians*); decapod crayfish, *Gebia littoralis* and *Calianassa subterranea*; and, under the rocks, a great number of isopods, Sphaeroma and Idothea. Farther up the bays, on the slightly silted saccocirrus sand, live a number of polychaetes: Arenicola, Glycera and Nereis.

Table 181

Open sea and more open bays		Closed inlets, harbours and seaports	
Rocks	Sand	Rocks, silty sand, artificial constructions	
Biocoenosis inhabiting coastal cliffs washed by waves and surf	Biocoenosis inhabiting Saccocirrus sand, beaches at and above sea-level	Mud shore biocoenosis with Nereis and Arenicola on cliffs and constructions above sea-level	Area, surface layers subject to violent action of waves Littoral zone Continental shelf
Biocoenosis characteristic of the upper line of Cystoseira growths	Biocoenosis in 5–9 m Cystoseira bed. Below it and commonly instead of it in the open sea, rocky sand or shell-gravel with Gouldia, Meretrix, *Tapes*, *Venus* or *Amphioxus* sand, at a mean depth of 21 m	Biocoenoses of Ulva, Enteromorpha and Zostera growths, silty sand with Cardium, Syndesmya, Vermes, Cystoseira on cliffs and piers	
Biocoenosis of the shell-gravel dwellers, less frequently of oyster bank		Biocoenosis of oyster bank, or mussel mud replacing it	Area, in the depths, unaffected by wave action Sublittoral zone Continental shelf
Isobath 27–55 m		Isobath 7–17 m	
Biocoenosis of mussel mud, at a mean depth of 38 m down to 55–66 m		Biocoenosis of mussel mud and Mellina mud	
Biocoenosis of Terebellides mud		None	
Biocoenosis of phaseolin mud, at a mean depth of 105 m		None	
Isobath 180 m			
The realm of hydrogen sulphide, below 180 m			

The small bivalves Cardium, Syndesmya and Loripes live in deeper places (22 to 25 m) on fine and dense sand; while on the bottom live *Gebia littoralis*; the crab *Portunus holsatus*, and a number of fish: Gobius, Blennius, Uranoscopus, Mullus and others.

At the same depths on coarser sand, with an admixture of shell gravel-lives an abundant fauna of worms: a large number of Turbellaria and poly, chaetes; the interesting archiannelid *Polygordius ponticus*; and a remarkable inhabitant of the Black Sea *Branchiostoma* (*Amphioxus*) *lanceolata*. At times the holothurians *Synapta digitata* and *S. hispida* and gerbil are found here in large numbers.

Some molluscs also are likewise most characteristic of sand bottoms; among the gastropods *Nassa reticulata*, and among the bivalves *Venus gallina*, *Gouldia minima*, *Divaricella divaricata*, *Merethrix rudis*, *Calyptraea chinensis*, *Mactra subtruncata*, *Tapes proclivis*, *Mytilus galloprovincialis*, *Cardium exiguum* and others.

As has been said above, at the head of the bays and inlets the facies of the rocks is gradually more and more reduced, while the sands become covered with mud. Inside all the bays and inlets, in quieter places protected from the waves, growths of Zostera, sheltering a very typical bottom-living fauna, are found everywhere at depths of 5·5 and even down to 9 m. *Z. marina* lives preferably on silt and silty sand floors, but *Z. minor* prefers pure sand. Zernov gives the following characteristics of the fauna of Zostera growths: 'A large number of mysids, amphipods, isopods, shrimps, different genera and species of pipefish, *Grenilabrus tinca* and other fish, the Medusa Cladonema and Sagitta (Spadella) swim among the Zostera leaves; innumerable Rissoa with Syllids planted on their shells crawl about their leaves, as well as many Tergipes; masses of various Rhabdocoela and Acoela; Cerithiolum, which are found there in immense masses, *Trochus* and other molluscs. At the approach of autumn Zostera becomes covered with bryozoans: Lepralia, Membranipora and the tunicates Didemnidae, which die off in the winter, causing the Zostera to sink under the weight of these accretions. Among the roots of Zostera there hide amphiurae, Stenelais, Lagis, Rhynchobolus, Gebia, Calianassa, Syndesmya, Cardium, Gastrana and other molluscs which live on sand, and in the more muddy places very numerous polychaetes, chiefly the two species *Nereis cultrifera* and *N. diversicolor*, but also Nephthys, Glycera, Arenicola, Lagis and others.

Somewhat higher than the Zostera growths, in the silts near sea-level, the same polychaetes which hide under Zostera roots live in large numbers: Arenicola, Nereis, Glycera and others.

Shell-gravel biocoenosis. At the lower limit of the zone of sand and Zostera growths, where the slightly muddy sand gradually passes into silty sand and sandy mud, there lies along the shore a fairly wide band of the so-called shell gravel—an accumulation of living and dead molluscs, mostly bivalves. Shell gravel is specially well displayed in places where, in Zernov's words, 'the effect of the waves is already too weak to break and powder it to sand, but is still strong enough to carry the main mass of silt particles over them and farther and deeper out into the Sea'. Shell gravel usually occupies separate, isolated areas on the shores of the Black Sea, not forming a continuous band. Well up inside the bays it usually rises to a depth of a few metres, while in the open sea it may be as deep as 55 to 65 m. Shell gravel consists mainly of the molluscs which inhabit the sand lying above it; it contains an admixture of oysters, mussels and some other forms. An oyster form called *Ostrea sublamellosa* (cliff oyster) lives on the cliffs, and the *O. taurica* variety (bank oyster) lives on the oyster-beds (Fig. 212).

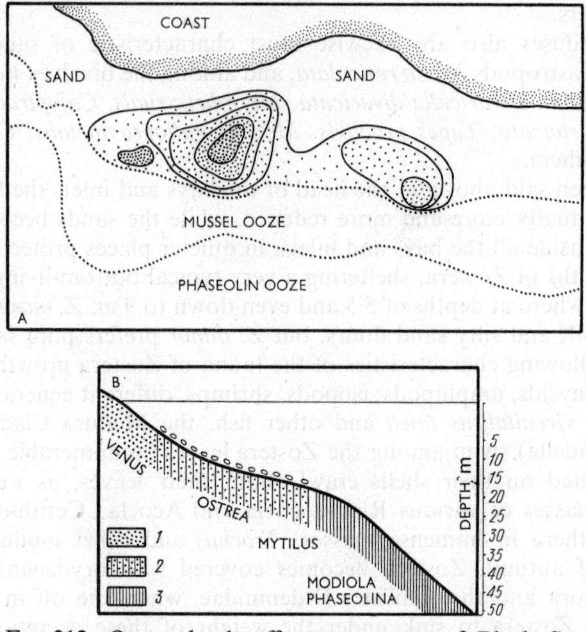

FIG. 212. Oyster bank off eastern coast of Black Sea (Nikitin, 1934). A in plan. B cross-section; *1* Sand with Venus; *2* Oyster bank; *3* Phaseolin ooze.

Thus the oyster-bed is a variety of shell gravel. Shell gravel is separated from the zone of sand lying above it by imperceptible stages, while the biocoenosis of deeper-lying mussel- and phaseolin-oozes is separated from the shell gravel much more sharply.

Apart from oyster the following molluscs are components of this biocoenosis: *Mytilus galloprovincialis*, *Pecten ponticus*, *Tapes rugatus*, *Venus gallina*, *Cardium edule*, *C. exiguum*, *Modiola adriatica*, *Merethrix rudis*, *Nassa reticulata*, *Gouldia minima* and others; it contains also the crustaceans Porcellana, Athanas, *Portunus arcuatus* and *P. marmoreus*; the hermit crab *Diogenes varians*; *Balanus improvisus*; a mass of polychaetes, sponges (especially the small boring sponge *Cliona stationis*) and hydroids. The shell-gravel biocoenosis is the Black Sea group which is richest in its composition.

H. Caspers supplements the picture of the biocoenosis range of the Black Sea bottom-living fauna given by Zernov with data related to the Gulf of Varna (Fig. 213). He distinguishes the following biocoenoses: a littoral one, with *Pachygrapsus* zostera; a sandy one with Corbula; that of the cliffs with Sabellaria and Pectinaria; and that of the central part and shell gravel.

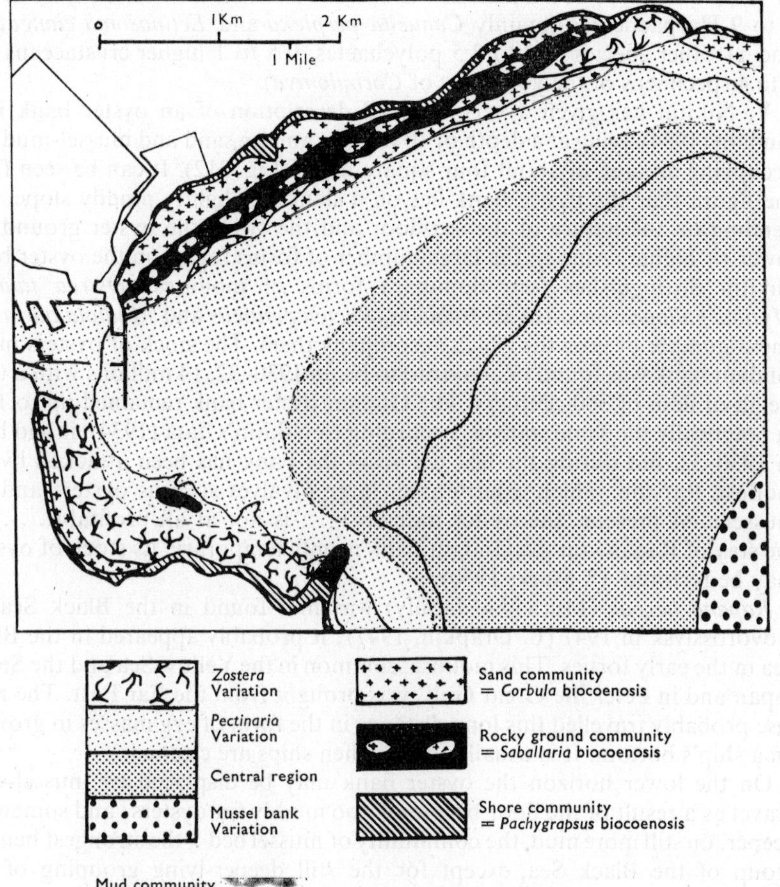

FIG. 213. Distribution of main bottom communities in Gulf of Varna (Caspers, 1957).

M. Bacesko (1957) has given a detailed description of the *Corbulomya maeotica* biocoenosis off the Rumanian coast of the Black Sea on littoral sand at depths of 1 to 20 m. This biocoenosis provides the basic stock of food for benthos-eating fish: Acipenseridae, flatfish, Mugilidae, bullhead, etc. The average biomass of this biocoenosis is 360 g/m² (with fluctuations from 280 to 1,034 g/m²), and the number of Corbulomya specimens reaches 145,000 per m². Besides Corbulomya, which sometimes furnishes up to 97 per cent by weight of the biocoenosis, the following are the most common: *Nassa neritea*, Venus, Angulus, *Paramysis kroyeri*, Cumopsis, *Pseudocuma longicornis pontica*, Gastrosaccus, *Pontogammarus maeoticus*, Nerine, Aricidea, *Spio filicornis* and others. Apart from macrobenthos the author gives the first comprehensive description of the microbenthos of the Black Sea. One cubic centimetre of sand was found to contain 250 to 900 Foraminifera, 50 to 120 nematodes, 1 to 9 Harpacticidae (mainly *Canuella perplexa* and *Ectinosoma elongatum*) and 11 other species (0·5 to 2·5 polychaetes, 0·5 to 1 higher crustaceans and 1 to 4 specimens of the young fry of *Corbulomya*).

V. Nikitin has given a very detailed description of an oyster bank near Gudaut (1934), lying at a depth of 10 to 30 m among sand and mussel-mud and occupying an area of about four square miles (Fig. 212). It can be seen from the figure that the oyster bank lies on a slanting, slightly muddy slope. Depending on the nature of the sea-floor and the swell, the oyster ground lies lower or higher. Among the large number of forms found on the oyster bank Nikitin distinguishes four dominant forms of molluscs: *Ostrea taurica*, *Mytilus galloprovincialis* var. *frequens*, *Pecten ponticus* and *Modiola adriatica*, and a number of growths which accompany them. The stock of oysters in the Gudaut bank was found (V. Nikitin) to be, in 1930–32, 14 millions with a total weigh of flesh of 300 centners. The Gudaut oyster bank remained up to 1949 in practically the same state as, according to Nikitin's data (1934), it had been in 1930–32, but during the last ten years the bank has been attacked by the mollusc Rapana, which exterminates large bivalves such as oysters and sea mussels. At present 'the oyster industry . . . is not at all profitable. . . . If the stay of Rapana on the Gudaut bank is only temporary, its stock of oysters may be restored' (I. Stark, 1950).

Rapana bezoar (Muricidae family) was first found in the Black Sea off Novorossiysk in 1947 (E. Drapkin, 1947); it probably appeared in the Black Sea in the early forties. This mollusc, common in the Yellow Sea and the Sea of Japan and in Peter the Great Gulf, was brought from the Far East. The mollusc probably travelled this long distance in the form of egg masses in growths on a ship's bottom. It is usually found when ships are cleaned.

On the lower horizon the oyster bank may be displaced by mussel-shell gravel as a result of the floor becoming too muddy for oysters; and somewhat deeper, on still more mud, the community of mussel bed—the strongest benthic group of the Black Sea, except for the still deeper-lying grouping of the phaseolin ooze—comes into force. As has been pointed out by Zernov, the fauna of the mussel-ooze 'is really, in most cases, the shell gravel fauna, except for oysters and other forms which cannot tolerate the ooze, so that mussels have taken up the dominant position'. Farther up, at the tops of the bays and inlets, the upper boundary of the mussel-ooze community rises to 9 to 11 m below the surface (off Odessa even to 1 m below the surface), while in the open sea it occupies a zone 55 to 78 m deep. For the mussel-ooze besides the dominant form—mussel—the following are most characteristic: among the molluscs; *Cardium simile*, *Meretrix rudis* and Tapes; the huge colonies of hydroids, *Aglaophenia pluma* and *Serturella polyzonias*; the tunicates: *Ascidiella aspersa*, *Ciona intestinalis*, *Botryllus schlosseri*, *Eugyra adriatica*;

and frequently large numbers of the nemerteans *Cerebratulus kowalevskyi*; the ooze-polychaetes *Melinna palmata* and *Terebellides strömii*; and the brittle star *Amphiura florifera*. Among the crustaceans the most typical is *Crangon crangon*. Among the plants Phyllophora is very characteristic. The most interesting feature of this group is the huge mass development of a typical littoral form—the sea mussel at depths of 27 to 65 m. In many places thesea mussel goes down in ocean and seas with tides to depths unusual to it as a littoral form; this occurs either in tideless seas with no littoral (the Baltic and the Mediterranean Seas), or owing to unfavourable conditions prevailing on the littoral (Cheskaya Guba). However, nowhere does the sea mussel accumulate in such huge masses at such low levels as in the Black Sea. In the Mediterranean (in the vicinity of Naples) the sea mussel does not go lower than 10 m. The cause of this mass development of sea mussel at a considerable depth must be sought in biocoenotic relationships. Apparently at higher levels sea mussel encounters some restricting rivals, which are absent at depths where the mussel bed occurs. The main species of mussel which inhabits the bed evolved an independent variety—*Mytilus galloprovincialis* var. *frequens*; this is also of interest.

The biocoenosis of the Phyllophora field. On some sectors of mussel bed, in quiet depths, huge accumulations of live (Phyllophora) or dead (Zostera) plants are formed and carried away by the currents. We have already mentioned the existence of a colossal accumulation of Phyllophora in the middle of the Sevastopol–Danube–Odessa area at depths of 27 to 55 m (mostly at 35–45 m). 'The Phyllophora fauna is very poor', writes Zernov, 'almost all the organisms living on Phyllophora are coloured brown-red—in full harmony with the colour of Phyllophora itself.

'The crustaceans such as Amphipoda, Isopoda are the most numerous here; there are some crabs (*Portunus arcuatus*), a few polychaetes, molluscs and small fish. Apparently the huge beds of Phyllophora prevent any considerable development of animal life.'

The biocoenosis populating the dead plants on the sea-bottom is specially well developed at depths of 35 to 45 m in Karkinitsk Bay, where Zostera, brought out from inside the bay, which is entirely overgrown by this sea-weed, is gathered in large masses. It is abundant also in the Bay of Taman and other places on the Black Sea coast. Masses of Amphipoda, Mysidae, Decapoda, molluscs, Turbellaria, and some small fish live in the accumulations of dead plants.

The phaseolin-ooze biocoenosis. This is even more original than that of the mussel. It is the deepest zone of benthic life in the Black Sea. Usually found first at 55 to 65 m (at times at 40 to 45 m; in some places at 80 m) with a sharp transition from the mussel-mud, the phaseolin ooze reaches on the average a depth of 180 to 185 m. *Modiola phaseolina* is the main component of this group.

Modiola phaseolina is an interesting example of the ecological aspect of many representatives of the Mediterranean fauna in the Black Sea. Outside the Black Sea *M. phaseolina* is widely distributed in the Atlantic Ocean, as far as the shores of Norway to the north, and is particularly abundant off the shores of England. It is comparatively rare in the Mediterranean Sea. *M. phaseolina* has a very wide vertical range; it is found from the littoral to shallow depths in the Atlantic Ocean, mostly to 100 m, and on hard or rocky sea-floors. In the Black Sea it is most abundantly developed at depths of 65 to 100 m, living only on soft mud floors, not rising above 40 m and not sinking down below 167 m (L. Yakubova, 1948). Almost everywhere in the Black Sea *M. phaseolina* is a dominant form at depths below 60 m, with a few hundred specimens per m^2.

Of other organisms commonly thriving in phaseolin mud one can point to the molluscs *Cardium simile*, *Syndesmya alba* and *Trophonopsis breviatus*; the sponge *Suberites domuncula*; the actinia *Cerianthus cestitus* and *Cyliste vicuata*; the worms *Terebellides strömi*, *Melinna palmata* and *Nephthys cirrosa*; the crustacean *Crangon crangon*; a number of amphipods; the echinoderms *Amphiura florifera* and *Cucumaria orientalis*; the tunicates *Ctenicella appendiculata*, *Eugyra adriatica*, and *Ciona intestinalis*. *Modiola phaseolina*, *Melinna palmata*, *Cerianthus vestitus* and *Amphiura florifera* are predominant among all these forms.

Sea-weeds become rare at 80 to 90 m; below this lies the pseudo-abyssal and its only group is the fauna of the phaseolin ooze.

The filter-feeding phenomenon. The bottom-living population of the Black Sea is characterized by a strong development of filter-feeding phenomena. Accumulations of bivalves (typical filter-feeders) and among them the ones of greatest mass—sea-mussel, oyster, Mytilaster and Modiola (*Modiola adriatica* and *M. phaseolina*)—form a wide ring from the water's edge to the limit of inhabited depth. The capacity of filter-feeders is huge, and the upper column of sea water permanently exposed to their action is freed from microsestonic suspension. The effect of the filter organisms on the bottom soils of the Black Sea is just as important. Ooze deposits are a result of their fecal pellets. In this way the apparently contradictory fact of large accumulations of sea-mussels being adapted to soft-deposit zones can be reconciled. Soft soils occur in quiet zones, and the sea-mussel usually inhabits well-washed areas of the sea-bed. Evidently the mussel-shell deposit areas, and partly those of phaseolin ooze, are by no means quiet zones; moreover, the soft ooze here may be formed by the molluscs themselves and may have a biogenic character. Without the filter organisms the oozes would not have been deposited in masses in these zones. However, this is so far only a hypothesis, which needs to be proved.

Fauna zonation. L. Yakubova (1935) used the qualitative distribution of the Black Sea benthos as a basis for the classification of the fauna according to three coastal zones (Fig. 214).

I. The eastern half of the Sea, from the southern coast of the Crimea, along the Caucasian coast and the eastern part of the coast of Anatolia. Yakubova considers the fauna of this area as the most typical of the Black Sea at present.

II. The southwestern zone, open to the influence of the more saline waters of the Bosporus, including the western part of the Anatolian coast and the southern half of its eastern part. A number of species not found in other parts of the Black Sea have been recorded here. Tuna, swordfish, lobster and a number of invertebrates are fairly common here. An exchange of fauna proceeds continuously between the Black Sea and the Sea of Marmora through the Bosporus. The waters of the Sea of Marmora, carrying its characteristic fauna, penetrate into the Black Sea by the lower current. Such

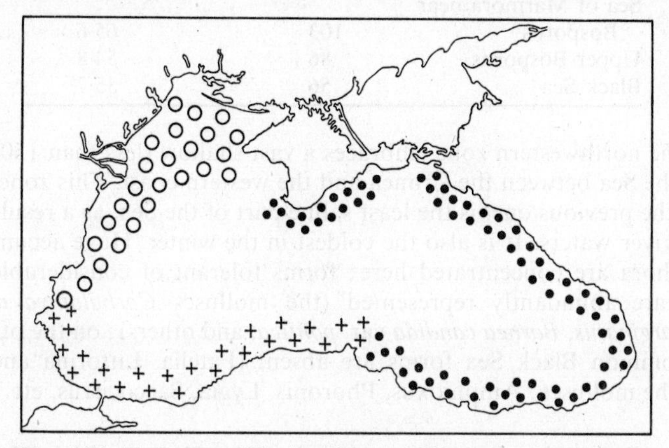

FIG. 214. Zoogeographical regions of Black Sea (Yakubova) (see text).

typical Mediterranean plankton as the Siphonophora Diphyes, the Radiolaria Acanthometra, and the polychaete Tomopteris are found in the Bosporus area of the Black Sea.

A number of the Mediterranean benthic forms have been discovered in the Bosporus region of the Black Sea, within the sphere of the lower Bosporus currents; these forms, apparently, do not penetrate very far into the Black Sea (Nikitin, 1927, Jakubova, 1948, Băcesko, 1959). They have been recorded at depths of 38 to 94 m (more than 60 species) and include such forms as the Coelenteratae *Phellia elongata* and *Virgularia mirabilis*; the echinoderms *Ostergrenia adriatica*, *Ophiura texturata*, *Ophiothrix echinata* and *Cucumaria orientalis*; the molluscs *Nucula sulcata*, *Turitella communis*, *Murex tarentinus*, *Venus bragniarti*, *Nassa incrassata*, *Corbula gibba*, *Fissurella graeca*, *Natica fusca*, *Gibbula deversa*, *Schismope striatula*, *Cyclonassa brusinai*, *Pandocia singularis*; the worms *Phascolosoma minuta*, *Paronais lira*, *Proclea graffi*, *Drilonereis filum*, *Polidora antennata*, *Sternaspis scuttata*; the crustaceans *Cymodoce erythrea euxinica*, *Elaphognathia monodi*, *Pontotanais borceai*, *Colomastix pusillus*, *Harpinia della-vallei*, *Philomedes interpuncta*, *Citereis jonesii*; 20 species of the Foraminifera and many others. They chiefly extend to the north along the western shores of the Sea.

The Bosporus fauna forms a kind of intermediate link between the faunas of the Black Sea and the Sea of Marmora.

O. Ostroumov (1894) gave an illustration of this fact, from the example of bivalves, as set out in *Table 182*.

Table 182

Area	No. of Mediterranean genera	Ratio of Mediterranean to Archipelago genera
Archipelago	157	100
Sea of Marmora near Bosporus	103	65·6
Upper Bosporus	86	54·8
Black Sea	56	35·7

III. The northwestern zone embraces a vast shallow (less than 150 m deep) part of the Sea between the Crimea and the western coast. This zone, in contrast to the previous one, is the least saline part of the Sea, as a result of dilution by river waters. It is also the coldest in the winter. Huge accumulations of Leophora are concentrated here; forms tolerant of considerable loss of salinity are abundantly represented (the molluscs *Corbulomya maeotica*, *Solen marginatus*, *Barnea candida* var. *pontica*, and others); on the other hand many common Black Sea forms are absent (Patella, Littorina and Pecten among the molluscs; Amphioxus, Phoronis, Lygia, Saccocirrus, etc.).

The lower limit of benthos. As mentioned above the lower limit of plankton distribution in the Black Sea slopes from west to east. The same is observed for benthos. V. Nikitin has shown (1938) that the lower limit of benthos runs at different depths in different areas (Fig. 215) (*Table 183*).

Only in the Bosporus area does the lower limit of benthos go down to a depth of 170 to 200 m. The area occupied by benthos is about 2,900 km². Hence in the areas of circular currents plankton penetrates deeper than benthos by about 25 to 40 m. The total area occupied by benthos in the Black Sea is 95,360 km² or a little more than 23 per cent of the total Sea area. The lower limit of bottom-life is related to a considerable decrease of oxygen-content (2 to 5 per cent) and an increase of carbon dioxide (pH 7·7 to 7·6).

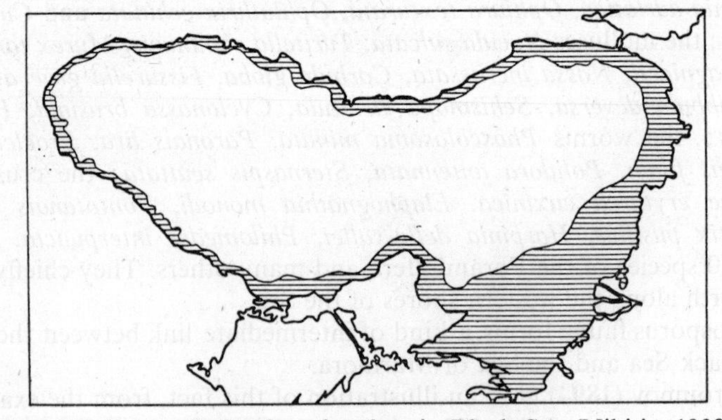

FIG. 215. Lower limit of zoobenthos in Black Sea (Nikitin, 1938).

Table 183. Depth of lower limit of benthos, m, and area of sea-bed occupied by benthos, km²

	Off western coast	In northwestern part	Off southern coast	Off Crimean coast	Off Caucasian coast
Depth	125–127	115–125	130–135	127–135	135–165
Sea-bed area	12,500	57,600	9,500	6,800	6,000

L. Yakubova pointed out (1935) that of the individual forms *Modiola phaseolina* penetrates deepest (180 m); then came *Amphiura stepanovi* (165), *Nephthys hombergii* (162); *Cerianthus vestitus* and *Melinna palmata* do not quite reach such depths. *Terebellides stroemi, Syndesmya alba, Cardium simile, Mytilus galloprovincialis* and Phoronis go down as far as 130 m. *Eugyra adriatica* (125 m) and *Suberites domuncula* live in rather shallower waters.

Quantitative distribution of zoobenthos. As distinct from all the other seas of the European part of the U.S.S.R., we possess only scarce data on the quantitative distribution of the Black Sea bottom-living fauna. For the purpose mentioned we can use only certain indications from the works of V. Wodjanitzky (1941), V. Nikitin (1938), V. P. Vorobieff (1938), L. Arnoldi (1941) and O. Mokievsky (1949).

As has been mentioned in the introductory chapter, the high summer temperature of the surface layer of the Black Sea brings about, especially in the enclosed bays, a high intensity of biological productivity. In summer on free surfaces, growths give a biomass of up to 30 or 40 kg/m². A thick pile of 30 to 35 cm diameter may be destroyed almost completely by marine borers in the three summer months (July to September).* The rock-burrowing molluscs are represented in the Black Sea by four species: *Petricola lithophaga, Barnea candida* var. *pontica, Pholas dactylus* and *Gastrochaena dubia* (V. Nikitin, 1951). Uninterrupted colonies of *Barnea candida* var. *pontica* and *Pholas dactilus* with a population-density of up to 2,500 specimens/m² have been discovered on the bare marl shale off the Caucasian shores.

M. Dolgopol'skaya (1954) has given the results of her experimental research on fouling in the Black Sea. The total annual weight of the fouling is up to 100 kg/m²; the main fouling organisms are: balanus, sea-mussels, bryozoa, ascidians and oysters. V. Wodjanitzky has pointed out (1941) that on mussel-shell gravel at 10 to 25 m deep the benthos biomass can reach 3·7 kg/m² and is often 1·5 to 2·0 kg/m². A biomass of up to 60 g/m² is obtained on the sand floor off the coast, and on the mussel-mud up to 250 or even 500 g/m².† On phaseolin ooze the biomass varies from a few grammes to 800 g/m².

* According to P. Ryabchikov (1957) three species of teredinids have been observed in the Black Sea: *T. navalis, T. utriculus* and *T. pedicillata.*

† O. Mokievsky has observed (1945) along the western coast of the Crimean peninsula, on the beach sand above sea-level, abundant colonies of crustaceans (Orchestia), molluscs (*Donacilla cornea*) and polychaetes (*Ophelia bicornis*) with a biomass of over 0·5 kg/m².

Wodjanitzky gives the total biomass of the Black Sea zoobenthos as 15 to 30 million tons. This amount is possibly a little overestimated. L. Arnoldi (1941)* (*Table 184*) gives more accurate data, but only for a small area of the southern coast of the Crimea (from Cape Fiolent to Alupka).

Table 184

Environment	Biocoenosis	Census of the population per m²			
		Mean number of specimens	Mean biomass g/m²	Minimum biomass g/m²	Maximu[m] bioma[ss] g/m²
I. Coastal pure sand	*Venus gallina* *Divaricella divaricata* *Mactra subtruncata* *Donax venustus* *Diogenes pugilator* *Tellinafabula*	1,926	108	8·7	262
II. Silty sand	*Venus gallina* *Mactra subtruncata* *Divaricella divaricata* *Tapes lineatus* *Gouldia minima* *Modiola adriatica* *Meretrix rudis*	1,844	388	140	767
III. Mussel mud	*Mytilus galloprovincialis* var. *frequens* *Meretrix rudis* *Modiola adriatica* *Cardium simile* *Mactra subtruncata* *Syndesmya alba* *Modiola phaseolina*	825	667	135	2,076
IV. Phaseolin ooze	*Modiola phaseolina* *Molgula euprocta* *Terebellides strömii* *Syndesmya alba* *Cardium simile* *Melinna adriatica*	2,258	138	0	654

Mean indices of biomass and the population-density per m² of the four biocoenoses listed in *Table 184* can be calculated from Arnoldi's data for a number of dominant and characteristic benthos species (*Table 185*).

Moreover, the *Mytilaster lineatus* biomass of 382 g/m² at 2,900 specimens/m² and the maximum biomass for *Modiola phaseolina* of 779 g/m² at 10,700 specimens/m² recorded by Arnoldi should be noted. These data closely approach V. Wodjanitzky's result.

Nikitin (1949) thinks that the mean benthos biomass for the Caucasian coast (not counting the mussel and oyster banks) can be taken as 136 g/m². If we use this amount for the populated part of the whole Sea we shall obtain a

* L. Arnoldi writes (1941) that the Karkinitsky Bay zoobenthos is in its biomass poorer than that of the open parts of the Sea, being on the average about 100 g/m².

Table 185

Biocoenosis	I No. of specimens	I Biomass g/m²	II No. of specimens	II Biomass g/m²	III No. of specimens	III Biomass g/m²	IV No. of specimens	IV Biomass g/m²
Venus gallina	126	60	248	131	5	5	0·5	0·02
Divaricella divaricata	595	7	858	5·8	—	—	1	0·02
Mactra subtruncata	473	22·3	127	34	51	17	—	—
Donax venustus	21	6·7	—	—	—	—	—	—
Diogenes pugilator	28	3·2	16	1·6	—	—	—	—
Tellina fabula	9	1·7	26	6·6	—	—	—	—
Tapes lineatus			29	52	12	17	—	—
Gouldia minima			116	9·7	17	2·5	0·5	0·2
Modiola adriatica			30	41	44	53	—	—
Meretrix rudis			43	18	94	53	—	—
Nassa reticulata			19	10	8	6	—	—
Mytilus galloprovincialis			6	32	185	464	3	3
Pecten ponticus			5	22	—	—	—	—
Cardium simile					63	10	27	3·3
Syndesmya alba					47	4·5	38	2
Modiola phaseolina					108	7·5	1,958	111
Molgula euprocta					—	—	72	13
Terebellides strömii					—	—	63	2
Melinna adriatica						—	58	1·4

total biomass for the Sea of approximately 12 million tons. This is also approximately the amount of total annual benthos production.

The change of benthos biomass with depth off the Caucasian coast shows an increase at depths of 10 to 50 m, i.e. on the shell gravel and mussel-mud (*Table 186*).

As shown by *Table 186* the largest number of benthos specimens is observed on mussel beds (50 to 100 m deep) and the largest biomass on the shell gravel (10 to 50 m). The number of molluscs and crustaceans invariably decreases with depth, while the number of worms increases.

Table 186

Depth m	Mean number of specimens	Mean biomass g/m²	Percentage ratio of individual groups: Molluscs	Worms	Crustaceans	Others	Soils
0–10	500	128	82·5	4·8	4·2	8·5	Mostly sand
10–30	680	171	90·3	2·9	1·0	5·8	Silty sand and shell gravel
30–50	884	176	88·3	7·5	0·8	3·4	Sandy silt and silt
50–70	1,204	89	64	31	0·7	4·3	Ooze
70–100	1,950	100	60	34·8	0·1	5	Ooze
100–130	582	26	21·5	72·5	0·02	6	Ooze
130–160	57	4	1·5	93	0	5·5	Ooze
Lower limit of benthos							

A similar picture of quantitative distribution of benthos (number of specimens and biomass) is given by Nikitin for the Anatolian coast. The maximum number of specimens was observed at 60 to 75 m (up to 1,500 specimens/m^2), and the greatest biomass at 35 to 50 m (up to 2,000 g/m^2).

The Black Sea is inferior to the Sea of Azov and superior to the Caspian Sea in the benthos biomass of the populated part of its floor. Comparing the benthos of the Black and Azov Seas V. Wodjanitzky (1940) comes to the conclusion that only about 50 per cent of the benthos of the former can be used by fish (food-benthos), whereas in the Sea of Azov it is almost entirely food-benthos. Hence taking into consideration its feeding properties the Sea of Azov benthos is four times more productive than that of the Black Sea, and when calculated for the whole surface of the Sea it is sixteen times more productive.

Quantitative estimate of microbenthos. In 1939–40 L. Arnoldi carried out the first quantitative recording of the microbenthos of the upper layers of the soil (1·5 to 2·5 m) in the northwestern part of the Black Sea. As numbers go, the first place is occupied by worms (nematodes, nemerteans, archianellides) ciliates, crustaceans and mollusc larvae.

The number of micro-zoobenthos specimens reaches 4·6 million per 1 m^2 (on the average 1·6 million) and its biomass 30 g/m^2.

The number of micro-phytobenthos (diatoms) reaches 30 to 50 million specimens per 1 m^2, giving a biomass of up to 10 g/m^2.

Summarizing the as yet insufficient data on the numbers of the Black Sea fauna one can draw up *Table 187*.

Table 187

Group	Biomass 10^3 tons	Annual production 10^3 tons
Plankton	10,000 to 12,000	150,000 to 200,000
Phyllophora	17,000	?
Other macrophytes	1,500	1,500
Zoobenthos	13,000 to 15,000	13,000 to 15,000
Dolphins	Up to 30	?

The presence of numerous inlets at all stages of their development (Fig. 216) is the characteristic peculiarity of the northwestern part of the Black Sea. N. Zagorovsky (1925–30), F. Mordukhai-Boltovskoy (1948, 1953) and Yu. Markovsky (1955, 1959) have studied the inlets. A description of the Bulgarian inlets is given by G. Paspalev, A. Volkanov and G. Caspers, and of the Rumanian ones by P. Bujor.

The Dniester, Sukhoy, Khadzhibeysky, Kuyal'nitsky, Greater and Lesser Adzhalitsky, Tiligulsky, Tuzlovsky *solonetz*, Berezansky and the Dnieper-Bug inlets (Fig. 216) are river valleys flooded (possibly several times) by the post-Pliocene sea when its level was much higher than at present. In the later, drier periods, when river waters were not abundant, the inlets would lose their connection with the Sea, being separated from it by a bar; their salinity would rise to saturation with lake salt, and black oily ooze rich in iron compounds, used in modern times for medical purposes, would be formed. Communication with the Sea might be established by an inrush of the Sea through the bar and to a certain degree by the percolation of sea-water through it. The suspension of river water supply to the inlets might, in the final account, lead to a complete drying up and the formation of a *solonetz*.

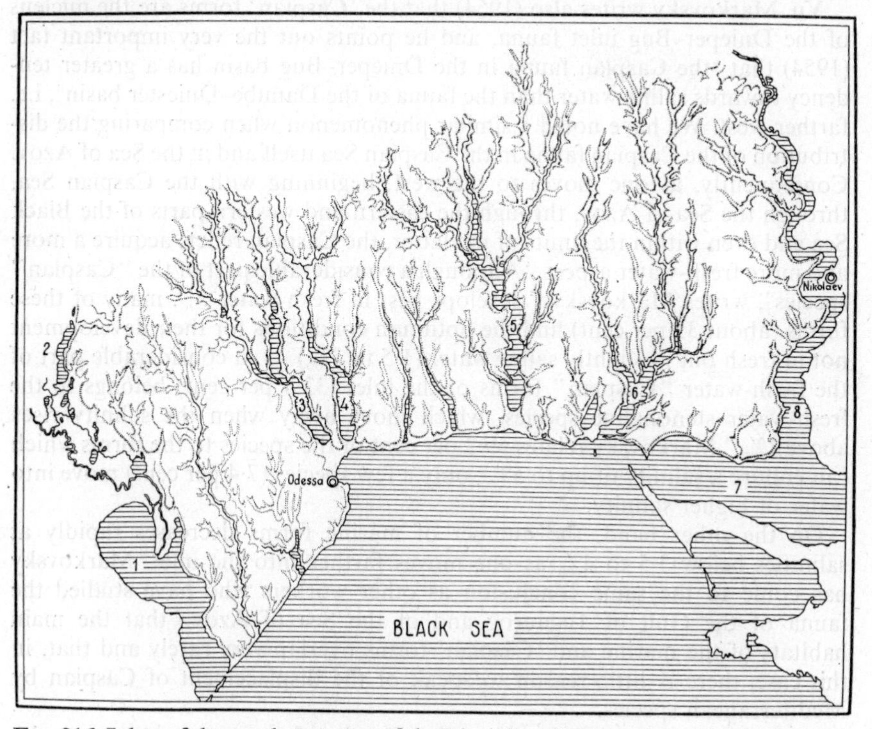

FIG. 216. Inlets of the northwest part of the Black Sea (Markovsky). *1* Dniester inlet; *2* Kutchurgansky inlet; *3* Khadzhibeysky inlet; *4* Kuyal'nitsky; *5* Tiligulsky; *6* Berezanksy; *7* Dnieprovsky; *8* Bug inlet.

The population of the inlets gives a clear picture of a mixture of the euryhaline marine (Mediterranean) fauna with a relict, Pontic, brackish-water fauna of the Caspian type and with fresh-water immigrants. The marine fauna of the inlets, qualitatively impoverished, and usually of a smaller size, does not, however, form dense settlements. On the other hand, an abundance of relict Pontic forms is observed in the inlets, which creates, in V. Sovinsky's expression (1902) 'a similarity between the fauna of the northwestern area (Gulf of Odessa) and that of the Caspian Sea'. 'We can consider', wrote A. Ostroumov (1897), 'the Bug inlet as a corner of the Pliocene basin, thrown up into the mainland and slightly renovated.'

Mordukhai-Boltovskoy (1961) points out that about 120 species of the animal 'Caspian' fauna live in the Azov–Black Sea basin, which comprises 40 per cent of the autochthonous Caspian Sea fauna, taking it as 300 to 305 species (without the Protozoa). The main part of this fauna comprises the amphipods (33 species), the mysids (8 species), Cumacea (10 species), molluscs (11 species) and fish (30 species).

Only 18 representatives of the Caspian fauna live in the open parts of the Black Sea, and in the Sea of Azov as many as 30, mostly fish.

Yu. Markovsky writes also (1954) that the 'Caspian' forms are the nucleus of the Dnieper–Bug inlet fauna, and he points out the very important fact (1954) that 'the Caspian fauna in the Dnieper–Bug basin has a greater tendency towards saline water than the fauna of the Danube–Dniester basin', i.e. farther west. We have noted a similar phenomenon when comparing the distribution of the Caspian fauna in the Caspian Sea itself and in the Sea of Azov. Consequently, as one moves to the west, beginning with the Caspian Sea, through the Sea of Azov, through the eastern and western parts of the Black Sea and even within the limits of the latter, the Caspian relicts acquire a more and more fresh-water aspect. 'Although a considerable part of the "Caspian" species', writes Markovsky, 'develops best in fresh water . . . many of these forms (about 35 per cent) find the optimum conditions for their development not in fresh but in slightly saline water (1·5 to 3‰) . . . a considerable part of the fresh-water "Caspian" forms of the inlet (33·4 per cent) belongs to the fresh-water stenohaline species, which move away when the salinity rises above 1‰.' Markovsky relates 59·2 per cent of the species to the forms which can endure a salinity of up to 5‰; only a few species (7·4 per cent) move into water of higher salinity.

On the other hand, the number of marine forms decreases rapidly at salinities below 3·5 to 4‰ as one moves farther into the inlet. Markovsky has come to the same conclusion as other workers who have studied the fauna of the Gulf of Taganrog and of the Sea of Azov—that the main habitats of the marine and 'Caspian' forms overlap very rarely and that, in this case, there is little reason to speak of the displacement of Caspian by Mediterranean species.

In the Dnieper and Don deltas the Caspian fauna comprises on rocky bottoms 80 to 100 per cent, on sands 70 to 86 per cent, on silty-sands 30 to 58 per cent, on grey muds 15 to 28 per cent, on black ooze in stagnant bodies of water 1 per cent (F. Mordukhai-Boltovskoy, 1948). This clearly shows the adaptability of this relict fauna to well-aerated rapid currents. Markovsky has identified 78 Caspian forms in the Dnieper inlet, among them two coelenterates, three polychaetes,* one leech, three gastropods, and six bivalves; the rest are crustaceans. Markovsky has recorded 64 forms in the Bug inlet (*Manyunkia caspica* should be added to them), among them two coelenterates, four worms, six bivalves, three gastropods and 50 crustaceans.

In analysing the biocoenoses of the Dnieper–Bug inlet Markovsky distinguished 28 bottom ones, 3 bentho-nectic and 15 plankton ones. The dominant forms comprise *Dreissensia polymorpha*, *Monodacna colorata*, *Clessiniola variabilis*, *Cardium edule*, *Adacna laeviuscula* sp. *fragilis*, *Adacna plicata*

* *Manayunkia caspica* must be added to them.

sp. *relicta*, *Vivipara vivipara*, *Theodoxus danubialis*, *Unio tumidus*, *Pontogammarus maeoticus*, *Corophium volutator*, *C. nobile*, *Balanus improvisus*, Oligochaeta, Tendipedidae, *Hypaniola invalida*, *Nereis* spp., *Mytilus galloprovincialis*. Half of them are 'Caspian' and 2 or 3 fresh-water forms. The average biomass of the bottom biocoenoses is from a few grammes to 1 kg per m^2.

The bentho-nectic biocoenoses are formed of 'Caspian' mysids; fresh-water Rotifera and crustaceans are greatly preponderant in the plankton, the Caspian fauna in them being represented only by *Eurytemora velox*.

The Dniester inlet is only slightly smaller in size than the Dnieper–Bug

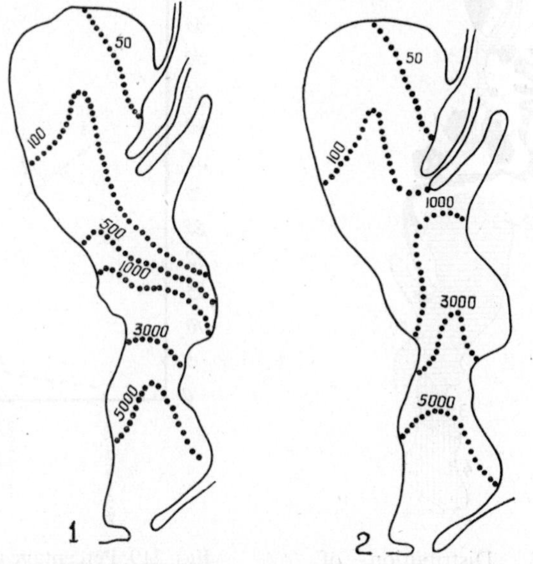

FIG. 217. Distribution of isohalines (Cl^-, mg/l.) in the Dniester inlet, 27 June to 1 July 1950: *1* Surface; *2* Bottom layer (Markovsky).

inlet (377 km^2 according to Markovsky); its salinity decreases gradually from south to north (Fig. 217), undergoing considerable fluctuations under the influence of the weather and the season of the year.

Yu. Markovsky writes (1953) that zooplankton of the inlet consists mainly of 'Caspian' crustaceans . . . which are represented in the Dniester inlet by fresh-water populations with a few purely fresh-water forms.

As in the Dnieper–Bug inlet, the plankton benthos of the Dniester inlet has a pronounced preponderance of 'Caspian' mysids with some admixture of 'Caspian' Cumacea and amphipods.

The bottom population of the inlet consists mainly of 'Caspian' forms. According to Yu. Markovsky (1953) their number decreases as one approaches the sea. If the inlet is divided into fresh-water, transitional and brackish-water parts, the fauna of the first two comprises 66 to 67 per cent of the

Caspian species, while 63·8 per cent of the last one consists of marine forms. A. Ostroumov had already pointed out in 1897 that the animal population of the seaward area of the inlet consisted mainly of marine species, which gave place to the 'Caspian' and fresh-water species farther up the inlet (Figs.

FIG. 218. Distribution of marine, relict and fresh-water bottom biocoenoses in the delta and the inlet of the Dniester. Biocoenoses: *1* Fresh-water; *2* Relict; *3* Marine or relict depending on salinity; *4* Marine (Markovsky).

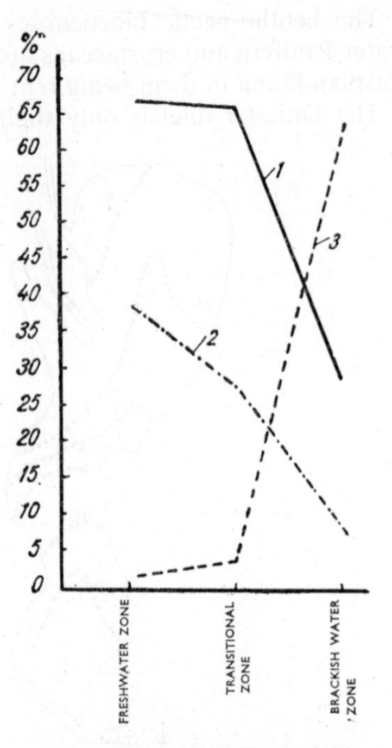

FIG. 219. Percentage relationship of the number of 'Caspian' fresh-water and marine species of bottom animals in various zones of the Dniester inlet (Markovsky). *1* Percentage, 'Caspian' species; *2* Percentage, fresh-water species; *3* Percentage, marine species.

218 and 219). Markovsky distinguishes nine bottom biocoenoses in the Dniester inlet with the following dominant forms: (*Pontogammarus maeoticus*, *Corophium volutator*, *Nereis* sp., *Corophium nobile*, *Dikerogammarus*, *Dreissensia polymorpha*, Monodacna, *Clessiniola variabilis*, *Micromelania lincta*, *Lithogliphus naticoides*, *Syndemya ovata* and Cardium), i.e. the 'Caspian' species are again predominant. Markovsky records in all more than 100 species of bottom and benthopelagic animals. The 'Caspian' species comprise 54 per cent in the Kuchurgan inlet and the lower reaches of rivers, and their

number is greatly reduced as we pass into the more saline waters of the inlet. 'Caspian' crustaceans settle down farther up the stream of a river, moving up the Dniester to its middle and upper parts. Twenty-four species of Gammaridae have been discovered in the Dniester and its inlet, seven of Corophiidae and nine of Cumacea. In the 17 biocoenoses distinguished, the 'Caspian' species are predominant in 13, and the first among them are: *Monodacna pontica*, *Dreissensia polymorpha*, *Clessiniola variabilis*, *Micromelania lincta*, *Pontogammarus maeoticus*, *Dikerogammarus villosus*, *Hypania invalida* and others.

The Kuchurgan inlet of the same river system, but situated to the north of the Dniester inlet and of a very low salinity (0·05 to 0·2‰ by chlorine), has a fauna characterized by the dominant role of its relict forms of Caspian aspect (Markovsky, 1953) both in its plankton (*Heterocope caspia*), its necto-benthos (Caspian mysids Paramysis, Mesomysis, Katamysis and Limnomysis), and also in its benthos (Hypania, Hypaniola, Adacna, Monodacna, Micromelania, Theodoxus, Dreissensia and others) (M. Yaroshenko, 1950).

Some data on the fauna of the Danube delta may form substantial additions to what has been said above. At one time the lower reaches of the Danube and the estuary zones of the rivers of the northwestern Black Sea were occupied by a wide arm of the sea, along the northwest side of which numerous inlets were formed (Figs. 220 and 221). Some excellent research was carried out on the fauna of the lower reaches of the Danube by Rumanian and Russian investigators, in particular by Yu. Markovsky (1955) on the Killisk delta. In the Killisk delta he recorded 140 species of invertebrates (without Protozoa) out of the total number of 412 species known for all the Danube delta (among them 58 molluscs and 186 crustaceans), including 36 species of molluscs and 43 species of crustaceans. In most cases half of the fauna, or more, consists of 'Caspian' forms (in Katlabug 62·8 per cent). The fresh-water aspect of the 'Caspian' species in the Danube and its delta is even more pronounced than in the other inlets of the northwestern part of the Black Sea and the characteristics of its plankton, plankton-benthos and benthos faunas are the same. The aboriginal fresh-water species are greatly predominant in the plankton, whereas in plankton-benthos the 'Caspian' species are just as predominant, thanks to the mysids, and in the benthos half of the species are 'Caspian' forms.

The fresh-water aspect of the Danube 'Caspian' forms which has been acquired to a great degree has been used, and may be used later on a much larger scale, for their acclimatization in bodies of fresh water of other river systems and even in the Dnieper (F. Mordukhai-Boltovskoy, 1950, 1952; Yu. Markovsky, 1952, 1954; P. Yuravel, 1950, 1952) where stable populations increasing the valuable components of fish-food resources may be created.

The greater fresh-water tendency of the Black–Azov Sea 'Caspian' species, as compared with that of the same community in the Caspian, and the strengthening of the 'fresh-water' aspect in the Black and Azov Seas from east to west is difficult to explain. The easiest way would have been to assume that the Pontic fauna remained in the Black and Azov Seas throughout the whole post-Pontic period, and altered here under the effect of the freshening of the waters of the Caspian Sea. There are, however, several serious objections to this. To explain this phenomenon by the salt composition of the Azov and

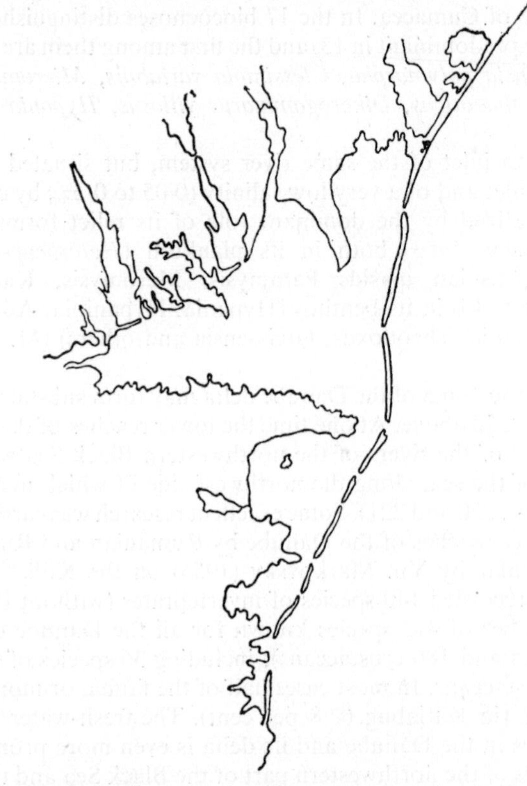

FIG. 220. Diagram of ancient estuary of river Danube (Antipa, 1910).

Black Seas or by competition (in virtue of the above-mentioned facts) with the Mediterranean fauna, which pushed the 'Caspian' forms into fresh waters, is even more difficult.

Fish and mammals

The Black Sea ichthyofauna, with its 122 species of marine fish and 34 of fresh-water fish, is about twice as rich as the Caspian Sea (77) and 25 per cent richer than the Barents Sea (114) in its variety of species. The characteristic difference from the fish of the Barents Sea consists of a much greater variety of commercial fish. In the Barents Sea only 10 per cent of the species are commercial, while in the Black Sea no less than 20 per cent are so.

A. Krotov (1949) includes in the list of the Pontic relict species of fish: *Percarina demidoffi*, *Lucioperca marina*, *Clupeonella delicatula* and six species of bullheads (among them *Mesogobius batrachocephalus*, *M. gymnotrachelus*, *Neogobius rata*, *N. platyrostris*, *N. syrman*). Krotov (1949) traces a connection with later immigrants from the Caspian Sea: the Acipenseridae (*Huso huso*, *Acipenser güldenstädti*, *A. stellatus*, *A. nudiventris* and *A. ruthenus*), Clupeidae (*Caspialosa kessleri pontica*, *C. brashnikovi maeotica*, *C. caspia nordmanni*, *C. c. tanaica*, *C. c. paleostomi*), salmon (*Salmo trutta labrax*), Benthophilus *Benthophilus macrocephali magistri* and *B. stellatus*), *Benthophiloides brauneri*,

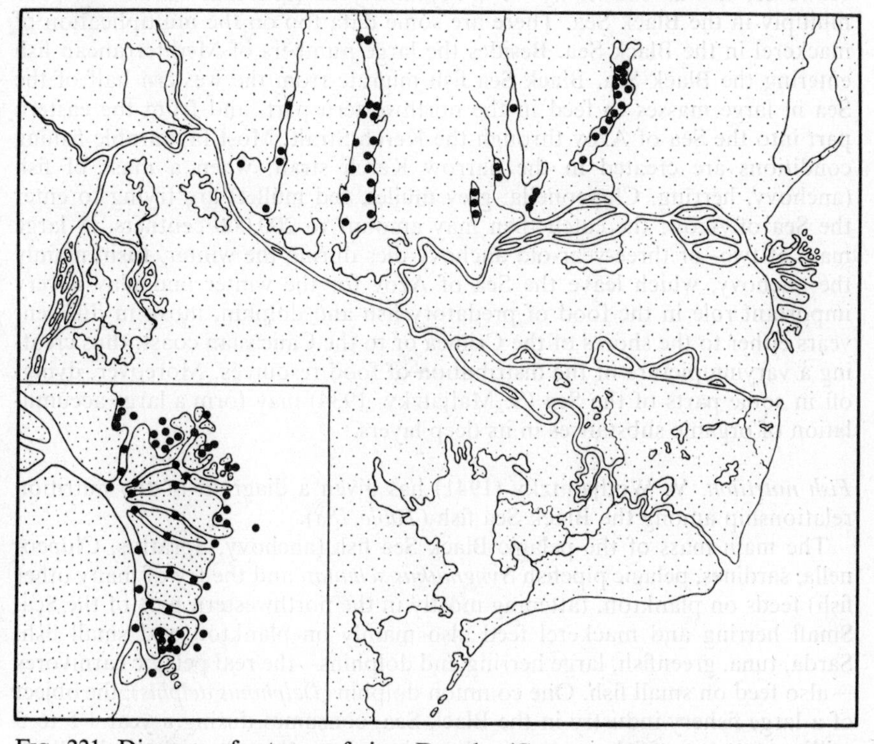

FIG. 221. Diagram of estuary of river Danube (Carausu, 1943). Localities where biological samples were taken.

Caspiosoma caspium, some species of bullheads (*Neogobius melanostomus*, *N. cephalarges*, *N. kessleri*, *N. fluviatilis* and *Proterorhinus marmoratus*) and the stickleback *Pungitius platygaster*; no fewer than 39 species in all. Most of the Black and Azov Sea fish are immigrants from the Mediterranean after the Dardanelles break-in. They comprise 60 per cent of the whole Black Sea and Azov Sea ichthyofauna, including the fresh-water fish.

In the Black and Azov Seas the process of species evolution also involved a number of fish of Mediterranean origin such as anchovy, with its Black Sea and Sea of Azov sub-species, the brill, garfish, red mullet and others. A number of fish which enter the Black Sea from the Mediterranean may also breed there (mackerel, Sarda). It has been proved by Wodjanitzky (1940) that many fish which need great depths for their development could not become acclimatized in the Black Sea, and for this reason among the Mediterranean communities fish with pelagic ova are predominant in the Black Sea.

Large numbers of anchovy, mackerel, Sarda, greenfish (*Pemnodon saltator*), hardtail, tuna, *Sprattus phalericus*, sardines and others enter the Black Sea in the spring through the Bosporus. Not long ago it was considered that neither mackerel nor Sarda nor tuna multiply in the Black Sea, but only feed there. However, it was shown by V. Wodjanitzky in 1936 that Sarda and tuna multiply in the Black Sea. There are some data too on the multiplication of mackerel in the Black Sea. Besides the large numbers of Mediterranean fish entering the Black Sea, Black Sea fish migrate from the western half of the Sea in large masses to feed in the northwestern part, and from the eastern part into the Sea of Azov through the Kerch Strait. Most favourable fishing conditions are created in the narrow Kerch strait, when a mass of fish (anchovy, herring, Clupeonella, grey mullet, red mullet) are trying to enter the Sea of Azov; the catch then may amount to 200,000 centners. A large mass of two- or three-year-old anchovy dies during the winter. Fish, mainly the anchovy, which leave the Sea of Azov for the winter and play a very important role in the food of predatory fish and dolphin, move in different years either to the shores of the Crimea or to the Caucasian coast, thus creating a varying picture of the distribution of food resources. Moreover, dying-off in some parts of the Sea (S. Maljatzky, 1934) may form a large accumulation of organic substances in its deep layers.

Fish nutrition. V. Wodjanitzky (1941) has given a diagram of the nutrition relationship among the Black Sea fish (*Table 188*).

The main mass of the pelagic Black Sea fish (anchovy, Sprattus, Clupeonella, sardines, pelagic pipefish *Syngnathus schmidti* and the fry of many other fish) feeds on plankton, fattening mostly in the northwestern part of the Sea. Small herring and mackerel feed also mainly on plankton and small fish. Sarda, tuna, greenfish, large herring and dolphins—the real pelagic carnivores—also feed on small fish. One common dolphin (*Delphinus delphis*), the object of a large fishery industry in the Black Sea, consumes during a year 1·5 to 3 million centners of fish, i.e. two or three times more than the yield of the Black Sea catch.

Moreover, *Phocaena phocaena* is common in the coastal areas of the Black Sea and in the Sea of Azov. The third dolphin species in the Black Sea, *Monachus monachus*, is the fourth mammal form of the Sea.

According to V. Moskvin's data (1940) the herrings of the northeastern part of the Black Sea differ greatly in their feeding habits, whereas *Caspialosa pontica* and *C. maeotica* are typical predators feeding mainly on small fish (chiefly anchovy) and large crustaceans. *C. tanaica* feeds on lower crustaceans (mainly *Calanus helgolandicus*) and sea-weeds (*Table 189*).

According to A. Makarov's data (1939) mackerel—also a typical pelagic carnivore—feeds mainly on Sprattus, anchovy, smelt and copepods. The diet of hardtail is very similar to that of mackerel; however, since it is a bottom-living fish, it feeds not on copepods but on mobile benthos organisms, mostly

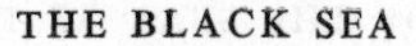

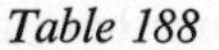

Table 188

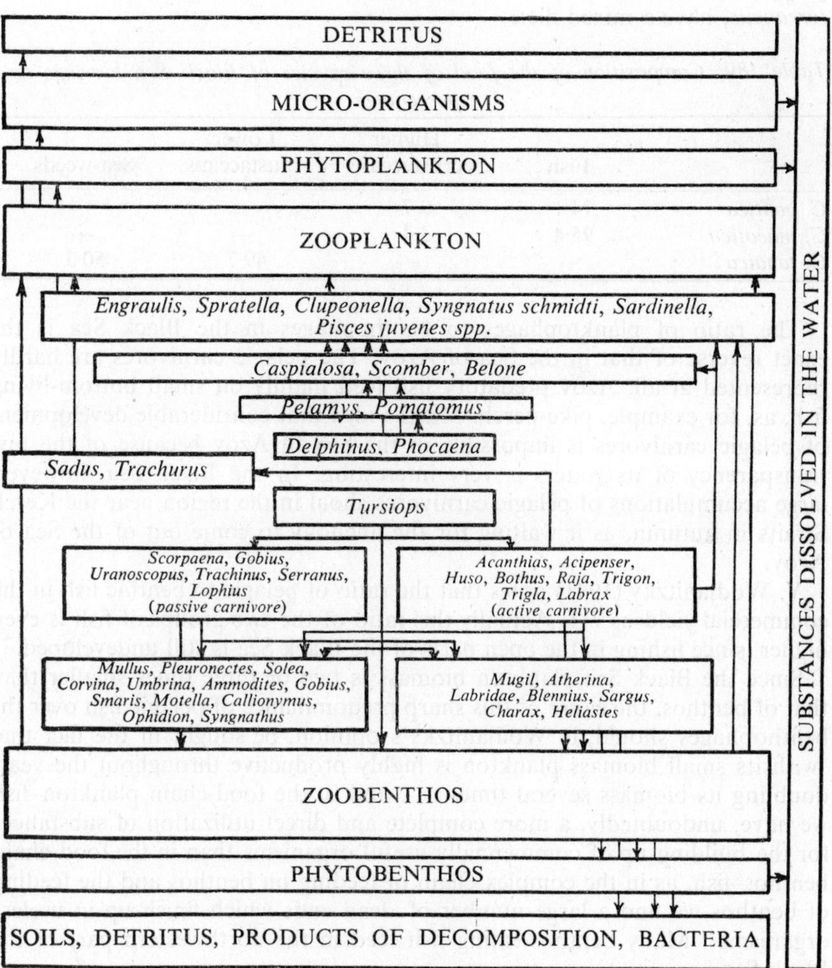

crustaceans. The food of the hardtail, like that of the mackerel, consists of approximately half fish and half crustaceans.

Apart from the pelagic carnivores one may distinguish a group of bottom-living carnivores: flatfish, Acanthias and some beluga, sturgeon and others. There is a large number of small fish among the benthophages, representative of Grenilabrus, Ophidon and Mullus genera, partly sturgeon, beluga, and starred sturgeon. Finally, some fish feed on detritus deposited on the bottom, and on members of the microbenthos. Among them grey mullet may be named.

V. Wodjanitzky (1941) notes that among the Black Sea fish there are fewer benthophages than planktophages; benthophages are richer in number of species and are of secondary importance in fishing, except for sturgeon and grey mullet. Some fish, for instance hardtail and *Gadus* (*gaidropsarus*) *mediterraneus*, have a mixed diet.

Table 189. Composition of the food of three species of Black Sea herrings as a percentage

	Fish	Higher crustaceans	Lower crustaceans	Sea-weeds
C. pontica	74·1	9·7	—	—
C. maeotica	95·4	3·4	—	—
C. tanaica	—	—	49·7	50·3

The ratio of planktophages to benthophages in the Black Sea is the exact reverse of that in the Sea of Azov. The pelagic carnivores are hardly represented at all. Azov predatory fish feed mainly on small bottom-living fish, as, for example, pike-perch. Marti's idea that considerable development of pelagic carnivores is impossible in the Sea of Azov because of the low transparency of its waters is very interesting. In the Black Sea, however, large accumulations of pelagic carnivores shoal in the region near the Kerch Straits in autumn, as if waiting for the anchovy to come out of the Sea of Azov.

V. Wodjanitzky (1941) notes that the ratio of pelagic to benthic fish in the commercial yields is 7:1. Actually this ratio of the two groups of fish is even higher, since fishing in the open parts of the Black Sea is still undeveloped.

Since the Black Sea plankton biomass is two or three times smaller than that of benthos, the cause of this sharp predominance of pelagic fish over the benthophages should, in Wodjanitzky's opinion, be sought in the fact that 'with its small biomass plankton is highly productive throughout the year, doubling its biomass several times . . . and in the food-chain plankton–fish we have, undoubtedly, a more complete and direct utilization of substances for the building up of commercially useful organisms than in the food-chain benthos–fish, as in the complex chain of feeding on benthos and the feeding of benthos we find a large number of dead ends which finish up in useless organisms'. Many benthos-eating fish feed in the northwestern part of the Black Sea.

L. Arnoldi and E. Fortunatova (1941) have carried out a comprehensive investigation of the biology and physiology of the nutrition of small, bottom-living coastal-water fish. They have elucidated the standards of the daily consumption of food, the feeding intensity, the gain in weight for various standards of feeding, the rate of digestion, the assimilation of food, etc., and the changes in all these indices with the season and with temperature.

Fisheries. The situation and the prospects of development of the Black Sea fisheries reflect in a most characteristic manner some peculiarities of the distribution of fauna in it.

Before 1939 the yield of our fisheries in the Black Sea was about 500,000 centners. The yield of those of other countries was about 360,000 centners (which corresponds to approximately 2·0 kg of fish per hectare calculated for the whole Sea surface).

General characteristics of Black Sea productivity

Our general idea of Black Sea productive peculiarities depends on the conception described above of vertical circulation adopted by us. If the vertical circulation goes down to the depth of the Sea, then the latter is not a bottomless well, absorbing large quantities of organic substances; but a great part of them is brought back into the inhabited zone. After his comprehensive examination of the problem V. Wodjanitzky (1954) came to the conclusion that the production processes are not weakened in the Black Sea as compared with those in other seas. To confirm his point of view Wodjanitzky reproduces V. Datzko's table, given here as *Table 190.*

Table 190

Group of organisms	Biomass 10^3 tons Wet weight	Dry weight	Annual *P/B* ratio	Annual production, 10^3 tons Wet weight	Dry weight	Percentage of dry substance
Phytoplankton in 0–50 m layer	3,600	360	300	1,000,000	100,000	10
Micro-organisms in 0–200 m layer	13,500	2,700	250	3,375,000	675,000	20
Zooplankton in 0–10 m layer	11,000	1,100	30	330,000	33,000	10
Zoobenthos	15,000	2,250	2·5	3,700	5,550	15
Phytobenthos*	20,000	2,400	1	20,000	2,400	12
Fish:						
Plankton-eating	5,000	1,500	0·5	2,500	750	30
Benthos-eating	700	310	0·5	350	105	30
Dolphin	50	17	0·35	17	10	35

* The figure is undoubtedly double what it should be.

In elucidating *Table 190* Wodjanitzky adduces the following considerations: that the quantities of nutrient salts (nitrates and phosphates) in the inhabited layer of the Sea are of the same order as in other seas (the nitrate content is somewhat decreased and there is a certain saturation with phosphates and ammonia); the salt ratio in the surface and in the depths is, moreover, the same.

In its inhabited zone the Black Sea cannot be considered as impoverished either in phyto- or zoo-plankton. In any case according to all these indices it is not poorer but richer than the Caspian Sea. As regards its fisheries, the Black Sea occupies a middle position between the Mediterranean and the Sea of Azov. Wodjanitzky thinks that its resources of pelagic fish (anchovy, sprat, Clupeonella, herring, mackerel, garfish, hardtail, Sarda, *Pomatomus saltatrix*, tuna and others) are very rich, and that from them the fishing industry can be greatly expanded.

Table 191. Quantity of plankton in the Black Sea, summer 1939 (S. Maljatzky)

Group		May–June	August
Total annual plankton biomass mg/m³	Mean	13·8	10·18
	Range	2·3 to 39·9	3·5 to 20
Calanidae	Mean	2,578	17·79
(No. of specimens)	Range	10 to 19,600	10 to 6,928
Sagittae	Mean	756	235
(No. of specimens)	Range	1 to 3,524	2 to 1,560
Phytoplankton	Mean	85·0	198·0
(mg/m³)	Range	34 to 6,620	310 to 4,780

M. Dobrzanskaya (1954) gives the comparative data on phytoplankton production, obtained from photosynthesis data for the different Seas (*Table 192*). It follows from them that (*1*) the Black Sea in this respect is not inferior

Table 192. Daily production of phytoplankton in the surface horizon of different Seas (ml/litre of glucose) (M. Dobrzanskaya, 1954)

Coastal areas of Black Sea, March 1948 to November 1950 (M. Dobrzanskaya)	0·32–0·90
Depths of Black Sea, March 1948 to November 1950 (M. Dobrzanskaya)	0·11–0·39
Southern part of Caspian Sea, August 1932 to October 1934 (S. P. Brujevitch)	0·19–0·75
Bay of Naples, February 1907 to August 1908 (A. Rutter, 1924)	0·71–0·94
Coasts of Sea of Norway, March 1922 (G. Gran)	0·30–0·37
Shores of Atlantic Ocean, August 1947 (Rayleigh and George)	0·68
Sargasso Sea, Atlantic Ocean, July to September 1947 (Rayleigh and George)	0·08–0·25

but superior to other Seas, and (*2*) that its surface waters are as productive in phytoplankton as the deeper waters.

10

The Sea of Azov

I. GENERAL CHARACTERISTICS

The Sea of Azov is a body of water attached to the Black Sea which is remarkable in many respects. It is essentially a broad, very shallow inlet of the Don, with water only slightly saline. Owing to a number of circumstances it is supplied with abundant mineral substances.

A rich bottom-population, an abundance of organic substances, great warmth in summer, and a readily established saline stratification cause the upper limit of the reduction zone to rise easily from the sea-floor into the water of the deepest, central part, with the consequent phenomenon of suffocation of the bottom-fauna.

The Sea of Azov is populated mainly by the most euryhaline forms of the Mediterranean fauna, chiefly molluscs, which are exceptionally abundant there. Relict Caspian Sea fauna lives only in the most eastern corner of the Gulf of Taganrog.

For a large number of Black Sea fish and for some river fish the Sea of Azov is a plentiful feeding ground in the warm season of the year.

The Sea of Azov is the most productive sea in the world, its fish catch being 80 kg/hectare in some years.

II. HISTORY OF EXPLORATION

First period

The first reliable information about the fauna of the Sea of Azov resulted from the research of A. Ostroumov (1892, 1896, 1897) and V. Sovinsky (1894, 1902). During the first fifteen years of the present century biological collections were made in the Sea of Azov by N. Borodin (1901) and S. Zernov (1901). All these investigations were concerned with classification of the fauna and the Sea as such was hardly studied at all, either as regards its hydrological conditions or its biology.

Second period

Investigations made in recent years have led to a situation where the Sea of Azov can now perhaps be placed among those seas of the U.S.S.R. which have been most comprehensively studied. From 1923 to 1927 the Azov and Black Seas scientific-industrial expedition, under the leadership of N. M. Knipovitch, worked in the Sea of Azov. N. Tchougounov (1926), a member of this expedition, has given in his work a general picture of the quantitative distribution of the fauna and some general principles of this distribution. An elaborate taxonomic-faunal investigation of the most interesting group of relict crustaceans of the basin of the Sea of Azov was carried out by A. Martynov

(1924), A. Derzhavin (1925) and others, independently of the Azov–Black Sea expedition.

Third period

Very valuable and thorough quantitative investigations of the fauna of the Sea of Azov have been carried out in the last few years by the Azov–Black Sea Institute of Fisheries and Oceanography and the Don–Kuban Fisheries Station. Among these works the most important from our standpoint are those of V. Vorobieff on the benthos of the Sea of Azov (1944) and on the Sivash fauna (1940), of A. Okul (1940) on the plankton of the Sea of Azov, of F. Mordukhai-Boltovskoy (1937) on the bottom-living fauna of the Gulf of Taganrog, and of V. Maisky (1940) on fish census. The work of A. Zhukov (1938) on the chemical conditions of the Sea, which hitherto had remained almost unexamined, must also be noted. All these investigations have been carried out in recent years.

In connection with the changes in the Caspian Sea conditions, as a result of hydro-power construction on the river Don, detailed investigations of the conditions and the biology of the Sea of Azov have been carried out by (A. Karpevitch, 1955, 1957; M. Zheltenkova, 1955; T. Gorshkova, 1955; V. Datzko, 1951; G. Pitzik, 1951; G. Pitzik and A. Novoshilova, 1951; I. Stark, 1951, 1955, 1956; E. Yablonskaya, 1955, 1957; V. Maisky, 1955; F. Mordukhai-Boltovskoy, 1948, 1953, 1960; A. Novoshilova, 1955, 1958).

III. PHYSICAL GEOGRAPHY, HYDROLOGY AND HYDRO-CHEMISTRY

Situation and size

The Sea of Azov, extending to 45° 17′ N latitude and from 34° 19′ to 39° 18′ 30″ W longitude is a very shallow water body (Fig. 222), which is greatly diluted in its eastern part by the rivers Don and Kuban and made more saline in its western part on account of evaporation. The Sea of Azov is connected with the Black Sea by the narrow Kerch Strait, and it can be regarded as a broad inlet of the Don. On the northwest the Sea of Azov is connected with the Sivash or Putrid Sea by the narrow Genichensk Strait (120 m). The surface area of the Sea of Azov is 38,000 km² (without Sivash); of this total 5,640·6 km² is the area of the Gulf of Taganrog. The surface area of the Sivash is 2,630 km².

Bottom topography

The greatest depth of the Sea of Azov is only 13¼ m. The average depth of the Gulf of Taganrog is 4·7 m, that of the Sea of Azov without the Gulf of Taganrog—7·2 m, and with it 6·8 m. The total volume of the Sea is 320 km³. The Sivash is very shallow, its greatest depth being no more than 3·6 m. A shallow zone of less than 5 m deep (Fig. 222) forms a narrow strip off the coast. Depths of 5 to 10 m encircle the body of water, except for the southern part of the Sea of Azov, occupying 42·7 per cent of its area. Depths of 10 m and more form 50·2 per cent of the total area. Hence the shallows (less than 5 m) occupy only 7 per cent of the Sea.

As one moves farther into the Gulf of Taganrog its depth decreases from 9 to 8 m in the central part of its western half. The greatest part of this half of

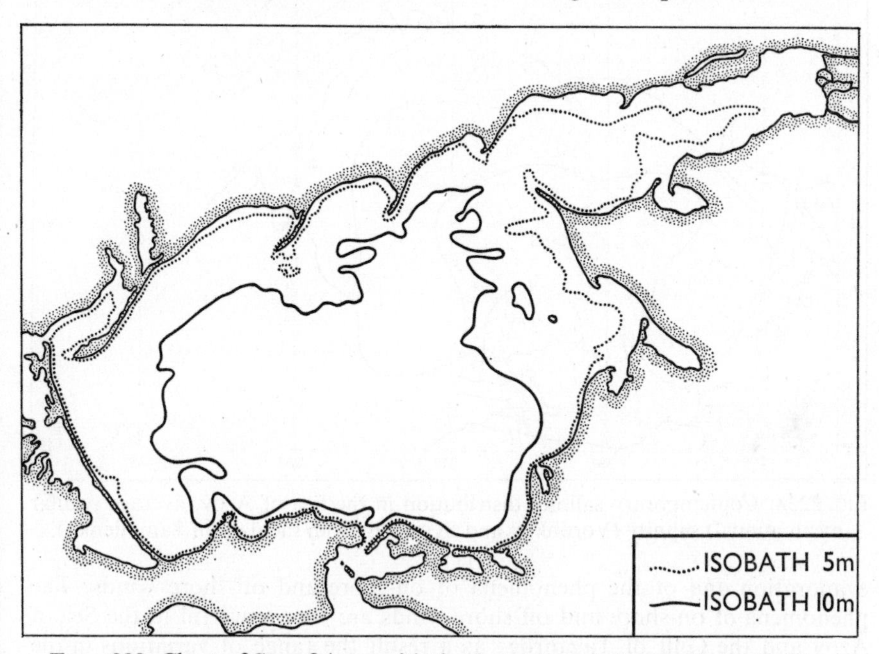

FIG. 222. Chart of Sea of Azov with the 5 and 10 m isobaths (Knipovitch).

the Gulf is 5 to 7 m deep, and the 4 m isobath approaches close to the coast. In the eastern part of the Sea, by contrast, large areas are occupied by shallow banks 2 to 3 m deep or less. The most eastern sector of the Gulf is a submarine delta of the river Don, with troughs—the continuation of the arms of the delta—which are divided by shoals. 53·6 per cent of the total area of the Gulf of Taganrog is 5 m deep or less.

Currents

Owing to the shallowness of the Sea, its water is in a state of perpetual horizontal motion and under the effect of the winds; various multiform systems of irregular currents are thus created. N. M. Knipovitch (1932), however, considers that there are many indications of the existence of some constant system of circular cyclonic current along the shores, circling round the central, deeper part of the Sea.

Fluctuations of water-level and water-balance

The water-level of the Sea of Azov and its various parts undergoes considerable fluctuations as a result of spring floods, of rainfall, of summer

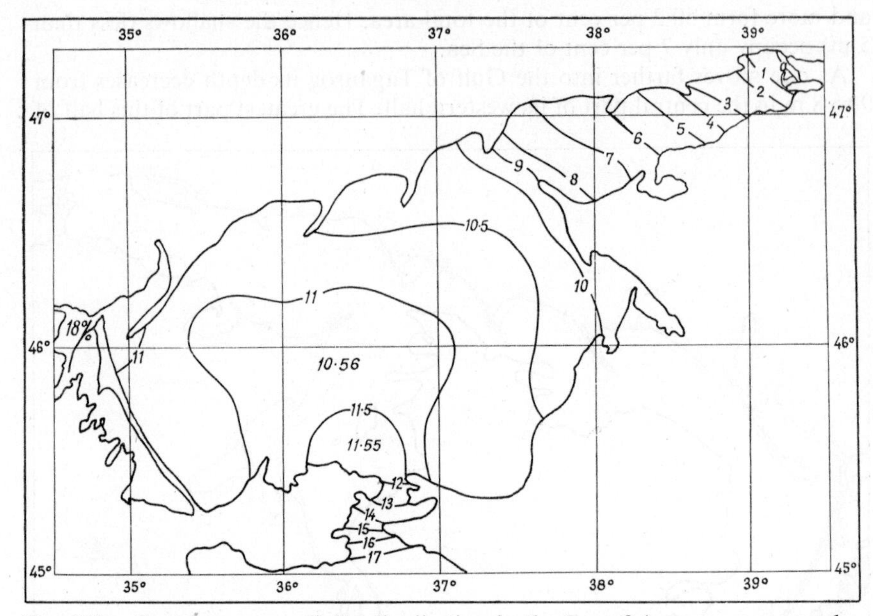

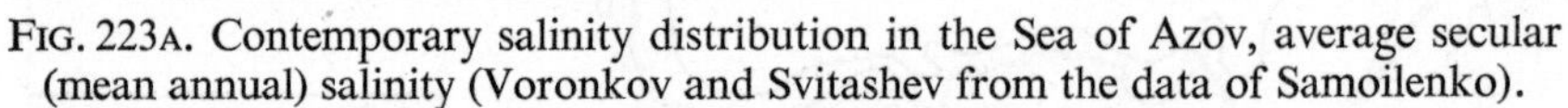
FIG. 223A. Contemporary salinity distribution in the Sea of Azov, average secular (mean annual) salinity (Voronkov and Svitashev from the data of Samoilenko).

evaporation and of the phenomena of on-shore and off-shore winds. The phenomena of on-shore and off-shore winds are very powerful in the Sea of Azov and the Gulf of Taganrog; as a result the range of variations in the

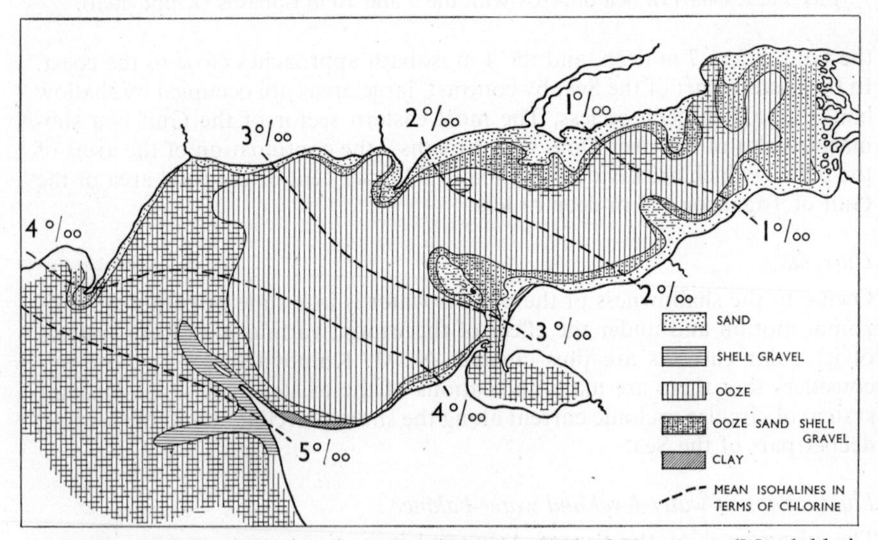

FIG. 223B. Distribution of soils and salinity in Gulf of Taganrog (Mordukhai-Boltovskoy).

sea-level reaches 4·44 m in the Gulf of Taganrog. The picture of the currents is therefore confused. However, it may be concluded that waters are carried out of the Gulf into the Sea mainly along the northern shore, while Azov waters enter it along the southern one. This can be clearly seen from the distribution of the isohalines (Fig. 223A, B) which also give a general picture of the range of salinity in the Gulf of Taganrog.

The water-balance of the Sea of Azov is made up of the elements given in *Table 193* (V. Samoilenko, 1947).

Table 193

Influx	km³	Consumption	km³
River discharge	41	Evaporation	29
Precipitation	14	Loss through the Kerch Strait	88 to 121
Inflow through the Kerch Strait	63 to 96	Loss through the Narrow Strait (into the Sivash)	4
Inflow through the Narrow Strait (out of the Sivash)	3		
Total	121 to 154	Total	121 to 154

Since the inflow of fresh water into the Sea of Azov is not fully matched by evaporation, the remaining surplus of water is distributed between the Genichensk and Kerch Straits. In early spring a surplus of saline water flows from the Sivash into the Utlyukski inlet through the Genichensk Strait, but for the rest of the year there is a prevailing current from the Sea into the Sivash. The exchange of waters through the Kerch Strait is irregular in character, being greatly affected by winds. The currents of the Kerch Strait play an important part in the hydrology and biology of the Sea of Azov: on the one hand, the surplus masses of less saline waters are carried out of the Sea of Azov by this current; on the other, the more saline waters of the Black Sea are carried in.

The Tsymlyansk dam on the river Don was completed in 1952. This led to the formation of the huge Tsymlyansk water reservoir above the dam, while below it new conditions in the river and the Sea began to form (A. Karpevitch, 1957). Twenty-three per cent of the average yearly discharge of the Don was intended to be removed for irrigation purposes. In coming years, as a result of hydro-power construction on the rivers Don and Kuban, the supply of nutrient substances into the Sea of Azov will be reduced by about 50 per cent, while the primary production of phytoplankton will decrease to about 40 per cent of the annual average (V. Datzko and M. Fedosov, 1955). Moreover, the salinity of the Sea of Azov will increase to 15‰. In 1952 the salinity of the Sea of Azov increased on the average about 0·41‰ by comparison with 1951. In 1953 it increased again by 0·32‰ (E. Vinogradova, 1955).

According to V. P. Vorobieff (1944) the average annual discharge of solid matter from the land into the Sea of Azov is of the order of 8·3 million tons, which gives on the average 12·9 cm³ per 1 m³ of water, whereas the discharge of dissolved substances is more than 13 million tons.

Transparency

The water of the Sea of Azov is only slightly transparent, owing to the large amount of organic and inorganic matter suspended in it. The limits of the fluctuations of transparency are 0·1 to 5·0 m; in the overwhelming majority of cases transparency does not extend farther than 2 m, and in 60 per cent of them farther than 1 m. On the whole the water is more transparent in the central and western parts of the Sea than in the east.

Temperature

Like the Black and Caspian Seas, the Sea of Azov, except for the Sivash, belongs to the bodies of brackish water, in the sense used by N. M. Knipovitch (1929), to which we referred earlier.

Some features of the hydrological conditions of the Sea of Azov are due to this brackishness of its waters. In winter time, with the surface water at freezing temperature and partly covered with ice, warmer and at the same time heavier waters are concentrated in the depths. At a salinity of 6‰* (by chlorine), the temperature at the surface at that time will be −0·58°, and at the bottom 1·67°. When the circulation is vigorous and the whole column of water has a temperature of about freezing point, then, in the spring, once the surface layers are warmed to 1·67° they rapidly sink and quickly warm the whole column of water to the temperature of the highest density, i.e. 1·67°. Further heating is mainly concentrated in the upper layers of water and passed over to the lower layers only gradually as a result of drifting circulations.

The summer rise in temperature of the waters of the Sea of Azov, and the mean annual temperature, are fairly high. Thus the mean annual temperature of the surface of the Sea for the four years 1924–27 was 11·28° for Taganrog and 12·4° for Temryuk.

In the four summer months at Temryuk the water temperature is higher than 20°, reaching 25° at times. The lowest average monthly temperature, which sometimes occurs in January, but usually in February, is about 0°; some lower temperatures have been recorded occasionally: −0·3° for Taganrog, −1·0 for Temryuk, −1·3 for Genichensk. On the other hand the highest average monthly temperature of water on the surface of the Sea, usually occurring in July, reaches 25·9° at Taganrog, and the highest single observations were 29·6° at Taganrog, 31·2° at Eisk, and 29·3 at Temryuk.

In autumn and winter as a rule an almost homothermic state is observed; the temperature varies only slightly with depth. Only in the spring, during the period of a quick rise of water temperature, is a considerable decrease of temperature with depth commonly observed. A strong wind brings about considerable changes in the range of temperature right down to the bottom.

* The salt ratio in the Sea of Azov, and especially in the Caspian, is somewhat different from that of typical sea-water. Hence it is impossible to obtain an accurate expression of its total salinity from the usual formula of the change in the chlorine content obtained by titration (weight of chlorine in grammes per kilogramme of water). For the Sea of Azov and still more for the Caspian Sea the so called ‘ chlorine numbers ’ are commonly used instead of salinity. The usual formula can be used to convert it into general salinity:

$$S‰=0{\cdot}030+1{\cdot}8050\ \mathrm{Cl}$$

Ice conditions

The considerable fall of temperature in December, January and February leads to the formation of ice, which proceeds the more readily owing to the shallow water and the low salinity of the Sea of Azov. Ice formation begins at the Gulf of Taganrog, where it remains longer than anywhere else. Ice formation is weakest off the southern shores.

In some years an almost continuous ice cover persists for 4 to 4½ months. In 1923–28 the period of ice varied in different parts of the Sea from 38 to 138 days, while the thickness of the cover ranged from 9 to 90 cm. Ice usually appears in the first half of December and disappears in the second half of March. 'Taking into consideration the considerable thickness of the ice fields', wrote N. M. Knipovitch (1932), 'which are 80 or even 90 cm thick, the masses of hummocks and the piling up of ice which sometimes reaches down to the sea bottom, one cannot help seeing that the freezing of such great masses of water with the separating out of large amounts of salts, would increase to a considerable degree the salinity of the sea in winter, particularly in so shallow a sea as the Sea of Azov.'

Salinity

The mean salinity of the Sea of Azov may be taken as 11·2‰; seasonal fluctuations of salinity are observed with a maximum in winter and a minimum in summer (Fig. 223A).

The salinity of the Sivash is unusual for the Sea of Azov. In the Northern Sivash a salinity of 40·0‰ has been observed and it increases even more farther south and west.

In the Sea of Azov itself maximum salinity (17·5‰) is found in the bottom layers in the area of the Kerch Strait—this is Black Sea water which is only slightly diluted.

The salinity of the Sea of Azov fluctuates considerably during the course of the year. Maximum salinity is found in the winter months when its rise is caused by the decrease in the river inflow and the freezing up of large masses of fresh water. Salinity begins to decrease gradually with the melting of the snows, and a period of minimum salinity is reached by the end of summer (September). In the eastern part of the Gulf of Taganrog the water is often almost fresh, while in the west, close to the entrance into the Sea of Azov, salinity rises to 4 to 5‰ (chlorine).

Gas conditions

The surface layers of the Sea of Azov usually contain an adequate amount of oxygen, owing to its shallow waters and its good aeration. Annual changes of oxygen content in the water-column are shown in Fig. 224A where they are compared with the course of phytoplankton development. Fluctuations of oxygen content are small (92 to 114 per cent saturation). The deep-water layers, however, owing to the abundant life in the Sea, the accumulation of huge masses of decomposed organic substances and the high temperature, may easily lose their oxygen and pass to a state of oxygen deficiency. This

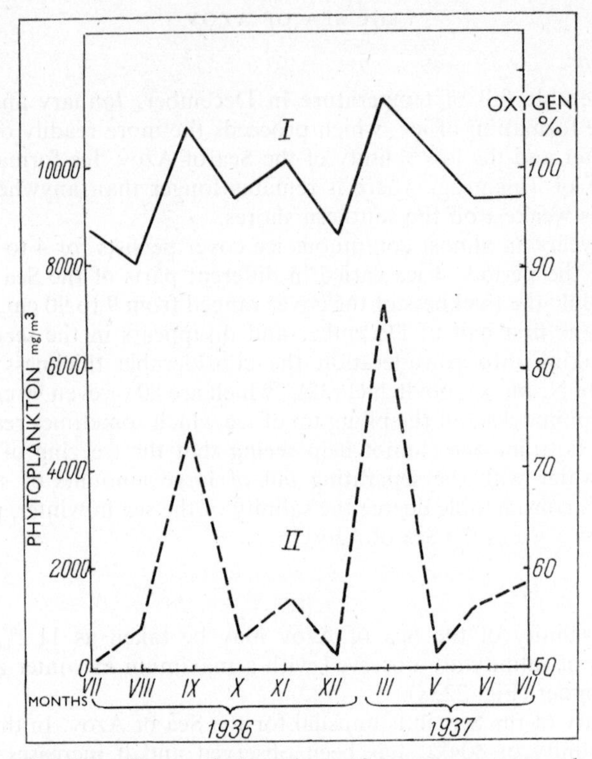

FIG. 224A. Seasonal alterations of oxygen content and the development of phytoplankton in the Sea of Azov (Zhukov). *I* Oxygen; *II* Phytoplankton.

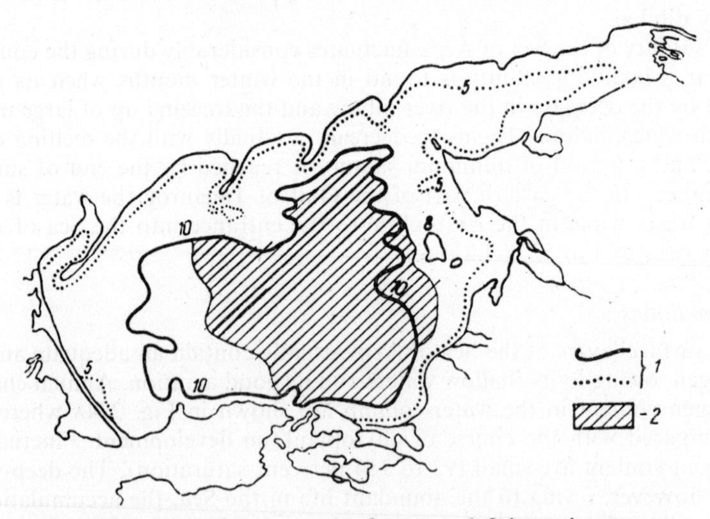

FIG. 224B. Area of occurrence of oxygen deficiency in summer: *1* Isobaths; *2* Main zone of possible oxygen deficiency (Fedosov).

occurs usually in May and continues until August. This state may develop with a catastrophic rapidity when conditions make vertical circulation difficult (calm weather, considerable warming up of the upper lower salinity layer) (Fig. 224B).

This is assisted also by the saline stratification which is especially apparent in the part of the Sea adjacent to the Kerch Strait: the more saline Black Sea waters entering the Sea of Azov through the Strait lie in the bottom layer where they are covered by the diluted waters of the Sea of Azov.

In June 1937 A. Zhukov observed a 40 to 80 per cent oxygen saturation in the bottom layers throughout the Sea, and in July phenomena of a very intense suffocation developed in the bottom layer, from which oxygen disappeared throughout most of the Sea. In August the situation became less acute and the September gales broke down the established stratification and the amount of oxygen near the bottom increased. Similar intense suffocation phenomena were observed in 1946.

Stormy weather mixes up the whole water-column and disturbs the stratification. The table given by Knipovitch is a good illustration of this (*Table 194*).

Table 194

)epth m	After calm weather				After stormy weather			
			Oxygen content				Oxygen content	
	t°C	S‰	cm³	% of saturation	t° C	S‰	cm³	% of saturation
0	24·96	10·72	6·945	120·09	21·76	10·46	4·34	73·43
5	24·96	10·72	6·55	114·91	21·75	10·50	4·32	73·10
5	22·56	10·72	1·09	18·41	—	—	—	—
2·5	21·96	10·81	0·0185	0·31	21·76	10·50	4·32	73·10

Bottom zones exposed to frequent suffocation phenomena are the poorest in benthos. Suffocation leads to a mass extinction of bentopelagic organisms; among fish some species of bullheads suffer most.

For some areas of the Sea of Azov the bacterium *Microspira aestuarii* is very characteristic; it is sometimes found in huge amounts reaching 56 million specimens per 1 g of soil. The total amount of bacteria can rise to 776 million specimens per 1 g of soil (in the Kazantip area). Sulphates are reduced by this bacterium, while carbonates are formed in the process and hydrogen sulphide is evolved; this can also contribute to a loss of oxygen content, since it is bound to be used for the oxidation of the hydrogen sulphide formed. Bacteria decomposing cellular tissues with the formation of marsh gas (methane), which requires for its further oxidation large amounts of oxygen, are important among the bacteria of the bottom of the Sea of Azov.

Nutrient salts

As regards nitrates, in July 1936 these were everywhere absent. They began to appear in August and by the beginning of the autumn (September–October)

Table 195. Changes in the concentration of plant nutrients, mg/m³, in the Sea of Azov (without the Gulf of Taganrog) in 1957 (by M. Fedosov and E. Vinogradova, 1955)

Month	Phosphorus	Silicon	Nitrogen+ammonia
March	32	240	198
April–May	5	85	159
June	11·6	188	74
July	53	233	100
August	16	318	155
September	21	(1,250)*	86
October	57	(1,335)*	61
November	(103)*	(2,190)*	54

* Bottom-samples in parentheses.

the nitrate content in the water had risen to 30 mg/m³. In November it increased to 60 and even to 90 mg/m³. A specially large amount of nitrates was observed in the Gulf of Taganrog (up to 150 to 200 mg/m³).

In 1937 the nitrates accumulated during the winter were exhausted in a short time by the spring bloom of phytoplankton. In April–May the nitrates disappeared completely, remaining only in the middle part of the Gulf of Taganrog in amounts of 80 to 300 mg/m³. By June–July 1937 there was a small accumulation of nitrates, but in August and September they had again disappeared from the whole area of the Sea. Even in the Gulf of Taganrog the amount of nitrates fell to 8 mg/m³ and only in the actual estuary of the Don did it reach 100 mg/m³. The waters of the Don carry 500 to 700 mg/m³ nitrogen in the form of nitrates.

On the other hand the amount of ammonium nitrogen in the Sea of Azov is exceedingly large, especially during the periods of the mass dying-off of plankton; for instance, after spring bloom (up to 900 mg/m³). This is obviously connected with the decomposition of a large bulk of organic matter. The picture of ammonia distribution is the reverse of that of oxygen. The amount of ammonia nitrogen in seas usually appears as a few tens of milligrammes per cubic metre of water, and it rarely exceeds 100 (Baltic and Mediterranean Seas). Only in the deep part of the Black Sea does the amount of ammonia nitrogen reach 1,000 to 1,200 mg/m³.

Unlike the nitrates, the phosphates remain all the year round in the waters of the Sea of Azov, although at times in small amounts; only in the upper layer may they be completely consumed (*Table 195*). In April to August phosphorus in the upper layer is either absent or remains at a level of 4 to 12 mg/m³; in the bottom layer it may increase from 30 mg/m³ to 200 or 300 mg/m³ in June, and then fall to 40 or 50 mg/m³ in August. The usual phosphorus content in sea-water in winter is 20, 40, 60 and even 90 mg/m³. The river Don contains from 50 to 150 mg/m³ of elementary phosphorus.

Silicic acid

Silicic acid content is as much as 2,050 to 3,500 mg/m³ in October and November; it falls, as spring approaches, to an average of only 250 mg/m³ in

March. In April and May its content falls to 50 mg/m³ in the surface layer and to 100 mg/m³ in the bottom one. These sharp fluctuations in silicic acid content should be attributed to its being consumed by plankton diatoms. During the autumn dying-off of plankton some silicic acid appears in the water again.

Thus the most typical features of the chemical conditions of the Sea of Azov are due to an abundant discharge of detritus and plant food by the river Don, which ensures an exceptionally intensive development of plankton and benthos life.

Chemical characteristics

However, a good supply of oxygen is required for the development of life on this scale and for the oxidation of huge amounts of organic substances. Since in the Sea of Azov the process of aeration is at times, and in the region of the Straits always, impeded by salinity and temperature stratification, catastrophic suffocation of the benthopelagic fauna may occur, accompanied by an accumulation of large amounts of ammonia in the bottom layer. Two maxima of nitrate and phosphate accumulation are observed during the year, with at times a complete consumption of nitrates in April–May and August–September. Owing to the shallowness of the Sea of Azov, large amounts of phosphates and silicic acid can accumulate on the bottom; they may also be dissolved in the water.

All aspects of the chemical conditions of the Sea of Azov are to a great extent determined by the course of phytoplankton development, both by its increased multiplication and its dying off. The oxidation conditions, the accumulation of ammonia, the phosphorus, nitrogen and silicon cycles all reflect the various phases of plankton development, especially because of the shallowness of the Sea.

The soils

A diagram of the distribution of soils appears in Fig. 225A. There are few rocky shores in the Sea of Azov, and these are mainly situated on the southern coast. A wide band of sands with a smaller or larger admixture of shell gravel encircles the central part of the Sea and of the Gulf of Taganrog, occupied by silty mud and shell-gravel mud. In the southern part of the Sea this band of sands is narrower than on the other shores, and the mud bottom approaches the coast more closely. The proportion of fines (less than 0·01 mm) in these muds reaches 30 to 50 per cent; in the silty muds of the central part of the Sea it is always in excess of 50 per cent. The deepest parts of the Gulf of Taganrog, beginning from a depth of 3·5 m, have a soft mud floor, with a characteristically large number of Ostracoda shells. F. Mordukhai-Boltovskoy (1937) thinks that these muds might be called Ostracoda muds (up to 50,000 or 100,000 and more live Ostracoda per 1 m²). Sand stretches in a more or less narrow band along the coast, entering deep into the Gulf only with shoal heads. Vast areas of the bottom, especially in the part of the Gulf farthest west, are occupied by mixed mud, sand and shell gravel.

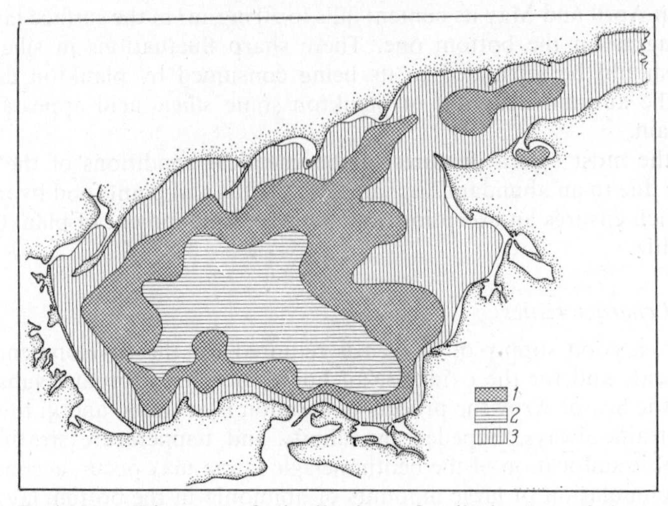

FIG. 225A. Diagram of distribution of soils in Sea of Azov (Vorobieff, 1949). *1* Ooze-shell gravel; *2* Clayish ooze; *3* Shell gravel on sand-ooze and ooze-sand.

The distribution of organic carbon in the upper layer of the sea-bed soils corresponds closely with the change in the nature of the latter (T. Gorshkova, 1955). It is most remarkable that no special accumulation of organic carbon is observed anywhere in the Sea of Azov, not even in its deep central part, as

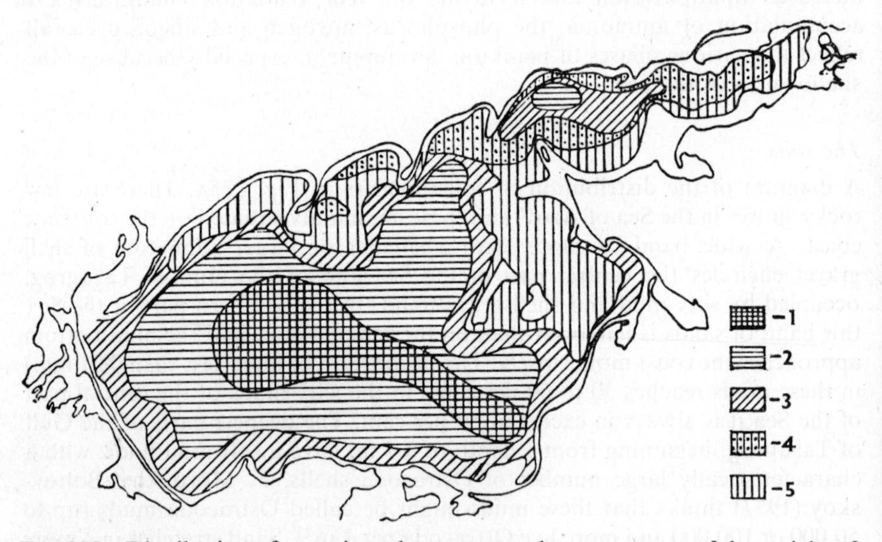

FIG. 225B. Distribution of organic carbon, expressed as percentage of dry weight of the substance in the upper layer of the Sea of Azov deposits (Gorshkova, 1955). *1* From 2·9 to 2·4%; *2* From 2·4 to 2·0%; *3* From 2·0 to 1·5%; *4* From 1·5 to 1%; *5* From 1 to 0·5%.

might have been expected from the high indices of plankton and benthos biomass and from the abundant amounts of organic substances brought in by the rivers (*Table 196* and Fig. 225B).

Table 196. Mean percentage of organic carbon in the sediments of different seas

Region	Maximum and minimum	Mean
Sea of Azov	0·6 –2·9	1·63
Barents Sea	0·15–3·12	1·28
Northern Caspian	0·25–3·0	0·63

Since large areas of the sea-bed of the Barents Sea, and especially of the Northern Caspian, are occupied by sand, and that of the Sea of Azov by muds, the data of *Table 196* may be considered very close to one another.

As has been revealed by the same author's examination of the salinity of the soil solutions of the Sea of Azov, the salinity of this Sea and that of the Gulf of Taganrog has increased during the last century.

M. Fedosov (1955) characterizes the genetic composition of the bottom-deposits of the Sea of Azov in the manner given in *Table 197*.

Table 197

Constituent	Percentage
Mineral river suspensions	45·5
Organic substances of river suspensions	1·4
Precipitates of organic substances formed in the Sea	13·5
Mineral and organic precipitates	6·3
Eolian deposits and products of the breakdown of the banks	33·3
	100·0

Nature of the shores

As V. Zenkovitch (1958) has pointed out, all the coastal waters of the Sea of Azov are exceptionally shallow; this is connected with the small depth of the Sea itself. The basin of the Sea, which receives the turbid waters of the Don and Kuban rivers and of the products of the wash-out of loess shores, is filled with mud, which rises to unusually shallow depths (of about 3 m).

Quaternary loess and sand deposits stretch along the whole northern shore of the Sea, the southern shore of the Gulf of Taganrog and the eastern shore down to Primorsko-Akhtarsk. Shores made of such deposits are intensively washed out and in some sectors this wash-out reaches a rate of 10 m/year. The shores of the Kerch and Taman peninsulas are more resistant, since there are some outcrops of hard Tertiary limestone. In the southeastern corner (Temryuk Bay) the wide delta of the Kuban river is cut off from the Sea by a long sandy bar. The Kuban enters the Sea by three separate mouths. Along the western coasts of the Sea stretches the shell-gravel sand bar—the Arabat

Strelka, behind which is situated the estuarine lake of Sivash with its greatly increased salinity. This lake is connected with the Sea by the Genichensk Strait.

The coasts of the Sea of Azov have two exceptional characteristics. A series of five narrow shoals, stretching out from the coast into the Sea at an angle of about 45° in a south-southwesterly direction, is situated in the north. The length of these shoals increases from east to west; the biggest is more than 50 km (Fedotova shoal with Biryichy Island). Their unusual formation is connected with the marked prevalence of easterly and northeasterly winds, owing to which the resultant of the action of the waves is oriented almost parallel to the present coast (A. Aksenov, 1955). The cause of this unusual orientation of the shoals is due to the deposits being shifted at maximum speed at an angle of about 45° to the direction of the waves.

The second characteristic of the shores of the Sea of Azov is that the basic material of accumulated forms consists almost exclusively of shell gravel brought out to the coast. The shoals on the eastern shore consist entirely of marine shell gravel. This rare phenomenon is connected, first with the very high productivity of the bottom-fauna, and secondly with the instability of the coastal loess which, when broken down, is too fine to be deposited on the shore.

IV. FLORA AND FAUNA

General characteristics

We know of no other sea in the world which can be compared with the Sea of Azov in the extreme intensity of its productive processes. This is the result of a whole series of factors, although there are some which have a reverse effect (for example, the occurrence at times of a pronounced oxygen deficiency and the formation of hydrogen sulphide in the bottom layers). Knipovitch rightly includes among the conditions contributing to the high productivity of the Sea of Azov: its shallowness, which facilitates the return of nutrient substances from the bottom into the water; an adequate exposure to sunlight of the whole water-column (in spite of its low transparency); favourable conditions for mixing and aeration and, finally, the large amounts of inorganic and organic matter brought in by the rivers, both in solution and in suspension.

Knipovitch also notes that the lowered salinity greatly affects the qualitative composition of the flora and fauna but does not hinder its very rich quantitative development.

The following should be added to these considerations. If the Sea of Azov were widely connected with the Black Sea and formed a part of it, like for instance the northwestern part of the Black Sea, its productivity would undoubtedly be less even though the amounts of nutrient salts carried from the shore and detritus were the same. All nutrient substances are accumulated in the Sea of Azov and, except for a comparatively negligible loss through the Kerch Strait, they are not carried out of it. We see something quite different in the area of the Black Sea mentioned above: nutrient substances and detritus are carried away in large quantities from the shallow coastal regions into the adjacent deeper parts, which considerably lowers the biological yield of those shallows.

The second important factor leading to high productivity of the Sea of Azov is the summer warming both of the whole water-column and of the sea-bottom for a long period from April to October. The heating of the upper layer of water of the Sea of Azov corresponds to approximately 3,800 degree-days annually, and that of the bottom-layer to a little less.

The intensity of the productive processes of the Sea of Azov may possibly be connected in some measure with the ice-formation process, or, more precisely, with the melting of ice. If this phenomenon has a wide impact in nature then, given that the shallow depths of the Sea, and the fact that its ice-cover composes one twentieth to one twenty-fifth of the whole volume of water, the effect of melted water on the development of life in spring must be particularly important.

Composition and heterogeneity of population

At present 226 species of invertebrates (Mordukhai-Boltovskoy, 1960) and 79 forms of fish have been shown to exist in the Sea of Azov. The list includes among the invertebrates 35 species of polychaetes, 33 species of molluscs, 30 species of lower and 61 species of higher crustaceans. Of the total number of 305 animal species, 165 belong to the Mediterranean and 75 species are Caspian relicts.

In recent years, as a result of the increase in the salinity of the Sea of Azov, a migration into it of Black Sea forms has begun. Thus a form of the genus Teredo, which had not hitherto penetrated farther than the Kerch Strait, has been found off Kazantip. On the other hand, the movement of more salt-loving forms from the Utlyuksky inlet and the Sivash into the Sea of Azov has also been observed. The qualitative composition of the population of the Sea of Azov is a biological factor of exceptional interest. It includes several heterogeneous groups.

The relicts of the Novo-Euxine Caspian fauna, now populating the least saline parts of the Sea of Azov and the eastern part of the Gulf of Taganrog (river mouths, inlets), provide some species which propagate throughout the whole Sea. To these relicts belong, among the coelenterates: *Ostroumovia maeotica* and *Cordylophora caspia*; among the polychaetes: *Hypania invalida, Hypaniola kowalewskyi* and *Manayunkia caspica*; among the molluscs: *Monodacna colorata, Dreissena polymorpha* and *Theodoxus pallasi*; among the Cumacea: *Pterocuma pectinata*; among the mysids: *Mesomysis kowalewskyi*; among the amphipods: *Cordiophilus baeri, Gmelina kusnetzowi, Dikerogammarus villosus, D. haemobaphes, Chaetogammarus ischnus, Pontogammarus robustoides, P. weidemanni, P. crassus, Amathillina cristata, Calanus curvispinum, C. maeoticus, Pontogammarus maeoticus*, and others. The last named evidently now finds the best conditions for its existence in the Sea of Azov. Fresh-water fauna in considerable numbers are mixed with this relict fauna in the least saline parts of the Sea.

The main mass of the fauna of the Sea of Azov consists, however, of Mediterranean immigrants; some of them have found exceptionally good conditions for mass development in the Sea of Azov. Among them the following should be noted first of all: Balanus, Cardium, Mytilaster, Syndesmya,

Nereis and others. All these forms are widely euryhaline, being found at a salinity of 7 to 27‰. Some of them can endure a very considerable lack of salinity (down to 2 to 3·6‰); others, on the contrary, prefer very high salinity, being found even at a salinity of 50 to 70‰. Among the Mediterranean immigrants the most important are the groups of polychaetes (32 species), molluscs (22 species) and amphipods (12 species). The considerable qualitative poverty of the Mediterranean fauna in the Sea of Azov is apparent if only from the fact that of the 137 species of coelenterates of the Mediterranean, only three species live in the Sea of Azov; of the 1,451 species of molluscs, only 22; of the 300 species of pelagic copepods, only 8; of the 51 species of crabs, only one—*Brachynotus lucasii*; of the 223 species of amphipods only 12 species, etc.

The remains of the more salinity-loving fauna of the ancient Black Sea period live as relicts in the western part of the Sea, in the Utlyuksk inlet and in the Northern Sivash. As typical Black Sea relicts the polychaete *Pectinaria neopolitana* and the mollusc *Loripes lacteus* may be named. The others have disappeared from the fauna of the Sea of Azov; but their shells are found everywhere in large numbers, as, for instance, *Venus gallina*, *Gastrana fragilis*, Tapes and others.

The ultra-haline forms so marked in the Sivash and found in large numbers at salinities higher than 30‰ are a characteristic element of the fauna of the Sea of Azov. The most typical of them are the crustaceans *Artemia salina* and *Chironomus salinarius*.

Zoogeographical zonation

The Sea itself can be subdivided according to its fauna in the following manner: the eastern part of the Gulf of Taganrog (relict, Novo-Euxine fauna with an admixture of some fresh-water species), the Sea of Azov itself and the western part of the Gulf of Taganrog (with the contemporary Azov–Black Sea fauna of Mediterranean origin); the Utlyukskyi inlet and the northern part of the Sivash (a mixture of the contemporary Azov–Black Sea fauna with Novo-Euxine relicts of the ancient Black Sea basin); and the remainder of the Sivash and the saline Kuban inlet (ultra-haline forms).

Immiscibility of the relict and Mediterranean faunas

B. Iljin (1930), F. Mordukhai-Boltovskoy (1937) and V. P. Vorobieff (1945), examining the relationship between the brackish-water and Mediterranean faunas, have noted that these two faunas rarely mix with one another. The brackish-water (relict) fauna is concentrated to the east of a line connecting the base of Krivaya shoal with the village of Porkaton, i.e. to the east of the isohaline 3·6‰ (Fig. 226A, B). To the west of a line from Mariupol to the base of Eisk shoal (7·2‰ salinity) the predominance of the Mediterranean fauna is just as marked. Between these two limits (3·64 to 7·25‰ or 2 to 4‰ by chlorine) live the most euryhaline members of both faunas (*Cyprideis littoralis*, *Corophium volutator*, *Macropsis slabberi*, *Nereis diversicolor*, *Hypaniola kowalewskyi* and some others). The number of species and the amount of biomass in this zone are much smaller than to the east or west.

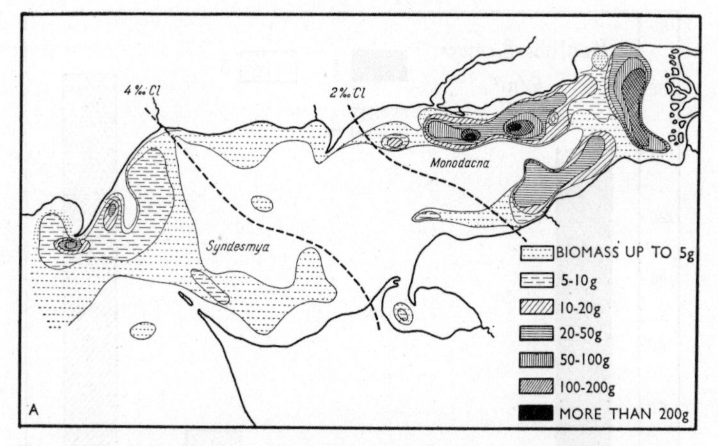

FIG. 226A. Distribution of biomass (g/m³) of Monodacna and Syndesmya in the Gulf of Taganrog (Mordukhai-Boltovskoy).

The marked interchange of relict and marine faunas in the Gulf of Taganrog affects not only the qualitative composition but also the quantitative ratio of these two components. In the eastern part of the Gulf there is a huge predominance of relict species in the biomass, while in the western part the marine forms are predominant (Fig. 227).

Thus not only do these two faunas not mix, but they are divided from each other by a distinctive intermediate area. This fact, it corresponds to reality, is of great theoretical interest, as we have said earlier.

Plankton

Qualitative composition of phytoplankton. As usually happens, the biomass of the vegetable part of the plankton of the Sea of Azov is considerably larger

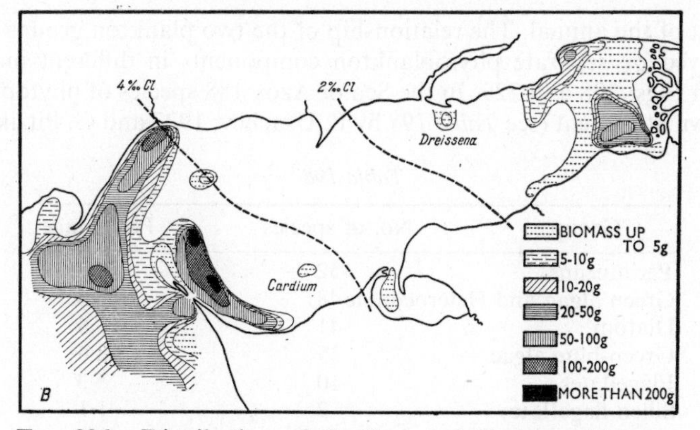

FIG. 226B. Distribution of Cardium and Dreissena biomass (g/m³) in the Gulf Taganrog (Mordukhai-Boltovskoy).

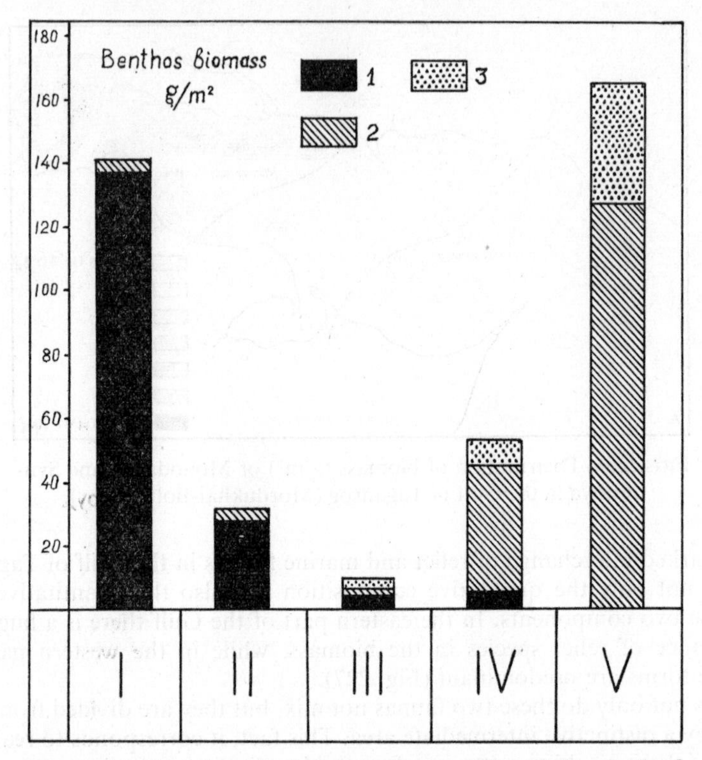

FIG. 227. Alterations in benthos communities of the Gulf of Taganrog from west to east (Mordukhai-Boltovskoy with some changes). *I* Cardium complex; *II* Ostracoda–Nereis community; *III* Ostracoda community; *IV* Monodacna–Dreissena community; *V* Monodacna–Unionidae community; *1* Mediterranean forms; *2* Fresh-water forms; *3* Relict forms.

than that of the animal. The relationship of the two plankton groups and the part played by separate phytoplankton components in different months is shown in Figs. 228 and 229. In the Sea of Azov 188 species of phytoplankton are known at present (see *Table 198* by P. Usachev, 1927 and G. Pitzik, 1951).

Table 198

Group	No. of species	Percentage
Peridineans	52	27·7
Green algae and Heterocontae	48	25·5
Diatom	41	21·8
Green-blue algae	35	18·6
Flagellates	10	5·3
Silico-flagellates	2	1·1
Total	188	100

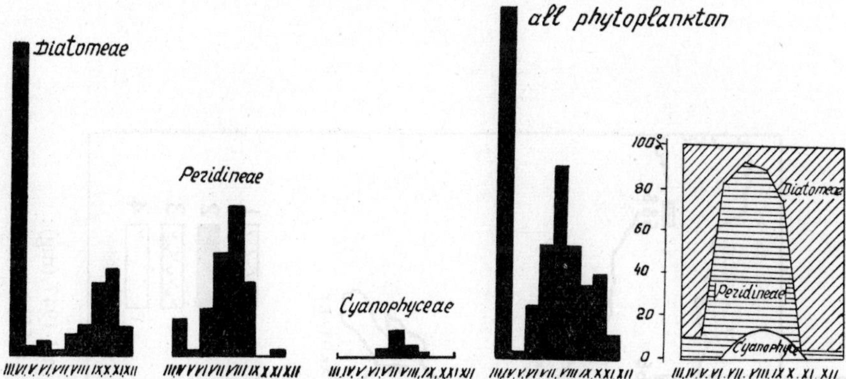

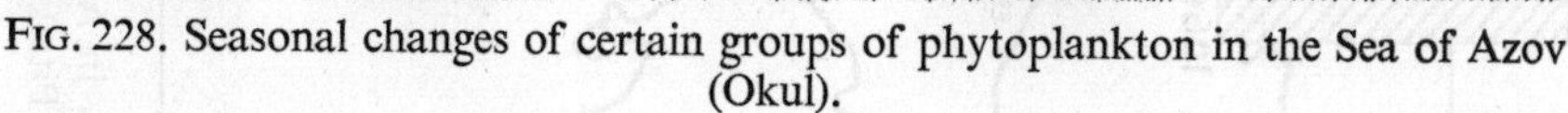

FIG. 228. Seasonal changes of certain groups of phytoplankton in the Sea of Azov (Okul).

There are only 32 species of mass forms among them. Among the Blue-green algae there are: *Microcystis feruginosa*, *Aphanizomenon flos aquae*, *Nodularia spumigena* f. *typica*, var. *lato-rea*, *Anabaena knipowitschi*, *A. hassalii* var. *macrospora*; among the Protozoa, Silico-flagellata: *Ebria tripartita*; among the peridineans: *Exuviella cordata*, *Proterocentrum micans* and *Glenodinium danicum*; among the diatoms: *Skeletonema costatum*, *Thalassiosira nana*, *Coscinodiscus biconicus*, *Leptocylindrus danicus*, *Rhizosolenia calcar-avis*, *Rh. radiatus*, *Chaetoceros subtile*, *Biddulfia mobiliensis*, *Ditylium brightwelli* and *Thalassionema nitzschioides*.

Phytoplankton biomass. The relative significance of phytoplankton in the productive processes is comparatively high, owing to the very weak development of coastal vegetation. As regards mass the main role in the phytoplankton is played by the diatoms (about 55 per cent of all the phytoplankton in the whole of the Sea), the peridineans (about 41·2 per cent of all the phytoplankton, chiefly in the open sea), and to a much lesser extent by the algae.

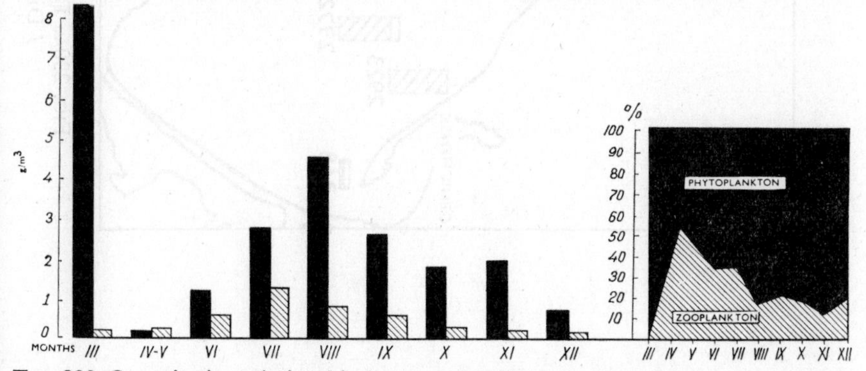

FIG. 229. Quantitative relationship between the phyto- and zoo-plankton of the Sea of Azov in various seasons of the year (Okul).

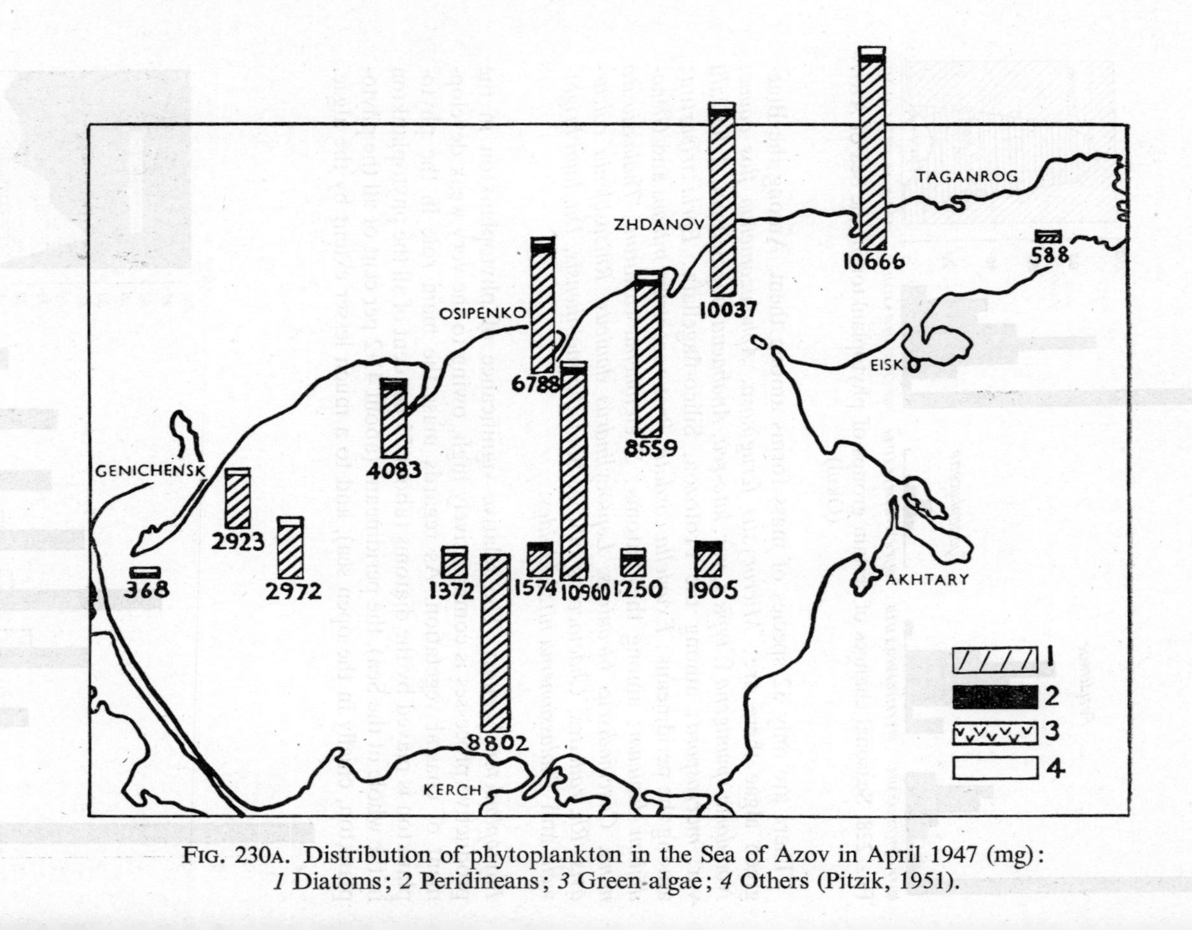

FIG. 230A. Distribution of phytoplankton in the Sea of Azov in April 1947 (mg): *1* Diatoms; *2* Peridineans; *3* Green-algae; *4* Others (Pitzik, 1951).

The blue-green algae (chiefly in the Gulf of Taganrog) constitute even at the time of their maximum bloom (summer) barely 13 per cent of all the phytoplankton, and on the average only 4·2 per cent.

Diatoms have two maxima: a larger spring one (March–April) (*Skeletonema costatum* and *Coscinodiscus* spp.), when the amount of diatoms reaches 7 g/m^3, and a late autumn one (October–November) (*Rhizosolenia calcar-avis, Leptocylindrus danicus, Ditylium brightwelli, Skeletonema costatum, Thalassionema nitzschioides, Thalassiosira nana* and different species of Chaetoceros and Coscinodiscus), with a maximum of up to 2 g/m^3. During the rest of the year the amount of diatoms decreases sharply (May, June, July, December, January, February). During the bloom periods the diatoms form 90 to 98 per cent of the total phytoplankton biomass. At times the biomass of the Sea of Azov reaches a colossal amount, one which has been found in no other sea. For August 1925 P. Usachev gives a plankton biomass of 270 g/m^3 (385 g/m^3 in other years) and for October 1924—106 g/m^3; moreover, the plankton consisted almost entirely of the diatom *Rhizosolenia calcar-avis*. As G. Pitzik has shown (1951), such a huge phytoplankton biomass has not been found since 1934 owing to a great reduction of the number of diatoms of *Rhizosolenia calcar-avis* during the periods of bloom, when it was no higher than 13 g/m^3, and usually about 2 to 4 g/m^3.

The peridineans form an almost equally important component of the Sea of Azov plankton. Their maximum multiplication takes place in the summer. Their summer bloom is preceded by a small early-spring bloom in March (about 0·85 g/m^3). At its maximum development, in August, the peridinean biomass is on the average about 3·5 g/m^3, consisting mainly of *Exuviella cordata, Goniaulax polyedra, G. triacantha, Proterocentrum micans, Peridineum knipowitschi*, and others; owing to their mass development the water is coloured reddish-brown.

Among the Cyanophyceae mainly *Nodularia spumigena* and, to a lesser extent, *Aphanizomenon flos-aquae, Microcystis aeruginosa* and some species of Anabaena develop in large masses. Volvocales and the green algae are mostly concentrated in the parts of the Sea with a lower salinity.

Blooming in patches is at times caused by a mass development of Flagellates of the orders Chrysomonadina and Cryptomonadina. Among the Silicoflagellates *Ebria tripertita* is predominant.

Phytoplankton development in the Gulf of Taganrog has some features peculiar to itself (Fig. 230A and B). In the first place, phytoplankton is considerably more developed here, and the blue-green algae (Microcystis and Aphanizomenon) are predominant during the whole warm season (June to November), reaching in the autumn a phytoplankton biomass of 85 to 93 per cent; the diatoms become markedly preponderant only in spring (Fig. 231).

The number of Aphanizomenon filaments may be more than 5·5 milliards/m^3, each of the filaments consisting of 100 to 150 cells. The number of peridineans and diatoms at one station also reached 4·5 millions of specimens/m^3.

All these quantitative data, which are mainly taken from the work of

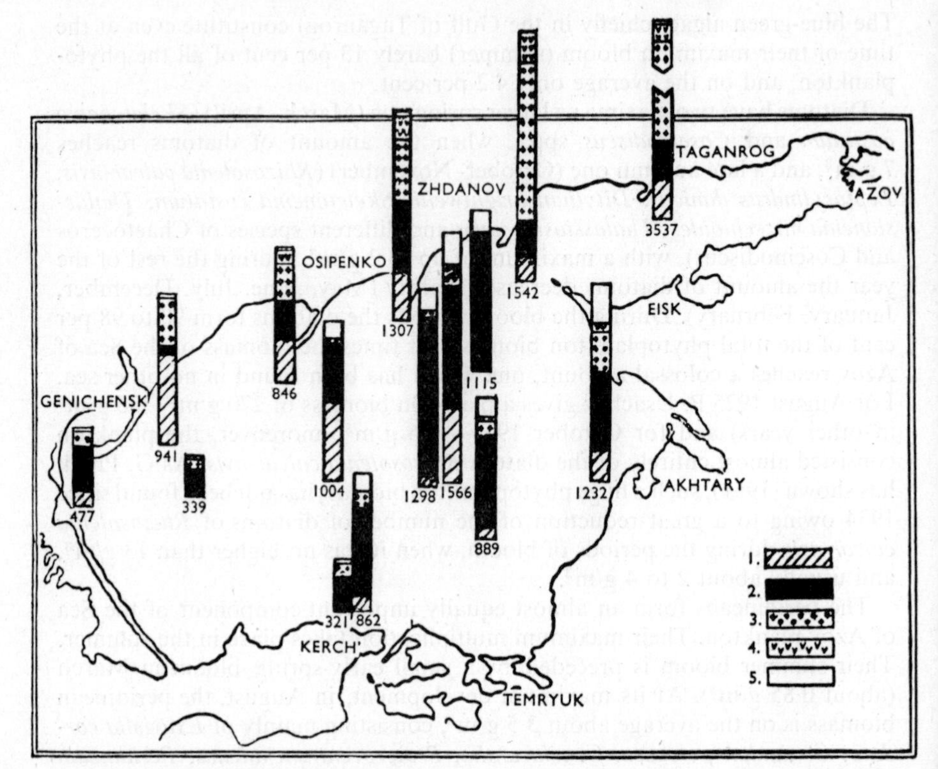

FIG. 230B. Distribution of phytoplankton in the Sea of Azov in July 1947 (mg): *1* Diatoms; *2* Peridineans; *3* Plus-green algae; *4* Green algae; *5* Others (Pitzik).

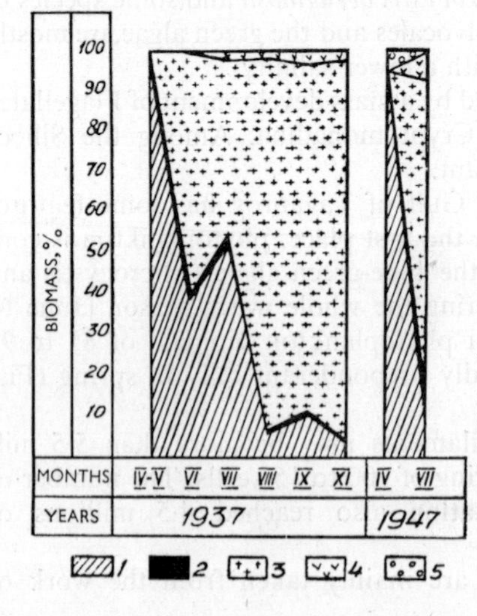

FIG. 231. Comparison of main groups of phytoplankton in the Gulf of Taganrog (Pitzik, 1951): *1* Diatoms; *2* Peridineans; *3* Blue-green algae; *4* Green algae; *5* Others.

A. Okul and G. Pitzik, relate to 1937 and 1950; the picture may have been different in other years. In particular P. Usachev (1927) notes that the blue-green algae play an important part in the life of the Sea of Azov. This contradiction may be explained by the erroneous picture obtained by the qualitative method of investigation, since the blue-green algae accumulate mainly on the surface of the sea. Apart from the spring, a mass development of the Sea of Azov plankton is also observed in the summer and autumn up to October. This course of plankton development, in the opinion of N. M. Knipovitch (1932), indicates that there is no shortage of nutrient salts in the water of the Sea of Azov; this is apparently due to the proximity of the bottom, the rapidity of the processes of mineralization and regeneration, and generally to a large amount of limiting nutrient salts.

The frequently observed saturation of the Azov Sea water with oxygen is the result of a similar huge accumulation of algae in the water-column. A case was mentioned above of the Sea of Azov phytoplankton reaching a density of 300 to 400 g/m^3, which approximately corresponds to the same amount of grammes by weight. If the depth of that station was 8 m, up to 2 or 3 kg of phytoplankton alone could have been concentrated in a water-column of 1 m^2 cross section. Moreover, the plankton is often very unevenly distributed—in patches and strips, carried about by currents and vertical movements of the water. A particularly important development of plankton can be observed in the western part of the Sea, sometimes in the middle part of the Gulf of Taganrog.

Qualitative composition of zooplankton. The qualitative composition of the Sea of Azov zooplankton (G. Pitzik and A. Novoshilova, 1951) can be expressed in the form of *Table 199.*

Table 199

Protozoa	14 species	Copepoda	31 species
Coelenterata	6 species	Mysidacea	11 species
Rotatoria	20 species	Cumacea	6 species
Chaetognatha	1 species	Amphipoda	2 species
Cladocera	17 species		
		Total	108 species

In addition the plankton usually contains a large number of the larvae stages of polychaetes, brozoans, Cirripedia and decapod crustaceans which live on the bottom. However, only 50 species in all are found in the main basin of the Sea of Azov, and only a few of these develop in large masses. Among the separate groups, divided according to their origin, those most characteristic of the Sea of Azov are the following:

I. Novo-Euxine relicts (mainly in the Gulf of Taganrog) *Evadne trigona, Cercopagis pengoi, Heterocope caspia, Calanipeda aquae dulcis* and others.

II. Mediterranean immigrants. Mainly among the Copepoda: *Acartia cluasi*, *Paracartia latisetosa*, *Centropages kroyeri*, *Labidocera brunescens*, *Oithona nana*; among the Tintinnoidae: *Tintinnopsis minuta*, *T. meunieri*, *T. tubulosa* var. *subacuta*, *T. relicta*, *Leptotintinnus pellucidus*, *L. botanicus*; among the Cladocera: *Podon polyphemoides*.

III. Fresh-water Cladocera and Rotatoria in the least saline sections (Leptodora, Asplanchna and others).

Calanipeda aquae dulcis, *Evadne trigona*, *Brachionus quadridentatus*, *B. plicatilis* and *Pedalion oxyuris* are particularly richly developed.

In the outer part of the Gulf of Taganrog Heterocope, Cercopagis and, in the least saline parts, the fresh-water Rotatoria, Cladocera and Cyclopidae are developed in large masses.

Zooplankton biomass. Quantitative investigations of the Azov Sea plankton were carried out by F. Mordukhai-Boltovskoy (1938) and A. Okul (1940), by G. Pitzik and A. Novoshilova (1951) and by A. Novoshilova (1955).

In the Sea of Azov the highest annual zooplankton biomass for the last 20 years was recorded in 1937 (*Table 200*). In recent years it has fluctuated

Table 200

Year	Mean annual zooplankton biomass, mg/m³, in Sea of Azov	Year	Mean annual zooplankton biomass, mg/m³, in Sea of Azov
1937	612	1941	502
1938	236	1947	388
1939	213	1948	132
1940	372	1949	386

considerably and was lowest in 1939 and 1948. Individual components of plankton groups have also shown significant variations in particular years. In the Gulf of Taganrog the zooplankton biomass has also fluctuated substantially from year to year. In 1937 it was very high (1,351·3 mg/m³) and still higher (up to 2,082·7 mg/m³) in 1949. As has been shown by investigations lasting for many years, before the flow of the river Don was controlled, the total zooplankton of the Sea of Azov in early spring (March–April) consists of 47 to 90 per cent Rotifera (Synchaeta). In May and June, side by side with Copepoda and Rotatoria, the number of the larvae of bottom invertebrates (Cirripedia, Vermes and Mollusca) increases greatly. In May 1949 and 1950 the biomass of the Cirripedia larvae formed 83 to 85 per cent of the total zooplankton biomass in the northeastern part of the Sea (A. Novoshilova, 1958). The number of Copepoda increases towards the beginning of the summer, reaching 65 to 95 per cent of the total biomass (slightly less in the Gulf of Taganrog), mostly on account of *Acartia clausi* and *Centropages kroyeri*, and in the Gulf of Taganrog *Calanipeda aquae dulcis* and *Heterocope caspia*.

Table 201. Fluctuations of zooplankton biomass in the Sea of Azov in mg/m³ (A. Novoshilova, 1958)

Year	Sea of Azov					Gulf of Taganrog			
	Feb	Apr	Jul	Aug	Oct	Apr	Jul	Aug	Oct
1938	55	63	463	367	272	175	1,835	240	747
1940	—	44	315	756	—	—	—	—	—
1941	—	63	942	—	—	—	—	—	—
1947	—	57	573	802	—	411	1,079	—	—
1948	—	26	—	263	—	180	—	740	793
1949	—	7	833	319	—	—	2,728	1,914	—
1950	—	76	493	214	—	—	—	—	—
1951	—	189	483	509	596	213	1,134	1,506	—
1952	—	174	784	—	246	109	884	—	—
1953	—	104	517	232	—	129	449	1,105	1,110
1954	—	32	120	131	133	99	352	818	831
1955	71	338	54	26	93	534	254	517	562
1956	—	30	245	77	35	306	519	693	1,994

This was observed also in the autumn, when the 'marine' plankton moved eastwards. In subsequent years the Sea of Azov zooplankton biomass decreased owing to the change in the flow of the river Don (*Table 201*).

General quantitative characteristics of zooplankton and its seasonal changes are given in Figs 232 and 233.

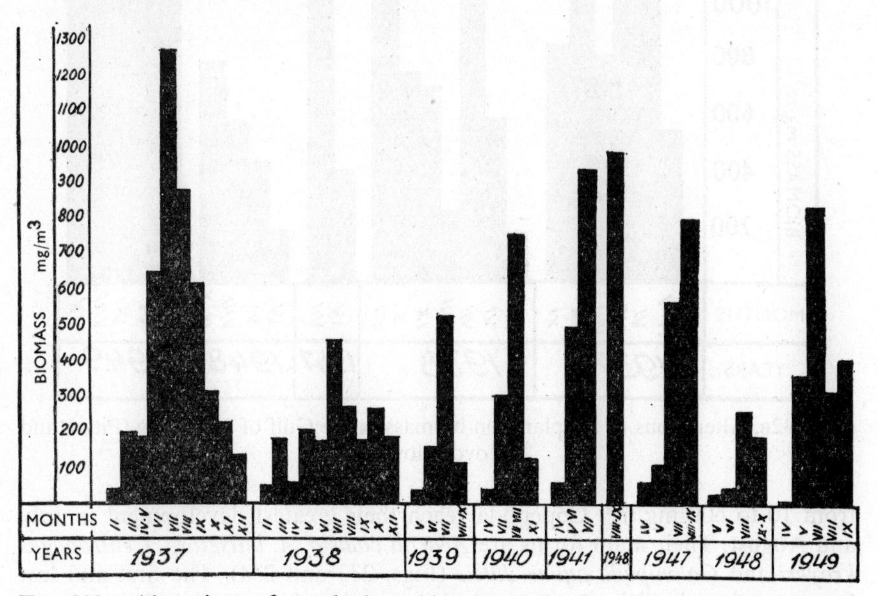

FIG. 232A. Alterations of zooplankton biomass in the Sea of Azov proper (Pitzik and Novoshilova).

Copepoda and Rotifera play a dominant part in the Sea of Azov zooplankton. Their annual mean biomass, according to A. Okul's data, is 210 mg/m³, i.e. more than 50 per cent of the total zooplankton biomass, with fluctuations

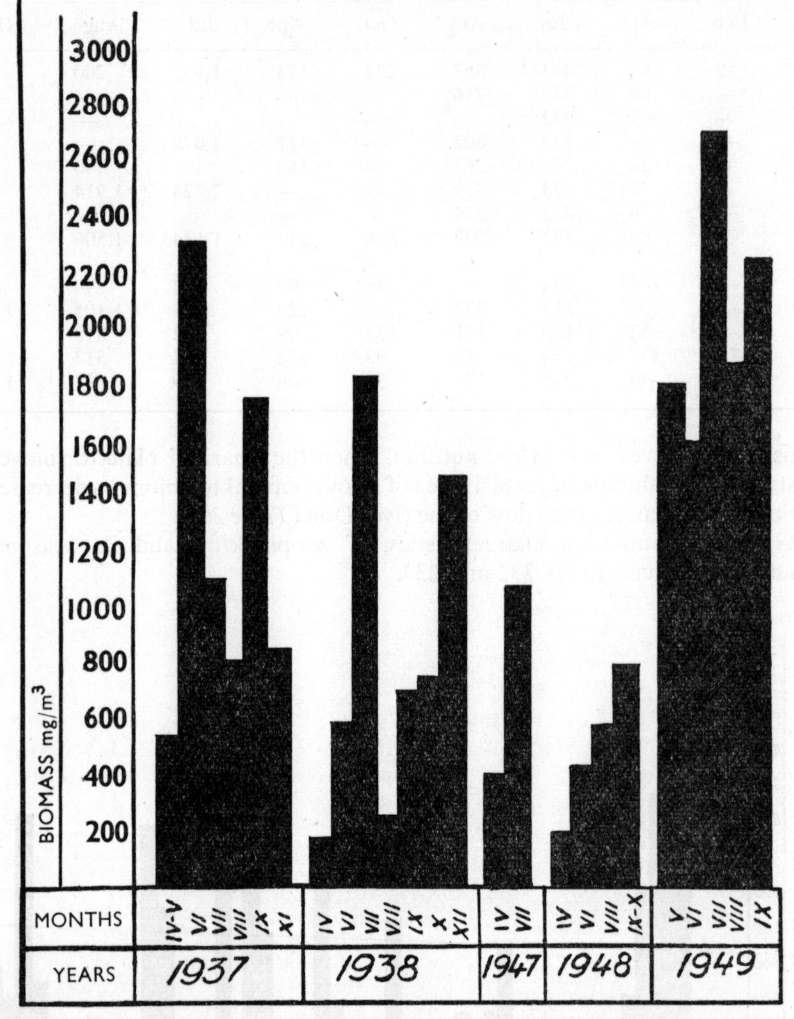

FIG. 232B. Alterations of zooplankton biomass in the Gulf of Taganrog (Pitzik and Novoshilova).

from 10 to 600 mg/m³. Copepoda reach their greatest development in July and August. Their main forms are *Acartia clausia*, *A. latisetosa*, *Centropages kroyeri* and *Calanipeda aquae dulcis* (Figs. 233 and 234). The first and last forms are found all the year round, the second and third reach their greatest development during the warmest part of the year. In the Gulf of Taganrog

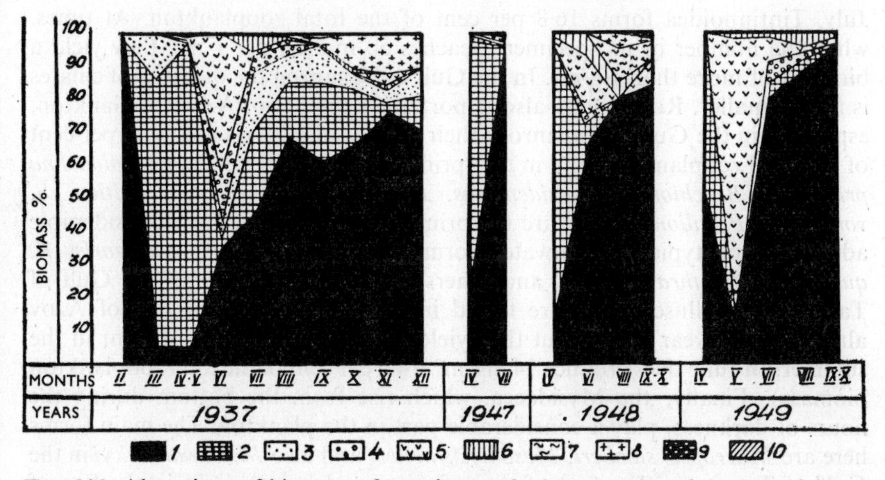

FIG. 233. Alterations of biomass of certain zooplankton species of the Sea of Azov proper: *1* Copepoda; *2* Rotatoria; *3* Tintinnoidea; *4* Mollusc larvae; *5* Cirripedia; *6* Cladocera; *7* Hydrozoa larvae; *8* Polychaeta larvae; *9* Mysidacea; *10* Others (Okul, 1941).

Copepoda development is even greater than in the open part of the Sea of Azov (on the average 70 per cent of all the zooplankton biomass; in fact 1,500 mg/m³, chiefly consisting of *Calanipeda aquae dulcis*). The relict form *Heterocope caspia* is very characteristic of the Gulf of Taganrog; there is a considerable admixture of fresh-water species in the most eastern part of the Gulf. Cirripedia larvae play a substantial part in the Sea of Azov in June; 42 per cent of zooplankton biomass consists of them, they yield up to 270 mg/m³. Their numbers are much smaller in the Gulf of Taganrog.

Among the other groups which go to form the Sea of Azov zooplankton, that of the marine Infusoria Tintinnoidea should be mentioned first; in spite of its minute size, it gives a mean annual biomass of 39 mg/m³ (9·6 per cent of the total zooplankton). During the period of its greatest development, in

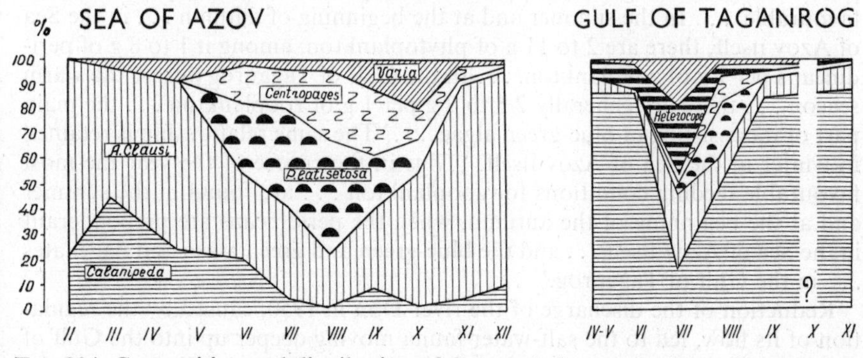

FIG. 234. Composition and distribution of Copepoda in the plankton of the Sea of Azov and the Gulf of Taganrog according to the months of the year (Okul, 1941).

July, Tintinnoidea forms 16·8 per cent of the total zooplankton. At times, when the number of its specimens reaches 50 million per 1 m³, they yield a biomass of more than 1 g/m³. In the Gulf of Taganrog the quantity of ciliates is much smaller. Rotifera are also important in the Sea of Azov zooplankton, especially in the Gulf of Taganrog; their annual biomass is about 25 per cent of the total zooplankton, and in the spring even 80 or 90 per cent. *Asplanchna priodonta*, *Brachionus quadridentatus*, *B. plicatiles*, *Synchaeta baltica*, *S. vorax* and *Pedalion oxyuris* are the principal forms. There is a considerable admixture of typical fresh-water forms, such as *Keratella cochlearis*, *K. quadrata*, *Triarthra longiseta* and others, in the eastern part of the Gulf of Taganrog. Mollusc larvae are found in the plankton of the Sea of Azov almost all the year round, but they yield a considerable development in the summer. In June they produce 94 mg/m³ (14·5 per cent of the total zooplankton biomass). Finally, the Mysidacea, which rise from the bottom during the hours of darkness, play a considerable part in the plankton. The main forms here are *Macropsis slabberi*, *Mesomysis helleri* and also *M. kowalewskyi* in the Gulf of Taganrog. The first of these forms produces at night in the Sea of Azov 152 mg beneath 1 m² of surface area, and in the Gulf of Taganrog even 185 mg; *Mesomysis kowalewskyi* in the Gulf of Taganrog produces 254 mg, and *M. helleri* in the Sea of Azov, 57 mg. A small part of the Sea of Azov zooplankton consists of Cladocera (*Evadne trigona* and *Podon polyphemoides*) and polychaete larvae. G. Pitzik (1951) gave an interesting comparison of the mass development of phyto- and zooplankton in the Sea of Azov and of the significance of the first as food for the second: 'Early in the spring phytoplankton develops in such colossal quantities, that the scarce zooplankton leaves much of it untouched. At that period for every gramme of zooplankton there is 30 to 70 g of phytoplankton, including 27 to 66 g of diatoms and 2 to 4 g of peridineans. With such a ratio the main mass of phytoplankton, dying off, is deposited on the sea-bottom; together with the detritus which is brought down in huge amounts by run-off from the land, it forms large deposits of organic matter. In late spring there are only 0·9 to 1·2 g of phytoplankton per 1 g of zooplankton . . . and the feeding conditions for zooplankton, and through it for plankton-eating fish as well, may become unfavourable. . . . In the summer and at the beginning of autumn . . . in the Sea of Azov itself, there are 2 to 11 g of phytoplankton, among it 1 to 8 g of peridineans per 1 g of zooplankton. . . . In the Gulf of Taganrog during the warm season . . . there are generally 2·5 to 7 g per 1 g of zooplankton . . . the main part of it consisting of blue-green algae. . . .' The same relationship is retained in winter in the Sea of Azov itself. 'Thus in the course of the year the most favourable feeding conditions for zooplankton . . . are found in the summer and at the beginning of the autumn, when the peridineans are preponderant in the Sea of Azov itself . . . and the blue-green and green algae and flagellates . . . in the Gulf of Taganrog.'

Reduction of the discharge of the river Don in 1950, caused by the regulation of its flow, led to the salt-water fauna moving deeper up into the Gulf of Taganrog and the fresh-water fauna receding. In 1951 the discharge of the Don was considerably greater, and the Gulf fauna moved in the opposite direction, but in 1952, when the Tsimlyansk reservoir was filled, the salinity of the Gulf waters rose again and 'marine' fauna again moved eastwards. There were no marked changes in the zooplankton biomass during 1950–52 (A. Novoshilova, 1955). A clear illustration of this process of changes in

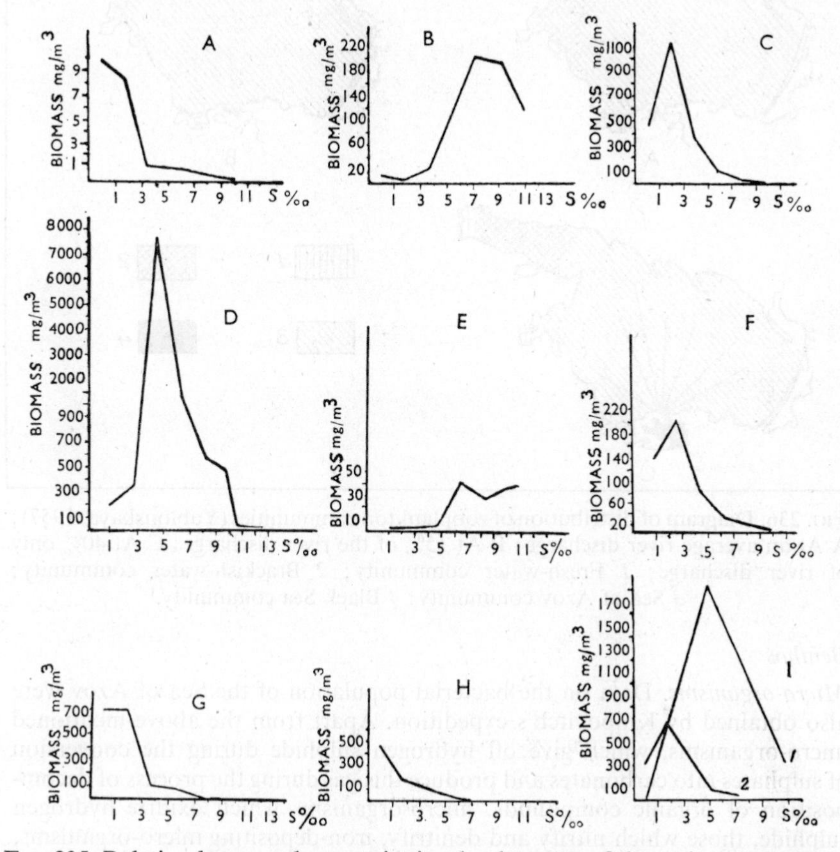

Fig. 235. Relation between the quantitative development of the main zooplankton species and the salinity of the waters (Yablonskaya, 1957). A Fresh-water Rotifera (*Brachionus angularis*, *Keratella cochlearis*, *Keratella quadrata*, *Polyarthra trigla*); B *Synchaeta* sp. (a spring form); C *Asplanchna priodonta*; D *Calanipeda aquae dulcis*; E *Acartia clausi*; F *Heterocope caspia*; G *Acanthocyclops vernalis*; H Fresh-water Cladocera (*Daphnia longispina*, *Diaphanozoma brachyurum*, *Laptodora kindtii*); I Mysidacea (1 *Macropsis slabberi*; 2 *Mesomysis kowalevskyi*).

numbers with a change of salinity, as related to the Rotifera and Crustacea, is given (Fig. 235) by Yablonskaya, who has also drawn a prognosis of the distribution of the main zooplankton biocoenoses in the Sea of Azov at different stages of the loss of river water due to irrigation measures (Fig. 236).

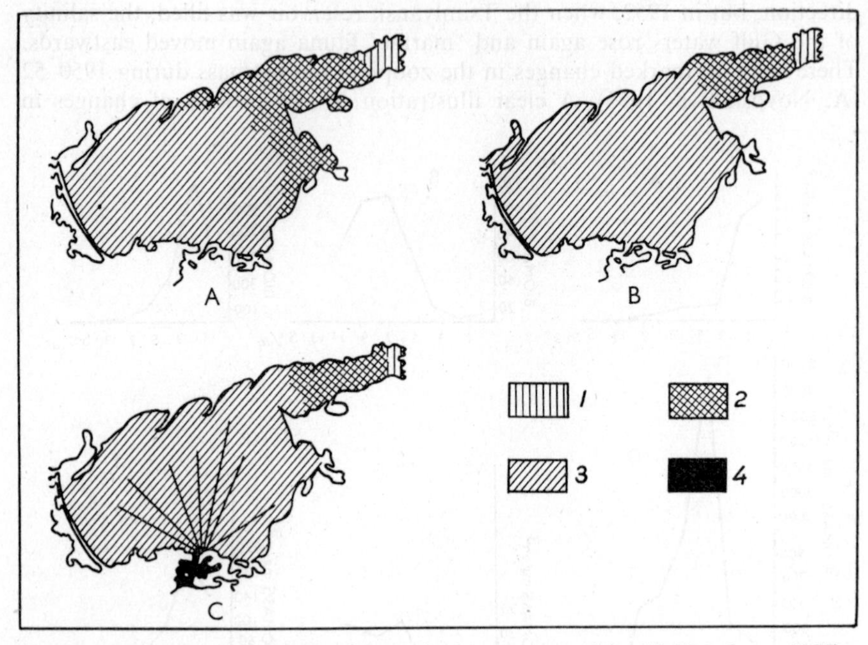

FIG. 236. Diagram of distribution of zooplankton communities (Yablonskaya, 1957): A At an average river discharge; B At 15% of the river discharge; C At 40% only of river discharge; *1* Fresh-water community; *2* Brackish-water community; *3* Sea of Azov community; *4* Black Sea community.

Benthos

Micro-organisms. Data on the bacterial population of the Sea of Azov were also obtained by Knipovitch's expedition. Apart from the above-mentioned micro-organisms, which give off hydrogen sulphide during the conversion of sulphates into carbonates and produce this gas during the process of decomposition of organic compounds, micro-organisms which oxidize hydrogen sulphide, those which nitrify and denitrify, iron-depositing micro-organisms, chitin-decomposing and other micro-organisms have been recorded in the composition of the Sea of Azov micro-flora. B. Isatchenko (1924) carried out a quantitative survey of the Sea of Azov bottom micro-organisms and obtained for some coastal areas the sum of 274 to 776 million specimens per gramme of the soil. If the average size of micro-organisms is 1 μ^3, and their average number 500 millions, than 1 g of the soil contains an approximate weight of 0·5 mg of micro-organisms. This, when converted to 1 m^2, would give a huge quantity for the mass of micro-organisms and gives some idea of the colossal processes taking place in the sea-bed, especially if we keep in mind that the annual production of micro-organisms in the Sea of Azov is hundreds and maybe thousands of times greater than its biomass.

Only within the area of the Kerch Strait itself is the quantity of micro-organisms greatly reduced.

The qualitative composition of the macrophytes of the Sea of Azov is considerably impoverished as compared with the Black Sea. Instead of the 221 species of green, red and brown algae of the Black Sea there are no more than 25 or 30 species in the Sea of Azov. The amount of algae decreases markedly as one moves eastwards, and at the entrance to the Gulf of Taganrog red algae are not found. In the Sea of Azov among the red algae the most widely distributed are *Ceramium diaphanum*, *Polysiphonia opaca* and *P. variegata*; among the green species, Enteromorpha and Cladophora. The macrophytes populate only a narrow band along the shore of the Sea of Azov. Apart from this among the flowering plants *Zostera marina*, *Z. nana* (*minor*), *Zannichelia pedunculata* and *Potamogeton marinus* are common in the Sea of Azov.

Continuous macrophyte beds are rare in the Sea of Azov, and only in the Utlyuksk inlet and in the northern Sivash are there abundant growths of Zostera, which are exploited commercially. According to V. Generalova the maximum biomass of bottom-algae of the Utlyuksk inlet is 22·4 tons, and that of calcareous plants 69·3 tons per hectare. According to the data of M. Kireeva and T. Shchapova (1939) in those areas the amount of Zostera occupying an area of 9,500 hectares is 25,000 tons dry weight.

According to V. Generalova (1951) Zostera forms about half of the total mass of water macrophytes in the Sea of Azov, red algae form 35 per cent and the green 15 per cent. Commercial stocks of macrophytes of the northwestern part of the Sea of Azov are small (*Table 202*).

Table 202

Area	Biomass, tons per hectare			
	Algae		Zostera	
	Mini.	Max.	Mini.	Max.
Utlyuksk Inlet	2,125	2,246	17,582	69,333
Arabat Strelka	2,000	—	16,000	—

Qualitative composition of zoobenthos (*Fig. 237*). We do not possess sufficient data for a complete list of species of the bottom-fauna of the Sea of Azov, but we can make use of the incomplete list drawn up by F. Mordukhai-Boltovskoy (1960). This list includes (with unimportant additions but without Protozoa) 292 invertebrate species and sub-species (*Table 203*).

The crustaceans occupy the first place by the richness of their specific composition and the number of specimens per unit area (about 3,670), but as regards biomass the bivalves are considerably superior to the rest. The Sea of Azov may be truly called the mollusc sea, or the Cardium–Syndesmya sea, as the Baltic Sea can be called the Macoma sea; this may be illustrated by the data given in *Table 204*.

The peculiar conditions of the Sea of Azov—its salinity lower than that of the Black Sea, its marked seasonal fluctuations of temperature, its long winter and shallow waters—lead to a definite selection of forms from the

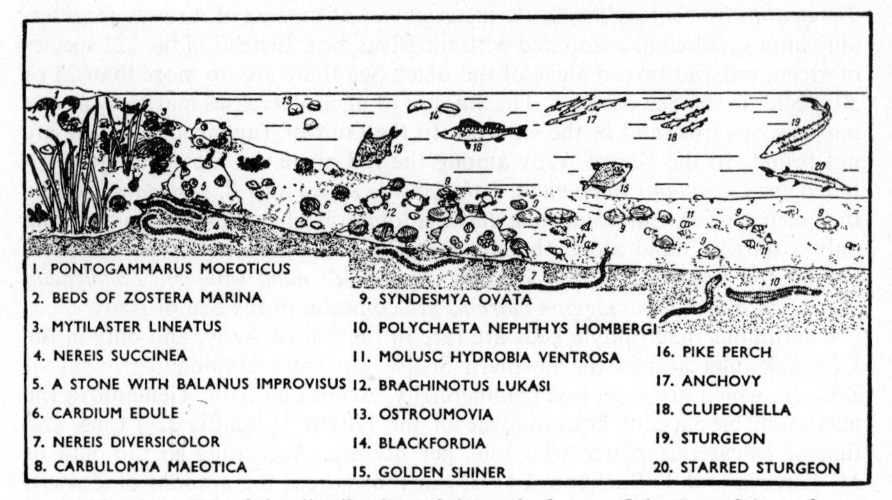

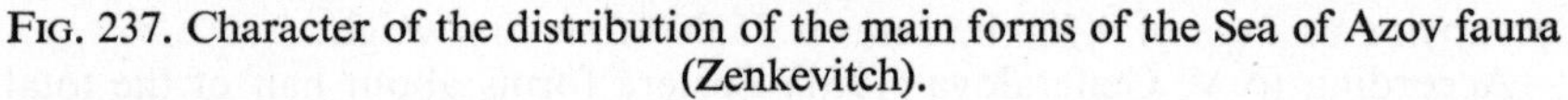

FIG. 237. Character of the distribution of the main forms of the Sea of Azov fauna (Zenkevitch).

considerably richer Black Sea fauna, which in its turn is a selected fauna from the Mediterranean. In spite of this, a certain number of Mediterranean forms find in the Sea of Azov conditions exceptionally favourable for their development and form huge accumulations. As a result, the communities of the Sea of Azov are often characterized by their large biomass and by their high productivity indices and, at the same time, by the extreme poverty of their qualitative composition (oligo-mixed communities). Of the 137 species of benthos only 30 species are found more or less frequently.

Table 203

Group	No. of species and sub-species	Group	No. of species and sub-species
Porifera	1	Copepoda	30
Coelenterata	7	Cirripedia	2
Turbellaria	4	Ostracoda	3
Nemertini	1	Amphipoda	29
Polychaeta	35	Mysidacea	11
Oligochaeta	6	Cumacea	10
Hirudinea	2	Isopoda	3
Bryozoa	2	Decapoda	8
Rotatoria	14	Chaetognatha	1
Gastropoda	15	Tunicata	1
Lammellibranchiata	19	Pisces	79
Cladocera	9		
		Total	292

Table 204

Group	Mean number of specimens/1 m²	percentage	Mean biomass g/m²	percentage
Bivalves	971	6·3	98·50	74·2
Crustaceans	11,345	74·0	15·26	11·6
Worms	1,939	12·6	7·50	5·8
Others	911	7·1	10·74	8·4
Total	15,166	100·0	132·0	100·0

For its salinity the Sea of Azov should be included, according to Remane's (1935) classification, in the mesohaline zone. The true relict brackish-water fauna is concentrated in the inner part of the Gulf of Taganrog, living there at a salinity below 3·6‰.

Zoobenthos biocoenoses. Bottom biocoenoses of the Sea of Azov, which were comprehensively investigated by V. P. Vorobieff (1944), F. Mordukhai-Boltovskoy (1939), and later by I. Stark (1951, 1955, 1958), can be divided first of all into two large groups:

(*1*) Relict biocoenoses, with early Pontic relicts as dominant species—Dreissena, Monodacna, Hypaniola and some species of Corophium and Pontagammarus.

(*2*) Mediterranean or Azov–Black Sea biocoenoses, with Ostracoda as dominant species as well as Corophium, Cardium, Syndesmya, Mytilaster, Corbulomya, Hydrobia, Balanus, Nereis, Sphaeroma and Pectinaria.

However, both these groups, especially the first, are distinguished by a strongly marked oligohalinity; this, and the small difference in their living conditions, leads to a great similarity in the type of biocoenosis, making easy the transition of various combinations into each other.

The general picture of the autumn distribution of bottom biocoenoses and of the biomass for 1934–35 is given in Fig. 238A, B. Let us consider the brief characterization of individual biocoenoses marked on the chart, beginning from the east.

Biocoenosis: Dreissena–Monodacna–Unionidae—In the most eastern corner of the Gulf of Taganrog, in front of the Don delta on the estuarial shallows, there are situated different variations of the Dreissena–Monodacna–Unionidae biocoenosis. Nearer to the Don, in the least saline part, Dreissena is predominant. Only the most hardy forms can endure sharp fluctuations of salinity and sometimes considerable drying-up caused by land winds. The mean biomass here is 13 g/m², of which *Dreissena polymorpha* forms 11·6 g/m². Among the other forms the relict crustaceans Cumacea (*Pterocuma sowinskyi, Stenocuma tenuicauda*, species of the Schizorhynchus genus), Mysidacea (*Metamysis strauchi, Mesomysis kowalewskyi*), Amphipoda (*Corophium curvispinum, Pontogammarus abbreviatus*), the species of Gmelina genus, Oligochaeta

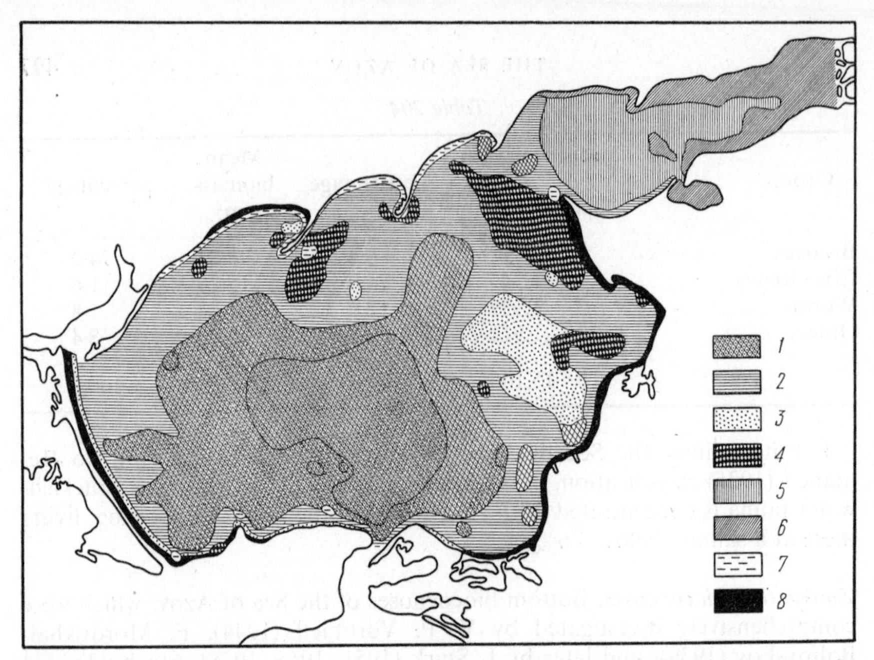

FIG. 238A. Distribution of bottom biocoenoses (see text) of the Sea of Azov in autumn 1934–35 (g/m³) (Vorobieff, 1944). *1* Syndesmya–Hydrobia; *2* Cardium; *3* Mytilaster; *4* Balanus; *5* Nereis–Ostracoda; *6* Monodacna–Dreissena; *7* Nereis; *8* Corbulomya.

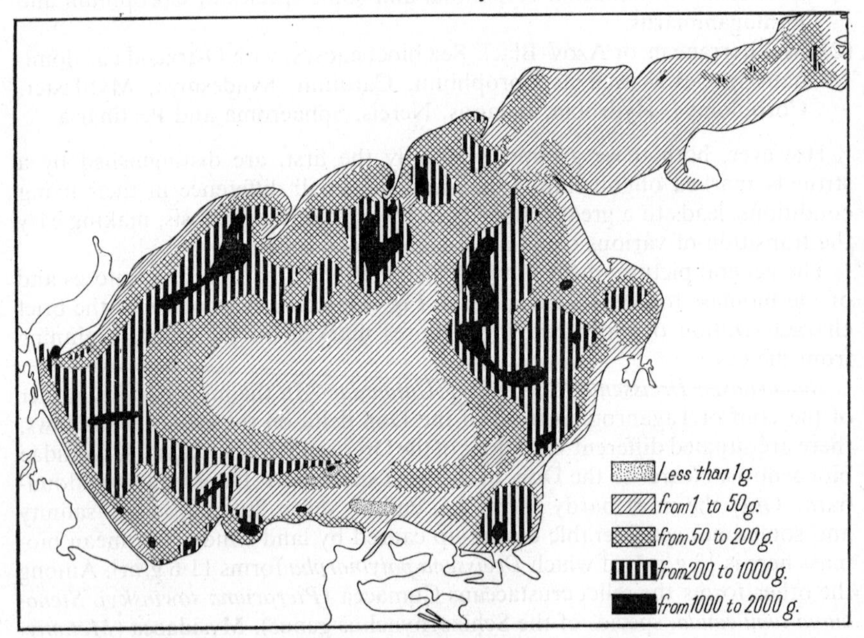

FIG. 238B. Distribution of benthos biomass of the Sea of Azov in autumn 1934–35 (g/m³) (Vorobieff).

(Tubificidae) and Chironomidae, are of importance. 89·3 per cent of the total biomass consists of molluscs, and 8·4 per cent of crustaceans. Marked variations of salinity, and its increase as one moves westwards, cause a decline in the number of species.

In the most westerly part of the biocoenosis, on coastal sands and shell gravel at depths of 1·5 to 3·5 m and around the Peschanye Islands, lives a very much impoverished (2·6 g/m²) variant of this biocoenosis, with a predominance of the relict polychaete *Hypaniola kowalevskyi*, the crustacean *Corophium volutator* and an oligochaete of the Tubificidae family. It is almost free of fresh-water elements and molluscs (mainly Monodacna), and resembles somewhat the following ostracode biocoenosis, but without the ostracodes or Tanypus. Apart from the above-mentioned forms, the presence of the relict crustaceans *Pterocuma pectinata* and *Gmelina ovata* and the generally pronounced relict aspect are characteristic of this group.

The Nereis diversicolor Ostracoda biocoenosis—In the western half of the Gulf of Taganrog, on the soft dark so-called Ostracode muds, lives the *Nereis diversicolor* Ostracoda biocoenosis, which also produces a number of variants. This biocoenosis penetrates far to the east along the deepest part of the Gulf. In the westward direction the marine forms become gradually dominant in it, although there is still a considerable admixture of Tubificidae and Tanypus. In the central, deeper part (below 4 m) of the Gulf of Taganrog Ostracoda are markedly predominant in the benthos. With a very low average biomass (9·12 g/m²) the biocoenosis has a strikingly large number of minute crustaceans, whose shells, in innumerable numbers, compose the basis of the sea-bed (the average number of live specimens of Ostracoda is 40,000 specimens per 1 m², at times up to 150,000, at a biomass of 3 to 6 g/m², comprising more than half the total biomass—58 per cent).

In the Eisk inlet the Amphipoda *Corophium volutator* (more than 6,000 specimens per 1 m² and 26 per cent of the total biomass) produces a large biomass. Colonies of the relict polychaete *Hypaniola kowalevskyi* are just as abundant here (up to 40,000 specimens per 1 m²). Among the other forms the following should be noted: *Nereis diversicolor*, Tubificidae, *Balanus improvisus*, *Cardium edule* and *Monodacna colorata*. In general 73·3 per cent of the total biomass consists at times of crustaceans.

In the western half of the sector occupied by the Nereis–Ostracoda biocoenosis, at a depth of 4 to 8 m, *Nereis diversicolor* becomes more and more significant. The biomass here is also low (an average of 23 g/m²) and 40 per cent of it consists of Ostracoda (up to 230,000 specimens per 1 m²). Worms (mainly *Nereis diversicolor* and *Hypaniola kowalevskyi*), comprising 47 per cent by weight of the biomass, are almost as significant. Among the other forms the molluscs *Syndesmya ovata* and *Cardium edule* and the crustacean *Corophium volutator* should be noted.

The Nereis succinea biocoenosis—In the rest of the Sea of Azov, throughout the coastal zone wherever there is a mud bottom, the biocoenosis *Nereis succinea* is found. The biocoenosis *Nereis succinea* is met in different biocoenotic combinations, in the main with Ostracoda, Balanus, Cardium, Hydrobia, Pterocuma, Mytilaster, Ampelisca and Corbulomya.

Nereis diversicolor lives mainly in the Gulf of Taganrog, *N. succinea* in the rest of the Sea. The variant *N. diversicolor*–Ostracoda lives in the Gulf of Taganrog all the year round. *N. succinea* possesses a more intensive faculty for spawning than *N. diversicolor*; it forms large numbers of eggs and it has some pelagic larvae and heteroneroid forms. *N. succinea* probably pushes its rival *N. diversicolor* out of the Sea of Azov into the Gulf of Taganrog, which is not suitable for *N. succinea* owing to its low salinity. In the Black Sea, however, with a salinity too high for *N. succinea*, *N. diversicolor* develops intensively, forming powerful populations, and competes successfully with another species—*N. cultrifera*.

Clamworms form excellent food for many fish of the Black and Azov Seas. Ninety per cent of them are assimilated by fish, compared with only 77 per cent of crustaceans, 85 per cent of fish and only 29 per cent of molluscs. The high content of nitrogen (64 per cent) and fats (16 per cent) in clamworms also increase their value as food.

As is known, Nereis of the Sea of Azov has been used for acclimatization in the Caspian Sea in order to increase the feeding value of the benthos for fish, primarily for the sturgeon. The results of this acclimatization are given in Chapter II. Naturally, since Nereis has developed hugely in the Caspian Sea, that system of competitive relationships with the local benthos is of great interest. May Nereis do real harm to the benthos population of the Caspian Sea? The system of synecological interconnection established for Nereis in the Sea of Azov is of interest for the solution of this problem. This has been comprehensively studied by I. Stark (1959). The latter confirms the well known fact that *Nereis succinea* and *N. diversicolor*, like many other nereides, thrive on ooze and vegetable detritus, and that they may take live components of zoobenthos only accidentally and passively, together with their main food, and that therefore they do no substantial harm to the rest of the infauna, oligochaetes and chironomids included. Stark finds proof of this in the frequency of the occurrence of dense nereides colonies within the areas of high indices of the number of specimens and biomass of those more passive forms of infauna which could have suffered from the nereides. Thus in the Gulf of Taganrog, where the nereid biomass is highest, chironomids, oligochaetes and Hypaniola reach their greatest development.

The Pontogammarus maeoticus biocoenosis—The only relict, and the most oligo-mixed, biocoenosis found throughout the whole of the Sea of Azov, apart from the Gulf of Taganrog, on sloping sandy beaches, right at the water's edge and within the regularly washed zone, is *Pontogammarus maeoticus*. The biomass and number of organisms in this biocoenosis varies greatly, reaching occasionally (in places with broken sea-weeds and detritus) 80,000 specimens of *P. maeoticus* per 1 m^2, with a biomass of 642 g/m^2. *P. maeoticus* does not tolerate an accumulation of rotting sea-weeds since it is a steno-oxybiotic form. *P. maeoticus* is also rare on pure sand. In unfavourable weather (strong swell, gales) and in winter time the whole mass of *P. maeoticus* migrates into deeper waters. This form is found up to 10 m deep as a component of almost all biocoenoses of the Sea of Azov.

The Cardium edule biocoenosis—The *Cardium edule* biocoenosis begins in the most westerly part of the Gulf of Taganrog; it is very widely distributed in the open parts of the Sea of Azov, and in 1934 occupied about one-third of its bottom.

A bottom-area of 10,000 km² of the Sea of Azov is occupied by this biocoenosis in the spring, and 12,000 km² in the autumn. The widening of its habitat is due to its pushing out other biocoenoses (*Nereis succinea*, Syndesmya, Mytilaster).

Cardium does not form such massive populations in the Black Sea as in the Sea of Azov, where it has found exceptionally favourable conditions for its mass development. *Cardium edule* is a typical filter-feeder since it lives on plankton and detritus suspended in water; it competes with Mytilaster, Balanus and Corbulomya in its feeding, forming with them a powerful filter. Huge plankton development and the abundance of detritus in the Sea of Azov create most favourable conditions for the existence of *C. edule*. This biocoenosis reaches its highest development on silty sand bottoms. This species is also widely distributed in the Atlantic Ocean, reaching the western part of the Murman peninsula in the north. The Baltic Sea also is thickly populated by it. In the northern part of the Atlantic *C. edule* is adapted mainly to the tidal zone and is a typical littoral organism. Thus it is a very widely distributed eurytopic species, with a great capacity for adapting itself to different conditions of life: temperature, salinity, soils and depths. This mollusc is devoured in large numbers by fish (in the Sea of Azov by bullhead, Acipenseridae, flat fish, golden shiner, roach, *Rutilus rutilus heckeli* and others); for many thousands of years it has also been used as food by man.

As a result of *C. edule's* capacity for adapting itself to different conditions of existence, numerous varieties have been evolved from it; *C. edule* var. *maeotica* lives in the Sea of Azov, while in the Utlyuksk inlet and the Sivash *C. edule* var. *picta* is also found.

In the Sea of Azov *C. edule* is found on various sea-bottoms, but it prefers soft beds. A single biomass of this mollusc varies from a few grammes to 2 kg and more per 1 m². *C. edule* does not require a great amount of oxygen but it cannot survive a considerable lowering of oxygen content. In the Sea of Azov its greatest numbers are adapted to a depth of 6 to 10 m. At a greater depth it is replaced by *Syndesmya ovata*. Since Cardium is fairly tolerant to considerable fluctuations of salinity it can compete successfully with all the forms of benthos of the Sea of Azov; Mytilaster alone pushes it out on the harder sea-bed of the Zhelezinskaya Bank, while Corbulomya does so on sand, or silty sand bottom at a depth of less than 4 m. *C. edule* begins to multiply during the second summer of its life, but its breeding reaches its greatest intensity only in its third or fourth summer. *C. edule* may perhaps breed three times a year, laying some tens of thousands of eggs.

A comparison of the rate of growth of *C. edule* off the English and German coasts shows that in the Sea of Azov it is much slower and that *C. edule* does not reach as advanced an age. As regards the rate of growth this can apparently be explained by lowered salinity and by the unfavourable aeration conditions of the Sea of Azov, and partly also by the higher temperature, causing earlier sexual maturity; the shorter life-span of the Azov *C. edule*

Table 205

Name of form	Spring: No. of specimens per 1 m²	Spring: Biomass g/m²	Autumn: No. of specimens per 1 m²	Autumn: Biomass g/m²
Cardium edule	395	279·10	1,426	754·61
Syndesmya ovata	1,464	93·83	462	42·03
Nereis succinea	139	7·58	463	5·42
Balanus improvisus	143	6·81	564	21·02
Hydrobia ventrosa	1,483	3·18	2,778	5·13
Mytilaster lineatus	1,211	4·60	140	11·51
Nephthys hombergi	33	1·54	76	1·19
Corbulomya maeotica	68	2·25	51	0·15
Ampelisca diadema	90	1·07	49	0·21
Ostracoda	913	0·10	2,000	0·10
Brachinotus lucasi	—	—	16	3·69
Others	91	5·81	154	0·66
Total	6,028	396·86	8,163	845·72

must be explained by the latter. In the Sea of Azov five-year-old *C. edule* are 23 to 26 mm long, while the English ones are 39 to 42 mm; moreover, off the shores of England they live up to nine years, and off the shores of the Murman peninsula to eleven years, and they attain an even bigger size. Cardium, like Nereis, takes part in various biocoenotic groupings in different parts of the Sea.

Cardium–Syndesmya is the most usual grouping found in the Sea of Azov, mostly at depths of 8 to 16 m and on mud-floors. The quantitative ratio of individual components for the whole *C. edule* biocoenosis is given in *Tables 205, 206* and *207*. Thus the gain in weight in *C. edule* biomass consists of the settling of the young, the migration of the one-year-old from the deeper parts, and the growth of all age groups. The loss of biomass is the result of the three first age groups being devoured (fish do not feed on four- and five-year-olds);

Table 206

Groups	Spring: No. of specimens per 1 m²	Spring: Biomass g/m²	Spring: Biomass %	Autumn: No. of specimens per 1 m²	Autumn: Biomass g/m²	Autumn: Biomass %
Lamellibranchiata	3,138	375·78	94·76	2,033	803·30	95·58
Gastropoda	1,483	3·18	0·80	2,778	5·13	0·60
Vermes	176	9·40	2·37	598	6·99	0·82
Crustacea	1,076	1·64	0·41	2,190	4·16	0·49
Balanus	143	6·81	1·71	564	21·02	2·49

Table 207

Forms	No. of specimens per 1 m²	Biomass g/m²
Cardium edule	467	151·5
Syndesmya ovata	2,740	151·3
Hydrobia ventrosa	14,321	14·85
Nephthys hombergi	45	1·69
Nereis succinea	54	2·14
Balanus improvisus	30	2·20
Ostracoda	1,563	0·16
Corbulomya maeotica	10	1·46
Others	19	0·96
Total	19,249	326·26

it is, moreover, possible to show that the comparative percentage of the young stages in the regions of intensive feeding of fish is very low as compared to regions where fish do not feed. On the Zhelezinskaya and Eleninskya Banks, where fish feed intensively, the young of Cardium forms only 12·4 per cent in comparison with the adults, while along the Arabat Strelka, where there are fewer fish, this percentage rises to 55·7.

Vorobieff (1944) has estimated the consumption by fish of young Cardium at 31 to 77 per cent by comparing these data. Knowing the numbers of settled young it can be calculated that the fish consume 644 specimens with a biomass of 102·4 g/m². Similar data were obtained by Vorobieff when he determined the amount of young Cardium eaten by fish from their intestinal content. It was calculated in the same way that the amount of one-year-olds consumed by fish is 70 per cent as compared with those under one year, and 184 per cent of two-year-olds. The loss of Cardium due to consumption by fish from May to November in the biocoenosis under consideration is given in *Table 208* (calculations were carried out for those under one year).

After making some corrections Vorobieff concludes that 661 g/m² of Cardium are consumed. The difference in the average biomass, from spring

Table 208

Age group	Consumption No. of specimens per 1 m²	Biomass g/m²
Under one year	644	102·40
One-year-olds	450	179·55
Two-year-olds	238	316·00
Three-year-olds	22	59·71
Four-year-olds	—	7·28
Total	1,354	664·94

to autumn, for the Cardium biocoenosis is 185 g/m². Hence to a first apoprximation, the actual production of Cardium in this biocoenosis is 1,146 g/m². The *P*/*B* coefficient for the original spring biomass will be 1,146:279=4: 1.

Balanus sometimes settles on mollusc shells in large numbers and take away their food and oxygen. On the other hand, Mytilaster young also settle at times on the Balanus cases and even on top of them, tightening up the cases with their bysus threads. By taking away its food and oxygen and in a purely mechanical manner Mytilaster young, when settling in masses, may destroy *B. improvisus*. The destruction of one of the components of this close symbiosis may cause the destruction of another, especially when a mass of *B. improvisus* settles on *C. edule*. The mollusc dies and stops the aeration of the water, and the Balanus settled there are deprived of their food.

In fish feeding-grounds masses of *C. edule* and *M. lineatus* are devoured and *B. improvisus* acquires a dominant position. Moreover, the last named grows more vigorously than its rivals, but it multiplies less intensively. It produces hundreds of eggs, while *C. edule* produces tens of thousands and Mytilaster hundreds of thousands. Thus the changes in the groupings Balanus, Mytilaster and Cardium, and their transition from one into another, are caused primarily by their struggle for the site, food and oxygen, and by their being eaten by fish. Large areas of sea-bed at depths of 6 to 8 m with hard soils, in cases when Cardium, Mytilaster and Syndesmya are devoured in masses by fish, are rapidly populated by the intensively developing Balanus, which has a very long period of puberty. This might be the reason why the *Balanus improvisus* biocoenosis is found in patches, mainly along the routes along which fish travel. Moreover, the considerable washing out of the bed soil during a violent swell affects Cardium and Mytilaster very strongly, while a low oxygen content kills off Balanus. That is why a biocoenosis with a marked predominance of Balanus is more often found in the autumn than in the spring, Its total area in the spring is 607 km², and in the autumn 2,200 km². Apart from on rocks and cliffs, which are rare in the Sea of Azov, Balanus develops best on shell gravel, either pure or with an admixture of sand or mud, at a depth of 4 to 6 m.

As with other bottom groupings of the Sea of Azov, so with the biocoenosis in which Balanus is predominant one can readily establish its plasticity and the most varied combinations with other mass benthos species, especially *Nereis succinea*, *Cardium edule*, *Mytilaster lineatus*, *Hydrobia ventrosa*, *Syndesmya ovata* and *Brachynotus lucasi*.

The *P*/*B* ratio of *Balanus improvisus* varies within the limits of 1 to 4·76 in different biocoenoses, depending on the density of the population of other species present and primarily, of course, on that of Balanus itself (intra-specific and inter-specific competition). Another variant of the Cardium biocoenosis, scattered in separate patches like the previous one, is the variant with a marked predominance of *Mytilaster lineatus*. The main accumulations of *M. lineatus* were adapted to the Zhelezinskaya Bank, off the craggy southern shores of the Sea of Azov and also to the coast of the Arabat Strelka. On the Zhelezinskaya Bank it had pushed out almost all the other biocoenoses. The total area occupied by this grouping—1,470 km²—is almost one and a half times greater in autumn than in spring. The species invariably accompanying *M. lineatus* are, in order of decreasing importance, Balanus, Cardium and *Nereis succinea*. In contrast to all the other biocoenoses of the Sea of Azov, the *M. lineatus* grouping is more stable and permanent. The quantitative ratio of different species in this biocoenosis is given in *Table 209*.

In the spring *M. lineatus* is represented in the biocoenosis by two age-stages; the one-year-olds (on the average 4,904 specimens per 1 m²) and the

Table 209

Species	Spring		Autumn	
	No. of specimens per 1 m²	Biomass g/m²	No. of specimens per 1 m²	Biomass g/m²
Mytilaster lineatus	5,277	279·00	10,810	600·83
Balanus improvisus	1,282	61·28	1,609	62·30
Cardium edule	203	38·85	83	63·35
Nereis succinea	230	16·02	915	9·06
Syndesmya ovata	36	11·20	9	0·53
Ampelisca maeotica	143	3·35	20	0·18
Mytilus galloprovincialis	6	5·11	—	—
Hydrobia ventrosa	358	1·40	146	0·23
Brachinotus lucasi	2	0·90	61	7·00
Microdeutopus gryllotalpa	49	0·21	686	0·50
Corbulomya maeotica	2·5	0·40	—	—
Others	117·5	1·00	305	1·80
Total	7,706	415·72	14,644	745·78

two-year-olds (374 specimens per 1 m²). It begins to multiply in April and ceases to do so in August. The two-year-olds breed in April; in May and June the one-year-olds also begin to multiply. In the autumn those under one year also begin to breed (7,812 specimens per 1 m²). During this time the number of one-year-olds and two-year olds is reduced (2,890 and 108 specimens per 1 m²) as a result of their being eaten by fish (bullheads, golden shiner, roach and the Acipenseridae). Thus the loss of one-year-olds from May to November is 2,014 specimens, and that of the two-year-olds 266 specimens per 1 m².

It has been established that the losses suffered by the one-year-olds per 1 m² are 160·32 g; of the two-year-olds, 81·66 g; and of those under one year 338·75 g. These data were obtained by examination of the variations of *M. lineatus* from different places, by the calculation of losses due mainly to their being eaten by fish, by the analysis of stomach-content of fish and by making use of the average weight of molluscs of a certain size. The total amount of all three age groups of *M. lineatus* eaten by fish from May to November is about 579·73 g/m^2. The autumn increment of biomass (*Table 209*), obtained in spite of this loss, is the result of intensive increase of the molluscs remaining in the population. The actual production of *M. lineatus* can be determined as 900 g/m^2, while the average *P*/*B* ratio is 3·22. This high ratio for the Sea of Azov is explained by its high temperature and the abundance of food.

The Syndesmya ovata *biocoenosis*—In the deepest part of the Sea, beyond the *Cardium edule* biocoenosis, there lay in 1934–35 the *Syndesmya ovata* biocoenosis, occupying an area of about 14,500 km^2; this latter is somewhat reduced in the autumn, since it is replaced by its contiguous *C. edule* biocoenosis. In the deepest part of the Sea (12 to 13 m), over an area of 4,500 km^2, the number of Syndesmya is small, and the gastropod mollusc *Hydrobia ventrosa* is predominant. In a wide zone surrounding this deepest part (10 to 11 m), over an area of 10,000 km^2, *Syndesmya ovata* is greatly preponderant, while at depths less than 9 m Syndesmya is replaced by Cardium.

S. ovata is one of the most numerous molluscs in the Sea of Azov. In the Black Sea it is mostly found in fairly shallow low-salinity sectors, especially under the roots of Zostera and the Chareal sea-weeds in lagoons and inlets. This species is widely distributed in the Mediterranean Sea and in the Atlantic Ocean off the coast of Europe. Specimens living on sand or shell gravel are larger in size (up to 25 mm) and have a thicker shell, while on mud soils they are smaller (up to 20 mm) and have a thin transparent shell. In the Sea of Azov they live in largest numbers on silt or silty sand. *S. ovata* feeds on detritus and dwells in the upper layer of the sea-bottom. It has extensible siphon-tubes which help it to endure the unfavourable gas conditions of the near-bottom layer. In general this species is hardier than *C. edule* and goes to greater depths in the Sea of Azov than other molluscs, excepting only *Hydrobia ventrosa*, and it is adapted to the zone of 'blackened shell gravel' with an admixture of mud, in which the proportion of fines is 40 to 50 per cent. In deep and less well-aerated sectors of the bottom Syndesmya displaces Cardium; both molluscs are found in almost equal numbers at depths of 9 to 10 m; in higher layers Syndesmya is replaced by Cardium. *S. ovata* is found at all depths from 1 to 13 m in the Sea of Azov, but it reaches a maximum at 10 to 11 m. However, in shallower places (4 to 6 m) *S. ovata* produces a second maximum on silty sand or shell gravel and mud, since it does not find there its powerful rivals Cardium and Mytilaster, which displace it at depths of 6 to 9 m.

This eurytopic capacity of *S. ovata* is also shown in its response to salinity. In the Sea of Azov it survives salinity fluctuations of 5·5 to 7·0‰ in the Gulf of Taganrog and up to 55‰ in the Sivash. Its optimum, however, is reached at 9 to 12‰. It can live in the presence of hydrogen sulphide and ammonia and can even exist for some time (5 to 8 days) under anaerobic conditions.

S. ovata is one of the favourite foods of almost all the bathypelagic fish of the Sea of Azov, especially sturgeon and golden shiner, and it has a high food-value, partly due to its small size and thin shell.

S. ovata has a very high fecundity: the number of its eggs reaches some hundreds of thousands. It breeds from the end of April to the end of September. *S. ovata* reaches its sexual maturity in the third year of its life, rarely in

Table 210

Species	Spring		Autumn	
	No. of specimens per 1 m²	Biomass g/m²	No. of specimens per 1 m²	Biomass g/m²
Syndesmya ovata	2,143	181·40	3,765	285·15
Cardium edule	49	15·72	62	48·75
Hydrobia ventrosa	3,663	5·00	2,893	4·66
Nereis succinea	93	4·83	142	5·26
Nephthys hombergi	48	1·99	73	2·95
Ostracoda	2,772	0·42	1,077	0·15
Corbulomya maeotica	28	0·57	2	0·10
Ampelisca diadema	17	0·26	0·4	0·00
Balanus improvisus	4	0·43	31	2·48
Mytilaster lineatus	—	—	21	2·46
Others	21	3·48	16·6	0·29
Total	8,838	214·10	8,083	352·25

the second. *S. ovata* has two mass larvae spat-falls, in June and in August–September. The characteristic features of the *S. ovata* biocoenosis and its separate components are shown in *Tables 210* and *211*.

The amount of *S. ovata* consumed by fish per 1 m² (it is the prey also of the small crab *Brachynotus lucasi*) was calculated by Vorobieff in a manner similar to that used for *Cardium edule* and appears by components in *Table 212*.

The processes of growth, however, prevail over losses, and by November the biomass is 100·75 g/m² greater than that of the spring. As for the preceding species in the winter natural mortality must take place, thereby bringing the autumn numbers down to the spring ones. The actual production of *S. ovata* is 377 g/m², and its *P*/*B* coefficient is equal to 2·05.

Table 211

Groups	Spring			Autumn		
	No. of specimens per 1 m²	Biomass g/m²	%	No. of specimens per 1 m²	Biomass g/m²	%
Bivalves	2,222	200·74	93·77	3,850	336·46	95·00
Gastropods	3,663	5·06	2·36	2,893	4·66	1·32
Worms	155	6·87	3·21	222	8·70	2·43
Balanus	4	0·43	0·20	31	2·48	0·70
Other crustaceans	2,722	0·93	0·43	1,086	1·88	0·53
Others	—	0·06	0·03	—	0·08	0·02

Table 212

Age group	No. of specimens	Weight, g
Under one year	3,756	68·36
One-year-olds	683	78·55
Two-year-olds	371	124·66
Three-year-olds	7	4·71
Total	3,817	276·27

The central, deepest (11 to 13 m) part of the Sea, over an area of 4,500 km², is inhabited by the variant Hydrobia–Nephthys–Syndesmya of this biocoenosis. It lives on grey liquid clay-mud with a small admixture of blackened shell gravel, which smells of hydrogen sulphide. This biocoenosis consists of about 16 species only; most of them, moreover, are temporary inhabitants, while the permanent components of the biocoenosis are *Hydrobia ventrosa*, *Nephthys hombergi*, *Nereis succinea* and *Syndesmya ovata*, which are the most eury-oxybiotic species. Among the other species only *Corbulomya maeotica* and *Cardium edule* are found more or less frequently. A remarkable feature of this group, which is determined by the phenomenon of suffocation frequently occurring there, is the marked uniformity of the age of the mollusc populations, which have settled after the suffocation and survive until the following one. Considerable numbers of *Cardium edule* migrate, as a result of a shortage of oxygen, into the neighbouring shallower sectors of the sea-bottom. The density of the population fluctuates greatly from zero up to 38,400 specimens per 1 m², and its biomass up to 120 g/m². The predominant biomass is, however, 10 to 15 g/m². The relationship between the components and the fluctuations from spring to autumn are given in *Table 213*.

Among all the species found in this grouping a gain in biomass is observed only with Syndesmya; moreover its *P*/*B* ratio is only 0·99 here. For all the

Table 213

Species	Spring		Autumn	
	No. of specimens per 1 m²	Biomass g/m²	No. of specimens per 1 m²	Biomass g/m²
Hydrobia ventrosa	2,736	6·43	3,131	6·28
Nephthys hombergi	213	2·94	1,182	2·07
Nereis succinea	36	2·25	49	1·42
Syndesmya ovata	49	2·65	82	5·29
Corbulomya maeotica	33	0·59	22	0·41
Cardium edule	—	—	21	3·02
Others	37	0·05	91	0·64
Total	3,104	14·91	4,579	19·13

others an increase in the number of specimens with a decrease of biomass is observed during the summer; this is either caused by replacement of the older age groups by the young, or is the result of a reduction of density and biomass.

The Corbulomya maeotica biocoenosis—This biocoenosis is adapted mainly to depths of 1 to 6 m off the coasts. It reaches its maximum at depths of 2 to 4 m on pure sand with shell gravel or on slightly silty sand. In the spring it occupies an area of 1,270 km², but in the autumn only 819 km², being replaced by *Cardium edule* which comes up from the deeper sector. The most usual components of this biocoenosis are *Nereis succinea*, *Ampelisca diadema*,

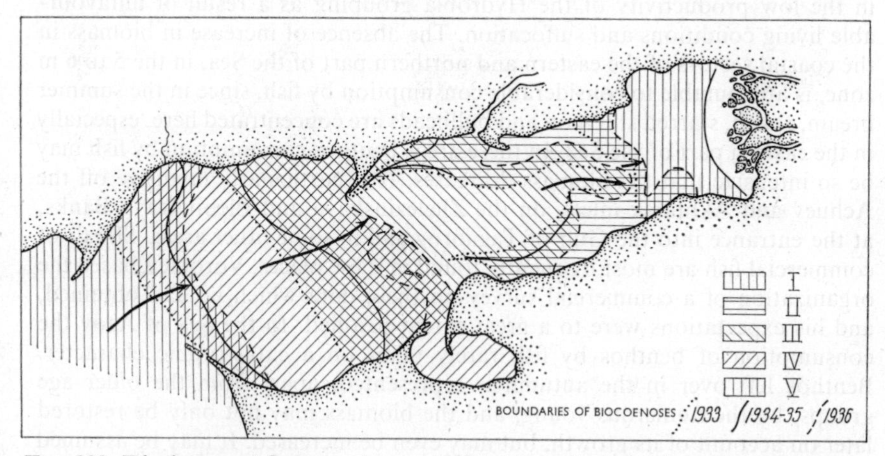

FIG. 239. Displacement from west to east of the boundaries of bottom biocoenoses of the Gulf of Taganrog under the effect of the rise of salinity in 1933–36 (Mordukhai-Boltovskoy, 1939). *I* Monodacna–Dreissena–Unionidae; *II* Monodacna; *III* Ostracoda–Hypaniola–Corophium–Tubificidae; *IV* Nereis–Ostracoda; *V* Cardium.

Cardium edule and *Syndesmya ovata*, which form different quantitative combinations with Corbulomya.

Many of the biocoenoses of the open parts of the Sea of Azov which have been considered live also in the Utlyuksk inlet, where they undergo great changes in their composition owing to a considerable admixture of Black Seas relicts, which have survived there as a result of somewhat higher salinity, and especially of such forms as *Cerithiolium reticulatum*, *Pectinaria neapolitana*, *Cardium exiguum*, *Rissoa euxinica*, *R. venusta* and others.

Seasonal and annual migrations of biocoenoses. A noticeable migration of marine benthic biocoenoses eastwards into the Gulf, brought about by the fluctuation of the outflow from the Don, was observed by F. Mordukhai-Boltovskoy (1939) when he compared quantitative-biocoenotic data on the Gulf of Taganrog benthos in 1933 with those for 1934–36 (Fig. 239). A considerable loss of salinity in the Gulf in 1932 was caused by the abundance of the Don spring outflow, which in previous years had been much lower and had caused a rise of salinity. As marine biocoenoses advance, the brackish water and relict biocoenoses recede eastwards. This is particularly noticeable in the case of the Monodacna biocoenosis in the east and those of Cardium and Syndesmya in the west.

The benthos biomass of the Sea of Azov undergoes considerable changes from spring to autumn. Generally it is doubled, but not in all sectors; at times it remains unchanged, at times it is reduced. The absence of changes in the biomass may be the result either of poor productivity, or high mortality, or a considerable consumption by fish. Throughout all the central part of the Sea the biomass remains almost unchanged; the cause of this must be sought in the low productivity of the Hydrobia grouping as a result of unfavourable living conditions and suffocation. The absence of increase in biomass in the coastal sectors of the eastern and northern part of the Sea, in the 5 to 6 m zone, is attributable to considerable consumption by fish, since in the summer bream, roach, starred sturgeon and bullheads are concentrated here, especially in the eastern part of the Sea. In these areas benthos consumption by fish may be so intensive that the biomass decreases. It is particularly intensive off the Achuev and Akhtarsk inlets, on the Zhelezinskaya and Eleninskaya Banks, at the entrance into the Gulf of Taganrog and in some other areas. Shoals of commercial fish are most frequently found in these places. Vorobieff based the organization of a commercial survey on these data which he had obtained, and his expectations were to a great extent justified. In the Sea of Azov the consumption of benthos by fish rarely takes on a catastrophic character. Benthos left over in the autumn is represented, apart from the older age groups, by the numerous young, and the biomass may not only be restored later on account of its growth, but may even be increased. It may be assumed that greater consumption corresponds to a greater concentration of fish. In his calculations of the amount of benthos consumed by fish Vorobieff takes 50 g/m as unity. Vorobieff fixed the grounds where fish would probably shoal for feeding in a similiar manner by examining the dynamics of benthos and the transition of one community into another, as a result of fish eating the benthos in spring time.

The distribution of benthos biomass in the Sea of Azov (see Fig. 238B) is very irregular and is characterized by considerable patchiness. Areas of high biomass alternate with sectors of very low biomass. In the open part of the Sea of Azov, in spite of its considerable variegation, it is possible to trace a concentric distribution of zones of increasing biomass from the centre of the Sea to its periphery, followed by a fall in biomass as the coast approaches. The outline of the biomass in a latitudinal cross section passing through the central impoverished zone is shown in Fig. 240; the ring of high biomass encircling the central deeper part is very evident here. Given the phenomenon occurring in the Sea of Azov of the suffocation of bottom fauna, and the equally massive phenomenon of the consumption of the fauna by fish, the huge spat-fall of larvae and the subsequent development of mollusc populations of uniform age can proceed over the areas—and in some years they are very wide areas—which have been freed from living organisms. The distribution of the large number of larvae is controlled by the direction of the currents. In this way the combination of currents and soils favourable to the development of the large numbers of larvae carried in by the currents, i.e. soils found red on their journey which either are slightly populated or have been altogether deprived of organisms, creates conditions for the development of the populations of uniform age which are so characteristic of the benthos of the Sea of Azov. The theory of soil–currents is expounded by the English investigator F. Davis (1924) for the North Sea and is more applicable to the Sea of Azov than to any other. The distribution of some patches

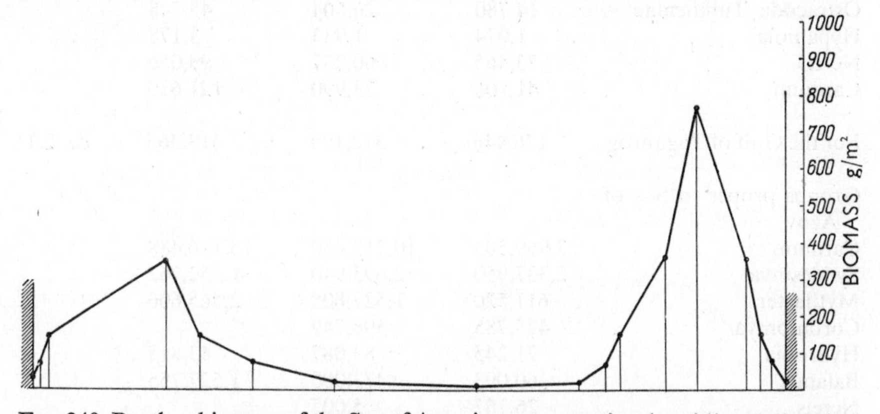

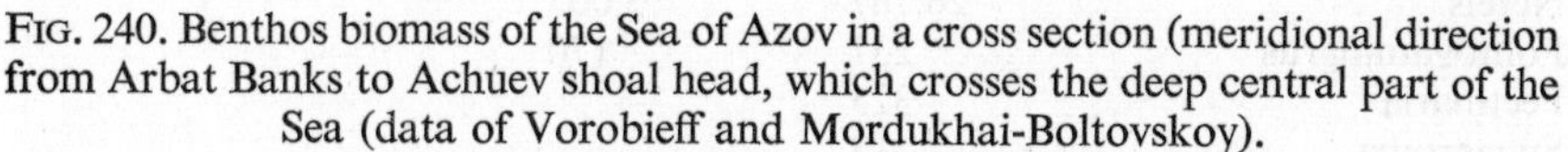

FIG. 240. Benthos biomass of the Sea of Azov in a cross section (meridional direction from Arbat Banks to Achuev shoal head, which crosses the deep central part of the Sea (data of Vorobieff and Mordukhai-Boltovskoy).

along a circular current in the Sea of Azov seems to confirm this point of view. These patches will move from year to year according to the life-span of the molluscs in the direction of the currents, depending on the distribution of soils and the bottom topography, and then after an interval they will occur again in their old places. Larvae will not be able to develop in places occupied already by a powerful population of some other organism; they will perish there in masses. Such patches of molluscs will exist for 3 to 4 years if the population neither dies nor is eaten by fish in a shorter time—which may be almost an annual occurrence in the deeper parts of the Sea of Azov.

General assessment of zoobenthos productivity. A quantitative investigation of benthos and its productivity carried out by Vorobieff and Mordukhai-Boltovskoy enabled the former to calculate the indices of biomass and productivity of the Sea of Azov benthos with the greatest accuracy possible at that time, both in its total and for the different biocoenoses discussed above and their variants for 1933–35 (*Table 214*).

A comparison of the biomass indices of the Sea of Azov with those of other seas shows that the Sea of Azov is in a class by itself. The average benthos biomass of the Sea of Azov was 418 g/m² in the autumn, while the average for the years 1934 and 1935 was 313 g/m².

Table 214

Groups	Biomass, tons Spring	Biomass, tons Autumn	Actual annual production tons	*P/B*
Dreissena	5,888	10,592	17,404	
Monodacna	69,741	125,533	216,432	
Ostracoda–Corophium	7,392	13,305	21,878	
Ostracoda–Tubificidae	14,780	26,604	43,748	
Hypaniola	1,074	1,933	3,178	
Nereis	33,465	60,237	99,056	
Cardium	41,106	73,990	121,670	
For the Gulf of Taganrog	176,446	312,194	513,366	*ca.* 2·1
Groups proper to Sea of Azov				
Cardium	3,969,503	10,215,450	13,116,488	
Syndesmya	2,337,950	2,693,940	1,352,762	
Mytilaster	611,520	1,527,808	2,565,606	
Corbulomya	425,785	398,749	—	
Hydrobia	71,245	83,087	43,815	
Balanus	60,093	473,000	1,527,755	
Nereis	26,767	5,005	—	
Pontogammarus	237	170	—	
Pectinaria	325	—	—	
Sphaeroma	13	—	—	
For the Sea of Azov proper	7,503,438	15,397,209	18,606,426	*ca.* 1·6
For the whole of the Sea of Azov	7,676,884	15,709,403	19,119,792	

Changes in the Sea of Azov benthos over a period of many years. I. Stark, continuing the researches of Vorobieff and Mordukhai-Boltovskoy, has prepared a series of comprehensive studies (1951, 1955, 1958) of the benthos of the Sea of Azov. She has brought greater precision into the picture of benthos distribution in the northeastern part of the Sea and the Gulf of Taganrog up to 1952. In her survey of the general course of quantitative changes of benthos, in the areas she investigated where Sea of Azov fish have their main feeding grounds, Stark notes that the loss of benthos biomass in areas of large concentrations of fish as a result of suffocation, consumption by fish and natural mortality, exceeds at some seasons of the year (summer and autumn) the gain by breeding and growth.

In other seasons (late autumn and spring) the picture is reversed, gain exceeding loss. The loss of benthos in winter time is due to natural mortality and sometimes to suffocation of the fauna. After a huge extinction of fish by suffocation in 1937 the quantity of benthos continued to decrease for several years, and Mytilaster was almost completely replaced by Cardium. The increase of benthos up to 1947 was mostly due to Cardium (Fig. 241). The amount of benthos continued to decrease, and by the autumn of 1948 its mean biomass was reduced to 106 g/m² in the northern part of the Sea of Azov. In Stark's opinion these changes in the quantitative composition of the benthos may have been partly the result of silting, linked with the abundance

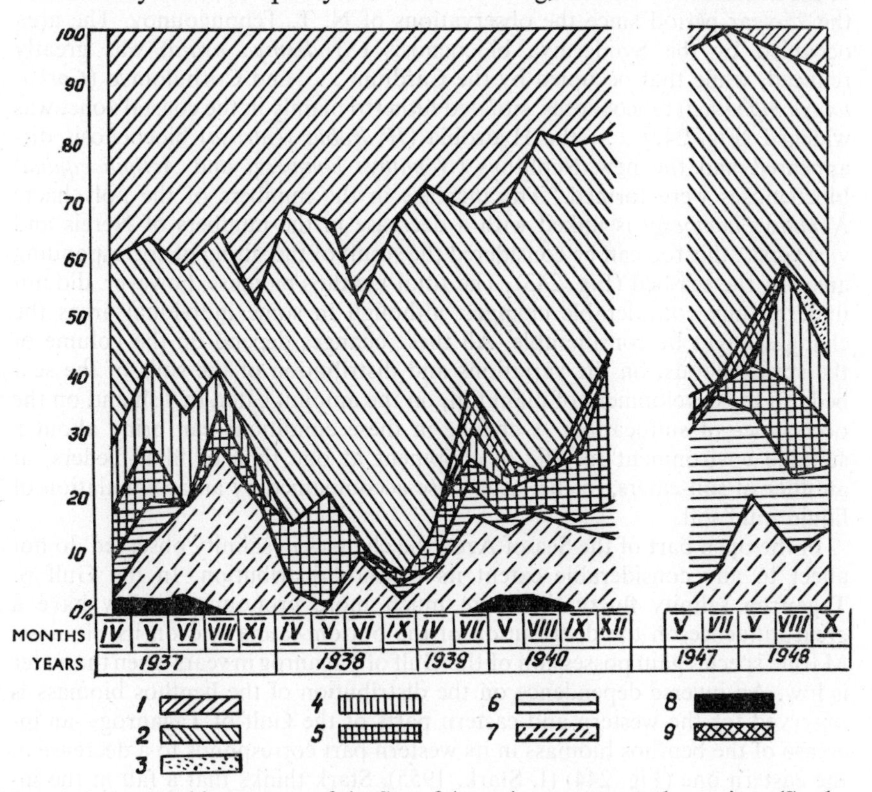

FIG. 241. Bottom biocoenoses of the Sea of Azov (occurrence at the stations (Stark, 1960)). *1* Mytilaster; *2* Cardium; *3* Brachynotus; *4* Syndesmya; *5* Balanus; *6* Hydrobia; *7* Nereis; *8* Corbulomya; *9* Nephthys.

of flood waters in 1937–39, which had an unfavourable effect on fauna which avoids soft mud bottoms (Mytilaster, Balanus and others).

Bottom-fauna of the Gulf of Taganrog varies considerably from year to year; Stark (1955), as well as Mordukhai-Boltovskoy (1948), connects these fluctuations with the changes in the spring floods of the river Don. During the years 1933–35 Cardium, Balanus, Hydrobia and other more salt-loving species were widely represented in the benthos. Those were years of low spring floods. In 1948, when floods were high, the role of these forms became insignificant, but after the exceptionally low floods of the Don in 1949 and 1950 a pronounced increase of marine fauna, principally the inferior food forms Balanus and Cardium, began to be observed. The exceptionally low floods of 1949 and 1950 evoked great changes in the benthos not only of the Gulf of Taganrog, but also of the whole Sea of Azov. In the eastern part of the Sea the Mytilaster biocoenosis almost completely disappeared, and, as I. Stark has pointed out (1955), 'in 1951 more substantial changes occurred in the benthos of the Sea of Azov than in the 15-year period since the work of Vorobieff and the 25-year period since the observations of N. T. Tchougounov. The area occupied by the Syndesmya biocoenosis (*Syndesmya ovata*) was greatly reduced, while that occupied by the Cardium . . . and Corbulomya (*Corbulomya maeotica*) biocoenoses, situated hitherto mainly in the coastal zone, was widened (Fig. 242) . . . the Hydrobia (*Hydrobia ventrosa*) biocoenosis disappeared and the new Nephthys (*Nephthys hombergi* and *Actinia equina*) biocoenoses were formed.' The increase in the numbers of the polychaete *Nephthys hombergi* is linked with a decrease in the numbers of Nereis and vice versa; this too can be considered the result of the silting of corresponding areas of the sea-bed (Fig. 243). The total benthos biomass, however, did not undergo any considerable changes, although in some individual areas the changes might be considerable. All these changes depend on the volume of the spring floods, on the variations and distribution of the soils of the sea-bed, on the development of plankton, on the amount eaten by fish and on the occurrence of suffocation. A change in these conditions can bring about a suitable environment for the development at one time of filter-feeders, at another of soil-eaters, in the latter case accompanied by an accumulation of liquid mud soil.

In the open part of the Sea of Azov the changes in salinity observed do not affect to any considerable extent its benthos distribution. In the Gulf of Taganrog salinity fluctuations are much more pronounced; they have a great influence on the distribution of the bottom-fauna and on its biomass. Marine species gain possession of the Gulf of Taganrog in years when the water is low. An inverse dependence on the distribution of the benthos biomass is observed for the western and eastern parts of the Gulf of Taganrog—an increase of the benthos biomass in its western part corresponds to a decrease in the eastern one (Fig. 244) (I. Stark, 1955). Stark thinks that a fall in the inflow from the river Don will not have a bad effect on the benthophage feeding grounds in the Sea of Azov proper, in spite of a pronounced decrease in the number of Syndesmya and an increase in that of Corbulomya Cardium and Mytilaster. The Gulf of Taganrog will be more densely populated by Cardium, Hydrobia, Nephthys and Syndesmya, but conditions for the feeding of the young would deteriorate, since the habitats of the small-sized forms of infauna (chironomids and Hypaniola) will be reduced; for adult fish the deterioration would be marked by a reduction in the numbers of Monodacna and Dreissena. Changes, however, were observed in the Sea of Azov also; with the increase of salinity, salt-loving forms such as *Actinia equina*, *Cardium exiguum*, *Cylista viduata*, *Pectinaria neapolitana*, *Glycera convoluta*, *Melinna palmata*, *Nassa reticulata*, *Cyclonassa kamyschensis* and several others penetrate into the basin through the Kerch Strait and the Utlyuksk inlet. The *Teredo navalis*, hitherto unknown in the Sea of Azov, has been recorded off Kazantip.

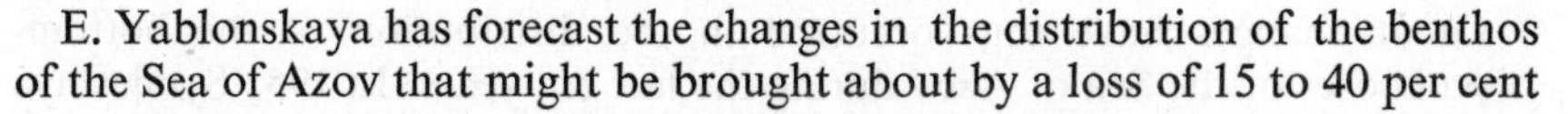

E. Yablonskaya has forecast the changes in the distribution of the benthos of the Sea of Azov that might be brought about by a loss of 15 to 40 per cent

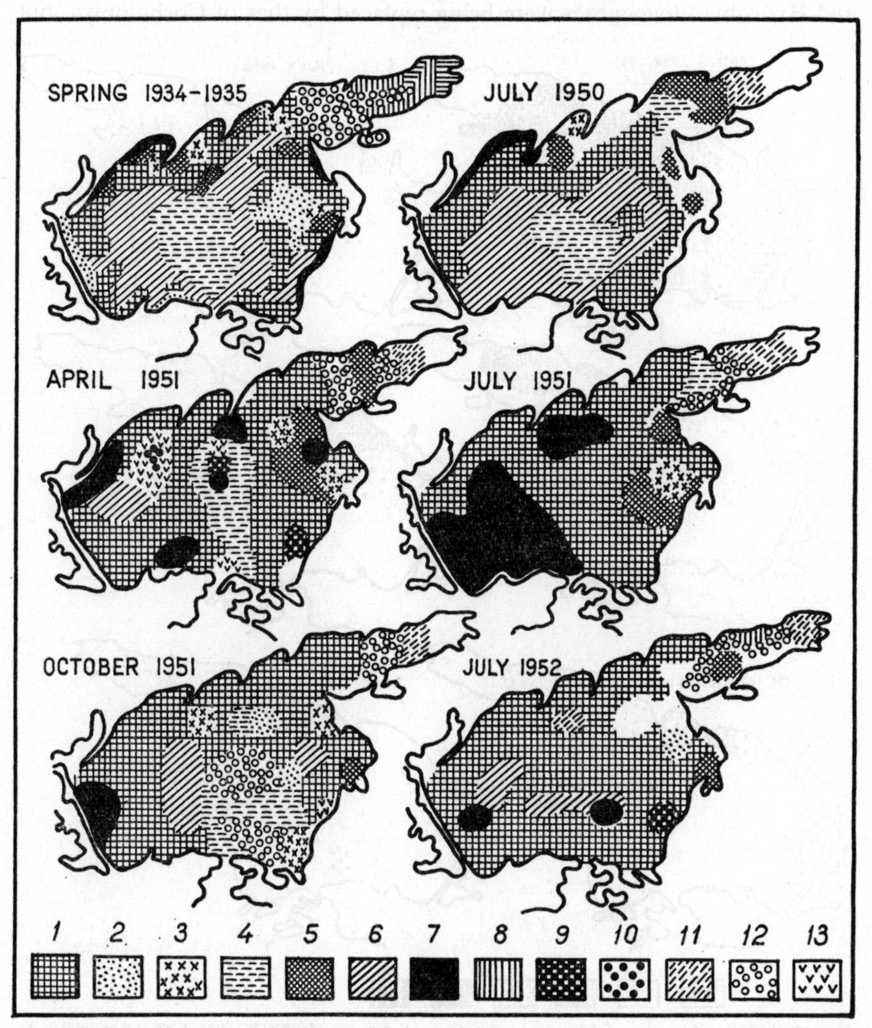

FIG. 242. Distribution of bottom biocoenoses in the Sea of Azov (Stark): *1* Cardium; *2* Mytilaster; *3* Balanus; *4* Hydrobia; *5* Nereis; *6* Syndesmya; *7* Corbulomya; *8* Monodacna; *9* Actinia; *10* Ampelisca; *11* Oligochaeta; *12* Ostracoda; *13* Nephthys.

of its river inflow on the basis of all earlier relevant research (Fig. 245). This mainly consists of a strong development of the Cardium, Balanus and Mytilaster biocoenoses and a reduction of the Hydrobia and Nereis biocoenoses, and, in part, a considerable development of the last named in the Gulf of Taganrog.

Great changes have thus occurred in the distribution of the bottom-biocoenoses of the Sea of Azov during the last ten years. In 1951 Syndesmya and Hydrobia biocoenoses were being replaced by that of Corbulomya, but

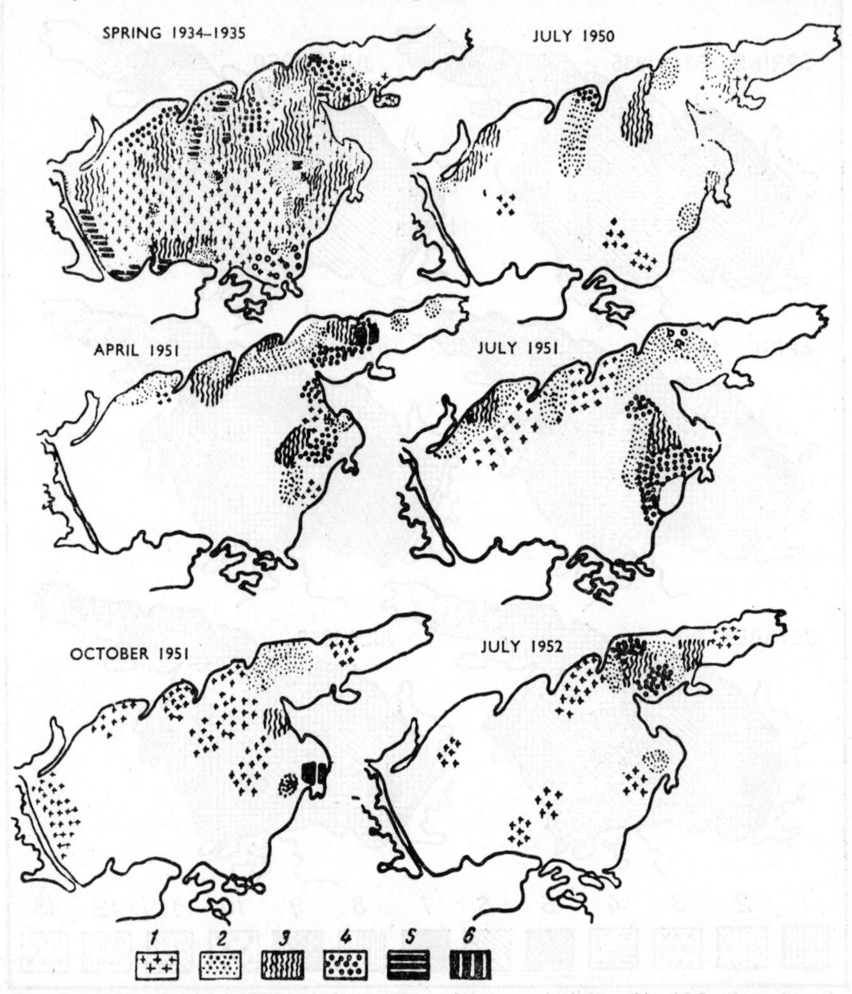

FIG. 243. Distribution of Nereis in the Sea of Azov, g/m³ (Stark). *1* Not less than 1; *2* From 1 to 5; *3* From 5 to 10; *4* From 10 to 25; *5* From 25 to 50; *6* From 50 to 100.

even in 1952 the latter was coming to be replaced by the biocoenosis of Cardium, Mytilaster, Balanus and others. In the southeastern part of the Sea the Syndesmya and polychaete biocoenoses began to appear again in 1955 and 1956 owing, possibly, to an increase in the run-off from the land. The biomass of the central part of the Sea increases considerably after years of low floods and drops again when there are heavy floods; the total average benthos biomass also undergoes considerable fluctuations (*Table 215*).

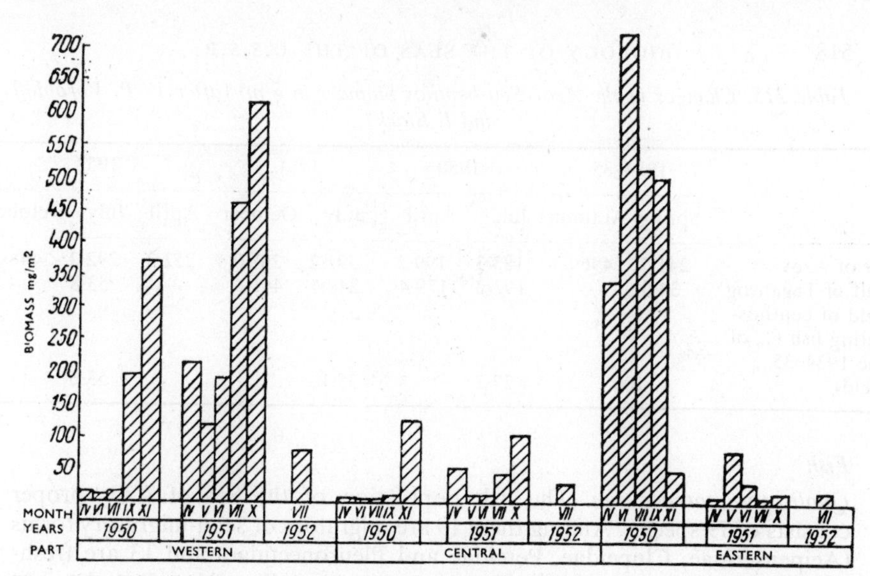

FIG. 244. Distribution of benthos biomass of the Gulf of Taganrog according to seasons and regions (Stark).

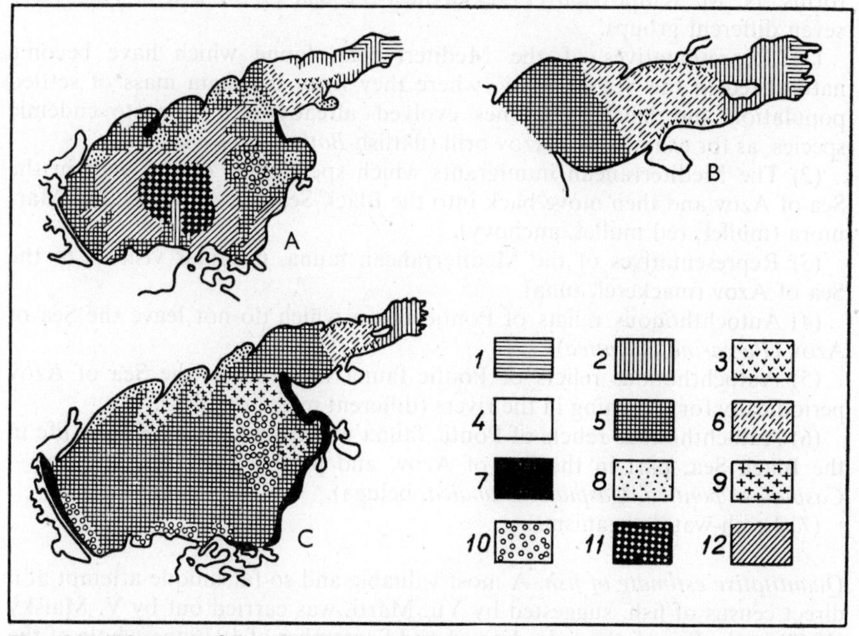

FIG. 245. Diagram of the distribution of bottom biocoenoses in the Sea of Azov and the Gulf of Taganrog (Yablonskaya, 1957). A At an average water discharge; B At about 85% water discharge; C At about 60% water discharge; *1* Dreissena; *2* Monodacna; *3* Hypaniola–Corophium; *4* Ostracoda; *5* Cardium; *6* Nereis–Ostracoda; *7* Corbulomya; *8* Nereis; *9* Balanus; *10* Mytilaster, mussel; *11* Hydrobya–Nephthys; *12* Syndesmya.

Table 215. Changes in the Azov Sea benthos biomass in g/m² (after V. P. Vorobieff and I. Stark)

	1934–35		1950		1951		1952		
	Spring	Autumn	July	April	July	October	April	July	October
Sea of Azov	241·7	496·0	183·3	199·2	391·2	267·0	252·3	292·2	448·1
Gulf of Taganrog	34·0	—	192·2	179·4	248·4	441·8	—	53·8	—
Yield of benthos-eating fish (% of the 1934–35 yield)	100		37·7		55·1			53·6	

Fish

Qualitative composition. The fish population of the Sea of Azov proper consists of 79 species. Among them 19 are migratory or semi-migratory forms (Acipenseridae, Clupeidae, Percidae and Pleuronectidae) and 13 are fresh-water ones. Cyprinidae, Gobiidae, Acipenseridae, Clupeidae, Percidae and Pleuronectidae families are outstanding in respect of the number of their forms. N. M. Knipovitch (1932) divides the fish of the Sea of Azov into seven different groups.

(*1*) Representatives of the Mediterranean fauna which have become naturalized in the Sea of Azov, where they form the main mass of settled population and have sometimes evolved already into separate endemic species, as for example the Azov brill (flatfish *Bothus torosus*).

(*2*) The Mediterranean immigrants which spend part of the year in the Sea of Azov and then move back into the Black Sea or even the Sea of Marmora (mullet, red mullet, anchovy).

(*3*) Representatives of the Mediterranean fauna, irregular visitors to the Sea of Azov (mackerel, tuna).

(*4*) Autochthonous relicts of Pontic fauna which do not leave the Sea of Azov (*Percarina maeotica*).

(*5*) Autochthonous relicts of Pontic fauna which leave the Sea of Azov periodically for spawning in the rivers (different migratory fish).

(6) Autochthonous relicts of Pontic fauna which spend part of their life in the Black Sea, part in the Sea of Azov, and part in the rivers (herring—*Caspialosa pontica*, *Caspialosa tanaica*, beluga).

(*7*) Fresh-water organisms.

Quantitative estimate of fish. A most valuable and so far unique attempt at a direct census of fish, suggested by Yu. Marti, was carried out by V. Maisky (1940) in the Sea of Azov. In August and September of 1936 the whole of the Sea of Azov was covered with about two hundred hauls using fine-meshed lampara in the open parts of the Sea and scraper off the shores. Each series of net hauls took 10 to 12 days. The shallowness of the Sea of Azov makes the use of the lampara or similar equipment specially handy for a census of fish throughout the Sea (Fig. 246).

As a result of his investigations Maisky produced a chart showing the quantitative distribution of every fish throughout the Sea. A tabular summary of the raw material resources for separate breeds of fish in the Sea of Azov is included here. These data are of exceptional interest, since this kind of information has not been obtained for any other sea; moreover, it gives much more accurate estimates of commercial resources of fish than those usually obtained with the aid of biostatic analysis (*Table 216*).

In the following years (1936–52) according to V. Maisky's data (1955)

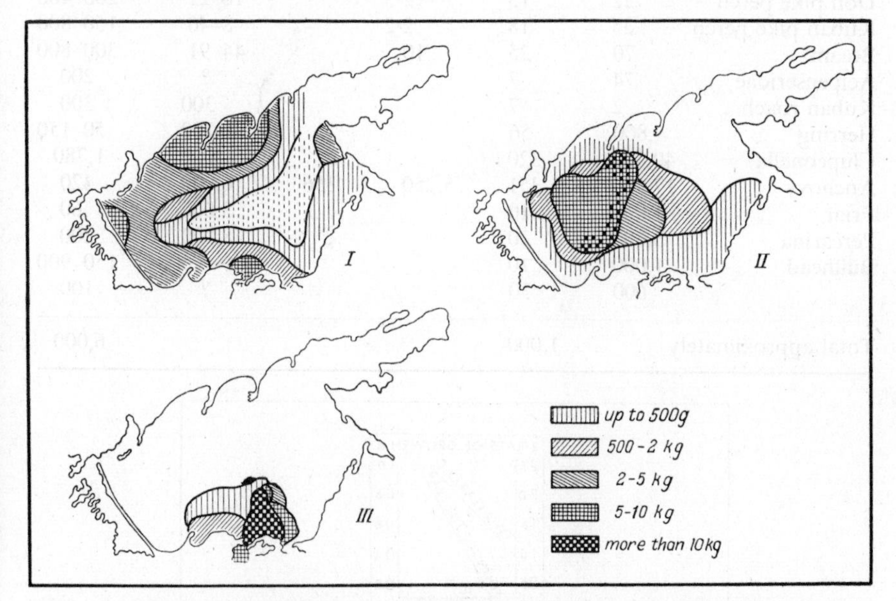

Fig. 246. Quantitative distribution of anchovy (yield of one catch of lampara) in the Sea of Azov in different seasons of 1933 according to the data of the census (Smirnov). I June–July; II September; III beginning of October.

'a great increase in the number of commercial shoals of migratory and semi-migratory fish and the reduction of the habitat of bream and Pelecus' were recorded. There were also some changes in the numbers of anchovy, Clupeonella, Percarina and Benthophilus. The quantities of other fish changed only little.

Using the same data of direct census Maisky gives for some fish a diagram of the movements of the whole Azov shoal: that of Azov Clupeonella (*Clupeonella delicatula delicatula*) is given in Fig. 247.

Although these data may not be very accurate, this is the first attempt to give a general quantitative picture according to age of fish in our Seas by direct calculation with quantitative collection equipment. Thus the total amount of fish, as determined by direct census, must be no less than 60,000 tons. The amount of benthos eaten by fish, as determined by V. P. Vorobieff from the data of his direct census, is of the order of 10 or 11 million tons; this

Table 216

Form	Under one year		One to two years old		Groups of marketable age	
	No. of specimens $\times 10^{-6}$	Centners $\times 10^{-3}$	No. of specimens $\times 10^{-6}$	Centners $\times 10^{-3}$	No. of specimens $\times 10^{-6}$	Centners $\times 10^{-3}$
Don pike perch	22	15	2·3	—	10–21	200–400
Kuban pike perch	25	18	2·2	—	8–40	150–800
Bream	70	25	10	—	44–91	300–800
Acipenseridae	74	7			?	200
Kuban roach	2	7			300	300
Herring	800	56			50–200	50–150
Clupeonella	40,000	320			66,000	1,780
Anchovy	17,500	351	5,250	356	6,000	420
Friar	1,000	10			3,000	60
Percarina	3,000	20			8,000	200
Bullhead	1,000	10			400–3,000	150–900
	600	30			?	100
Total approximately		1,000				6,000

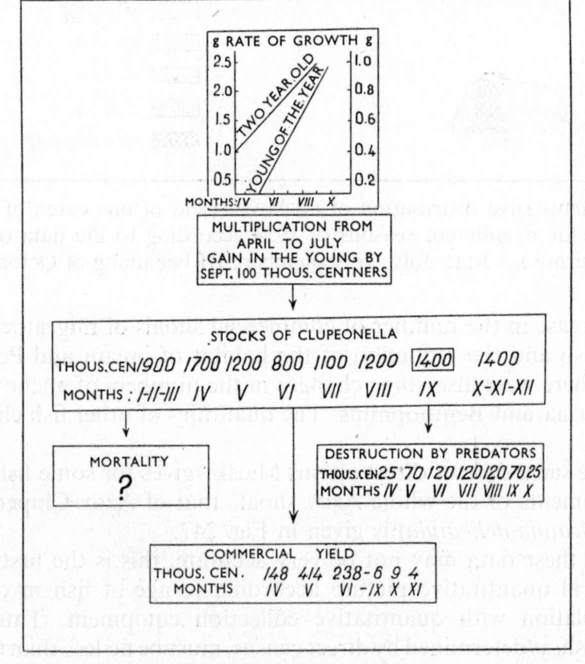

FIG. 247. Diagram of population movements of Sea of Azov Clupeonella in 1937 (Maisky).

would correspond approximately to 600 to 900 thousand tons of fish, i.e. similar results are obtained by both methods.*

Feeding of fish. The high benthos- and plankton-productivity of the Sea of Azov determines the exceptional qualities of this body of water as a feeding ground not only for the Azov fish, but also partly for those of the Black Sea (herring, anchovy, red mullet, grey mullet, etc.). Herring, anchovy and other pelagic fish prey on zooplankton; bullhead, Percarina, Benthophilus and Atherinopsis feed on benthos. In their turn they serve as food for pike perch. Some fish, like striped mullet (*Mugil cephalus*) and mullet (*Mugil auratus*), live mostly on detritus.

So far there has been no general summary of fish nutrition in the Sea of Azov like that made by A. Schorygin for the Caspian Sea. The fullest quantitative data exist on the nutrition of anchovy and some other plankton-eating fish (A. Okul, 1939 and A. Smirnov, 1938). Of the benthos-eating fish the bream alone has so far been thoroughly studied (V. P. Vorobieff, 1938). Finally, for the predatory fish there are some data on the nutrition of pike perch (N. Tchougounov, 1931; V. Maisky, 1939 and V. P. Vorobieff in manuscript). In recent years comprehensive studies of the nutrition of Sea of Azov fish have been made, and were published in 1955 (E. Bokova, M. Zheltenkova, V. Kornilova, V. Kostyuchenko, E. Fesenko and M. Sheinin).

Plankton-eating fish. During periods of its multiplication the mass of plankton in the Sea of Azov must be not less and very probably larger than the mass of benthos. Taking into account the fact that the production of the Azov phytoplankton must considerably exceed that of benthos, it becomes clear that the plankton of the Sea of Azov has a higher productivity than its benthos. The intensively productive Azov plankton serves as a plentiful source of food for the fish which gather there from the Caspian Sea and from the rivers to fatten.

The Azov anchovy (*Engraulis encrassicholus maeoticus*)—one of the main commercial objectives of the Black and Azov Sea fisheries—enters the Sea of Azov in the spring (April–June) for intensive feeding and spawning. The anchovy leaves the Sea of Azov from the second half of August till the end of November; it hardly feeds at all during its stay in the Black Sea.

Coming into the Sea of Azov the anchovy begins to feed intensively (Fig. 248). A. Smirnov (1938) and A. Okul (1940) have shown that the western half of the Sea serves as a specially rich feeding ground. Plankton forms the main part of the anchovy's food; when this is short, it feeds on benthos (polychaetes, molluscs). The anchovy's feeding proceeds intensively and by June its repletion index is 128; by July it is 117. In some individual areas of the Sea its repletion index may be even higher (up to 210). In the coastal areas in June it feeds mainly on worms (40 per cent), copepods (30 per cent), barnacles (13 per cent) and molluscs (10 per cent). At that time phytoplankton constitutes a small part (2 per cent) in the anchovy's diet. In some individual

* The census of anchovy carried out recently from the air (I. Golenchenko, 1947) leads to the conclusion that the resources of anchovy in the Sea of Azov are considerably larger.

cases anchovy stomachs were filled with polychaetes and small Hydrobia only.

Copepoda form the main food of anchovy and Atherina and even more so of Clupeonella (Fig. 248). The intestines of these three fish contain on the average 60 to 70 per cent by weight of copepods (85·8 per cent in Clupeonella,

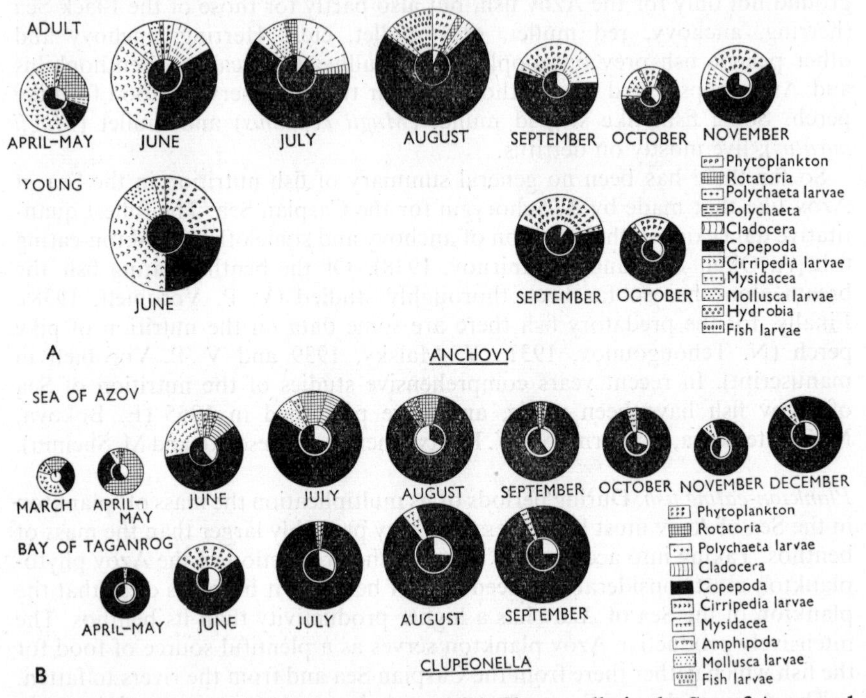

FIG. 248. Food spectra of (A) anchovy and (B) Clupeonella in the Sea of Azov and their changes during the year. The area of the circle corresponds to the value of the repletion index. White sector within the circle is the percentage of empty stomachs (Okul, 1941).

40 per cent in anchovy, 56·5 per cent in Atherina). For herring, however, Copepoda are not an important item of diet.

In spring Rotifera constitute a large part of the food of fish, ranging from 25 to 63 per cent for Clupeonella and up to 21 per cent for anchovy. For a short period in June (at the time of their mass occurrence) Cirripedia larvae may acquire an important place in the nutrition of plankton-eating fish; anchovy food includes 33 to 37 per cent of them, that of Clupeonella 25 per cent, of Atherina 10 to 14 per cent and of herring 4 per cent. In spring and autumn Mysidacea (mainly *Macropsis slabberi*) plays an important role in the nutrition of Atherina and herring, forming 31 to 47 per cent and 21 per cent of the whole content of stomachs of herring and Atherina respectively. Mollusc larvae have little feeding value for fish (1 to 4 per cent). Herring eat large numbers of fish fry and young fish.

Taking into consideration the indices of repletion of the intestines and the time of digestion, Okul has arrived at an index of daily food consumption (the ratio of the weight of food consumed during a day to the weight of the body of the fish). Taking into consideration the stock of food for plankton-

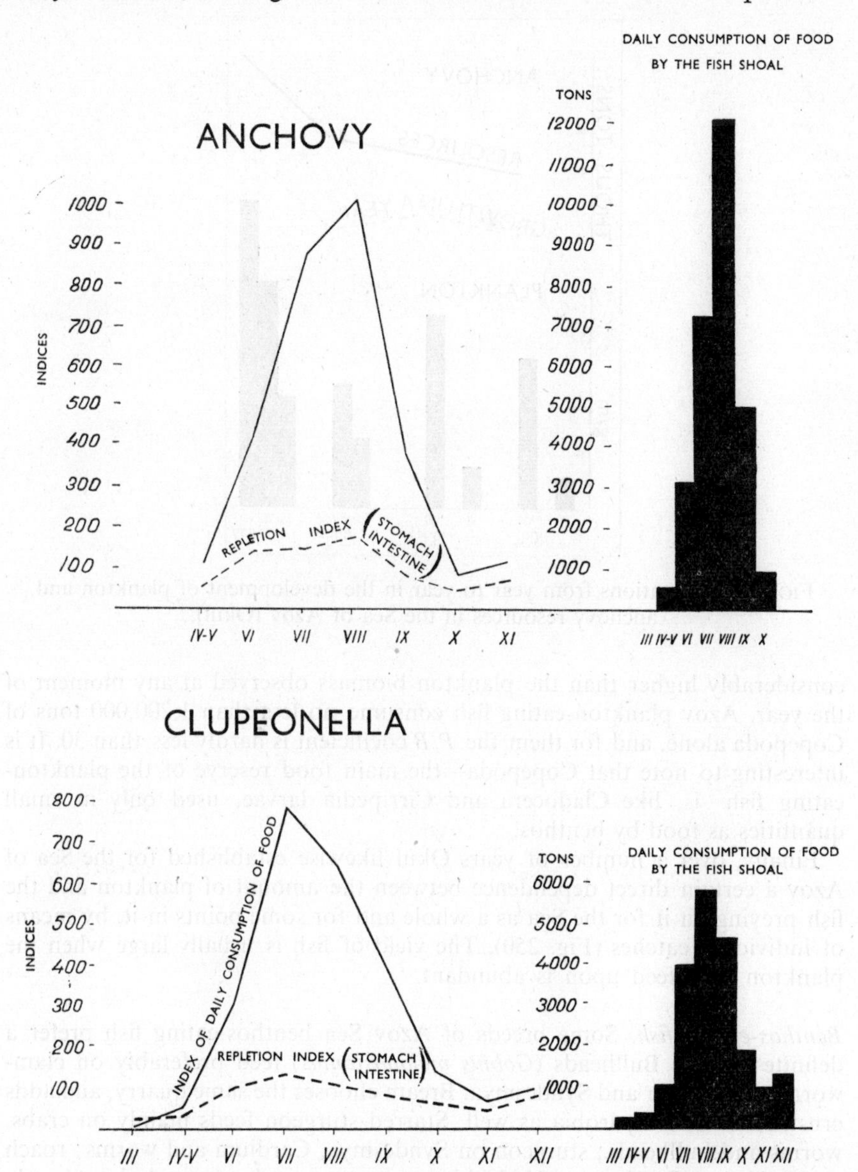

FIG. 249. Daily consumption of food by anchovy and Clupeonella in the Sea of Azov. On the left-hand side consumption by individuals, on the right by the shoal as a whole (Okul).

eating fish in the Sea of Azov (Fig. 249), he calculated the total amount of plankton consumed. In 1937 this quantity for the Sea of Azov was 1,700,000 tons, and for the Gulf of Taganrog 200,000 tons. This amount is

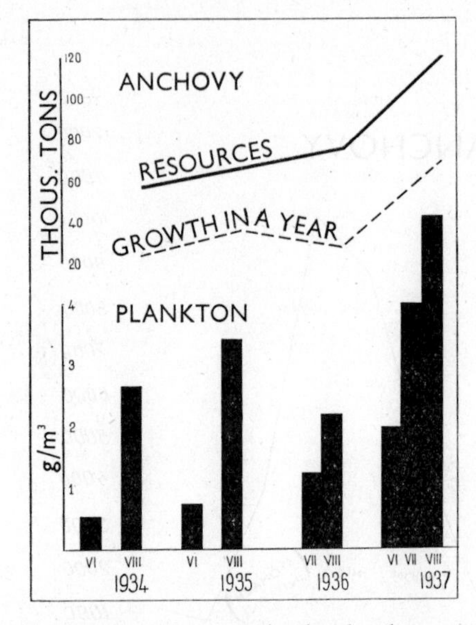

FIG. 250. Alterations from year to year in the development of plankton and anchovy resources in the Sea of Azov (Okul).

considerably higher than the plankton biomass observed at any moment of the year. Azov plankton-eating fish consume no less than 1,200,000 tons of Copepoda alone, and for them the P/B coefficient is hardly less than 30. It is interesting to note that Copepoda—the main food reserve of the plankton-eating fish—is, like Cladocera and Cirripedia larvae, used only in small quantities as food by benthos.

Finally, over a number of years Okul likewise established for the Sea of Azov a certain direct dependence between the amount of plankton and the fish preying on it for the Sea as a whole and for some points in it, by means of individual catches (Fig. 250). The yield of fish is usually large when the plankton they feed upon is abundant.

Benthos-eating fish. Some breeds of Azov Sea benthos-eating fish prefer a definite quarry. Bullheads (*Gobius melanostomus*) feed preferably on clam-worms, Mytilaster and Syndesmya. Bream chooses the same quarry, and adds crustaceans and Hydrobia as well. Starred sturgeon feeds mainly on crabs, worms and bullheads; sturgeon on Syndesmya, Cardium and worms; roach on Mytilaster, Syndesmya, Hydrobia, crustaceans and worms. As has already been shown by Tchougounov the Azov Sea benthos is suitable for fish to feed on almost exclusively.

In the Gulf of Taganrog the western part is the most important feeding ground; the main mass of adult fish remains there temporarily on its way to spawn in the river Don and on the way back again; fish fry and immature fish are fattened there to a great extent. Huge shoals of fish under one year old, of one-, two- and three-year old pike perch, bream, carp, Pelecus, herring, etc. gather in the Gulf of Taganrog, especially in summer and autumn. Only the Clupeidae prey mainly on plankton; the other fish feed on benthos. Of the benthos only the large Unionidae, Monodacna and Dreissena are used in small amounts by fish: all of the rest is consumed by fish.

As shown by V. P. Vorobieff (1938) bream is a real polyphage. In the course of its life, however, bream changes its diet. Its fry feeds mainly on plankton, then bream begins to prey on the larvae of insects, worms and crustaceans; large adult bream lives on worms, molluscs and large crayfish.

Predatory fish. The pike perch is the main commercial fish of the Sea of Azov; in the amount of its yield it is inferior only to Clupeonella (721,000 centners in 1937). As a predator pike perch preys mainly on fish; prawns form an addition to its food. It is the main consumer of small fish in the Sea of Azov. Together with other predators, such as herrings and bullheads (*Mesogobius melanostromus* and *Neogobius syrman*), beluga, catfish, Pelecus, *Aspius aspius* and others, it destroys a huge amount of small fish; it could in this respect appear as a rival of man. As Maisky has noted (1939), pike perch fattens mainly in the Gulf of Taganrog and the eastern part of the Sea of Azov. In the course of a year it destroys 3 to 3·5 million centners of small fish, a quantity much higher than that taken by man from the whole fishing industry in the Sea of Azov. In addition bullhead comprises 55 to 60 per cent, Clupeonella 14 to 15 per cent and anchovy 11 to 12 per cent of the food eaten by the pike perch.

In spring and summer pike perch feeds mostly on Clupeonella and anchovy, and in the autumn almost exclusively on bullhead. The pike perch's annual consumption of fish, according to Karpevitch's data, is about seven times its own weight.

Fisheries. The fisheries of the Sea of Azov at present bring in about 1·5 million centners (1·15 million centners in 1930, and 2·75 million centners in 1936); but the yield of the most valuable fish—pike perch, golden shiner, herring and Acipenseridae—has decreased. The catch of Clupeonella, and particularly of bullhead, has increased (L. Berdichevsky, 1957).

The catch in the Sea of Azov (without the Kerch Strait) was 1·05 millon centners in 1957, comprising 90 thousand centners of pike perch, 41 thousand centners of golden shiner, 80 thousand centners of roach (*Rutilus rutilus*) and 733 thousand centners of bullhead. In 1937 the catch of different breeds of fish was only the following: 81,900 tons of Clupeonella, 72,100 tons of pike perch, 50,400 tons of anchovy, 34,100 tons of bream, 3,900 tons of roach, 1,200 tons of carp, 7,500 tons of Acipenseridae, 6,200 tons of herring. 4,400 tons of bullhead and 11,900 tons of other fish, totalling 277,500 tons.

The yield from the fisheries in the Sea of Azov constituted then some 90 per cent of all the fish caught in the Azov–Black Sea basin; only 10 per cent of this came from the Kerch Strait. In recent years the proportion has dropped to 65 per cent or so. The yield from the whole area of the Sea of Azov is 73 kg per hectare (in some years up to 82 kg/hectare).

V. CONCLUSION

V. Pauli (1939) gives a very good description of the Sea of Azov as a eutrophic sea: 'In the Sea of Azov not only do the reduction processes fall behind the activity of the producers, but the production itself does not correspond to the amount of biogenic compounds. According to the data for phosphorus pentoxide, and probably some other biogenic compounds as well, these are not completely used up by the autotrophic population even at the time of maximum plankton development.'

The masses of organogenic compounds brought down by the rivers Don and Kuban into the Sea of Azov are only partly consumed by fish. Considerable quantities of them are converted into the organic compounds of plankton organisms and are not used by fish. An appreciable part of the biogenic compounds is carried away into the Black Sea.

Datzko has given the biomass of the annual production of the main groups of the Sea of Azov population (*Table 217*).

Table 217

Group	Biomass, 10^3 tons			Annual production 10^3 tons	Annual P/B ratio
	Wet weight	Percentage of total biomass	Dry weight		
Micro-organisms	250	3·2	50	175,000	700
Phytoplankton	1,000	13	100	340,000	340
Zooplankton	200	2·7	20	600	30
Zoobenthos	4,800	63·5	720	12,000	2·5
Fish	1,300	17·4	390	800	0·6

Forecast of changes in the biological productivity of the Sea of Azov in connection with reduction of river inflow. The hydrology and biology of the Sea of Azov are bound to change as a result of hydrotechnical construction on the river Don and the losses which it will involve in river inflow and in a certain part of the dissolved or suspended substances brought down by the Don into the Sea. A number of investigators have speculated on these possible changes.

The salinity of the Sea of Azov would increase by 2‰ with an assumed loss of 10 km³ of Don water, and by 5‰ with a loss of 20 km³. Taking into consideration the fact that in the south Russian seas fisheries are concentrated mainly in the less saline parts, V. Samoilenko (1955) supposes that a reduction of the less saline parts and a decrease of the inflow of organic biogenic subtances would lead to a drop in the level of biological productivity and would have an unfavourable effect on the fisheries of the Sea of Azov. As a result of the building of hydrological installations the feeding areas for fish might be reduced and their passage into rivers for breeding might be hindered.

F. Mordukhai-Boltovskoy (1953) approaches this problem from a different angle. He starts from the assumption that as things are at present (before the construction of the Volga–Don canal) the Don waters bring into the Sea of Azov an excess amount of plant food, which causes a superfluous development of plankton and an over-accumulation of organic substances in the central parts of the Sea; this led to a constant oxygen deficiency and to the suffocation of fish and bottom-fauna over large areas of the sea-bed. In this worker's opinion the loss of 10 km^3 of river water and the freedom of reservoirs from suspended matter will have a favourable effect on the oxygen conditions of the Sea and on the yield of fish, since it will free the Sea from over-accumulation of organic matter. A loss of 20 km^3 of Don waters must lead to a shortage of food supply and to a lowering of productive yield, both as a result of that shortage and as a result of the great reduction of habitat areas (low-salinity water) for semi-migratory fish.

Later this problem was again considered by E. Yablonskaya (1955), A. Karpevitch (1955) and a number of other investigators, and the results of their work are given in a two-volume symposium *Reorganization of Fisheries in the Sea of Azov* (1955). Yablonskaya does not share Mordukhai-Boltovskoy's view on the over-accumulation of organic substances on the bed of the Sea of Azov. According to the data of T. Gorshkova (1955) such over-accumulation has not been observed, and Yablonskaya therefore assumes that the productive capacity of the Sea of Azov would not be improved by the drop in the outflow from the river Don and by the settling down, as precipitates in reservoirs, of the plant food substances which reached the Sea before control of outflow from the river was fairly fully utilized. Yablonskaya therefore thinks that with a 15 per cent drop in the river outflow zooplankton production, both in the Gulf of Taganrog and in the Sea proper, would be somewhat lowered, while at a 50 per cent loss of river outflow Azov plankton production might go down by about 40 per cent. Benthos biomass in the Gulf of Taganrog might increase as a result of the immigration of larger-sized components of fauna from the west, but its importance for feeding will be reduced. In Yablonskaya's opinion (see also Stark) the benthos biomass of the Sea of Azov proper would change little. Fish feeding on this mass of organisms—the plankton eaters (mainly anchovy and Clupeonella)—will be somewhat less in number. At present benthos-eating fish do not consume all the benthos available, and when the river outflow is reduced they will on the whole have enough food, although this will apply to a different extent for different species of fish.

E. Yablonskaya (1957) describes the changes in the conditions of the Sea of Azov connected with the control of the flow of the river Don in the following way: 'the first 4 years (1951–55) were characterized by a reduction of the flow of the Don (in 1921–51 an average of 26·2 km³ a year; in 1952–55 an average of 19·4 km³ a year), by a reduction in the biogenic discharge into the Sea (*Table 218*) and by its transformation in the water reservoir and in the river, as a consequence of which its primary food-value was lowered; the salinity of the Sea rose by almost 2‰, causing a marked reduction in the provision of food for the plankton-eating fish, and as a result their productivity became almost 2·5 times lower than the average before the control of the river waters'.

Among the inhabitants of the Gulf of Taganrog, according to Yablonskaya's data, there is a series of forms the mass development of which is adapted to a salinity of 4 to 9‰ (Fig. 235); they belong to brackish-water and fresh-water types. Yablonskaya has made a diagram, based on all existing data, of the future distribution of bottom biocoenoses corresponding to a loss of 15 and of 40 per cent of the river water (Fig. 236); plankton and benthos would react differently to a change in the salinity of the Gulf, which would be occupied mainly by brackish-water plankton and Sea of Azov benthos.

Table 218. A comparison of some indices of the biological conditions of the Sea of Azov before and after commencement of control of flow of the river Don (E. Yablonskaya)

Characteristic	Average before control	1955
Phosphorus compounds	2,016	650
Nitrogen (spring) compounds	179	97
Nitrogen (summer) compounds	327	58
Zooplankton biomass	475	40
Production of plankton-eating fish (anchovy and Clupeonella) in thousands of centners	4,990	1,844
Peridinean, per cent	88·9	20·3
Diatoms, per cent	3·9	78·7

VI. THE SIVASH, OR PUTRID, SEA

Situation and area

The Sivash, or Putrid, Sea is a peculiar, large (2,700 km²), subsidiary body of water of the Sea of Azov. Situated to the west of it, the Sivash is connected with it by the shallow (2 to 3 m) and narrow (120 m in width) Tonky Strait. It is separated from the Sea of Azov by the long and narrow Arabat Strelka, and it comprises a complex system of inlets connected by straits and of numerous islands.

The greatest depth of the Sivash hardly reaches 3·2 m in its southern part, while its average depth changes from 0·63 m in its northern part to 0·86 m in the south. With a volume of water of about 1 km³ the ratio of its volume to its area is equal to 1/1,300, while the corresponding ratio for the Sea of Azov is 1/150.

Salinity

The salinity of the Sivash is greatly increased by a considerable preponderance of evaporation over precipitation and inflow of water from rivers. The gradual increase in salinity in the Sivash is shown in Fig. 251. In the southern part of the Sivash the salinity rises to 124 to 166‰.

Salts dissolved in Sivash water consist mainly of sodium chloride, magnesium chloride, magnesium sulphate, magnesium bromide, potassium chloride, calcium sulphate and calcium bicarbonate, sodium chloride, magnesium chloride and magnesium sulphate being considerably preponderant; the salt composition of Sivash water differs little from that of the ocean (*Table 219*).

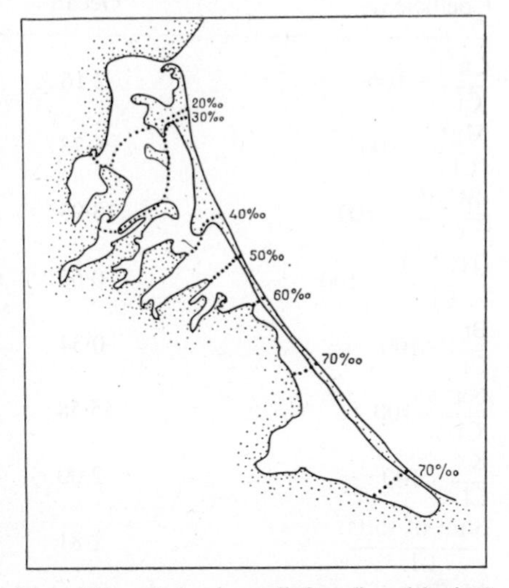

FIG. 251. Gain in salinity (in chlorine) in Sivash from north to south (Zhukov from data of Vorobieff).

There is a higher content of sulphates and carbonates in the water of the Sea of Azov as a result of the considerable inflow of river waters. The Azov waters entering the Sivash are concentrated and freed from excess of calcium carbonates and sulphates; thus there occurs a gradual return to the salt ratio common in the ocean. This process is called by Danilchenko and Ponizovsky 'normalization of Sivash brine'; to illustrate this they give the data set out in *Table 220*.

Table 219. Salt composition of waters of the ocean, Black and Azov Seas, and the Sivash (Percentage weight of the salt) (P. Danilchenko and A. Ponizovsky, 1954)

Salt	Ocean (after Ditmar)	Black Sea	Sea of Azov	Eastern Sivash off Chongarsk Strait	Western Sivash (Sergeevsky body of water)
Sodium chloride	77·68	79·40	76·90	79·00	78·35
Potassium chloride	2·10				2·09
Magnesium chloride	9·21	8·92	9·81	9·87	9·39
Magnesium sulphate	6·39	6·33	6·80	6·51	6·95
Magnesium bromide	0·21	0·20	0·21	0·21	0·17
Calcium sulphate	3·70	3·64	3·79	3·65	2·82
Calcium bicarbonate	0·74	1·52	2·72	0·76	0·21
Overall salinity, percentage weight	3·53	1·83	1·03	4·08	12·89

Table 220. Change in the chlorine coefficients of the waters of the ocean, Black and Azov Seas, and the Sivash (P. Danilchenko and A. Ponizovsky, 1954)

Coefficients	Ocean	Black Sea	Sea of Azov	Eastern Sivash
$\frac{Ca^{2+}}{Cl^-} \times 100$	2·16	2·49	3·08	2·22
$\frac{Mg^{2+}}{Cl^-} \times 100$	6·73	6·75	7·05	6·79
$\frac{(SO_4)^{2-}}{Cl^-} \times 100$	13·93	13·54	14·80	14·45
$\frac{(HCO_3)^-}{Cl^-} \times 100$	0·66	2·00	3·55	0·24
$\frac{Br^-}{Cl^-} \times 100$	0·34	0·33	—	0·34
$\frac{Na^+}{Cl^-} \times 100$	55·58	55·45	56·90	55·29
$\frac{K^+}{Cl^-} \times 100$	2·00	2·20		1·98
$\frac{\text{Sum of salts}}{Cl^-}$	1·81	1·81	1·85	1·80
$\frac{MgSO_4}{MgCl_2}$	0·67	0·70	0·71	0·66

M. Bozhenko (1935) determines the sum total of the stock of salts in the Sivash as 190 million tons, including 309,000 tons of elemental bromine and 7·1 million tons of magnesium.

Temperature

The shallow waters of Sivash become considerably warmed in the summer (up to 30° to 35°). On the other hand in the winter their temperature falls to −1° or −2° (and even to −3° in the southern part), and the northern and some of the central Sivash is covered with ice.

According to Vorobieff either a mass extinction or a migration of animals into the deeper parts of the Sivash occurs as a result of the sharp seasonal temperature fluctuations and of a partial freezing of the whole column of water.

Oxygen

Oxygen content decreases sharply from north to south. A litre of water in the north of the Sivash contains 5·51 cm³ of oxygen, in the central part 4·0 cm³, and in the south 1·88 to 1·75 cm³. The phenomenon of bottom-fauna suffocation occurs more readily in calm summer weather in the Sivash than in the Sea of Azov; this is due to the shallow depth of water and to the large amounts of oxygen used in the decay of organic substances.

Phosphorus and nitrogen

A further characteristic is the insignificant content of phosphates and nitrates in Sivash waters which was noted by Vorobieff. Only in winter has an appreciable accumulation of these substances been recorded.

Soils

According to Vorobieff the prevailing soils are 'muds of varying colour and density, with an admixture of sand, shell gravel and organic remains. These muds are mainly composed of huge amounts of plant remains, detritus and plankton, which dies off in salt water, brought from the Sea of Azov and the Utlyuksk inlet (autochthonous matter) and also of the plants of the Sivash itself, which develop in huge masses. In the northern part the mud consists of dead ditch-grass, Zostera, dog whelk and the green algae Cladophora; in the central and southern Sivash it consists of Cladophora and green-blue algae. The small crustacean *Artemia salina*, which develops in enormous numbers in the summer, must play an important role in mud formation of the southern Sivash.' The processes of the decay of organic substancesare limited owing to the high salinity and large amounts of organic matter deposited among the bottom sediments.

'Organisms most tolerant of hydrogen sulphide, methane and other gases liberated during the processes of decay, such as Sphaeroma, Idothea, Gammarus, the fly larvae, nemertines and others, are found in huge quantities among decaying sea-weeds on the shores of the Sivash.'

Spionidae, Pectinaria, Syndesmya and Cardium are found in muddy sand, and Clymene, Nereidae, Syndesmya, Cardium, Hydrobia, Chironomidae and others in muds.

Distribution and composition of fauna

Vorobieff (1940) has made a comprehensive study of the distribution of life in the Sivash, and we shall be using his data below.

As one moves up into the bay there is a change in the qualitative composition of the fauna with the increase of salinity—the marine forms become less numerous and the number of the typical ultrahaline forms increases (Figs. 252 and 253).

Huge amounts of plankton and larval forms of benthos are constantly brought into the Sivash by the Azov Sea waters; a kind of compulsory colonization of the Sivash is going on. Most of the larvae and adult organisms which find themselves in the Sivash either perish, or live for only a short time, or settle in the Northern Sivash. We have every reason to assume that if it were not for this constant influx of Azov Sea forms the population of the Sivash would be much poorer in variety and biomass, since most of the species which survive in the Sivash have a very low productivity and a sharp decrease in their biomass occurs throughout most of the year.

At the present time only the ultrahaline species live in the central and southern Sivash. The Novo-Euxine and ancient Black Sea relicts are the first to disappear as one moves into the Sivash, then the Azov–Black Sea species and the fresh-water halophilic ones.

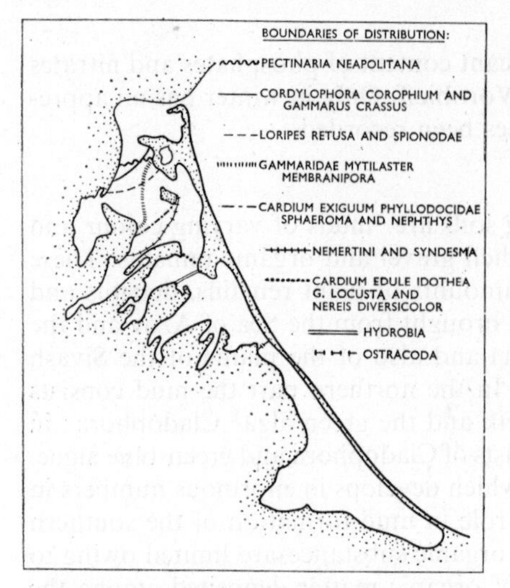

FIG. 252. Limit of distribution in the depth of the Sivash of some Azov–Black Sea forms (Vorobieff).

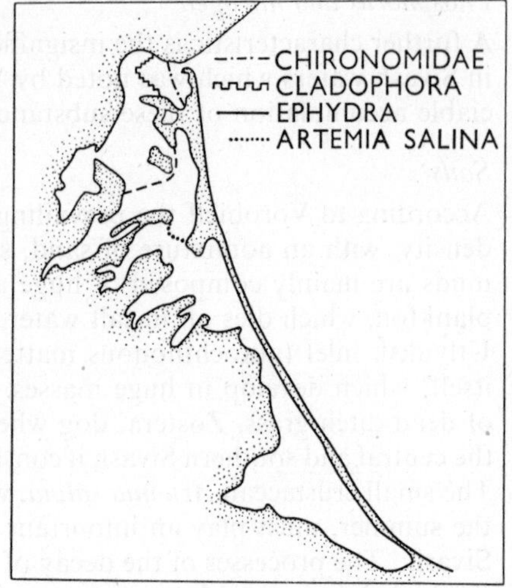

FIG. 253. Northern boundary of distribution of ultrahaline forms in the Sivash (Vorobieff).

Vorobieff gives the number of animal and plant species inhabiting various parts of the Sivash as in *Table 221*.

Of the 40 species of zoobenthos in the Sivash 18 (39·9 per cent) are Novo-Euxine relicts, 5 (11·1 per cent) are ultrahaline forms, 19 (42·2 per cent) are Azov–Black Sea forms and 3 (6·7 per cent) are ancient Euxine relicts.

Of the 75 species of zooplankton 6 (7·98 per cent) are Novo-Euxine relicts, 9 species (12·9 per cent) are ultrahaline forms, 59 (79·4 per cent) are Azov–Black Sea forms and 1 (1·33 per cent) is a Novo-Euxine relict. The occasional drying up by the wind of large areas of the bottom is a characteristic phenomenon of the Sivash; one part of its fauna perishes, while another develops the ability to survive the dry periods by burrowing into the sea-bed.

Plankton

Plankton distribution, according to Vorobieff, is as set out in *Table 222*.

Plankton biomass throughout the Sivash comprises 22,440 tons in February,

Table 221

Group	Sections of Sivash			
	1st northern	2nd northern	Central	Southern
Benthos	40	38	5	2
Zooplankton	56	55	23	9
Phytoplankton	43	70	34	16
Fish	53	9	1	—

Table 222

Group	Zooplankton		Group	Phytoplankton	
	No. of species	Percentage		No. of species	Percentage
Protozoa	24	30·24	Chlorophyceae	10	10·7
Coelenterata	1	1·26	Cyanophycae	7	7·49
Vermes larvae	2	2·53	Diatomacaea	54	58·27
Rotatoria	9	11·34	Peridineae	21	22·47
Entomostraca	33	42·02	Flagellata	1	1·07
Mollusca larvae	2	2·53			
Total	79	100	Total	93	100

9,540 in May–June, 19,184 in July, 9,161 in August, 5,910 in September and 6,412 in November (an annual average of 26,063). Consequently there are two maxima in plankton development: in spring and autumn.

Benthos

Summer suffocation of the Sivash bottom-fauna in calm weather is a common occurrence; as a result, the deeper-lying mud beds are much more sparsely populated. Summer, moreover, is the least favourable season for the development of bottom-fauna; winter and especially spring are the most favourable. As a result, seasonal changes in benthos biomass in the Sivash are observed on mud bottoms in the deeper parts: a decrease from summer to autumn as a result of suffocation, further winter reduction, and an increase in the spring (a further drop in the spring may in certain cases be caused through consumption of it by fish). 'The fact that sand and a mixture of silty sand and shell gravel are the most productive soils in the northern Sivash is explained by the same reasons, i.e. in the last analysis by the aeration conditions at the bottom.'

Among the large forms of the benthos only *Chironomus salinarius* and fly-larvae are found on the muds in the central and southern parts of the Sivash. Macrobenthos is absent from coarse-grained soils, while the fly larvae are adapted best to silty sand with shell gravel; the anaerobic conditions of mud soils are not favourable to them. Here the biomass is very small, fluctuating between 1 and 12 g/m². In the most saline part (60‰) it drops to a few grammes or fractions of a gramme.

Phytobenthos presents a different picture since the inner parts of the bay are considerably overgrown with the ultrahaline *Cladophora siwaschensis*, which is absent from the outer parts of the bay. The increase of the amount of phytobenthos at a chlorine content of 20 to 40‰ is explained by the intensive development of Zostera and Ruppia under these conditions.

Of the nine bottom-communities established for the Sivash the following are the most numerous: Cardium, Syndesmya, Hydrobia, Chironomus, Artemia and Cladophora.

In the northern Sivash the mollusc *Cardium edule* is present in various combinations as the dominant species, with a number of others. In the summer it is associated with Chironomus, *Syndesmya ovata* and *Gammarus locusta*, in the autumn with *Hydrobia ventrosa*, Chironomus, Syndesmya and Pectinaria, in the winter with Chironomus, Hydrobia and Syndesmya, in the spring with Syndesmya and Hydrobia. Among the other forms *Nephthys hombergi*, Mytilaster, *Nereis diversicolor*, *N. zonata* and Chironomus may be noted.

In the northern Sivash the mean biomass is 200 to 300 g/m² (*Table 223*).

Table 223

Species	No. of specimens per 1 m²	Biomass g/m²
Cardium edule	1,172	145·2
Chironomus	10,680	25·6
Syndesmya ovata	343	18·3
Gammarus locusta	396	7·1
Nephthys hombergi	157	3·0
Mytilaster lineatus	17	2·6
Hydrobia ventrosa	920	2·3
Nereis zonata	146	1·7

In the summer other forms are present only in small numbers. In autumn the numbers of Hydrobia may attain 17,230 specimens per 1 m² with a biomass of 44·54 g/m². The numbers of Pectinaria (up to 13 g/m²) and of *Nereis diversicolor* (up to 5·9 g/m²) are considerably increased. Lamellibranchiata composes from 66·7 to 93·9 per cent of the total biomass, Hydrobia in autumn up to 13 per cent, Vermes up to 11·5 per cent, Chironomidae by the end of the winter up to 18 per cent.

In the outermost part of the bay the Syndesmya biocoenosis is preponderant in benthos almost in the same combination of species, but with a biomass of up to 400 to 500 g/m².

The site occupied by the Syndesmya biocoenosis (1st northern Sivash) gives shelter to a fairly abundant ichthyofauna. According to N. Tarasov's data (1927) 53 species of fish were recorded which feed there, but rarely penetrate into the second part of the northern Sivash. Vorobieff suggests that 'all the production of this biocoenosis is completely consumed by fish'.

In the autumn Hydrobia becomes the dominant form in the area formerly occupied by the Cardium biocoenosis, and partly in the first northern Sivash inhabited by the Syndesmya biocoenosis. The distribution of Loripes, Mytilaster, Gammarus and Vermes (Nephthys and Nereis) communities is limited in time and space.

More than two-thirds of the Sivash area is occupied by the *Chironomus salinarius* biocoenosis. This biocoenosis inhabits some parts of the northern Sivash and the whole of the central and southern Sivash. Chironomus is found in the central Sivash in various combinations with the same Hydrobia, Cardium, Gammarus, Ostracoda and Artemia; in the northern Sivash, with

Gammarus, Ostracoda and Artemia; and in the southern only with Artemia, which all dies out in the second half of the summer.

In the central and southern Sivash the biocoenoses acquire a sharply pronounced oligo-mixed character and are really a combination of two species, Chironomus and Artemia. In summer the mean biomass of these organisms is 18·8 and 2·3 g/m², in autumn 24·5 and 0·5 g/m², in winter 2·7 and 0·0 g/m², and in spring 7·7 and 0·03 g/m² respectively; Ostracoda and Ephydra are mixed with these two forms in small numbers only.

Together with *Artemia salina* and Chironomus, *Cladophora siwaschensis*, which inhabits the central and southern Sivash in vast numbers, gives this area its particular character.

On the whole benthos biomass decreases gradually as one moves farther into the Bay; this can be seen on the charts in Fig. 254. On the other hand we observe that sites of increased biomass as well as the main vegetation growths lie close to the eastern shores.

In winter the benthos biomass of all the biocoenoses falls sharply.

The mean annual biomass of the outer half of the northern Sivash is equal to 360 g/m², that of the inner 140 g/m². The mean annual biomass of the central Sivash comprises 22 g/m², and of the southern 4·26 g/m².

The macrophytes play an important part in the phenomena of biological production in the Sivash. In the first northern Sivash, where Cladophora is weakly developed owing to low salinity, there are Zostera and Ruppia; in the rest of the Sivash Cladophora produces a very high biomass. Owing to the large amounts of Cladophora in the central and southern Sivash, the mean annual total biomass of the whole (zoo- and phyto-) benthos is found to be approximately uniform throughout the area:

1st northern Sivash	564 g/m²
2nd northern Sivash	514 g/m²
Central Sivash	257 g/m²
Southern Sivash	515 g/m²

Fish

Of the 12 species of fish living permanently in the Sivash the flatfish *Pleuronectes flesus luscus*, some bullheads, pipefish, sea horses and sticklebacks may be noted. Of all these species only the flatfish and the bullhead (*Zostricola ophiocephalus*) have some commercial significance.

Eight species of fish (all commercial) enter the Sivash to feed: two species of grey mullet (*Mugil auratus* and *M. cephalus*), anchovy (*Engraulis encrassicholus maeoticus*), herring (*Caspiolosa maeotica*), Atherina (*Atherina pontica*), jackfish (*Trachurus trachurus*), garfish (*Belone acus*) and bullhead (*Gobius fluviatilis*).

Finally there are about 30 species of Azov Sea fish which occasionally visit the Sivash.

The limits of the distribution of some fish are given in Fig. 255.

Fish fed in the Sivash grow faster and fatter. Grey mullet, which goes into the Black Sea to spawn, is particularly fat.

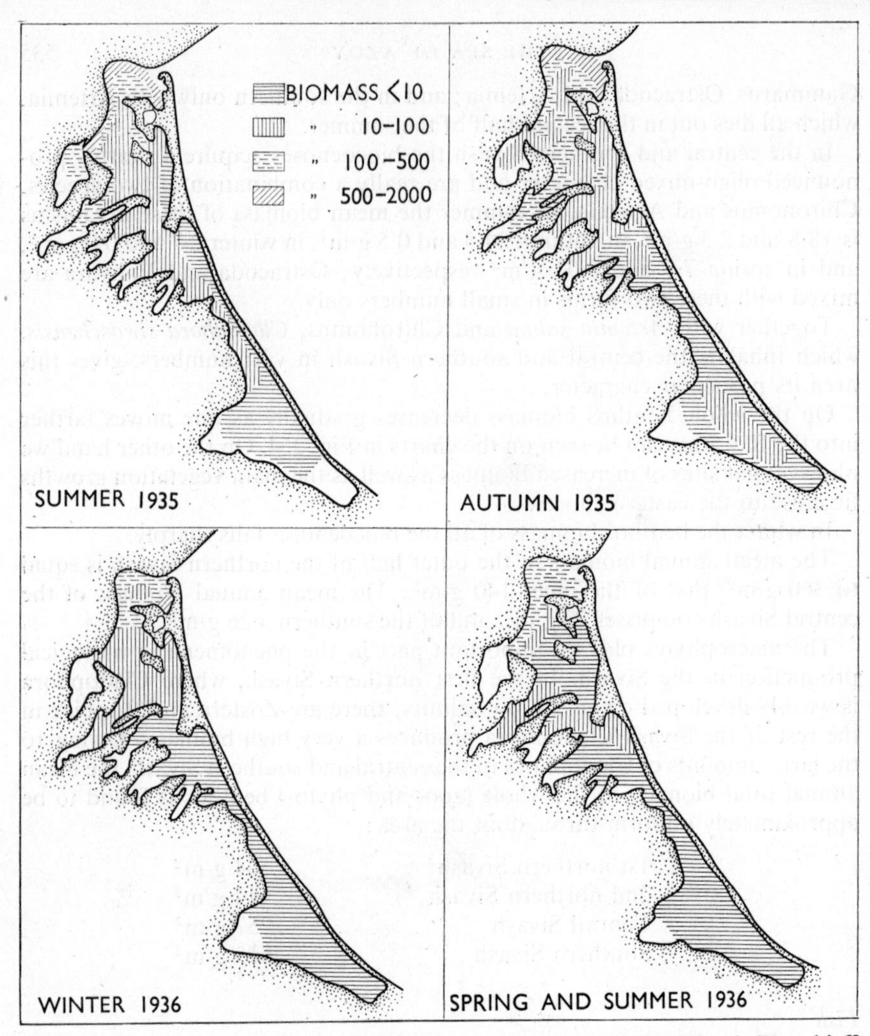

FIG 254. Seasonal distribution of benthos biomass (g/m^3) in the Sivash (Vorobieff, 1944).

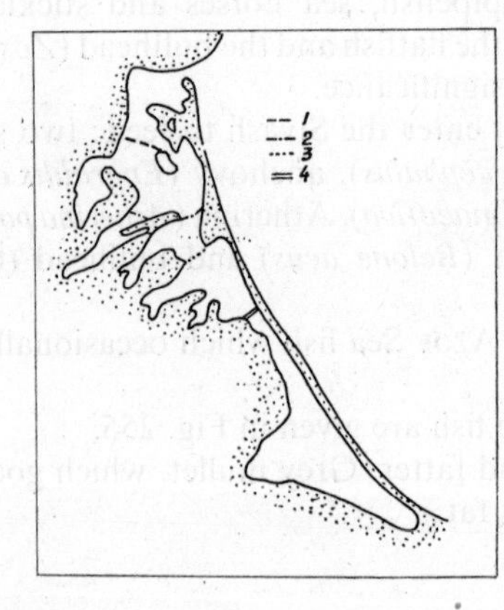

FIG. 255. Limit of penetration of some fish into the Sivash (Vorobieff). 1 *Engraulis encrassicholus*; 2 *Pleuronectes flesus luscus*; 3 Young gobiidae; 4 Young Mugil.

The average catch of grey mullet during the last 20 years constitutes 80 to 90 tons; in some years, however, it has risen to 550 tons (1923). The grey mullet which feed in the Sivash are mostly young.

Some of the anchovy entering the Sea of Azov from the Black Sea in April occasionally get into the Sivash and find excellent feeding there on plankton. Some dozens of tons are caught. Up to 150 tons of other pelagic fish are caught in the Sivash including *Atherina pontica*, which feeds on plankton and on some small bottom-dwellers.

In addition it has been established that in spring considerable numbers of flatfish migrate from the Sivash into the Utlyuksk inlet and the Sea of Azov. Finally in some areas of the northern Sivash commercial production reaches the very high rate of 100 kg/hectare. In the second (southern) part of the northern Sivash the production is only 15 kg/hectare, while in the central and southern Sivash it is insignificant.

A certain loss of salinity might have a favourable effect on the Sivash fisheries. In Vorobieff's opinion this could be achieved by separating off the western and southern Sivash from its main part by dams and by digging a channel through the Arabat Strelka into the central Sivash.

A deepening of the channels connecting the Sivash with the Sea is desirable in order to facilitate the entry and return of fish from the Sea of Azov. In this way a wider area of the Sivash could be used for intensive fishery.

Vorobieff estimates in the following manner the size of the main groups of organisms in the northern Sivash, by applying the methods used by I. Petersen for Danish waters: 'The total amount of fish in the northern Sivash, when all food is used, may be estimated at 21,000 tons. When only two-thirds of the food resources are used this quantity becomes 14,000 tons.' Vorobieff estimates the annual resources of plant food for the zoobenthos as 628,000 tons: 'With 10 as a coefficient, 62,800 tons of benthos could have developed from these stocks. When only two-thirds of the food is used this amount becomes 41,900 tons, which approaches the data actually recorded.' Further calculations lead Vorobieff to the conclusion that of the 1,322,000 tons of phytoplankton and phytobenthos produced in the Sivash annually only a small part is consumed by animals.

11

The Caspian Sea

I. GENERAL CHARACTERISTICS

The Caspian Lake–Sea is the largest enclosed body of water in the world, and is exceptional in its peculiarity.

Salinity-stratification of its waters is much less pronounced than in those of the Black Sea; an oxygen supply, sufficient for the penetration of individual numbers of its fauna to their limiting depths, is provided by water circulation. However, the density of the population is high only in the upper horizon; below 100 m life is very much restricted owing to a shortage of oxygen.

The Sea has been apportioned to separate zoo-geographical provinces and its fauna is composed mainly of remarkable, relict, genetically heterogeneous forms—the remains of relict marine faunas, formerly much more widely distributed, which have survived in other marine and fresh bodies of water in Eurasia and which are linked in origin with the Tethys fauna.

Immigrants from the Arctic basin, from the Black and Azov Seas (Mediterranean fauna) and from fresh waters are added to this nucleus of Caspian fauna.

In the struggle for existence the Caspian fauna is inferior to the biologically stronger fauna of the open seas; this makes the Caspian Sea exceptionally suitable for acclimatization.

Fisheries are very rich in the Sea, and its yield is original in its specific composition.

II. HISTORY OF EXPLORATION

First period

The first data on the Caspian Sea biology are found in the works of P. Pallas (1741–1811) and S. Gmelin (1745–74). Important biological data were brought back by the expeditions of K. Baer (1853–56) and O. Grimm (1874 and 1876).

Second period

The next period, of a closer, more comprehensive study of the Sea, is connected with the name of N. M. Knipovitch, who organised and carried out three expeditions in it in twelve years (1904 to 1915) before the war, which interrupted its further exploration for many years.

Knipovitch's first expedition worked in 1904, the second in 1912 and 1913 and the third in 1914–15. A general picture of the distribution of the depths of the Caspian Sea, its currents, temperature, salinity, oxygen and hydrogen sulphide content, as well as that of plankton, benthos and fish was obtained by Knipovitch's expeditions. Seasonal changes in some of these phenomena were also recorded. These expeditions provided the physico-geographical, hydrological and biological foundation on which wider and profounder researches were to be based in Soviet times.

Third period

Little was added to our knowledge of the Caspian Sea during the sixteen years following Knipovitch's expedition. In this period the following should be noted: N. Tchougounov's work on the census of the North Caspian benthos (1923), on the feeding of the young of commercial fish (1918), and on the North Caspian plankton (1921); and A. Derzhavin's thorough examination of starred sturgeon, vobla and bream (1915, 1918 and 1922), and certain others.

The herring expedition (1930) and the All Caspian Fisheries Expedition (1931–34) concentrated their attention almost exclusively on scientific-trade problems.

Fourth period

In 1932 large-scale biological investigations were begun in the Caspian Sea by the Oceanographic Institute and its branches which have eventually developed into a comprehensive study of all sections of oceanography within the system of work of the All Union Institute of Marine Fisheries and Oceanography. During this fourth period the study of the hydrochemical conditions, of the quantitative distribution of life and the phenomena of biological productivity and of means of acclimatization have become particularly important and widely developed.

The Astrakhan (1904) and Baku (1912) Scientific Fisheries Stations have played an important part in the study of the Caspian Sea.

III. PHYSICAL GEOGRAPHY, HYDROLOGY, HYDROCHEMISTRY AND GEOLOGY

Situation and size

The Caspian Sea (see Fig. 256) extends in a north–south direction and is about 1,204 km long, with a width of from 204 km (opposite the Apsheron peninsula) to 566 km (in its widest part).

It lies between 47° 13′ and 36° 34′ 35″ N latitude and between 46° 38′ 39″ and 54° 44′ 19″ E longitude. The area of the Sea is 436,000 km^2. Its volume is about 77,000 km^3, with an average depth of 180 m. The northern part of the Caspian (north of a line Chechen Island to Tyub-Karagan Point) has an average depth of only 6·2 m and its volume is less than 1/100 of that of the whole Sea (0·94 per cent), whereas in area the Northern Caspian constitutes about 27·73 per cent of the whole. The Central Caspian, if it is bounded on the south by a line from Zhiloy Island to Kuuli Cape, forms a little more than one-third of the volume (35·39 per cent), and about 36·63 per cent of the area of the whole Sea, its average depth being 175·6 m and its greatest about 770 m.

The Southern Caspian, which is the deepest part of the Sea, has a greatest depth of about 1,000 m and an average depth of 325 m. In volume this part is a little less than two-thirds of the whole body of water (63·67 per cent); and its surface area is 35·64 per cent. The depths of the Central and Southern

Caspian are divided by a comparatively shallow ridge running to the east from the Apsheron peninsula at a depth of not more than 200 m.

The Northern Caspian is exceptionally shallow and is mostly not more than

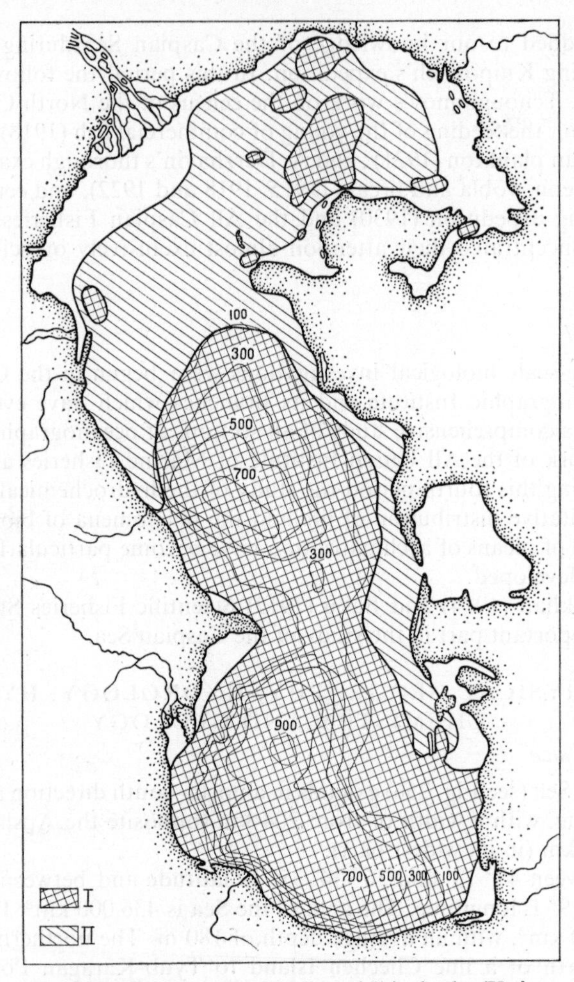

FIG. 256. Chart of Caspian Sea with isobaths (Knipovitch, 1936) and soils (Klenova). *I* Detritus and fine-grained fraction; *II* Coarse fraction.

10 m deep. There is a somewhat deeper part in its eastern region, the so-called Gur'evskaya Furrow.

Sea-bed

The bottom topography is closely linked with the distribution of bottom-deposits and detritus, as well as with that of the benthos biomass. Thick, soft mud deposits (*batkaki*) are formed—frequently right at the shore and in shallow water—under favourable conditions (bottom topography, slow currents) from the large accumulation of detritus brought down by river water and retained by vegetation. Detritus and fine-grained soil fractions moved away from the shores and were carried into the deep Central and Southern Caspian depressions, which thus become encircled by a wide belt of the coarse fraction, mainly huge beds of shell gravel (Fig. 256). This peculiarity—the transfer of detritus from shallows to depths, and an abundance of pure shell-gravel floors—is of cardinal importance for the phenomena of biological productivity taking place in the Sea; it decreases considerably its potential level, both as regards benthos and also, apparently, as regards plankton.

The organisms populating the Sea, the molluscs most of all, are of extreme importance in the formation of the sea-bed. According to A. Kolokolov's computations (1940) the ratio of plant nutrients to terrigenous substances in the North Caspian sea-bed is about 1:1. Dead molluscs remain in those parts of the Sea where they lived and sea-beds rich in shell gravel are formed, and are thus most productive as regards benthos.

Sea level

The level of the Caspian Sea, averaged over the last century, has been 25·45 m below the ocean level. Moreover, it is not constant from year to year, but undergoes considerable seasonal variations and fluctuations which may last for many years. The average level of the Caspian Sea (for the hundred years 1830 to 1929) is 327 cm from zero on the Baku sea-gauge (its level being 28·73 m above sea-level). The highest level of the Sea, 363 cm above zero on the Baku sea-gauge, was recorded in 1896, and the lowest in very recent years. In 1945 the level of the Caspian Sea was only 134·26 cm, and it is continuing to fall. Thus in the last 50 years the range of the fluctuations of the level of the Caspian Sea has been 229 cm. In the last 17 years (1929–46) it has fallen by almost 2 m (187 cm); the decrease is proceeding fairly uniformly. Only in 1942–44 was there some indication of a break in this uniformity, when the level of the Sea rose by 11·5 cm as compared with 1941; by 1945, however, its level had dropped again by 20·5 cm as compared to 1943.

There is reason to suppose that the catastrophic drop in the level of the Caspian Sea, caused by the considerable decrease of river inflow (from 1930 to 1943) has now been stabilized at the level of about 130 cm above zero on the Baku sea-gauge. A further insignificant drop of the level to 110 to 115 cm above zero on the Baku sea-gauge may be expected in the coming years.

In the opinion of most investigators (L. Berg, S. P. Brujevitch and others) these changes in the level of the Caspian Sea are the results of the fluctuations in the amounts of fresh water received by the Sea from the rivers and from rainfall minus evaporation. According to a different view the changes are caused by the movements of the earth's crust (I. Gubkin, P. Pravoslavlev and others).

A number of mountain ranges in the Southern Caspian, stretching from north to south (Fig. 257), were discovered by recent investigations (V. Solov'evt 1958) with the use of an echo sounder. In Solov'ev's opinion they are of recen, formation; this indicates the continuance of structural processes, which could naturally be linked with the change of sea-level. Similar mountain-forming processes may probably be discovered also in the Central Caspian.

Although the second explanation may have some truth in it, it is possible to show, as has been done in a graphic form by Brujevitch, that the fluctuations in the level of the Caspian Sea are in close accord with the quantity of water supplied by the rivers. The mightiest water-artery feeding the Caspian Sea, the Volga, brings into it on the average about 270·8 km³ of water each year. According to G. Bregman's calculations about 75·6 per cent of the whole supply of fresh water is brought by the river Volga (the average annual inflow from rivers, measured over many years, has been 355 km³). The conformity between the fluctuations of sea-level and those of the inflow of the Volga waters is so close that the direct influence of the latter on the level of the Sea has been established (Fig. 258).

Zenkevitch considers that the greatest part of the shore of the Caspian Sea

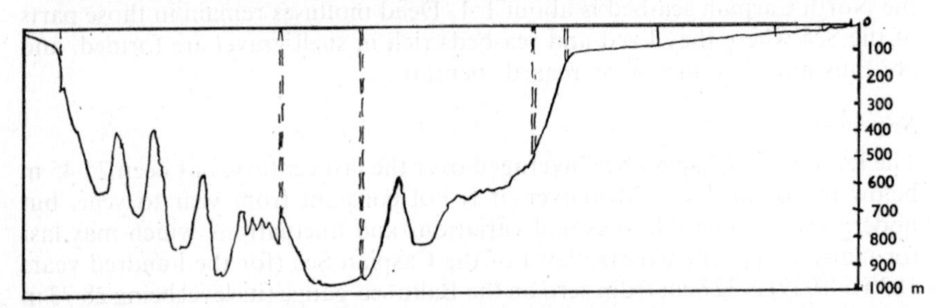

FIG. 257. One of the latitude contours of the Caspian Sea bottom in its southern part (Solov'ev, Kulakova and Agapova).

bears a definite imprint of the effect of a considerable lowering of its level, characteristic of the whole Quaternary period. A huge lowland area was submerged by the ancient Caspian in the north, and now its shores are moving southwards along the completely flat surface of the ancient sea-bed. Only the extensive delta of the Volga is under the influence of fluvial factors and is growing as a result of alluvial accretion. All along the rest of the shore the morphology is not clearly defined, and the water's edge may recede up to 20 km to the south, due to the effect of on-shore and off-shore winds.

The western (Caucasian) shore consists of relatively solid Neogene carbonate rock. Nevertheless alluvium-bearing currents may be formed along this coast. Alluvium deposited by them is supplied by large rivers (Samur, Sulak, etc.) and by the washed out sea-bed, from which a mass of shell gravel is cast up on to the beach. South of the Apsheron peninsula the coast is more irregular with a number of headlands and a whole archipelago of islands, mud-volcanic and others, lying to seaward. Farther south, within the area of the delta of the river Kura, the stretch of friable alluvial shore begins and extends to within the boundaries of Iran.

The abundant shallows round the Apsheron peninsula have a peculiar structure. Complex tectonic structures have been discovered on the bottom, some of them oil-bearing, and marine petroleum works have been set up there.

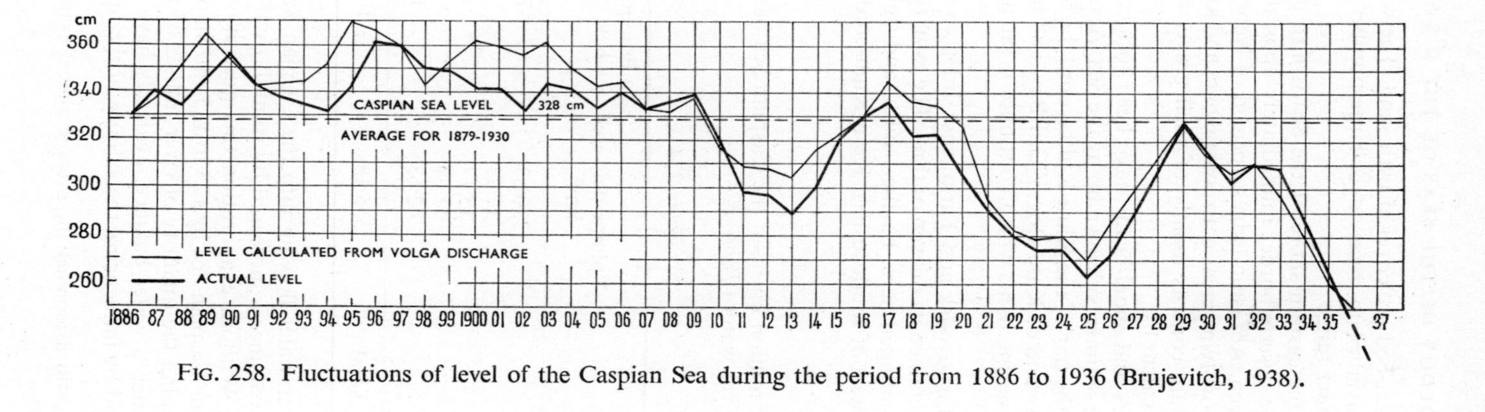

FIG. 258. Fluctuations of level of the Caspian Sea during the period from 1886 to 1936 (Brujevitch, 1938).

Large areas of the sea-bed are covered with sand. The whole southern shore of the Sea is an alluvial plain, receiving a large number of rivers which flow down from the El'burz range.

The structure of the eastern shore of the Sea is also peculiar. There is no river inflow, and the deserts border immediately upon the Sea. The contour of this shore is uneven. Abrasion ledges, formed of Neogene carbonate rock, alternate here with low-lying areas with coastal bars and long shoal-heads. The eastern coast alluvium consists mainly of shell gravel and oolitic grains (a variety of granular calcite).

Large coastal bars and shoal-heads have been formed in many places on this coast by marine sediments thrown up by the Sea. Among them the following may be noted: the bar of the Kara-Kul lagoon, the bars and shoal-heads of Krasnovodsk Bay and of Kara-Bogaz-Gol Bay, and likewise Ogurchinsky Island and the submarine bank which continues it far to the south (V. Zenkevitch, 1957).

In the area of Krasnovodsk and Turkmensk Inlets, with its peculiar structure, the coast has retained its uneven outline. The estuary of the ancient Oxus (Amu-Dar'ya) was situated here. Farther south, and right up to the frontier of Iran, the sand desert of southwestern Kara-Kum borders the Sea.

Water balance

The huge area—3·7 million km²—of the Caspian Sea basin receives annually about 355 km³ of river water (*Table 224*):

Table 224

River	Volume delivered km³	Proportion of whole delivery %
Volga	270·83	76·3
Kura	17·22	4·9
Ural	13·17	3·7
Terek	11·31	3·2
Others	42·65	11·9
Total	355·18	100

This mass of river water flowing into the Caspian Sea, comprising about 1/250 of its whole volume, is increased by rainfall to 451 km³ or to 1/176 of the whole volume. Without evaporation this quantity of water might have raised the level of the Caspian Sea by 123 to 125 cm* in one year. The climatic conditions determining the quantity of river inflow, of rainfall and evaporation would, with such a water balance, evidently have a considerable effect on the sea-level, and by influencing the salinity of the upper layers of the Sea

* V. Prishletzov (1940) determines the average annual evaporation from the whole Caspian Sea as 86·6 cm.

cause, as we shall see below, considerable changes in the phenomena of biological productivity.

According to Brujevitch's computations (1938) the level of the Caspian Sea would remain practically constant with an average Volga inflow of 257 km^3. The level would inevitably drop with a decrease in the inflow, and would rise with an increase (Fig. 258).

Fluctuations of the level of the Caspian Sea are complicated by seasonal changes; during the first half of the summer after the floods, the level is at its highest, and it is at its lowest at the beginning of winter.

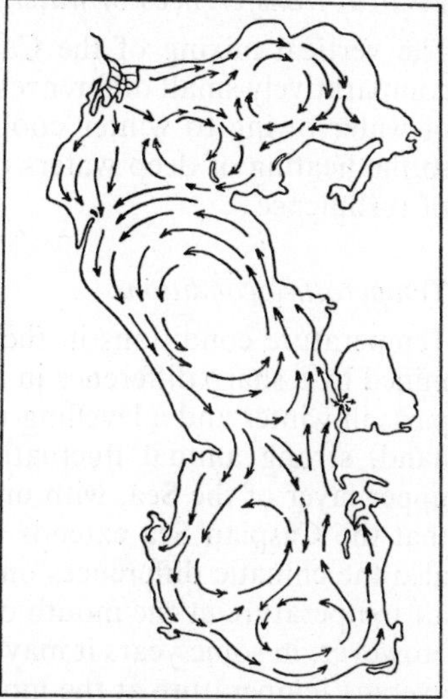

FIG. 259. Currents of the Caspian Sea (A. Mikhalevsky, 1931).

Currents

The movements of the water masses of the Caspian Sea, like those of any other sea, are expressed in a system of vertical and horizontal displacements due to different causes. The Caspian Sea is encircled by a large cyclonic current, forming two powerful halistatic areas in the Southern and Central Caspian (Fig. 259). The speed of this current along the western side of the Central Caspian may reach, according to Stokman (1938), 20 cm/sec. On the approach to the shallows of the Northern Caspian the main mass of waters, moving from the south along the eastern shore of the Sea, turns to the west and, farther on, to the south, receiving the main mass of the discharge waters of the Northern Caspian. Part of these waters passing the Mangyshlak peninsula is diverted into the Northern Caspian.

There is a separate cyclonic current in the southern part of the Southern Caspian with its own halistatic area in the centre. Part of the waters moving southwards along the western side of the Central Caspian runs away from the western shores, at the latitude of the Apsheron ridge, and passes to the eastern side. The Volga waters move south partly along the western coast, partly directly east, creating two anticyclonic gyrations: one to the northwest from the northern end of Kulaly Island, the other to the northeast over the Ural trench. The existence of a circular movement of waters over the Ural trench is confirmed by the accumulation of soft silty deposits in the trench, by the presence of hydrogen sulphide, and by the absence of hydrogen sulphide in the sea-bed encircling the trench as a result of the washing-out effect of the circular current. In the Northern Caspian, however, especially in summer, the picture of the permanent currents is changed by strong winds owing to the shallowness of the Sea, and by on- and off-shore winds (A. Milkhalevsky, 1931).

According to N. Gorsky (1936) the system of the winter under-ice currents of the Northern Caspian differs greatly from what has just been described.

Saline Central Caspian waters slowly fill the Ural trench, flowing in between Kulaly Island and the Central-Zhemchuzhnaya Bank close to the Buzachi peninsula. A compensating current of fresh water runs mostly along the western shore of the Northern Caspian.

Vertical transferences of water masses

The vertical mixing of the Caspian Sea water masses is well assured, with comparatively small differences in the density of the surface and deeper layers of water owing to winter cooling, to the effect of on- and off-shore winds, to the heating of deep waters owing to adiabatic processes, and as the result of turbulence.

Temperature conditions

Temperature conditions in the Caspian Sea are very peculiar and are determined by a sharp difference in temperature between its southern and northern parts in winter and a levelling-up of the temperature in summer. On the other hand, strong annual fluctuations of temperature are characteristic in the upper layer of the Sea, with uniform temperature in its deeper part. The fact that the Caspian Sea extends for 1,200 km from north to south determines also the climatic differences on land adjacent to the Sea. The average annual air temperature at the mouth of the river Ural is 7·8° C, and at Pehlevi 15·6°. However, in some years it may reach 19·5° (Inlet of Astrabad). In January the average temperature at the mouth of the river Ural is −10·5°, and at Pehlevi +5·9°. In July the difference between the air temperatures of the shores of the Northern and Southern Caspian is only 3° to 3·5°.

Since the Sea is heated mostly from its surface, the difference in the air temperatures of areas adjacent to the northern and southern parts of the Sea controls the difference in the surface temperature of the Sea. The nature of the distribution of surface temperature and its seasonal changes are well illustrated by Fig. 260. Almost all the northern part of the Sea is commonly (with variations in different years) covered with ice for four months a year (December to March). The ice-cover attains a thickness of 40 to 50 cm, and in the northeast even of 70 cm; the temperature of the water drops to −1°. For the surface layer of the Sea January and February are the coldest months, and July and August the warmest. The heating of the Sea in spring and its cooling in autumn start at the coastal shallows, gradually spreading to the centre and into the depths. In the hottest time of the year the surface temperature may rise to 30° and even 30·8°. The seasonal range of temperature fluctuations is sharply pronounced in the upper layer and grows gradually less and less with depth, and finally at 400 to 450 m it completely fades away; below this lies a layer of a practically constant temperature, with a somewhat higher temperature in the Southern Caspian depression (a little below 6°) as compared with that of the Central Caspian (slightly below 5°). As in any other sea, time is required for the heating to be transferred into the depths and with increasing depth this delay becomes greater. Knipovitch has shown that in 1914–15 the maximum heating of surface water occurred at the end of

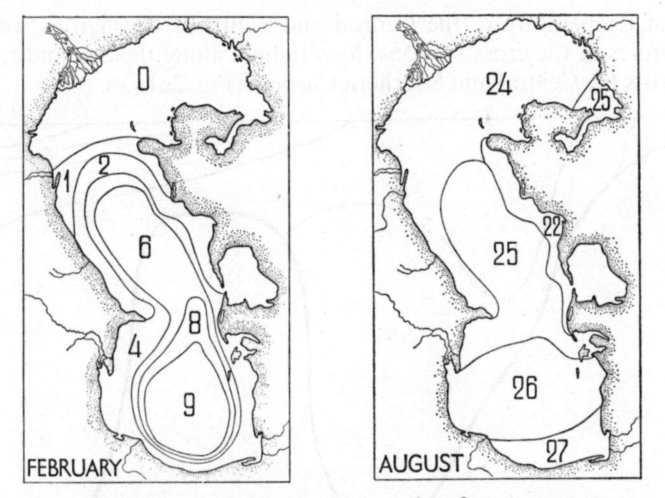

FIG. 260. Diagrammatic distribution of surface temperatures of the Caspian Sea in (A) February and (B) August.

July and the beginning of August. At a depth of 50 m the highest temperature was reached by the end of August, at that of 100 m in January, while deeper still the greatest rise of temperature was in February; that is, with a delay of six months. At a time when it is winter on the surface of the Sea, at a depth of 300 to 400 m there is a 'hydrological summer'. Below 400 m the temperature remains constant. As an example the average annual data may be given (*Table 225*); these allow a comparison to be made of the vertical

Table 225

Depth m	Central Caspian: Mean temp. 21 Feb to 8 Mar 1934	Central Caspian: Mean temp. 25 Jul to 12 Oct 1934	Southern Caspian: Mean temp. 21 Feb to 8 Mar 1934	Southern Caspian: Mean temp. 25 Jul to 12 Oct 1934
0	5·94	22·03	9·05	24·18
50	5·78	6·63	8·92	9·58
100	5·62	5·76	7·20	7·11
200	5·27	5·29	6·11	6·14

Depth m	Central Caspian: Mean annual temperature			Southern Caspian: Mean annual temperature		
300	5·07	5·01	4·96	5·91	5·93	5·96
400		4·88			5·90	
500		4·82			5·93	
600		4·86			5·93	
700		4·83			5·92	
800					5·96	
900					5·94	

course of temperature in the Central and Southern Caspian as well as the temperatures in the cross sections, longitudinal along the Sea and transverse ones across the Central and Southern Caspian (Fig. 261A, B, C).

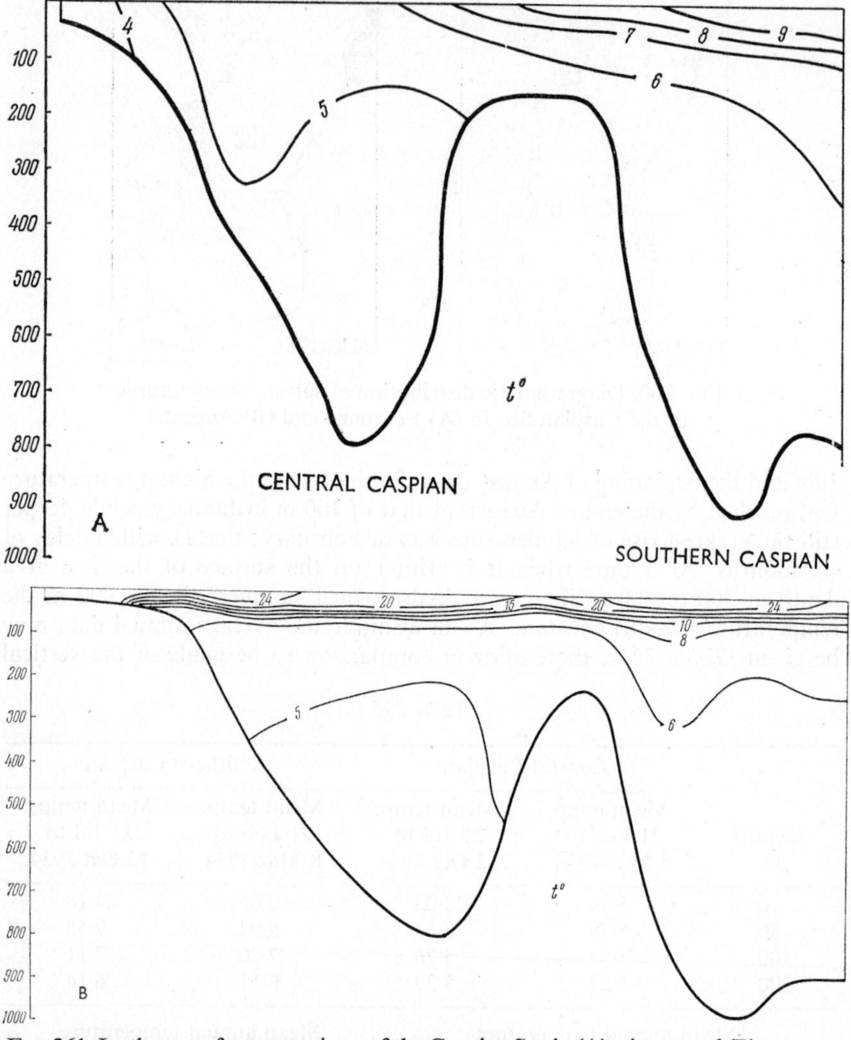

FIG. 261. Isotherms of cross sections of the Caspian Sea in (A) winter, and (B) summer (Brujevitch, 1937).

The temperature of the deep waters of the Caspian Sea varies but little and in practice it may be considered constant. Over the last 20 years a difference of only 0·05° has been recorded in the depths of the Sea (according to Brujevitch, 1937).

It had already been established by the work of Knipovitch that there is a rise of temperature of a few hundredths of a degree in the bottom layer of the two Caspian Sea depressions.

N. Gorsky (1936) explains this by two causes: the heat radiated from the earth's crust, and the rise of temperature obtained as a result of the compression of water at great depths (adiabatic process).

The temperature conditions of the Northern Caspian differ considerably

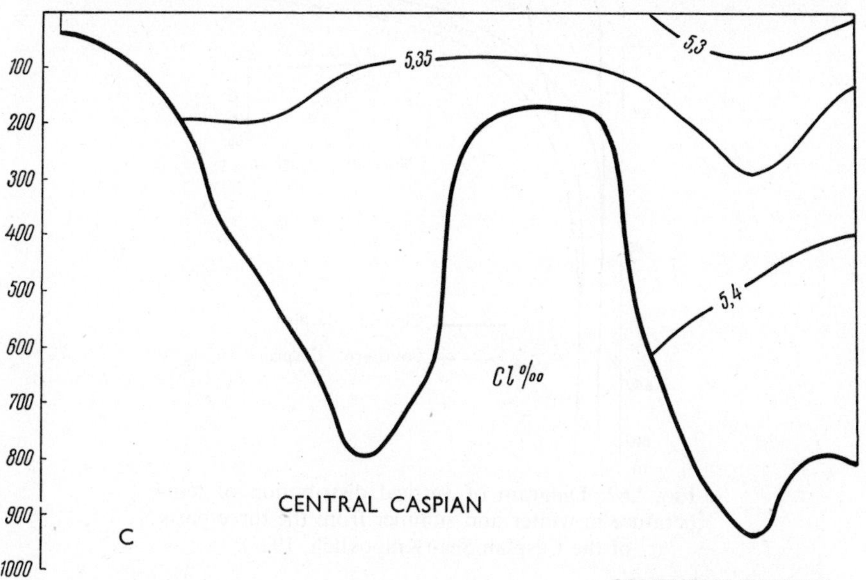

FIG. 261C. Isohalines (by chlorine) of the cross sections of the Caspian Sea (Brujevitch).

from those of the Central and Southern. In consequence of its shallowness and of the ease with which its water is displaced by wind and of the vigorous phenomena of the on- and off-shore winds, stratification is hardly maintained at all in the Northern Caspian. The isolines usually run vertically not horizontally, i.e. changes of temperature, salinity, etc. run not from the surface of the Sea to its bottom, but from the centre to the shores. Hence each of the three large parts of the Caspian Sea has its own definite temperature characteristics (Fig. 262).

Ice conditions

Only the Northern Caspian has an ice-cover every winter. First of all, with the onset of the frosts, huge 'young shore ice' is formed in the shallows where the water is of low salinity. After two weeks the deeper part of the sea is covered with ice. This delay is due to the higher salinity of the central part of the Northern Caspian and to its greater swell which breaks the crust of the congealing ice. Strong variable winds destroy the ice, even when the central part of the Sea has been frozen, causing some clearings and the formation of drifting ice fields. The fields drift at varying speeds and constantly collide with each other: some get broken up, and at times one field is forced on top

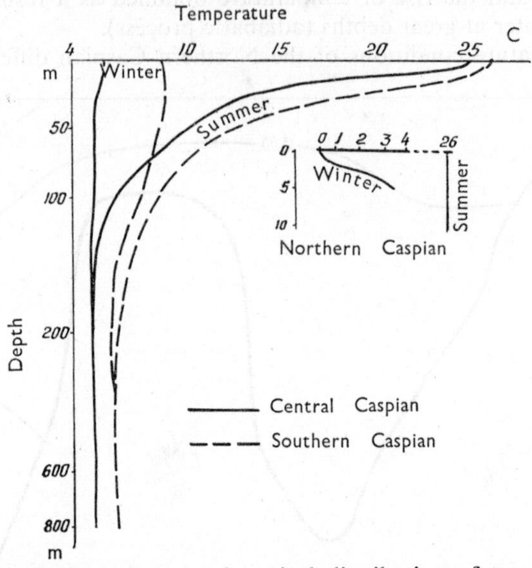

FIG. 262. Diagram of vertical distribution of temperature in winter and summer from the three parts of the Caspian Sea (Knipovitch, 1923).

of another. Thus there are formed embacles and lump ice, that is, big floes which go aground and grow bigger on account of more drifting floes sliding on top of them. The limit of solid ice is more or less permanent. It runs along the 12 m isobath from the northern end of Kulaly Island to Tyuleni Island.

Salinity

The salinity of the Caspian Sea differs greatly from that of the ocean both in the ratio of its components and in their sum. According to S. P. Brujevitch (1937) the average composition of the waters of the Caspian Sea, the river Volga and the ocean are determined by the data expressed in percentages appearing in *Table 226*.

The chlorine coefficient of the Caspian Sea may be taken as 2·396 (by Lebedintzev, 2·386) and its average salinity as 12·80 to 12·85‰. Alternatively the salinity may be represented as in *Table 227* (according to Knipovitch, 1923).

As shown by the tables, Caspian waters are poor in sodium and chlorine and rich in calcium and sulphates by comparison with the ocean; this difference in the salt ratio makes its water approximate more to river water.

The surface salinity of the Central and Southern Caspian is fairly uniform; it is contained between the isohalines of 12 and 13‰. Only in the far south-eastern corner of the Sea (Krasnovodsk Bay) is the surface salinity above

Table 226. Total salinity

Salts of	Caspian Sea		Volga at	
	Earlier data 12·63 to 12·89‰	Brujevitch 12·68 to 12·94‰	Astrakhan 0·19856‰	Ocean 35‰
Na	24·69	24·82	6·67	30·593
K	0·63	0·66		1·106
Ca	2·59	2·70	23·34	1·197
Mg	5·66	5·70	4·47	3·725
Cl	41·67	41·73	5·46	55·292
Br	0·08	0·06	—	0·188
SO_4	23·82	23·49	25·63	7·692
CO_3	0·86	0·84	34·43	0·207

13‰. To the north the 12‰ isohaline runs somewhat south of the boundary between the Northern and Central Caspian. Farther north salinity falls fairly sharply at the delta of the rivers Volga and Ural. A picture of the distribution of the surface salinity is given by Figs. 263A and 263B.

In the open parts of the Sea salinity increases with depth, as shown in *Table 228* which gives the average annual salinities for August 1933.

Vertical salinity distribution is also given in the foregoing diagrams (Fig. 261A, B, C).

The quantity of river water and precipitation received by the eastern shores is very low, since evaporation is considerable. As a result a greater or lesser rise of salinity is observed in all the inlets of the eastern part of the Caspian Sea. In Kaidak, which no longer exists, salinity reached 59·52‰ in 1934 (with a chlorine number of 25·01). In the inner parts of Krasnovodsk Bay salinity is almost as high, but it reaches its maximum in Kara-Bogaz where at times it goes up to 200‰. S. P. Brujevitch (1950) has pointed out that a decrease of river inflow has caused a considerable rise of salinity in the Northern Caspian. Thus in 1939 the average surface salinity reached 5·42‰ in chlorine, i.e. a salinity observed in the depths of the Central and Lower Caspian (*Table 228*).

Table 227

Salt	Caspian Sea	Ocean
NaCl	62·15	78·32
$MgSO_4$	23·58	6·40
$MgCl_2$, $MgBr_2$	4·54	9·44
$CaCO_2$	1·24	0·21
KCl	1·21	1·69
$CaSO_4$	6·92	3·94
	99·64%	100·00

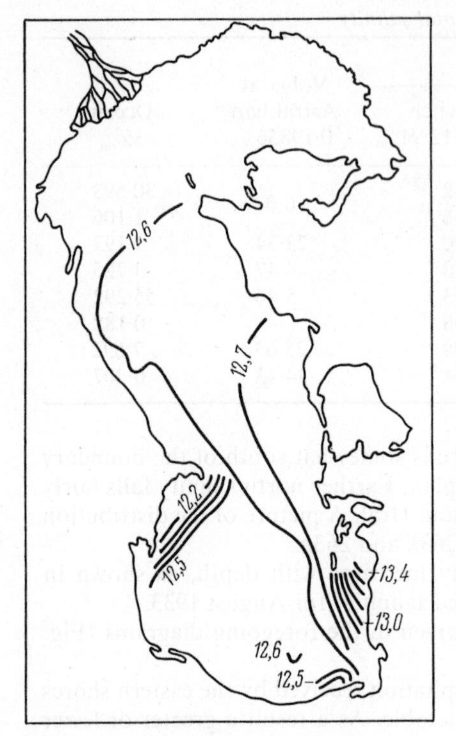

FIG. 263A. Distribution of surface salinity (‰) of the Caspian Sea in February and March 1934 (Brujevitch, 1950).

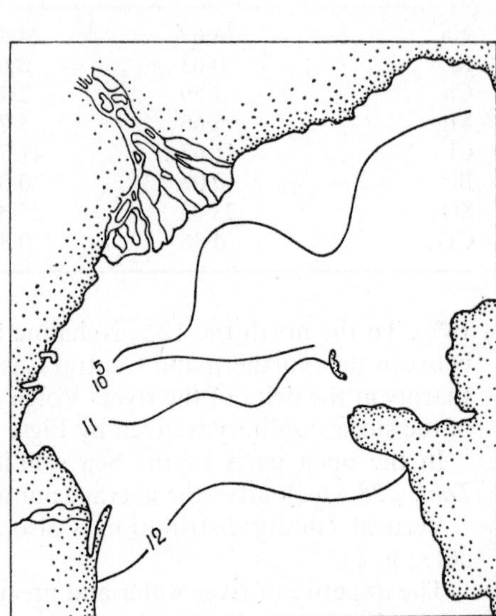

FIG. 263B. Distribution of surface salinity of the northern Caspian Sea in June 1934 (‰) (Ivanov).

The difference in the salt ratio of Caspian and ocean waters (*Table 227*), which appeared as a result of the separation of the Caspian Sea from the ocean and which is gradually rising owing to the metamorphism by river discharge, makes it possible to calculate the approximate period of time of the existence of the 'lake' phase of the Caspian Sea. S. Brujevitch (1939) has calculated it in

Table 228

	Salinity ‰				
Depth, m	0	50	100	200	300
Central Caspian	12·59	12·66	12·68	12·72	12·76
Southern Caspian	12·61	12·65	12·68	12·74	—
Depth, m	**400**	**600**		**800**	**900**
Central Caspian	12·76	12·78		12·84	—
Southern Caspian	12·82	12·84		12·87	12·90

relation to chlorine, magnesium and the sulphates. He considers the 'lake age' of the Caspian to be about 15,000 years.

In the salt balance of the Caspian Sea the carrying away of the salts beyond the limits of the Sea by the wind plays a definite role. L. Blinov (1950) determines by means of complex computations the amount of salts carried away from the surface of the Caspian Sea beyond its limits as 62,400 tons per day (at an average wind speed of 6 m/sec), which is about 30 per cent of the total accession of salts from the river inflow (according to S. P. Brujevitch it is 195,000 tons per day).

Oxygen

The oxygen conditions of the Caspian Sea are the result of the following factors. In summer the oxygen content at the surface of the Sea is near saturation: 98 per cent in the Central Caspian and 94 per cent in the Southern. In the Northern Caspian the picture is rather more varied, but on the average the oxygen content is more than 90 per cent. There is a slight supersaturation in the winter throughout the whole surface of the Sea (103 to 105 per cent). Changes in oxygen content with depth are shown in *Table 229* and in Fig. 264.

Table 229

Average amounts and seasonal differences in the content of oxygen dissolved in water for various parts of the Caspian Sea as percentage of saturation

Depth m	Central Caspian Feb–Mar 1934	Southern Caspian Feb–Mar 1934	Seasonal variations	
			Central Caspian	Southern Caspian
0	101	104	3	10
10	101	103	4	8
25	99	101	13	11
50	95	94	21	24
100	88	75	14	20
200	56	50	5	10
400	(32)	25	—	—
600	17	13	0	7
800	—	4	—	4

The decrease of oxygen content with depth in the Caspian Sea is not nearly so pronounced as that of the Black Sea. As we have seen, the much weaker saline stratification does not hinder the penetration of the vertical displacement of water into the depths. It is evident from the comparison given that in the Central Caspian the oxygen content is higher than in the Southern.

Substantial changes have taken place in oxygen distribution in the column of Caspian waters in the 40 years since the last works of N. M. Knipovitch (1914–15). Oxygen was then entirely absent near the bottom of the Central

Caspian. In 1934 even at the greatest depths there was some 0·13 to 0·64 cm^3/l. of oxygen. According to N. M. Knipovitch's data (1914–15) for the Central Caspian, at a depth of 700 m oxygen was disappearing and hydrogen sulphide appearing (up to 0·3 to 0·4 cm^3/l.). A smaller amount of hydrogen sulphide was recorded in the Southern Caspian. In 1934 S. Brujevitch recorded some small amounts of hydrogen sulphide (about 0·2 cm^3/l.) in the Southern Caspian at a depth of 700 m.

As in the Black Sea, the hydrogen sulphide is mainly the result of anaerobic

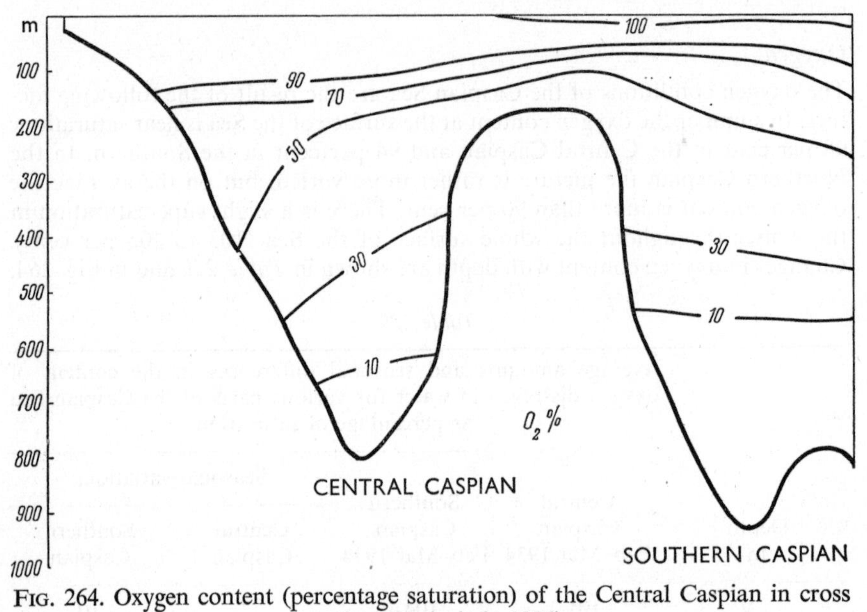

FIG. 264. Oxygen content (percentage saturation) of the Central Caspian in cross section (Brujevitch, 1934).

reduction of sulphates due to the activities of bacteria of the Microspira type. Moreover A. Pelsh (1936) discovered in the Caspian Sea a new group of bacteria (Hydrogenthiobacteria) capable of synthesizing hydrogen sulphide from solid sulphur and gaseous hydrogen. In contrast to that of the Black Sea, animal life in the Caspian Sea penetrates to the greatest depths.

Suffocation phenomena of the type found in the Sea of Azov have not been recorded in the Caspian Sea. If they do exist in the Northern Caspian they are probably local and limited; this is confirmed by the absence from the Caspian of zones of blackened shell gravel, so typical of the Sea of Azov. This is explained by the wide distribution of sand and large-grain soils in the shallows encircling the Caspian depths, which indicates a sufficient aeration of the bottom layer in shallow areas. It is different in the shallows with mud-accumulations, where a very marked shortage of oxygen (4 to 20 per cent of saturation) has been recorded at times. A mass accumulation of soft mud-beds in protected regions and bottom hollows, however small, is due to abundant organic substances, either brought by the rivers (allochthonous), or gathered in the Sea itself as the remains of dead animals and, still more, dead plants (autochthonous). Such regions are most frequent in the Northern Caspian, often in very shallow places. In the eastern part of the Northern Caucasus, in the Kaidak and Mangishlak areas, and in Krasnovodsk Bay large areas of the bottom are covered by muds many metres thick, the so-called batkaki, rich in organic substances with a thick bacterial crust, evolving huge amounts of methane and hydrogen sulphide. According to A. Sadovsky (1929) a 4 cm

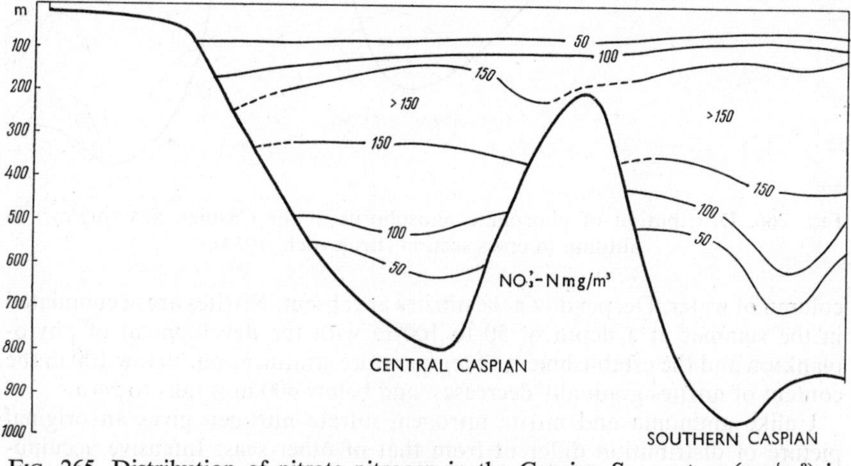

FIG. 265. Distribution of nitrate nitrogen in the Caspian Sea waters (mg/m^3) in cross section (Brujevitch, 1934).

layer of mud is accumulated there annually. Throughout the northern shore of the Northern Caspian, in Agrakhansk Bay and in Krasnovodsk Bay, we find similar zones of huge deposits of decaying organic matter. They also fill the central part of the Ural trench. Under certain conditions, when the water in these shallows gets thoroughly mixed by a gale, the top layer of the soil may be washed away and hydrogen sulphide may enter the water. These phenomena may sometimes become acute and lead to suffocation. It is a purely local phenomenon, linked with the occurrence of muds rich in hydrogen sulphide in very shallow areas.

Let us now consider the content of nitrogen, phosphorus and silicon compounds in the Caspian Sea waters (Figs. 265, 266 and 267).

Nitrogen

Ammonia nitrogen content in the Caspian is about the same as that of the Baltic and North Seas, higher than in the ocean, but in deeper layers much lower than that in the Black Sea. Its amount in the Caspian fluctuates within a few tens (20 to 50, and in the Southern up to 70 mg/m^3).

The nature of the distribution of nitrites is similar to that of other seas. In winter the nitrites are found fairly uniformly distributed within a 50 to 100 m

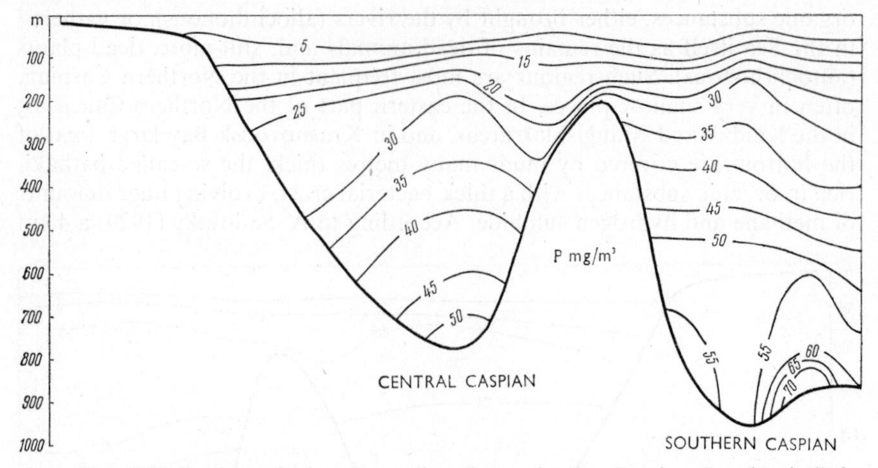

FIG. 266. Distribution of phosphate phosphorus in the Caspian Sea (mg/m³) in autumn in cross section (Brujevitch, 1934).

column of water. Deeper down the nitrites are absent. Nitrites are accumulated in the summer at a depth of 50 to 100 m with the development of phytoplankton and the establishment of temperature stratification. Below 100 m the content of nitrites gradually decreases, and below 400 m it falls to zero.

Unlike ammonia and nitrite nitrogen, nitrate nitrogen gives an original picture of distribution different from that of other seas. Intensive accumulation of nitrates proceeds at 100 to 600 m (mainly at 200 to 400 m). Above 100 m, within the zone of intense vertical circulation and the consumption of plant nutrients, the nitrate content is either very low (in winter in the Central Caspian 5–10–15 mg per 1 m³) or absent (in the summer). The lower limit of

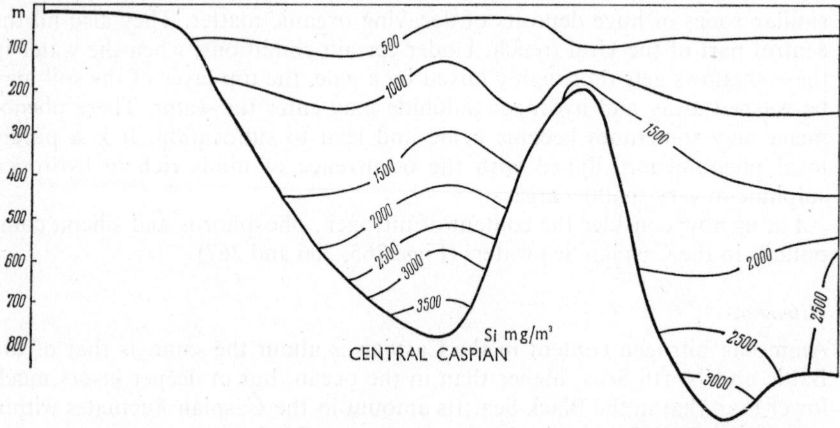

FIG. 267. Distribution of silicon in the Caspian Sea (mg/m³) in autumn in cross section (Brujevitch, 1934).

the layer rich in nitrates is linked with the horizon of the sharp fall of oxygen content. Within the water column, at 200 to 400 m deep, nitrate nitrogen content fluctuates between 110 and 180 mg/m³; below 600 m nitrates disappear.

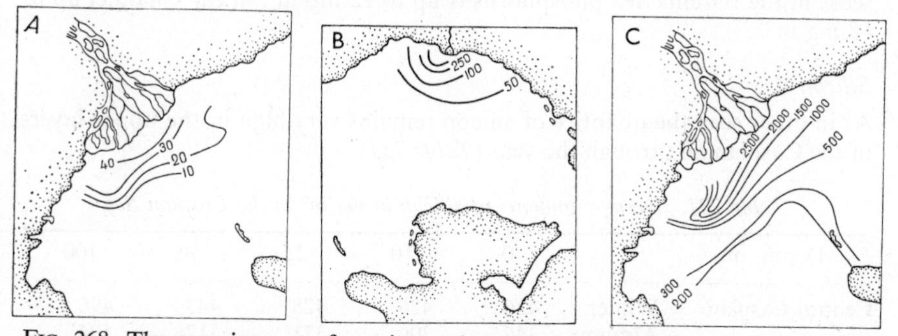

FIG. 268. The carrying out of nutrient substances by river waters in the northern Caspian (mg/m³). A Phosphorus content by the end of August (Brujevitch and Ivanov); B Nitrates in front of the Ural delta in February and March (Brujevitch and Fedosov); C Silicon in September (Brujevitch and Ivanov).

This is similar to the distribution of nitrates in the Black Sea, only the upper zone of impoverishment is thinner there (above 50 m); it frequently contains a considerable amount of nitrates. The lower limit of this zone is at 200 m. Both Seas have similar amounts of nitrates.

The Caspian waters are kept continuously enriched in nutrient salts by river waters (Fig. 268).

Phosphorus

As in other seas the phosphates are completely absent from the upper layer of the Caspian Sea in summer. In winter they are found in small amounts in the upper layer, but not everywhere (up to 6 to 9 mg/m³). From 100 m downwards the phosphorus content increases to 60 to 80 mg/m³ (*Table 230* and Fig. 266).

Table 230. Average amounts of phosphate phosphorus in mg/m³ in the Caspian Sea

Depth, m		0	10	25	50	100
Central Caspian	Winter	4·2	4·2	4·8	6	9
	Autumn	0·1	0·2	0·4	3·8	11
Southern Caspian	Winter	1·0	1·2	1·3	1·6	11
	Autumn	0·3	0·1	0·1	2	11
Depth, m		**200**	**400**	**600**	**800**	**900**
Central Caspian	Winter	27	38	53	(75)	
	Autumn	24	35	44	(52)	
Southern Caspian	Winter	24	37	50	76	78
	Autumn	24	41	49	—	65

Seasonal fluctuations in phosphorus content in the upper layer of the Caspian Sea are very small—in the Southern Caspian about 1 mg/m³, in the Central Caspian up to 4·5 mg/m³; these data are commonly much higher in other seas: in the Barents Sea phosphorus is up to 22 mg/m³, in the Channel up to 18 mg/m³.

Silicon

As in other seas the quantity of silicon remains very high in the upper layers of the Caspian all through the year (*Table 231*).

Table 231. Average amounts of silicon in mg/m³ in the Caspian Sea

Depth, m		0	10	25	50	100
Central Caspian	Winter	426	426	428	443	496
	Autumn	346	306	371	517	594
Southern Caspian	Winter	321	305	246	317	486
	Autumn	226	212	245	331	547
Depth, m		**200**	**400**	**600**	**800**	**900**
Central Caspian	Winter	910	852	3,019		
	Autumn	907	1,485	2,560		
Southern Caspian	Winter	747	1,355	2,040	2,193	2,319
	Autumn	749	1,315	2,116	—	2,742

There is more silicon in the upper layer in winter, while in the summer the largest quantity is found at a depth of 50 to 100 m; this is connected with the development of plankton and its regeneration in a deeper layer from the sinking dead plankton. Seasonal fluctuations in silicon content in the upper layer are similar to those observed in the Barents Sea and the Channel (about 100 mg/m³).

Vertical zonation

S. P. Brujevitch has established a definite vertical zonation of the Caspian Sea waters on the basis of his comprehensive study of the hydrochemistry of the Sea; it is related mainly to the distribution of plant nutrients. Brujevitch (1938) calls it structural zonation (*Table 232*).

Table 232

Zones	Depth, m	Subzones	Depth, m
I. Zone (impoverishment) of consumption of plant nutrients	0–100	IA Photosynthesis	0–25 (50)
		IB Nitrites	50–100
II. Zone (aggregation) of accumulation of plant nutrients	Below 100	IIA Nitrates	100–400 (600)
		IIB Reduction	Below 400 (600)

The upper zone is the area of phytoplankton activity, with intensive photosynthesis proceeding mainly in the 25 to 50 m layer. Below 100 m there is accumulation of organic matter and plant nutrients caused by the sinking down of the remains of dying plankton, while vertical circulation is not sufficiently strong to bring them up in any considerable quantities; thus accumulation is greater than consumption. Within the zone of impoverishment of plant nutrients only the 25 to 50 m layer (on the average 35 m) is characterized by intensive photosynthesis (the subzone of photosynthesis). Deeper down, sunlight does not penetrate in the amounts required for intensive phytoplankton development. The nitrites are accumulated below the photosynthesis subzone as a result of the decomposition of plankton organisms, which sink into this subzone (the nitrites subzone). The two subzones of the upper zone are divided in summer time by a layer with a sharp temperature drop and are hardly mixed at all. The upper zone is intensively mixed when the surface water is cooled, and plant nutrients, which had disappeared from the upper layer in the summer, are distributed throughout its whole column. Within the accumulation zone the oxygen content decreases while the plant nutrients increase with depth. A considerable accumulation of nitrates, mostly at depths of 200 to 400 m, is characteristic of the upper part of this zone; at a greater depth (below 400 m) ammonia nitrification becomes impossible owing to a shortage of oxygen and the process stops at the ammonia stage. A sharp decrease of oxygen content is characteristic of the lower boundary of the nitrate subzone.

Mean data along the cross section Kurinsky Kamen'–Ogurchinsky Island for August 1933 are given in *Table 233* and in Fig. 269. The letters and Roman figures correspond to Brujevitch's zones and subzones in *Table 232.*

Table 233

Zones	Sub-zones	Depth m	t° C	S‰	pH	O %	P mg/m³	Si mg/m³	Nitrate nitrogen mg/m³	Nitrite nitrogen mg/m³	Ammonia nitrogen mg/m³
	A	0	25·03	12·61	8·42	97	1·1	194	7	0·0	53
		10	24·81	12·62	8·41	96	1·3	197	7	0·0	—
		25	24·57	12·63	8·41	94	1·5	193	4	0·0	—
	B	50	10·45	12·65	8·30	89	2·2	214	13	1·3	—
		100	7·90	12·68	8·22	71	7·0	265	19	0·5	—
I	A	200	6·20	12·74	8·00	46	26·0	561	115	0·2	—
		400	5·86	12·82	7·85	22	40·0	1,000	100	1·1	—
	B	600	5·87	12·84	7·74	3	56·0	1,637	17	0·0	—
		800	5·87	12·87	8·72	0	67·0	1,855	18	0·0	—
		900	5·88	12·90	7·74	0	70·0	2,000	—	0·0	70

Naturally none of these boundaries remains constant, especially in different parts of the Caspian Sea, and some of them frequently do not coincide with each other. Sharp changes in quantities of phosphates do not coincide with the boundary of the accumulation of nitrates and silicic acid, etc. The main zones of enrichment have the following sequence: silicic acid, nitrates, phosphates.

L. A. Zenkevitch had suggested a little earlier (1932) a different vertical

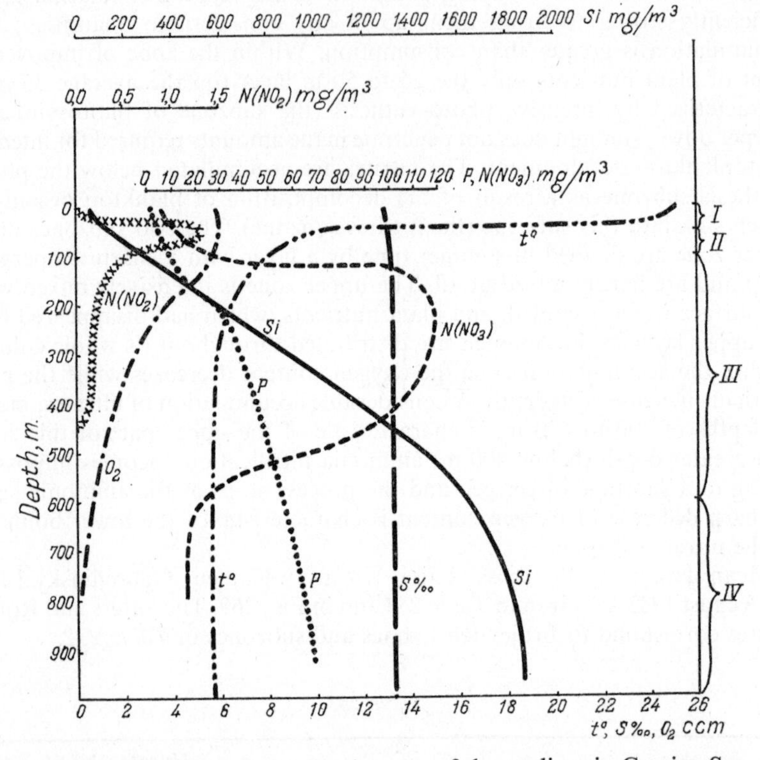

FIG. 269. Distribution of main elements of the medium in Caspian Sea waters. *I* Subzone of photosynthesis; *II* Nitrites subzone; *III* Nitrates subzone; *IV* Reduction subzone (Zenkevitch, 1947).

division of the water column into zones for the Barents Sea based chiefly on oxygen conditions (see Barents Sea). The two diagrams, however, can be contrasted.

Chemical conditions of the Northern Caspian

Hydrochemical conditions of the Northern Caspian differ greatly from those of the rest of this Sea because of its instability, its strong seasonal fluctuations, and its greater dependence, owing to its shallowness, on winds and the chemical properties of its soil. Slightly less than 300 km³ of fresh water are brought into the Caspian Sea each year by the rivers; rainfall adds about 18 km³, and about 100 km³ is lost by evaporation, so that the annual gain in fresh water is of the order of 200 km³, i.e. about one-fourth of the whole volume of water of the Northern Caspian. The volume of winter ice in the winter is about 10 per cent of the whole volume of water. Intensive early summer flooding, which freshens this part of the sea, considerable seasonal fluctuations of water-exchange with the Central Caspian, sharp fluctuations in the amounts of plant nutrients brought in with fresh waters, all these factors make the Northern Caspian saline conditions unstable and changeable. The large river-mouth areas of the Sea become almost completely freshened under the effect of river water. Salinity increases in the south, and on the boundary between the Northern and Central Caspian (along the line Chechen' Island–Mangishlak peninsula) the average salinity is 5·1‰ by chlorine* (the general salinity being 12·1‰). Salinity decreases to the north of this line. The Northern Caspian mainly has a salinity of 8 or 9‰: only in the estuaries of the rivers Volga and Ural does the salinity drop sharply. Huge amounts of plant nutrients are brought into the Northern Caspian with the fresh water; they are found in amounts maximal for the whole of the Caspian Sea just to seaward of the Volga and Ural delta: up to 40 mg phosphorus, up to 2,800 mg silicon, up to 250 mg nitrogen as nitrates per 1 m^3. The junction of the fresh waters rich in plant nutrients with the more saline waters is a place of huge plankton development (up to 2,000 to 4,000 mg/m^3). A kind of powerful phytoplankton filter is created and only a very small quantity of plant nutrients passes through it, so that outside it the quantity of plankton diminishes sharply to a few or a few tenths of mm^3 per 1 m^3. Hence, since the plant nutrients are almost completely used up by the great gatherings of plankton just seaward of the deltas, the Sea is supplied with it not directly from the river inflow, but only from detritus plant nutrients and from the diluted organic, and probably colloidal, compounds. The bottom deposits of the zone situated to seaward of the deltas play the role of a storehouse for a definite period. The distribution of huge silt deposits in the Northern Caspian, forming wide bands in front of the Terek, Volga and Ural estuaries, is in complete accord with this.

Changes in depth of vertical circulation

Being distributed throughout the whole Sea, plant nutrients drift finally into the deep depressions of the Central and Southern Caspian; return from there is difficult and rare. However, there is another factor which influences the return of plant food from the deep depressions, which act as huge storehouses.

The upper layer of the Sea would get either more or less saline as a result of an increase or decrease of river inflow, which would also cause either a rise or a fall of the level of the Caspian. However small the salinity fluctuations of the upper layer of the Sea they would affect the vertical mixing of waters. With increase of salinity in the upper layer the lower limit of vertical circulation goes deeper (possibly only by a few tens of metres), especially in winter; deeper layers of the sea rich in plant nutrients will then be drawn into

* The usual Knudsen formula for the determination of the total salinity of marine water from the chlorine numbers cannot be applied to the Caspian Sea, and the coefficient 2·38, established by Lebedintzev, is used instead—$S‰ = Cl \times 2{\cdot}38$.

the circulation, and in spring the upper column of water will be better 'fertilized' than in years when the upper layer becomes fresher and the lower limit of circulation moves upwards. As a result there may be years more or less favourable for the quantitative development of phytoplankton, and consequently of zooplankton and all the succeeding links in the food chains.

During the last few years the level of the Caspian has gone down by 2 m. At the same time these years were characterized by an extremely vigorous plankton development. Brujevitch has pointed out that during a 22 cm fall in the level of the Sea from 1933 to 1934 the salinity of the upper 100 m column of water must have been raised by almost 0·1‰. The quantity of nutrient salts at a depth of 50 to 100 m in 1934 was higher than that in 1933; this probably indicates their rise from great depths as a result of more intense vertical circulation (*Table 234*).

Table 234

Depth m	Phosphorus, mg/m³			Silicon, mg/m³			Nitrate nitrogen, mg/m³		
	Aug 1933	Feb 1934	Oct 1934	Aug 1933	Feb 1934	Oct 1934	Aug 1933	Feb 1934	Oct 1934
0	1·1	0·8	0	194	392	253	7	0	0
10	1·3	0·7	0	197	351	266	7	0	0
25	1·5	1·3	0	193	262	267	4	0	0
50	2·2	4·0	5	214	346	391	13	0	0
100	7	11·0	12	265	469	612	19	70	85

IV. FLORA AND FAUNA

General characteristics

The Caspian Sea fauna (Fig. 270), qualitatively very poor, is very varied in its origin; its basic forms are descended from the Tertiary marine fauna, which underwent considerable evolution as a result of changes in the orography and in the whole hydrological conditions of the Sea. The remains of the fauna of Tertiary seas of the Sarmatian and Pontic periods are represented by such characteristic groups of the Caspian Sea as: herrings, bullheads, Benthophilus; the molluscs by various forms of Cardae (except *Cardium edule*); and by Dreissena, Bryozoa Victorella, the polychaetes Hypania, *Hypaniola Parhypania* and perhaps *Manayunkia caspica*; some of the Turbellaria; all the Decapoda except prawns and Heteropanope; Cumacea; most of the mysids; Gammaridae; Porifera; the medusa Moerisia and the hydroid Cordylophora. Later immigrants from the northern (Arctic community) and western (Mediterranean community) seas and from fresh waters are mixed in considerable numbers with this basic part of the fauna.

This fourfold genesis of the Caspian Sea fauna is a striking peculiarity of its biology. During the periods of its history when its salinity was greatly reduced it became a body of almost fresh water (for example the Glacial transgression); at least into some of its component parts, a freshwater fauna made its way there and partly adapted itself to the subsequent rises in salinity. Such were the cyprinids and perch, the most important among fish, all or almost all the gastropods, tubificid worms, some of the Turbellaria, and a considerable number of animal and plant planktons. Two main components of the modern Caspian population, the original marine and fresh-water faunas, having lived together through the phases of its subsequent history had become, in a remarkable manner, interlocked with each other, acquiring similar biological characteristics and similar distribution throughout the Sea. Both groups include some typical 'marine' forms living exclusively in the most saline parts of the Sea, some 'brackish-water' ones, some tolerant to various degrees of salinity, and other forms which

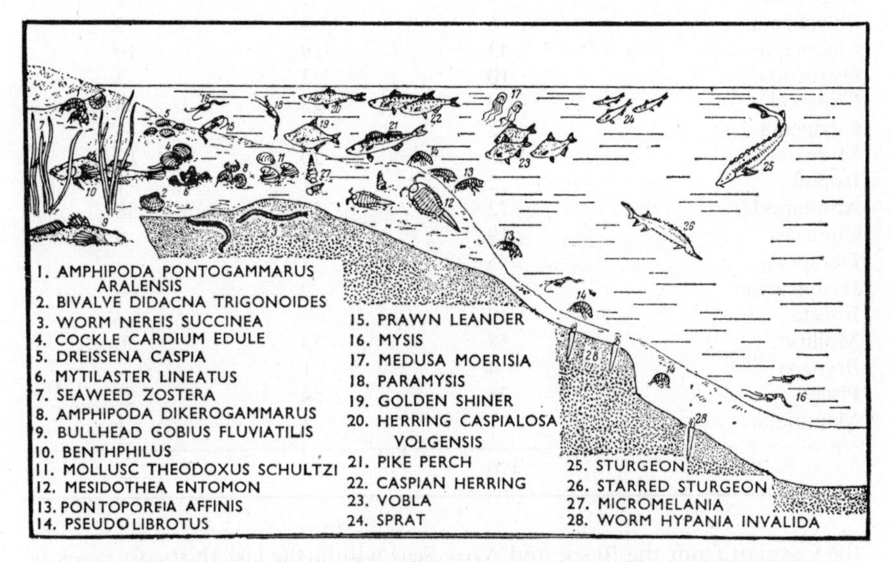

FIG. 270. General distribution of Caspian Sea fauna (Zenkevitch, 1951).

have migrated into fresh water. Recent immigrants from the Black and Azov Seas and from the north, from the Arctic basin, have joined these basic groups of the Caspian fauna. However these genetically heterogeneous communities retain some of their biological and physiological peculiarities.

The present-day distribution of an organism throughout a sea often does not provide us with a clue as to its genesis. This should be considered mainly as the result of subsequent changes in salinity. The time and means of penetration of many groups and individual representatives of the Caspian fauna into the Sea, their migration into fresh waters and their subsequent life in the body of water remain obscure.

Derzhavin (1951) and Mordukhai-Boltovskoy (1960) revised the list of the present-day fauna of the Caspian Sea. It now comprises 727 animal species (374 genera)—538 free-living specimens (301 genera) (see *Table 235*), 170 parasite forms (67 genera) and 23 species (14 genera) which have penetrated into

Table 235. Composition of the fauna of the Caspian Sea, except the parasites

Animal group	Total number	Endemic forms of the Black, Azov and Caspian Seas	Endemic forms of the Caspian Sea
Poriferae	5	4	4
Coelenterata	3	2	1
Turbellaria	34	29	29
Nematodes	9	3	3
Rotatoria	40	2	2
Oligochaeta	4	2	2
Polychaeta	6	4	2
Cladocera	43	19	16
Ostracoda	10	3	3
Copepoda	50	23	23
Cirripedia	2	—	—
Mysidacea	20	20	13
Isopoda	2	1	1
Amphipoda	72	72	38
Cumacea	19	19	9
Decapoda	5	1	—
Hydracarina	2	2	—
Insecta	9	—	—
Mollusca	58	53	50
Bryozoa	4	1	—
Pisces	78	54	25
Mammalia	1	1	1
Total	476	315	222

the Caspian from the Black and Azov Seas within the last thirty–forty years, either with or without the help of man. The general composition of the Caspian Sea fauna cannot be considered as finally established, since many groups (among them Protozoa and Vermes) have not yet been sufficiently described.

The data given in *Table 235* shows that 'of the total number, 695, of the Caspian species (excluding the parasites) 315 species are limited in their distribution by the basins of the south Russian seas. The list of the Caspian endemic forms, in the strict sense of this term, contains 222 species. Besides this, the presence of 50 sub-species of Protozoa, polychaetes, crustaceans and fish, found only in the Caspian Sea, stresses the endemic character of the Caspian fauna.' (A. Derzhavin, 1951.)

It is also clear from this computation that the Caspian Sea is now the main habitat of the ancient autochthonous fauna of the south Russian seas. Derzhavin believes, however, that the considerable number of representatives of the Caspian fauna peculiar to the Black and Azov Seas should not be underestimated.

According to his evaluation of the Caspian Sea fauna, Poriferae, Coelenterata, Turbellaria, annelides, higher crustaceans, hydrachnid molluscs and fish comprise 308 species and 138 genera. Of these the endemic forms of the Black, Azov, Caspian and Aral Seas comprise 263 species (89 per cent) and 72 genera (52·2 per cent), among them 32 genera (23·2 per cent) and 174 species (58·9 per cent) of Caspian forms endemic in the strict sense. On the other hand, among the 170 species of parasites 21 species are endemic forms of the Caspian Sea. No endemic genera have been recorded among the parasites. Among the separate groups of the autochthonous Caspian fauna, Poriferae and Coelenterata are the first to attract attention. Four species of Poriferae inhabit the Caspian Sea—two species of the genus Metschnikovia (*M. intermedia* and *M. tuberculata*) together with *Protoschmidtia flava* and *Amorphina caspia*.

All the four species belong to the Renieridae family of the Cornacuspongia order. The four species of Poriferae are Caspian endemics, while the species of the genus Metschnikovia are related to the Baikal Baicalospongia and Ochrid Ochridospongia.

One of the three autochthonous Caspian Coelenterata, *Polypodium hydriforme*, occupying an ambiguous place among the orders of the sub-class Hydroidea, is a parasite on the ova of Acipenseridae inhabiting the basins of the Caspian, Black and Aral Seas. The Medusa *Caspionema* (*Moerisia*) *pallasi*, a strictly endemic form of the Caspian Sea, does not possess the hydroid stage; it belongs to the Clavidae family (Leptolida order). The hydroid *Cordylophora caspia* belongs to the same order; in contrast to the Caspionema it lacks the medusa stage. Cordylophora with some other forms probably penetrated into the Caspian Sea when this was joined to the Baltic Sea by canals in the last century; it was widely propagated in the Caspian and has migrated from it, by means of shipping, into different parts of the world; it has now become a cosmopolitan form (L. A. Zenkevitch, 1940). Cordylophora is also known in the Kurun Lake (lower Egypt).

M. Tikhy has recorded as early as 1916 the existence of a plankton hydroid in the Caspian Sea; he did not give a detailed description of it and no one else has recorded it since. The three closely related forms of polychaetes inhabiting the Caspian Sea—*Parhypania brevispinis*, *Hypania invalida* and *Hypaniola kowalewskii*—of the Ampharetidae family, are typical Caspian autochthonous forms. The first is found only in the Caspian Sea, and the two others are known in the inlets and rivers of the basins of the Black and Azov Seas.

Manayunkia caspica (Sabellidae family), a Caspian endemic form, is closely related to the Manayunkia of North America, Europe and Asia and to those of Lake Baikal. Manayunkia possibly penetrated into the Caspian Sea with the Arctic community forms in the post-glacial age; however it does not have a cold-water aspect as other relict immigrants have, and its occurrence (M. Bacesko, 1948) in the Danube is an indication of its earlier (pre-Khvalyn) genesis and of its penetration into the Pontic basin from the northeast by fresh-water routes.

Among the Caspian autochthonous forms one of the most prominent places is occupied, side by side with molluscs and fish, by crustaceans, mainly Peracarida; 136 species of this last inhabit the Caspian Sea. All Caspian mysids belong to the sub-family Mysini, the family Mysidae and the genera Hemimysis (1 species), Mysis (4 species), Schistomysis (1 species), Paramysis (10 species), Caspiomysis (1 species), Katamysis (1 species), Diamysis (1 species), and Limnomysis (1 species). Only Caspiomysis is strictly endemic to the Caspian Sea. Katamysis and Limnomysis are endemic forms of the Pontic–Caspian region. The others have a wider distribution in the oceans. The Mysis genus stands apart. Most mysids are representatives of plankton-benthos, but *Paramysis loxolepis* and the species of the genus Mysis (except *M. caspia*) belong to plankton; they make daily vertical migrations of some hundreds of metres (up to 500 m). Representatives of the genus Mysis, evolved from the Arctic immigrant *Mysis oculata* var. *relicta*, have retained their Arctic aspect, living in depths of more than 50 m. A number of Caspian mysids penetrate fresh waters and become adapted to them.

Among the Cumacea order representatives of 8 genera (Pseudocumatidae family, Pseudocuma, Stenocuma, Pterocuma, Volgocuma, Caspiocuma, Schizorhynchus, Chasarocuma) and 19 species live in the Caspian Sea. Derzhavin has pointed out that they have probably all evolved from one ancestral form of the genus Pseudocuma, and that they all converge (morphologically and biologically) on the Cumacea community of the ocean fauna. All the 19 species of Cumacea inhabit only the Pontic–Caspian region, and 10 species are strictly endemic to the Caspian. Some Caspian Cumacea have also penetrated into fresh waters in the basins of the Caspian Sea (10 species), of the Azov Sea (9 species), and of the Black Sea (9 species plus two doubtful ones). Cumacea live at the bottom; however they are involved in the diurnal rhythm of vertical migrations.

The large order Isopoda is represented in the Caspian Sea by 3 species only of varied genesis. *Iaera sarsi* is an endemic form of the Pontic–Caspian region. *Mesidothea entomon* f. *caspia* is an immigrant from the Arctic. The third form, *Nannoniseus caspius*, described by O. Grimm in 1875 from one specimen, has not been recorded by any one else in the Caspian Sea. Iaera inhabits the shallow littoral zone, while Mesidotea, in contrast, retaining its Arctic aspect, does not rise into the upper warmed layers.

Among the higher crustaceans the order Amphipoda is the richest in species and the most characteristic of the Caspian fauna. All Caspian amphipods (72 species) belong to the only sub-order—Gammarideae—and mostly to the Gammaridae (60 species) and Corophiidae (8 species) families. Of the other four species two Pseudalibrotus species and one of Pontoporeia are immigrants from the far north, while *Caspicola knipovitschi*, an original form described by Derzhavin, forms a separate family—the Caspicolidae. Except for these forms the Caspian Amphipoda belong to two families. The following genera are particularly rich in species: Gmelina (5 species), Amathillina (5 species), Niphargoides (11 species), Pontogammarus (10 species), Stenogammarus (6 species), Dikerogammarus (4 species), Chaetogammarus (4 species), and Corophium (8 species). The other genera—Niphargus, Boeckia, Gmelinopsis, Gammaracanthus (Arctic immigrant), Cardiophilus,

Derzhavinella, Zernovia, Behningiella and Sowinskya—have only one species each, while Gammarus, Pandorites and Iphigenella have two each. The endemic nature of the two main families of Caspian amphipoda is shown in *Table 236*.

Table 236. Endemic nature of Amphipoda of the Caspian fauna (*Gammaridae and Corophiidae families*) (*A. Derzhavin*)

Family	Total number		Pontic–Caspian endemics				Caspian			
	Genera	Species	Genera		Species		Genera		Species	
			No.	%	No.	%	No.	%	No.	%
Gammaridae	19	60	16	84·2	60	100	6	31·6	30	50
Corophiidae	1	8	0	0	8	100	0	0	4	50

This clear picture of specific endemism is broken only by *Stennogammarus ischnus* and *Corophium curvispinum*, which have recently penetrated from the Baltic Sea through some water systems. Generic endemism is broken (if we except the Arctic immigrants Pseudalibrotus, Pontoporeia and Gammaracanthus) by the genera of the Corophiidae family, widely distributed outside the limits of the Pontic–Caspian region. Thirty-five species of Caspian Amphipoda have adapted themselves to life in river systems. Of the order Decapoda two species of the Astacidae family (river crayfish) are known in the Caspian (*Astacus leptodactylus* and *A. pachypus*) and two species of the Palaemonidae family, brought there by man, while the shrimps *Leander rectirostris* and *L. squilla* are found.

The group of molluscs represented by the classes Gastropoda (according to Lindholm, 37 species) and Lamellibranchiata (21 species) are no less characteristic and significant in the fauna of the Caspian Sea.

Of the Neritidae family (Prosobranchia, Diotocardia) two species are known for the Caspian Sea—*Theodoxus pallasi* and *Th. schultzii*. The latter is strictly endemic to the Caspian Sea, whereas the first has also been recorded in the inlets of the northwestern part of the Black Sea, in Lake Top'yaton, and in the Sea of Azov. The three families of the Monotocardia order—Valvatidae (1 species), Hydrobiidae (3 species) and Micromelaniidae (19 species)—are much richer in species.*

Of the Hydrobiidae family Derzhavin points out 3 species—*Lithoglyphus exiguus*, *Hydrobia pusilla* and *H. grimmi*—and representatives of the Micromelaniidae family—19 species, belonging to 4 genera—Micromelania (6 species) Nematurella (3 species), Caspia (7 species), and Clessiniola (3 species). All these 19 species are Pontic–Caspian endemic forms, only *Gaspia gmelini* and *Clessiniola variabilis* live outside the Caspian in the inlets of the Black and Azov Seas. Thus the strictly Caspian endemic nature of this group is well emphasized.

* V. Lindholm did not publish a complete description of the gastropod molluscs of the Caspian Sea, and, using the description of Derzhavin, 23 species are given here.

The taxonomic composition of the Caspian Lamellibranchiata has been more thoroughly studied than that of the Gastropoda. Apart from *Mytilaster lineatus*, a recent immigrant from the Black Sea, and *Syndesmya ovata*, transferred from the Sea of Azov, all the Caspian bivalves are endemic forms of the Pontic–Caspian basin. They are represented by three tribes of the Heterodonta suborder, one species of the Corbiculidae family (*C. fluminalis*), five species of the genus Dreissena (*D. polymorpha, D. rostriformis, D. caspica, D. grimmi, D. andrussovi*), one species of Cardium (*C. edule*), two species of Monodacna (*M. caspia* and *M. edentula*) and seven species of the genus Adacna (*A. trigonoides, A. crassa, A. pyramidata, A. longipes, A. barbot-de marnyi, A. baeri* and *A. latens*). Except for *Cardium edule*, which had penetrated into the Caspian Sea through Manych in the Khvalyn period, and *Dreissena polymorpha* and *Corbicula fluminalis* (an ancient fresh-water immigrant), which have migrated far beyond the limits of the Caspian Sea, the endemic nature of the bivalves is most pronounced; in Derzhavin's opinion they are all autochthonous forms of the Pliocene Seas. Sixteen species are endemic forms of the Caspian, while Didacna is an endemic genus of it (*Table 237*) (A. Derzhavin, 1951).

Table 237

Total amount of Caspian molluscs			Number of endemic forms among them			
			Pontic–Aralo–Caspian		Caspian	
	Genera	Species	Genera	Species	Genera	Species
Number	16	57	0	53	4	50
Percentage	100	100	62·5	93·0	25·0	87·7

The heterogeneous nature of the Caspian fauna is well illustrated in the Turbellaria group. V. Beklemishev established (1915) the presence of 29 species of Turbellaria in the Caspian Sea (Triclada—6 species, Acoela—11, Alloeocoela—5, Rhabdocoela—7). Twenty-seven species of Turbellaria are endemics; in fact there are no less than two endemic genera. In Beklemishev's opinion 18 species of Turbellaria are undoubtedly marine forms (Acoela, part of Rhabdocoela and the majority of Alloeocoela); they originated in the Tertiary period when the Caspian basin was still connected with the ocean. The 7 species of Rhabdocoela are ancient (Tertiary) immigrants from fresh water into the Caspian Sea. The other species have only recently come from fresh waters.

The so-called negative features are more sharply pronounced in the population of the Caspian Sea than in that of the open sea; many typically marine groups are either completely absent from the Caspian or represented by very few species. Strictly speaking only fish, crustaceans and, to a smaller extent, the molluscs are varied here. The number of species of these three groups constitutes about 60 per cent of all the species of the free-living animals of the Caspian.

A very large number of endemic forms (about 60 per cent) are also characteristic of the Caspian Sea.

The very vigorous development of new species brought in from the Azov and Black Sea helps one to understand the biological properties and productivity of the Caspian population. On the other hand, at different periods of the Tertiary and Quaternary epochs some individual representatives of the Caspian autochthonous fauna left the Caspian basin through the river systems, rapidly settled in a vast territory, and in some cases acquired a cosmopolitan nature. Caspian fauna, especially its fish and crustaceans, readily migrate into the fluviatile systems, penetrating far upstream.

Brackish-water character of Caspian autochthonous fauna

The small salinity range tolerated by the brackish-water relict Caspian fauna is its remarkable peculiarity. In contrast to the Sea of Azov immigrants this fauna is incapable—as has been shown experimentally (A. Karpevitch, G. Belyaev and Ya. Birstein, 1946; N. Romanova, 1956)—of enduring high salinity (Fig. 271). Karpevitch has proved experimentally from forms of the two faunas that in contrast to the immigrants from the west (euryhaline marine forms) the brackish-water forms have a considerable stenohalinity. The distribution of these forms throughout the Caspian Sea is determined by these characteristics. On the other hand, it has been shown by the experiments of G. Belyaev and Ya. Birstein (1946) that a salinity of about 15‰ is lethal for the Caspian brackish-water mysids, while for some species of Gammaridae it becomes lethal at about 20 to 25‰. The most saline areas of the Caspian Sea (20 to 25‰) are densely populated by euryhaline marine immigrants from the west—*Mugil auratus* and *M. saliens*, *Syngnathus nigrolineatus caspius*, *Cardium edule*, *Pomatoschistus caucasicus*. Among the Caspian relicts only the herring *Caspiolosa caspia salina*, and the crustacean *Dikerogammarus aralensis* are associated with them. The first is found only within the areas of high salinity, the second throughout the whole Caspian Sea; it is particularly abundant in the Aral Sea.

N. Romanova (1956) has studied experimentally the survival, in various conditions of salinity, of the highest mass species of crustaceans of the Caspian Sea. She has divided them into three groups:

(*I*) Species distributed throughout the Caspian Sea which enter the rivers of the Caspian basin (saline limits 0 to 13‰).
(*II*) Species distributed throughout the Caspian Sea, which do not enter fresh water (salinity range 2 to 13‰).
(*III*) Species characteristic only of the Central and Southern Caspian (salinity range 8 to 20‰).

The low tolerance of most brackish-water Caspian crustaceans of a rise in salinity was confirmed by the experiments of Romanova and Karpevitch. The majority of these crustaceans die at a salinity between 14 and 20‰.

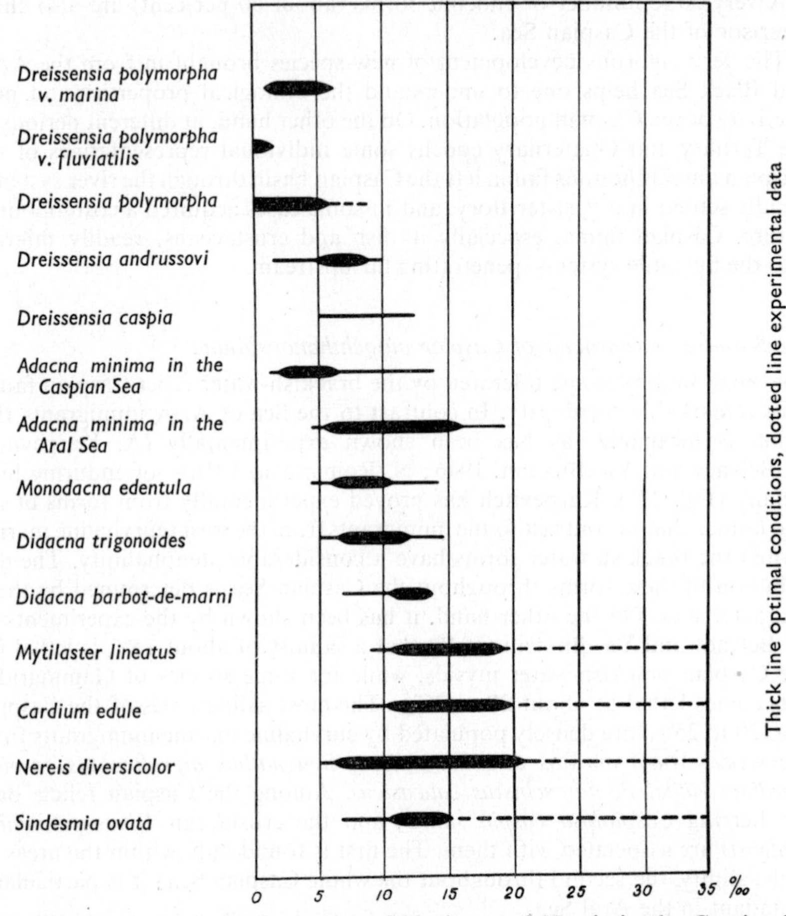

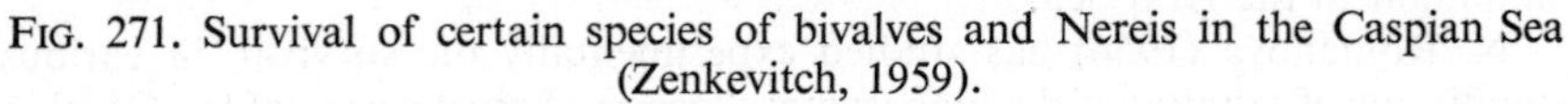

FIG. 271. Survival of certain species of bivalves and Nereis in the Caspian Sea (Zenkevitch, 1959).

Negative features of the Caspian fauna

The negative features of the Caspian fauna, as compared to the fauna of the open seas, consist of the complete depletion of such groups as Radiolaria, calcarean and horny Poriferae, Siphonophora, true medusae, Anthozoa, Ctenophorae, Polyclada, nemertinians, echiurids, sipunculids, priapulids, brachiopods, chaetognaths, pantopods, crabs, chitons, scaphopods, cephalopods, echinoderms, Enteropneusta, tunicates, Acrania, skates, sharks and cetaceans. Moreover, many typical marine groups are very poorly represented here, such as, for example, Foraminifera, Poriferae, Hydrozoa, Polychaeta, Bryozoa, Decapoda, Gastropoda and most of the order of bivalves.

There is a marked preponderance of crustaceans and fish in the fauna of the Caspian Sea, while the majority of the marine groups are absent.

The free-living fauna of the Barents Sea comprises approximately 2,000 species, the Mediterranean 6,000, and the Caspian only 538; the last is about 27 per cent of that of the Barents Sea and 9 per cent of that of the Mediterranean. Moreover this low proportion differs greatly for various groups (*Table 238*).

Table 238

Groups	Barents Sea		Mediterranean Sea		Caspian Sea			
	No. of species	% of total fauna	No. of species	% of total fauna	No. of species	% of Barents Sea fauna	% of Mediterranean fauna	% of Caspian Sea fauna
Echinodermata	62	3·1	101	1·7	0	0	0	0
Bryozoa	272	14·0	138	2·3	4	1·6	3	0·7
Polychaeta	200	10·0	433	7·2	6	3·0	1·4	1·3
Bivalvia	64	3·2	366	6·1	23	36·0	6·4	4·3
Gastropoda	150	7·5	937	15·6	32	21·0	3·4	6·0
Higher crustacea	152	7·6	620	10·3	118	78·0	19·0	22·0
Fish	121	6·0	529	8·7	78	64·0	15·0	12·6
Fish and higher crustaceans	273	13·6	1,196	19·0	196	72·0	14·0	36·4

Evidently the migration into brackish waters is much easier for the higher crustaceans and fish than for other animals, since they can endure the subsequent changes of salinity of the water body much more readily. This is due to their integuments which protect their body from osmotic processes.

Formation of species

The process of vigorous species formation undergone by its many forms is a characteristic peculiarity of the Caspian Sea fauna; groups of numerous species were evolved here and their transitions are often indistinct. Such are herrings, bullheads, Benthophilus, Amphipoda, mysids, Cumacea, Dreissena, and others.

K. Kiselevitch (1923) considers that all the numerous forms of Caspian herrings have evolved from the one species *Caspialosa caspia*. G. Sars (1927) came to the conclusion, as a result of his study of Caspian crustaceans, that all the members of the Cumacea species have evolved from the same ancestral form, an immigrant from the Mediterranean. This feature is even more pronounced for the remarkable faunas of Lakes Baikal and Tanganaika.

A definite part of the autochthonous fauna of the Caspian Sea is a relict of the Tertiary seas which had begun to evolve by the end of the middle Miocene under the effect of the fall in salinity.

Sovinsky points out the huge preponderance (89·39 per cent) of forms peculiar to the Pontic–Caspian–Aral area in the Caspian Sea fauna, among which almost three-quarters of the forms are found in the Caspian Sea only.

Cosmopolitan species

Foraminifera can be cited as an example of a widely cosmopolitan group. Shokhina, who studed Foraminifera in the Mertviy Kultuk and Kaidak Inlets, has distinguished six deep-water forms for that area belonging to the genera Elphidium, Rotalia and Discorbis. Among them the most frequently met are *Rotalia beccarii*, *Elphidium polyanum* and *Discorbis vilardeboana*. All three forms are widely distributed in the Atlantic and Pacific oceans and the seas connected with them. *Nonion depressulum* and *Elphidium granulosum*, pointed out by Behning, and *Ammobaculites* pseudospirale, mentioned by Voloshinova, can be added to these six forms. Moreover, Shokhina has discovered four species of plankton Foraminifera: *Globigerina bulloides*, *Gl. triloba*, *Globorotalia crassa* and *Globigerinella aeguilateralis*. Hence there are indications that 13 forms of Foraminifera have been recorded in the Caspian Sea. The most numerous form, Rotalia, gives on sandy beds up to 2,500 specimens and on silt up to 15,000 (in one case 60,000 specimens) per 5 g of soil. The next most common form, *Elphidium polyanum*, reaches 5,000 specimens per 5 g of soil.

History of the fauna

Humboldt formulated a theory in the forties of the last century, according to which the Aral–Caspian basin was widely connected with the Arctic Ocean through the western Siberian lowlands by the end of the Miocene epoch. In Suess's opinion a new northern fauna had penetrated into the Sarmatian Sea through this so-called Humboldt Strait. However Suess's theory of the northern genesis of the Sarmatian fauna had no further development and his assumption of the existence of a direct link between the Caspian Sea and the Arctic Ocean to both east and west of the Ural Mountains, at all events since the Eocene period, has been refuted. Th. Fuchs (1887) denied the theory of the northern genesis of the Sarmatian fauna. In his opinion it was an original fauna, evolved in this body of water as a result of its isolation and of the rise in salinity.

Since it was difficult to derive the Sarmatian fauna from the fauna of the Middle Miocene basin Andrussov and Mushketov deduced that it was evolved from the remains of the Oligocene fauna of the Turanian basin, which had become adapted to less saline water and had migrated from the east into the Sarmatian basin, then in a state of formation. Andrussov assumes that the Sarmatian Sea was populated by (*1*) forms which arrived from the east, (*2*) forms which had survived since the time of the Middle Miocene Sea, and (*3*) forms evolved during the Sarmatian Era.

The origin of the Akchagyl fauna, which has much in common with the Sarmatian, is just as difficult to trace. The Pontic Sea, which followed the abundantly saline Sarmatian Sea, had lost much of its salinity and was populated by fresh- and brackish-water faunas. This in turn was replaced by a saline Akchagyl Sea, and a rich fauna, similar to the Sarmatian one, appeared in it again. N. Andrussov (1911), and after him I. Gubkin (1931) and A. Archangelsky (1932), think that some shelter existed, where the Sarmatian fauna survived the Pontic period, and that it returned to the Caspian Sea in the Akchagyl period. In the opinion of V. Kolesnikov (1941) the cyclic changes of Caspian mollusc faunas in the Tertiary epoch noted by Andrussov is explained not by the survival of one sheltered fauna, but by consecutive migrations of Mediterranean species into the Caspian basin. Moreover, during some definite eras fresh-water forms migrated into the Caspian Sea. Thus, for example, Kolesnikov thinks that the fauna of the Apsheron period, which has been studed in more detail, has three origins: (*1*) the greatly altered remains of the former Akchagyl population; (*2*) fresh-water immigrants, including among others *Dreissensia distincta*, *Dr. polymorpha*, *Dr. caspia* and Nematurella, and (*3*) the considerably changed immigrants from the Black Sea area. Among the 75 Apsheron molluscs 12 are very similar to, and four are identical with, the present Caspian forms.

Fresh-water immigrants

The more or less ancient fresh-water immigrants constitute a considerable part of the fauna of the Caspian Sea. Such colonization of the Caspian Sea occurred several times during its history in its periods of greatest freshening. Many of the origins of the fresh-water immigrants of the Caspian Sea are lost in the distant past. It has been noted, for example (B. Dybovsky, 1933, V. Bogachev, 1932), that the very original Caspian gastropods should be considered as immigrants from the fresh waters of the Pliocene; this would explain their close relationship with the Baikal molluscs. *Manayunkia caspia* among the polychaetes, Acipenseridae and some other fish, and possibly seal, are probably ancient immigrants from the fresh waters of the Pliocene. For some forms, the cyprinids for example, a fresh-water genesis seems more evident, and many of them have apparently migrated during the late post-glacial transgression, when the Caspian Sea received its last large party of fresh-water immigrants.

It seems certain that the Caspian Sea, and especially the Aral, were energetically colonized by fresh-water forms, and V. Beklemishev and V. Baskina-Zakolodkina (1933) have shown that this movement was not only furthered by the decrease of salinity of the water. They have proved for these Seas the importance of the nature of the salinity of the Caspian and Aral Seas, i.e. the ratio of the magnesium and calcium ion concentrations, which brings the saline waters of our southern sea-lakes close to fresh water. The ratio $Mg/Ca = 1{\cdot}34$ in the Aral Sea makes it most suitable for the existence of the fresh-water crustacean Daphnia. In Caspian waters this ratio (2·5) is higher but still less than that in the Black Sea (3·12); the higher survival of Daphnia in the Caspian rather than in the Black Sea waters might be explained in this way.

Mediterranean elements

After the final separation of the Caspian and Black Seas and the linking of the latter with the Mediterranean and its colonization by Mediterranean fauna, some of its species penetrated into the Caspian, and even the Aral, Sea. Three periods can be distinguished in the history of the Neogene colonization of the Caspian Sea by Mediterranean organisms. The first and most ancient of these periods apparently belongs to Khvalyn times; it is linked with the penetration of some six species through the Kuma–Manych depression (*Zostera nana*, *Cardium edule*, *Fabricia sabella*, *Atherina mochon pontica caspia*, *Syngnathus nigrolineatus caspius*, *Pomatoschistus caucasicus*).

The second period, which started in the twenties of this century, is linked with the accidental or purposeful bringing in of species by man; nine Mediterranean species have penetrated into the Caspian Sea during this period (*Rhizosolenia calcar-avis*, *Mytilaster lineatus*, *Syndesmya ovata*, *Nereis diversicolor*, *Leander squilla*, *L. rectirostris*, *Mugil auratus*, *M. saliens*, *Pleuronectes flesus*); the fish *Gambusia affinis* was also imported about this time.

The third period was the time of the establishment of a direct water route between the Caspian and Azov Seas by the Volga–Don canal and the auto-immigration into the Caspian Sea of nine new Mediterranean forms (*Blackfordia virginica*, *Membranipora* (*Electra*) *crustulenta*, *Balanus improvisus*, *B. eburneus* and *Rhithropanopues harrisii* spp. *tridentata*, the polychaete *Mercierella enigmatica*, *Monodacna colorata*, *Corbulomya maeotica* and *Podon polyphemoides*). This third period, which began a few years ago, will probably turn later on into a long, complex and extremely curious process of the reconstruction of the Caspian Sea fauna, as a result of the free influx of the most euryhaline members of the Mediterranean flora and fauna.

Apart from the above-mentioned 23 animal species, ten new sea-weed species have been discovered in the Caspian Sea: first, *Ceramium diaphanum* and *C. tenuissimum* (M. Kireeva and T. Shchapova, 1957); secondly, *Ectocarpus confervoides* f. *fluviatilis* and *Polysiphonia variegata* (G. Zevina, 1958). Apparently none of these four forms was present in the Caspian in the 'thirties (Kireeva and Shchapova). A number of sea-weed forms, hitherto unknown in the Caspian Sea (*Acrochaeta parasitica*, *Ectochaete leptochete*, *Enteromorpha tubulosa*, *E. salina*, *Entoneme salina*, *Acrochaetium daviesii*) were found by Zevina in the growths fouling hydrotechnical constructions.

Thus the 'Mediterranean' group in the Caspian Sea comprises only 28 species, including one diatom, ten bottom-living algae, one marine flowering plant, one medusa, one bryozoan, two barnacles, two shrimps, one crab, two polychaetes, three molluscs, one cladocer and three species of fish.

The process of the colonization of the Caspian Sea by new members of flora and fauna and an exceptional mass development of some of them in their new habitat (Mytilaster, Mugil, Rhizosolenia, Leander, Nereis, Syndesmya and Balanus) is linked with a number of curious ecological (synecological) phenomena. First of all, with some of them an extremely intensive development, similar to a kind of 'biological explosion', has been observed. Thus *Rhizosolenia calcar-avis*, which penetrated into the Caspian Sea early in the 'thirties, probably in small numbers, had by 1934 multiplied into several million tons, forming two-thirds of the whole mass of plankton. The first wave of exceptional mass development was followed by a drop in its numbers and the biocoenosis, into which the new form entered and adapted itself, limited its development. Immigrants from distant seas are of particular interest among the new forms of the Caspian fauna. There are two of these in the composition of the Caspian Sea fauna: the medusa *Blackfordia virginica* (B. Logvinenko, 1959) and the crab *Rhithropanopeus harrisii* sp. *tridentata*

(T. Nebolsina, 1959). The original home of both forms is on the northeastern shores of North America. The medusa has apparently come to the Sea of Azov directly, while the crab arrived in the Black Sea via Dutch coastal waters (Zuyder Zee). This latter brackish-water form had originally immigrated from North America and was described in the Zuyder Zee as a new form, *Heteropanope tridentata. Rh. harrisii* found favourable conditions for its existence in the Sea of Azov and the Don estuary; in its further travel it proceeded by canal into the Caspian Sea where it found a fourth home.

A. Karpevitch (1958) and E. Bokova (1958) have raised the problem of the utilization of Caspian crustaceans as an acclimatization stock for the Aral and Baltic Seas and for Lake Balkhash. The ecology and physiology of a number of mass forms of Caspian crustaceans were carefully studied and the following were recommended for the Aral Sea and Lake Balkhash: *Mesomysis* (*Paramysis*) *kowalewskyi*, *M. baeri* and *M. intermedia* (Karpevitch), and for the Aral and Baltic Seas *Schizorhynchus bilamellatus*, *Pterocuma pectinata* of the Cumacea, and *Corophium nobile* and *C. curvispinum* of the Amphipoda (Bokova). The three mysids were transported in the adult stage into the Aral Sea in the summer of 1958. The results of this attempt at acclimatization are so far unknown.

Bogachev was the first to record in 1928 the mollusc *Mytilaster lineatus* in the Caspian Sea; he thinks that it was brought from the Black Sea during the civil war from Batum on small craft, the undersides of which are often covered with clumps of Mytilaster. Closing its valves tightly the mollusc can endure life in the air for a long time.

The history of the colonization of the Caspian Sea by this mollusc Mytilaster and of the annual increase of its biomass was studied by V. Brotzky and M. Netzengevitch (1940). As early as 1932, according to their data, Mytilaster had already moved from the Baku area, following the main currents, along the coast of the Southern Caspian, colonized the eastern shore of the Central Caspian and penetrated into the southern part of the Northern Caspian. In the following years it moved still father north and along the western coast of the Central Caspian (Figs. 272 and 273); its biomass was growing rapidly. In 1938 Mytilaster biomass in the Caspian constituted five million tons, and if we include the growths on the cliffs this quantity will be at least doubled.

Besides actual growth of the Mytilaster biomass the increase of its relative significance in the total biomass has also been observed. Thus, for example, in 1933 on the eastern shore of the Southern Caspian Mytilaster composed only 18 per cent of the total benthos biomass; by 1935 it composed as much as 89 per cent, and in the following years more than 90 per cent. Moreover, it overwhelmed the growth of other benthos components, as may be seen by comparing data for the western coast of the Southern Caspian (*Table 239*).

It is difficult to decide at the moment whether Mytilaster acclimatization in the Caspian Sea is favourable or unfavourable for its fisheries. On the one hand Mytilaster no doubt suppresses the development of some valuable food forms, in particular Dreissensia; on the other, it now forms part of the diet of many commercial fish. In the Southern and to some extent also in the Central Caspian sturgeon feed on this mollusc to a considerable extent; starred sturgeon, marine pike-perch, the roach *Rutilus frisii kutum* and some other fish are beginning to eat it. Ducks, wintering on the shore of the Caspian, feed intensively on the Mytilaster of the neighbouring cliffs. They have begun to winter in places colonized by it where they had never appeared before owing

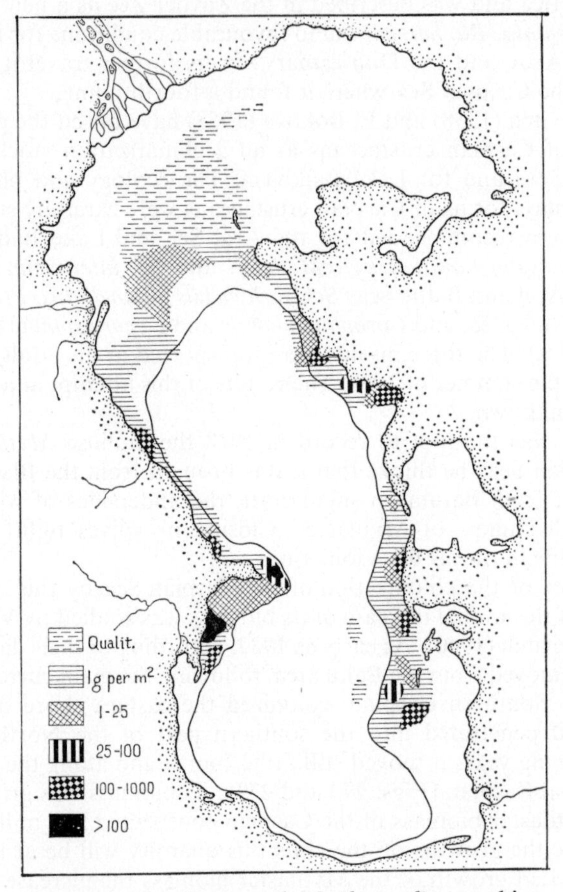

FIG. 272. Distribution of *Mytilaster lineatus* biomass in the Caspian Sea in 1938 (Brotzky and Netzengevitch).

to the absence of food. Black Sea grey mullet (*Mugil auratus* and *M. saliens*) were successfully acclimatized in the Caspian in 1930. The prawns *Leander rectirostris* and *L. squilla*, brought in with the grey mullet, have multiplied as prolifically as Mytilaster during the last thirty years.

According to Yu. Marti's data (1940, 1941) the fry chiefly of *M. auratus*, and in considerably smaller numbers of *M. cephalus* and *M. saliens*, were brought into the Caspian Sea. *M. cephalus* fry do not easily endure transport and must have perished. *M. auratus* is now widely distributed throughout th-

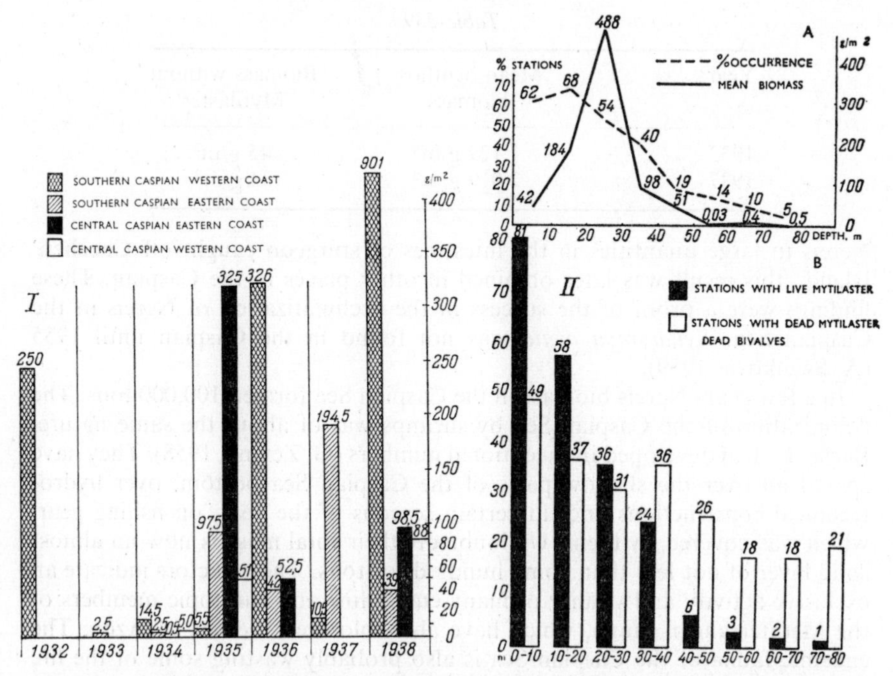

FIG. 273. *Mytilaster lineatus* biomass (g/m²). *I* In Central and Southern Caspian according to the years; *II* Distribution with depth; A Occurrence (% stations) and mean biomass (g/m²); B Ratio between the living and the dead Mytilaster (Brotzkaya and Netzengevitch).

Caspian Sea; it has penetrated into the northern part and in particular into Mertvyi Kultuk. *M. saliens* is adapted mainly to the western shore, where it lives with *M. auratus*. On the Turkmen coast *M. saliens* is more numerous than *M. auratus*.

Finally, in 1939 and 1940, Nereis and *Syndesmya ovata* were brought from the Sea of Azov into the Caspian Sea for acclimatization in order to increase food resources for commercial fish.* Sixty-one thousand specimens in all of Nereis and 18,000 specimens of *Syndesmya ovata* were put overboard in different places of the Caspian Sea (L. A. Zenkevitch, Ya. Birstein and A. Karpevitch, 1945).

In the autumn of 1944 N. Spassky (1945) recorded for the first time

* In the course of the transplantation of Nereis into the Caspian Sea there was a theory that the transplanted species was *Nereis succinea*.

Some time later this belief altered and doubts arose. The first one to express doubt was Dr. Joel W. Hedgpeth (1957), who in his 'Treatise' published some critical notes referring to my paper on the Caspian Sea. Presently material on the Nereis from the Caspian Sea was forwarded to the prominent specialist working with the Polychaeta, Olga Hartman. She classified this species as *Nereis diversicolor* (1960). The careful examination of Nereis coming from the Caspian Sea (V. Chlebovitsch, 1962) has confirmed the wide-range distribution of this species throughout various seas, whereas *Nereis succinea* was not discovered.

Table 239

Year	Mean benthos biomass	Biomass without Mytilaster
1932	1,129 g/m^2	45 g/m^2
1937	2,019 g/m^2	34 g/m^2

Nereis in large quantities in the intestines of sturgeon caught off Chechen' Island; this result was later obtained in other places in the Caspian. These findings were a proof of the success of the acclimatization of Nereis in the Caspian Sea. *Syndesmya ovata* was not found in the Caspian until 1955 (A. Saenkova, 1959).

In a few years Nereis biomass in the Caspian Sea formed 100,000 tons. The colonization of the Caspian Sea by shrimps was of about the same nature. Barnacles had developed in exceptional numbers (G. Zevina, 1958). They have spread all over the shallow parts of the Caspian Sea bottom, over hydrotechnical constructions and, in certain seasons of the year, on fishing gear, which was covered by them. Undoubtedly their total mass is now an almost solid layer of not less than some hundreds of tons. These factors indicate an exclusive activity and vitality of many euryhaline and eurytopic members of the Mediterranean fauna, which have also colonized the Sea of Azov. The endemic fauna of the Caspian Sea is also probably wasting some of the life resources of this Sea, and it may not be very powerful in its struggle with its most active Mediterranean rivals. Such detritus-eating forms as the red mullet and Nereis are certainly wasting some of the Sea resources. On the other hand, Mytilaster is in close competition with the local Dreissensia as a filter feeder and fouling organism; barnacles, which arrived later, are a closely related biological form, and possibly also take part in the rivalry. Hence two acclimatizations can be distinguished: that of intrusion, when the local forms (Nereis, Mugil) remain undisturbed, and when they are dislodged (Mytilaster, Rhizosolenia) (L. A. Zenkevitch, 1940). Shrimps, perhaps, have established some relationship with local mysids. While some forms are undoubtedly useful in the Caspian Sea (Nereis, Syndesmya, Mugil) the usefulness of others is not clear (Leander, Mytilaster), and others still play a negative role (Rhizosolenia, Balanus and possibly Mytilaster).

The unusual fate of many new immigrants into the Caspian Sea has emphasized the conceptions of potential habitat and of the acclimatization stock (L. A. Zenkevitch, 1940). For most of the land and marine forms their actual habitat is probably far from occupying all that part of the biosphere in which these forms could live, and into which, for some reason, they cannot penetrate. All these parts of the biosphere form potential habitats for them. On the other hand, many species could live in areas where they are absent if they were brought into them. Such forms belong to the acclimatization stock for these areas. The most successful acclimatization of the Baltic herring *Clupea harengus membras* in the Aral Sea can, from this point of view, serve as a good example for the Soviet Seas. It is quite probable that, for the Caspian and Aral Seas on the one hand, and for the Baltic Sea on the other, many members of their faunas could have been included in their reciprocal acclimatization stocks, and some of them have already been used by Nature itself (Dreissensia, Cordylophora and others in the Baltic Sea, and the Arctic immigrants in the Baltic and Caspian Seas). The utilization of acclimatization stocks, especially in the Caspian and Aral Seas, offers man the prospect of many possibilities for the reconstruction of the fauna of these Seas under conditions of forthcoming changes in their salinity.

Arctic immigrants

The fourth component of the Caspian fauna—the Arctic immigrants from the Arctic basin—is in all respects just as remarkable. At present the following are included in this group of forms: (1) *Limnocalanus grimaldi*, (2) *Mesidothea entomon* spp. *glacialis*, (3) *Pseudalibrotus caspius*, (4) *Ps. platyceras*, (5) *Pontoporeia affinis microphthalma*, (6) *Gammarcanthus loricatus caspius*, (7) *Mysis caspia*, (8) *M. microphthalma*, (9) *M. macrolepsis*, (10) *M. amblyops*, (11) *Stenodus leucichthys*, (12) *Salmo trutta*. The seal *Phoca caspia*, the polychaete *Manayunkia caspia* and, according to Dogel and Bykhovsky, some fish parasites of the genera Corynosoma, Crepidostomum, Bunocotyle and others should most probably be included in this group.

There is no doubt at present that these organisms penetrated into the Caspian Sea from the north after the latter became isolated from the Black Sea. These Arctic immigrants are very thinly represented in the Black Sea. They have deviated very slightly from their original forms. The ten main Arctic immigrants comprise two groups of animals—crustaceans and fish, i.e. the two groups best able to endure the freshening of the water. As we shall see below this indicates a fresh-water route for their migration from the north; this has already been suggested by O. Grimm (1888), K. Kessler (1877), R. Gredner and, in a more definite form, by V. Sovinsky (1902).

As early as 1916 Sv. Ekman pointed out the closer family relationship of the Caspian forms of the Arctic community with their relatives from the Arctic Ocean, compared with those of the Baltic Sea. This led Ekman to assume the probable former existence of a direct link between the Caspian Sea and the Arctic Ocean; therefore he does not accept the suggestion of the penetration of some forms, for example *Limnocalanus grimaldi*, by a fresh-water route. Ekman is inclined to relate the moment of the penetration of this crustacean into the Caspian Sea either to the end of the Tertiary period or to one of the inter-glacial eras. The former existence of a direct link between the Caspian Sea and the Arctic Ocean had been suggested before by G. O. Sarz.

However, in spite of these difficulties the view that the Arctic community penetrated into the Caspian Sea in the post-glacial era through river and lake systems, as has been suggested by Kessler, must be accepted. Further support for this opinion was given by the Swedish geologist A. Högbom (1917).

Attempts to trace the route of the Arctic community into the Caspian Sea through the Humboldt Strait have been abandoned. Högbom thinks that eastern Europe was flooded by water melting from receding ice, which, on the other hand, prevented its escape to the north, and therefore this water flowed southward, carrying with it Arctic organisms which populated the freshened or fresh-water inlets which extended far to the south of the Arctic Sea.

E. F. Gurjanova in 1933 and P. Pirozhnikov in 1937 introduced a new approach to this problem. Since the Caspian forms of crustaceans are closest of all to those of the Kara Sea and are often almost indistinguishable from them, Gurjanova suggested that this must be just where the Caspian immigrants came from. Pirozhnikov transferred the ideas expressed by Högbom on the elastic glacier effect to the Ob–Yenisei plain. The main argument against this point of view rests in our ignorance of the distribution of the original Caspian species in the Arctic basin in the post-glacial era. It is quite possible that at that time they also inhabited the European part of the Arctic basin and that later, when the temperature rose, they were pushed eastwards beyond Novaya Zemlya.

L. Berg's hypothesis (1928) is just as plausible; according to it the penetration of the northern organisms into the Caspian Sea from the Baltic took place through the extensive Rybnoe Lake, which in the post-glacial era overflowed the shores of the Baltic Sea and of Lakes Ladoga and Onega (and also Beloozero and Shesna which were connected with the Caspian Sea) and deposited the striated clays discovered by S. Jakovlev on the watershed between Lakes Onega and Beloozero. In Pirozhnikov's opinion this hypothesis is contradicted by the absence now of Stenodus and Pseudalibrotus in the Baltic Sea; however, as was noted by A. Derzhavin (1939), *Stenodus leucichthys* is found in the Baltic basin, and Pseudalibrotus could have lived in the Baltic Sea under the severe conditions of the Ice Age and could have disappeared with the rise in temperature.

Finally A. Podlesniy (1941) admits the possibility that *Stenodus leucichthys* and salmon penetrated into the basin of the Caspian Sea from the Northern Dvina through the Kol'sko-Vychegodsk confluence of the North and South Kel'tma rivers. He suggests that both forms of the salmon family had penetrated to the south more than once even in the post-glacial era.

The intrusion of Caspian fauna into fresh waters

Apart from the fact of the original marine groups being, in the history of the Caspian fauna, the forms best able to endure a considerable fall of salinity, they evolved a number of new forms which could move even farther; these, pressed on by phases of increase of salinity which set in after phases of freshening, penetrated into fresh waters. Here again we see mainly the same two groups—crustaceans and fish—best fitted, owing to their more or less impenetrable integuments, to retain the hypertony of their perivisceral fluid in relation to environment.

Table 240

Isopoda 1; Amphipoda 35; Cumacea 10; Mysidacea 6; Decapoda 1. Total 53

Ya. Birstein (1935) has pointed out that 44 species—53 according to A. Derzhavin (*Table 240*)—of Caspian crustaceans have immigrated into the river Volga.

No fewer than 18 species of Caspian fish of marine origin have penetrated into rivers. Among the other groups only a few forms of the Caspian autochthonous fauna succeeded in penetrating into fresh waters: *Cordylophora caspia* and possibly *Polypodium hydriforme* among the coelenterates; *Dreissena polymorpha* among the bivalves; some species of Theodoxus and Melanopsis among the gastropods; and among the polychaetes *Hypania invalida* and *Hypaniola kowalewskyi*. Hence crustaceans and fish occupy the first place; there are only seven species of molluscs, three of coelenterates and two of polychaetes.

Two theories have been suggested to explain the occurrence of Caspian crustaceans in the fresh water of the Pontic–Caspian basin. According to one hypothesis they are typical relicts, i.e. they continue to live where they were left by the receding sea (A. Derzhavin, 1912, 1924, 1939; A. Behning, 1924; S. Zernov, 1934 and others); or they have migrated up the rivers beyond the limits of Caspian transgressions. According to the second theory these forms are active immigrants from the Caspian Sea into the rivers (A. Skorikov, 1903; V. Zykov, 1903; L. Berg, 1908; V. Beklemishev, 1923; Ya. Birstein, 1935).

In principle there seems no difference between the two theories. The discrepancy centres mainly on the problem of the place where the euryhalinity of crustaceans living at different salinities was developed: whether it occurred in the Sea itself or in its inlets, which covered the lower course of the present-day Volga and other Caspian rivers. No objections were raised against the capability of Peracarida to move by some means or other against the current and settle down. The freshening of a considerable part of the Sea and the development of the euryhaline forms in the Sea itself seems to us more plausible. This freshening may have occurred during the melting of the ice when a considerable amount of melt-water flowed into the Caspian Sea. In his last work A. Derzhavin (1939) also relates the appearance of mysids in the lower reaches of the Volga to the inter-glacial era, marked by the Baku transgression of the Caspian Sea which was caused by the inflow of glacier waters.

The migration of the marine animals from the Sea into the rivers proceeded no doubt as a result of a subsequent increase of salinity in the Sea, i.e. in this case the phenomenon known as 'saline pulsations' took place. When the freshening of the Sea is followed by a rise in salinity, a definite part of its fauna is unable to adapt itself to this greater salinity and therefore gathers in places of lowest salinity—mouths and estuaries of rivers, for example. This process consists both of extinction and of active and passive transference, differing in degree for various biological forms. Into the complex, multiform phenomenon of the change-over of marine organisms to life in fresh water there are interwoven both moments of relict state and moments of passive and active immigration. Furthermore the same species may be a relict in one part of its habitat and an immigrant in another.

The marine Peracarida of the Volga (except for its very lowest reaches) are probably immigrants from the Caspian, or a freshened inlet of it where they had settled. Some species enlarged their habitat by passive immigration, attaching themselves to boats and living ensconced in the encrustations on the hulls. The absence from Caspian rivers of sedentary marine forms of molluscs (except for the passive immigrant *Dreissena polymorpha*) and of polychaetes underlines the importance of a capability for active migration in the colonization of rivers. According to A. Derzhavin (1939) these species do not live in the rivers because their plankton larvae are carried away by the current. However, the Caspian Ampharetidae (and the great majority of other members of this family) do not have plankton larvae; on the other hand the existence of such larvae in the case of *Dreissena polymorpha* has not prevented the latter from densely populating the whole of the Volga. Colonization by way of passive immigration has been extremely effective for Caspian animals. *Cordylophora caspia*, *Victorella parida*, *Dreissena polymorpha*, *Stenogammarus ischnus* and *Corophium curvispinum* have moved farthest northward, as far as the Baltic Sea. The four forms could easily have been propagated by river-craft. *Cordylophora caspia* outdistanced the others and at present it is becoming cosmopolitan. It has been found in North and South America, in Australia, New Zealand and China, so far everywhere in large sea ports, where it is brought by ships. However, the last rise in salinity of the Caspian basin after the glacial transgression was not the sole cause of the colonization of the river systems by a number of forms. Such 'waves' of immigration have taken place many times in the history of the south Russian bodies of water. Ya. Birstein and Vinogradov (1934) have noted, in the process of the immigration of river crayfish, three such 'waves' even before the isolation of the Caspian Sea from the Black Sea. The fresh-water medusa Craspedacusta is, no doubt, also a very ancient immigrant from some bodies of water, ancestors of the Sarmatian basin (L. A. Zenkevitch, 1940).

The correlation between the Caspian, Baikal and Okhrida faunas

The family ties between the Caspian fauna and those of some very remote bodies of water, in particular those of Lakes Baikal and Okhrida, are evident. The Caspian Porifera Metschnikovia is akin to the Baikal Lubomirskiidae and the Okhrida Ochridospongia. The gastropod molluscs Micromelaniinae belong, together with the Baikal Baicaliinae, to one Micromelaniidae family, members of which live elsewhere only in Lake Okhrida. The polychaete genus Manayunkia has some of its forms in Lake Baikal and in the Caspian Sea. Finally a whole number of the Caspian and Baikal sandhoppers are undoubtedly related; this was proved not only morphologically but also by the results of the precipitation reaction. In the opinion of A. Martynov (1924) and D. Taliev (1941) the links between the Caspian Sea and Lake Baikal are explained by the migration of some Caspian forms into fresh water in the Tertiary period; they then migrated extensively and reached Lake Baikal, where they have maintained themselves to this day. G. Vereshchagin (1941) thinks 'that the Caspian and Lake Baikal are two centres of the development of marine fauna which had intruded into inland waters; moreover the ancestors of these forms, which lived in the pre-Sarmatian Seas on the one hand, and in the east-Asiatic Seas on the other, were not identical, but were similar in different groups in a different way'. Indeed, Vereshchagin thinks that the marine organisms penetrated into the Caspian Sea much later than into Lake Baikal.

Zoogeographical situation of the Caspian Sea

V. Sovinsky (1902) examined the typical Caspian fauna, which is fairly markedly repeated in the Aral Sea and which abundantly populates, as we have seen, the fresher parts of the Black and Azov Seas, and he had full reason to distinguish a separate Pontic–Caspian–Aral marine zoogeographical province consisting of two parts: 'The Black–Azov Seas part, which has retained its Caspian fauna only in the freshened section; and the Caspian–Aral one, which kept its original fauna completely intact.' According to Sovinsky this province is part of the Celtic–Boreal region.

However, V. Uljanin (1871) justly pointed out the great preponderance of Mediterranean fauna in the Black and even the Azov Seas; thus the inclusion of these Seas in one single Pontic–Caspian–Aral province is artificial. Derzhavin considered this problem in 1925 and came to the correct conclusion of the existence of a Caspian zoogeographical brackish-water and fresh-water province, but not of a Pontic–Caspian–Aral marine one; he thus brought in an important correction of principle into the appellation given by Sovinsky.

Caspian fauna with its peculiar history of development and the complexity of its origin from different sources could hardly be included in the Atlantic–Boreal region. It seems more correct to consider it as a separate biogeographical unit, since we cannot relate it to any one marine zoogeographical region. Thus we can assume that the Caspian fauna belongs to a separate brackish-water region of partly marine, partly fresh-water origin.

The micro-organism population of the Caspian Sea

Micro-organisms probably play a much greater role in the Caspian Sea than in many other bodies of water. Huge chemical processes take place here with their assistance. Desulphurizing bacteria with a more or less strong reducing effect are found in every bottom sample, as has been shown by A. Maliyants (1933). They are as important here as in the Sea of Azov. Thick bacteria films and whole coverings are formed in the upper layers of mud floors, in the more or less enclosed shallows of the eastern shores and off the deltas of rivers with deposits of organic matter carried there by the rivers.

The chemical role of Caspian Sea micro-organisms has not yet been properly investigated; however, some valuable data for the understanding of the main bacterial processes, and, in particular, for their quantitative estimation are given in the works of Voroshilova and Dianova.

The decomposition of organic matter proceeds, especially in the accumulation zones, by means of putrifying bacteria. In the middle part of the Kaidak, for instance, their number rises to 1,000 to 2,500/cm^3, whereas in the purer waters of the Northern Caspian there are only 1 to 60 specimens/cm^3. They do not descend into the depths of the sea-bed. Ammonia and hydrogen sulphide are the products of their (life) activity. Further decomposition of the compounds (nitrification) proceeds under the action of the nitrate and nitrite bacteria. Ammonium compounds are oxidized to nitrites in water, and to nitrates in the soil, since the nitrate bacteria are absent from water. The denitrifying bacteria, reducing nitrites and nitrates, are opposite in their function to the previous nitrifying ones and are usually found in all the samples. The nitrogen fixer, the anaerobic *Clostridium pasterianum*, which sometimes goes down 80 cm into the sea-bed, performs the function of nitrogen accumulation.

Anaerobic bacteria of methane and hydrogen fermentation of cellular tissue, stimulating the process of carbohydrate decomposition, are of great significance in the decomposition of organic residues in the soil. Large amounts of methane and hydrogen are contained in the mud bottoms of the Caspian shallows. At times these gases bubble up to the surface. A kind of 'boiling' has at times been observed on the dump wrack lying off the Volga estuary, formed by the mass of gas bubbles rising from the bottom. This process is neutralized by micro-organisms which live in the uppermost layer of the bottom; they require a certain quantity of oxygen for their development and have an oxidizing effect on the compounds of sulphur (sulphur micro-organisms), methane (methane micro-organisms) and hydrogen (hydrogen micro-organisms) formed at greater depths. The column of water is protected from the entry of hydrogen, methane and hydrogen sulphide by the presence of these three groups of micro-organisms in the uppermost layer of the bottom soil. This film, as previously noted, can be destroyed by violent disturbances of the water caused by wind, and the harmful gases may then enter the water and poison it. The slight disturbances common in these shallows bring to the surface of the floor the oxygen required for the development of thioneine, methane and hydrogen micro-organisms, which, besides protecting the water from poisonous gases, give a brown colour to the upper layer of the floor. Deeper down, there usually lie thick layers of black, stinking mud.

This protective film in its turn serves, according to Voroshilova and Dianova, as a substratum for the development of huge amounts of unicellular algae, which synthesize organic matter. In Butkevitch's opinion life would have completely disappeared from Caspian waters if this bacterial film, with its reducing effect on hydrogen sulphide, methane and hydrogen, had been removed.

The presence of a huge number of micro-organisms in the Northern Caspian (100,000 to 400,000 and up to 17,000,000 specimens per one millilitre of water) had already been recorded by V. Butkevitch (1938). The number of micro-organisms is, as usual, related to the total amount of plant and animal life, or to the amount of decaying organic remains (*batkaks*). Kriss points out that the amount of micro-organisms in the waters of the middle parts of the Northern, Central and Southern Caspian varies generally between 100,000 to 300,000 specimens per 1 ml of water. Below 100 m the amount of bacteria drops to a few thousands (Figs. 274 and 275). According to V. Butkevitch's calculations the biomass of the Northern Caspian micro-organisms is 50 to 250 mg/m^3, and even 1 g/m^3 off the Volga. Kriss, however, says that these values are about twice too high. In the central and southern parts of the Caspian Sea, according to Kriss, if the average biomass of micro-organisms is taken as 36 mg/m^3 (or 7·2 mg/m^3 dry weight) within the layer of active photosynthesis (0 to 50 m), the coefficient of its daily increase is 0·35. The amount of decomposed organic matter will be 11·2 mg/m^3. In Kriss's opinion

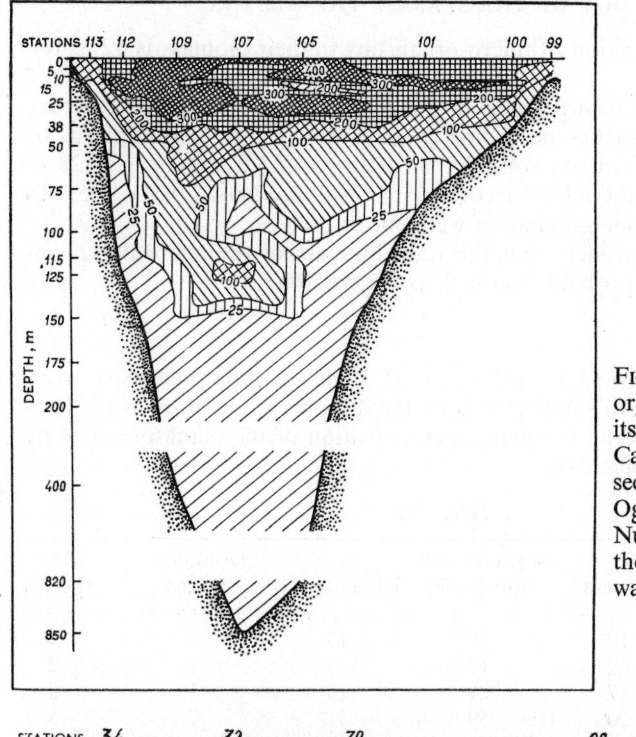

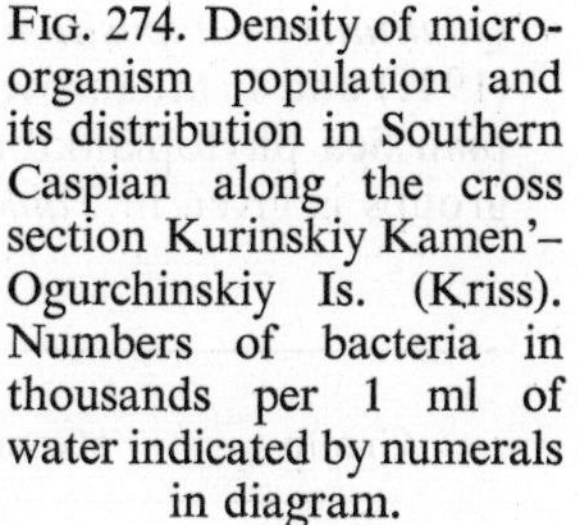

FIG. 274. Density of micro-organism population and its distribution in Southern Caspian along the cross section Kurinskiy Kamen'–Ogurchinskiy Is. (Kriss). Numbers of bacteria in thousands per 1 ml of water indicated by numerals in diagram.

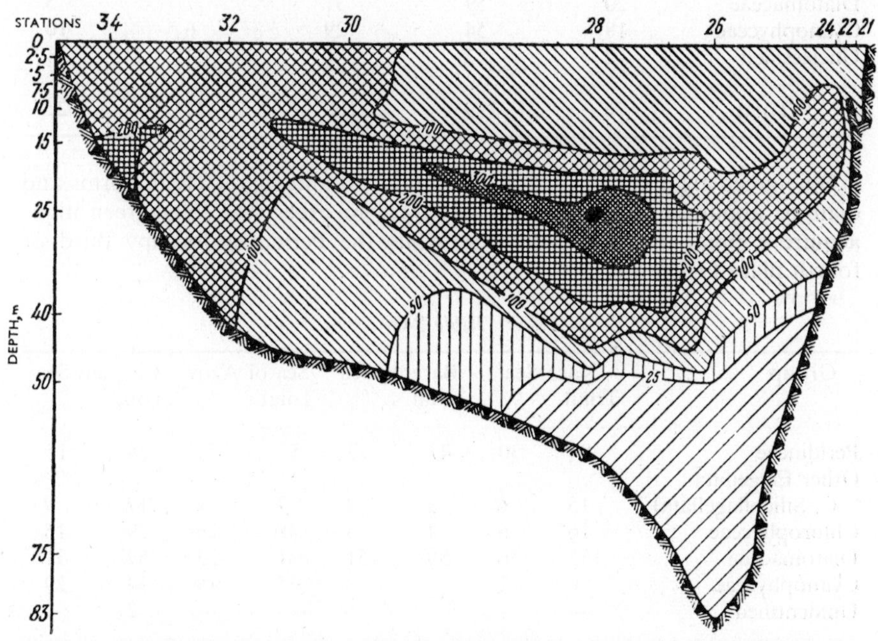

FIG. 275. Distribution of micro-organism population density in Central Caspian along the cross section Makhach–Kala–Sagunduk (Kriss). Numbers of bacteria in thousands per 1 ml of water indicated by numerals in diagram.

the ratio of the production of micro-organisms to their biomass is 127·7 for the Caspian Sea.

The number of micro-organisms in the bottom-soil of the Northern part of the Caspian Sea reaches, according to A. Zhukova (1955), 12 milliards of cells per one gramme of wet soil, in the Southern and Central parts 128 to 897 millions, and in the inlets, according to D. Evdokimov (1937), 105·7 to 1,627·6 millions per one gramme of wet soil.

A. Kriss (1958) considers that the total biomass of the micro-organisms in the Caspian Sea is probably as much as 1,600,000 tons.

Plankton

Qualitative composition of phytoplankton. P. Usachev's comprehensive work (1941) and I. Makarova's data (1957) on the diatoms are used by us for Caspian Sea phytoplankton. The general composition of the plankton algae by groups is given in *Table 241.*

Table 241

Group	Genera	Species and subspecies	Percentage	Dominant species	Main species
Peridineae	10+	28+	15	1	2
Other Flagellata	9+	17	9	7	2
Chlorophyceae	17	29	15	1	2
Diatomaceae	20	59	31	7	5
Cyanophyceae	18	54	29	6	10
Unclassified	2	2	1	—	—
Total	76+	189+	100	22	21

Blue-green algae constitute half the dominant and characteristic forms and diatoms about 34 per cent. Thus, contrary to other seas, blue-green algae acquire a predominant significance, while the Peridineae occupy third or fourth place (*Table 242*).

Table 242

Group	Kara Sea		Barents Sea		Sea of Azov		Caspian Sea	
	Total	%	Total	%	Total	%	Total	%
Peridineae	84	30	47	43	52	28	28	15
Other Flagellata (+Silicoflagellata)	15	6	3	3	7	4	17	9
Chlorophyceae	16	6	4	3	48	26	29	15
Diatomaceae	155	56	56	51	41	23	59	31
Cyanophyceae	6	2	—	—	35	19	54	29
Unidentified	—	—	—	—	—	—	2	1
Total	276	100	110	100	183	100	189	100

I. Makarova (1957) distinguished 59 species, subspecies and forms of diatomaceous algae in the phytoplankton of the Central and Southern Caspian. There are 17 species and varieties of Chaetoceros (*Ch. wighami*, *Ch. paulsenii*, *Ch. subtilis*); 10 species of Coscinodiscus (*C. jonesianus*, *C. j.* var. *commutatus*); and 6 species of Thalassiosira. Thus more than half the Caspian diatoms belong to these three genera. Among the other genera *Sceletonema costatum*, *Cyclotella caspia*, *Actinocyclus ehrenbergi*, and among the immigrants *Rhizosolenia calcar-avis* are the dominant forms. The fact that, contrary to animal groups, endemism among the diatoms is poorly marked, is most characteristic. Makarova points out *C. radiatus* and *C. perforatus* as the only two endemic species; both belong to the widely distributed genus Thalassiosira (*Th. caspica* and *Th. variabile*). There is also one species of just as common a genus, *Actinocyclus paradoxus*. On the other hand, there is a pronounced predominance of marine–brackish-water, brackish-water and cosmopolitan forms among the plankton diatoms (about 62 per cent). The composition of the Caspian Sea diatoms has a very great similarity with that of the north-western part of the Black Sea and the Sea of Azov.

Thirty-five per cent of Caspian species are common with those of the lower Volga and its delta; 37 per cent of the species are common with those of the Aral Sea, but the greatest similarity is observed with the Sea of Azov (114 common forms, or 63 per cent). The species common with the Black Sea constitute 36 per cent, mainly among the diatoms and peridineans; there are no common species among the blue-green algae. Hence as regards its phytoplankton composition the Caspian Sea lies between the Sea of Azov and the Aral Sea.

Phytoplankton biomass. Among the peridinean algae one species—*Exuviella cordata* with two variants (*typica* and *aralensis*)—plays an exceptional role in the biology of all parts of the Caspian Sea; it forms the basic food of plankton animals and plankton-eating fish, producing at times a biomass of 4·5 to 6·5 g/m^3, mostly on the western side of the Northern and Central Caspian. This is probably due to the presence of a powerful current, carrying plant food and running along the western coast. The intensive development of *Rhizosolenia calcar-avis* since 1934 has resulted in a pronounced decrease of Exuviella. Among the other peridineans *Prorocentrum micans* var. *scutellum* and *Gonyaulax polyedra* have most significance in the Caspian Sea.

As in the Sea of Azov, and contrary to the open seas, green algae play an important part in the Caspian Sea phytoplankton, especially in its northern part and still more in its freshest part. The majority are fresh-water forms. *Dictyosphaerium ehrenbergianum* var. *subsalsa*, *Oocystis socialis* and *Botryococcus braunii* are the most widely distributed green algae. Among the diatoms the dominant species in the plankton up to 1934 were *Skeletonema costatum*, *Actinocyclus ehrenbergii*, *Coscinodiscus biconicus*, *Chaetoceros subtilis*, *Ch. wighamii*, *Thalassionema nitzshioides*. A new form, *Rhizosolenia calcar-avis*, appeared in the Caspian Sea in 1934 and later became the dominant form of the whole phytoplankton. The distribution of the diatoms in the northern part of the Sea is given in Fig. 276.

The diatoms play a very important role in the Caspian Sea phytoplankton. The diatom biomass in the Central Caspian constitutes 12 to 20 per cent of the total phytoplankton; their quantity is even higher in the Northern Caspian, especially in its northwestern corner, where it has been known to reach 10 g/m³. Mass development of *Rhizosolenia calcar-avis* was first recorded in the Caspian plankton in 1934 in its south-westernmost corner (more than 6 g/m³); by 1935 it had already spread through the whole of the Sea. *Rh. calcar-avis* produces a biomass of 5 or 6 to 9 g/m³ in different places in the Sea

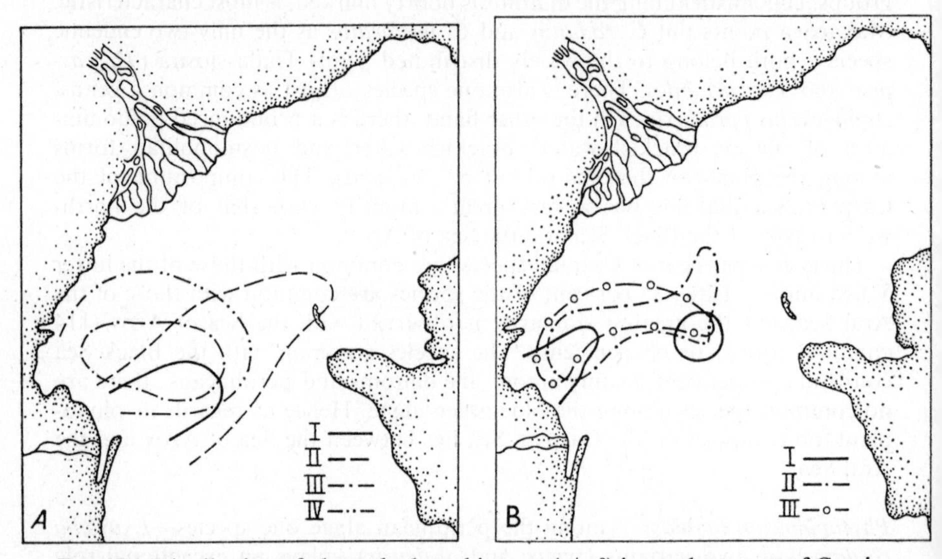

FIG. 276. Distribution of phytoplankton biomass (g/m³) in northern part of Caspian Sea (Usachev). A August 1934; *I* Exuviella biomass 4·5 to 6·5 g/m³; *II* The main zone of Exuviella gathering; *III* Isoplankta of diatoms 0·8; *IV* Isoplankta of diatoms 0·3; B September 1934; *I* Exuviella 0·1 to 0·2 g/m³; *II* Diatoms 0·3 to 0·8 g/m³; *III* Blue-green algae 0·3 to 0·5 g/m³.

(Fig. 277). In some cases it constitutes 99 per cent of the total phytoplankton; it commonly exceeds 80 per cent. This is a completely unprecedented example of a mass development of one single form and of the displacement by it of 20 to 25 per cent of another mass form, *Exuviella cordata*, which even in 1934 constituted 56 to 78 per cent of the whole mass of phytoplankton. Its average number of specimens is 10^8 m³; that of Rhizosolenia is 2×10^7. This situation remained unchanged in 1936. In 1937 the Rhizosolenia biomass decreased* on the average to 0·06 to 2·16 g/m³.

Among the blue-green algae of the Caspian Sea the dominant species are the following: *Aphanizomenon flos-aquae*, *Nodularia spumigera*, *N. harveyana*, *Anabaena bergii*, *A. bergii* var. *minor* and *Merismopedia tenuissima*. Blue-

* High indices of the phytoplankton biomass were observed, however, only off the coast; in the Central part of the Sea the amount of phytoplankton is measured in tens of milligrammes per cubic metre (10 to 20 mg/m³).

green algae reach their highest development in the Northern Caspian, where their summer and autumn bloom is observed and where their biomass rises to 0·4 to 0·7 g/m³, consisting mainly of *Aphanizomenon flos-aquae*. If the mean biomass of the Caspian phytoplankton in the autumn of 1934 be taken as 1·2

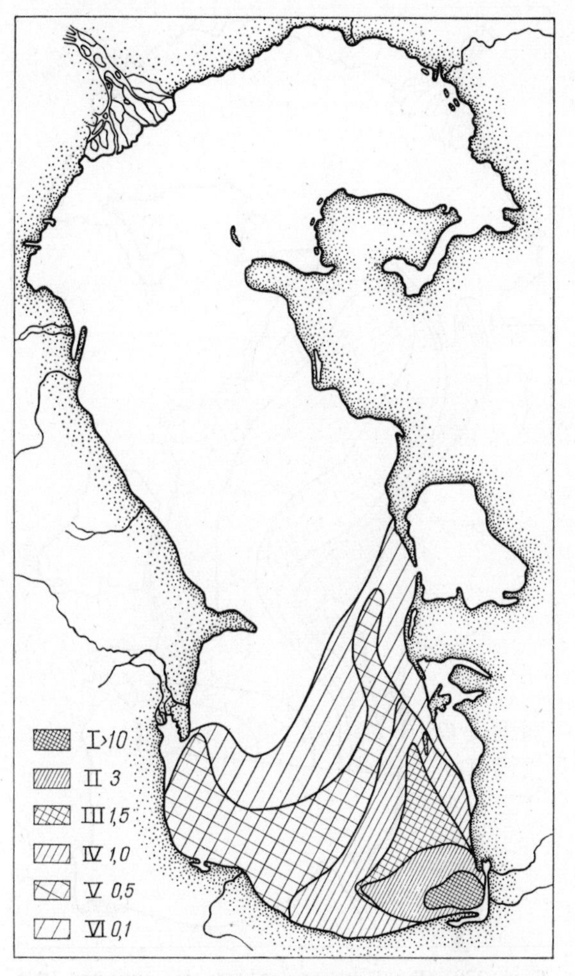

FIG. 277. Quantitative development of *Rhizosolenia calcar-avis* in 1934 (Usachev).

g/m³, then by 1935 it had increased to almost 2 g/m³ and in 1936 to 3 g/m³. The whole of this increase is due to Rhizosolenia. The largest plankton accumulations are adapted to the Northern, and partly to the Central, Caspian—mainly on the western side, where a discharge current enriches the water with plant food carried down by the Volga (Figs. 278 and 279).

The main mass of the Caspian phytoplankton is adapted to the upper

25 m layer of water. There is every reason to think that phytoplankton caught in deeper layers is in a moribund state. As a result, in late autumn and winter, with the decrease in production on the surface, the maximum phytoplankton may move to deeper layers (Fig. 280). In the Central Caspian Rhizosolenia

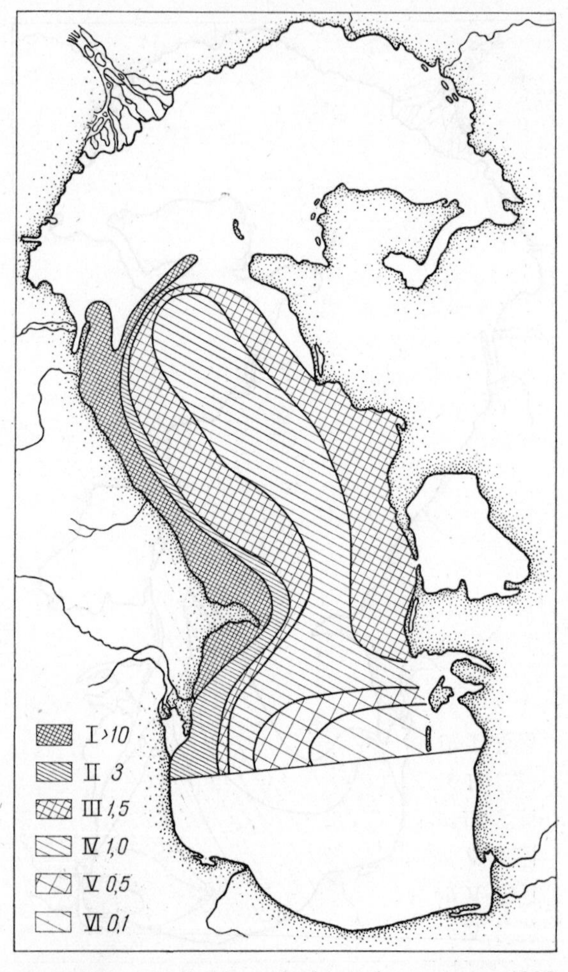

FIG. 278. Total phytoplankton in autumn 1935 (Usachev).

was still absent in 1934, and Exuviella was the dominant form. With the appearance and prompt domination of Rhizosolenia, Exuviella had to cede its place (Fig. 281). Changes in the total phytoplankton biomass and in the relationship between Exuviella and Rhizosolenia in 1934 to 1936 are given in *Table 243*.

The general quantitative distribution of surface phytoplankton throughout

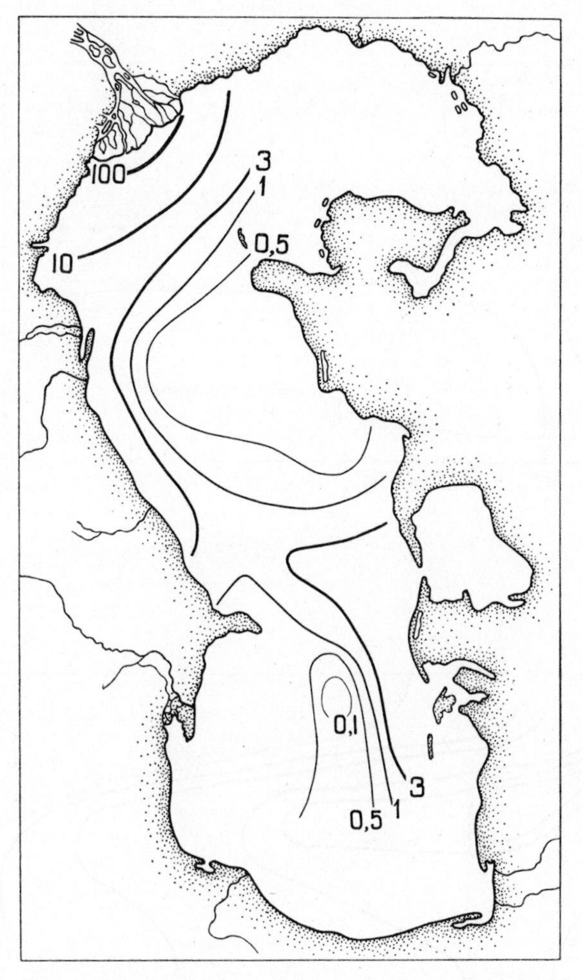

FIG. 279. Distribution of mean biomass of surface phytoplankton (g/m³) from June to August 1936 (Usachev).

Table 243

Year	1934	1935	1936
Mean phytoplankton biomass, g/m³	1·2	2·0	3·0
Exuviella only (%)	33	—	14
Rhizosolenia only (%)	15	75	50

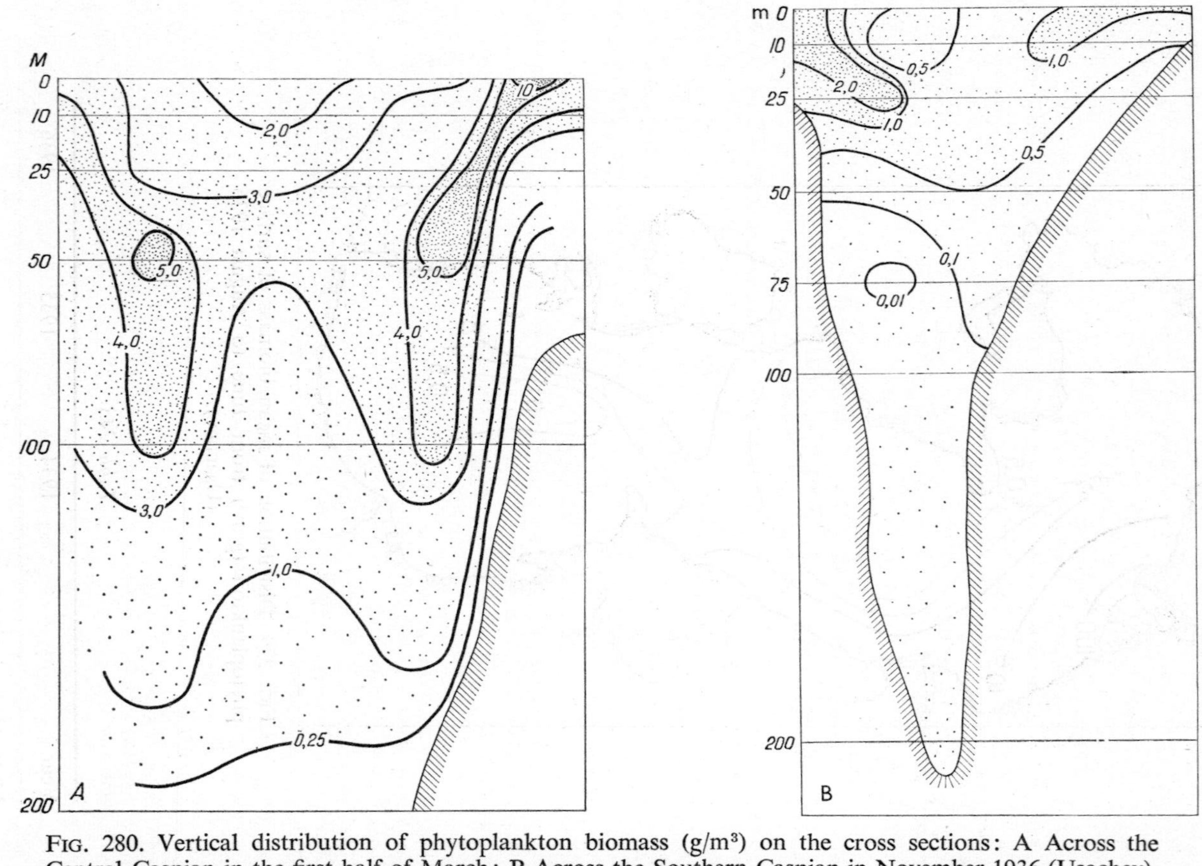

Fig. 280. Vertical distribution of phytoplankton biomass (g/m^3) on the cross sections: A Across the Central Caspian in the first half of March; B Across the Southern Caspian in November 1936 (Usachev).

the Caspian Sea in 1935 is given in Fig. 278. It is evident that the plankton biomass in the estuarian zone of the Caspian Sea had already reached the huge amount of 100 g/m³ (in some individual cases 140 g/m³).

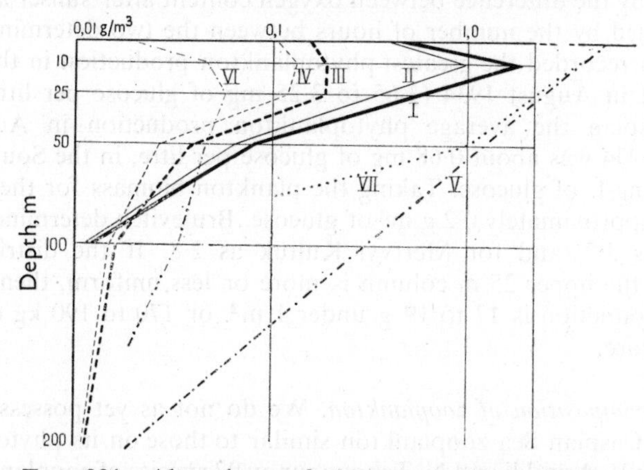

FIG. 281. Alterations of the mean phyto-plankton biomass (g/m³) with depth (*I*) and of that of Exuviella separately (*II*) in September 1934 in the coastal part of the Northern Caspian. *III* and *IV*: same for Central Caspian; *V* and *VI*: same for Southern Caspian with the appearance of Rhizosolenia; *VI*: same for Rhizosolenia separately (Usachev).

Usachev has compared the phytoplankton biomass of the Caspian and Azov Seas. The mean phytoplankton biomass of the Sea of Azov during the bloom of *Rhizosolenia calcar-avis* was found to be 2·0 to 5·2 g/m³ higher than that of the Caspian Sea; in 1925 it was 100 g/m³ higher.

Phytoplankton productivity. Valuable data on the characteristics of plankton distribution in the Sea are obtained from the quantitative estimation of phytoplankton (productive part of plankton). The determination of productivity on the basis of biomass data is most difficult and at present almost impossible. As we have seen in Vorobieff's work on the Sea of Azov, such data can be computed for the benthos since the indices of growth, multiplication, dying off, and consumption by fish can be obtained. The problem, however, generally becomes most difficult for plankton species. It can be solved in part for zooplankton. Let us recall, for example, the Barents Sea plankton, 80 to 85 per cent of which is composed of a one-year-old population of *Calanus finmarchicus*. The estimation of phytoplankton productivity cannot be approached by means of population census. On the other hand, the existence of phytoplankton is closely linked with the chemistry of the water, with the amounts of oxygen, carbon dioxide, phosphorus and nitrogen present, and with its pH value.

S. P. Brujevitch (1937) has determined phytoplankton productivity in the

Caspian Sea by the daily changes in oxygen content and pH in the sea itself, that is by the difference between the afternoon maximum and the night minimum of oxygen content. The average hourly consumption of oxygen was determined by the difference between oxygen content after sunset and before sunrise divided by the number of hours between the two determinations.

Brujevitch recorded the greatest phytoplankton production in the Mërtvyi Kultuk inlet in August 1934 (3·65 to 3·25 mg of glucose per litre). In the Central Caspian the average phytoplankton production in August and September 1934 was about 0·68 mg of glucose per litre, in the Southern part about 0·75 mg/l. of glucose. Taking the plankton biomass for the Southern Caspian as approximately 0·2 g/m^3 of glucose, Brujevitch determines its daily P/B ratio as 3·7, and for Mërtvyi Kultuk as 2·8. If the distribution of plankton in the upper 25 m column is more or less uniform, then the daily plankton production is 17 to 19 g under 1 m^2, or 170 to 190 kg of glucose under 1 hectare.

Qualitative composition of zooplankton. We do not as yet possess sufficient data on the Caspian Sea zooplankton similar to those on its phytoplankton. According to V. Arnoldi and N. Tchougounov 92 species of zooplankton were recorded for the whole of the Northern Caspian in the proportions shown in *Table 244*. The fresh-water forms consist mainly of Rotatoria and Cladocera.

Table 244

Fresh-water forms	56·5%	Rotatoria	45·2%
Brackish-water forms	7·5%	Cladocera	28·6%
Marine	33·8%	Copepoda	21·7%
Indifferent	2·2%	Others	4·5%

According to these investigators 115 zooplankton forms have been distinguished in the Azov, Caspian and Aral Seas; of these 60 per cent are fresh-water and 40 per cent marine and brackish-water forms. The Northern Caspian has the greatest similarity with the Aral Sea (25 per cent common forms).

A. Kusmorskaya made a detailed study of the Northern Caspian zooplankton in 1938 (Fig. 282). According to her data the qualitative composition of Northern Caspian zooplankton does not differ from the characteristics given in *Table 244*. Among the Protozoa, Tintinnoidea are the most numerous and most widely distributed; they are represented by three species: *Tintinnus mitra*, *Codonella relicta* and *Tintinnopsis* spp.; moreover, the first of them is not found in Mërtvyi Kultuk and Kaidak, where *C. relicta* and *Tintinnopsis* spp. reach their highest development. The Coelenterata are represented by the medusa *Caspionema pallasi*, by its hydroid and by a hydroid of a new form not yet described. The most numerous Rotifera are *Asplanchna priodonta*, three species of Brachionus (*B. bakeri*, *B. pala*, and *B. mülleri*) and a few species of Synchaeta and *Ceratella aculeata* var. *tropica*. The distribution of many fresh-water species is limited to the estuarian zones of the rivers;

they are not found at salinities above 4 to 5‰. On the other hand, a series of forms characteristic of brackish waters *Brachionus mülleri*, *Synchaeta vorax*, *S. neapolitana*, and others) have been successfully distinguished.

Cladocera are even more sharply divided into fresh- and brackish-water forms. The first group includes the fairly numerous representatives of the families Sididae, Daphnidae, Bosminidae and Chydoridae, which move far out to sea only during the flooding of rivers. The second group consists of genera of the Polyphemidae family (Polyphemus, Cercopagis, Apagis and Evadne), which avoid places of considerably lowered salinity. *Evadne trigona*

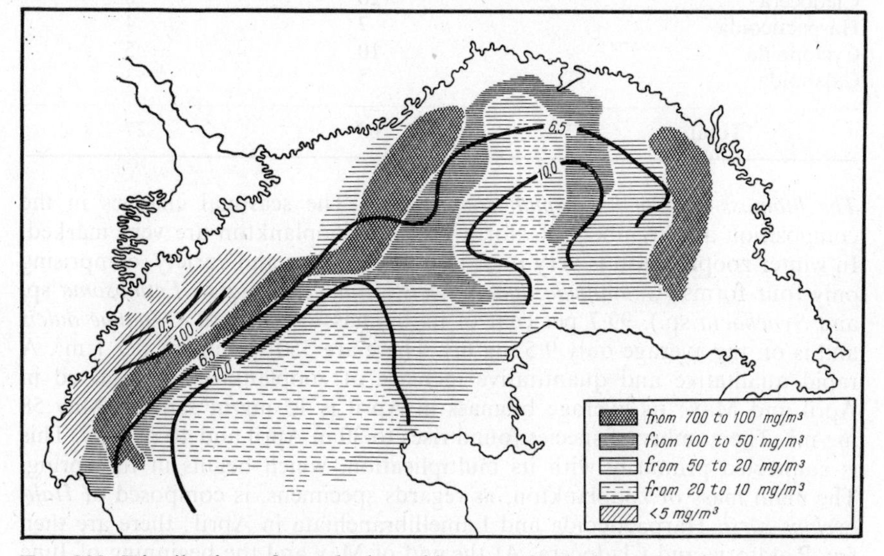

FIG. 282. Distribution of zooplankton biomass of Northern Caspian and the isohalines in September 1935 (Kusmorskaya).

and *Cercopagis gracillima* are the most widely distributed and numerous representatives of this group. Among the Copepoda the dominant form for the whole Northern Caspian zooplankton is *Calanipeda aquae dulcis*—an extremely eurybiotic and widely distributed species. From February to November inclusive, Calanipeda comprises on the average 50 per cent of the total zooplankton biomass. *Halicyclops sarsi* is also very numerous and widely distributed. *Heterocope caspia* is much more stenohaline, avoiding both an increase and decrease of salinity. The rest of the Copepoda are found much less frequently and in smaller numbers. Among them too it is possible to distinguish a group of species connected with fresh water (*Cyclops* spp., *Nitocra incerta*, *Schizopera tenera*, *Nannopus palustris*, *Diaptomus gracilis*, *Eurytemora affinis* and others) and the group of species connected with saline water (*Eurytemora grimmi*, *Idyaea brevicornis*).

Kusmorskaya gives the composition of zooplankton in the western half of the Northern Caspian and in the Mangishlaksk area of the Caspian Sea in the form shown in *Table 245*.

Table 245

Groups	Number of species in the	
	western half of Northern Caspian	Mangishlaksk area
Tintinnoidea	—	2
Coelenterata	—	2
Rotatoria	21	5
Cladocera	20	6
Harpacticoida	7	4
Cyclopoida	10	5
Calanoida	5	3
Total	63	27

The biomass of North Caspian zooplankton. The seasonal changes in the composition and numbers of North Caspian zooplankton are very marked. In winter zooplankton is very poor in both numbers and variety, comprising only four forms (*Calanipeda aquae dulcis*, *Halicyclops sarsi*, *Ectinosoma* sp. and *Synchaeta* sp.). 99·7 per cent of its biomass consists of *C. aquae dulcis* and is on the average only 9·5 mg/m³. There are 350 specimens per 1 m³. A rapid qualitative and quantitative increase of zooplankton is observed in April and May: its average biomass in April is 15 mg/m³ and in May 58 mg/m³. The number of species found rises to 30 in April and 40 in May. This is connected primarily with its multiplication, which begins in the spring. The main mass of zooplankton, as regards specimens, is composed of *Halicyclops sarsi*, Harpacticoida and Lamellibranchiata in April; there are then few Rotatoria and Cladocera. At the end of May and the beginning of June the flood waters move much farther south and therefore the number of freshwater Rotatoria and Cladocera increases considerably. Intensive multiplication of almost all plankton forms proceeds simultaneously, chiefly that of Calanipeda, which by that time occupies first place in the biomass. Further growth of zooplankton biomass takes place in the summer, and in the mouth of the river Volga it increases by 70 per cent by August as compared with April. The intensive multiplication of the majority of planktons continues, and in this respect the August plankton does not differ much from that of May. In August the mean biomass in the western half of the Northern Caspian (less productive in zooplankton than the eastern half) constitutes 60 mg/m³, the average number of specimens being 6,950 per 1 m³. An extinction of zooplankton was observed in September 1934. It could not be considered a consequence of strong changes in the hydrological conditions of the Sea, since in this respect the difference between August and September is slight. It may be that the food resources of the Sea were exhausted by September. The zooplankton biomass dropped at that time to 15 mg/m³. In September 1925 zooplankton was found to be much richer than in the previous year. The average zooplankton biomass then was 100 mg/m³. Some differences were also observed in the relationship between individual groups: thus, for example, in September 1934 Rotifera comprised 9 per cent, and in September 1935 17 per cent, of the zooplankton biomass. A gradual drop of zooplankton biomass takes place in October and November, accompanied by an increase in the relative significance of Calanipeda. The average zooplankton biomass for October 1935 was 92 mg/m³, 56 per cent of it being Calanipeda; for November 1935 the average biomass was 35 mg/m³ with 65 per cent Calanipeda.

This difference between the September data of 1934 and 1935 can be explained by the hydrological conditions of the Northern Caspian in 1935. In autumn 1935 the southern part of the Northern Caspian was exceptionally enriched by plant food, brought, apparently, from great depths of the Central Caspian and carried far to the north owing to the increased flow of Central Caspian waters. This brought about an intensive Rhizosolenia bloom in the southern and middle parts of the Northern Caspian and also, no doubt, favoured zooplankton development.

Zooplankton distribution is not uniform in the Northern Caspian (see Fig. 282). As early as 1921 N. Tchugunov distinguished there three plankton zones characterized by their specific composition and the extent of quantitative development of zooplankton, controlled primarily by salinity: (*1*) the mouths of the Volga and Ural rivers with their lowered salinity of 0·3 to 0·4‰; (*2*) the zone of mixing of the saline and fresh waters, with a salinity of 8 to 9‰, approximately within the 12 to 18 ft bar of material carried down by the rivers; (*3*) the saline zone, with a salinity of 10 to 12‰ exposed to the direct influence of the Central Caspian, occupying the southern and central part of the western half of the Northern Caspian. The boundaries between these zones are naturally very unstable, change frequently, and can approach each other depending on the amount of flood water, wind, etc.

The zooplankton of the first zone is poor, and consists only of fresh-water species.

The next zone, richest in number and wealth of zooplankton, is populated by typically brackish-water organisms. In early spring the average zooplankton biomass of this zone is 16·5 mg/m³, say three times higher than in the first zone; by the end of May and the beginning of June it is 92 mg/m³, in August 130 mg/m³, in September 160 mg/m³ and in October* 154 mg/m³. It was in this zone that the maximum phytoplankton development was recorded.

The zooplankton of the third zone is considerably poorer both in numbers and variety of species. Several species are not found here and the remaining ones do not reach mass development. The average zooplankton biomass of this zone in August 1935 was 20 mg/m³, in September 1935 27 mg/m³, and in October 1935 only 13 mg/m³.

The difference in zooplankton biomass in these zones is controlled by other factors as well as salinity, which limits the range of one or another species; as has been shown by Kusmorskaya, plant food content in various areas is of great significance in this respect.

* The data for May, June, August, September and October are given only for the western part of the Northern Caspian.

A remarkable coincidence between quantitative development of zooplankton and of bacterial flora is evident from the data gathered by Kusmorskaya (1938). On the cross section Volga delta–Mangistau maximum numbers of micro-organisms and zooplankton are found together, falling exactly within the area of confluence of river and sea waters (Fig. 283). The same coincidence was recorded for Mërtvyi Kultuk and Kaidak. It might reflect both

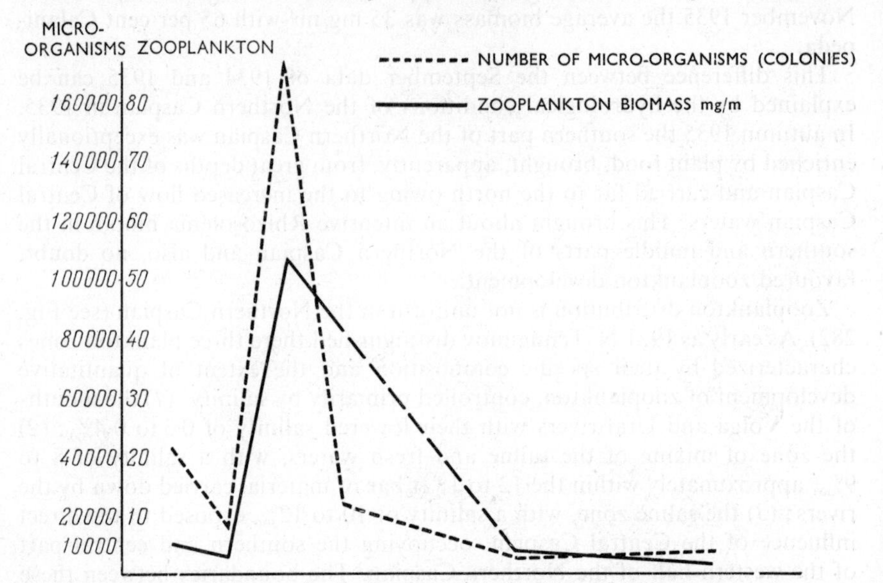

FIG. 283. Quantitative distribution of bacteria and zooplankton along the cross section Volga delta–Mangistau (Kusmorskaya).

an indirect and a direct dependence of zooplankton on micro-organisms. Micro-organisms decompose organic matter and enrich the waters with plant food. The development of phytoplankton biomass is due to it; this in its turn serves as food for zooplankton. Moreover plankton Copepoda feed directly on micro-organisms, and bacterial flora is used to feed zooplankton.

Taking Knipovitch's value of 793 km³ as the volume of the Northern Caspian, Kusmorskaya calculated the absolute amounts of zooplankton biomass and has obtained indices for the whole Northern Caspian as given in *Table 246*.

Zooplankton biomass of Central and Southern Caspian. Quantitative data on Central and Southern Caspian zooplankton are contained in the works of M. Idelson (1941) and V. Jashnov (1938, 1939). According to Idelson the largest zooplankton biomass is found in the 0 to 100 m layer; below that it decreases regularly with depth (*Table 247*).

The relationship between separate groups changes simultaneously (Fig. 284). Copepoda are the dominant groups in the 0 to 100 m layer, comprising 96 to 99 per cent of the total biomass in the Central Caspian and 71 to 95 per

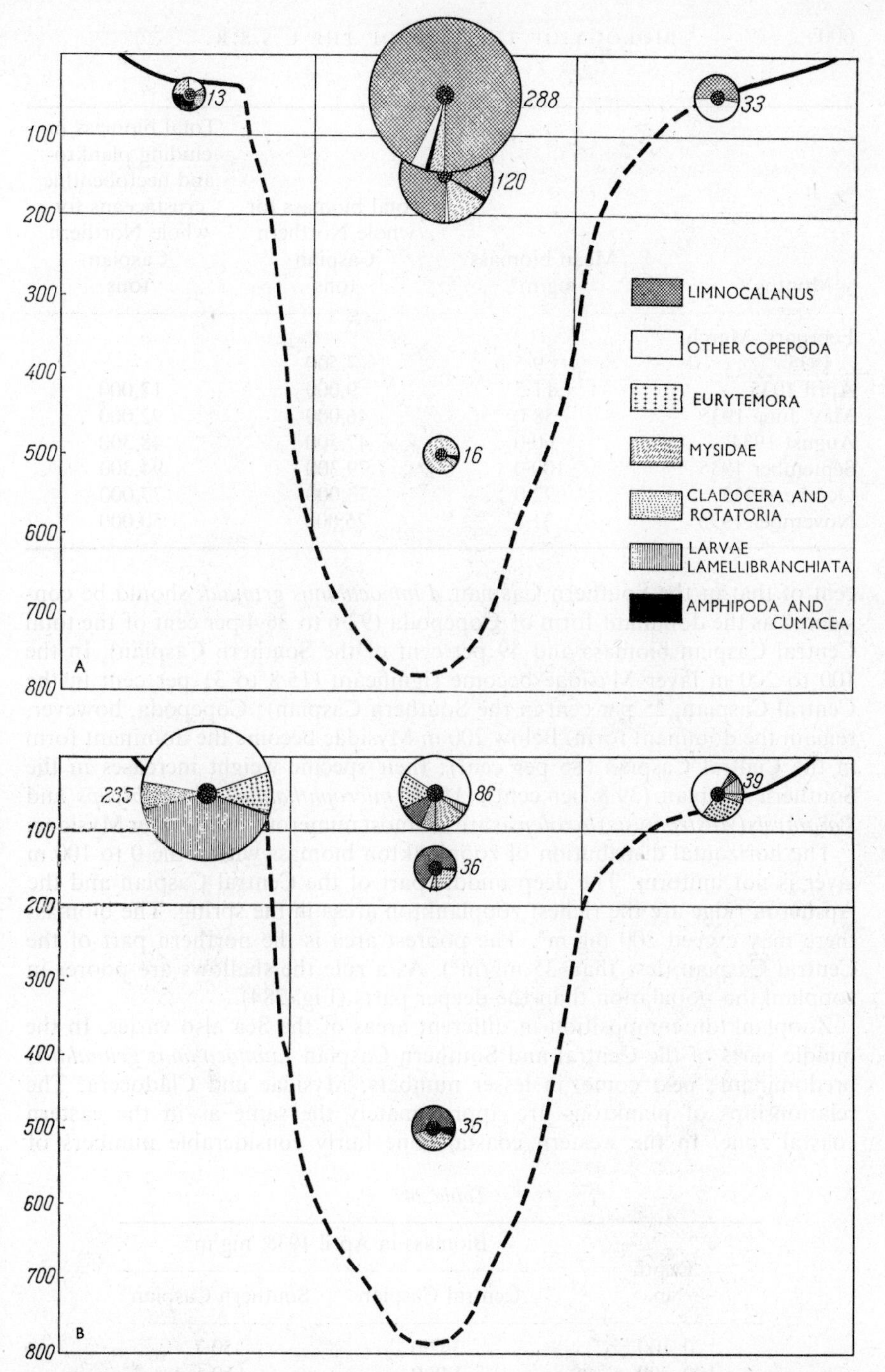

FIG. 284. Vertical distribution of zooplankton along the cross section through the central part of the Central Caspian, Divichi–Kenderli Bay, April (A) and August (B) (Idelson).

Table 246

Months	Mean biomass mg/m³	Total biomass for whole Northern Caspian tons	Total biomass including plankto- and nectobenthic crustaceans for whole Northern Caspian tons
February–March 1935	9·5	7,500	—
April 1935	11·5	9,000	12,000
May–June 1935	58·0	46,000	92,000
August 1934	60·0	47,500	48,300
September 1935	100·0	79,300	94,300
October 1935	92·0	73,000	77,000
November 1935	31·5	25,000	50,000

cent of that in the Southern Caspian. *Limnocalanus grimaldi* should be considered as the dominant form of Copepoda (92·6 to 36·4 per cent of the total Central Caspian biomass and 49 per cent of the Southern Caspian). In the 100 to 200 m layer Mysidae become significant (15·8 to 31 per cent in the Central Caspian, 25 per cent in the Southern Caspian); Copepoda, however, remain the dominant form. Below 200 m Mysidae become the dominant form in the Central Caspian (86 per cent); their specific weight increases in the Southern Caspian (39·8 per cent). *Mysis microphthalma, M. amblyops* and *Paramysis* (*Austromysis*) *loxolepsis* are the most numerous deep-water Mysidae.

The horizontal distribution of zooplankton biomass within the 0 to 100 m layer is not uniform. The deep middle part of the Central Caspian and the Apsheron ridge are the richest zooplankton areas in the spring. The biomass there may exceed 200 mg/m³. The poorest area is the northern part of the Central Caspian (less than 25 mg/m³). As a rule the shallows are poorer in zooplankton population than the deeper parts (Fig. 284).

Zooplankton composition in different areas of the Sea also varies. In the middle parts of the Central and Southern Caspian *Limnocalanus grimaldi* is predominant; next come, in lesser numbers, Mysidae and Cladocera. The relationships of planktons are approximately the same as in the eastern coastal zone. In the western coastal zone fairly considerable numbers of

Table 247

Depth m	Biomass in April 1938, mg/m³	
	Central Caspian	Southern Caspian
0–100	362·0	50·7
100–200	148·0	50·1
200–sea bed	23·8	22·9

Rotatoria, Lamellibranchiata (larvae), Mysidae, Amphipoda and Cumacea, as well as fish-fry, are found in addition to Copepoda, which remain the predominant group.

In the Central and Southern Caspian the total amount of zooplankton biomass and its qualitative composition change considerably with the seasons.

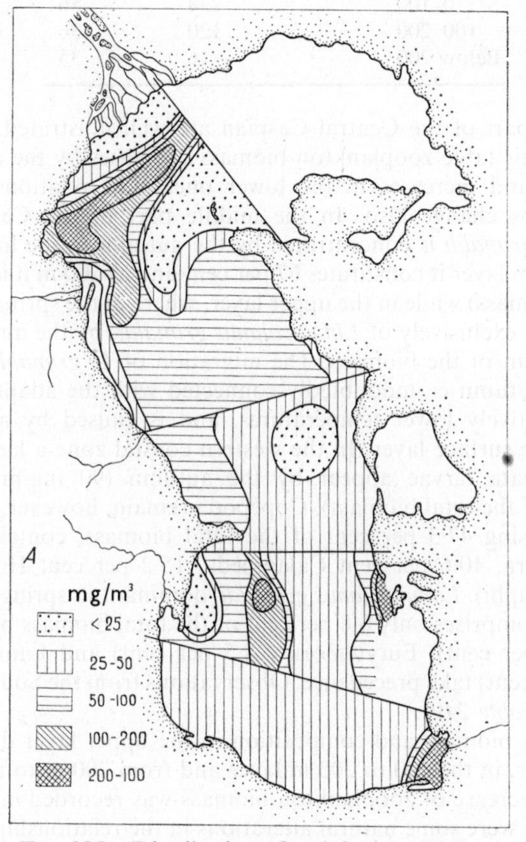

FIG. 285A. Distribution of zooplankton biomass of Central and Southern Caspian in autumn 1934 (Jashnov).

Unfortunately there is no material available for the assessment of this phenomenon. A comparison can only be drawn from the data (by Idelson) for March–April and August, and for December for the Southern Caspian. This comparison shows an increase of zooplankton concentration in the western coastal zone of the Central Caspian by the autumn, which at that time becomes richer in zooplankton (235 mg/m³) than the central (86·2 mg/m³) and eastern coastal zones (39 mg/m³). According to Jashnov's data a similar distribution of plankton population was recorded in the autumn of 1934–35 (Fig. 285A). The seasonal changes of the vertical distribution of zooplankton

Table 248

Layer m	Biomass, mg/m³ Apr 1938	Aug 1938
0–100	238	86
100–200	120	36
Below 200	16	35

in the middle part of the Central Caspian are well illustrated in *Table 248*. As shown in this table zooplankton biomass decreases by the autumn in the upper layers, and increases in the lower ones. The relationships between different groups change also. In the middle part of the Central Caspian *Limnocalanus grimaldi* is concentrated by the autumn in the lower layers (in the 100 to 200 m layer it constitutes 67 per cent and at 200 m it is 54·2 per cent of the total biomass) while in the upper layer, where in the spring the plankton consists almost exclusively of *Limnocalanus grimaldi*, by the autumn it forms only 9·7 per cent of the biomass. The migration of *L. grimaldi* to the lower layers in the autumn is undoubtedly connected with the adaptation of this species to relatively lower temperatures, and is caused by a considerable warming of the surface layer. In the western coastal zone a large number of Lamellibranchiata larvae appear by the autumn (90 mg/m³, comprising 42·2 per cent of the total biomass). Copepoda remain, however, the dominant group (comprising 47·3 per cent of the total biomass, containing 11·6 per cent Eurytemora, 10·6 per cent Calanipeda, 15·2 per cent Halicyclops and 9·2 per cent nauplii). *Limnocalanus grimaldi*, dominant in spring in the eastern coastal zone, comprises only 6·8 per cent of the total biomass by the autumn, nauplii (42·6 per cent), Eurytemora (28·5 per cent) and Lamellibranchiata larvae (9·2 per cent) take precedence. Observations from the Southern Caspian are shown in *Table 249*.

Zooplankton biomass and composition in the upper layer did not change much. However, in the 100 to 200 m layer and from 200 m to the sea-floor a considerable decrease of zooplankton biomass was recorded in March 1939; moreover there were some natural alterations in the relationships between the separate groups: Limnocalanus was the dominant form in April 1938 (68 and 56 per cent) while second place was occupied by the mysids (25 and 39·8 per cent); in December 1938 and in March 1939 in particular these

Table 249

Layer m	Biomass, mg/m³ Mar 1938	Apr 1938	Dec 1938
0–100	52	51	40
100–200	5	50	22
Below 200	8	23	23

animals changed places, the mysids occupying the first place (54 to 98 per cent), while the Limnocalanus biomass went down to 4·2 to 22·7 per cent.

The Central Caspian zooplankton biomass is subject to both seasonal and annual fluctuations. The data for the spring of 1938 and 1939 showed an increase of zooplankton biomass in 1939 (the average biomass for 1938 was 287

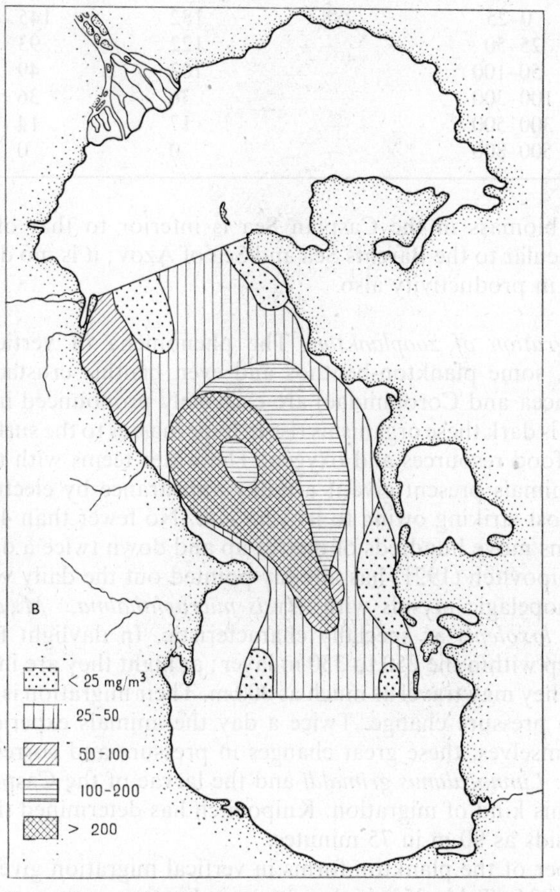

FIG. 285B. Distribution of zooplankton biomass of Central and Southern Caspian in May 1939 (Idelson).

mg/m³, for 1939—362 mg/m³) while its qualitative composition remained unchanged (Fig. 285B). The same fact was recorded for phytoplankton. In autumn 1938 the zooplankton biomass was higher (86·2 mg/m³) than in the autumn of 1934 (55 mg/m³). There are no similar observations for the Southern Caspian. Similar indices were, however, obtained for this part of the Sea in 1938 and 1939. Plankton biomass data from different parts of the Sea (Jashnov) are given in *Table 250* for the autumn of 1934; Rhizosolenia, however, is not included.

Table 250

Depth m	Zooplankton biomass in Caspian Sea, mg/m³		
	Northern	Central	Southern
0–25	288	182	145
25–50	—	122	93
50–100	—	103	49
100–300	—	36	36
300–500	—	17	14
500–800	—	0	0

Plankton biomass in the Caspian Sea is inferior to that of many other seas, in particular to the Barents Sea and Sea of Azov; it is, no doubt, inferior to the latter in productivity also.

Vertical migration of zooplankton. The phenomena of vertical migration of plankton, some plankton-benthos and even benthic crustaceans (for example Cumacea and Corophiidae) are extremely pronounced in the Caspian Sea. While it is dark these organisms rise in huge masses to the surface, attracted by its large food resources and oxygen. The water teems with them, and the masses of animals present give it a milky appearance by electric light. This process is most striking owing to its very size. No fewer than 4 to 5 millions of crustaceans move hundreds of metres up and down twice a day.

N. M. Knipovitch (1921) has already pointed out the daily vertical migration of bathopelagic mysids with *Mysis microphthalma*, *M. amblyops* and *Austromysis loxolepis* as specially characteristic. In daylight the maximum numbers keep within the 250 to 350 m layer; at night they are in the top layer of the Sea. They may travel as much as 300 m. Their migration is accompanied by a 30 atm pressure change. Twice a day the animals experience, without harm to themselves, these great changes in pressure and correspondingly in temperature. *Limnocalanus grimaldi* and the larvae of the Caspian sprat also experience this kind of migration. Knipovitch has determined the rate of rise of some mysids as 90 m in 75 minutes.

The number of the plankton forms in vertical migration given by Jashnov for August 1934 (*Table 251*) is even more indicative.

V. Bogorov (1939) has given a comprehensive description of the vertical

Table 251

Depth m	Amount of plankton, ton/km³			
	Central Caspian		Southern Caspian	
	day	night	day	night
0–50	1·1	9·7	0·7	7·7
50–100	3	1·9	0·9	3·4
100–400	16·8	6·0	6·3	1·5

migration of *Eurytemora grimmi* in the Caspian Sea. This crustacean never forms a maximum in the surface layer. It starts its upward movement from the depths in the afternoon. At midnight it begins to sink again. This is clearly pronounced in the early morning hours, and by 8 o'clock in the morning almost all the *Eurytemora grimmi* are already at a depth of 50 to 83 m, where they remain till their next ascent. The nature of the changes is shown in *Table 252*, which includes the data for all the stages (in number of specimens

Table 252

Depth m	Hour of the day 6 p.m.	8 p.m.	11–12 p.m.	2 a.m.	5 a.m.	8 a.m.	11 a.m.	2 p.m.
1–10	928	1,600	1,680	1,358	50	4	6	40
10–25	2,863	3,240	2,396	3,378	373	—	—	2,250
25–50	1,595	277	765	1,109	1,201	709	6	2,010
50–83	—	15	65	37	62	5,413	3,181	1,610

per 1 m^3). No significant changes in the process of migration for different ages have been recorded for *E. grimmi*, but such changes were noted for the Northern Sea *Calanus finmarchicus* by A. Nicholls (1953). The rate of upward movement of these small Copepoda is about 2 cm/sec (72 m/h); their descent is almost as rapid.

Borgoov has given an interesting estimation of the biological significance of the vertical migration of *E. grimmi*. An average of 7 mg/m^3 of living matter is transferred during one day. It is understandable that the feeding significance of plankton in different layers changes sharply in connection with these movements. A certain layer can contain very different amounts of food-forms at various times of the day. Bogorov has established the feeding value of a given layer (the product of mean biomass by the number of hours, corresponding to the given state of the biomass) and the feeding intensity of a given layer (quotient of mean biomass divided by the number of hours for a given biomass). For *E. grimmi*, one of the most important food-plankton of the Caspian Sea, these values are given in *Table 253*.

Table 253

Depth m	Feeding value	Feeding intensity
0–10	48	1·3
10–25	210	0·9
25–50	120	0·5
50–83	180	2·2

The 10 to 25 m and 50 to 83 m layers have the highest feeding value, while the highest feeding intensity is found in the 0 to 10 m and 50 to 83 m layers, since a huge number of organisms is gathered there for a short time. Using the data obtained by S. Marshall and A. Orr (1955) and by A. Nicholls (1937) for *Calanus finmarchicus*, V. Bogorov (1939) calculated the volume of oxygen consumed by the whole *Eurytemora grimmi* population and the carbon dioxide liberated by it in various layers of water in 24 hours. When it is dark the main oxygen consumption takes place in the top layer (0 to 25 m); when light, in the 50 to 83 m layer (*Table 254*).

Table 254

Horizon	0–10	10–25	25–50	50–83
Daily oxygen consumption, cm^3/m^3	30	80	50	90
Carbon dioxide increase, cm^3/m^3	24	64	40	72

The coefficient of daily vertical distribution of the highest mass of plankton can be calculated from these data. From the data of a definite station, collected at a definite hour, it is possible to calculate the distribution of plankton at any moment of the day, using the previously established coefficients of daily vertical distribution of organisms according to stage and sex.

For Eurytemora the coefficients of daily vertical distribution have been calculated in the form given in *Table 255*.

Table 255

Depth m	Time of catch								Coefficient of distribution	
	6 p.m.	8 p.m.	11–12 p.m.	2 a.m.	5 a.m.	8 a.m.	11 a.m.	2 p.m.	Day	Night
0–10	20	30	30	20	5	1	1	1	2	25
10–50	50	60	50	60	20	—	—	39	15	55
25–50	30	9	18	18	70	11	1	30	28	19
50–85	—	1	2	2	5	88	98	30	55	2

The converse picture is obtained for the day and night distribution of *E. grimmi*. A similar method of calculation is less reliable when the stations are not complete or only one sample was taken.

Benthos

Qualitative composition of phytobenthos. Kireeva and Shchapova's interesting and comprehensive research on macrophytes (1939, 1957) should not be omitted from the list of oceanographic work done in the Northern Caspian in the last 15 years. A very full picture of their distribution in number and species is given for the eastern and northeastern coast of the Sea. Before all else the specific composition of the Caspian Sea macrophytes is characteristic, as compared to the flora of other seas (*Table 256*).

In the Mediterranean and Black Seas red algae predominate, then come the

Table 256

roup of ottom algae	Mediterranean Alboran coast No. of species	%	Black Sea No. of species	%	Sea of Azov No. of species	%	Caspian Sea No. of species	%	Baltic Sea No. of species	%
ue-green lgae	67	13·6	—	—	—	—	33	28·0	55	15·1
reen algae	78	15·9	54	24·5	12	46	46	40·0	132	36·2
ed algae	258	52·5	103	46·6	11	42·5	29	25·0	78	21·4
rown algae	89	18·0	64	28·9	3	11·5	8	7·0	100	27·3
Total	492	100	221	100	26	100	116	100	365	100

brown and finally the green. In the Caspian Sea there is a reverse relationship between these species: the first place is occupied by the blue-green and green algae, the percentage of brown and red is low, and their ratio to the first is even lower. The Baltic Sea ratio is somewhat similar.

The qualitative poverty and the ratio between the separate groups of the Caspian Sea macrophytes is related to the historical past of the Sea and to its low salinity. Apart from the algae tabulated, on the eastern shores of the Sea five species of flowering plants are widely distributed: *Zostera nana*, *Ruppia maritima*, *R. spiralis*, *Najas marina* and *Potamogeton pectinatus* (63 forms in all).

T. Shchapova (1938) thinks that the majority of brown and red algae belong to the transformed Sarmatian and later Pontic flora, and that owing to the occurrence of numerous and considerable losses of salinity in the Caspian basin a whole series of marine species has disappeared, while new forms of fresh-water origin have settled in. Some marine forms could have penetrated here from the west very recently. It is probable that *Zostera nana* was one of them. The evolution of a brackish-water flora was furthered by the history of the Caspian Sea; moreover the mass development of the charial algae is of particular interest. Thus the complete analogy between the Caspian flora and fauna becomes evident.

Distribution and biomass of phytobenthos. Shchapova distinguishes three main groupings of bottom-living macrophytes according to the type of the sea-bed soil.

On rocky soils, chiefly on the western and eastern coasts, green and red algae with the highest percentage of marine forms are preponderant. The highest horizon is inhabited by *Cladophora glomerata flavescens*, *Cl. nitida* and *Enteromorpha intestinalis*. At a depth of only 0·3 to 0·4 m green algae already yield their place to red ones (*Laurencia paniculata*, *Polysiphonia elongata* and *P. violacea*). Among brown algae *Monosiphon caspius* is common here.

On shallow sand–shell-gravel soils *Zostera nana* is the highest developed form and, to a much lesser extent, *Ruppia maritima* and *Polysiphonia sertularioides*. Exceptionally large growths of Zostera are found in the Mangishlak area and, apparently, in the southeasternmost part of the Sea. Zostera is easily detached from the bottom by the swell and, since it floats, it gets scattered throughout the Sea, often forming heaps of wrack in places distant from that of its original growth. The main accumulations of the second form —*Polysiphonia sertularioides*—are recorded in the southeastern parts of the Sea.

Charial algae (*Chara intermedia*, *Ch. polyacantha*, *Ch. aspera* and *Ch. crinita*) grow in huge amounts on the shallow (0·2 to 2 m) hydrogen sulphide silt soils of the eastern coast, mostly in inlets and behind the islands, etc. Macrophyte sea-weeds in the Caspian Sea do not sink deeper than 25 m owing to the poor transparency of its waters. The biomass distribution of algae is very patchy, rising at times almost to 30 kg/m³ with the growths of charial algae and sometimes dropping to insignificant amounts; it is adapted mainly to within 2 m of the surface. *Zostera nana* biomass reaches 1 kg/m³ at some places, but is commonly about 200 to 300 g/m³ (wet weight). Total raw resources of this commercial plant constitute about 700,000 tons of wet weight in the Caspian Sea. Its yield in the area of the Apsheron peninsula alone is about 1·5 to 2 thousand tons. Red algae are especially abundant along the western coast of the Caspian Sea. Off Svinoi Island they have a biomass of up to 3·6 kg/m³, consisting mostly of *Laurencia paniculata*. In other areas the red algae *Ceramium diaphanum* and *Polysiphonia sertularioides* predominate. Among the green algae *Enteromorpha ampressa* and *Cladophora* spp. are preponderant with their biomass of a few kilogrammes. Charial algae give 2 to 3 kg/m² biomass in some areas. Brown algae do not form any considerable biomass in the Caspian Sea. The total biomass of Caspian macrophytes is of the order of 3 million tons of wet weight, with an average *P*/*B* ratio about unity. A chart of the macrophyte biomass of the eastern shores of the Caspian Sea is given in Fig. 286.

The maximum macrophyte biomass is found in the Caspian Sea near soft-soil shores, the minimum near rocky floors. This has led Kireeva and Shchapova to assume that the Caspian is more of a lake than a sea by the distribution of its phytobenthos biomass.

Qualitative composition of bottom-living fauna. As has been mentioned above, the Caspian Sea fauna is considerably inferior in its variety to that of the open sea, both in the total number of its species and in the relationship between its separate component groups. *Table 256* contains some plankton-benthos and plankton groups.

The difference between the composition of the marine and Caspian Sea fauna is shown in *Table 257*.

It is evident from this table that in full-salinity seas Porifera, Coelenterata, Polychaeta and Bryozoa form groups as varied as those of the molluscs, crustaceans and fish, while in the low-salinity waters of the Black, Caspian and Baltic Seas the last three groups constitute only 50 to 65 per cent of the groups mentioned. Moreover one of the greatest characteristics of the Caspian Sea—the poverty of its qualitative composition—is shown graphically in *Tables 257* and *258*.

Table 257. Composition of Caspian Sea bottom living fauna

Groups	No. of species	Groups	No. of species
Foraminifera	9	Amphipoda	72
Porifera	4	Isopoda	2
Coelenterata	4(1)*	Cumacea	19
Turbellaria	34	Mysidacea	20
Nemertini	1	Decapoda	5(3)
Hirudinea	2	Chironomidae	3
Oligochaeta	4	Hydracarina	2
Polychaeta	6(1)	Bryozoa	4(1)
Ostracoda	10	Lamellibranchiata	23(4)
Cirripedia	2(2)	Gastropoda	32
		Pisces	78(3)
		Total number of free-living animals	336(15)

* The composition of the Caspian Sea fauna, especially the Protozoa which are not listed here except for Foraminifera, has not been fully investigated yet. Data in parentheses give numbers of species which have recently penetrated into the Caspian Sea.

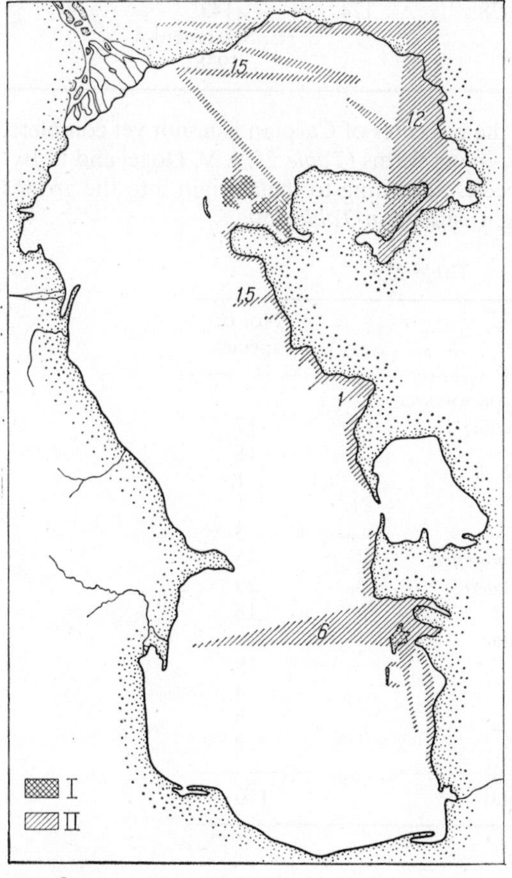

FIG. 286. Distribution of the biomass of macrophytes of the eastern coast of the Caspian Sea (Kireeva and Shchapova).

Table 258

Groups	Caspian Sea	Barents Sea	Black Sea	Baltic Sea including Arcona area
Foraminifera	9	115	9	?
Porifera	4	94	42	0
Hydrozoa and Anthozoa	4	139	44	24
Turbellaria	34	27	79	?
Nemertini	1	20	27	?
Polychaeta	6	200	123	25
Gephyrea	—	11	0	1
Bryozoa	4	272	12	3
Brachiopoda	—	4	—	0
Higher crustaceans	118	361	214	32
Lamellibranchiata	23	87	5	24
Pantopoda	—	24	5	0
Gastropoda	32	150	74	5
Echinodermata	—	62	4(5)	2
Ascidia	—	50	16	0
Pisces	78	174	143	30

(E. Slastenenko 1938)

Fish-parasite fauna. The list of the parasites of Caspian fish, not yet complete, may be added to that of the free-living forms (*Table 259*). V. Dogel and B. Bykhovsky (1939) divide these species according to their origin into the groups (except forms of uncertain origin) shown in *Table 260*.

Table 259

Groups	No. of species
Flagellata (Trypanosoma, Trypanoplasma)	17
Myxosporidia	18
Microsporidia	1
Coccidia	1
Infusoria	3
Trematoda monogenea	45
Trematoda digenea	29
Cestodes	18
Acanthocephala	5
Nematoda	19
Hirudinea	4
Copepoda	8
Branchiura	2
Total	170

Table 260

Groups according to origin	Fresh water		Marine		Total
	Non-endemic	Endemic	Non-endemic	Endemic	
Southeastern	—	2	—	—	2
Southern	19	8	—	9	36
Northern	10	—	2	2	14
European	91	—	2	—	93
Total	120	10	4	11	

It follows from *Table 259* that the parasite fauna of Caspian fish consists mainly of fresh-water species (94·3 per cent). Parasites of marine origin comprise only 5·7 per cent of the total number of species and are chiefly peculiar to the herring family, Acipenseridae and bullheads. Of the 22 endemic Pontic–Caspian–Aral forms only 7 inhabit the Caspian Sea alone. Of special interest among these two species of northern origin are the parasite of the seal *Carynosoma strumosum* and the Caspian herring parasite, *Bunocotyle cingulata*, neither of which has any genetic link with the north.

It is most characteristic that a large number (22) of the Caspian fish parasites live in fish in their larval stage and in birds when adults. This is no doubt linked with the exceptional abundance of diving birds in the Caspian Sea. Only eleven larvae of such species are recorded for Aral fish and only ten for the Neva Inlet. The Caspian Sea is in general much richer in fish-parasites than the Aral Sea. On one particular kind of fish 119 species of parasites were recorded in the Caspian Sea and only 70 in the Aral. The comparison of the data on the Caspian and Aral sturgeon *Acipenser nudiventris* is particularly indicative in this respect (before the appearance of *Nitzschia sturionis* in the Aral Sea).

On this subject Dogel and Bykhovsky write as follows: 'We see that not one of the (first eight) specific Acipenseridae parasites has survived in the Aral Sea. All the Aral parasites of the sturgeon *Acipenser nudiventris* have either an accidental character or (Asymphilodora, Macroseroides) have moved on to it from fish of different kinds.' Dogel and Bykhovsky explain the greater abundance of fish-parasites in the Caspian Sea as compared with the Aral Sea by the greater variety of invertebrates in the Caspian fauna, since the latter serve as intermediate hosts to parasitic worms; and also by the historical past of the Aral Sea. On the other hand Caspian fish and, in particular, Acipenseridae are poorer in marine parasites and richer in endemic and fresh-water forms than Black Sea fish.

Among the Caspian fish-parasites recorded a number of forms are harmful to fisheries: Ligula, afflicting annually some millions of specimens of cyprinoids; Caligus, which causes the emaciation of carp; Dioctophymidae larvae, which form tumours in the intestines of Acipenseridae; Eustrongylides larvae, causing red boils in the muscles of pike perch, and others.

Vertical distribution of zoobenthos. O. Grimm had already pointed out in 1877 the vertical zonality of the distribution of Caspian fauna and had established three faunal zones covering the upper 300 m. A similar division of the Sea was suggested by N. M. Knipovitch (1921), based on the distribution of a series of hydrological and biological factors. He suggested four zones for the Central Caspian and three for the Southern. The upper zone (100 to 200m), with its seasonal temperature fluctuations and a larger oxygen content, was further divided into sub-zones by Knipovitch. The second zone is characterized by a lower oxygen content and a fairly constant temperature (down to 450 m). According to Knipovitch the third zone with a constant temperature and low oxygen content extends in the Southern Caspian to the sea-bed and in the Central to 750 m. Below it lies the fourth zone, characterized by the presence of hydrogen sulphide. According to Knipovitch the limit of bottom life lies at 415 m in the Central Caspian and at 460 m in the Southern. The main mass of benthos lives in the two upper zones. More recently S. P. Brujevitch (1937) suggested a diagram for the vertical division of the Sea according to chemical indices, of which mention has been made above.

As has been shown by recent research the maximum depths for bottom-living organisms are greater than those suggested by Grimm and Knipovitch, the 400 to 500 m deep water column was found to contain some benthos, although here it is poor both in number and variety (Fig. 287). *Hypania invalida* was discovered down to maximum depths (960 m); Pseudolibrotus was caught in plankton nets below 600 m. Some mysids were found at almost the same depth. They can all, apparently, exist on very small amounts of oxygen.

In the Central Caspian bottom fauna becomes very scarce at about 100 m. Crustaceans of Arctic origin live here: *Mesidothea entomon*, *Pseudolibrotus platyceras*, *Ps. caspius*, *Pontoporeia affinis*, *Mysis caspia*, *M. microphthalma* and *M. amblyops*. *Amathillina spinosa*, *Pandorites podoceroides*, *Niphargoides grimmi*, *Stenocuma diastyloides* are found down to a depth of 150 m. An almost complete absence of molluscs is characteristic; only very rarely would a grab bring up *Dreissena grimmi*, *Dr. rostiformis*, *Micromelania spica*, *M. caspia* and *M. elegantula*. Deeper down (to 400 m) the Oligochaeta and *Hypania invalida* are found. In the Southern Caspian, only *Hypania invalida* and the Arctic mysids were found.

The specific deep-water fauna is absent from the great depths of the Caspian Sea. These are inhabited first by the forms of Arctic origin, adapted to low temperature; secondly by Caspian autochthonous forms, descendants of the shallower fauna, which acquired a deep-water aspect. The fauna is much richer above 100 m. Bivalves begin to play a dominant role here by their biomass (up to 90 per cent). However, at a depth of 50 to 100 m, the greatest mass forms are absent: *Mytilaster lineatus*, *Dreissena polymorpha*, *Dr. caspia*, *Didacna trigonoides*, *D. barbot-de-marnyi*, *D. crassa*, all the Adacna species, *Cardium edule*, *Theodoxus pallasi*, Hydrobia, all the species of the Pontogammarus genus, almost all of the Pterocuma, Turbellaria and *Cordylophora caspia*. Instead the original fauna of the large, higher crustaceans are most developed here: *Amathillina spinosa*, *Dikerogammarus caspius*, *D. grimmi*, *D. macrocephalus*, *Gammarus placidus*, *Paramysis eurylepis*, *Metamysis inflata* and some gastropods: *Micromelania elegantula*, *M. dimidiata*, *Theodoxus schultzi*.

At depths of less than 50 m the Arctic species disappear, the number of large crustaceans decreases considerably, while *Mytilaster lineatus*, *Dreissena caspia* and *Dr. rostriformis* appear in large numbers, and *Dr. polymorpha*.

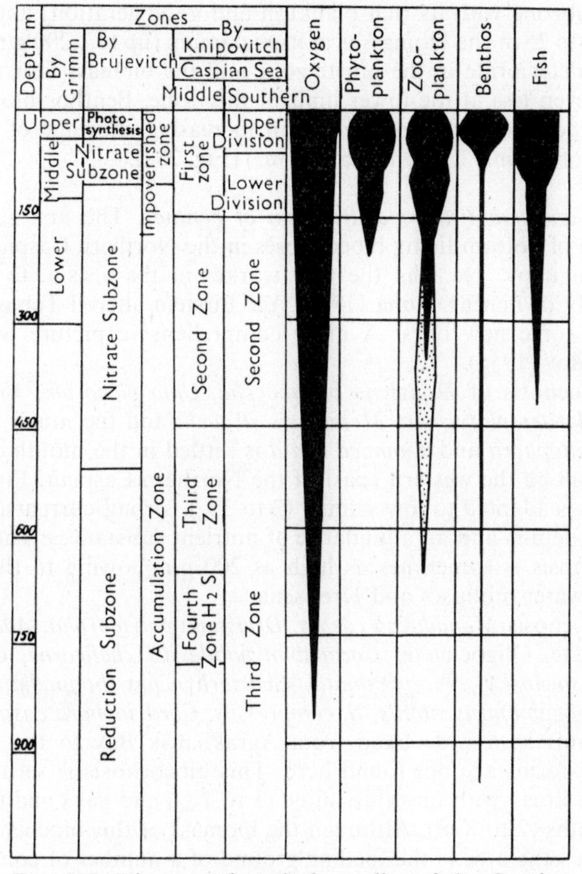

FIG. 287. Diagram of vertical zonality of the Caspian Sea (Zenkevitch, 1947).

Didacna baeri, *D. protracta* and species of the genera Pontogammarus, *Dikerogammarus haemobaphes* and others appear in smaller numbers. On sand silt above 15 m *Pontogammarus maeoticus*, *Dikerogammarus haemobaphes*, *Mytilaster lineatus*, *Theodoxus pallasi* and other Gastropoda are preponderant, while the Cardidae, except *Didacna trigonoides*, are almost absent. *Pontogammarus maeoticus* lives in huge numbers on sands right at the edge of the water, forming a biocoenosis very similar to that of the Sea of Azov (the zone of overwash).

The Caspian benthos is distributed into definite zones; moreover widely eurybathic forms and groups such as, for example, *Hypania invalida* (0 to 900 m), Oligochaeta (0 to 400 m), Chironomidae (0 to 400 m), *Dreissena grimmi* (5 to 300 m) and some others may be noted.

The vertical distribution of benthos agrees best with Brujevitch's 'structural zones'. The best conditions for benthos development are found in the photosynthetic subzone with its rich plankton and good aeration; and in fact at a depth of 15 to 25 m the biomass is at its maximum (up to 1,200 g/m^2). Feeding conditions deteriorate in the nitrite zone and the biomass falls to 70 to 150 g/m^2, and even less at the lower limit of this zone. Benthos biomass is very low in the accumulation zone, with an increasing shortage of oxygen and foodstuffs (often only a fraction of 1 g/m^2) (Fig. 288).

Qualitative and quantitative distribution of benthos. The first survey of the distribution of bottom-living biocoenoses in the Northern Caspian was given by N. Tchugunov. He was the first worker in the U.S.S.R. to use a grab for the study of marine fauna (1923). Ya. Birstein altered Tchugunov's data and added some new ones. A more comprehensive picture was given by L. Vinogradov (1955).

The biocoenosis of *Dreissena polymorpha*, *Unio pichorum*, *Viviparus viviparus*, *Pandorites platycheir*, *Metamysis strauchi* and the much rarer *Volgocuma thelmatophora* and *Limnaea ovata* is settled in the mouth of the Volga and partly along the western coast of the Northern Caspian (Fig. 289). This biocoenosis is adapted to low salinity (2 to 3‰), strong currents, a hard seafloor, small depths and an abundance of nutrient substances. The biomass of this biocoenosis is sometimes as high as 200 g/m^2 owing to the numerous large fresh-water molluscs and Dreissena.

The biocoenosis *Monodacna caspia*, *Dreissena polymorpha*, *Adacna plicata*, Chironomidae, Oligochaeta, *Corophium nobile*, *C. chelicorne*, *C. monodon*, *Pterocuma sowinskyi*, *Pt. pectinata*, *Schizorhynchus bilamellatus*, *Gmelina pusilla*, *Stenogammarus similis*, *S. compressus*, *Cordylophora caspia* and some others extends as a wide band from Agrakhansk Bay to the Ural River. Fresh-water forms are not found here. This biocoenosis is settled on a soft sea-floor, in areas with unstable saline (3 to 7‰) and gas conditions, and in shallow depths (2 to 8 m). Although the biomass of this biocoenosis is fairly low (12 g/m^2) the area is the feeding ground of a number of commercial fish (vobla, golden shiners and others).

The remaining part of the Northern Caspian, except for the Ural Trench and the transition zone to the Central Caspian, is occupied by the hard-seabed biocoenosis, adapted to depths of 8 to 12 m and a salinity of 5 to 9‰, with *Didacna trigonoides* as a dominant species. Among the other forms *Monodacna caspia*, *Dreissena polymorpha*, *Dr. caspia*, *Adacna plicata*, *Theodoxus pallasi*, *Niphargoides caspius*, *N. corpulentus*, *Corophium chelicorne* and *Dikerogammarus haemobaphes* are most developed here. The average biomass is 28 g/m^2. Ninety-five per cent of the total biomass here is composed of molluscs, whereas in the previous biocoenosis they formed only 86 per cent.

The soft soils filling the Ural Trench are inhabited by a small community

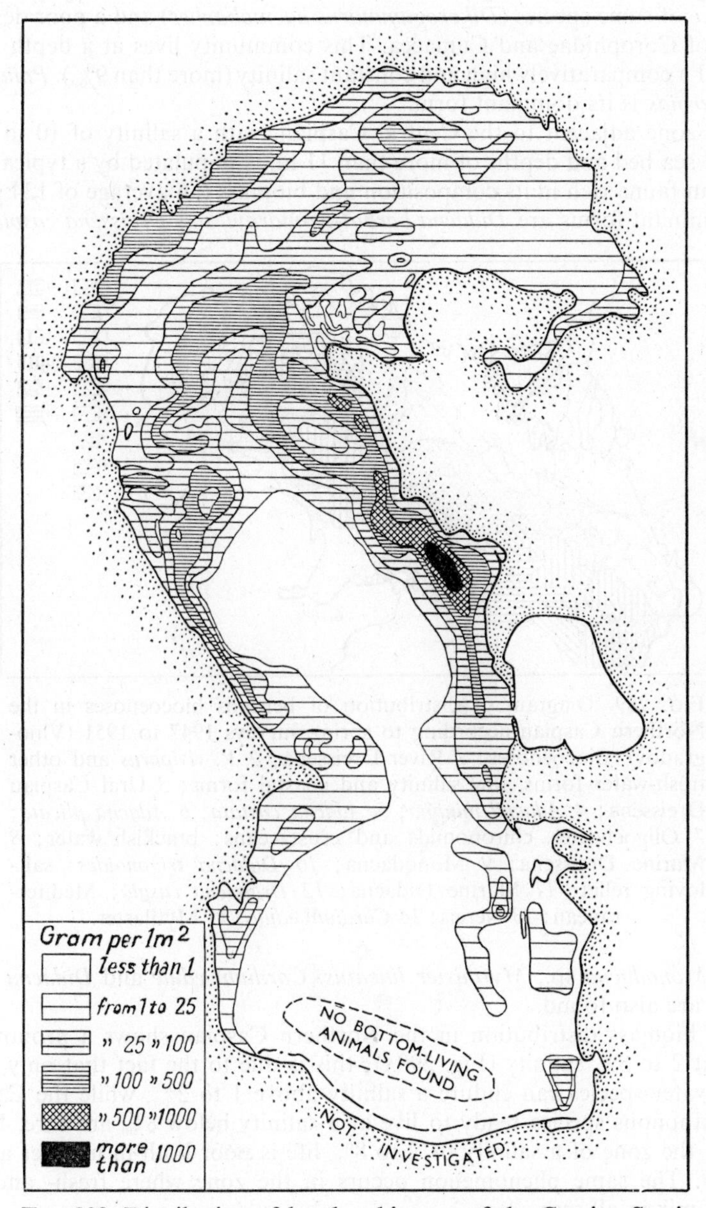

FIG. 288. Distribution of benthos biomass of the Caspian Sea in 1935 (Birstein, Briskina and Ryabchikov).

(average biomass—11·28 g/m^2) which differs from the preceding one by the absence of some species (*Dikerogammarus haemobaphes*) and a poor development of Corophidae and Cumacea. This community lives at a depth below 11 m at a comparatively high and constant salinity (more than 9‰). *Pandorites podoceroids* is its dominant form.

The zone adjacent to the Central Caspian, with a salinity of 10 to 12‰, a hard sea bed and depths of more than 11 m, is populated by a typical mid-Caspian fauna rich in its composition and biomass (an average of 124 g/m^2). Its dominant forms are *Didacna barbot-de-marnyi* and *Dreissena caspia*, and

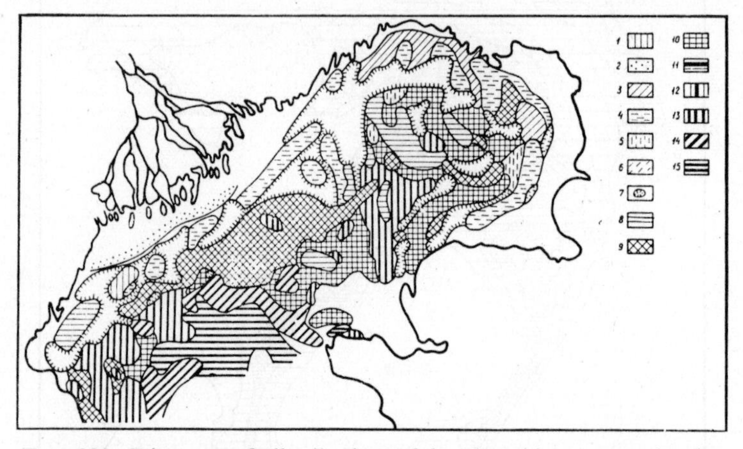

FIG. 289. Diagram of distribution of benthos biocoenoses in the Northern Caspian according to spring surveys 1947 to 1951 (Vinogradov). Biocoenoses: *1* River Dreissena; *2* *V. viviparus* and other fresh-water forms, low salinity and coastal forms; *3* Ural–Caspian Dreissena; *4* *Adacna minima*; *5* *Adacna costata*; *6* *Adacna plicata*; *7* Oligochaetes, chironomids and crustaceans: brackish water; *8* Marine Dreissena; *9* Monodacna; *10* *Didacna trigonoides*: salt-loving relict; *11* Marine Didacna; *12* *Dreissena caspia*; Mediterranean; *13* Nereis; *14* *Cardium edule*; *15* Mytilaster.

some *Monodacna* sp., *Mytilaster lineatus*, *Cardium edule* and *Didacna trigonoides* are also found.

The biomass distribution in the Northern Caspian shows a pronounced drop at 2 to 8‰ salinity (Fig. 290A); this is due to the fact that only a few fresh-water species can endure a salinity above 1 to 2‰, while the Caspian autochthonous species ready to live at a salinity below 8‰ are rare. Hence within the zone of a salinity of 2 to 8‰ life is poor both in number and in variety. The same phenomenon occurs in the zone where fresh- and sea-waters mix in all seas.

Here, however, apart from salinity the gas conditions of the bottom layer are also of great importance. Salinities of 2 to 8‰ are found within the zone of the 12 to 18 ft heap of wrack. The soft soils here owe their origin to the deposition of suspended particles under the effect of the coagulative action

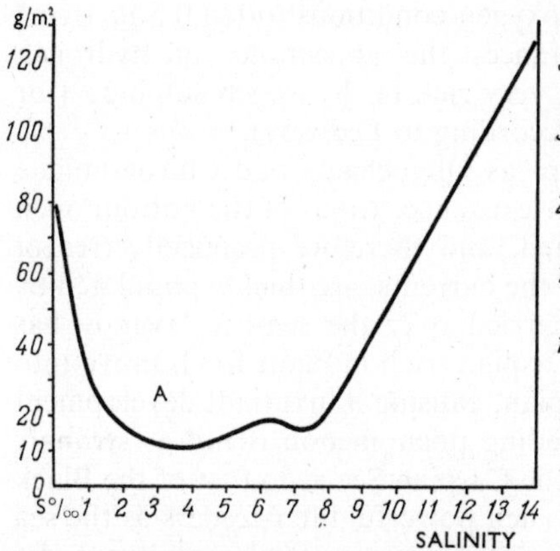

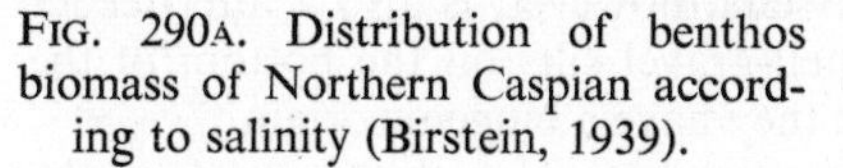
FIG. 290A. Distribution of benthos biomass of Northern Caspian according to salinity (Birstein, 1939).

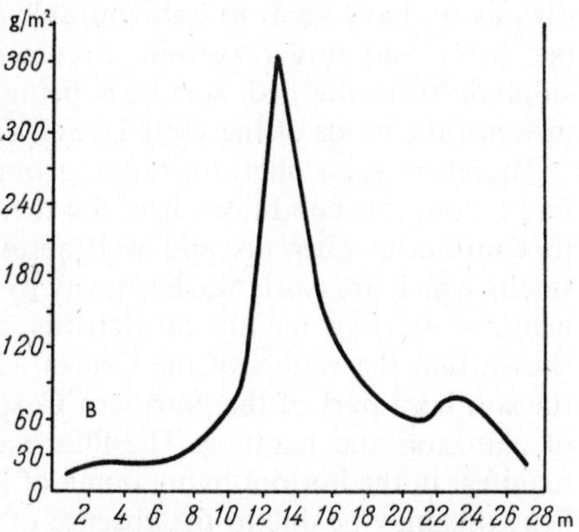

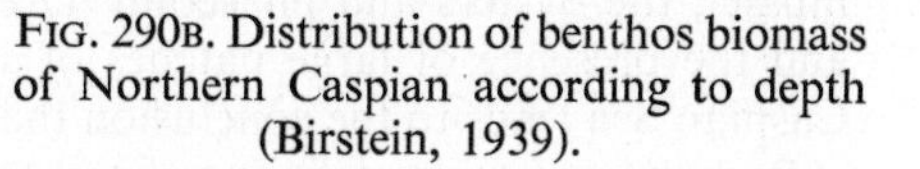
FIG. 290B. Distribution of benthos biomass of Northern Caspian according to depth (Birstein, 1939).

of sea-water. In calm weather a definite vertical stratification is observed in this zone, since the fresh waters of the Volga and Ural flow over the saline sea-water. When the processes of decomposition of the organic substances of the sea-bed become intensive owing to conditions of vertical stratification, oxygen is used for the oxidation of the soil and the bottom layer loses much of its oxygen. This oppresses many benthic animals and the heap of wrack becomes inhabited by euryoxybiotic forms which can live in water deficient in oxygen. This problem was discussed above when dealing with brackish water.

In the Northern Caspian the main benthos biomass is found at depths of 12 to 16 m, whereas its average depth is only 6 m (Fig. 290B). The relationship between the benthos biomass and the nature of the sea-bed is just as indicative. It has been shown for many seas that on mobile hard floor (gravel, shell gravel, large-grain sands) the fauna becomes scarce and sometimes disappears.

This, however, is not so in the Caspian Sea. Low biomass indices are found on soft beds, situated chiefly along the 12 to 18 ft of wrack (*Table 261*). This is

Table 261

Sea-bed	Mean biomass, g/m²
Shell–gravel	79·0
Sand–shell–gravel	32·2
Sand	23·9
Sand–shell–gravel–ooze	26·7
Ooze–shell–gravel	18·8
Ooze	8·8
Ooze with hydrogen sulphide	0·9

due, as we have seen, to unfavourable oxygen conditions (often 0·5 to 1 cm^3 per litre) and under certain circumstances the appearance of hydrogen sulphide from the bed, soft beds being very rich in hydrogen sulphide (for instance the muds of the Ural Trench according to Fedosov).

Therefore such oligo-oxybiotic groups as Oligochaeta and Chironomidae find favourable conditions here for their existence. Areas of the bottom open to continuous currents and well aerated, and therefore practically free of smelts which are easily washed away by the currents, are thickly populated by benthos, feeding mainly on detritus carried over the sea-bed. Ivanov has shown that the waters of the Central Caspian, rich in plant food, move into the southern part of the Northern Caspian, causing a luxuriant development of plankton and benthos. The filter-feeding phenomenon is not as strongly manifest in the bottom-living fauna of the Caspian Sea as in that of the Black Sea; this may be due to the absence of such powerful filter-feeders as the sea mussel, the oysters and phaseolin. Dreissena, however, is also a filter-feeder and the presence of large patches of shell-gravel silts on the bottom of the Caspian Sea leads to the conclusion that they have a biogenic origin.

Perhaps a certain deficiency in the representation in the Caspian of the filter-feeding phenomena has conditioned such a luxuriant development in it of a typical filter-feeder, the alien Mytilaster—a development which is not characteristic of it in its native habitat, the Black and Azov Seas.

The process of the accumulation of silt soils may possibly increase in the areas of the dense settlements of Mytilaster in the Caspian Sea.

During the last 25 years much qualitative and quantitative research has been carried out on the bottom-living fauna of the Caspian Sea. The Northern Caspian has been investigated in particular detail.

On the average the benthos biomass of the Northern Caspian has remained unaltered, except for its catastrophic drop in 1937–38, which was followed by fairly slow regeneration over many years. A second, less violent drop was recorded in 1946 and 1947 (*Table 262*).

As shown by *Table 262* the drop in biomass is in both cases controlled mainly by the decrease in the number of molluscs and, to a lesser extent, by that of the crustaceans in 1937 and 1938. Birstein suggests that at that time some suffocation phenomena took place as a result of oxygen shortage. Bivalves are markedly predominant in the Northern Caspian benthos; among other groups Nereis stands out sharply (*Table 263*).

These data on the state of benthos in the Northern Caspian can be supplemented by those given by V. Osadchikh (1958) for 1954 and 1956. The total benthos biomass increased during this period by 30 per cent, mainly owing to worms (by 98 per cent) and crustaceans (by 70 per cent). Oligochaete biomass increased by 193 per cent and that of Nereis by 59 per cent. The chironomid biomass increased very greatly (by 355 per cent). The food available for adult fish rose by 25 per cent and for young fish by 46 per cent. Considerable patches of Syndesmya were formed (*Table 264*).

It is evident from the data in *Table 264* that the intrusion of Nereis has had no harmful effect on local fauna; neither the oligochaetes nor the chironomids have been affected, as might first have been expected if this effect existed.

Table 262. Mean Northern Caspian biomass (g/m^2) 1935–55

Groups	1935 spr*	1937 aut*	1938 spr	1940 spr	1941 aut	1944–45 aut	1946 aut	1947 spr	1948 aut	1949 spr	1954	1956
Vermes	0·82	0·28	0·19	3·16	1·76	3·25	2·45	3·30	3·12	2·38	3·35	6·50
including Nereis	—	—	—	—	—	1·17	1·40	1·32	1·96	1·50	1·12	1·91
Chironomidae	0·99	0·05	0·17	0·39	0·17	0·38	0·44	0·73	0·23	0·11	0·09	0·37
Crustacea	2·63	0·38	0·38	1·36	3·22	3·41	2·09	1·72	1·21	1·97	2·47	3·93
Mollusca	35·88	7·59	4·0	10·19	13·23	26·15	9·94	12·87	25·94	26·01	12·67	17·40
including Syndesmya	—	—	—	—	—	—	—	—	—	—	—	0·22
Total	40·32	8·30	4·74	15·10	18·38	33·19	14·92	18·62	30·50	30·37	18·64	30·30

* spr—spring, aut—autumn.

Table 263. Benthos composition in Northern Caspian, g/m², in 1949

Groups	Biomass	Groups	Biomass
Oligochaeta	0·79	Monodacna	6·30
Ampharetidae	0·08	Adacna	1·62
Nereis	1·5	Didacna	4·63
Hirudinea	0·008	Cardium	0·89
		Dreissena	6·56
Total of Vermes	2·38	Mytilaster	5·61
Chironomidae	0·11	Gastropoda	0·40
Gammaridae	0·70	Total of Mollusca	26·01
Corophiidae	0·82		
Cumacea	0·35	Total of benthos	30·37
Total of crustaceans	1·87		

Table 264. Benthos composition in Northern Caspian in 1954 and 1956, g/m² (V. Osadchikh, 1958)

Organism	1954 Within the zone of commercial fish distribution	1956 Within the zone of commercial fish distribution	1956 Throughout the zone investigated
Dreissena polymorpha	3·51	4·49	5·15
Adacna minima	2·25	1·22	1·16
Monodacna	4·89	5·41	5·93
Didacna trigonoides	1·84	3·03	3·77
Cardium edule	0·12	0·22	0·75
Mytilaster lineatus	0·06	0·004	0·42
Syndesmya ovata	—	0·0003	0·22
Total of molluscs	12·67	14·37	17·40
Corophiidae	0·91	1·61	1·40
Gammaridae	0·90	1·41	1·40
Cumacea	0·66	1·18	1·13
Total of crustacea	2·47	4·20	3·93
Nereis	1·12	1·78	1·91
Oligochaeta	1·50	4·40	4·12
Ampharetidae	0·73	0·47	0·47
Total of worms	3·35	6·65	6·50
Chironomidae	0·09	0·40	0·37
Total biomass	18·64	25·62	28·20

The Nereis biocoenosis (L. Vinogradov, 1953) has not replaced, and could not have replaced, the biocoenosis of small Adacna, higher crustacean and chironomid larvae. Only in one place (Tyuleni Island), forming 1·8 per cent of the whole area, has the Nereis biocoenosis taken the place of an oligochaete biocoenosis, but it formed a biomass there two to seven times (in different years) greater than the oligochaete biocoenosis. The examination of benthos throughout the whole Caspian Sea carried out in 1956, 18 years after the 1938

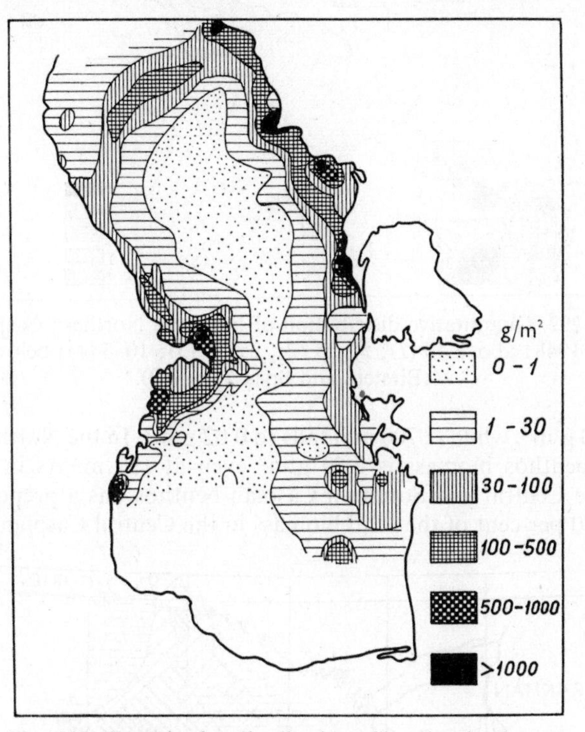

FIG. 291. Quantitative distribution of benthos in Central and part of the Southern Caspian in 1956 (g/m²) (Romanova, 1960).

survey (N. Romanova, 1960), has revealed considerable changes in the nature of the distribution of the bottom-living fauna (Fig. 291). The eastern shores of the Northern and Central Caspian are richer in benthos than the western ones. The main mass of benthos is formed by Mytilaster, with a pronounced decrease in the amount of Dreissena, Didacna, Monodacna and Adacna (63 per cent of total biomass in the Central Caspian, and 94 per cent in the Southern). The part played by Cardium is increased, and Nereis is strongly developed (Fig. 292) on soils rich in organic matter (Fig. 293). In its central parts the Sea is deeper than 200 m and the benthos biomass there falls below 1 g/m². Total benthos biomass reaches its maximum at depths of 10 to 25 m. In the Southern Caspian at depths of 200 to 300 m the biomass decreases to

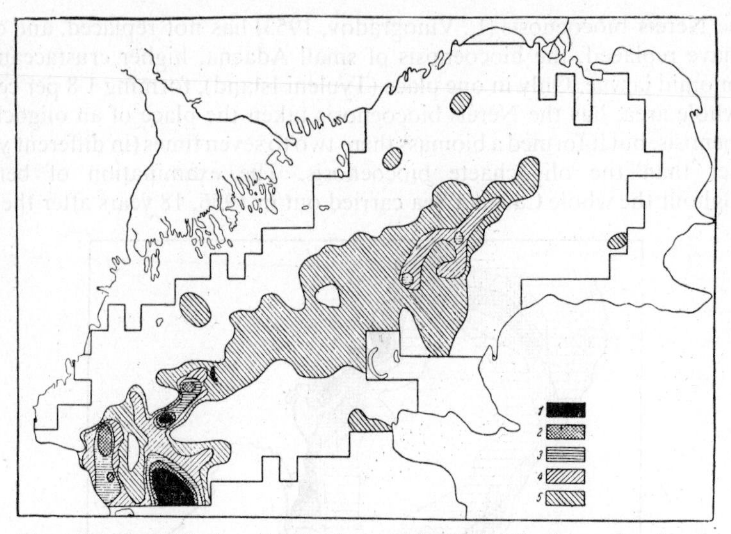

FIG. 292. Quantitative distribution of Nereis in Northern Caspian in June 1948: above 50 (*1*); 50–25 (*2*); 25–10 (*3*); 10–5 (*4*); below 5 (*5*) (Birstein and Spassky, 1952).

0·60 to 0·70 g/m², while at 700 m it falls to 0·02 g/m². In the Northern Caspian the mean benthos biomass is 7·59 g/m² even at 150 m. As in the Central Caspian the Central and Southern Caspian benthos has a preponderance of molluscs (90 per cent of the total biomass in the Central Caspian, 98 per cent

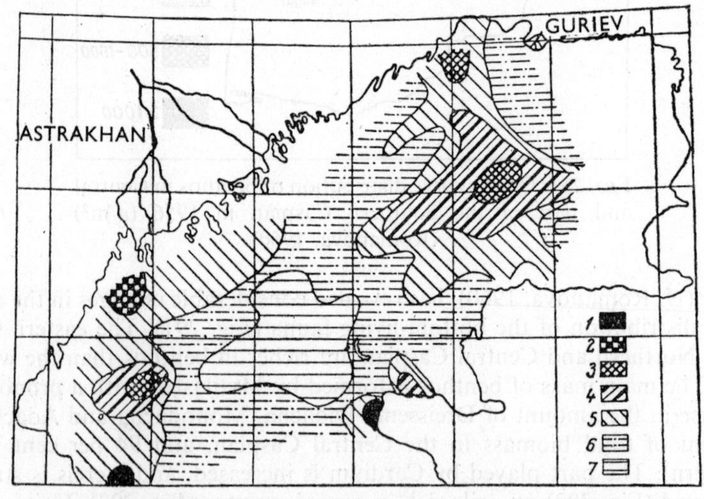

FIG. 293. Distribution of organic substances in the soils of the Northern Caspian as percentages (Yastrebova, with data of Gorshkova added): above 3 (*1*); 3–2 (*2*); 2–1·5 (*3*); 1·5–1 (*4*); 1–0·5 (*5*); below 0·5 (*6*); trace (*7*).

in the Southern). In the Central Caspian the higher crustaceans, Gammaridae and Corophiidae, which penetrate to great depths and give a biomass of about 6 g/m^2, develop in considerable numbers. The Nereis biomass reaches 0·6 to 0·8 g/m^2, based on the whole Sea area, and 3·5 to 5·0 g/m^2 for the areas no deeper than 200 m. Its favourite habitats are Mytilaster concretions, where it apparently uses the mollusc faeces and pseudofaeces rich in organic matter. 'The vigorous development and the wide eurybiotic capacity of the members of Mediterranean fauna which have penetrated into the Caspian Sea have often been recorded', writes N. Romanova (1959). 'The considerable adaptability of the immigrants, their higher viability than that of the local autochthonous fauna, is illustrated by the composition of the Southern Caspian fauna. Exceptionally high biomass is always due to the development of species of Mediterranean fauna: Mytilaster, Cardium and Nereis', with this difference between Mytilaster and Nereis, that the first crowds out other bivalves in its development, while the second does not crowd anything out when growing in large numbers.

A detailed survey of Nereis colonies, of their utilization by fish and of the change in the composition of the bottom biocoenosis, was again organized in 1948 and 1949; a series of experimental researches was also carried out. The results of this work were published in a special volume (1952).

Special attention was naturally paid to Nereis and Syndesmya in their new habitat. As has been mentioned above, the worm was discovered in the Caspian Sea in 1944, i.e. five years after its transplantation. By that time the

Table 265. Benthos composition of Central and Southern Caspian

No. in order	Organism	g/m^2		Percentage of total Biomass		Thousands of tons	
		Central	Southern	Central	Southern	Central	Southern
1	Nereis	0·6	0·8	0·98	0·65	68·8	76·7
2	Oligochaeta	0·5	0·3	0·76	0·24	57·4	28·7
3	Polychaeta	0·2	0·1	0·3	0·08	22·9	9·6
	Vermes	1·3	1·2	1·98	0·97	149·1	115·0
4	Chironomidae	0·21	0·07	0·33	0·04	24·1	6·7
5	Isopoda	0·8	0·08	1·22	0·07	91·8	7·6
6	Amphipoda:						
	(a) Gammaridae	2·1	0·4	3·2	0·3	240·9	38·4
	(b) Corophiidae	2·4	0·5	3·64	0·4	275·3	47·9
7	Cumacea	0·5	0·3	0·76	0·24	57·4	28·7
	Malacostraca	5·8	1·28	8·82	1·01	665·4	122·6
8	*Balanus improvisus*	0·22	0·3	0·34	0·25	25·2	28·7
9	*Mytilaster lineatus*	41·5	114·1	62·9	94·38	4,761·4	10,942·2
10	*Dreissena distincta*	11·6	0·03	17·6	0·02	1,330·9	2·8
11	*Cardium edule*	1·0	4·1	1·51	3·4	114·7	393·2
12	Didacna	3·6	0·02	5·46	0·02	413·0	1·9
13	Monodacna	0·3	0·1	0·45	0·01	34·4	9·6
14	Adacna	0·4	—	0·61	—	15·9	—
	Molluscs	58·4	118·35	88·53	97·83	6,670·3	11,349·7
	Total	65·93	121·1	100	100	7,534·1	11,622·7

main sandy silt areas of the Northern Caspian, hitherto practically uninhabited (Fig. 294), were already populated by Nereis. Nereis can endure a scarcity of oxygen and can exist for a long time in its absence (A. Karpevitch, 1952). The habitat of Nereis was charted with greater precision during the extensive investigations of the Northern Caspian bottom-living fauna carried out in 1948–49 (Fig. 292). Its total biomass was found to be 1·4 to 1·7 million centners. If we take into consideration the worms consumed by fish and their

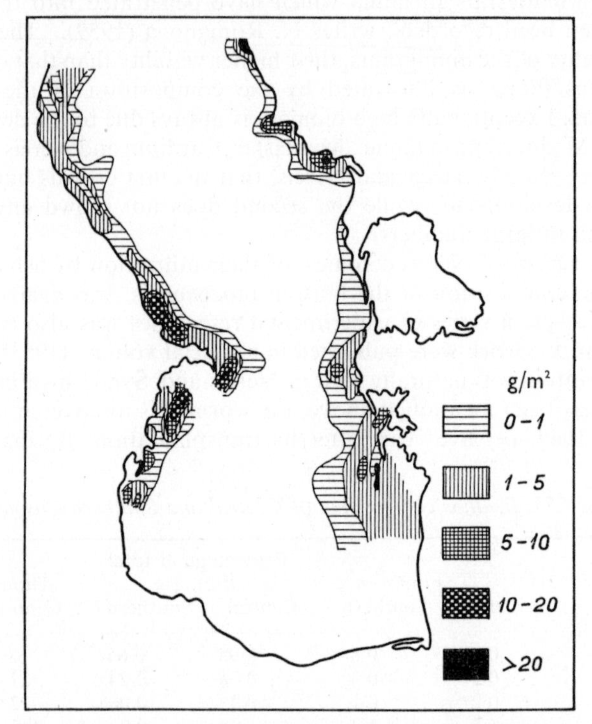

FIG. 294. Distribution of Nereis in Northern and the northern part of the Southern Caspian in summer 1956 (Romanova, 1960).

mass mortality after spawning, the annual production of Nereis in the Northern Caspian must be two or three times larger still.

According to the latest survey, carried out in 1954 and 1956 (V. Osadchikh, 1958), the habitat of Nereis and its numbers have remained unchanged in the Northern Caspian.

The benthos survey of 1956 covered also the Central Caspian and part of the Southern (N. Romanova, 1959); a picture of the quantitative distribution of Nereis obtained showed quantitative indices similar to those for the Northern Caspian (Fig. 294). Thus the total quantity of the Nereis biomass in the Caspian Sea reaches one million tons, while its annual production is two to three times greater. The fate of another immigrant into the Caspian Sea

—*Syndesmya ovata*—is quite different. It was discovered only in 1955 (A. Saenkova, 1956) and so far its propagation has been limited to individual patches in the southern part of the Northern Caspian. On the average it gave in 1956 a biomass of 0·22 g/m^2 in the area investigated (V. Osadchikh, 1958), and a total of about 200,000 to 300,000 centners. Before 1956 *Syndesmya ovata* was not recorded in either the Central or the Southern Caspian. There are reasons to believe that the first transplantation of Syndesmya into the Caspian Sea gave no results, while that of 1948 was successful.

A careful study of the biology of Nereis has shown (G. Belyaev, 1952) that the worms can live in huge numbers (up to 8,900 specimens with a biomass of up to 870 g/m^2, and with some specimens growing to 14 cm in length and to more than 2 g in weight) in shallow lagoons and inlets of the northwestern part of the Caspian Sea on silty sand soils. The author notes that on these sites Nereis evidently feeds exclusively on soil detritus rich in organic matter. Young and adult worms can easily live through a fall of salinity down to 1‰ or less; fertilization and egg development require a salinity of not less than 5‰. Nereis mass multiplication takes place in shallows in the spring and in greater depths in summer, moreover heteronereis stages are formed which leave the burrows inhabited by immature worms. The worms die after spawning; the whole cycle of their development is accomplished in one year, or perhaps even in one summer. These observations are supplemented by a comprehensive study of the feeding of Nereis (E. Yablonskaya, 1952) which has shown that Nereis, which spends most of its life actually in the soil, 'has developed a capacity for swallowing as food the upper layer of the soil with all its components . . . using, instead of detritus, films at different stages of destruction and plants and animals living in them when they are within reach, without any special selection or hunting for them . . . moreover, the natural conditions of the Nereis environment would make the latter impossible in the majority of cases'. Owing to this manner of feeding, animal remains are very rare in the worms' intestines. V. Beklemishev (1950) has studied in detail the feeding of *Nereis pelagica* in the Barents Sea. The intestines of this worm are always filled with algae, with a little admixture of animals which were taken in with the algae. *N. diversicolor* and *N. virens*, as well as *N. succinea*, have adopted the same manner of feeding. The jaws of all these species of Nereis, arranged exactly alike, are not a weapon of attack on living victims, but an instrument for raking algae and detritus into their mouths.

A. Zhukova (1954) has shown experimentally that Nereis, fed on microorganisms and yeast, develops and grows normally. She has thus proved the detritus feeding of this worm and confirmed Yablonskaya's data. A survey of the feeding of fish in the Northern Caspian (N. Sokolova, 1952; Ya. Birstein, 1952) has shown that, since Nereis colonies appeared in the Caspian Sea, starred sturgeon has almost exclusively passed over to a Nereis diet, and sturgeon and a number of other fish have added a considerable amount of it to their diet.

The nutrient qualities of Nereis, both as fat and as protein, and its calorific value are certainly high (*Table 266*).

The calorific value of Northern Caspian benthos has increased greatly with

Table 266. Nutrient value of Caspian invertebrates (E. Bokova, 1946; L. Vinogradov, 1948; M. Zheltenkova, 1939)

Foodstuff	Content, percentage of dry weight			Calorific value k cal/g
	Fats	Proteins	Ash	
Caspian molluscs (*Dreissena polymorpha*)	1·23	10·16	83·06	0·63
Caspian crustaceans (Gammaridae and Corophiidae)	6·47	53·71	25·59	3·13
Nereis diversicolor	7·73	66·88	13·82	5·58

its colonization by Nereis, and in 1946–49 21 to 30 per cent of its total calorific value was due to Nereis.

Changes in benthos distribution (quantitative and qualitative) in the Caspian Sea are controlled not only by the distribution of new immigrants, but also by its rise in salinity, especially in the Northern Caspian.

Mytilaster, Cardium and Nereis have moved far northwards; on the other hand *Dreissena polymorpha* and *Didacna trigonoides*, much less tolerant of salinity, have receded to the northwest and reduced the area of their habitat.

Zoobenthos biomass of the Caspian Sea. The following is a count of the benthos biomass in the different areas of the Caspian Sea:

Southern	116,227 tons
Central	10,000,000 tons
Northern	6,100,000 tons
Total	27,622,700 tons

Thus almost four-fifths of all bottom fauna are concentrated in the Central Caspian. Plankton does not form such accumulations there, especially along the eastern shores; the cause of the abundance of benthos is as yet unknown.

Food value of zoobenthos of Caspian Sea. Data on the qualities as food of the main species of the Caspian and Azov–Black Sea fauna are of interest. E. Bokova (1946) gives some interesting information on this aspect in her work (*Tables 267, 268, 269*). It is evident from these data that species of the genus Adacna have the highest food value among the Caspian molluscs. Mytilaster and Syndesmya are close to them in their properties (*Table 267*).

The molluscs occupy first place in the Caspian benthos and in the diet of Caspian fish.

Crustaceans are different in their nutrient qualities and it is evident from *Table 267* that crustaceans, which occupy second place in the diet of Caspian fish, are much superior to the molluscs in their significance as food.

The average percentage of protein and fat content in crustaceans is more than five times higher than that in molluscs, while the ash content is correspondingly three times lower.

Table 267

Form	Percentage dry weight Protein	Fat	Ash
Caspian			
Didacna trigonoides	5·10	1·11	91·00
D. barbot-de-marnyi	6·06	0·90	88·60
Adacna minima	17·53	2·33	75·60
A. laeviuscula	14·80	1·30	72·10
A. plicata	12·56	2·0	—
Dreissena polymorpha	9·93	0·68	86·81
Mediterranean			
Cardium edule	5·62	0·95	92·90
Mytilaster lineatus	14·41	1·72	72·80
Syndesmya ovata	13·00	1·24	71·54
Average for all the Caspian molluscs (except Syndesmya)	10·16	1·23	83·05

Food indices of worms (and insect larvae) are even higher than those of the crustaceans. Nereis, acclimatized in the Caspian Sea, has the most favourable food indices (*Table 269*).

Fish

The Caspian Sea fish, according to A. Derzhavin, include 78 species (*Table 270*).

The last four families in *Table 270*, which includes two species of grey

Table 268

Form	Percentage dry weight Protein	Fat	Ash
Caspian			
Paramysis baeri	73·10	6·00	16·00
Paramysis baquensis	51·25	5·00	27·00
Metamysis strauchi	70·25	8·30	14·17
Average for mysids	63·37	6·87	19·18
Pontogammarus maeoticus	54·77	9·40	25·00
Dikerogammarus haemobaphes	50·31	8·50	24·10
Stenogammarus similis	49·18	3·80	33·50
Pandorites platycheir	46·49	9·37	35·29
Average for amphipods	48·83	7·21	29·68
Pterocuma pectinata / *Pterocuma sowinskyi*	29·20	3·17	40
Average for all crustaceans	53·71	6·47	25·59
Mediterranean			
Leander nectirostius	71·85	4·44	13·98

Table 269

Species	Percentage dry weight		
	Proteins	Fat	Ash
Caspian			
Chironomids	66·12	7·60	10·40
Oligochaetes	63·70	5·00	5·85
Mediterranean			
Nereis	66·88	7·73	13·82

mullet, flatfish and mosquito-fish, were introduced into the Caspian Sea fauna by man. Of the 38 aboriginal genera of the Caspian fish, eleven—Caspiomyzon, Caspialosa, Neogobius, Mesogobius, Proterorhinus, Asra, Caspiosoma, Hyrcanogobius, Benthophiloides, Benthophilus and Anatirostrum—are endemic forms of the Pontic–Caspian–Aral region; of these Caspiomyzon, Asra, Anatirostrum and 22 other species exist only in the Caspian Sea. The greatest variety of species is given by the Gobiidae, Cyprinidae, Clupeidae and Acipenseridae families. The Clupeidae and Gobiidae families are exceptional in their process of forming small taxonomic units. For example, *Caspialosa caspia* has five forms and *Caspialosa brashnikovi* has seven forms (subspecies).

Table 270. Composition of Caspian Sea ichthyofauna

Family	Total number of species	Among these, number of endemic forms:				
		Pontic–Caspian species	Aral		Caspian	
			Percentage	Species	Percentage	Species
Petromyzonidae	1	1	100	1	100	0
Acipenseridae	5	3	60	0	0	2
Clupeidae	9	9	100	4	55·5	14
Salmonidae	2	1	50	1	50	1
Esocidae	1	0	0	0	0	0
Cyprinidae	15	55	33	1	7	9
Cobitidae	2	1	50	1	50	0
Siluridae	1	0	0	0	0	0
Gadidae	1	0	0	0	0	0
Gasterosteidae	1	1	100	0	0	0
Syngnatidae	1	1	100	0	0	1
Atherinidae	1	0	0	0	0	1
Percidae	4	2	50	0	0	0
Gobiidae	30	30	100	16	53·0	8
Mugilidae	2	0	0	0	0	0
Pleuronectidae	1	0	0	0	0	0
Poeciliidae	1	0	0	0	0	0
Total	78	54	69·3	25	32·0	35

A most characteristic feature of the Caspian Sea ichthyofauna is the wide range of its species between those of fresh and saline waters, with most varied forms of adaptation to water of different salinity—from fresh water (with the development of settled breeds) to the high salinity of the eastern inlets of the Caspian Sea. Thus *Caspialosa caspia salina* lives at a salinity of 35·8‰. The western species *Pomatoschistus caucasicus*, *Syngnathus nigrolineatus caspius* and *Atherina mochon pontica caspia* live and multiply at a salinity of 59·5‰. Derzhavin correctly remarks that: 'such a variation in the behaviour of Caspian fish is a manifestation of a wide adaptation during the Quaternary history of this body of water to the changing conditions of water, climate and salinity in different parts of the Caspian Sea'. The formation of one single fauna from marine and fresh-water forms through a complex history of a fauna of diversified genesis is graphically shown from the example of Caspian fish; in individual biological groups of this fauna fresh-water and marine forms are found side by side. A prolonged coexistence under changing conditions had erased the features linked with the early diversified genesis of species and a single fauna was evolved, bound together by its conditions of existence in a given body of water and by the history of the latter.

Biological groups of fish. Among the fish of the Caspian Sea the group of migratory fish inhabiting the Sea itself and moving up the rivers for spawning is chiefly distinguishable. Vobla, Acipenseridae (except sterlet), *Stenodus leucichthys*, salmon and some herrings may be included in this group. The second group, of semi-migratory fish, includes primarily those which keep to the less saline areas of the Sea and move up the rivers for spawning (pike perch, golden shiner, carp and Pelecus), and secondly those which keep only to the much more diluted waters of the river mouths and also move upstream for spawning (*Abramis ballerus*, *Abramis sapa*, *Rutilus rutilus*, *Aspius aspius* and others). The third group consists of the native river fish. They are either absent or rare even in the areas of the Sea with a reduced salinity (sterlet, Tinca, *Carassius auratus*). Finally, the fourth group comprises fish which very rarely enter waters of lowered salinity (marine pike perch, some varieties of the South Caspian herrings such as *Caspialosa brashnikovi grimmi*, *C.b. kisselevitschi*, *C. caspia knipovitschi*, *C. brashnikovi autumnalis*, Clupeonella and a series of the species of bullheads and Benthophilus). Some of them move to the shore for spawning, others make regular migrations from the Central and Southern Caspian into the Northern. Marine pike perch and three breeds of Southern Caspian herrings never enter the zones of lowered salinity at all. Most of these groups include species of ancient autochthonous forms and fresh-water immigrants.

The great differences in the manner of life of the Caspian fish attracted the attention of workers long ago. K. Kessler (1887), the author of the first biological classification of fish, based his work on his observations of Caspian fish.

Fish migration. The exceptional richness in migratory fish is the interesting feature of the Caspian Sea (and also of the Sea of Azov). All the Acipenseridae (except sterlet), Salmonidae and Cyprinidae of the Caspian Sea enter a river for spawning and then return to the Sea. Among the herrings *Caspialosa volgensis* and *C. kessleri* are migratory fish. The latter enters the Volga, with its gonads still immature, from the beginning of April till the end of June, moving upstream as far as Gorki, going up the Oka to Serpukhov and Kaluga, and up the Kama to beyond Molotov. *Caspialosa volgensis* spawns mainly in the lower Volga (up to Saratov); only a few of the fish go farther upstream. Side by side with these there are semi-migratory herrings which spawn in the pre-delta and delta of the Volga (*C. caspia aestuarina*, *C. suvorovi*) and herring which enter fresher waters of the Sea for spawning but do not go upstream (*C. brashnikovi* with its varieties and *C. caspia* with its sub-species). Thus an examination of these herrings, so closely related to each other, reveals a series of gradual transitions from the migratory to the marine fish.

The migrations of Caspian herring within the limits of the Sea are regular and fairly complex. In winter they all gather in the southern and central parts of the Caspian (Fig. 295A), mostly within the area open to the influence of the warm current running from the shores of Iran along the eastern coast of the Southern Caspian.

With the coming of warm spring weather, herrings approach the western and part of the eastern shores of the Central and Southern Caspian, while some breeds move into the Northern Caspian (Fig. 295B). The more cold-loving herrings (*C. brashnikovi*, Alosa and the migrant herrings) are the first to approach the shore. When the temperature of the coastal waters rises above 12° C the herring move northward where the water is still much cooler. They keep in the open sea away from the shore. Only some endemic Southern Caspian herring can endure a comparatively high temperature, and they spawn off the coast at a temperature of 12° and even higher.

In summer the main mass of herrings is gathered in the Northern Caspian. The fry of migratory herrings (*C. brashnikovi*, *C. sphaerocephala* and *C. saposhnikovi*) come down to this area from the rivers Volga and Ural, attracting the predatory herring which have remained in the Northern Caspian after spawning, feeding on the fry of migratory herring and on the sprat. In the summer large numbers of migratory herrings and of the Central Caspian Alosa are found in this region.

The entry of herrings into the warmer Central Caspian waters begins in the autumn with the arrival of colder weather in the Northern Caspian. Herrings and sprat young-of-the-year are the first to leave; they are followed by adult predatory herrings preying on them. With the drop in temperature herrings move farther and farther south (Fig. 295C), lingering in shallow inlets and bays, where they feed on plankton (*C. caspia*) and on the young fish (predatory breeds). Moreover, they move much more slowly than in the spring, keeping to the upper layer of water (15 to 25 m), since in the autumn only a shallow layer is heated.

Apart from the two herring species above, *Caspiomyzon wagneri*, two species of Salmonidae (*Stenodus leucichthys* and *Salmo trutta caspius*) and the Acipenseridae should be included in the group of migratory fish of marine origin. Usually these fish make long spawning journeys; moreover, there are

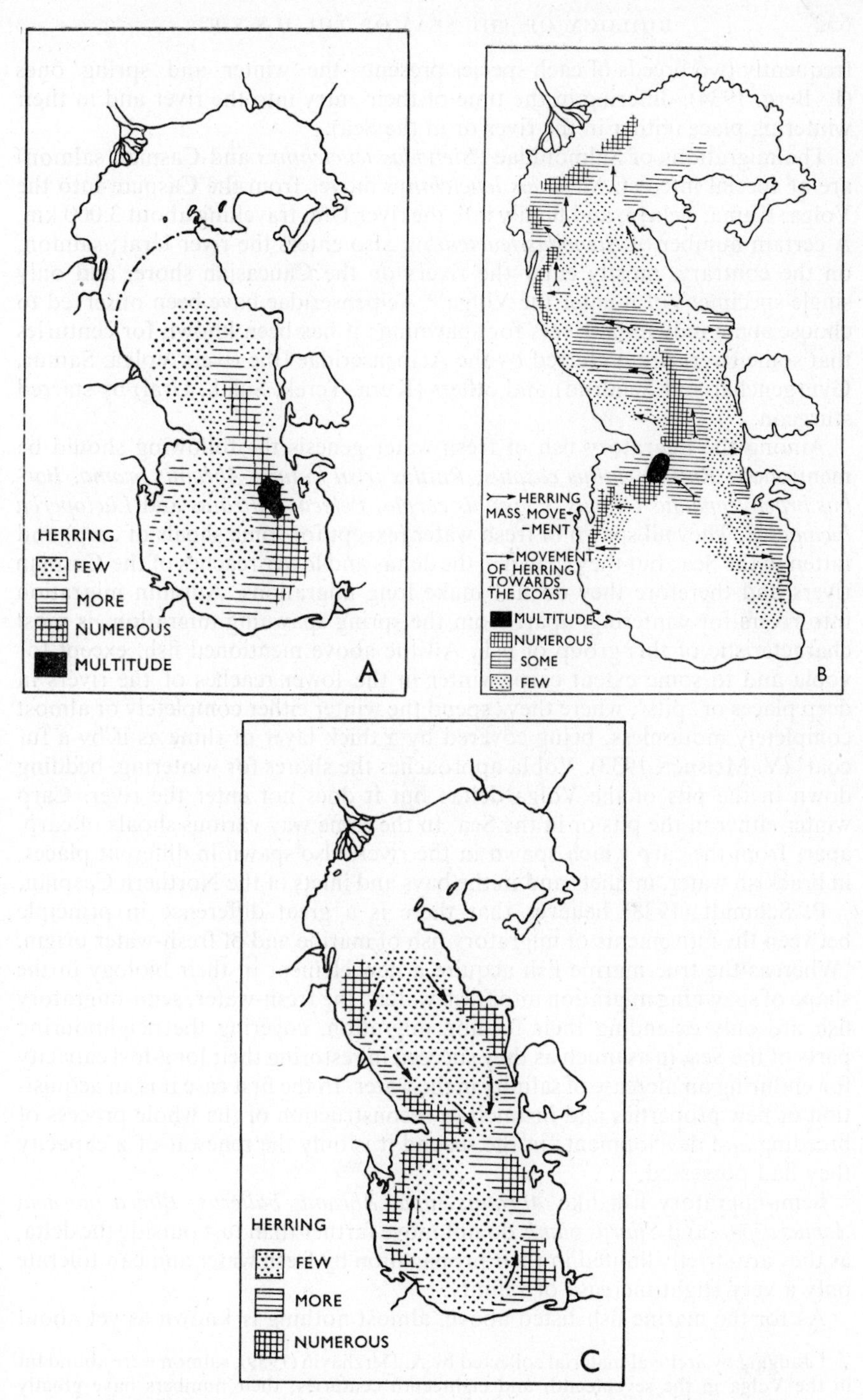

FIG. 295. Distribution of herring in the Caspian Sea (Tchugunov, with some alterations): A In winter and early spring; B In spring; C In autumn.

frequently two breeds of each species present—the 'winter' and 'spring' ones (L. Berg, 1934), differing in the time of their entry into the river and in their wintering place (either in the river or in the Sea).

The migrations of Salmonidae (*Stenodus leucichthys* and Caspian salmon) are of special interest. *Stenodus leucichthys* moves from the Caspian into the Volga, Kama, Belaya, and finally into the river Ufa, travelling about 3,000 km. A certain number of *Stenodus leucichthys* also enters the river Ural; salmon, on the contrary, mostly enter the rivers on the Caucasian shore, and only single specimens of it enter the Volga.* Acipenseridae have been observed to choose some individual rivers for spawning; it has been known for centuries that some rivers are preferred by the Acipenseridae (the rivers Volga, Samur, Gyurgenchai and Sefidrud) and others (Kura, Terek, Sulak, Ural) by starred sturgeon.

Among the migratory fish of fresh-water genesis the following should be mentioned; *Rutilus rutilus caspius*, *Rutilus frisii kutum*, *Abramis brama*, *Barbus brachycephalus caspius*, *Cyprinus carpio*, *Pelecus cultratus* and *Lucioperca lucioperca*. They all spawn in fresh water (except for some shoals of carp) and fatten in the Sea; but they spawn in the deltas and lower reaches of the Caspian rivers and therefore they do not make long migrations. Autumn migration into rivers for wintering, apart from the spring spawning migration, is most characteristic of this group of fish. All the above mentioned fish, except for vobla and to some extent carp, winter in the lower reaches of the rivers in deep places or 'pits', where they 'spend the winter either completely or almost completely motionless, being covered by a thick layer of slime as if by a fur coat' (V. Meisner, 1933). Vobla approaches the shores for wintering, bedding down in the pits of the Volga delta; but it does not enter the river. Carp winter either in the pits or in the Sea. In the same way various shoals of carp, apart from the carp which spawn in the river, also spawn in different places, in brackish water, in inlets and in the bays and inlets of the Northern Caspian.

P. Schmidt (1938) believes that there is a great difference in principle between the movements of migratory fish of marine and of fresh-water origin. 'Whereas the true marine fish acquire a new element in their biology in the shape of spawning migration into fresh waters, the fresh-water, semi-migratory fish are only extending their feeding migration, covering the neighbouring parts of the Sea, in as much as they succeed in restoring their long-lost capacity for enduring an increase of salinity in the water. In the first case it is an acquisition of new properties and instincts, a reconstruction of the whole process of breeding and development; in the second it is only the renewal of a capacity they had possessed. . . .'

Semi-migratory fish like *Abramis sapa*, *Abramis ballerus*, *Blicca bjorna*, *Aspius aspius* and *Silurus glanis* do not move farther than just outside the delta, as they are strictly limited in their propagation by fresh water and can tolerate only a very slight increase of salinity.

As for the marine fish listed above, almost nothing is known as yet about

* Judging by archival material collected by A. Derzhavin (1939), salmon were abundant in the Volga in the seventeenth and eighteenth centuries; their numbers have greatly decreased since then.

their migration (except for that of herrings). In the literature there are but few indications of the approach to the shores of some bullheads and marine pike perch for spawning (N. Tchugunov and F. Egerman, 1932). Fish of Mediterranean origin (Atherina, Pomatoschistus and Syngnathus) move into the saline southeastern corner of the Caspian Sea for spawning, which they do at a salinity of 30‰.

The question of the causes which compel fish to accomplish long and complicated migrations is an extraordinarily intricate one. To solve it we have to turn to geological data. Some workers point to the extreme importance of the post-glacial loss of salinity of the Caspian Sea and its effect on the working out of the migrational rates of Caspian fish. Ya. Birstein writes (1935) that 'the difference between a sea and a body of fresh water at that time had probably become so negligible that for assimilated (formerly) marine fauna the river was no longer an alien medium; fresh-water fish also could readily extend their habitat into the Sea, which was formerly closed to them owing to its physicochemical conditions. The subsequent gradual increase in salinity had apparently only slightly affected the habitats of fresh-water fish which had mainly been formed in post-glacial time; it may, however, have somewhat reduced their distribution in the Sea. It may have been this, in fact, which assigned fish to the biological types—migratory, semi-migratory and fresh-water non-migratory—which have already been established by Kessler.' Schmidt thinks that 'the migratory routes of the herring now observed may have begun to be developed at the end of the glacial period. When with the beginning of the ice recession great torrents of fresh water began to flow towards the Sea, some species of herring, probably already more adapted to fresh water, used them for spawning, and the range of their migrations increased more and more with the further withdrawal of ice and the lengthening of the rivers. Other herring species have remained marine or semi-migratory forms up to our time.'

Numerous species of the Clupeidae are the main consumers of plankton; not all, however, for some of them are predators (Fig. 296). Among the plankton-eating Clupeidae three pelagic species of the genus Clupeonella (Clupeonella and *Sprattus phalericus*), which form large colonies in the Caspian Sea, are distinguished by their small size. Volga and Caspian herrings are also plankton eaters, whereas the Brashnikov and Saposhnikov herrings are typical predators. Some forms have a mixed diet as, for example, *Caspialosa kessleri*. A. Behning (1938) showed that plankton Copepoda (*Eurytemora grimmi*) feed mostly on Flagellata and unicellular algae. Mysids feed also on these forms, as well as on small crustaceans. Sprats and herring-fry feed mostly on copepods, while *Caspialosa caspia* feeds on copepods and pericardians. The seal feeds on sprats and on *Caspialosa caspia*. A general diagram of the food chain of Caspian plankton-eaters can be drawn from the data available (Fig. 297).

Feeding of benthos-eating fish. The problem of the nutrition and feeding correlations of Northern Caspian benthos-eating fish has been carefully investigated by Schorygin (1952). His research can be regarded as a model of this type of study.

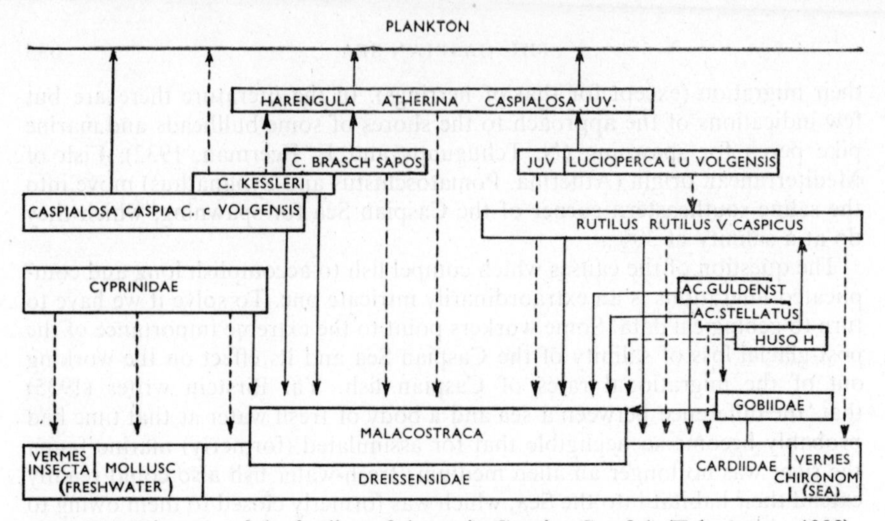

FIG. 296. Diagram of the feeding of the main Caspian Sea fish (Tchugunov, 1928).

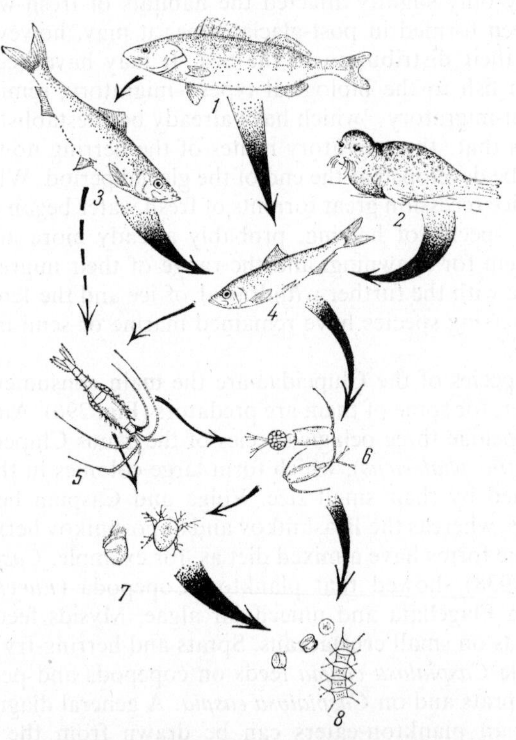

FIG. 297. Diagram of the feeding series of Caspian planktophages (Behning, 1938, with some additions). *1* Pike perch, starred sturgeon; *2* Seal; *3* Herring predators (*C. braschnikovi*); *4* 'Peaceful' herring (*C. caspia*, Clupeonella); *5* Large crustaceans (Pericardia); *6* Small crustaceans (Calanipeda); *7* Small zooplankton; *8* Phytoplankton.

Benthos-eating fish of the Caspian Sea can be divided into four groups: worm eaters in a wide sense (including chironomids), and those which live on molluscs, crustaceans and fish (usually called predators); moreover, individual fish are transitional types as regards their diet. As may be judged from *Table 271* sturgeon and two species of bullheads—*Pomatoschistus* (*Bubyr*) *causasicus* and *Knipovitschia longicaudata*—feed on worms; vobla, *Benthophilus stellatus* and *B. macrocephalus* and the bullheads *Gobius melanostamus affinis* and *G. kessleri* feed on molluscs. Predators and crustacean eaters often have a mixed

Table 271. General character (percentage basis) of fish diet in Northern Caspian

Breed	General nature of diet				Main nutrient groups
	Worms and chironomids	Molluscs	Crustaceans	Fish	
,turgeon	96	—	—	1	Chironomidae
'omatoschistus caucasicus	88	—	6	6	Chironomidae
Knipovitschia longicaudata	44	—	22	34	Chironomidae, Gammaridae
Benthophilus stellatus	—	100	—	—	Adacna, Didacna, Monodacna
B. macrocephalus	1	80	18	2	Gastropoda, Monodacna
Vobla	1	82	7	1	Dreissena, Monodacna
Gobius melanostomus affinis	8	54	34	0·4	Gammaridae, Cardium, Dreissena
G. kessleri	—	52	22	26	Gammaridae, Cardium, Gobiidae
Hyrcanogobius bergi	9	—	91	—	Cumacea, Gammaridae
Gobius fluviatilis pallasi	5	14	71	8	Gammaridae, Corophiidae
G. caspius	—	18	69	8	Gammaridae, Mysidae
Golden shiner	9	15	54	0·2	Cumacea, Corophiidae, Adacna
Carp	16·5	18	36	1	Gammaridae, Dreissena, Corophiidae
Starred sturgeon	1	0·5	46	45	Mysidae, sprat
Caspialosa saposhnikovi	1	1	39	56	Mysidae, sprat
Salmon	6	2	20	68	Gobiidae, sprat
Caspialosa sphaerocephala	—	—	10	82	Sprat
Pike perch	—	—	10	89	Gobiidae, sprat
Caspialosa brashnikovi	—	—	4	96	Sprat
Beluga	—	1	1	98	

diet. The bullheads *Hyrcanogobius bergi*, *Gobius fluviatilus pallasi*, *G. caspius*, pike perch and carp may be considered typical crustacean eaters; while the typical predators are belugam pike perch, *Caspialosa saposhnikovi*, *Caspialosa brashnikovi* and *C. sphaerocephala*. Starred sturgeon and sturgeon also have a mixed diet.

Some less pronounced transitions also exist between the typical crustacean and mollusc eaters. *Gobius melanostomus affinis*, *G. kessleri*, *G. pallasi*, *G. caspius*, golden shiner and carp have a mixed diet of this type. However, in all these cases except for the first two, the consumption of crustaceans is greatly in excess of that of molluscs.

A comparison between the main nature of diet and the average index of repletion brings out a definite dependence: the higher the calorific value of food the lower the index of repletion. Moreover, the indices of repletion vary greatly for different fish—from 26 for starred sturgeon to 368 for *B. stellatus*. Mollusc-eating fish have the highest index of repletion (from 107 to 368); it varies from 75 to 211 for worm eaters. When fish is the basic diet the repletion indices fall to 26 to 120 and, finally, with a diet of crustaceans the indices range from 27 to 79. In general indices of repletion are inversely proportional to the calorific value of food, as illustrated by the following data:

Gammaridae	3·92 cal/g	Vobla	1·00 cal/g
Corophiidae	2·34 cal/g	Bullheads	0·76 cal/g
Chironomidae	2·34 cal/g	Benthophilus	0·63 cal/g
Sprat	1·47 cal/g	*Dreissena polymorpha*	0·63 cal/g

This regularity is somewhat broken only by worm-eating fish, since for food of high calorific value the indices of repletion are high.

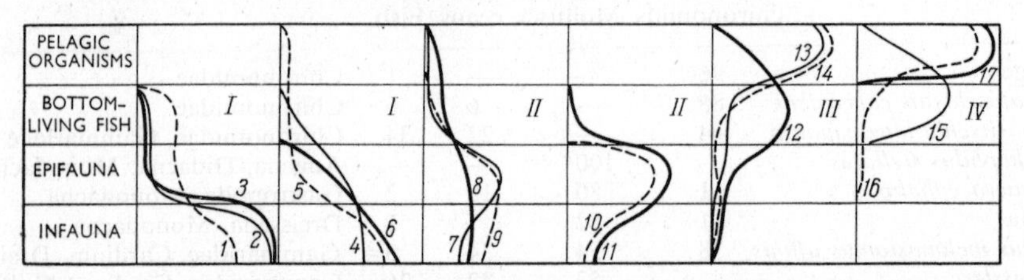

FIG. 298. Vertical distribution of fish feeding grounds in the Caspian Sea (Schorygin, 1952). 1 *Knipowitschia longicaudata*; 2 *Bubyr caucasicus*; 3 Sturgeon; 4 *Benthophilus marmoratus*; 5 Golden shiner; 6 *Hyrcanogobius bergi*; 7 Carp; 8 *Gobius fluviatilis pallasi*; 9 *Gobius melanostomus affinis*; 10 Vobla; 11 *Benthophilus stellatus*; 12 Sturgeon; 13 Casp. Alosa; 14 Starred sturgeon; 15 Pike perch; 16 *Casp. braschnikovi*; 17 *Casp. sphaerocephala* (*agrakhanskaya*).

A fish's choice of food is to a considerable degree correlated with its manner of life: fish living in a definite horizon use mainly organisms adapted to this horizon. If food organisms are divided into pelagic and benthonectic, epifauna and infauna, we get a basic adaptation of each fish to a certain horizon (Fig. 298). Typical predators, pike perch, and the dolginskaya and agrakhanskaya herrings feed mainly on pelagic organisms. Morover, pike perch feed mostly on bottom-living fish (bullheads and vobla), and herring on pelagic fish (sprats). Starred sturgeon and *Caspialosa saposhnikovi* eat benthos (both the epifauna and the infauna), although pelagic organisms are predominant in their diet.

Carp, vobla and some bullheads feed mainly on epifauna, while sturgeon, *Pomatoschistus caucasicus* and *Knipovitschia longicaudata* prey mainly on the infauna.

The change of diet with age of the sturgeon is interesting (Fig. 299 IV). When less than 50 cm long it feeds almost exclusively on Gammaridae, passing first to Corophiidae as it grows and then to river crustaceans. Simultaneously fish and Nereis acquire more and more significance in its diet, comprising 40 per cent of its food when the sturgeon is 60 cm long. However, with further growth the sturgeon does not remain on a diet of fish; it begins to eat more and more molluscs (Cardidae, Mytilaster and Nereis). When a sturgeon reaches 170 to 180 cm it feeds exclusively on molluscs and Nereis. This change is

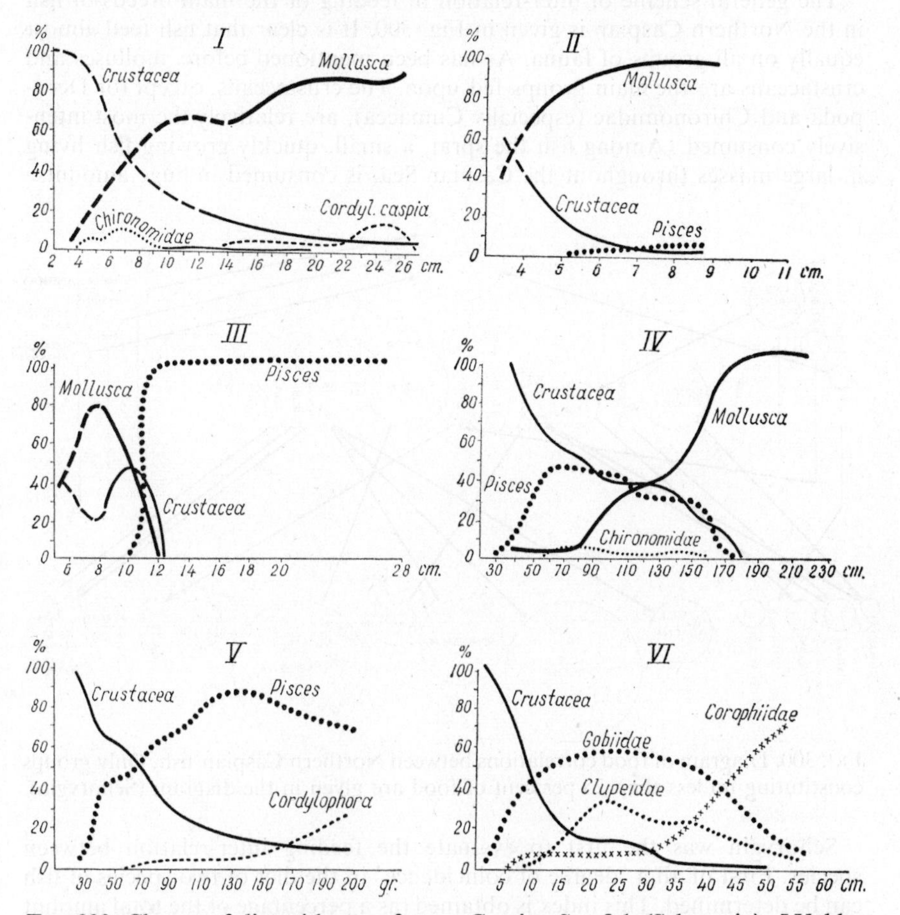

Fig. 299. Change of diet with age of some Caspian Sea fish (Schorygin). *I* Vobla; *II Benthophilus macrocephalus*; *III Gobius kessleri*; *IV* Sturgeon; *V Caspialosa saposhnikovi*; *VI* Pike perch.

connected with the approach of sexual maturity. Generally speaking sturgeon is a typical euryphague.

Competition for food. The examination of the inter-relation in feeding among the different species is one of the essential problems in the study of fish nutrition; moreover, as has been noted by Schorygin it is equally important 'to establish between which species, where, when, and for which foodstuffs such competition arises, and also, if possible, to determine the degree of competition. It is equally important to study the nature of the effect of the consumers we examine on food provision and to determine the strength of this effect on individual food groups.'

The general scheme of inter-relation in feeding of the main breeds of fish in the Northern Caspian is given in Fig. 300. It is clear that fish feed almost equally on all groups of fauna. As has been mentioned before, molluscs and crustaceans are the main groups fed upon. The crustaceans, except for Decapoda and Chironomidae (especially Cumacea), are relatively the most intensively consumed. Among fish the sprat, a small, quickly growing fish living in large masses throughout the Caspian Sea, is consumed in huge amounts.

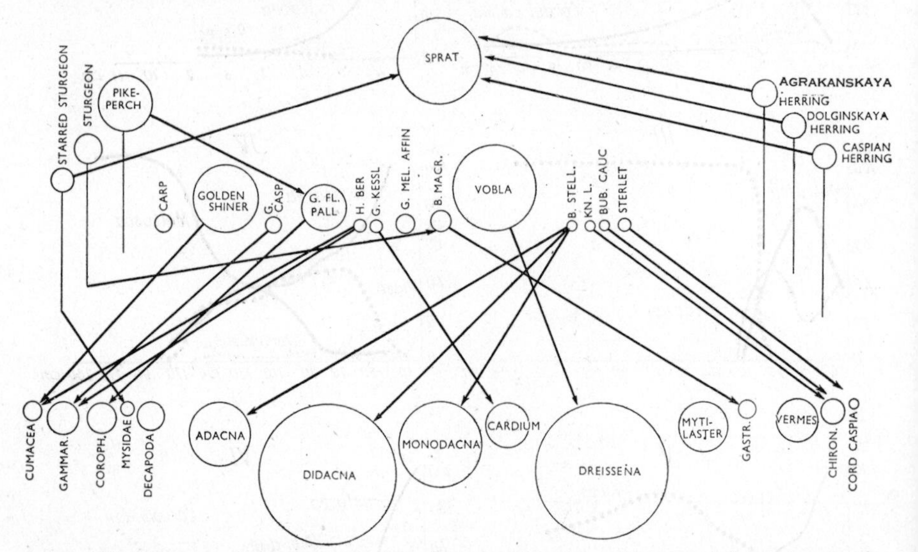

FIG. 300. Diagram of food correlations between Northern Caspian fish. Only groups constituting no less than 25 per cent of food are given in the diagram (Schorygin).

Schorygin was the first to evaluate the feeding inter-relation between species. First of all a 'degree of coincidence' in the diet of two species of fish can be determined. This index is obtained (as a percentage of the total amount of food) when the percentage composition of the diets of two fish is compared, as the sum of smaller percentages. The basis of this simple method of calculation can be illustrated by a graph (Fig. 301) where the area of the coincidence of the diet of the two species is defined by the smaller ordinates, independently of which kind of feeding the species belong to. This index (food coincidence, denoted *Fc*) will decrease with the increase of the precision of determination of the specific composition of food. It was found that the nature of vobla diet is nearest to that of Benthophilus and the bullhead *Gobius melanostomus affinis* (36 to 39 per cent); this similarity is much weaker with carp and golden shiner (27 per cent) and with other fish it scarcely exists. Golden shiner diet is much like that of some bullheads (32 to 61 per cent), and least like that of carp (34 per cent). The diet of cyprinoids is usually coincident with that of some bullheads (25·6 per cent); however, between the members of this family this coincidence is even greater (29·3 per cent). The diet of the Clupeidae examined has a high coincidence coefficient (75·9 per cent); with pike perch the coefficient is 26·2 per cent, with the Acipenseridae 24·8 per cent; it is low with cyprinoids 6·7 per cent and with Gobiidae 7·5 per cent. The various Acipenseridae species differ greatly in their diet (16 per cent), yet not so much as do cyprinoids (14·3 per cent), but more than Gobiidae (17·1 per cent) and Clupeidae (24·8 per cent) and so on.

The food-coincidence coefficient, while giving an idea of the relative similarity between the diets of rival species, does not express the intensity of their competition. Schorygin distinguishes also the amount and intensity of it. The amount of competition is the ratio of the part of their diet for which they compete to their total consumption. The intensity of the competition is the ratio between the demand made, in the shortest possible interval of time, by the rival organisms on the food for which they are competing and the availability of that food. The product of the amount of competition by its intensity expresses the force of competition. Comparative food competition of fish in the Northern Caspian as given by Schorygin is shown in *Table 272* (in conventional units).

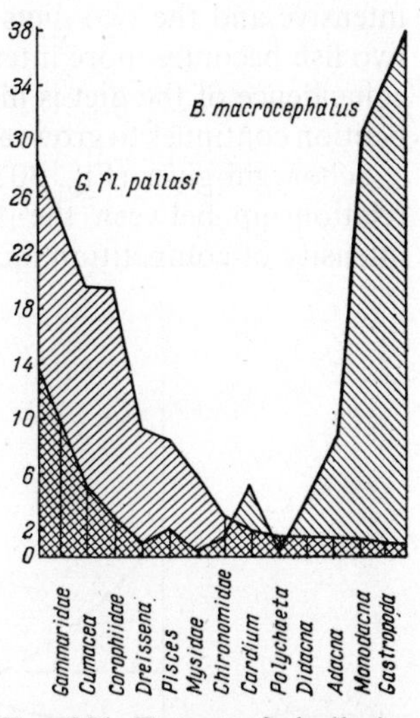

FIG. 301. Extent of similarity between nature of feeding of *Benthophilus macrosephalus* and *Gobius fluviatilis pallasi* (Schorygin).

It is clear from these data that intraspecific competition is, on the whole, higher than intrageneric, and the competition between the genera is weaker than between the forms of the same genus. Thus with cyprinoids the intraspecific competition is on the average expressed by 170 conventional units, and the intrageneric one by 121; with the Gobiidae it is only 41, with the

Table 272

Competitor	*B. macrocephalus*	*G. mel. affinis*	*G. fluv. pallasi*	Vobla	Golden shiner	Starred sturgeon	Sturgeon	Pike perch
Benthophilus macrocephalus	20	5	18	20	32	0·5	0·8	0·1
Gobius melanostomus affinis	5	7	24	7	29	1	2	0·6
G. fluviatilis pallasi	18	24	67	13	144	16	10	13
Vobla	20	7	13	46	29	1	2	0·6
Golden shiner	32	29	144	29	291	16	8	6
Starred sturgeon	0·5	1	16	1	16	100	27	39
Sturgeon	0·8	2	10	2	8	27	175	50
Pike perch	0·1	0·6	13	0·6	6	39	50	35

Acipenseridae 7, and with pike perch 3·3. With Acipenseridae intraspecific competition is on the average 133, intrageneric 101; with pike perch 44, with cyprinoids 7, and with Gobiidae 5 (conventional units).

By May the competition between golden shiner and vobla becomes less intensive and the two diets become more similar. In June the feeding of the two fish becomes more intensive and the competition is more acute, while the coincidence of the diet is much lessened. By August the intensity of the competition continues to grow, and both the amount and the intensity are increased.

Schorygin gives (Fig. 302A) a general picture of the dynamics of the food relationship between the two forms of fish. By the summer feeding and intensity of competition increase, but the two diets become less similar, since

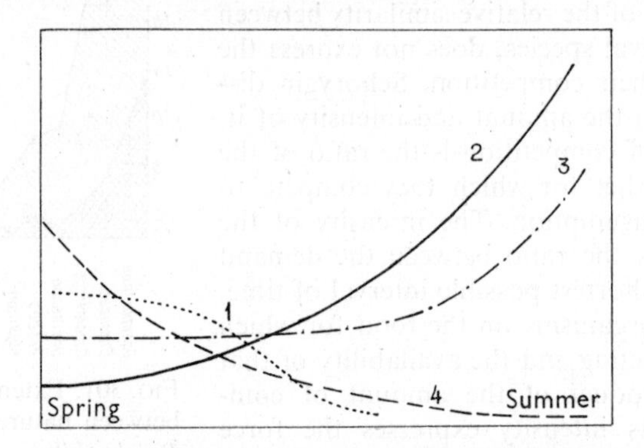

FIG. 302A. Diagram of food correlation of two fish (Schorygin): *1* Feeding ground coincidence; *2* Competition intensity; *3* Competition tension; *4* Volume of competition.

the two fish have by then driven each other away to feed on different organisms. The force of competition remains practically the same, with a decrease in the coincidence of the diet and a corresponding growth of competition. At the same time, although the two species begin to feed in different areas, the force of the rivalry between them begins to grow. Then, if the intensity of competition still increases its force begins to grow rapidly and a complete (forced) divergence may take place both as regards food and feeding grounds; following a decrease in intensity of competition the reverse process may take place.

The degree of elasticity in the diet of different breeds of fish plays an important part in the course of these changes. Schorygin has also tried to evaluate this latter. The degree of stability of the diet of a definite fish in different seasons and areas can be determined from the indices of food coincidence (*Fc*), and the mean value of this can also be found. Taking the value complementary to 100 of the mean thus obtained, we shall have the index of variability of diet. The results obtained in this way for six fish are given in *Table 273*. The elasticity of diet develops with increase of the regional and seasonal variations in the composition of the food. This effect can be excluded from our calculations by determining the extent of the variations in the provision of food, by the method used to determine changes in the nature of the diet. The ratio of the second value to the first is the index of the extent of the elasticity of the diet, regardless of the variations in provision of food. These indices are given in *Table 273*.

Table 273

Elasticity of diet	Sturgeon	Starred sturgeon	Pike Perch	Vobla	*Gobius fluviatilis pallasi*	Golden shiner
Without corrections for changes in available food	75	68	60	58	51	52
With a correction for changes in available food (ratio of degree of change of nature of diet to that of available food)	1·9	1·7	1·4	1·4	1·2	1·1

The elasticity in the diet of sturgeon and starred sturgeon is high; that of golden shiner is the lowest. It should be noted also that in the Northern Caspian the variability of the nature of the diet is greater than that of the provision of food. Finally Schorygin has introduced one more new conception—the feeding activity of fish, meaning the capacity of the organism to maintain its peculiar type of nutrition. The feeding activity and elasticity of the sturgeon, pike perch, and to some extent of the starred sturgeon, are high. Pike perch has a high activity but a low elasticity and vobla, on the contrary, a high elasticity with low activity. In his later work A. Schorygin (1948) has compared the results of his observations in 1935 with those of 1941. During that time the edible fauna had decreased by 56 per cent and the changes in benthos had brought about a change in the composition of fish diet. However, the force of competition for food between the six fish chosen (three species of bullheads, vobla, golden shiner and sturgeon) has remained practically unchanged. This is explained by the high elasticity of fish diet and is achieved by: (*1*) a separation of the feeding grounds of different species, (*2*) the divergence in the nature of their diet, and (*3*) by a more even utilization of food provided. The former strong competition was weakened, while the weak food link grew stronger (Fig. 302B). Seven or eight years after Schorygin's observations his method of quantitative examination of fish food competition was repeated by Ya. Birstein (1952), and it was found that competition for food in 1948–49 was considerably weaker than in 1941 (Fig. 302C). It was clear from his detailed examination of fish nutrition over these years that the slackening of competititon for food between the fish-benthophages is due to a huge development of Nereis which took place at that time, and which provided the fish with some millions of centners of supplementary foodstuffs of high calorific value.

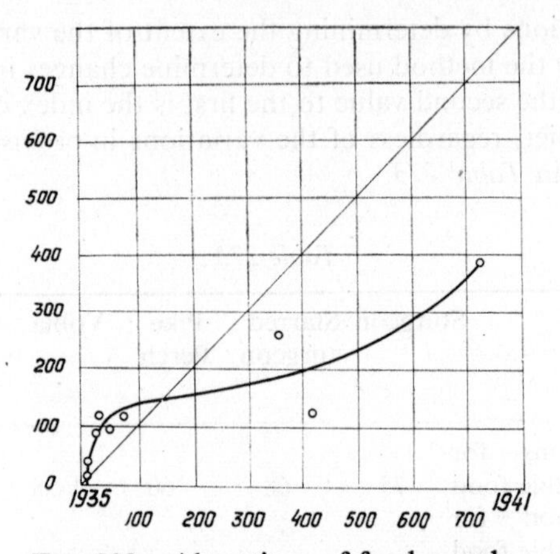

FIG. 302B. Alterations of food correlations of benthos-feeding fish of the Caspian Sea from 1935 to 1941 (Schorygin). The intensity of food correlation between rival pairs of species of fish during the period examined is given in circles as indices of magnitude. The diagonal line corresponds to the position of points when food correlations remain permanent.

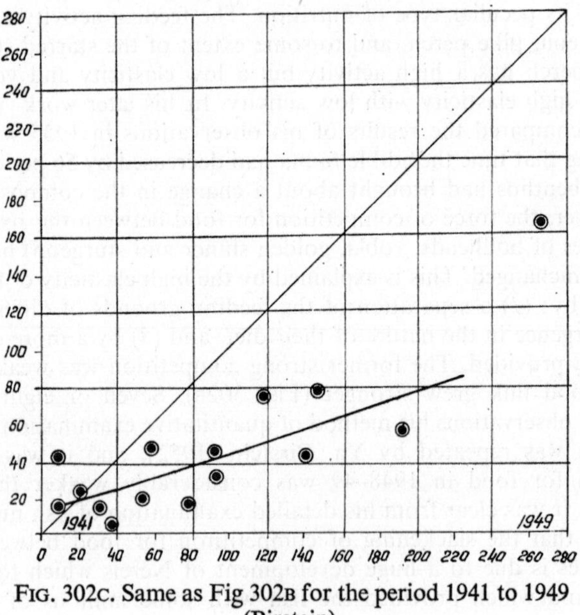

FIG. 302C. Same as Fig 302B for the period 1941 to 1949 (Birstein).

Yield of fish. Fish yield in the Northern Caspian in 1935 was about 31·6 kg/hectare (24 kg/hectare for benthophages), in the Sea of Azov 73 kg/hectare, in the Aral Sea 4·5 kg/hectare, and in the North Sea about 17 kg/hectare (in ponds 60 to 160 kg/hectare, and when fertilized up to 2,000). Thus the yield of fish from the Caspian Sea is comparatively high. The *F/B* coefficient for these Seas is also most significant. For the Northern Caspian it is about 1/12, for the Sea of Azov 1/20, for the Aral Sea 1/50, for the North Sea 1/140. Hence North Caspian benthos is utilized in the most efficient manner, and evidently there is strong rivalry for food between its consumers. Partly in connection with this, and partly owing to the existence of an abundant provision of food in the form of nereids* in the Sea of Azov, fish grow in it much better than in the Caspian Sea.

Schorygin's comprehensive examination of fish nutrition in the Northern Caspian makes it possible to come to a most reliable prognosis of the state of fish feeding under possible changes in the conditions and surface of the body of water. On the other hand, the examination of Caspian fish nutrition and a comparison of its results with data on the growth of commercial fish points to the existence of competition between some fish and to a considerable rivalry as regards provision of food. This in fact led to the idea that the Caspian Sea could be widely used for the acclimatization of the Mediterranean (Azov–Black Seas) fauna.

Commercial fish resources. The rough quantities of fish resources of the Caspian Sea given by some authors are based mostly on data from commercial statistics and on the examination for age of catch.

The Caspian Sea occupied the first place in our fisheries during the first two decades of this century. Later, however, owing to vigorous development of fisheries in the Barents Sea and in the Far Eastern Seas the Caspian trade dropped to third place. Recent yields of the Caspian fisheries were only 65·4 per cent (4·3 million centners in 1954) of the 1913 catch (L. Berdichevsky, 1957). This reduction has affected the most valuable breeds of fish—herring, vobla and pike perch; the yield of Acipenseridae is about half that of 1913, but it has remained on the same level since 1930. Sprat fishery has developed greatly. The fisheries of the Caspian Sea have changed a great deal during the last 30 years (*Table 274*).

Table 274. Yields of fish in the Caspian Sea (in thousands of centners) since 1930 (L. Berdichevsky, 1957)

Breed	1930	1940	1950	1954
Pike perch	909	348	314	333
Golden shiner	374	612	713	374
Acipenseridae	135·2	89·4	130·1	129

In 1956 the catch of fish in the Caspian Sea was 4·3 million centners (*Table 275*).

* The data given refer to the period before the implantation of Nereis.

Table 275. Yields of fish in the Caspian Sea in 1956

Breed	Catch 10³ centners	Breed	Catch 10³ centners
Starred sturgeon	64	Catfish	128
Sturgeon	54	Pike	123
Beluga	10	Vobla	623
		Herring	410
Total Acipenserida	128	Sprat	1,883
		Grey mullet	8
Pike perch	217	Other fish	355
Golden shiner	270		
Carp	161	Total catch	4,306

Avifauna

Much serious damage to the fisheries of the Caspian Sea is caused by fish-eating birds, chiefly cormorants, herons, sea-gulls and pelicans (A. Pakhulsky, 1951). The stock of fish-eating birds in the Caspian is more than six hundred thousand head and the quantity of fish consumed by them (1948) is about a million centners a year, 70 per cent of which is taken by cormorants. Moreover, the birds propagate a series of intestinal fish-worms; sea-gulls are the cause of violent epidemics of ligulosis affecting a great number of vobla.

Gulf of Karabugas

The Gulf of Karabugas is most remarkable; it can be considered as the final stage of the process of the eastern Caspian inlets turning saline; these, with their narrow links with the Sea, run deep into a desert country with a hot and dry climate. The ratio of the content of ions in the Caspian waters when they are concentrated, which does not alter in the Mërtvyi Kultuk and Kaidak inlets (as S. Makarov and D. Enikeev (1937) have shown) does, in the Gulf of Karabugas, alter in the direction of an increase in the content of sodium sulphate.

The Gulf of Karabugas is the largest sodium sulphate body of water in the world. The area of the Gulf of Karabugas (about 14,000 to 15,000 km²) as well as its depth and salt content have changed considerably owing to fluctuations in the level of the Caspian Sea (this has dropped by 193 cm between 1929 and 1945) and in its depth and the form of its connection with the Caspian Sea.

The greatest depth of the Gulf of Karabugas is now only 4·5 m, whereas once it was 9 m. The level of the Caspian Sea is 3 m higher than that of the Gulf of Karabugas.

In 1939 the inflow from the Caspian Sea to the Gulf of Karabugas decreased from 25 km³ to 6 km³; it rose again, however, in 1946 to 12 to 14 km³ owing to the deepening of the strait. The water of the Gulf of Karabugas has become considerably more saline in the last 60 years:

in 1897 salinity comprised 16·4 per cent by weight
in 1929–30 salinity comprised 20·5 to 21·0 per cent
in 1938 salinity comprised 28·1 per cent.

The limit of saturation is reached at this last salinity.

If we take 26·24 per cent by weight as its present mean salinity, its composition will be the following:

SO_4^{2-} ions represent 6·24 per cent by weight
Cl^- ions represent 11·89 per cent by weight
Mg^{2+} ions represent 2·76 per cent by weight
Na^+ ions represent 5·35 per cent by weight

The ratio Cl^-/Mg^{2+} is 4·31.

The waters of the inlet contain about 17·88 milliard tons of salts, among them 9·3 milliard tons of sodium chloride, 5·33 of magnesium sulphate and 2·8 of magnesium chloride. More than 8 milliard tons of mirabilite and other salts were precipitated on the bottom of the Gulf of Karabugas in the winter of 1949–50.

In winter, when the temperature of the waters of the Gulf of Karabugas falls, mirabilite (Glauber salt) is precipitated. The salinity of the Gulf of Karabugas is now twenty times higher than that of the Caspian Sea.

In 1897 the A. Spindler and N. Andrussov expedition discovered a mass of *Artemia salina* in the inlet; now owing to the rise of salinity this crustacean has disappeared from the inlet; only its eggs are found in large numbers on the shores. Animal organisms are absent from the inlet; its waters, however, are teeming with various representatives of microflora—algae and micro-organisms. The alga *Aphanothece salina*, forming huge, slimy colonies off the shores, and the Flagellates *Dunaliella viridis* and *D. salina*, with their profuse flowering during the precipitation of Glauber salt, are the two mass forms. There are, according to A. Pel'sh (1936), about 530,000 cells of Dunaliella to a gramme of solid salt mass, and on the average 21,000,000 micro-organisms to 1 cm^3 of the water of the Gulf of Karabugas.

V. CONCLUSIONS

S. P. Brujevitch tries to draw a comparison of total biomass and production of the whole body of water from the data on the numbers of the main components of the fauna and flora of the Caspian Sea. This table cannot be considered as very accurate, but the orders of quantities given for most of the groups can be taken as more or less valid (*Table 276*).

Table 276. Biomass and production of individual groups of Caspian Sea hydrobiontes and their content of nitrogen and phosphorus (S. P. Brujevitch, 1941) Weight, thousands of tons

Group	Year	Biomass					Annual	Annual production		
		Wet weight	Dry weight	% dry weight	N	P	P/B ratio	Wet weight	Dry weight	% dry weight
Bacteria	1935	8,000	1,600	18	200	20	500	4,000,000	800,000	5·87
Phytoplankton	1934	3,500	350	3·8	13·2	2·4	300	1,000,000	100,000	10·7
Zooplankton	1934	5,000	500	5	50	5	30	150,000	15,000	1·6
Zoobenthos	1935	30,000	4,500	49	450	45	4	1,200,000	18,000	1·9
Phytobenthos	1935	3,000	375	4	6	0·7	1	3,000	375	0·04
Fish	1934–36	6,000	1,800	20	170	21	0·5	3,000	900	0·10
Marine mammals		70	21	0·2	2·1	0·24	0·35	25	7	0·001
Total		55,600	9,150	100	891	94	—	—	—	100
Annual catch of fish	1934–37	450	130	—	13	1·6	—	—	—	—
Phytoplankton	1936	11,000	1,100	—	—	—	—	—	—	—

12
The Aral Sea

I. GENERAL CHARACTERISTICS

The most easterly Sea in the system of large bodies of water of the south Russian geosyncline is the Aral Sea, which is the fourth biggest enclosed sea in the world.

For the most part well heated in the summer and well aerated, the Aral Sea has practically the same salinity as that of the Caspian and Azov Seas; but the ratio of the different salts approaches that characteristic of fresh water, even more than in the case of the Caspian Sea.

As result of a most complex geological history of alterations in its orography and salinity the Aral Sea has qualitatively poor flora and fauna. However, a small number of autochthonous Caspian forms still live in the Aral Sea, which is the extreme point of the penetration eastwards of the most active immigrants of Mediterranean fauna.

The Aral Sea is considerably inferior to other south Russian Seas in its biological productivity; however, it seems to offer very wide possibilities for ameliorative measures aimed at an increase in the yield of fish by means of fertilization, fish-breeding and acclimatization.

II. HISTORY OF EXPLORATION

First period

The first data on the flora and fauna of the Aral Sea were collected in the nineteenth century by several expeditions. Among them the following should be noted: A. Butenev's expedition in 1841, in collaboration with the naturalist A. Leman; A. Butakov's expedition in 1848–49 and, finally, the Aral–Caspian expedition of 1874, with the participation of the zoologist V. Alenitzyn: the materials obtained were worked up by I. Borshchov (1877), N. Andrussov (1897), K. Kessler (1877) and others.

A most comprehensive investigation of the Aral Sea was carried out by L. Berg's expeditions in 1900 to 1902 and 1906; the result was the first comprehensive monograph describing the Aral Sea, published in 1908.

Second period

The next stage in the closer investigation of the Aral Sea with particular reference to its commercial wealth is linked with the activity of the Aral Fishery Station, which was inaugurated in 1929 in the town of Aralsk.

A. Behning (1934, 1935), V. Nikitinsky (1933) and G. V. Nikolsky worked at this station. The latter was responsible for a comprehensive monograph (1940) which brought together all existing information on the Aral Sea, particularly in regard to fish.

III. PHYSICAL GEOGRAPHY

Size and level

The greatest length of the Aral Sea is 428 km, and its greatest width 284 km (Fig. 303). Its area is 64,500 km^2: i.e. in size it occupies fourth place among the

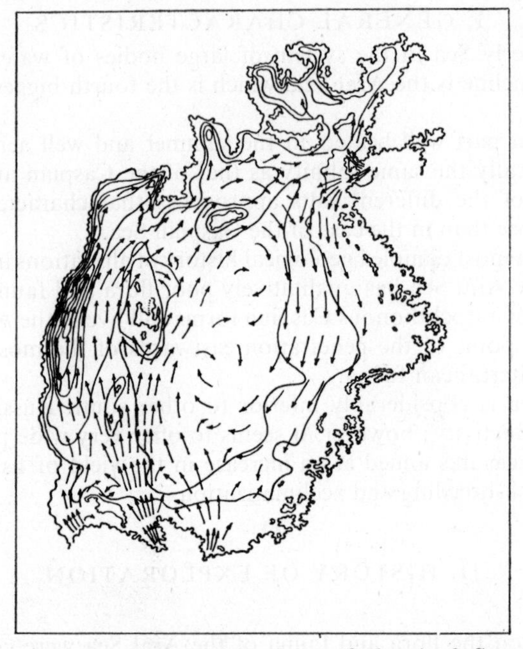

FIG. 303. Bathymetric chart of the Aral Sea (Nikolsky, 1940). Currents indicated by arrows (Kulichenko, 1944).

lakes of the world (after the Caspian Sea, Lake Superior and Lake Victoria). The volume of the Aral Sea is 10^3 km^3.

The level of the Aral Sea is 79·5 m higher than that of the Caspian and 52 m higher than that of the ocean.

Water balance

The water balance of the Aral Sea was determined by V. Samoilenko (1947) as given in *Table 277*.

Table 277

Gain	km^3/year	Loss	km^3/year
River inflow	54	Evaporation	58·09
Rainfall	5·36	Leakage through sea-bed	1·27
Total	59·36		59·36

Bottom topography

The greatest depth (67 m) occurs near the western shore of the Sea (Fig. 303); the predominant depths are 10 to 30 m, with an average depth of 16·2 m.

The Aral Sea is divided into two basins by a submarine ridge with a system of islands stretching from north to south: the smaller, but deeper, western basin and the eastern one which does not exceed 30 m in depth.

The northern part, separated from the rest of the Sea by the Kuch-Aral island, is called the Maloe More.

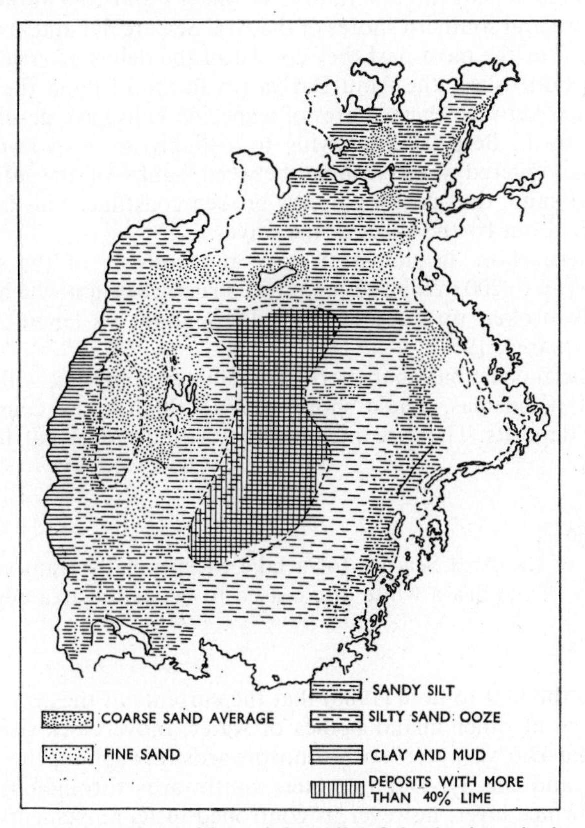

FIG. 304. Distribution of the soils of the Aral sea-bed (Kulichenko, 1944).

Soils

Grey mud covered by a thin brown layer is the predominant bed of the Aral Sea (Fig. 304). Black mud, owing its colour to the presence of a colloidal ferrous hydroxide, is found in the western deeper part of the Sea and in some inlets.

Freshly brought up black mud usually smells of hydrogen sulphide. Huge masses of rotting filamentous algae, forming a complete felt-like cover over the bottom, are concentrated in the western, deeper part of the Sea; the formation of hydrogen sulphide is facilitated by their presence.

River mouths are characterized by brown clay mud.

Sand floors, passing over into mud beds at depths below 10 m, form a wide band along the northern, eastern and southern coasts of the Aral Sea.

According to K. Gilzen's data (1908) the Aral Sea bed contains very little organic matter. The carbon content recorded at 15 stations fluctuates from 0·07 to 0·43 per cent. Its nitrogen content was determined at two stations as 0·0187 and 0·0068 per cent; the ratio C/N was 6·7 and 10·6 at these places.

The western and southern shores of the Aral Sea are flat and low (V. Zenkovitch, 1962). For the most part they consist of the deltas of great rivers overgrown with bullrushes: the Amu-Dar'ya (to the south) and the Syr-Dar'ya. In a wide area between them shores of a specific kind have developed, called 'Aral' type by L. Berg (1908). Owing to a slight rise in its level the Sea in this area has entered some troughs between banks of the adjacent wind-borne desert sand, thus creating a very broken coastline. This latter is being slowly levelled out by the effect of the waves.

The western shore is almost straight and consists of the steep *chinka* escarpment (up to 200 m high) of a faulted structure origin which has by now been greatly broken up by landslides. Throughout its length this coast is steep (V. Lymarev, 1957).

The northern coast has characteristic laminated contours, with a few large islands and peninsulas. These shores are not high; they consist of loose Quaternary deposits. They are intensely abraded, forming small local currents of alluvium.

Transparency

The waters of the Aral Sea are for a lake exceptionally transparent: in the western part of the Sea a white disc ceased to be visible at a depth of 24 m.

Currents

L. Berg was the first to note (1908) that the currents of the Aral Sea, in contrast to those of other inland bodies of water, move clockwise (Fig. 303); thus the Amu-Dar'ya waters spread northwards throughout the western part of the Sea, and the Syr-Dar'ya waters southwards throughout the eastern part. The surface layer, however, is controlled in its movements by the prevailing winds. Owing to the shallowness of the Sea and to its low coastline the phenomena of strong on- and off-shore winds sometimes occur to a marked degree.

In August, the warmest time of the year, the average temperature of the surface waters of the open part of the Sea is 24° to 25°, while in the depths of the western depression it is 2·3°. In June, however, the average temperature near the bottom falls to 0·3° (*Table 278*). The layer of sudden change usually occurs at a depth of 16 to 28 m, while in the shallow eastern part the water is warmed down to the bottom and the layer of sudden change is not found (*Table 278*).

Table 278. Mean temperature of Aral Sea waters

Depth	Feb	Apr	Jun	Aug	Oct	Dec
			Deep western depression			
0	1·0	4·2	18·8	24·2	16·3	5·0
5	1·0	3·3	16·0	21·3	16·9	5·0
10	1·0	2·7	12·0	20·1	16·5	4·9
20	1·0	1·5	4·3	13·4	16·3	5·0
30	1·0	—	2·4	6·4	9·8	4·6
40	—	—	0·4	3·5	4·5	—
50	—	—	−0·2	2·7	4·2	4·0
60	—	—	−0·3	2·3	3·7	—
			Central part of the Sea			
0	0·7	5·3	19·4	23·7	14·4	2·5
5	—	—	17·2	23·6	14·4	—
10	—	—	14·5	22·9	14·3	—
20	—	—	9·4	21·9	14·4	—

Surface waters are cooled in the autumn (October and November), while in winter the whole column of water acquires a near-zero temperature. In mid-winter conditions the temperature falls to freezing point and ice begins to form on the surface.

Ice conditions

Water usually begins to freeze in the northern part of the Sea at the end of November, and two or three weeks later in the southern part. At first ice forms near the shores and the northern inlets freeze up; then the whole of the Maloe More and the eastern shores freeze. The open part of the Bolshoe More is usually free of ice. Ice does not finally disappear until the second half of April.

Salinity

As has been mentioned above, the salt composition of the Aral Sea differs from that of ocean waters, even more than do those of the Caspian Sea, and as regards the ratio of individual salts it approximates to fresh water (*Table 279*).

Sodium, magnesium and calcium, and among the compounds sodium chloride (54 per cent), magnesium sulphate (26 per cent) and calcium sulphate (15 per cent) are preponderant in the Aral waters.

The average salinity of the Aral Sea is about 10‰ (Fig. 305). A fall of salinity is observed in the mouths of the rivers, while in the inlets of the south-eastern part of the Sea salinity rises to 14‰ as a result of intense evaporation. A state approaching homohalinity is established in winter and spring; in the summer the surface waters lose some of their salinity.

A forecast of the change of salinity of the Aral Sea associated with a possible future decrease of incoming river water and a fall of sea-level has been made by L. Blinov (1956). The relationship of average salinity to sea-level

Table 279

	Percentage of salts in waters of:			
	Ocean	Caspian Sea	Aral Sea	Lake Superior
Sodium	30·593	24·82	21·30	
Potassium	1·106	0·66	0·79	5·52
Calcium	1·197	2·70	5·00	22·42
Magnesium	3·725	5·70	5·41	5·35
Chlorine	55·292	41·73	33·93	1·89
Bromine	0·188	0·06	0·03	—
Sulphates	7·692	23·49	31·29	3·62
Carbonates	0·207	0·86	1·75	47·42
Silicates	—	—	—	12·76
Nitrates	—	—	—	0·86
Iron + aluminium	—	—	0·50	0·16
Total	35·00	12·8	10·19	0·06

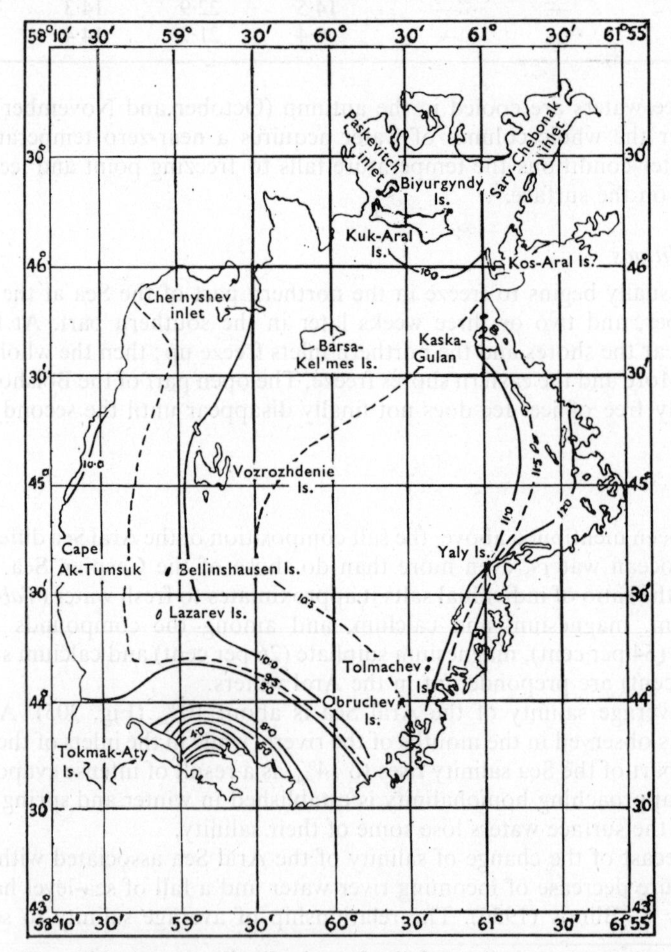

FIG. 305. Average distribution of salinity over many years in the upper layer of the Aral Sea (Blinov, 1956).

is given in Fig. 306, and the distribution of surface salinity of the Aral Sea, should its level drop by 5 m, is given in Fig. 307. If the sea-level dropped 10 m below what it is now, the salinity of the surface waters would increase by another 7‰.

The essential elements of the balance of the saline mass of the waters of

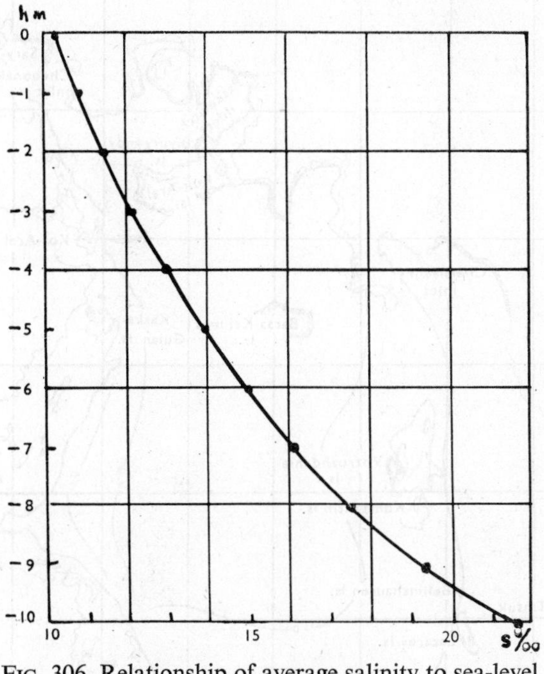

FIG. 306. Relationship of average salinity to sea-level of the Aral Sea (Blinov).

the Aral Sea under certain geographical and climatic conditions of the area are as follows (L. Blinov, 1956):

Salts deposited by rivers	12,850,000 tons
Salts carried away by winds	101,120 tons
Salts supplied from atmosphere	64,800 tons.

The total mass of salts in the Aral Sea is about 1,050,000,000 tons with an average salinity of 10·3‰. L. Blinov also determined the volume of water which leaks away through the soil as 1·26 km³, and assumes that this loss of salt compensates for the average annual salt supply by rivers.

As a result of a most detailed examination of the salinity of the waters of the Aral Sea and of its balance L. Blinov (1958) has come to the important conclusion that 'in relation to their saline (ionic) composition, the waters of the Aral Sea must be regarded as the strongly metamorphosed waters of the river discharge feeding the Sea. As a result of the processes of metamorphism the waters of the Aral Sea, and those of the Caspian Sea, became an

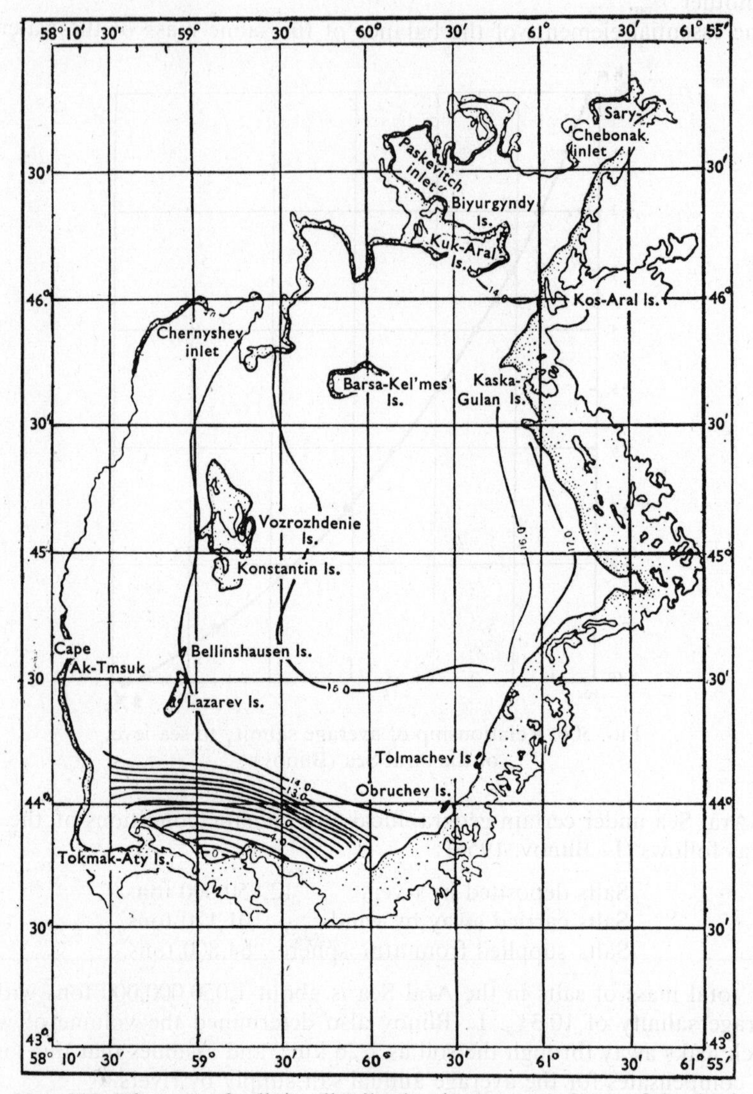

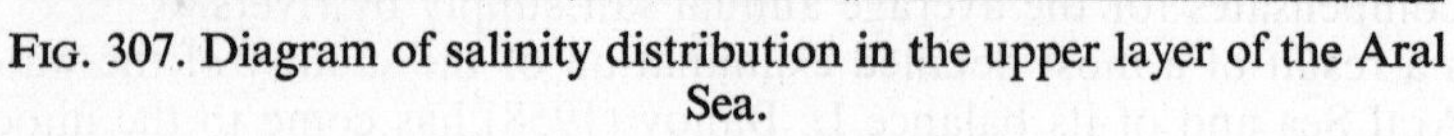
FIG. 307. Diagram of salinity distribution in the upper layer of the Aral Sea.

intermediate type between the hydrocarbonate calcium waters of the land and the sodium chloride waters of the ocean . . . although as regards their salt-forming ions the waters of the Aral Sea are closer to typical mainland waters than those of the Caspian. The salt system of the waters of the ocean and of the Caspian Sea is Cl–Na–SO, and that of the Aral Sea is Na–Cl–Mg.'*

Oxygen content

In summer time the waters of the Aral Sea are, as a rule, supersaturated with oxygen (at times up to 130 per cent saturation) even over the areas of black mud smelling of hydrogen sulphide. The great transparency of the water at comparatively shallow depths causes an abundant development of sea-weeds on the bottom of the Aral Sea, even at considerable depths, and the peculiar distribution of oxygen, which increases with depth, is also a direct result. Oxygen content below 81 per cent has never been observed in the Aral Sea. The presence of hydrogen sulphide has never been recorded, neither in the deepest parts and near the sea-floor, nor even where the sea-bed was known to contain hydrogen sulphide in its soil (mainly in the western basin).

The concentration of hydrogen ions

As regards the concentration of hydrogen ions the Aral waters differ from those of other big lakes; the pH index is comparatively small (7·2 to 7·8).

Plant nutrients

The distribution of plant nutrients in the waters of the Aral Sea has some peculiar characteristics. There is a normal active reaction, which on the average gives only small seasonal fluctuations (8·20 to 8·34) throughout the whole Sea.

These waters are very poor in phosphates. Their average content (P mg/m^3) in certain years (L. Blinov, 1956) varied within the limits 1·0 to 4·2 mg/m^3. Over a period of years the largest amount of phosphates, recorded in August 1949, was 23·1 P mg/m^3. In contrast with other Seas the quantity of phosphates here decreases with depth, often down to zero (10 to 20 m), and there is no accumulation of phosphorus in the depths. In the near-bottom layer phosphates are rapidly used up by vegetation. The average phosphate content in the upper layer of the Sea is given in *Table 280* (L. Blinov).

The nitrate content is also very low; it was found to be no more than 5 mg/m^3 in individual samples. Some increase was recorded only in the estuarine zones. There is more nitrogen in ammonium salts in the Aral Sea waters, its content reaching 80 mg/m^3. However, ammonium nitrogen is apparently of very little use. L. Blinov (1956) points out that it would hardly be possible to find another place affording a more monotonous picture of an 'analytical zero' of phosphorus and nitrogen than the Aral Sea. The content of silicic acid in the Aral Sea is considerably lower than in other seas; however,

* L. Blinov (1956) has investigated the chlorine number of the Aral Sea waters and has worked out the following formula for the determination of the salinity of total salts in terms of chlorine:

$$S\text{‰} = 0{\cdot}264 + 2{\cdot}791\ \text{Cl}\text{‰}$$

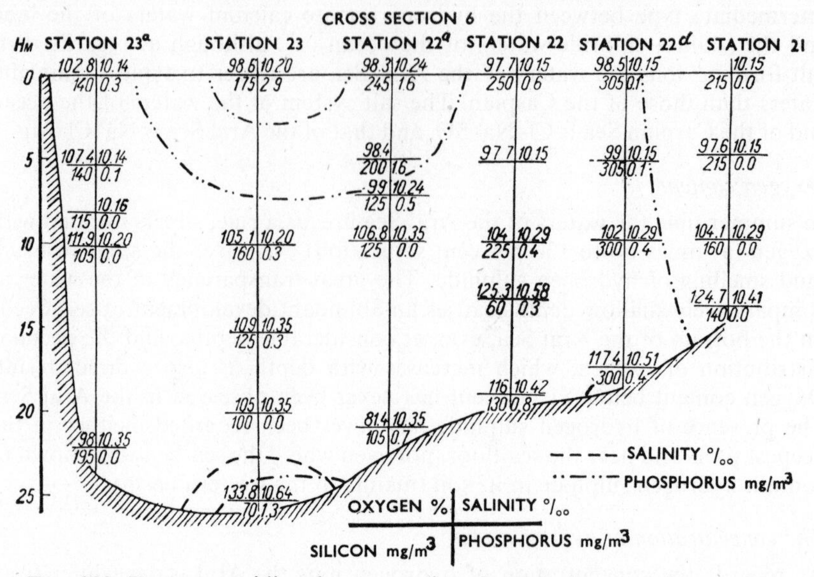

FIG. 308. Eastern meridional cross section through the central part of the Bol'shoe More, 3 to 6 June 1950 (Blinov).

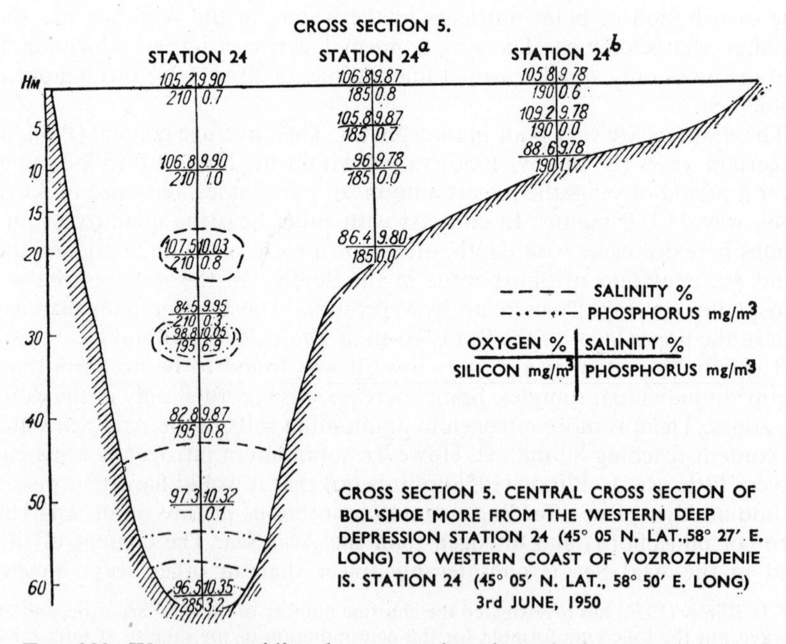

FIG. 309. Western meridional cross section through the central part of Bol'shoe More. 3 June 1950 (Blinov).

Table 280. Mean content of phosphates (P *mg/m*^{3})

Period	Northern section	Central section	Southern section
May–June	0·7	0·8	1·8
August–September	0·8	3·1	2·5
October	0·8	0·8	—

it never decreases to zero. Whereas there are hundreds and thousands of mg/m^3 of silicic acid in the surface waters of the Caspian Sea, there is only 150 to 250 mg/m^3 in the Aral Sea.

The hydrophysical and hydrochemical characteristics of the Aral Sea are given in Figs. 308 and 309.

IV. FLORA AND FAUNA

The general characteristics of the population of the Aral Sea and its history have been given above.

Composition of phytoplankton

The Aral Sea plankton is poor in numbers and in species.

A. Behning (1935) gives the following basic composition of phytoplankton:

Cyanophyceae	6 species
Flagellates	11 species
Conjugatae	2 species
Chlorophyceae	2 species
Diatomaceae	18 species

Among these 39 forms the most common blue-green algae are *Chroococcus turgidus*, *Merismopedia glauca* and *Anabaena bergi*; among flagellates—*Exuviella cordata aralensis*, *Prorocentrum obtusum*, *Glenodinium trochoideum*, *Gonyaulax levanderi*, *Peridinium achromaticum*, *P. subsalsum*, *Diplosalis caspica* and *D. pillula*; among the conjugates—*Spirogyra* spp. and *Mougeotia* spp. and among the green algae—*Oocystis socialis*, *Botryococcus braunii*; among the diatoms—*Actinocyclus ehrenbergi*, *Chaetoceras wighanii*, *Ch. subtile*, some *Campylodiscus* spp., *Coscinodiscus granii* var. *aralensis*, *Sceletonema costatum*, *Melosira borreri*, *Thalassiosira dicipens*, *Bacillaria paradoxa* and others.

The flagellates are of essential significance in the Aral Sea nannoplankton, forming the basic group in the food of Rotifera and Crustacea.

The diatoms dominate the plankton by their mass; the principal form among them is *Actinocyclus ehrenbergi* var. *crasa*, which sometimes produces over a million specimens per 1 m^3. Actinocyclus is the usual food of *Diaptomus salinus*, the highest mass form of Aral Sea zooplankton, which in its turn is the basic food of the young of most fish.

Botryococcus braunii is also of significance in the phytoplankton and in the food of zooplankton.

Thus the main supply of food for the zooplankton consists of flagellates, diatoms and to a lesser degree of green algae.

Composition of zooplankton

There are 24 main zooplankton forms in the Aral Sea, including:

Tintinnoidea	2 species
Rotatoria	8 species
Cladocera	7 species
Copepoda	7 species

In addition, the plankton usually contains a great many *Dreissena polymorpha* larvae (up to 10,000 specimens per 1 m³) and small-sized (and, in the hours of darkness, also fully grown) *Pontogammarus aralensis*.

The most usual zooplankton forms are: Infusoria *Codonella relicta* (up to 40,000 specimens per 1 m³); the Rotifera *Floscularia mutabilis*, *Synchaeta vorax*, *S. neapolitana* and *Rattulus marinus*; among the Cladocera *Ceriodaphnia reticulata*, *Moina microphthalma* (up to 3,000 specimens per 1 m³), *Cercopagis pengoi*, *Evadne camptonyx* (up to 12,000 specimens per 1 m³), and *E. anonyx*. Among the Copepoda *Diaptomus salinus* (producing up to 8,500 specimens per 1 m³) is the most important in the Aral Sea. This form is greatly predominant over all the other zooplankton forms; it is the main food of fish-fry, and sometimes of adult fish (stickleback, Pelecus, Chalcalburnus). According to V. Pankratova (1935) *D. salinus* forms 58 per cent of the food of carp-fry, 32 per cent of that of Chalcalburnus, 20 per cent of that of bream, and 10 per cent of that of vobla. In the open parts of the Sea *Mesocyclops leuckarti* and *M. hyalinus* (up to 600 specimens per 1 m³) are the most common of the Copepoda.

In August the total zooplankton biomass is on the average 0·5 g/m³. Copepoda biomass sometimes yields up to 230 mg/m³, Cladocera up to 650 mg/m³ and the larvae of molluscs up to 160 to 170 g/m³.

In A. Behning's opinion (1935) no less than 95 per cent of the total biomass of Aral zooplankton is composed of Dreissena larvae and of all stages of *Diaptomus salinus*. Thus the Aral zooplankton is an example of the pronounced predominance of a few forms (olygomixed).

Horizontal and vertical distribution of plankton

A. Behning (1935) has distinguished in the Aral Sea three areas differing from each other in their qualitative and quantitative plankton composition: the open Sea, the coastal areas and the estuarine reaches (Fig. 310).

The area of the open Sea is exposed to smaller fluctuations of temperature and salinity (10·3 to 10·5‰), while in the depths the temperature remains low (between 4·5° and 9·5°) all through the year. This area includes the central part of the Bol'shoy More and the open parts of the northern inlets of the Maloe More. There is 3·2 times more plankton (up to 1,200,000 specimens per 1 m³) in the depths than there is in the surface layer (up to 370,000 specimens per 1 m³) mainly owing to *Actinocyclus ehrenbergi*. The mean biomass in the open Sea, according to G. V. Nikolsky (1940), is 3·23 cm^3 per 1 m^3. *Diaptomus salinus*, Cladocera and Dreissena larvae make daily vertical migrations; in daytime they keep mainly at a depth of 10 to 20 m (Fig. 311).

'These daily plankton migrations', says A. Behning, 'have real significance in the life of the Sea. They enable the plankton animals to use all layers of water in their search for food; masses of diatoms are found by them in daytime in the depths—Actinocyclus, Campylodiscus, Pleurosigma—and by night in the upper layer they find flagellates and other species of phytoplankton.'

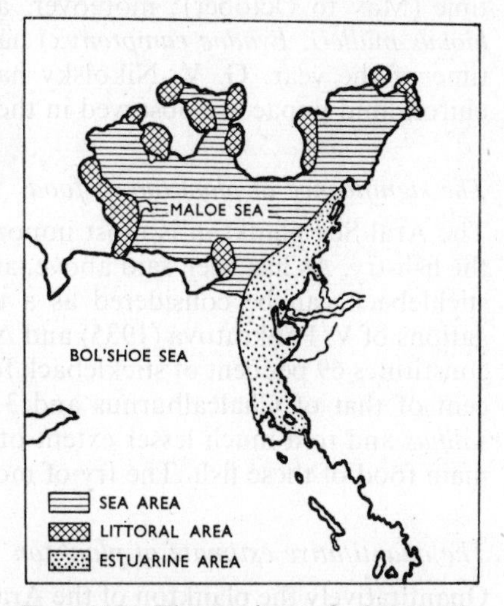

FIG. 310. The region of the north-western part of the Aral Sea according to plankton composition (Behning).

In bays and inlets, which usually have a somehat higher salinity and are subject to greater temperature and salinity fluctuations, the most common forms among the plankton, according to A. Behning, are the algae *Chroococcus turgidus*, *Oscillatoria tenuis*, *Lyngbya aestuarii*, two species of peridinians Cyclotella and *Melosira Borreri*, among the animals the Rotifera *Brachionus bakeri*, *B. mülleri*, and *Colurella adriatica*, and among the Crustacea *Halicyclops aequoreus*, *Cyclops viridis* and *Alona rectangula*. The mean plankton biomass is here about 2·75 mg/m^3. Near the mouth of the rivers Amu- and Sur-Daria,

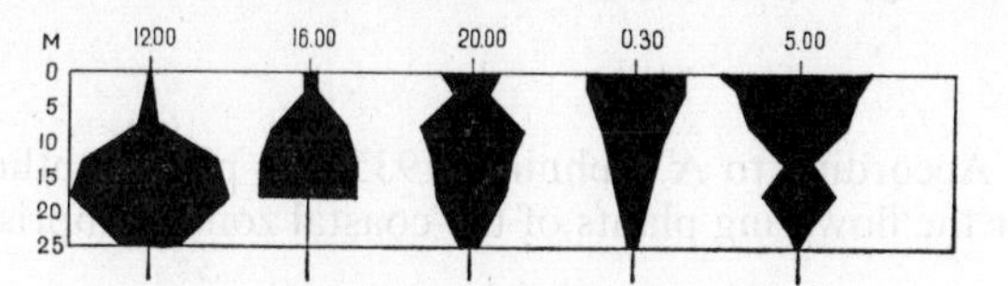

FIG. 311. Vertical migrations of plankton in the Aral Sea in August 1933 according to the number of specimens (Behning).

within the areas of the lower surface salinity, the plankton composition changes, many forms of the saline Aral waters are not found, and there is a considerable admixture of fresh-water forms. The most characteristic are the following: *Microcystis aeruginosa*, *Dinobryon sertularia*, *Ceratium hirundinella*, *Eudorina elegans*, *Fragilaria crotonensis*, *Keratella aculeata* and *Diaphanosoma brachyurum*. At the confluence of fresh and saline waters there is an increase of plankton biomass caused by the high content of plant nutrients in the river waters. The average wet volume of plankton in the Syr-Dar'ya estuary is 3 mg/m^3.

Seasonal changes of plankton

The Aral Sea plankton is more abundant in variety and numbers in summer time (May to October); moreover, a number of forms (for example *Brachionus mülleri*, *Evadne camptonyx*) have a maximum growth in the warmest time of the year. G. V. Nikolsky has pointed out that a large number of chironomid pupae are observed in the plankton, mainly in the autumn.

The significance of plankton as food

The Aral Sea plankton is most important as food for the bottom-fauna and the fish-fry. As has been said above, among the adult fish of the Aral Sea only stickleback can be considered as a typical plankton eater. As the investigations of V. Pankratova (1935) and A. Behning (1935) have shown, plankton constitutes 69 per cent of stickleback food, 16 per cent of that of Pelecus, 9 per cent of that of Chalcalburnus and 3 per cent of that of bream. *Diaptomus salinus* and to a much lesser extent other Copepoda and Cladocera form the main food of these fish. The fry of most fish feeds on plankton.

The quantitative estimate of plankton

Quantitatively the plankton of the Aral Sea is somewhat inferior to that of the Caspian and much poorer than that of the Sea of Azov (and other central Asian lakes except Lake Balkhash) (Fig. 312). Its average biomass is about 3 cm^3/m^3 and the number of specimens of plankton organisms is of the order of 8 to 9 millions, mainly flagellates and the diatoms Actinocyclus, Exuviella, Proterocentrum, Glenodinium, Diplosalis and other nannoplankton forms.

The quantitative distribution of the plankton of the Aral is illustrated in Fig. 312. The inadequacy of the nutrient salts is regarded by Nikolsky as the cause of the poverty of plankton in the Aral Sea.

Benthos

Phytobenthos. According to A. Behning (1935) the phytobenthos of the Aral Sea, except for the flowering plants of the coastal zone, comprises the following groups:

Chlorophyceae	4 species
Diatomaceae	25 species
Rhodophyceae	1 species
Characeae	1 species
Phanerogamae	1 species

Among these 32 forms the flowering plant *Zostera nana*, the green algae *Vaucheria dichotoma* and *Cladophora gracilis*, the red algae *Polysiphonia violacea* and *Characea alga Tolypella aralica* are the specially large mass forms.

Zostera mainly inhabits silty sand soils in the shallower areas of the bottom of the eastern and northern parts of the Sea. Large accumulations of it are found there. As in the Black and Caspian Seas, Zostera forms floating fields in the Aral Sea and great masses of it are cast up on the shore. Bottom sea-weeds go down much deeper than Zostera, and these sea-weeds (mainly *Vaucheria dichotoma*) form a thick cover on grey mud down to depths of 26 m. The Charial sea-weed *Tolypella aralica* forms abundant beds on black

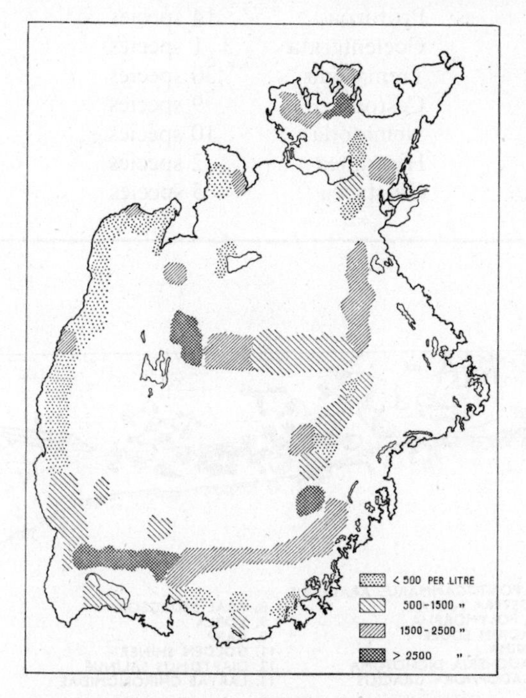

FIG. 312. Quantitative distribution of plankton in the Aral Sea in summer 1932–33, number of specimens per litre (Behning).

ooze which smells of hydrogen sulphide, mainly in bays and inlets more or less separated from the Sea. The thin brown film covering the mud soils comprises a huge number of diatomaceous algae.

The qualitative composition and quantitative distribution of zoobenthos (Fig. 313). Qualitatively zoobenthos is as poor as plankton; it comprises only 48 forms:

Foraminifera	2 species	Amphipoda	1 species
Nematoda (free-living)	7 species	Gastropoda	2 species
Turbellaria	12 species	Lamellibranchiata	4 species
Oligochaeta	3 species	Trichoptera	2 species
Bryozoa	1 species	Chironomidae	6 species
Harpacticoida	5 species	Hydracarina	1 species
Ostracoda	3 species		

Fish-parasites. Seventy-one species of different fish-parasites should be added to this list. According to V. Dogjel and B. Bykhovsky (1934) they are distributed among the following groups:

Protozoa	14 species
Coelenterata	1 species
Trematoda	30 species
Cestoda	9 species
Nematoda	10 species
Hirudinea	2 species
Crustacea	5 species

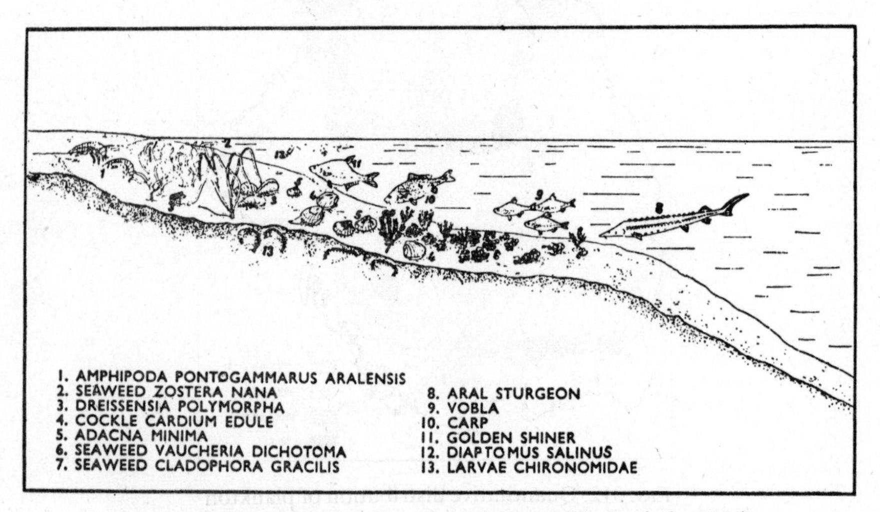

FIG. 313. Zonal distribution of Aral fauna (Zenkevitch, 1951).

For the Sea itself only 33 species of parasites have been confirmed. All the others are inhabitants of low-salinity areas. Among these parasites the Coelenterata *Polypodium hydriforme* and the Trematoda *Nitschia sturionis*, brought into the Aral Sea with starred sturgeon during its acclimatization, are of great interest.* About a hundred specimens of starred sturgeon were introduced into the Aral Sea from the Caspian Sea, without being disinfected against parasites.

The parasite of the gills of the starred sturgeon is the trematode Nitschia, which is widely dispersed in the Caspian Sea and does little harm there. No more than 40 specimens per fish have been recorded in that Sea. Once in the Aral Sea, however, the trematode transferred to the local sturgeon Acipenser and caused a serious epizootic epidemic which led to high mortality among fish. Up to 600 trematodes have been counted on one sturgeon Acipenser.

Over a period of some years the number of Trematoda dropped sharply;

* There is, however, an opinion that *Nitschia sturionis* existed in the Aral Sea before the starred sturgeon was introduced.

however, the stock of sturgeon Acipenser was not restored to its former numbers.

It was discovered in 1945 that the Aral sturgeon Acipenser was infected, in addition to the trematode, by a parasite of the roe of Acipenseridae fish well known in the Caspian Sea—the coelenterate *Polypodium hydriforme*. The poor multiplication of Acipenser sturgeon when the epizootic epidemic caused by Trematoda was over may have been due to its infection by *Polypodium hydriforme*. V. Dogjel and B. Bykhovsky noted the general poverty of the parasite-fauna of the Aral fish (two to three times poorer than the parasite-fauna of Neva Inlet in the Gulf of Finland), caused by the properties of the Aral waters and by the absence among the rest of the fauna of vector forms, the intermediate hosts.

Mass zoobenthos forms. The most common benthos forms are the Oligochaeta *Paranais simplex* and *Nais elinguis*; among Ostracoda *Cyprideis littoralis*, widely distributed in the Azov and Caspian Seas; only one representative of higher Crustacea, *Pontogammarus aralensis*; among molluscs *Adacna minima*, *Dreissena polymorpha* and, much more rarely, *Cardium edule*; and among the insects, the larvae of caddis flies and of chironomids. The highest number of specimens recorded and the weight of these forms per 1 m³ are given in *Table 281*.

Table 281

Form	No. of specimens	Biomass g/m²
Oligochaeta	600	1·3
Ostracoda	920	0·2
Amphipoda	750	6·8
Adacna minima	700	32·8
Dreissena polymorpha	2,000 (25,625)	66·15 (955)
Cardium edule	80	9·8
Trichoptera	80	4·0
Chironomidae	1,840	33·2
Hydrobia	462	—
Dikerogammarus aralensis	150	2·0

It is evident from *Table 281* that even the highest mass forms, such as for example Dreissena, which in the Caspian Sea frequently produces a few kilogrammes per 1 m³, do not produce more than a few dozen grammes in the Aral Sea. The Dreissena genus is represented in the Aral Sea (according to N. Husainova, 1958) by four species—*Dr. polymorpha* with two variants (*obtusecarinata* and *aralensis*), *Dr. caspia*, *Dr. pallasi* and *Dr. rostriformis*. *Cyprideis littoralis*, at times found in the Sea of Azov in hundreds of thousands of specimens per m³, is in the Aral Sea no higher than 1,000 with a biomass of 0·2 g/m². The same holds true of plants. The highest Zostera biomass recorded is only 90 g/m², Tolypella 9·5 g/m², and Vaucheria 531 g/m². The total weight of all the plants rarely exceeds 0·5 kg/m².

Bivalves are usually preponderant in the benthos biomass, constituting at times 94 per cent of its total. Chironomids occupy second place, Phryganidae third, and *Pontogammarus aralensis* fourth. Other benthos groups are of little significance.

All the organisms of Aral benthos are consumed by fish, but only a certain proportion of those of the Azov and Caspian benthos are taken. This fact

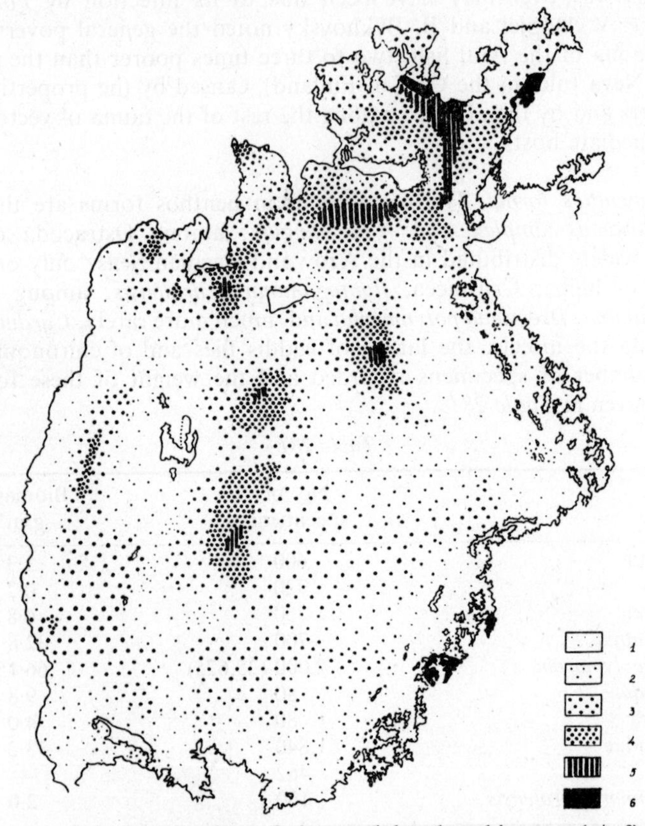

FIG. 314. Distribution of the total benthos biomass (g/m²) of the Aral Sea in 1954–57 (Yablonskaya).

must be taken into consideration when estimating the food significance of Aral benthos. The significance of benthos as food is thus relatively higher in the Aral Sea.

Uniform distribution, within the limits of one biotope, and the absence of areas of great concentration, are characteristic of Aral benthos. Even Dreissena does not form extensive accumulations here. The phenomenon of bottom-fauna suffocation has not been recorded in the Aral Sea.

The quantitative and qualitative distribution of the zoobenthos of the Aral Sea has more than once been investigated by V. Nikitinsky (1933), A. Behning

(1935) and I. Kulichenko (1944). The most recent comprehensive study was undertaken by E. Yablonskaya (1959), who has distinguished seven main biocoenoses. Practically the whole Sea is encircled (Fig. 315, 1) at little depth (2 to 10 m) by a zone of vegetation. *Dreissena polymorpha* is the predominant form. The mean mass of charial algae is 67·158 g/m²; among the Zostera in the Maloe More—22·255 g/m²; among the soft macrophytes

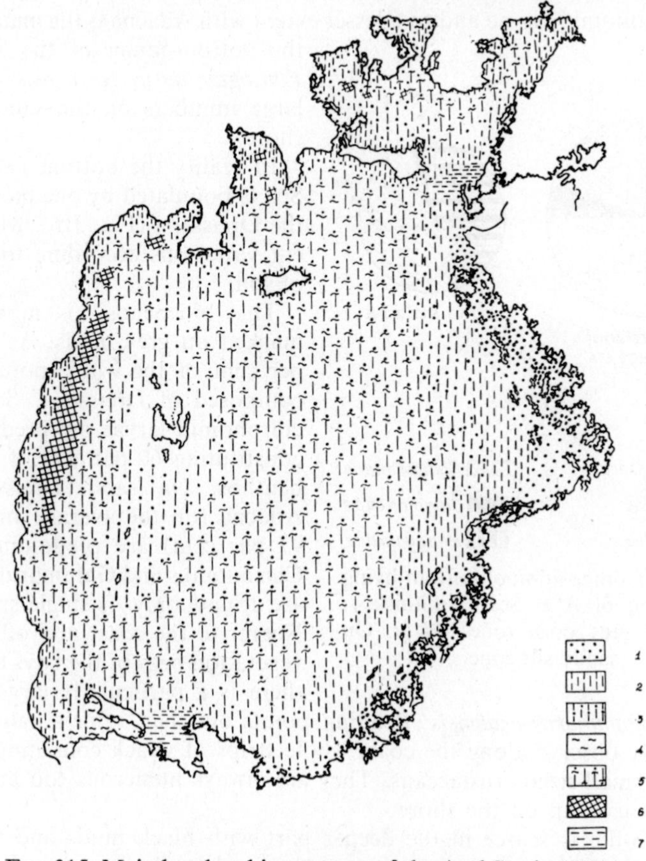

FIG. 315. Main benthos biocoenoses of the Aral Sea in 1954 to 1957 (Yablonskaya). See text for interpretation.

(Potamogeton and others)—10·874 g/m². This zone is followed by the sandy zone, which has a predominance of *Adacna minima* (Fig. 315, 2) with a biomass of 6·181 g/m². Still deeper (10 to 24 m) on the silty sand (Fig. 315, 3) the Dreissena and Adacna biocoenosis develops with a biomass of 15 to 14 g/m². Chironomid larvae are the dominant form on the mud soil of Adzhibai Inlet (Fig. 315, 4), producing a biomass of up to 16·2 g/m². All the central part of the Sea, with depths down to 27 m, on sand and grey mud soils is populated by the Chironomus, Dreissena and Adacna biocoenosis

(Fig. 315, 5) which forms a biomass of 20 g/m² in the Bol'shoe More and of 58·8 g/m² in the Maloe More. In the western depression on black mud with Vaucheris at depths of 28 to 60 m, Dreissena is predominant with a biomass of 12 to 18 g/m² (Fig. 315, 6), but at depths of 40 to 60 m the biomass drops to a few tens of milligrammes per 1 m². In the Syr- and Amu-Daria estuarine zones Adacna biocoenosis with an average biomass of 5·290 g/m² develops on brown soils at depths of 4 to 10 m. *Dreissena polymorpha* in combination with chironomid larvae and to a lesser extent with Adacna is the main form of the bottom-fauna of the Aral Sea. *Pontogammarus aralensis* lives in large numbers on the sands of the shore.

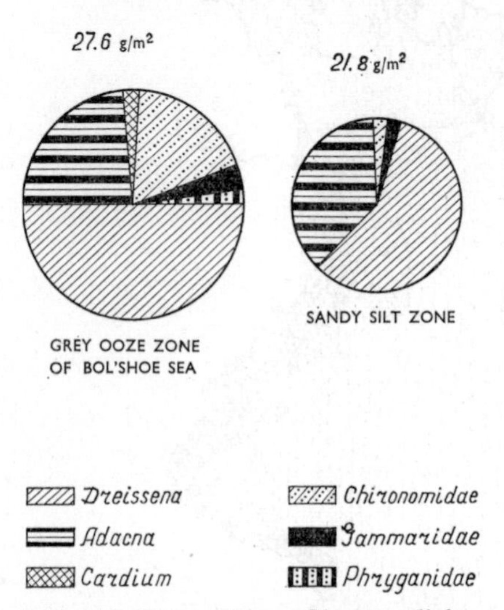

FIG. 316. Composition of bottom-living population of Aral Sea (Nikitinsky): *Left:* On grey ooze zone; *Right:* On sandy silt zone.

In reality the bottom of the Aral Sea is populated by one biocoenosis, the Dreissena (Fig. 316), with different variations according to the type of soil.

This biocoenosis is most clearly marked on grey muds. At times 80 per cent of the whole population is composed of Dreissena. Sometimes chironomid larvae are predominant, constituting 60 per cent of the total benthos. On sands Dreissena and Adacna (on the average more than 97 per cent) are predominant; the Chironomus and Gammaridae larvae are found only as single specimens. Nearer to the coast and off it in the vegetation beds of the bays and inlets there is a particularly large number of *Pontogammarus aralensis*. Behning points out that 'after a gale one can frequently observe along the coast whole strips of wrack consisting entirely of these small-sized crustaceans. They are always numerous too among the sea grass cast up on the shore.'

Bottom-life is scarce in the deeper part with black muds and hydrogen sulphide, and in some areas it may not be found at all.

In the shallower areas covered by black mud (40 to 50 m) benthos is poorly developed and is represented mainly by Nematoda, Oligochaeta and Ostracoda.

Benthos is richest in shell-gravel areas where, according to Behning, it reaches 40 g/m². Bottom-life is scarce or even completely absent opposite the mouths of both great rivers and, like that of the black muds, it is represented here by Nematoda, Oligochaeta, Ostracoda and chironomid larvae.

A survey of the distribution of bottom fauna in the Adzhibai inlet (south-western corner of the Sea) was undertaken by P. Dengina in 1957. The salinity of the Sea (measured by chlorine) varies from 4‰ at the end of the

Amu-Darya delta to 6·0‰ at the entrance to the Sea. Most of the inlet floor is occupied by a bed of *Zostera nana*; in summer there are up to 3,000 stems per 1 m². Dengina points out that Zostera 'is of great significance for the zoobenthos, since it serves as a substratum for the fixation of sessile forms (Dreissena) and as a habitat for the not very mobile forms. Bacterial flora developing on the stems and leaves of Zostera serves as food for cladocerans, insect larvae and molluscs. Zostera is the food of almost all benthophagic fish; it offers good shelter for the young of commercial fish which float down from the delta waters.'

Among the bivalves three forms of Dreissena (*D. polymorpha*, *D.p.* var. *aralensis* and *D. caspia*), *Adacna vitrea* var. *minima* and *Cardium edule*—and among the Gastropoda *Hydrobia ventrosa* and *Theodxus pallasi* belong to the highest mass forms. Ostracoda (*Cyprodeis littoralis*, *C. torosa* and *Hemicythera sicula*) play an important role in the benthos.

Among the crustaceans *Dikerogammarus aralensis*, and among the bryozoans *Victorella bergi* develop in large numbers. The larvae of insects are found everywhere, sometimes in large numbers. The mean zoobenthos biomass of the inlet has been determined by Dengina as 11·7 g/m² in the spring and 12·2 g/m² in the summer.

The data for the mean benthos biomass of the Aral Sea given by different investigators range from 16 to 18 g/m² (Behning) to 21 g/m² (Kulichenko) and 23 g/m² (V. Nikitinsky). Benthos is most abundant in the Maloe More (owing to Dreissena) and in some areas of the central part of the Bol'shoe More (due to chironomids). Benthos biomass is commonly 20 to 40 g/m². The benthos biomass of the Aral Sea undergoes considerable fluctuations over a period of years (*Table 282*).

Table 282. Mean benthos biomass, g/m²

Soil	1936 spr	1936 sum	1936 aut	1937 spr	1937 sum	1937 aut	1938 spr	1938 sum	1938 aut	1939 spr
Mud	16	22	16	29	61	29	39	43	34	27
Clayey mud	10	13	11	10	32	18	14	19	23	16
Sandy mud	12	20	13	14	54	23	10	21	13	18
Silty sand	10	11	6	13	19	12	6	16	17	10
Sand	11	12	8	10	30	27	17	8	8	10

Making a general estimate on the basis of the quantitative data of Aral Sea benthos, the three above-mentioned workers do not incline to the view that its benthos is very poor. On the contrary Nikitinsky and Kulichenko believe that the Aral benthos with its high quality as food forms a satisfactory stock of food for the present fish population.

Thus, in contrast to the Caspian Sea and like our other seas, the Aral Sea benthos biomass is greater on soft bottoms than on hard ones; this can probably be explained by the peculiarities of both bodies of water and by the conditions under which the different types of soil were formed in them.

Benthos biomass is highest in the summer; in the autumn it is somewhat higher than in the spring.

The causes of this type of seasonal change lie mainly in the intensity of the summer feeding of the fish.

Fish

Qualitative composition. The Aral Sea fish are represented by 11 families and 24 species; the family Cyprinidae alone comprises 12 species (50 per cent) and the Percidae 3 species (13 per cent); the other 9 families (including Acipenseridae, Salmonidae, Siluridae, Esocidae and Gasterosteidae) are represented by only one species. Seven species were brought into the Sea by man in recent years.

The transplantation of the Caspian *Caspialosa caspia aestuarina* and two species of Mugil into the Aral Sea was apparently not successful; the herring and mullet died out, because of the low winter temperature of the Aral Sea.

G. V. Nikolsky (1940) notes that the fauna of the Aral Sea comprises three genetic communities: (*1*) the remains of the upper-Tertiary fauna, (*2*) representatives of Aral–Caspian fauna and (*3*) representatives of northern Siberian fish. The Aral–Caspian forms constitute 45 per cent of the fish. They are mainly members of the cyprinid family. The fish of the Aral Sea are much poorer than those of the Caspian. Among the large lakes only Balkhash and Issyk-Kul' are poorer in fish species. There are only nine endemic forms (38 per cent) among the fish of the Aral Sea; moreover, the majority of them are sub-species: there is only one endemic species (Aral barbel).

The complete disappearance from the original Aral fauna of the members of the families Clupeidae and Gobiidae, which are so characteristic of the Caspian Sea, is most remarkable. Among the 24 species of Aral fish 14 are common to it and to the Caspian Sea and 10 belong to other different subspecies. Thus the Aral Sea fish are closely related to those of the Caspian Sea. 'It is well known that a gradual decrease in the number of fish species is observed', wrote Nikolsky, 'as one moves from west to east—from the Black Sea through the Caspian and Aral Seas to Lake Balkhash. Thus the number of species in the Black Sea (without the basin, Slastenenko's data) is more than 170. In the Caspian Sea the number of species falls below 100, in the Aral Sea to 20 and in Lake Balkhash to 8.' Nikolsky thinks that the 'fish of the Aral Sea were evolved from those of the Amu-Daria and its ancient tributary Syr-Daria.

Fish feeding. G. V. Nikolsky (1940) distinguishes two main biological groupings of Aral Sea fish—that of the open Sea and that of the coastal zones; the absence of small, benthos-feeding, comparatively immobile fish is highly characteristic of the Aral Sea (also there are no fish which live permanently away from the coast). The majority of Aral fish are good swimmers feeding on pelagic and bottom fauna.

The main commercial fish—golden shiner, vobla, bream, *Abramis sapa*, Pelecus and Chalcalburnus—feed in the open parts of the Sea from the middle of May to October at depths of 15 to 30 m and on the grey mud; nevertheless none of the species multiplies there. According to G. Nikolsky, 'the main items of fish diet in this part of the Sea, both in the epilimnion and in the hypolimnion are amphipods (*Pontogammarus aralensis*). Bivalves and gastropod molluscs play a much smaller role. Air insects, mainly caddis fly and chironomids, are of significance in the diet of fish living in the epilimnion (bream, *Abramis sapa* and vobla in the spring and autumn, and Pelecus and Chalcalburnus throughout the year); thus the typical pelagic fish is absent from the Aral Sea and the food which in the Caspian Sea is taken by Clupeonella is not used here.' Since there are no small pelagic fish there are no pelagic predators, which are so typical of the Black Sea and to a lesser extent of the

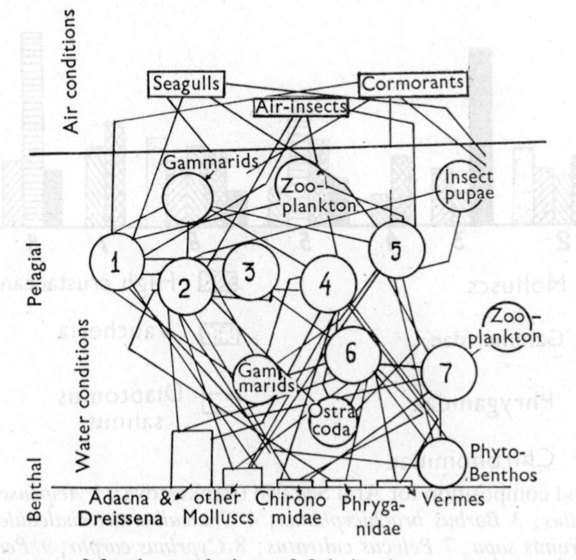

FIG. 317. Diagram of food correlation of fish in the open parts of the Aral Sea (Nikolsky). 1 *Pelecus cultratus*; 2 *Abramis sapa*; 3 *Lucioperca lucioperca*; 4 *Rutilus rutilus;* 5 *Chalcalburnus chalcoides*; 6 *Abramis brama*; 7 *Pungitius platygaster*.

Caspian. G. V. Nikolsky notes that the food chain of pike perch turned in the Caspian Sea towards the pelagic forms: plankton—Mysidae—Caspialosa—pike perch; in the Aral Sea it consists mainly of benthos: plankton—Pontogammarus—Pelecus—pike perch—*Abramis sapa*.

According to the nature of their diet the Aral fish can be distinguished into zoobenthophages, planktophages, and predators; phytophages are poorly represented here, and there are no mud-eaters.

Food correlations of fish of the open parts of the Aral Sea are given in Fig. 317.

The coastal grouping of Aral Sea fish comprises a large number of species of plant-eaters (rudd and some carp).

There is only one typical planktophage here, as well as in the open parts of the Sea—stickleback.

The composition of food for the fish, which also inhabit the open parts of the Sea, changes considerably near the shores, where gammarids become less and molluscs more significant; Ostracoda is added to the diet. Some shorter food chains make their appearance (for example: phytobenthos—rudd—pike perch); plankton is even less important.

V. Pankratova (1935) has shown that fish feed more on vegetable food in the winter than in the summer, and more on animal food in the summer than in the winter. According to this worker (Fig. 318) *Acipenser nudiventris* feeds exclusively on molluscs. The diets of vobla (*Rutilus rutilus aralensis*) and

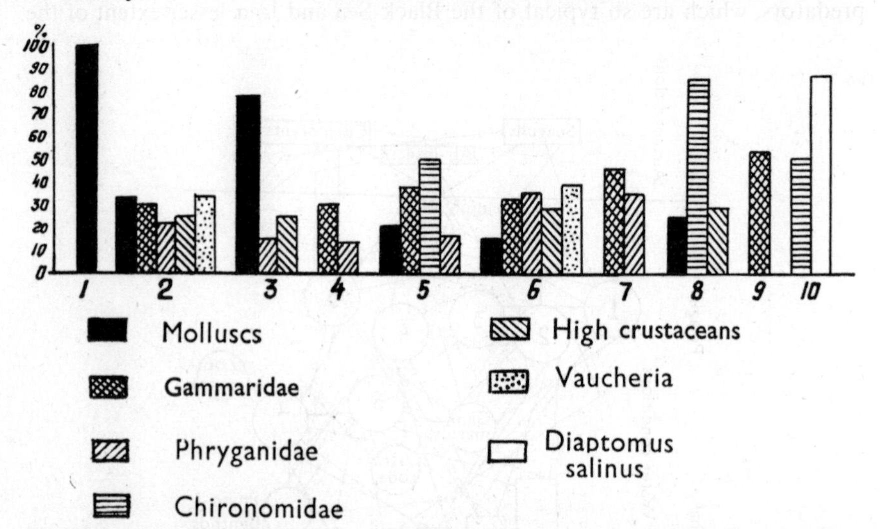

FIG. 318. Food composition for Aral Sea fish (Pankratova). 1 *Acipenser nudiventris*; 2 *Rutilus rutilus*; 3 *Barbus brachicephalus*; 4 *Chalcalburnus chalcoides*; 5 *Abramis brama*; 6 *Abramis sapa*; 7 *Pelecus cultratus*; 8 *Cyprinus carpio*; 9 *Perca fluviatilis*; 10 *Pungitius platygaster*.

bream (*Abramis sapa*) are the most varied, and the ratio of their components is very similar. Vegetable food is most significant in both diets: for vobla 63·5 per cent of fish had some remains of vegetable food in their intestines, and 49·5 per cent of them had only vegetable food in their intestines. Among the animals molluscs and insect larvae are predominant in the vobla's diet. Forty per cent of bream (*Abramis sapa*) had vegetable food (Vaucheria, and other filamentous algae), and among the animals caddis and beach fleas are predominant.

Barbus brachycephalus feeds mostly on molluscs, and to a much smaller extent on gammarids and higher plants.

Chalcalburnus chalcoides aralensis feeds on gammarids and phriganids, and *Abramis brama* eats all the benthos, but mostly gammarids and chironomid larvae. *Pelecus cultratus* preys almost exclusively on animals and mainly on beach fleas. It swallows also a number of land insects which fall into the water.

The main diet of *Cyprinus carpio* is chironomid larvae, and to a lesser extent molluscs, pelagic crustaceans and plants. *Perca fluviatilis* feeds exclusively on gammarus, and *Pungitius platygaster aralensis* is a typical planktophague. Its main food is *Diaptomus salinus*, and a supplementary one is chironomid pupae. *Silirus glanis*, *Lucioperca lucioperca*, *Aspius aspius illiodes* and *Esox lucius* are predators which feed on fish and very rarely eat other animals and plants.

Acclimatization measures. In recent years acclimatization measures in the Aral Sea have acquired a systematic character. In this work the high food value of the benthos, in spite of its small biomass, is taken into consideration as well as the great poverty of plankton food and the presence of considerable amounts of mostly vegetable organic detritus.

Adult *Acipenser stellatus* was brought from the Caspian Sea in 1933–34. Acclimatization measures were again undertaken in 1948–56. *Acipenser stellatus*, however, was brought as roe from the delta of the Ural river. Both species of grey mullet (*Mugil auratus* and *M. saliens*) and with them both species of prawns (*Leander adspersus* and *L. squilla*) were also brought from the Caspian Sea into the Aral Sea in 1954–56, while during the same years the roe of *Clupea harengus membras* came from the Baltic Sea. The transplantation of Baltic herring and its successful development in the Aral Sea is of special interest, the more so since in its new habitat the fish grows quicker and larger in size (two or three times larger). The severe temperature conditions of the Aral Sea might cause some doubts about the acclimatization of grey mullet; but as a mud-eater it has plenty of food there. So far it has not been discovered in the Aral Sea.

Two species of Caspian bullheads (*Pomatoschistus caucasicus*, and *Gobius melanostomus affinis*) and three species of Caspian mysids (*Mesomysis kowalewskyi*, *Mesomysis intermedia* and *Paramysis baeri*) were brought into the Aral Sea with the grey mullet (1958).

The fish *Atherina mochon pontica caspia* was brought in by accident. A future possibility is the transplantation into the Aral Sea of forms successfully acclimatized in the Caspian Sea—Nereis and Syndesmya and others. The success of the transplantation of the Baltic herring into the Aral Sea is an indication that other inhabitants of the Baltic might later be transplanted too. Among the invertebrates the bivalve *Macoma baltica* seems to offer some possibility of acclimatization in the Aral Sea.

Fishery. Carp, bream and vobla are the main items of commercial fishery in the Aral Sea. Chalcalburnus, catfish, *Abramis sapa*, barbel pike, pike perch and *Aspius aspius* are of less importance. The total catch in recent years (1956) has reached 459 centners. In 1956 there was a total yield of 166,000 centners of bream, 100,000 centners of carp, 57,000 centners of vobla, 25,000 centners of pike, 23,000 centners of Chalcalburnus, and 9,000 centners of pike perch. Fishing has so far been done mainly in the in-shore areas, chiefly in the mouths of rivers.

THE FAR EASTERN SEAS OF THE U.S.S.R.

13

General Characteristics of the Far Eastern Seas and of Adjacent Parts of the Pacific Ocean

I. GENERAL CHARACTERISTICS

A quarter of the coast of the U.S.S.R. is washed by the Pacific Ocean and the Seas of the Far East. Only a seventh of the whole coast is actually washed by the waters of the Pacific, while six-sevenths of it consists of the shores of the Seas of Japan and of Okhotsk and the Bering Sea. [The total area of the three Seas (4,872,000 km^2) is almost double the area of the European Seas of the U.S.S.R. from the White and Barents Seas to the Aral Sea (2,842,500 km^2). The volume of the Far Eastern Seas (6,741,300 km^3) is seven times greater than that of the European Seas (978,300 km^3)].

There is a free exchange of water through the numerous straits between the three Seas and the Pacific. The whole mass of water of the Bering Sea has free access to the Pacific through its many deep straits (down to 5,000 km), and therefore it can be considered as a bay of the Ocean. This is true to a lesser extent of the Sea of Okhotsk since, apart from its surface and modified near-bottom layers, its waters have the same characteristics as those of the neighbouring Pacific.

The Sea of Japan is the most isolated from the Pacific, owing to the shallowness (not more than 130 m) of the four straits which connect them.

The Sea of Japan has not, however, a reduced salinity; as a whole this approximates to that of the Ocean; its depths are well supplied with oxygen as a result of considerable mixing in winter.

A small shelf and great depths are characteristic of our Far Eastern Seas. Only the northern and northeastern parts of the Bering Sea are occupied by vast shallows, which constitute about half of its whole area. The shelf zone is very narrow in the Sea of Okhotsk and narrower still in the Sea of Japan. This influences the composition and especially the biological properties of its fauna.

The Seas of Japan and Okhotsk and the Bering Sea extend in a southwestern and northeasterly direction for almost 5,000 km. Whereas the climate of the northern parts of the Sea of Okhotsk and of the northwestern parts of the Bering Sea is arctic and severe, and both contain large masses of ice for several months, the small Kuril Bar and the southern part of the Sea of Japan closely approach the tropical zone. In the northwesterly part of the Pacific, as also in that of the Atlantic, the cold and warm water zones occur very close to each other, and as a result masses of cold water move from the north and masses of warm water move from the south (Gulf Stream, Kuroshio). This is in contrast to the northeastern sides of the oceans, where the extent of these zones is considerably greater, and the boundaries between the cold, temperate and warm water zones are spread out and the sharpness of the division between them is less distinct (Fig. 319).

As a result of the convergence of the cold and warm waters on the western side of the Ocean off the shores of Japan, the 0° and 16° isotherms are separated in winter by only 10°, whereas off the American shores the zone of eparation is more than 30°. In summer there is a 15° belt between the isotherms 10° and 26° on the western side of the Ocean and 40° on the eastern. This influences not only the climate of the coastal regions of the mainland but also the whole biological environment, and most of all the marked phenomena of oceanic convergence on the western side of the Ocean.

These peculiarities create conditions in the northwestern part of the Pacific Ocean for the existence of quantitatively very rich flora and fauna, and zones

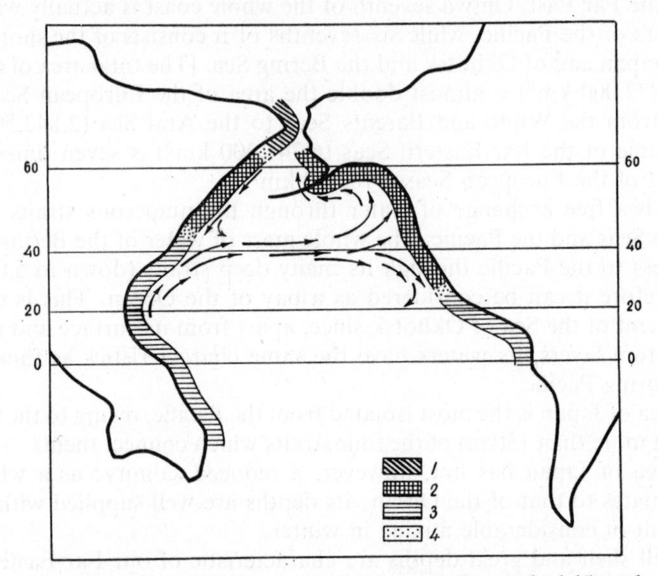

FIG. 319. Diagram of the Arctic (*1*), boreal (*2*), tropical (*3*) and mixed (*4*) zones on both sides of the Pacific Ocean.

of heterogeneity where Arctic boreal and subtropical meet. There are some mixed tropical and subtropical zones. This is most apparent in the zone where the waters of the Oyashio and Kuroshio meet in the pelagic region; we are therefore led to the conclusion that a mixed zone exists here rather than a subtropical region, since the boreal and tropical fauna and flora resemble each other very closely and are partly intermixed.

The qualitative variety of the population is increased also as a result of the great vertical range (down to 1,100 km) and of the much greater biotopic variety (a large number of archipelagos and the presence of coastal features). The fauna of the northwestern part of the Pacific and its adjacent seas is at least twice as rich as that of the seas of northwestern Europe. The deep-water fauna of the Sea of Okhotsk, the Bering Sea and the adjacent part of the Pacific (with the Aleutian, Kuril-Kamchatka and Japanese trenches) is extremely rich; its variety is probably considerably greater than that of any other part of the world ocean.

The flora and fauna, rich in variety and quantity, contain a number of species which are, or could be, of great commercial value—some 200 of the total of 800 species among fish alone. Oysters and scallops could first be added to the list of organisms exploited commercially; and then the huge variety of molluscs and crustaceans (primarily the Kamchatka crab), the large stock of marine algae (Laminaria and Alaria) and marine flowering plants (Zostera and Phyllospadix). Whales, fur-seals, walruses, sea lions, sea otters and other marine mammals could also be added to this list of the abundant and still almost untapped resources.

The exceptional abundance of life in some regions of the northwestern part of the Pacific is striking. The meeting zone of the Oyashio and Kuroshio waters is the richest among them; very many fish are attracted by the abundance of plankton, the fish in their turn being followed by large shoals of squids, whales and flocks of birds.

II. HISTORY OF EXPLORATION

Three hundred years ago (1648) the Cossack Semёn Dezhnev rounded the Chukotsk Peninsula and sailed through the straits (which should really have been called after him), entering the Pacific Ocean from the north. The Russians, who at that time were settled on the far-distant northeastern border of Asia hunting sea beasts, must have had some knowledge of sea fish and mammals and of the geography of the regions in which they swam. V. Bering's expedition (1725 to 1743), one of the greatest geographical undertakings in the history of ocean exploration, marked the beginning of a more systematic study of the flora and fauna of the Far Eastern Seas. Numerous documents form the legacy of this expedition. The naturalists S. Steller and S. Krasheninnikov, who took part in the expedition, gave the first, very valuable observations on the flora and fauna of the Far Eastern Seas and their shores.

At the end of the eighteenth and the beginning of the nineteenth centuries the ships of numerous Russian expeditions ploughed the northern part of the Pacific Ocean. Descriptions of the coastline of northern Asia and America were made by these expeditions. Biologists often participated. The expeditions of I. Billings and G. Sarychev (1785 to 1793), I. Kruzenshtern and Yu. Lisyansky (1803 to 1806), O. Kotzebu (1815 to 1818) and others are particularly well known.

The second period of the exploration of the Far Eastern Seas and the beginning of the systematic study of their flora and fauna are linked with the names of the members or collaborators of the St Petersburg Academy of Sciences—I. Voznesensky, A. Middendorf, L. Shrenk, N. Grebnitzky and others. The voyage of Admiral S. O. Makarov (1886 to 1889) in the corvette *Vityaz* was of exceptional importance in the history of the exploration of the Pacific.

At the beginning of this century several large expeditions were sent out to investigate the commercial wealth of the Far Eastern Seas. The most significant among them were the researches of V. Brazhnikov (1899 to 1904), P. Schmidt (1900 to 1901) and V. Soldatov (1907 to 1913).

The last and most fruitful period in the exploration of the Far Eastern Seas, of their environment, flora and fauna, including the deep-water fauna, and assessment of their commercial wealth, began in the 'twenties of the present century with the works of K. Derjugin, P. Schmidt (since 1925) and their collaborators (P. Ushakov, A. Ivanov, N. Tarasov, E. Gurjanova, G. Lindberg, P. Moiseev, G. Ratmanov, A. Taranetz and many others). The organization of the first Pacific Scientific-Industrial Station, and since 1929 of the Institute of Scientific Research on Marine Fisheries and Oceanography (T.I.N.R.O.) has been of great significance in the development of further work. The exploration of the Far Eastern Seas was developed on a particularly large scale in 1932 and 1933 under the leadership of K. Derjugin and P. Schmidt in connection with the Second International Polar Year. The State Hydrological Institute and the Pacific Institute of Fisheries and Oceanography sent out five research ships (including the *Rossinanta*, *Dal'nevostochnik* and *Gagara*) for a thorough survey of the Chukotsk and Bering Seas and the Seas of Okhotsk and Japan. Trawlings down to 3,800 m were carried out and a varied deep-floor fauna was found both in the Sea of Okhotsk and in the Bering Sea as well as in the adjacent part of the Pacific. As a result of this work many aspects of the conditions and biology of the Far Eastern Seas came to light for the first time; the huge amount of data collected was examined and classified by many workers over a number of years. One of the most important results of this survey was the creation of the Pacific Institute of Fisheries and Oceanography and the further development of its activity in the succeeding 25 years, when two branches were organized on Kamchatka and Sakhalin. Research was done by the Institute, mostly along scientific-industrial lines, but also in the field of general oceanography. Fifty volumes of its *Bulletin* have since been published.

The State Hydrological Institute and the Zoological Institute of the Academy of Sciences of the U.S.S.R. continued their research into the Far Eastern Seas during the 27 years since Derjugin's expedition. The most significant data were obtained by the Kuril–Sakhalin expedition, organized in 1947 to 1949 jointly by the Zoological Institute and the Pacific Institute of Fisheries under the leadership of Lindberg.

Japanese explorers have done much important work on the Seas of Japan and of Okhotsk. One of the biggest Japanese expeditions, headed by a professor of the Tokyo Institute of Fisheries, X. Marukava, took place from 1915 to 1917. It carried out an extensive survey of the hydrology, biology and fisheries of the Seas of Japan and of Okhotsk. Four ships took part in the expedition.

The discovery of large feeding aggregations of Far Eastern salmon in the northwestern part of the Pacific and to the southeast of Kamchatka may be considered as a great achievement of Japanese biologists. An important part in the success of this commercial prospecting expedition was the location of areas of very abundant development of plankton, in a region where cold and warm waters—rich feeding grounds for salmon—meet.

Research on a large scale by the Institute of Sea-weed Research of Hokkaido University has continued for many years under Professor Yamada, studying commercial sea-weeds in the regions surrounding Hokkaido Island.

In 1949 the ship *Vityaz* (Fig. 320) was sent by the Institute of Oceanology

FIG. 320. *Vityaz*, the exploration vessel of the Institute of Oceanology of the Academy of Sciences of the U.S.S.R.

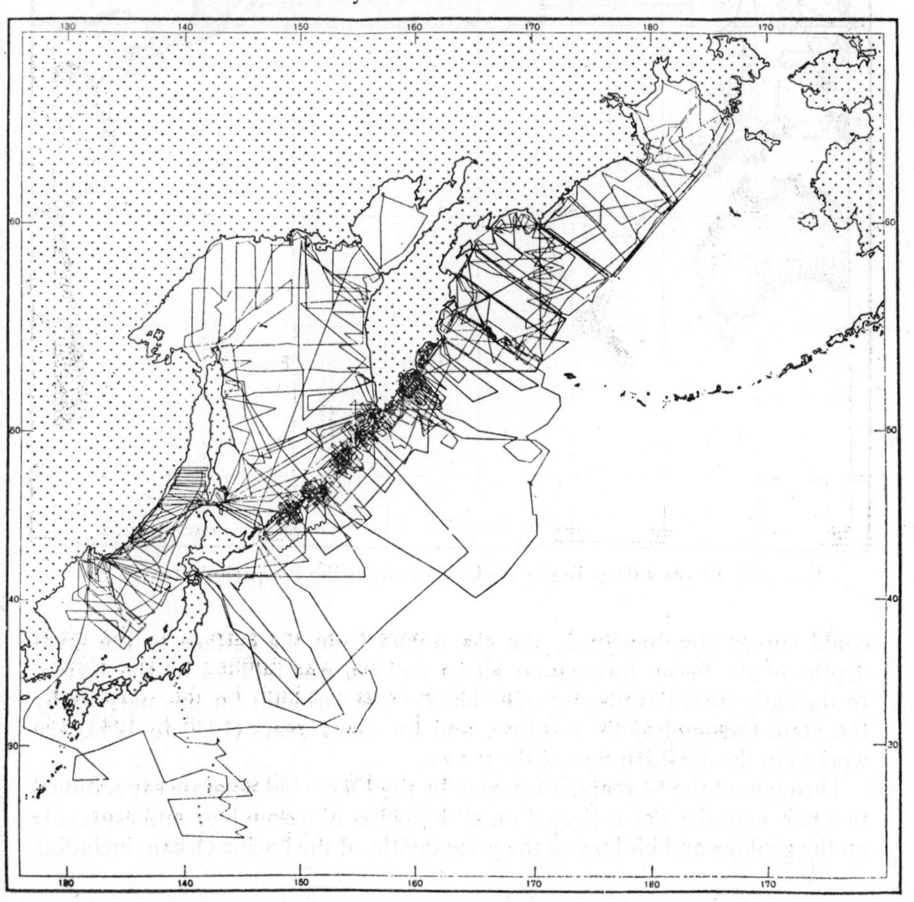

FIG. 321. *Vityaz* survey in the Pacific Ocean in 1949–56.

of the Academy of Sciences for a broad, many-sided survey of the Far Eastern Seas and of the northern part of the Pacific Ocean. During the International Geophysical Year (1957–59) the work done by this expedition was further extended to cover all the northern part of the Pacific Ocean (Figs. 321 and 322).

The old idea of Soviet oceanologists of a floating marine laboratory, which

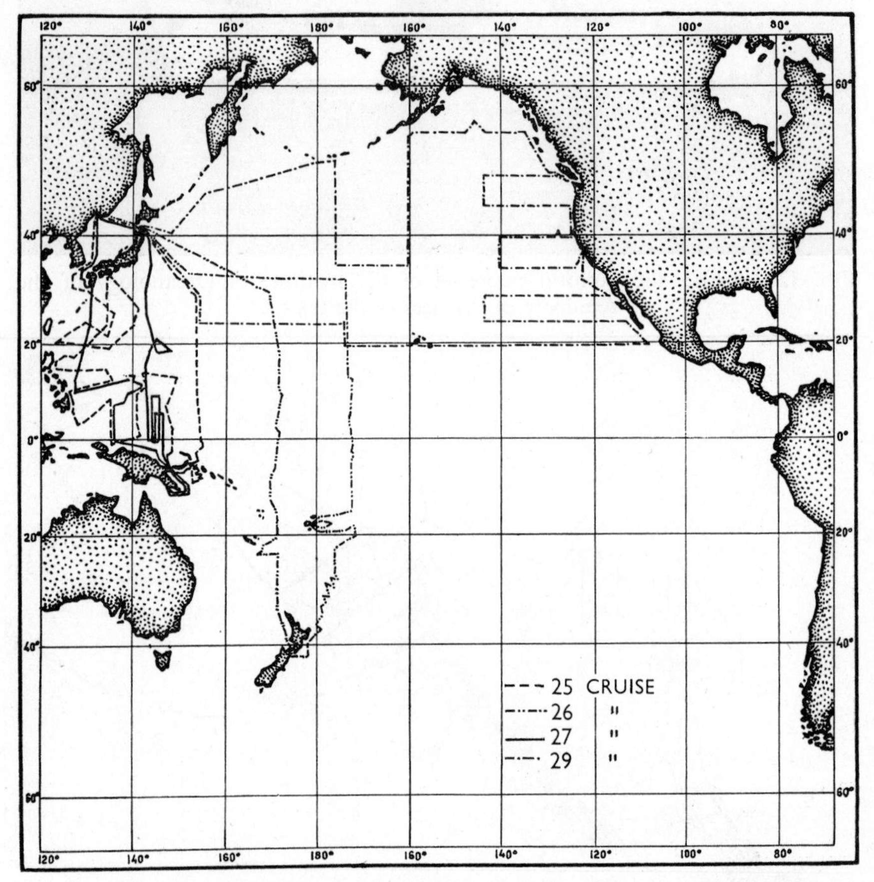

FIG. 322. *Vityaz* survey in the Pacific Ocean during the period of 1957–59.

could survey simultaneously the sea waters from the surface to the great depths of the ocean throughout all its regions, was fulfilled by the *Vityaz*. In the early 'twenties the research ship *Perseus* was built for this purpose by the State Oceanographic Institute, and for many years (1920 to 1943) she worked in the northern seas of the U.S.S.R.

Throughout the 12 years of research by the *Vityaz* (30 separate expeditions) rich new material was collected on all branches of oceanology and especially on the geology and biology of the great depths of the Pacific Ocean, including the bottom topography and the depths of the greatest ocean trenches, the composition and distribution of marine deposits, the composition and distribution of deep-water fauna, etc. (Figs. 321 and 322).

Most of the papers on the survey of the Far Eastern Seas are published in the *Bulletin* of the Pacific Institute of Fisheries and Oceanography, in the *Proceedings* of the Institute of Oceanology of the Academy of Sciences of the U.S.S.R. and in the series 'The Exploration of the Seas of the U.S.S.R.', which was first published by the State Hydrological Institute together with the Pacific Institute of Fisheries and Oceanography. Since 1941 the papers have been appearing under the title *The Survey of the Far Eastern Seas of the U.S.S.R.*, published by the Zoological Institute of the Academy of Sciences, and in the periodicals *The Survey of the Seas of the U.S.S.R.*, *The Fauna of the U.S.S.R.*, and *The Proceedings of the Zoological Institute of the Academy of Sciences of the U.S.S.R.* published by the same institute.

III. PHYSICAL GEOGRAPHY OF NORTHWESTERN PART OF PACIFIC OCEAN

Coastline and bottom topography

The coastline, bottom topography, circulation of the water masses and some phenomena of their geological past are the most characteristic features of these Far Eastern Seas.

The northwestern part of the Pacific Ocean is characterized by a rich development of coastal features and by the presence of numerous islands which form three great arcs—namely, the Japanese, Kuril and Aleutian, and the Alaska and Kamchatka Peninsulas, which cut off the Seas of Japan and of Okhotsk and the Bering Sea from the Ocean. The hydrology, chemistry and biology of the three Seas bordering the northeast of Asia are greatly influenced by the width and depth of the straits. The basin of the Sea of Japan is separated from the Pacific by shallow straits (not deeper than 130 m); its depths, however, are well aerated, and its geological past has left a deep imprint on its fauna. The straits connecting the Sea of Okhotsk with the Ocean are deep; they fall short of the greatest depth of the Sea by only 1,350 m (*Table 283*). The huge masses of the deep waters of the Sea of Okhotsk suffer, however, from a pronounced shortage of oxygen. The straits leading into the Bering Sea offer little impediment to the exchange of its waters with those of the Ocean, and therefore the Sea of Okhotsk, situated to the south of the Bering Sea, has a much more severe climate.

The present bottom topography of the Far Eastern Seas is characterized by a small shelf and a large zone of great depths. The areas of the three zones (the shelf, the bathyal and the abyssal) are about equal (Fig. 323). The three Seas, however, differ greatly in this respect. The Sea of Japan has a small shelf, and the abyssal zone is predominant in its bottom topgraphy. The Sea of Okhotsk has a fairly limited abyssal zone, and its bathyal zone is greatly developed, whereas the Bering Sea has an extremely limited bathyal zone and a large shelf in its northeastern part. Its shelf and the abyssal zone occupy practically equal areas (forming about 90 per cent of the total area of the Sea)

Table 283. Maximum depths of the deepest Pacific trenches of the Far Eastern Seas, and of the straits which connect them with the Pacific Ocean

Location	Depth m	Location	Depth m
Trenches		*Straits*	
Mariana	11,034	Bering	58
Tonga	10,882	Kamchatka	4,420
Kuril–Kamchatka	10,382	Kruzenshtern	1,920
Philippine	10,265	Boussole	2,318
Kermadec	10,047	Nevel'	*ca.* 5
Far Eastern Seas		La Perouse	53
Sea of Japan	3,669	Sangar	130
Sea of Okhotsk	3,372	Korea	105
Bering Sea	4,420		

This is of great significance for the development of the population of these Seas.

The presence of one of the deepest oceanic trenches—the Kuril–Kamchatka trench, which goes down to 10,382 m (according to G. Udintzev's latest calculations, 10,542 m)—is a most important factor in the structure of the earth's crust in the northwestern part of the Pacific.

The Kuril–Kamchatka trench (Fig. 324) is only one sector of the huge Pacific Ocean ring of faults in the earth's crust, high mountainous formations and depths of more than 11 km (Mariana trench). Each trench is a

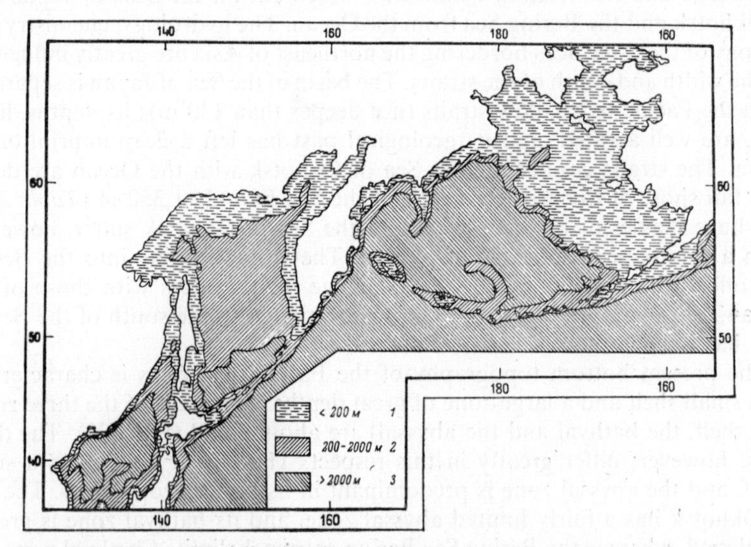

FIG. 323. Chart of the distribution of the continental shelf (*1*) continental slope (*2*) and the deep floor (*3*) in the Seas of Japan and Okhotsk and the Bering Sea (Ushakov, 1953).

complex formation, some hundreds of kilometres wide (Fig. 325). It does not consist merely of a mountainous range of islands (the Kuril bank is a double

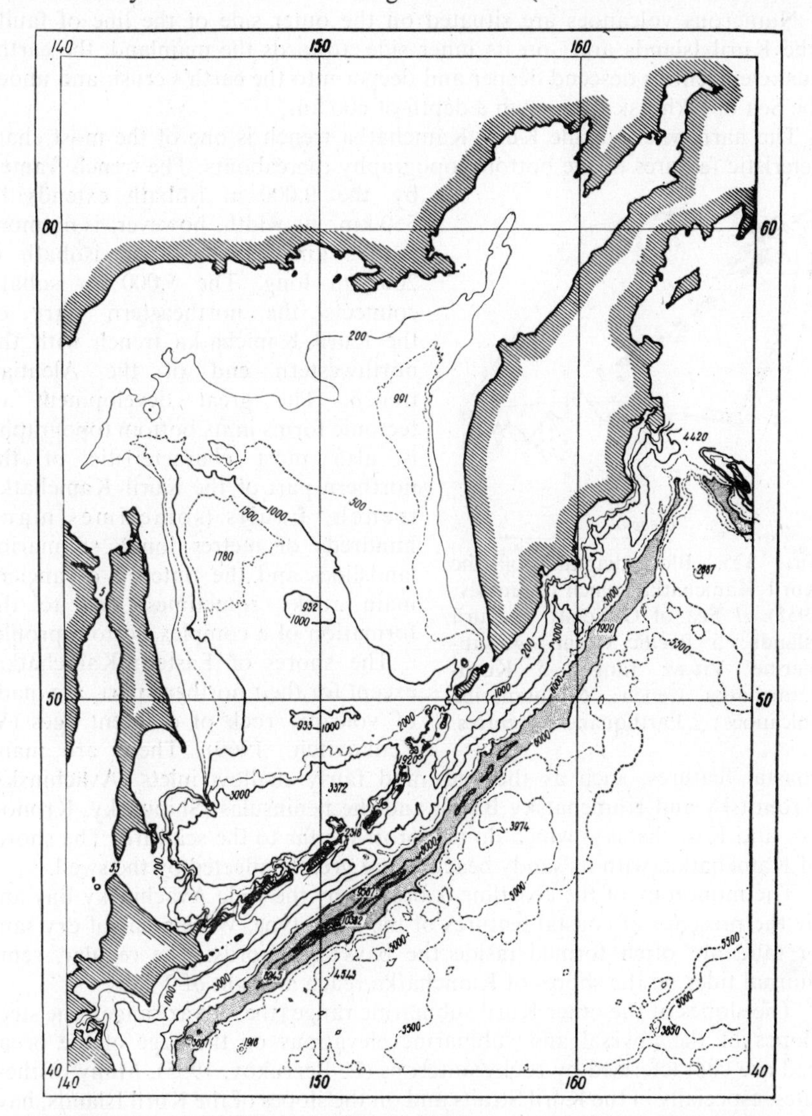

Fig. 324. Sea-bed relief of the Sea of Okhotsk and the Kuril–Kamchatka trench (Udintzev).

formation—the western range with summits above water and the submarine eastern range, the 'Vityaz'). The southern hollow of the Sea of Okhotsk is adjacent to the range of islands to the west; to the east of it lies the trench and elevation of the plateau edge. This mountainous formation can be regarded as a fault in the earth's crust and an advance of the mainland massif on the ocean bed, leading to mountain formations.

Numerous volcanoes are situated on the outer side of the line of faults (the Kuril Islands arc); on its inner side, towards the mainland, the earthquake epicentres descend deeper and deeper into the earth's crust, and under the Sea of Okhotsk they reach a depth of 600 km.

The narrowness of the Kuril–Kamchatka trench is one of the most characteristic features of the bottom topography thereabouts. The trench framed by the 9,000 m isobath extends to 550 km; its width, however, is no more than 5 km. The 6,000 m isobath is 200 km long. The 5,000 m isobath connects the northeastern part of the Kuril–Kamchatka trench with the northwestern end of the Aleutian trench. The great development of tectonic forms in its bottom topography is also most characteristic of the northern part of the Kuril–Kamchatka trench. Faults (sometimes many hundreds of metres long), submarine landslides and the outcrop of ancient main rocks sometimes lead to the formation of a complex bottom profile.

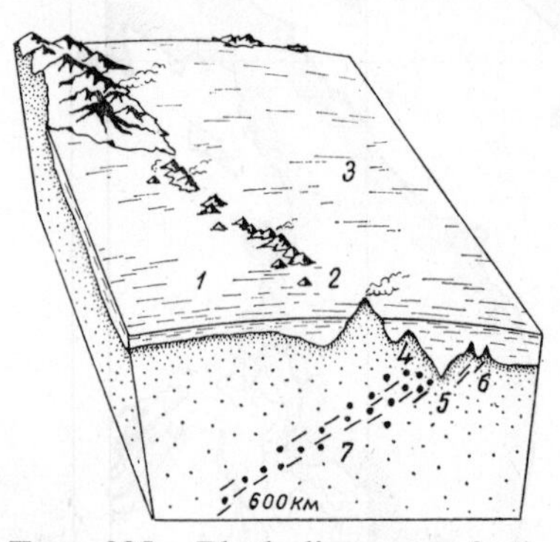

FIG. 325. Block-diagram of the Kuril–Kamchatka trench (Udintzev, 1955). *1* Sea of Okhotsk; *2* Kuril Islands; *3* Pacific Ocean; *4* Submarine Vityaz range; *5* Kuril-Kamchatka trench; *6* Submarine volcanoes; *7* Earthquake epicentres.

The shores of Eastern Kamchatka, except for their northern part, are made of volcanic rock of different ages (V. Zenkovitch, 1960). There are many coastal features, such as the wide and fairly shallow inlets (Avachinsky, Kronotsky and Kamchatsky Bays), and the peninsulas (Shipunsky, Kronotsky and Kamchatsky) which do not protrude far to the seaward. The shores of Kamchatka, with its sandy beaches, are greatly affected by the swell.

The monotony of the coastline is broken by the wide Avachinsky Bay and by the presence of coastal features of the fjord type. Wide areas of dry sand or mud are often formed inside the bays and fjords. The regular, semi-diurnal tides on the shores of Kamchatka reach a height of 2·5 m.

The slopes of the outer Kuril submarine range (the Vityaz range), the steep slopes of the abyssal and submarine elevations on the edge of the ocean bed are characterized by rocky outcrops (P. Bezrukov, 1955). Many of these sites, especially in the Kuril Straits and on the slopes of the Kuril Islands, have a gravel–pebble floor. At certain points there is in the deposits a considerable admixture of the products of submarine eruptions—pumice, lapilli and volcanic slag.

Sand floors are greatly developed on the slopes of the coast of Kamchatka, and in the region of the Kuril Islands (down to a depth of 3,000 m), while diatomaceous oozes are accumulated in the trenches. In general the northwestern part of the Pacific, and the Sea of Okhotsk, are exceptionally rich in diatomaceous oozes (Fig. 326); this is the result of the intensive development of diatoms in these regions.

Geological past of the Far Eastern Seas

The problem of the geological past and the palaeogeography of the Far Eastern Seas is exceptionally important. The nature of the alterations endured and the differences in the past of the Seas of Japan and of Okhotsk and the Bering

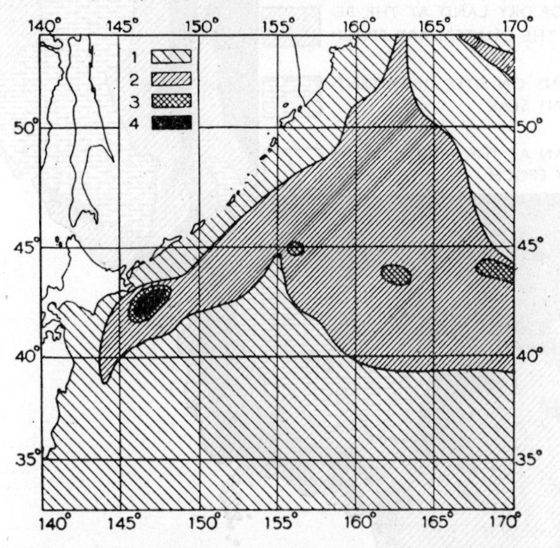

FIG. 326. Distribution of deposits of amorphous silica produced by diatoms (as percentage of dry weight of soil) (Bezrukov): *1* Less than 1%; *2* From 10 to 20%; *3* From 20 to 30%; *4* More than 30%.

Sea during the Tertiary and Quaternary Periods are two most important problems.

In his work on the Quaternary geology of Hokkaido Island the Japanese geologist Minato (1955) maintains the existence of a strong mainland glaciation in the Ice Age, noting its traces on Hokkaido Island. Having examined all the available data he considers there were two periods of considerable fall of temperature (two Ice Ages, one much earlier than the other) and great fluctuations of the sea-level, marked by a series of terraces at different horizons up to a height of 200 m above sea-level. On the other side Minato envisages considerable shifts of the coastline to seaward, during which the Islands of Japan must have been joined to the mainland.

The Tertiary and Quaternary Periods of the history of the Far Eastern Seas are characterized by the difference in the past of the Bering and Okhotsk Seas on the one hand and that of the Sea of Japan on the other. The first two basins retained their broad link with the Ocean; the past of the Sea of Japan was very complex, and it is still not sufficiently known. Was there a period of complete isolation of the Sea of Japan from the Ocean, and were its waters then fresh? Is H. Yabe's (1929) hypothesis true (Fig. 327)? Were the basins of the Okhotsk and Bering Seas dry land at the beginning of the Quaternary

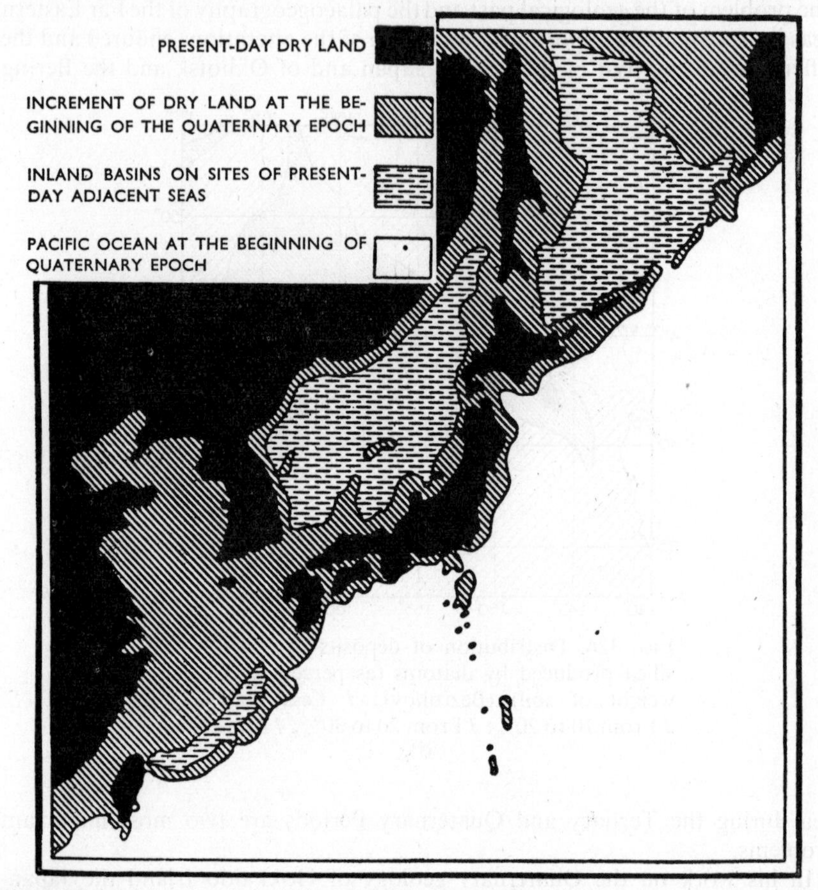

FIG. 327. Mainland relief of Far Eastern Seas at the beginning of the Quaternary period (H. Yabe).

Period and to what period should the appearance of their deep trenches be ascribed?

G. Lindberg's series of works on the palaeogeographic past of the north-western part of the Pacific (1948, 1953, 1956) are most interesting. An examination of the contemporary geographical distribution of fresh-water fish has led this worker to the conclusion that in the recent geological past some river systems now cut off from each other by the sea were then linked through areas of the mainland which are now submerged. The examination of the contemporary bottom topography of the Far Eastern Seas led Lindberg to the conclusion that these Seas were formerly dry land, either partly or even wholly; and that even during the Quaternary Period, when the single common river systems did exist, the level of the Ocean underwent a considerable change (up to 500 m). This worker suggests that during the Quaternary Period the Far Eastern Seas underwent alteration of the phases of regression and transgression no less than three times. In addition to such fluctuations of the sea-level G. Lindberg also maintains that the formation of the Seas of Japan and of Okhotsk and the Bering Sea trench was due to downwarping. He casts doubts upon the permanent or even more or less prolonged existence of the trenches and of the Pacific Ocean itself and of 'the existence in comparatively recent times of a continental link joining the Islands of Melanesia, Micronesia and Polynesia to the Hawaiian Islands and likewise to southeast Asia' (1948).

According to the latest opinion of Soviet geologists (P. Kropotkin, 1956, I. Andreeva and G. Udintzev, 1958) the trench in the Sea of Japan is very ancient (lower Palaeozoic). In its structure it closely resembles other trenches on the western edge of the Pacific, and the bed of the Ocean; it should therefore be regarded as a relict of this bed.

Bottom deposits of 1·5 km thick were found in the southern part of the Sea of Japan by seismo-acoustic methods. Associated with this, many geologists assume a raising of the edges of the Sea of Japan at the end of the Pliocene Period, until the Sea was completely separated from the Pacific (P. Kropotkin, 1954, 1956).

The history of the existence of links between the Bering Sea and the Arctic Ocean is equally obscure. The solutions of all these problems are most important for the understanding of the history of the fauna and in particular of such phenomena as amphi-boreal distribution.

The analysis of long cores from the sea-bed and the examination of their content of the remains of diatomaceous Radiolaria, Foraminifera, spores and plant pollen are exceptionally valuable for the understanding of the palaeo-geographical past of the Far Eastern Seas and of the palaeo-climatic changes.

T. Sechkina (1959) has analysed a 17 m long core obtained from the *Vityaz* in 1957 from a depth of 3,504 m in the northern part of the trench in the Sea of Japan, approximately on the latitude of the Strait of Sangara. The quantitative and qualitative compositions of the diatoms were found to alter considerably with the length of the core. Sechkina divided the core according to its diatom content into five horizons (0 to 140 cm, 140 to 280 cm, 280 to 590 cm, 590 to 1,033 cm and 1,033 to 1,706 cm). The uppermost horizon resembles the contemporary one in the composition of its diatoms; the second one differs from it greatly, reflecting a considerable decrease of temperature. In contrast, the diatoms of the third horizon bear witness to a considerable rise of temperature and there is in it a pronounced admixture of tropical diatoms, while the Arctic ones are absent. The upper four metres of the fourth horizon are, as it were, 'dumb', containing no diatoms. There is a thin (23 cm) layer of cold-water Arctic flora of diatoms under it (the 'dumb' column corresponds to the beginning of a great fall in temperature). The 'dumb' layer probably corresponds to the period of the greatest fall in temperature, to a short period of diatom plankton vegetation, to a considerable loss of terrigenous substances and to a dispersion of diatoms in its mass.

The 7 m long section of the core is characterized by the predominance in the lower horizon of warm-water forms which, however, are not found at the lower end of the core, and by the absence of Arctic species; it resembles in its composition the first and third horizons.

According to the data given there were two periods of glaciation (Ice Ages) and two inter-glacial periods when the temperature was higher.

The 17 m long core may possibly have penetrated into the Quaternary deposits; during that period the Sea of Japan retained its marine nature. If the Sea of Japan was ever isolated from the Ocean, this isolation cannot have taken place in the second half of the Quaternary Period.

A. Zhuze (1954) examined in a similar way the remains of the diatoms in the soils of the Okhotsk and Bering Sea beds, taking 27 m long cores from a depth of 3,355 m in the Sea of Okhotsk and a 16·5 m core from 3,638 m in the eastern trench of the Bering Sea. He distinguishes five main horizons and establishes the synchronism of the alterations of the two Seas, which have the same characteristics as the soils of the Sea of Japan. Zhuze has also established the local sequence: in the upper 150 to 185 cm the composition of the diatoms tallies with that of the present period. The second 3·5 m thick horizon is characteristic of a period of lowered temperature; while the third horizon, lying inside the sediments at a depth of 5 to 11 m corresponds to the period of the rise of temperature, the fourth again to a fall in temperature, and the fifth to a rise.

Therefore this worker assumes also 'that the monoliths examined cover a period of two Ice Ages and two inter-glacial epochs in the northeast of the U.S.S.R.'. The Ice Ages are characterized by sediments with a weak qualitative and quantitative development of diatoms, of predominantly Arctic forms, and a considerable admixture of neritic and fresh-water forms; the periods of warming up by an increase of oceanic warm-water forms, and a great abundance and rich variety of diatoms. The 27 m long core from the Sea of Okhotsk, however, belongs entirely to Quaternary deposits.

Currents, salinity and temperature

Cold masses of water (Oyashio) move from the north along the whole of the western coast of the Bering Sea, Kamchatka and the Kuril Islands, while the strong warm current, Kuroshio—the Gulf Stream of the Pacific (Fig. 328)—flows from the south along the shores of Japan to meet them. The warm Pacific waters penetrate into all the three Seas. They enter the Sea of Japan through the Korea Strait, the Sea of Okhotsk through the North Kuril Straits and the Bering Sea through the Aleutian Straits.

In summer more abundant warm currents move farther north, penetrating deeper into the Far Eastern Seas. In winter the main streams of Kuroshio move northeastward and eastward much farther to the south, and the intensity of the currents is greatly slackened in the northern part of the Ocean. This can be seen even better from the distribution of surface isotherms (Fig. 329). In summer the Aleutian Islands are skirted by the 10° isotherm and in winter by that for 2°; at that season the isotherm 12° lies close to 40° N latitude, where in summer the 20° isotherm passes.

The southern limit of the cold layer is subject to substantial fluctuations over many years (M. Uda, 1955), which have a pronounced effect on biological

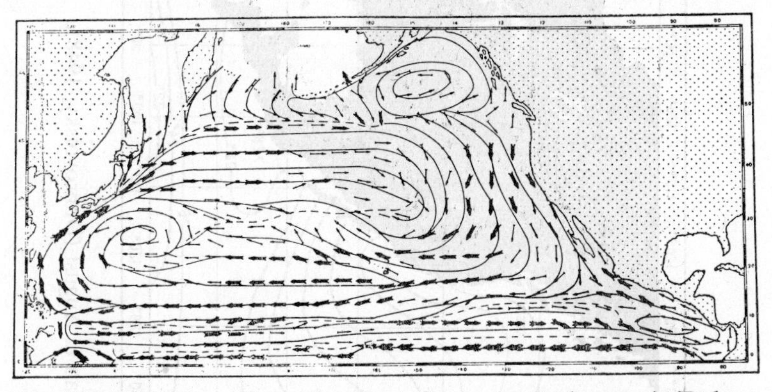

FIG. 328A. Diagram of continuous surface currents (summer) (Dobrovolsky, 1948).

phenomena. In 1933 this limit passed close to the Kuril Islands; in subsequent years it moved farther and farther southeast, and in 1953 it had moved away between 200 and 500 miles from its position of twenty years earlier.

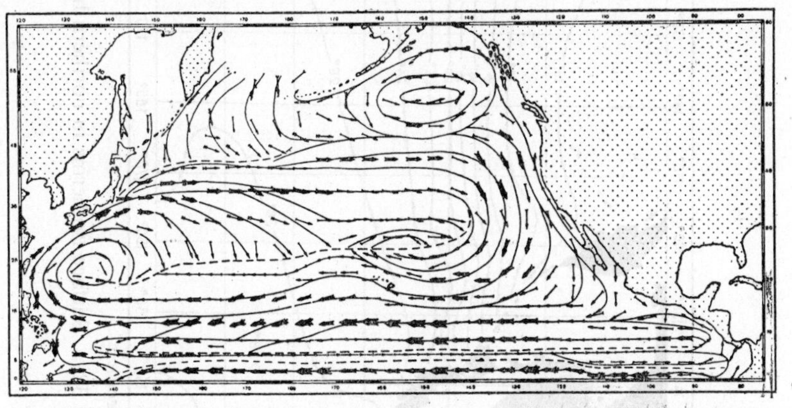

FIG. 328B. Diagram of continuous surface currents (winter) (Dobrovolsky).

The Ivasi catastrophe may have been connected, either directly or indirectly, with these fluctuations.

A clear picture of the changes of temperature, salinity, oxygen, phosphorus and silica content is given in Figs. 330, 331, 332 and 333.

The amplitude of temperature fluctuations becomes less with depth. In the Kuroshio region the amplitude is 13·5° (10·5° to 24°) on the surface; at a depth of 200 m it is 2·5° (9° to 11·5°); at 500 m barely one degree; while at

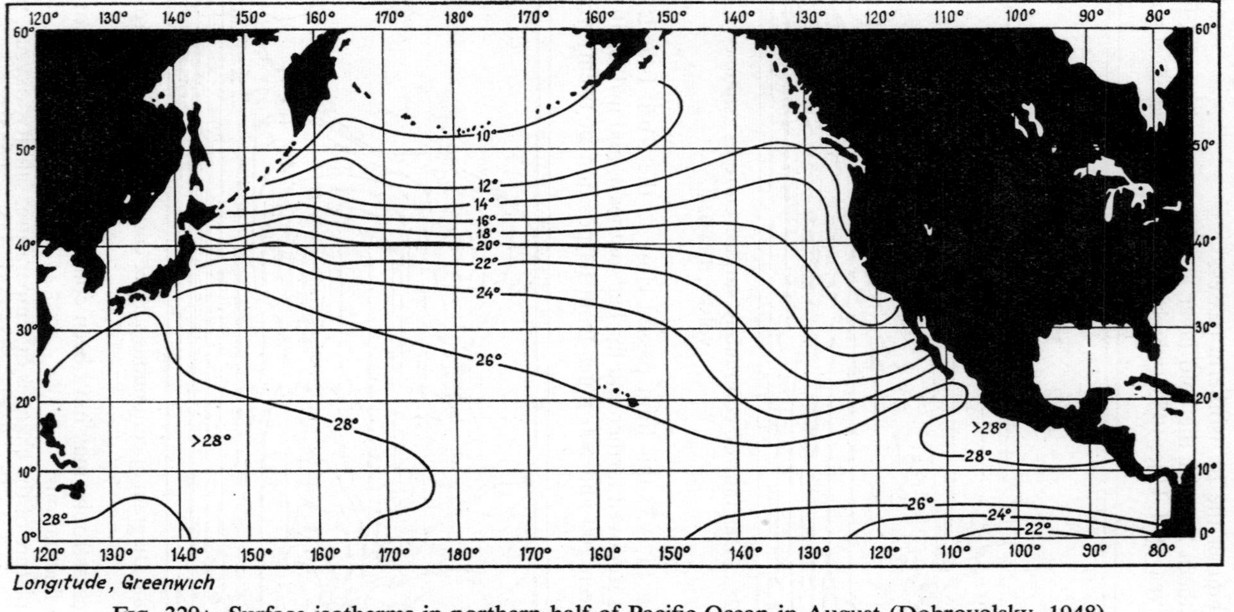

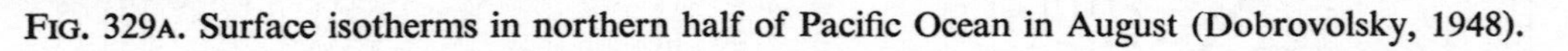

FIG. 329A. Surface isotherms in northern half of Pacific Ocean in August (Dobrovolsky, 1948).

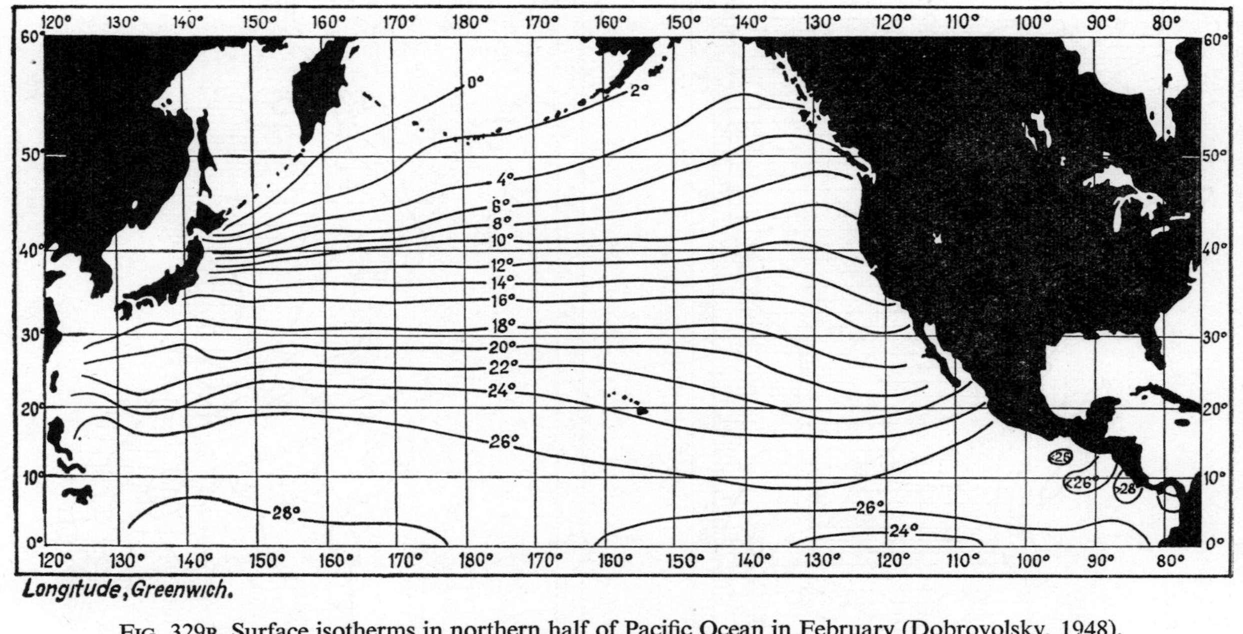

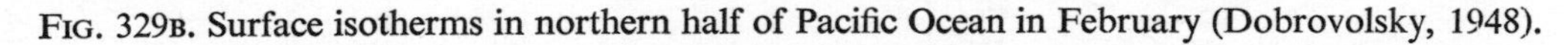
FIG. 329B. Surface isotherms in northern half of Pacific Ocean in February (Dobrovolsky, 1948).

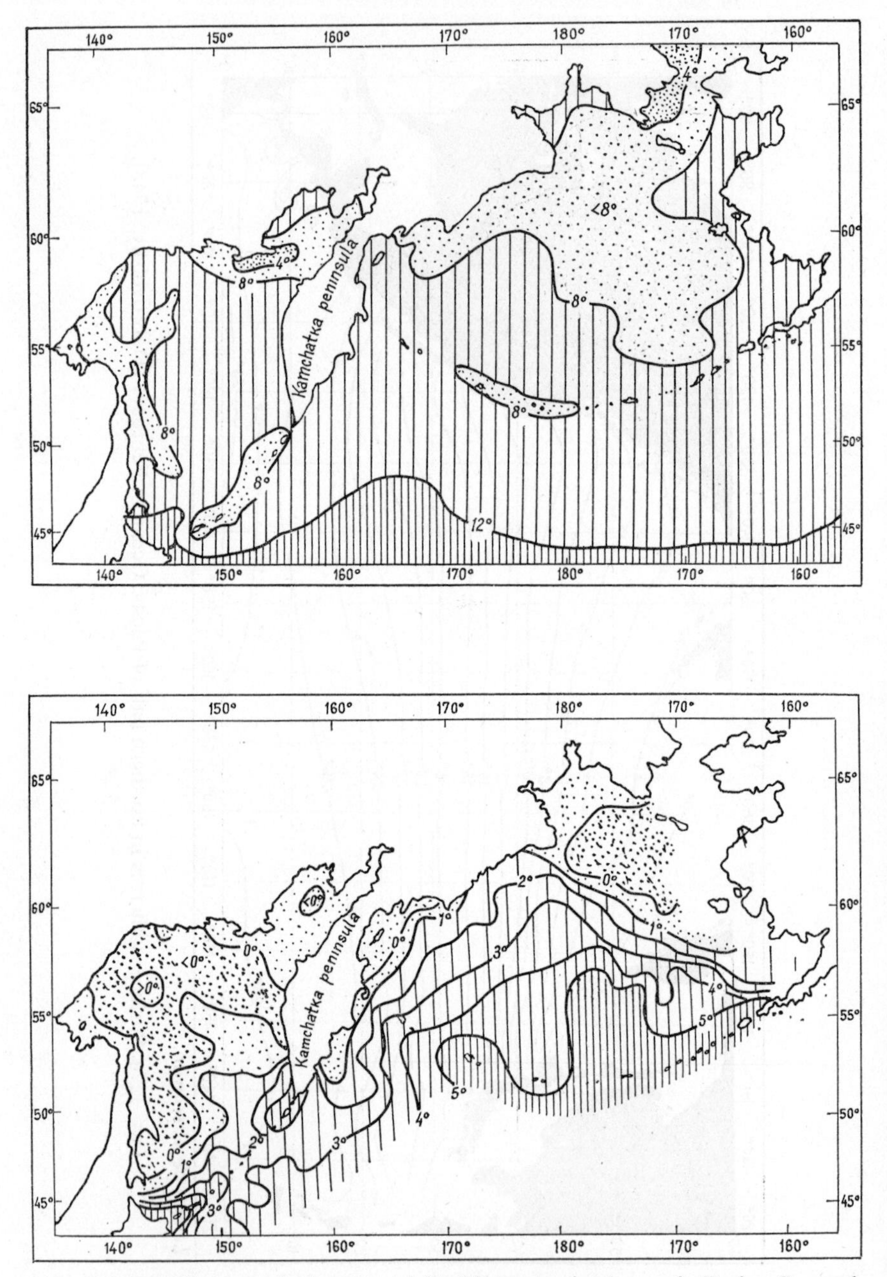

FIG. 330. Distribution of (A) ten- and (B) fifty-metre isotherms in Bering Sea and Sea of Okhotsk in July to September (Ushakov, 1953).

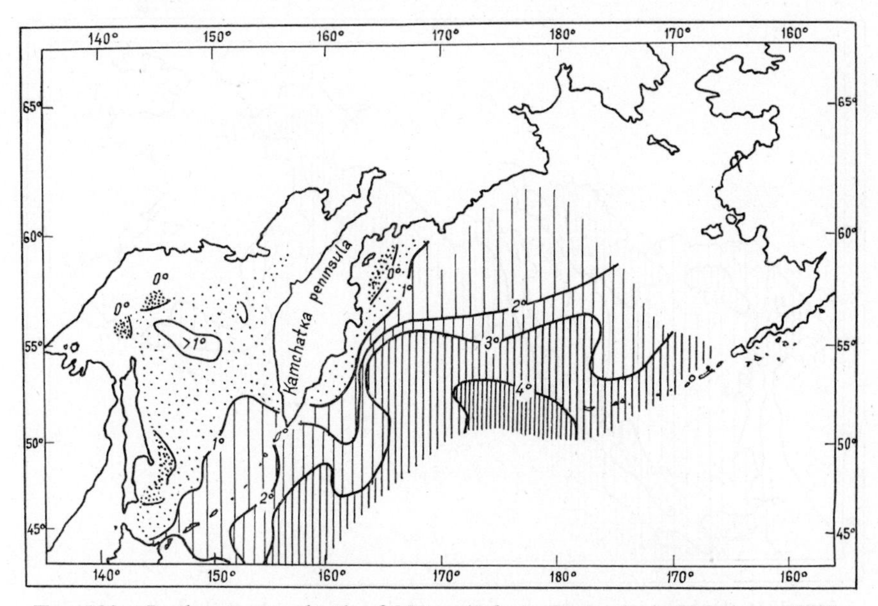

FIG. 330C. Isotherms at a depth of 200 m (July to September) (Ushakov, 1953).

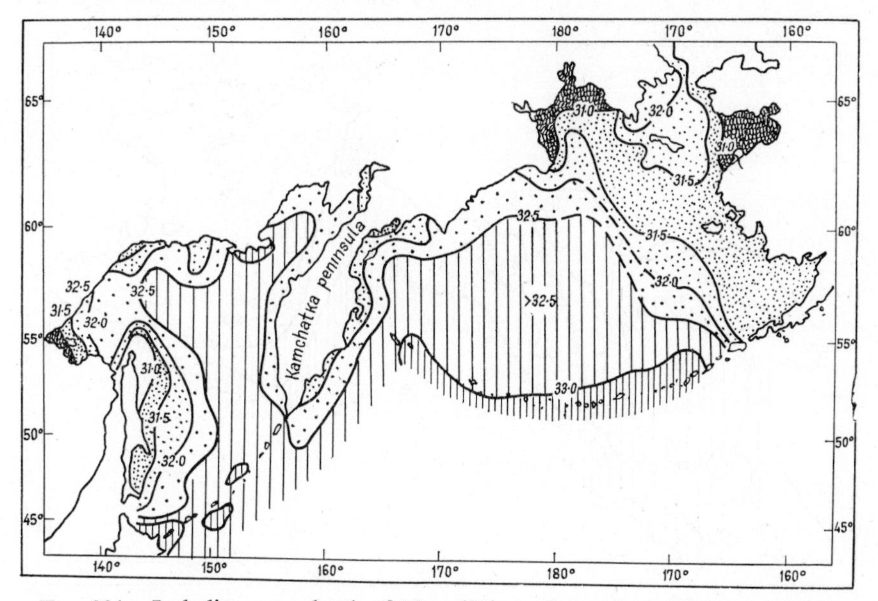

FIG. 331A. Isohalines at a depth of 10 m (July to September) (Ushakov, 1953).

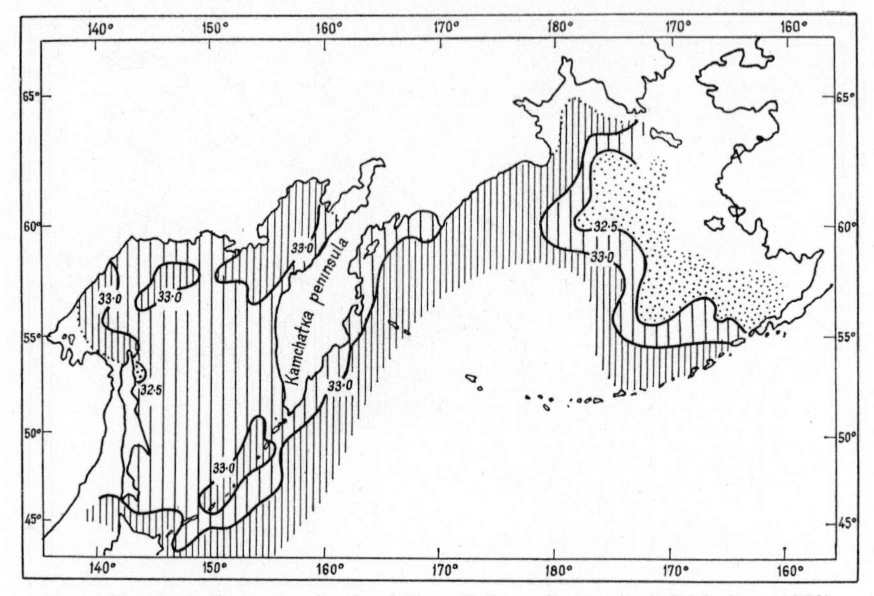

FIG. 331B. Isohalines at a depth of 50 m (July to September) (Ushakov, 1953).

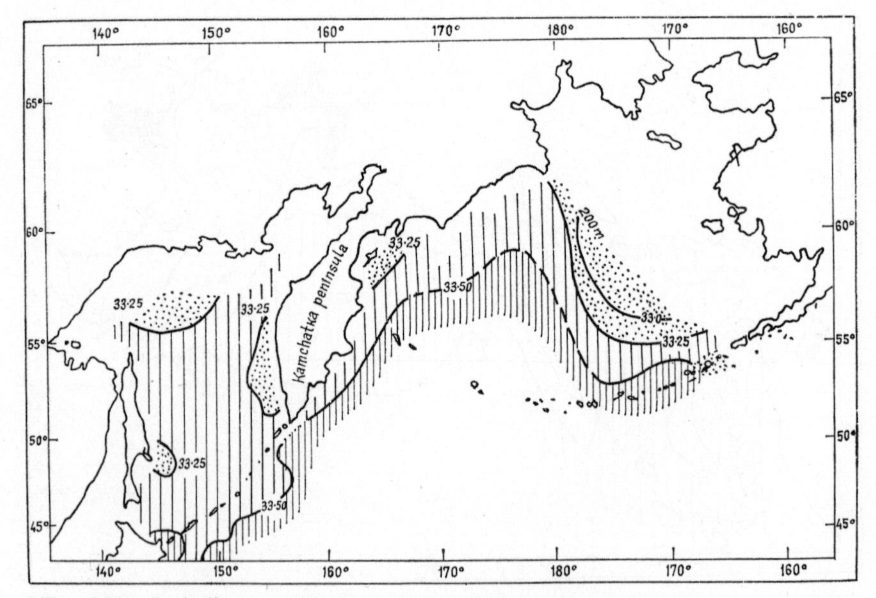

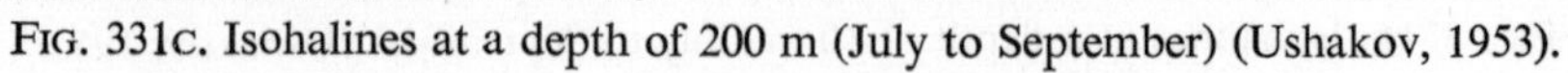
FIG. 331C. Isohalines at a depth of 200 m (July to September) (Ushakov, 1953).

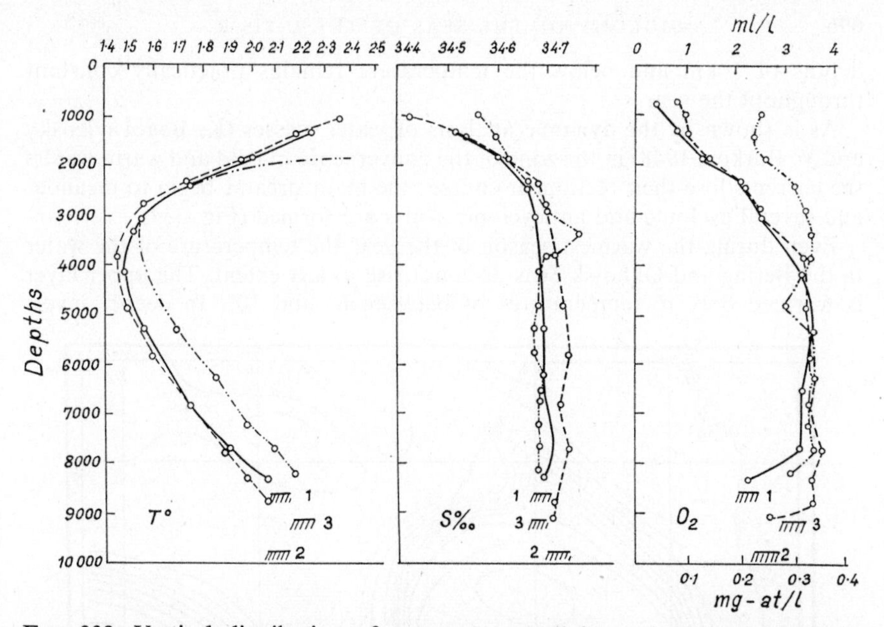

FIG. 332. Vertical distribution of temperature, salinity and oxygen content in Kuril–Kamchatka trench and Philippine deep (Bogoyavlensky). Continuous line—15 May; dotted line—30 June 1953 in Kuril–Kamchatka trench; chain-dotted line—23 January 1948 in Philippine deep. Data from *Albatross*.

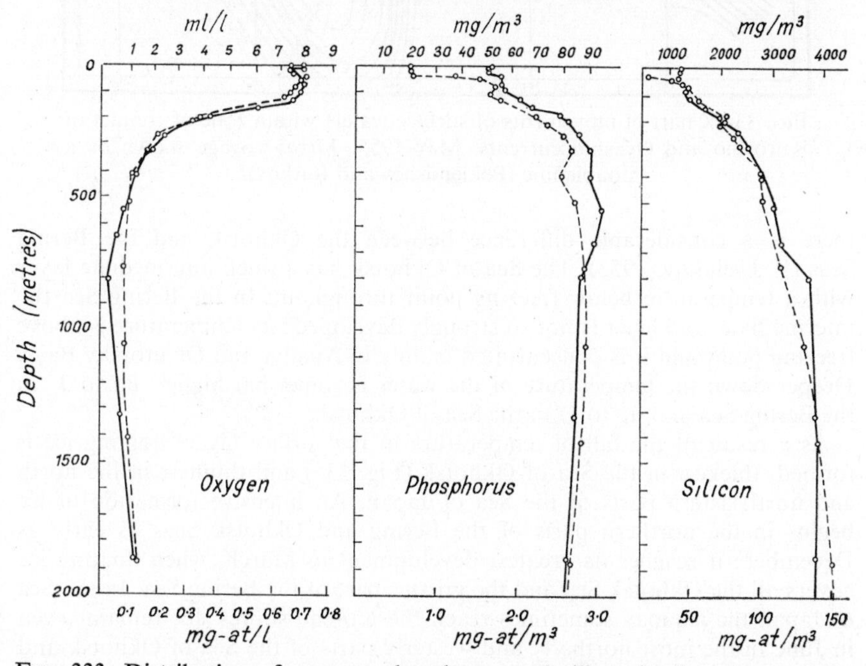

FIG. 333. Distribution of oxygen, phosphorus and silicon in the waters of the 'shallows' of the Kuril–Kamchatka trench in May and June 1953 (Bogoyavlensky). Continuous line—15 May; dashed line—30 June.

depths of 1 km and below the temperature remains practically constant throughout the year.

As is shown by the dynamic analysis of water masses (K. Bogoyavlensky and V. Burkov, 1948) in the zone of the convergence of cold and warm waters the currents lose their rectilinear course; the main streams begin to meander and several cyclonic and anticyclonic swirls are formed (Fig. 334).

Even during the warmest season of the year the temperature of the water in the Bering and Okhotsk Seas does not rise to any extent. The upper layer is warmed only to temperatures of between 6° and 10°. In deeper layers

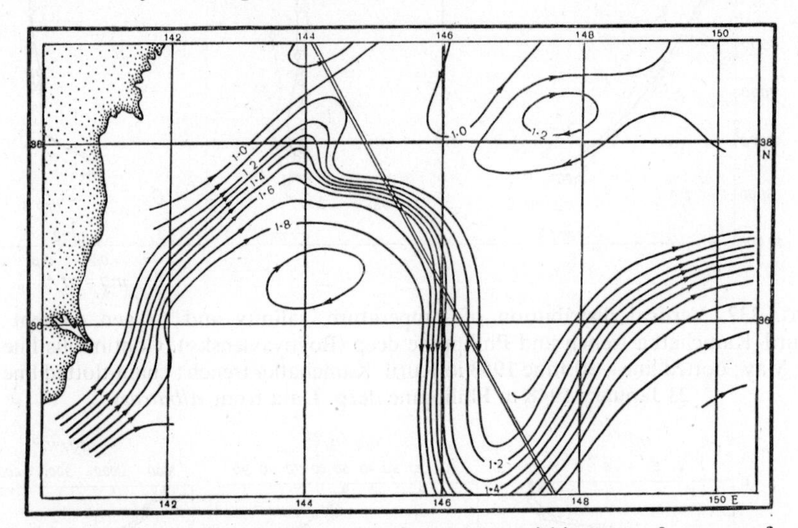

FIG. 334. Chart of movements of surface waters within zone of contact of Kuroshio and Oyashio currents, May 1955. *Vityaz* voyage shown by a double line (Beklemishev and Burkov).

there is a considerable difference between the Okhotsk and the Bering Seas (P. Ushakov, 1953). The Sea of Okhotsk has a thick intermediate layer with a temperature below freezing point throughout. In the Bering Sea the intermediate cold layer is not so strongly developed; its temperature is above freezing point and it is concentrated mainly in Anadyr and Olyutorsky Bays. Deeper down the temperature of the water is somewhat higher, up to 3° in the Bering Sea and up to 1° in the Sea of Okhotsk.

As a result of the fall of temperature in the surface layers floating ice is formed, thickest in the Sea of Okhotsk (Fig. 335) and thinnest in the north and northeastern parts of the Sea of Japan. An intensive formation of ice begins in the northern parts of the Bering and Okhotsk Seas as early as December; it reaches its greatest development in March, when floating ice covers all the Okhotsk Sea and the greater part of the Bering Sea. In the Sea of Japan the ice may sometimes reach the Korean shores. Ice remains even in June in the most northerly and westerly parts of the Sea of Okhotsk and in the north of the Bering Sea, especially in the Bay of Anadyr. As late as May there is ice in the northern part of the Tartary Strait. The ice is carried out into the Ocean through the Kuril Straits and along the Kamchatka coast. Large areas of the Okhotsk and Bering Seas are covered with ice for almost eight months. As for the other seas of the U.S.S.R., this phenomenon is found only in those off the Siberian coast.

The salinity of the Far Eastern Seas (apart from on their littoral and in the mouths of the rivers) does not exhibit pronounced fluctuations (P. Ushakov, 1953), but varies merely within the limits 31 to 33·5‰ (Fig. 331). The surface waters of the northwestern part of the Sea of Okhotsk (the influence of the

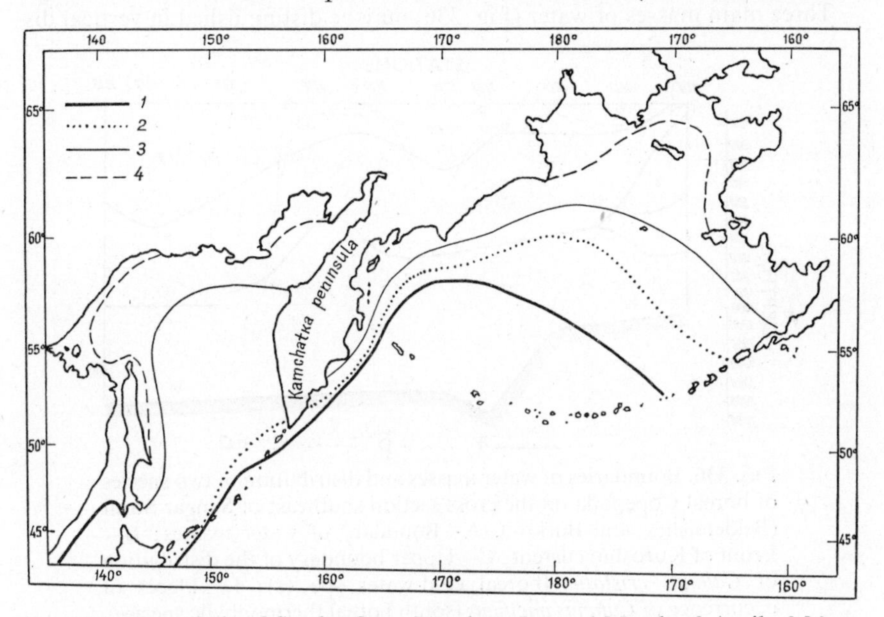

FIG. 335. Mean limit of floe-ice from March to June: *1* March; *2* April; *3* May; *4* June (Ushakov, 1953).

Amur) and of the Bay of Anadyr (the Anadyr River) have lost some of their salinity. At a depth of 50 m their salinity varies within the limits 32·5 to 33‰ and at a depth of 200 m within those of 33·25 to 33·50‰ (P. Ushakov, 1953).

The salinity of the Sea of Japan is somewhat higher; along the western coast the salinity of the surface waters is below 34‰, along the eastern coast it is above 34‰. With depth this difference disappears and the salinity rises to 34·5‰.

Vertical changes of temperature, salinity, and the contents of oxygen, phosphorus and silicon over the 'shallows' of the Kuril–Kamchatka trench are shown in Figs. 332 and 333.

The oxygen conditions of the Okhotsk and Bering Seas are practically the same as those of the adjacent parts of the Pacific. This is one of their most characteristic peculiarities as 'inlets' of the Pacific. Their oxygen content decreases gradually with depth, reaching only 10 per cent of saturation in the

Sea of Okhotsk and only 7 per cent in the Bering Sea at depths of between 1,000 and 1,500 m. Farther down the amount of oxygen rises again to 20 to 25 per cent of saturation.

The satisfactory oxygen supply in the deeper waters of the Sea of Japan, in spite of the isolation of its deep trench, is of special interest. The oxygen content of the deep waters of the Sea of Japan does not fall below 67 to 70 per cent of saturation (P. Ushakov, 1953). This is due to strong processes of vertical circulation in autumn and winter, caused by the cooling of the surface waters.

Three main masses of water (Fig. 336) may be distinguished in vertical dis-

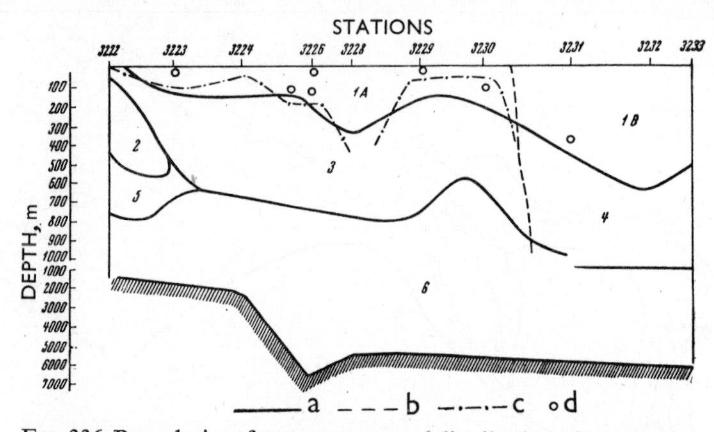

FIG. 336. Boundaries of water masses and distribution of two species of boreal Copepoda on the cross section southeast of Sangar Strait (Beklemishev and Burkov). A—Boundary of water masses; B—Front of Kuroshio current; C—Upper boundary of the distribution of *Calanus cristatus* (boreal cold-water species); D—Places of occurrence of *Calanus pacificus* (south boreal thermophylic species). *1a*—Modified subtropical water mass in the zone of mixing; *1b* Subtropical water mass (proper); *2*—Cold intermediate layer; *3*—Zone of interaction of subtropical and sub-Arctic waters; *4*—Intermediate layer of lowered salinity; *5*—Warm intermediate layer; *6*—Deep oceanic waters.

tribution over the Kuril–Kamchatka trench and in the Bering Sea (K. Moroshkin, 1955; A. Bogoyavlensky, 1955 and D. Smetanin, 1958 and 1959). These are:

(*1*) Upper sub-Arctic water masses (0 to 200 m), wherein all indices are subject to most pronounced seasonal alterations. These are the waters modified by local conditions (in the Bering Sea and over the Kuril–Kamchatka trench). In their turn they may be divided into the surface layer subject to summer heating (0 to 50 m), and a deeper (down to 200 m), cold intermediate layer. The salinity of these waters is slightly higher than 32‰.

During the period of spring bloom the amount of oxygen reaches 130 to 175 per cent of saturation; the amount of phosphates in terms of phosphorus decreases from 60 or 70 to between 20 and 10 mg/m³ or less; that of nitrates from 350 to between 20 and 40 mg/m³, and of silicon from the range 1,000 to 1,300 down to 200 to 300 mg/m³. Phytoplankton production was calculated from the amount of plant food as 75 g of carbon under 1 m² (D. Smetanin, 1959). Moreover, if in the coastal waters off Kamchatka the 'yield' during the spring reaches 125 g/m³ in terms of carbon, in the open regions of the Ocean it falls to 5 or 6 g/m³, i.e. by about 25 times. Vertical changes in the content of oxygen and plant food and in the ranges of temperature and salinity in spring at various places in the central Kuril–Kamchatka trench are given in *Tables 284, 285* and *286*.

Table 284

Depth m	Oxygen (percentage)	Phosphorus (mg/m³)	Silicon (mg/m³)
0	105–132	9–56	240–1,000
25	108–113	43–59	560–1,020
50	100–104	58–69	860–1,060
100	92–97	71–74	1,120–1,200
200	24–90	76–84	1,180–1,700

Table 285

Depth m	Temperature °C		Salinity ‰		Oxygen (percentage)		pH	
0	1·30	1·3	33·24	33·20	8·08	8·55	8·13	8·17
50	1·10	0·58	33·26	33·29	8·08	7·71	8·12	8·09
100	0·90	1·16	33·26	33·42	8·06	5·90	8·05	8·02
200	2·68	2·48	33·82	33·74	2·70	3·00	7·80	7·83
300	3·32	2·46	34·02	33·84	0·85	2·54	7·71	7·79
500	3·14	3·01	34·20	34·10	0·50	1·04	7·61	7·64
1,000	2·60	2·40	34·45	34·42	0·61	0·80	7·61	7·71
1,500	2·20	2·17	34·59	34·55	1·05	1·02	7·78	7·78

Table 286

Depth m	Temperature °C	Oxygen (percentage)	Phosphate phosphorus (mg/m³)	Ammonium nitrogen (mg/m³)	Silicon (mg/m³
0	1·60	122	47	375	1,400
100	0·80	99	56	390	1,400
200	3·15	20	85	590	2,740
500	3·10	6·5	88	615	3,700
1,000	2·45	9	83	600	4,260
2,000	1·72	32	78	560	4,560
4,000	1·44	44	69	480	4,160
8,000	1·92	46	62	—	3,900

(*2*) The lower sub-Arctic water mass may in its turn be divided into two layers—a layer (200 to 1,400 m) with a much lowered oxygen content, an increased amount of nutrient salts and a higher temperature; and a lower-temperature layer with an oxygen content of 32 to 46 per cent of saturation. This water mass likewise may be regarded as locally modified water, which enters mainly from the Bering Sea in the winter and sinks down from the Sea of Okhotsk. The rate of the movement of these waters southwards reaches 10 to 13 cm/sec at a depth of 600 m.

(*3*) Deep Pacific Ocean water masses (below 1,400 m) and bottom water, which is in constant reaction with bottom sediments. Deep water masses are characterized by their great homogeneity and by their comparatively low oxygen content (D. Smetanin, 1959) (3 to 4 ml of oxygen per litre as against 5 or more in the Atlantic Ocean) and by their increased content of plant food. Smetanin considers that this phenomenon is linked with the greater age of these waters as compared with those of the Atlantic.

In Smetanin's expression (1959) the waters of the ultra-abyssal of the Kuril–Kamchatka trench are, as it were, deep water spread out vertically; they are in constant movement (probably from north to south) at the same speed as the waters above them (A. Bogoyavlensky, 1955). The temperature of this water falls to 1·45°, but below 4,000 m it rises to 2·15° at the bottom (adiabatic process); its salinity increases to 34·75‰, its oxygen content to 3·6 ml per litre and the amount of phosphates to 60 mg/m^3 in terms of phosphorus.

IV. COMPOSITION OF FLORA AND FAUNA

The flora and fauna of the Pacific Ocean are in general richer than those of the Atlantic, and similarly the population of its northwestern part is considerably richer than that of the corresponding parts of the Atlantic.

The general taxonomic composition of the flora and fauna of the northwestern parts of the Pacific cannot be considered as well known; some groups have been studied in sufficient detail, others much less (Porifera, Coelenterata, Gastropoda and others); the taxonomy of some groups—Turbellaria, Nematoda, Actinia, bottom nemertines, Harpacticoidea and others—has hardly been established at all. The composition given in *Table 287* should only be taken as preliminary.

The complete list of the fauna of the northwestern part of the Pacific Ocean contains no fewer than 6,000 animal species. It is apparently considerably richer than that of the Atlantic Ocean fauna in the same latitudes.

The richness of the fauna of the Far Eastern Seas and the antiquity of its origin is accentuated by its abundant parasite fauna, studied by V. Dogjel and his pupils (A. Akhmerov, B. Bykhovsky and others).

About 900 parasite forms are known now, and one may assume that their actual number is much greater. This number is composed of species of 130 Protozoa, 400 Trematoda, 20 Cestoidea, 120 Nematoda, 80 Crustacea, 10 Gastropoda and 120 others.

The richness of the flora and fauna of the northern part of the Pacific may be demonstrated also from many other examples. Thus, for example, among

Table 287. Composition of flora [A. Zinova, 1954, 1960 and E. Zinova, 1940, 1954] and fauna [P. Ushakov, 1953 and P. Ushakov and others 1955, with some additions]

Group	Sea of Japan [northern part]	Sea of Okhotsk	Bering Sea [western part]	Total
Sea-weeds:				
Diatoms [plankton]	82	64	66	—
Green algae	56	58	25	79
Brown algae	109	105	46	143
Red algae	214	136	67	246
Total	379	301	138	468
Invertebrates:				
Foraminifera	>160	>400	>140	~600
Radiolaria	—	120	106	~200
Ciliata	—	~25	—	—
Porifera [Cornacuspongida]	70	101	50	>150
Coelenterata [Hydroidea]	99	185	132	>200
Nemertini [pelagic]	—	10	40	15
Polychaeta	>300	244	220	420
Hirudinea	12	4	8	15
Echiuroidea	>5	8	8	~20
Sipunculoidea	11	9	5	12
Bryozoa	~250	>200	—	~350
Copepoda [pelagic]	39	93	49	224
Cirripedia	~20	17	11	25
Isopoda	78	85	75	~175
Amphipoda	254	250	210	~500
Cumacea	49	48	25	65
Euphausiacea	4	4	—	6
Decapoda	125	96	62	~175
Pantopoda	30	29	20	~50
Bivalvia	—	~150	>200	~350
Gastropoda	—	154	—	~400
Cephalopoda	15	20	13	37
Amphineura	26	25	47	47
[all molluscs]	[~300]	[~262]	[~250]	[~750]
Brachiopoda	9	6	7	15
Echinodermata	~188	~160	186	>275
Ascidia	43	49	46	~80
Vertebrates:				
Pisces [T. Rass]	615	276	315	~800
Mammalia	—	—	—	35
Total number of animals	>3,250	>3,000	>2,500	~5,200

130 species (64·6 per cent) and 30 genera (90 per cent) of the family Laminariales, 84 species and 27 genera are known in the northern part of the Pacific Ocean (mainly along the Asian coast); in the northern part of the Atlantic 8 species and 5 genera are known. Thirty-five species of Laminariales are known for the Bering Sea, 40 for the Sea of Okhotsk and 32 for the Sea of Japan (4 species only are known for the Yellow Sea).

P. Ushakov (1953) points out 'that the occurrence in many groups of "bunches" or "fans" of numerous very similar and, in most cases, not sufficiently distinguished new subspecies and varieties is a distinctive feature of the Far Eastern fauna. It bears incontestable witness to very violent contemporary processes of the formation of new species. These processes, moreover, are most intensive in the Sea of Okhotsk.'

Indeed, this phenomenon of the specific richness of the flora and fauna of the northwestern area of the Pacific Ocean (within the limits of the boreal region) is observed not only in the Far Eastern Seas but also in the composition of the deep-water fauna of the adjacent part of the Pacific Ocean. Echiuroidea, Cephalopoda, Amphipoda, Isopoda, and especially Pogonophora (A. Ivanov, 1959) and Pisces may serve as examples. This is possibly due partly to the insufficient investigation of this region of the Ocean; but mainly it is the result of the considerable antiquity and great variety of the physico-chemical conditions of the northwestern part of the Pacific and of some specific geochemical peculiarity.

Some fauna groups of the northwestern part of the Pacific display an abundance of species both in the shallow and deep-water fauna. Foraminifera, Radiolaria, Polychaeta, Amphipoda, Mollusca, Echinodermata, Pogonophora, Pisces and Mammalia belong to these groups. Note that the last three belong to these groups; Pogonophora is particularly indicative in this respect. Half of all the known species of this group have been recorded for the northwestern part of the Pacific; not only the species but likewise the genera, families and orders (Fig. 337). In contrast, as yet only one representative of the genus Siboglinum, out of 11 genera and a large number of species, has been found in the Altantic Ocean.

Plankton

The group Calanoida occupies an exceptionally dominant position in the oceanic plankton of the temperate zone (boreal region). Among the great choice of species of this group the most significant in the Far Eastern Seas are the following: *Pseudocalanus elongatus*, *Calanus tonsus*, *Eucalanus bringii*, *Calanus cristatus*, *Metridia pacifica*, *Scolecithricella minor* and *Pareuchaeta japonica*. *C. cristatus*, *C. tonsus*, *E. bungii*, *P. japonica*, *M. pacifica*, *Sc. minor* var. *orientalis* and others are endemics of the Far Eastern Seas (K. Brodsky, 1955). The boreal aspect of this group of Calanoida is accentuated by the close resemblance of many of the above-mentioned forms to the boreal Atlantic forms.

The boreal Far Eastern plankton is replaced by the tropical plankton in the zone where the waters of the currents of Kuroshio and Oyashio meet. This group is predominant in the upper layer of the Bering and Okhotsk Seas; a considerable admixture of cold water forms is observed only in the very northern part of these Seas. Its distribution is limited in the Sea of Japan by the warm waters of the Tsushima current, which brings warm-water plankton. Bathypelagic Calanoida (400 to 3,000 m) are more widely distributed; however, they disappear completely from the fauna of the Sea of Japan (except

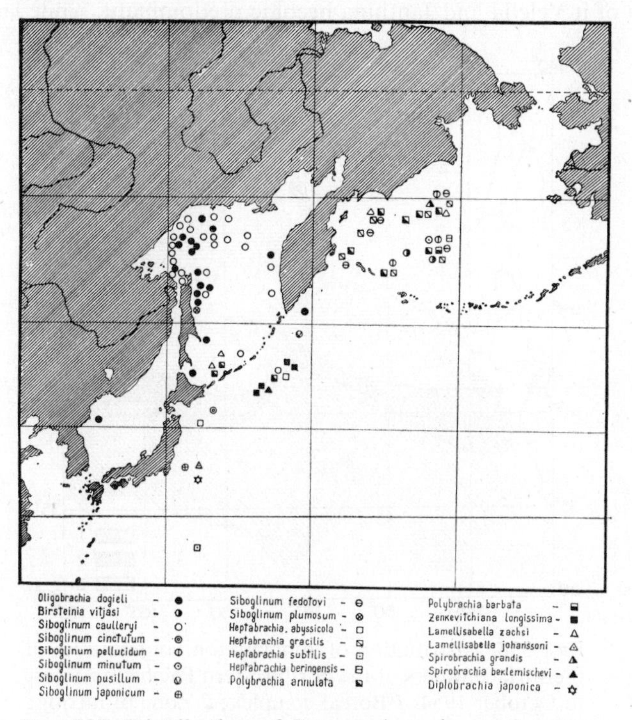

FIG. 337. Distribution of Pogonophora in northwestern part of the Pacific Ocean (Ivanov, 1959).

for certain upper bathypelagic forms) which are retained in the shallow straits.

Two hundred and twenty-four species of Calanoida have been established for the northern part of the Pacific Ocean, including 39 for the Sea of Japan, 71 for the Sea of Okhotsk and 49 for the Bering Sea.

Among the Calanoida of the Far Eastern Seas certain species are of exceptional significance for fish and cetaceans. Off the eastern coasts of Kamchatka *Eucalanus bungei* and *Calanus cristatus* form the main food of the herring. In the Sea of Japan the pilchard feeds mostly on *Paracalanus parvus*, *Pseudocalanus elongatus* and *Calanus pacificus*. The whales *Balaenoptera physalis*, *B. borealis*, *B. musculus* and *Megaptera nodosa* feed on Copepoda, mainly *Calanus cristatus*.

As has been mentioned above, the sub-Arctic waters of the Kuril current (Oyashio) meet the warm waters of Kuroshio off Honshu Island in 40° to

42° N latitude and react on each other. The boundaries of these zones agree closely with the distribution of certain mass forms of plankton (Fig. 338). To the north of the zone of mixing of the waters plankton is typically boreal, with a predominance of *Calanus cristatus*, *C. plumchrus*, *Eucalanus bungii bungii* and *Metridia ochotensis* (K. Beklimishev and V. Burkov, 1953). To the south of it Velella and Janthina become predominant, while large masses

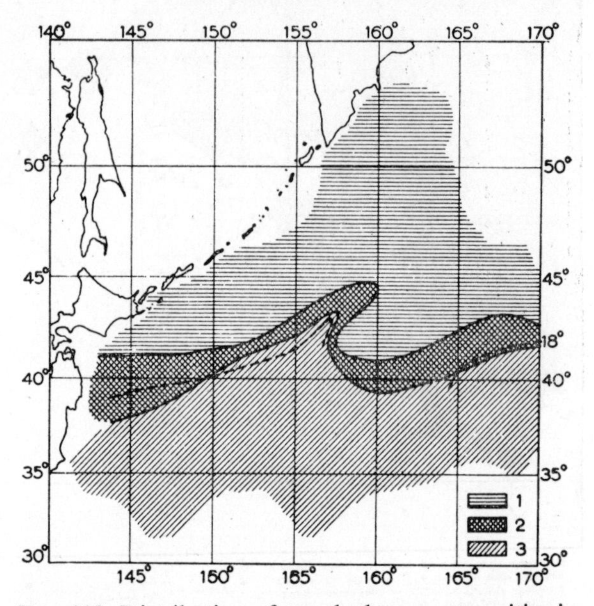

FIG. 338. Distribution of zooplankton communities in the surface waters of the northwestern Pacific in August to October 1954. *1* Boreal complex; *2* Zone of mixing; *3* Tropical complex. Dashed line is an 18° isotherm on the surface of the water (Bogorov and Vinogradov, 1955).

of Doliolum and Salpae, Lepas, Physalia, Porpita, Cestus and others make their appearance.

This type of replacement of the population of certain waters is clearly seen in the phytoplankton too (G. Semina, 1958) (Fig. 339). Bogorov has given an exceptionally clear and complete picture of the distribution of zooplankton within the zone of the meeting of the Kuroshio and Oyashio currents (the Polar front). North of latitude 40° to 42° surface waters have a winter temperature below 3° and a summer temperature of up to 14° or 15°. South of this zone of sub-Arctic convergence (the Polar front) the temperature rises to 26° to 28° in summer, while in winter it is 18° to 20°. The convergence zone is 100 miles wide in summer and several times wider in winter. To the north of it the boreal plants (*Thalassiosire nordenskjoldii*, *Chaetoceras convolutus*, *Ch. atlanticus*, *Ceratium longipes*) and the animals (*Calanus plumchrus*, *Eucalanus bungii*, *Calanus cristatus*, *Sagitta elegans*, *Euphausia pacifica*, *Thysanoessa longipes*) and other forms are predominant in the surface plankton; they are replaced in the south by the sea-weeds *Rhizosolenia bergonii*, *Chaetoceras lorenzianus*, *Climacodium biconcavum*, coccolithines, and animals, *Cestus amphitrites*, Velella, Physalia, Pteropoda and Heteropoda; and from among the Copepoda members of the genera Herocalanus, Undinula, Copilia, Sapphirina, Salpas, Halobates and many others.

Since the convergence zone has no population which is peculiar to itself

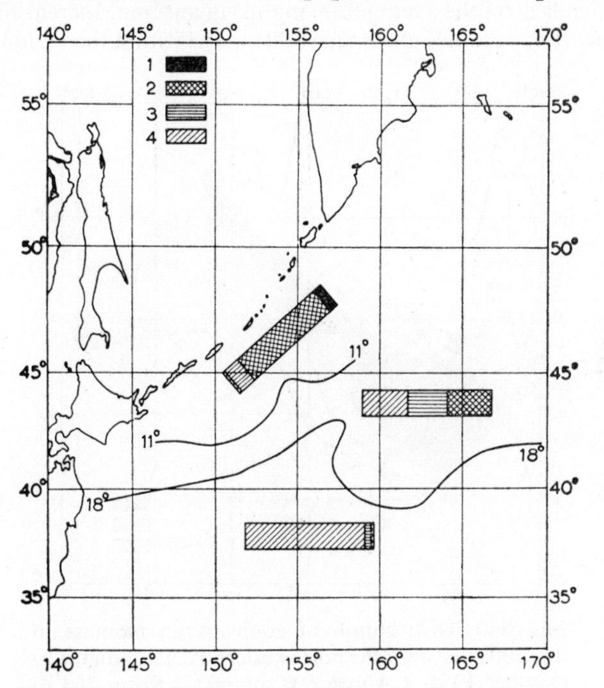

FIG. 339. Distribution of phytoplankton (as percentage of total number of species) in boreal waters, zone of mixing and northern waters of Kuroshio. *1* Cold water species; *2* Temperate cold water species; *3* Temperate species; *4* Warm water species. August to October 1954 (Bogorov).

alone in this part of the Pacific, Bogorov thinks that it does not possess the importance of a subtropical zone but only of a 'blending' zone, of the meeting of the tropical and boreal planktons. In the boreal waters north of the convergence zone peridinean sea-weeds constitute about one-third of the total number of plankton species, while south of it the number of diatom species is three or four times greater than that of the peridineans. In the northern part boreal phytoplankton species constitute 79 per cent (I. Smirnov, 1956), to the south 0·5 per cent; warm-water species, however, form 93·5 per cent. In general phytoplankton and zooplankton are similar in distribution.

Many plankton sea-weeds, among them *Rhizosolenia alata* and *Coscinodiscus viridis* as cold-water forms, and *Planktoniella sol* and *Vultar sumatranum* as warm-water forms, may serve as good indicators of the warm (Kuroshio) and cold (Oyashio) waters of the northwestern part of the Pacific Ocean (G. Semina, 1958). Alterations in the plankton density (Fig 340) and in the indices of its primary production (Fig. 341) are just as characteristic. Off the Kamchatka coast primary production in the autumn of 1955 was 20 times higher than in the tropical region. Plankton biomass in the waters adjacent to the Kuril Islands is on the average 200 mg/m³ in autumn. Increasing gradually to the southeast, it becomes more than 500 mg/m³ within the region of greatest

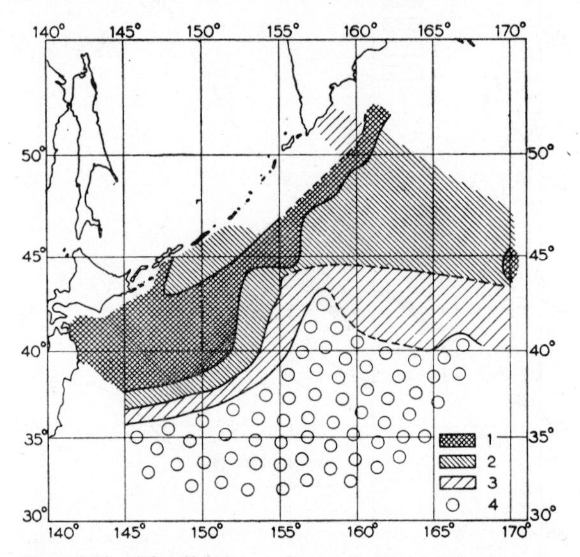

FIG. 340. Distribution of zooplankton biomass in 0 to 100 m layer of the northwestern Pacific, August to October 1954. *1* Above 500 mg/m³; *2* From 250 to 500 mg/m³; *3* From 100 to 250 mg/m³; *4* Below 100 mg/m³ (Bogorov and Vinogradov).

vertical mixing (V. Bogorov and L. Vinogradov, 1955), reaching at times 2,000 to 3,000 mg/m³. Still farther to the southeast the plankton biomass falls to 50 or even 20 mg/m³. However, it has to be taken into account that in the warm tropical waters the number of plankton generations is considerably higher and the period of multiplication much longer, thus compensating for the small indices of isochronous biomass. In the Kuril–Kamchatka region, for instance, *Calanus plumchrus* has only two multiplication maxima, the spring and autumn ones, and only two seasonal generations. The dominant forms of the surface euphotic zone (0 to 200 m) in Kuril (boreal) waters have been given above.

In May and June 1953 the 0 to 200 m layer contained 31·2 per cent of the total zooplankton biomass of the whole huge water column of the Kuril–Kamchatka trench. The transition zone immediately below it contained another 31·8 per cent. The 4 km layer of the deep waters of the trench held only 2 per cent of the plankton biomass of the 8 km deep-water column. The plankton biomass of the 0 to 50 m layer varies from 100 to 1,100 mg/m³ in different places and at different hours of the day. A pronounced decrease of plankton biomass, followed by a consecutive increase in the 200 to 300 m layer, is characteristic of the cold intermediate layer of the Kuril region. Farther down the biomass decreases rapidly to between 1,000 and 1,200 m, after which its rate of fall decreases; but at a depth of 6 to 8·5 km it falls to 0·5 mg/m³. Within the trench itself at this depth there is only 1·2 g/m² of

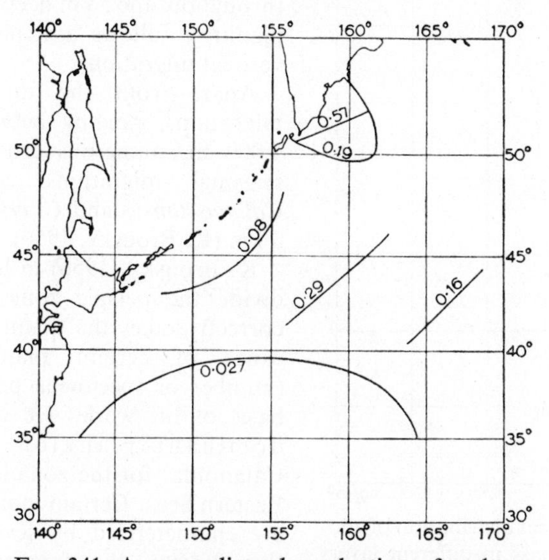

FIG. 341. Average diurnal production of carbon, mg/l, in the northwestern Pacific. August to October 1954, determined by the oxygen method (Bogorov and Beklemishev).

plankton biomass. Some species of Copepoda, Amphipoda and Ostracoda are characteristic of the ultra-abyssal plankton. Many planktons there lose their red colour, which is typical of the deep-water plankton, and acquire a dirty grey colour. Apparently (V. Bogorov and L. Vinogradov, 1955) the differences in the quantitative development of plankton in the boreal and tropical regions of the northwestern part of the Pacific are retained even with a transition to the deep floor (Fig. 342), hence the suggestion that the organic substances of the production zone are carried away in the vertical direction more than they are in the horizontal. Life phenomena which develop in the surface zone of the Ocean influence bottom fauna and the organic components of the sea-bed. The distribution of silica in the soils of the northwestern part of the Pacific Ocean, corresponding to the abundant development of plankton diatoms in the surface layer, is a good illustration of this correlation (Fig. 326).

M. Vinogradov (1954) has established some curious phenomena of the vertical migrations of plankton. Diurnal vertical migrations of many plankton species of the surface zone are either absent or only feebly developed, being determined either by the season of the year or by the age of the organism, the latter being much more important. On the contrary, species inhabiting much greater depths (for instance *Metridia pacifica*, *M. ochotensis*, *Parathemiato japonica*) descend many hundreds of metres and rise again. There are reasons for thinking that throughout the 5 km deep Ocean waters plankton follows a steplike system of vertical migrations.

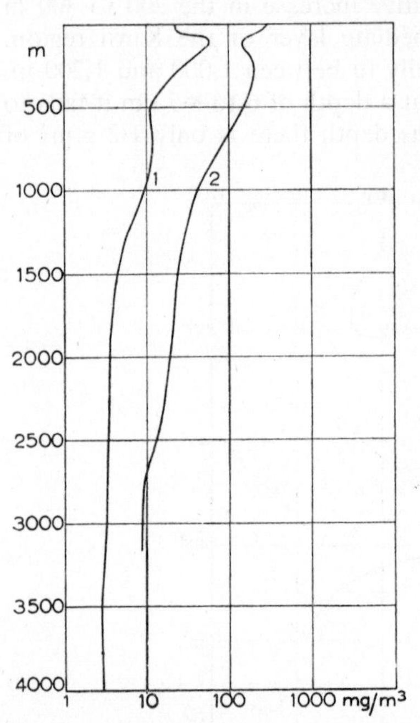

FIG. 342. Vertical distribution of zooplankton biomass in different layers at the deep-water stations in the northwestern Pacific. *1* Tropical waters; *2* Boreal waters (Bogorov and Vinogradov).

Apart from the diurnal vertical migrations, ranging between 300 and 5,000 m, numerous crustaceans have seasonal migrations extending for *Calanus tonsus* and *C. cristatus* to 2 or 3 km (K. Brodsky, 1956).

K. Brodsky (1956) in his attempt to divide the pelagic zone into districts correctly takes the quantitative significance of certain plankton species (number of specimens per m^3) as the basis of his work. He uses only one dominant plankton group, the Calanoida, for the zonation of the Far Eastern Seas. Certain individual species are characterized by several quantitative indices—the frequency of their occurrence, the number of specimens per m^3, the percentage of the number of specimens to the total number of Calanoida. The main forms of Calanoida are: *Pseudocalanus elongatus*, *Calanus tonsus*, *C. cristatus*, *Eucalanus bungii*, *Metridia pacifica*, *Scolecithricella minor*, *Pareuchaeta japonica* and *Microcalanus pygmaeus*. Brodsky's proposal to include the northwestern part of the Seas of Japan and of Okhotsk, and of the Bering Sea, and the southeastern part of the Chukotsk Sea is based on the distribution of Calanoida in the boreal regions. Moreover, he distinguishes the northern Japanese, northern Okhotsk and northern Bering provinces, all three with *Calanus finmarchicus* as a predominant form; this is widely distributed in the boreal and Arctic waters of the Atlantic and Arctic Oceans. Brodsky calls the fauna of these three provinces pan-Arctic: 'similar to the Arctic, but not identical with it, i.e. analogous but not homologous'.

The vertical distribution of Calanoida in the northwestern part of the Pacific Ocean is as follows: poor variety of species in the surface waters; a still smaller number of species in the cold intermediate layer; the greatest abundance of species in the bathypelagic zone, and a decrease in the number of species in the abyssal. The same phenomenon has been noted by V. Dogjel and V. Reschetnjak (1956) for the Radiolaria, when the greatest specific abundance was at a depth of 200 to 2,000 m.

Benthos

The fauna of the littoral and sublittoral. The exceptionally rich flora and fauna of the littoral and sublittoral of the Ocean coast of the Komandorski Islands, of Kamchatka and the Kuril Islands have not so far been investigated sufficiently. E. F. Gurjanova (1935) has given a colourful description of the littoral fauna of the Komandorski Islands.

The littoral flora and fauna of the Komandorski Islands are very rich both in numbers and variety. The sea surrounding the islands does not freeze; its water has an almost oceanic salinity. Even in winter only close inshore and after a storm does the temperature of the surface water fall to −1·2° C; farther out into the sea it varies from 0·5° to 1·5°, and reaches 9° to 11° in summer. At greater depths the temperature is still 2° to 2·5° even in winter (Gurjanova). Littoral flora and fauna live within the 4 m layer, and some individual organisms are considerably nearer to the surface. The tidal zone of the Komandorski Islands is characterized by the irregularities of the tides, as a result of which it may either remain submerged for several days or dry out.

'The Bering expedition', writes Gurjanova, 'cast up by a storm on the shores of Komandor, found there herds of fur seals, millions strong, thousands of sea lions, herds of sea cows and sea otters and thousands of polar foxes. All these large animals fed off the shores of the islands on sea-weeds, invertebrates and fish . . . the bottom of the sea round the islands is overgrown with whole submarine forests of huge sea-weeds. These Macrocystis and Nereocystis sea-weeds, sometimes attaining heights of some dozens of metres (up to 300 m), *Alaria fistulosa*, with a thallus 10 to 12 m long, Laminaria, Thalassiophyllum, and others, form dense submarine forests, which rise to the surface from depths of 20 or 30 m.' This vegetation has a very rich fauna of invertebrates. The Bering Island littoral is inhabited by 7 species of chiton, 6 species of Anomura, 6 of crabs, 4 of starfish, 2 of sea urchins, 2 of holothurians and a multitude of species of worms, molluscs crustaceans, actinians, bryozoans and ascidians. This fauna is peculiar to the softer soils of the littoral. 'However, the cliffs which rise above the water level', writes Gurjanova, 'beaten by the swell, are also densely inhabited. Thick beds of vigorous *Laminaria longipes*, *L. dentigera*, *Thalassiophyllum clathrum*, with their powerful rhizoids, whole carpets of soft, ramified and cortical bryozoans, Porifera and actinians, continuous settlements of the large acorn barnacles *Semibalanus cariosus*, and complex ascidians, develop intensely on these cliffs, constantly washed by the swell. Red algae, bright red sponges and large chitons rise here from the sublittoral.' Quiet coves with sandy bottoms have columns of the polychaetes *Schizobranchus insignis*, and large gastropods, *Argobuccinum*, spp. and *Natica clausa*, while the sands are inhabited by a multitude of large-sized Bivalvia—Spisula, Siliqua and Tellina. The Komandor littoral fauna in general has a warm-water aspect, reflected by the variety of its biocoenoses and a large number of warm-water forms of sea-weeds and invertebrates (Thalassiophyllum, Amphiroa, Acmaea pelta, Strombella, *Pholas crispata*, *Pholedidea penita*, *Tapes stominea*, and others) and by the rich development of the sublittoral fauna.

The narrow shelf zone of the eastern shores of Kamchatka and the northern Kuril Islands has also an exceptionally rich bottom fauna (Bivalvia, Polychaeta, Crustacea, Echinodermata and others), which in the summer attracts numerous shoals of commercial fish—pollack, cod, flatfish, sea bass and Kamchatka crab. The intensive development of the fauna is the result of the abundance of littoral vegetation and plankton. A. Kuznetzov carried out a detailed investigation of these regions and established (1959) the presence of 16 biocoenoses; *Modiolus modiolus*, *Mytilus edulis*, Porifera, Hydroidea, *Echinarachnius parma*, *Astarte rollandi*, *A. alaskensis*, *Macoma calcarea*, *Cardium ciliatum*, *Ophiura sarsi*, *Ophiopholis aculeata*, *Pavonaria finmarchica* (?), *Asteronyx loveni*, *Astarte icani*, *Ampelisca macrocephala*, *Brisaster townsendi*, *Acila castrensis*, *Brisaster latifrons*, *Artacama proboscidea*, *Ammotrypane aulogaster*, *Rhodine gracilior*, *Pista vinogradovi*.

The predominance of Arctic and Arctic–boreal species (30 species or 48·3 per cent of the 64 dominant and characteristic species) in the fauna is evident from this list of the composition of the main forms and a quantitative analysis of their predominance. The eastern shores of Kamchatka and of the northern Kuril Islands are washed by cold waters flowing from the Bering Sea. The boreal species constitute 38·8 per cent of the main species, and the cosmopolitan ones 9·7 per cent (6 species). The number of subtropical–boreal species among the main species is very small—only 2, or 3·2 per cent. This is in strong contrast with the composition of the shelf fauna of the southern Kuril Islands. Many of the above mentioned forms (9 out of 20) are mass forms of the lower Arctic seas including the Barents Sea. The somewhat original vertical distribution of the cold- and warm-water zoogeographical communities corresponds to the distribution of the water masses (A. Kuznetzov, 1959). Arctic–boreal biocoenoses are developed most intensely at a depth of 100 to 200 m (at a temperature of about 0° C) and at 500 to 1,200 m (at a temperature of 2° to 2·5°). The water mass at 0 to 100 m deep is considerably warmed up in summer, while at 200 to 500 m the temperature remains between 3° and 4°.

The bottom fauna of these regions is characterized by high density indices (*Table 288*).

The rich littoral population of the southernmost Kuril Island, Kunashir (O. Kusakin, 1956), has much in common with the littoral population of the southern part of the northern Japanese shore, some areas of southern Sakhalin and the shore of the southern Kuril Islands, and it can be included in the south-boreal province of the boreal region, with considerable influence from the subtropical littoral flora and fauna. Among the south-boreal and subtropical species the following should be mentioned: the hydroids *Campanularia platycarpa*; the Porifera *Grantessa nemurensis*; the polychaetes *Achistocomus sovieticus*, *Staurocephalus japonica*, *Audouinia tentaculata* and *Polymnia trigonostoma*; the amphipod family Talitridae; the isopods *Ligia cinerescens*, *Excirolana japonica*, *Dynoides denticinus*, *Cleantis isopus*; the decapods

Table 288. Biomass of bottom-living biocoenoses of eastern shores of Kamchatka and northern Kuril Islands

Region	Biomass of biocoenoses, g/m³, at depths of 0–500 m		
	Lowest	Highest	Mean
Kamchatka Bay (0–500 m)	3·5	588	174
Kronotsky Bay (0–2,000 m)	0·9	1,182	206
South-eastern tip of Kamchatka and eastern side of northern Kuril Islands	25·8	10,536	495
Western side of northern Kuril Islands	9	1,135	268

Pachycheles stevensii, Pandalus latirostris, Spirontocaris ochotensis mororani, Puggetia quadridens, Cancer gibbosulus, Eriocheir japonicus; the molluscs *Turbo sangarensis, Potamides aterrina, Purpura japonica, Pecten jessoensis, P. swiftii, Venerupia philippinarum, Ostrea gigas*; the echinoderms *Distolaterias elegans, Lysatrosoma anthosticta, Aphelasterias japonica*, and many others.

In the so-called Nemuoro Sea, which is situated between Kunashir Island and the small Kuril Ridge, the two heterogenous faunas—the cold-water fauna of the shallows of the Bering and Okhotsk Seas and the warm-water fauna of subtropical origin common with that of the southeastern part of the Sea of Japan—are, in view of their hydrological environment and the distribution of water masses, exceptionally well mixed with each other. The north-Pacific boreal fauna, which does not penetrate farther north than the Nemuoro Sea (P. Ushakov, 1951), forms the basic stock of the whole fauna.

The fauna of the southeastern end of the Sea of Okhotsk is nearer in its composition to that of the Sea of Japan than to that of the Sea of Okhotsk.

Whereas the exchange of fauna between the Seas of Okhotsk and Japan through the Tartary Strait is greatly restricted, it proceeds on a large scale through the Sengara Strait (P. Ushakov, 1955). Warm-water fauna of the southern Kuril Islands penetrates there through the Sengara Strait with the warm Tsushima waters (Soya current). Along the western side of the Sea this fauna only reaches the Gulf of Peter the Great. On the other hand, some cold-water species of the Sea of Okhotsk can penetrate south along the Sakhalin coast into the Sea of Japan, mostly during the cold season.

The abyssal fauna of the Kuril–Kamchatka trench. For ten years (1949–59) the Institute of Oceanology of the Academy of Sciences of the U.S.S.R. has carried out a study of the Pacific Ocean deep-water fauna using the *Vityaz*. To start with this work proceeded side by side with that done on the Danish vessel *Galathea*. Both expeditions brought to light much new knowledge on the fauna of the oceanic depths, of that living not only in the ocean bed, but also in the trenches, down to their greatest depths.

The research done by the *Galathea* is particularly significant, since it covered the deep waters of the whole tropical zone of the Ocean. This team surveyed the greatest depth of the Ocean and their collections of fish and other bottom-living fauna are of great value. The *Galathea* collections have enriched our knowledge with the description of many new animal forms, of which some (for instance Neopilina) are of exceptional importance. The *Vityaz* survey was concentrated mainly in the northwestern part of the Pacific Ocean. It was therefore carried out in a most detailed manner, attention being directed chiefly to the changes of biological phenomena in a meridional

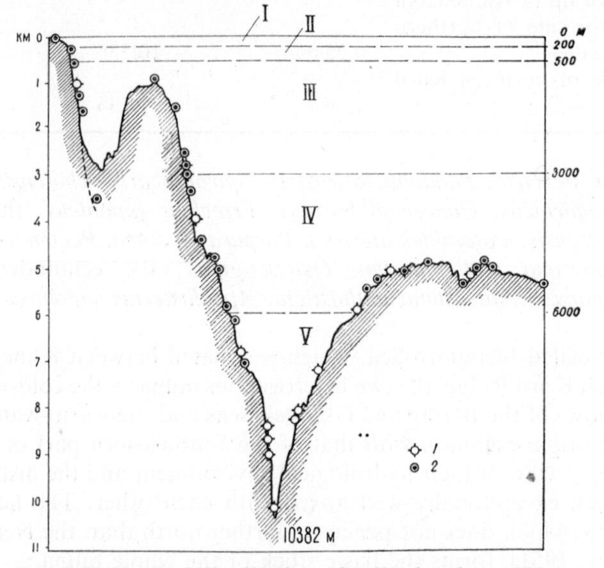

FIG. 343. Vertical distribution of collection from *Vityaz* gathered by trawling (*1*) and by bottom grab (*2*) through the cross section of the Kuril–Kamchatka trench, 1949 to 1955. *I* to *V*—Vertical zones, see *Table 289*.

direction, and vertically—from the surface to the greatest depths. The *Vityaz* and *Ob* explorations made it possible to draw a picture of the meridional changes of phenomena (geographical zonation) from the Bering Strait to Antarctic waters, and to obtain quantitative indices for pelagic and bottom life, which is of particular importance. The Kuril–Kamchatka trench was explored in great detail (Fig. 343).

Many new species and groups of deep-water animals were found in the *Vityaz* collections, among them the large new group of Pogonophora (Fig. 337).

Quantitative indices for the trawling collection were also obtained by means of the trawl-graph. Grab samples down to more than 7 km were obtained—trawls reached the greatest depths of the trenches.

The vertical zonality of the distribution of life had to be reconsidered owing to the intensive development of the investigation of the whole water column of the ocean. The works of Ya. Birstein, N. Vinogradova and Yu. Chindonova (1955, 1958) mark the beginning of this exploration. They have subdivided the pelagic area of the Pacific into zones. N. Vinogradova, moreover, suggested a system of division for the bottom-living fauna (1955, 1956). In later years all the *Vityaz* biologists were faced with this problem and it was found that the same zonation scheme is applicable to the pelagic and bottom life (Fig. 344) of the northwestern part of the Pacific Ocean.*

This scheme is fairly similar to that of Y. Hedgpeth (1957). For the equatorial zone and for the Antarctic waters this scheme might require some alterations.

It is clear from this scheme that transitional horizons, where two neighbouring faunas are intermingled, should be distinguished between the sublittoral and bathyal as well as between the latter and the abyssal (*Table 289*).

Such zones as the supralittoral (above sea-level), the littoral (the tidal zone), the sublittoral (the photosynthesis zone), the zone of the propagation of plant organisms, the bathyal (the zone of the continental shelf), and the abyssal (the zone of the ocean bed) are definite and established conceptions. The two transitional horizons, a separate ultra-abyssal zone (zones of oceanic trenches) and the division of the abyssal into two sub-zones need further explanation. The convenience of this scheme has been checked on a series of groups of invertebrates, the Pogonophorae, undoubtedly one of the most remarkable groups of the bottom-living fauna of the Okhotsk and Bering Seas and of the adjacent part of the Pacific Ocean.

The first representative of this group (*Siboglinum weberi*) was described by M. Caullerie (1914) from the collection of the *Siboga* expedition as a member of a new family of a new group of animals. This first Pogonophora was found in the waters of the Malayan Archipelago. The second specimen of the group (*Lamellisabella zachsi*) was found by Ushakov in the Bering Sea. A series of new forms of this remarkable group of animals was found (A. Ivanov, 1949, 1952, 1955, 1957, 1959, 1960) at the beginning of the researches of the *Vityaz*, when many new species of it were rapidly discovered. The place occupied by Pogonophorae in the system of animal classification, as an independent group of much taxonomic significance, was then determined (sub-phylum or even phylum). Since the first research of Ivanov, the promoter of this remarkable group, Pogonophorae were found in other places in the world ocean and in the old collections of different expeditions, where they had been placed in jars with polychaetes owing to the superficial resemblance of their tubes. Up to the beginning of 1959 42 species of Pogonophorae have been recorded, but not yet fully described, and assigned to 11 genera and a few families and orders. The collections made by the *Vityaz* and other expeditions contain some dozens of so far undescribed forms. New Pogonophorae forms are brought by every

* At first the following terms were suggested for depths below 6 to 7 km and for the fauna populating them: super-oceanic depths and super deep fauna (L. Zenkevitch, 1953). Later, however, Ya. Birstein suggested better terms—ultra-abyssal zone and ultra-abyssal fauna. In 1956 the term Hadal (from the name of the mythological god Hades, the ruler of the underground kingdom and the dead souls) was introduced by A. Brunn.

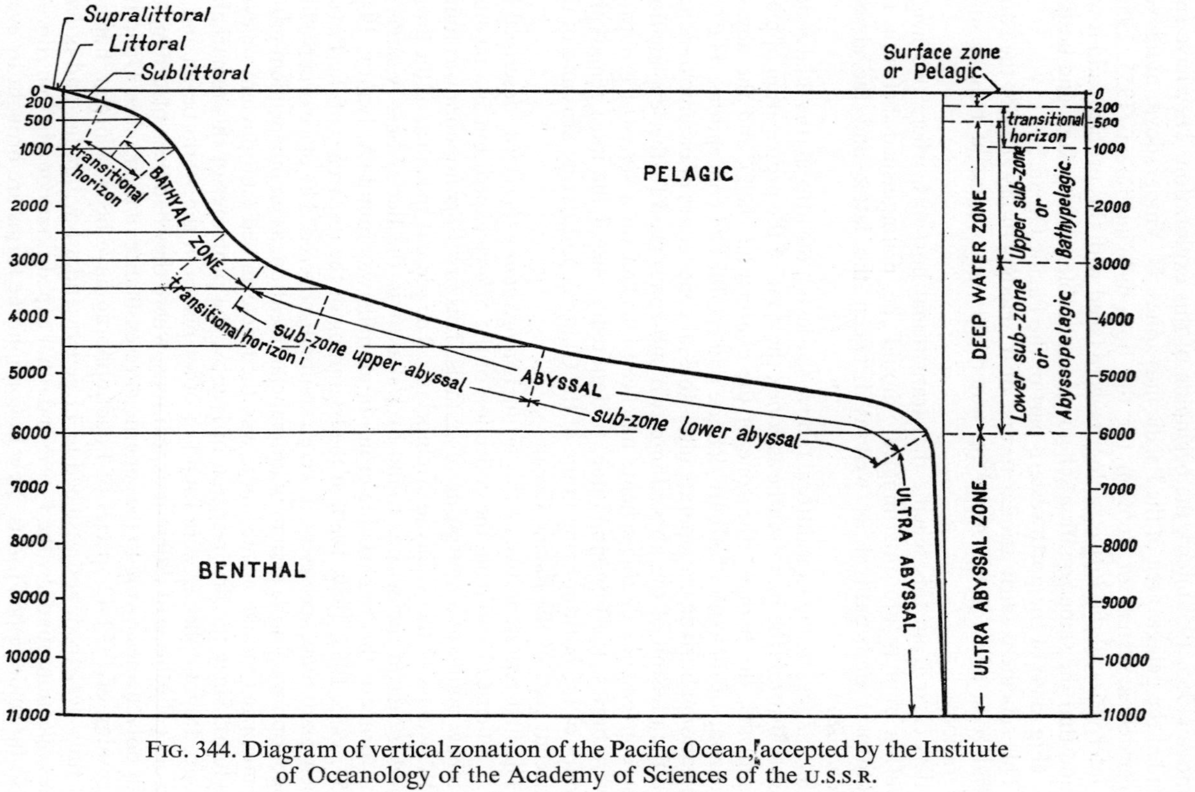

FIG. 344. Diagram of vertical zonation of the Pacific Ocean, accepted by the Institute of Oceanology of the Academy of Sciences of the U.S.S.R.

Table 289. Scheme of vertical zonation of fauna of northwestern part of Pacific Ocean

Benthos		Plankton	
Zone	Sub-zone	Zone	Sub-zone
I. Supralittoral		I. Surface or epipelagic 0 to 200 m	
II. Littoral ± 0 m			
III. Sublittoral 0 to 200 m			
Transitional horizon 200–500–1,000 m		Transitional horizon 200–500–1,000 m	
IV. Bathyal 500 to 1,000 m down to 2,500 to 3,000 m		II. Deep water 500 to 1,000 m down to 6,000 m	I. Uppermost or bathypelagic 500 to 1,000 m down to 2,000 to 3,00 m
Transitional horizon 2,500 to 3,500 m			II. Lower or abyssopelagic 2,000 to 3,000 m down to 6,000 m
V. Abyssal 3,000 to 3,500 m down to 6,000 m	I. Upper abyssal 300 to 3,500 m down to 4,500 m		
	II. Lower abyssal from 4,500 m to 6,000 m		
VI. Ultra-abyssal below 6,000 m		III. Ultra-abyssal below 6,000 m	

new expedition, and there is little doubt that soon this group will comprise some hundreds of species.

Judging by the intensive researches of the *Vityaz*, it is possible so far to assume to some extent that the main abundance of Pogonophorae species is concentrated in the Far Eastern seas and the northwestern part of the Pacific Ocean (Fig. 337), as well as in the northern hemisphere. Only forms of the genus Siboglinum, Oligobrachia and Polybrachia the richest in species, have so far been found in the Atlantic Ocean. Only one species of this genus has been recorded in Antarctic waters. *Diplobranchia belajevi* is the only species of this group so far reported from the Indian Ocean. Soviet expeditions have discovered in the Arctic basin *Polybranchia gorbunovi* in its eastern sector and *Siboglinum hyperboreum* off the eastern coast of Greenland; these have been found also in the Bering Sea. The Pacific Ocean is generally much richer in Pogonophorae, although they are unevenly distributed there. Only two species, *Krampolinum galatheae* and *Lamellisabella zachsi* are known from the eastern part of the Pacific, the Gulf of Panama. *Galathea* and *Vityaz* trawling in the Philippines and in the Mariana, Tonga and Kermadec trenches have not produced any Pogonophorae. The seas of the Malayan Archipelago have a more abundant Pogonophora fauna. However, so far only *Siboglinum weberi*, *S. pinnulatum*, *S. taeniaphorum* and *Galathealinum brunni* are known there—only four species of two genera. Four species of Siboglinum were found in the northern part of the Coral Sea (*S. microcephalum*, *S. buccelliferum*, *S. robustum* and *S. frenigerum*). The *Vityaz* found four species of Siboglinum (*S. vinculatum*, *S. variabilis*, *S. bogorovi* and *S. tenuis*) in the waters of the northern island of New Zealand.

Thus 20 species of Pogonophorae belonging to six genera are known outside the northwestern part of the Pacific, while in the latter 22 species belonging to nine genera have been found. Twenty-five new species of Pogonophora have been found in the Indian Ocean (*Vityaz*, 1959–60).

The Pogonophorae are typical deep-water organisms; in three areas, however, they rise to depths which are unusual for them: in the Sea of Okhotsk, (*Siboglinum caulleryi* to 22 m, *S. plumosum* to 119 m and *Oligobrachia dogieli* to 142 m); in the seas of the Malayan Archipelago (*Siboglinum pinnulatum* and *S. taeniaphorum* to 260 m); and in the Atlantic Ocean (*Siboglinum ermani*, *S. atlanticum*, *S. inermis Oligobrachia ivanovi*, and *Polybrachia capillaris* to 300 to 340 m; and in the Barents Sea (Nereilinum, to 170 m)). Many of these species descend to great depths, some even to the ultra-abyssal (for instance, *Siboglinum caulleryi* from 22 m to 8,164 m). As to their ascent to the upper layers in the Sea of Okhotsk, we are dealing, apparently, with a case similar to the rising of deep-water forms to the surface waters in the Arctic, a phenomenon well known for the Atlantic sector of the Arctic basin, the Sea of Okhotsk and the Antarctic. The ascent of deep-water forms to shallow depths has neither been investigated in detail nor sufficiently explained.

E. Vinogradova has recently studied this problem (1955). She points out that the ascent of the deep-water fauna to shallow depths unusual for them has been observed also in tropical latitudes. 'This kind of ascent is very pronounced in some areas of the West Indies and the seas of the Malayan Archipelago . . . thus, for example, the sea urchin *Pygmaeocidaris prionigera*, usually found at depths of 2,000 to 3,000 m in the Molo Strait of the Malayan Archipelago, has been recovered from a depth of only 69 to 91 m. The same has been observed of the deep-water family of sea urchins Echinothuriidae and Aspidodiadematidae, the Porifera Hyalonema and Farrea and the crabs Ethusina and others. . . . In that respect the region of the Banda Sea and the Key Islands is particularly remarkable, since an apparent mass ascent of the deep-water fauna to shallow depths is observed there. . . . The plateau on which the Key Islands are situated lies in shallow water and the temperature of the water falls below 10° to 13°. A mass ascent of deep-water fauna to the shallows is observed within the area of this plateau, which falls sharply away into the great depths of the Banda Sea. This deep-water fauna consists of most varied species of sea urchins, holothurians, starfish, glass sponges and others.'

Such a peculiarity in the vertical distribution of deep-water fauna may possibly be connected with the manner of its formation.

It is therefore even more astonishing that in the Bering Sea, where in general several deep-water forms have a tendency to rise to the upper horizons (E. F. Gurjanova, 1936), and in the neighbouring Sea of Okhotsk Pogonophorae were found only in a few cases at depths of less than 1,400 m (one case) and 1,693 m (two cases), and that usually they do not rise in the sea above 2,800 to 3,000 m.* Of the three Far Eastern Seas the highest number of Pogonophorae species has been recorded in the Bering Sea (11), seven of which appear, so far, to be endemic to it. Of the five species recorded in the Sea of Okhotsk only *Siboglinum plumosum* can provisionally be regarded as endemic. So far only one species has been discovered in the Sea of Japan, *Oligobrachia dogieli*, which had obviously penetrated from the Sea of Okhotsk where it lives at a depth of 119 to 572 m. Eight species of Pogonophorae have been described for the Kuril–Kamchatka trench, four of them endemic to it. Three endemic species have been found in the Japanese trench.

Echiuroidea (mainly of the family Bonelliidae) form a most original and characteristic element of the abyssal and ultra-abyssal fauna of the north-western part of the Pacific; there are eleven species of them (L. Zenkevitch, 1957, 1958) belonging to seven genera. Such an abundance of Echiuroidea is not known for any other region of the ocean. Echiuroidea are extremely poorly represented in the *Galathea* collection; there was only one specimen each among the material gathered by *Challenger* and *Ziboga*. There were none at all in the *Valdivia* collection. One of its species may be considered as a bipolar form. Echiuroidea (*Prometor benthophila*) are very rarely found on the eastern side of the Pacific Ocean. A group of ultra-abyssal forms can be clearly distinguished among the Echiuroidea (*Table 290*).

As a result of the researches of the *Vityaz* into the deep-water fauna it was found possible to widen considerably the limits of distribution in the depths of many groups of fauna (*Table 291*).

* In the Antarctic also at a depth of 3,000 m.

Table 290

Species	Depth of occurrence, m
Jakobia birsteini	6,150–8,100
Vitjazema ultraabyssalis	5,560–9,735
V. aleutica	7,286
Alomasoma nordpacifica	520–7,820
A. chaetifera	7,286
Bonellia pacifica	3,800–4,130
B. achaeta	3,500–5,540
Tatjanellia gracilis	3,940–5,020
T. grandis	2,970–3,400
Eubonellia valida	412–1,240
Listriolobus pelodes	1,580

Foraminifera, Hexacorallia, Nematoda, Polychaeta, Echiuroidae, Harpacticoida, Amphipoda, Isopoda, Gastropoda, Bivalvia and Holothurioidea penetrate deepest of all. In contrast Bryozoa, Brachiopoda and Decapoda descend least far into the depths. The deepest occurrence of fish—that of *Careproctus amblystomopsis* of the family Liparidae (A. P. Andriashev, 1955) (Fig. 345)—was in the Kuril–Kamchatka trench at a depth of 7,230 m; later, however, this fish was recorded in the Japanese trench at a depth of 7,579 m. This fish, according to Andriashev's terminology, is a secondary deep-water dweller. The variety of species of the fauna decreases rapidly with increasing depth, especially with the transition into the ultra-abyssal depths of the trenches (Fig. 346).

In the Kuril–Kamchatka trench 45 benthos species were found at a depth of 6,860 m, 41 at 7,210 to 7,230 m, 20 at 8,330 to 8,430 m, 9 at 8,610 to 8,660 m, 18 at 9,000 to 9,050 m, and 6 at 9,700 to 9,950 m.

The fact that the number of benthos species alone decreases with depth is of special interest. Plankton behaves differently (Fig. 347). The highest qualitative variety (calculated from Copepoda) is found not in the surface zone, but at depths between 2,000 and 5,000 m. Unfortunately this phenomenon has not yet been explained. It is best illustrated for Calanoidae in the Kuril–Kamchatka trench (Table 292). The same is noted in the case of pelagic Gammaridae (*Table 293*).

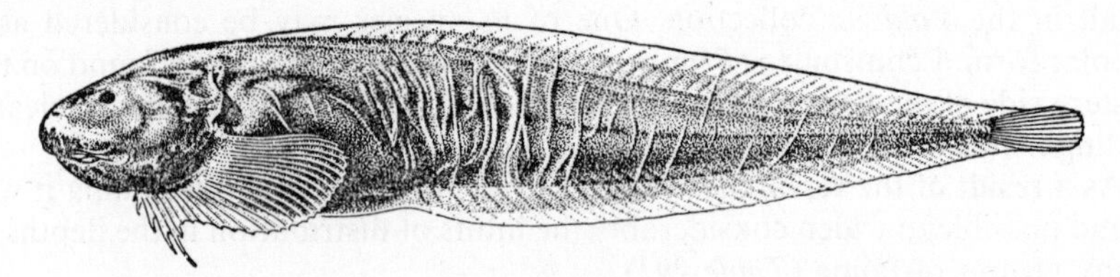

FIG. 345. *Careproctus* (Pseudoliparis) *amblystomopsis andriashev*; absolute length 238 mm. Kuril–Kamchatka trench, depth 7,230 m.

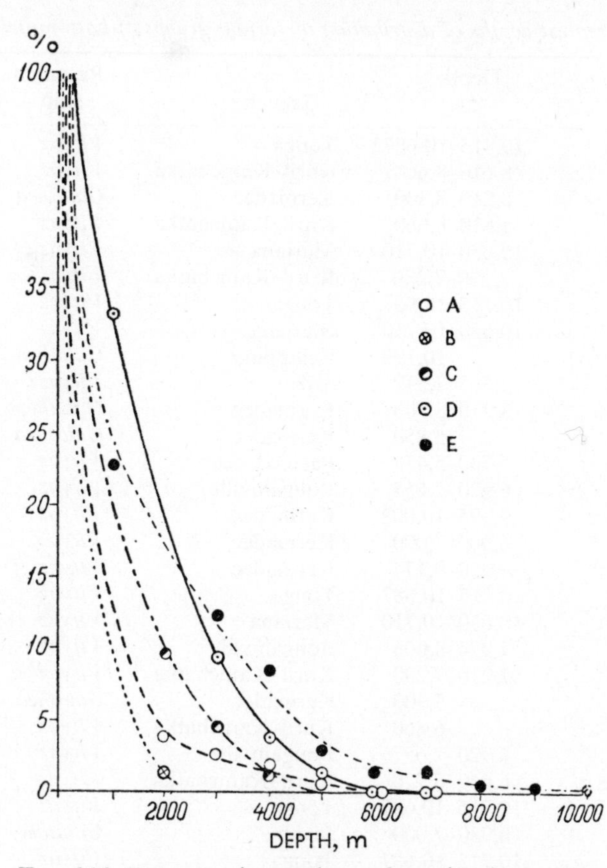

FIG. 346. Decreases in numbers of species (percentage basis) in certain groups of marine bottom-living invertebrates with increase of depth (Zenkevitch, Birstein and Belyaev). A Polychaeta; B Pericardia; C Pogonophora; D Asteroidea; E Holothurioidea.

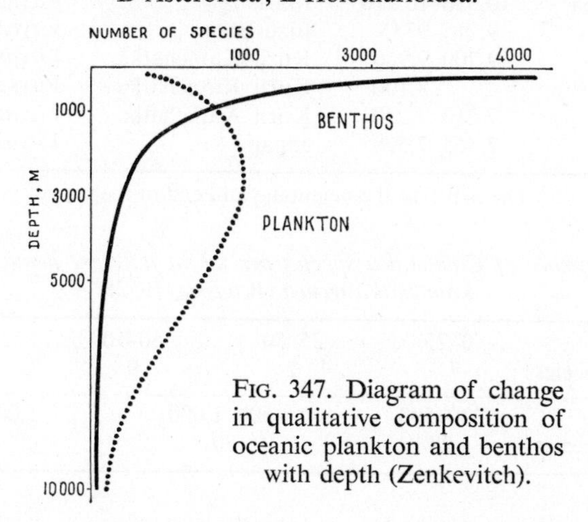

FIG. 347. Diagram of change in qualitative composition of oceanic plankton and benthos with depth (Zenkevitch).

Table 291. Greatest depths of distribution of various groups of bottom-living animals

Group	Depth m	Trench	Research ship	Year
Foraminifera	10,415–10,687*	Tonga	*Vityaz*	1957
Porifera	8.610–8,660	Kuril–Kamchatka	*Vityaz*	1953
Hydrozoa	8,210–8,300	Kermadec	*Galathea*	1952
Octocorallia	8,610–8,660	Kuril–Kamchatka	*Vityaz*	1953
Hexacorallia	10,630–10,710	Mariana	*Vityaz*	1958
Nemertini	7,210–7,230	Kuril–Kamchatka	*Vityaz*	1953
Nematoda	10,715–10,687	Tonga	*Vityaz*	1957
Polychaeta	10,630–10,710	Mariana	*Vityaz*	1958
Echiuroidea	10,190	Philippine	*Galathea*	1951
Priapuloidea	7,565–7,579	Japan	*Vityaz*	1957
Sipunculoidea	8,210–8,300	Kermadec	*Galathea*	1952
Bryozoa	5,850	Kermadec	*Galathea*	1952
Brachiopoda	5,730–5,458	Pacific Ocean	*Vityaz*	1957
Ostracoda	6,920–7,657	Bougainville	*Vityaz*	1957
Harpacticoida	9,995–10,002	Kermadec	*Vityaz*	1958
Cirripedia	6,960–7,000	Kermadec	*Vityaz*	1952
Tanaidacea	8,928–9,174	Kermadec	*Vityaz*	1958
Amphipoda	10,715–10,687	Tonga	*Vityaz*	1957
Isopoda	10,630–10,710	Mariana	*Vityaz*	1957
Cumacea	7,974–8,006	Bougainville	*Vityaz*	1957
Mysidacea	7,210–7,230	Kuril–Kamchatka	*Vityaz*	1953
Decapoda	5,300	Kermadec	*Galathea*	1952
Pantopoda	6,860	Kuril–Kamchatka	*Vityaz*	1953
Loricata	6,920–7,657	Bougainville	*Vityaz*	1957
Solenogastres	6,660–6,770	Kuril–Kamchatka	*Vityaz*	1953
Gastropoda	10,715–10,687	Tonga	*Vityaz*	1957
Scaphopoda	6,930–7,000	Javan	*Galathea*	1951
Bivalvia	10,715–10,687	Tonga	*Vityaz*	1957
Octopoda	8,100	Kuril–Kamchatka	*Vityaz*	1949
Asteroidea	7,587–7,614	Mariana	*Vityaz*	1955
Ophiuroidea	7,974–8,006	Bougainville	*Vityaz*	1957
Echinoidea	7,250–7,290	Banda Sea	*Galathea*	1951
Holothurioidea	10,630–10,710	Mariana	*Vityaz*	1958
Crinoidea	9,715–9735	Idzu-Bonin	*Vityaz*	1956
Pogonophora	9,700–9,950	Kuril–Kamchatka	*Vityaz*	1953
Enteropneustra	8,100	Kuril–Kamchatka	*Vityaz*	1949
Ascidiae	7,210–7,230	Kuril–Kamchatka	*Vityaz*	1953
Pisces	7,565–7,579	Japan	*Vityaz*	1957

* The depth at the beginning and end of the trawl.

Table 292. Number of Calanoidea species per m³ at different depths of the Kuril–Kamchatka trench (Brodsky, 1952)

Horizon, m	0–25	25–50	50–100	100–200
Number of species	7	7	9	10

Horizon, m	200–500	500–1,000	1,000–4,000
Number of species	28	30	87

Table 293. Number of species of pelagic Gammaridae at different depths of Kuril–Kamchatka trench (Ya. Birstein and M. Vinogradov, 1955). The zones correspond to those in Fig. 338

Zones and sub-zones	No. of species
Surface	1
Transitional	1
Upper abyssal	13
Lower abyssal	12
Ultra-abyssal	6

Quantitative development of different groups varies greatly with the horizon (Eig. 348). While Porifera (Hondrocladia, Hyalonema) are predominant at a depth of 1,000 to 2,000 m, holothurians (Elpiidae) and starfish (Porcellanasteridae) are the main groups between 2,500 and 7,000 m; still farther down holothurians become predominant in terms of biomass. At times the number of Pogonophorae specimens is remarkable. Thus, for example, about 3,000 specimens of Elpiidae, more than 4,000 tubes of Pogonophorae, mainly Zenkevitchiana, and about 100 specimens of *Echiuroidea vitjazema* were brought up from a depth of 9,000 m in one sweep at one of the stations in the Kuril-Kamchatka trench.

The qualitative variety of plankton increases with depth, while its numbers decrease steadily (*Table 294*) by no less than 1,000 times from the surface to the great oceanic depths; and probably, if we include the coastal areas and the periods of the greatest development of surface plankton, by several thousand times.

An interesting comparison of the vertical distribution of plankton biomass in the Kuril–Kamchatka, Mariana and Bougainville trenches is given by M. Vinogradov (1958) (*Table 294*).

Table 294. Vertical distribution of plankton biomass (mg/m³)

Depth, m	Kuril–Kamchatka trench	Mariana trench	Bougainville trench
0–50	508	24·0	127
50–100	376	14·9	107
100–200	288	10·9	32·8
200–500	59·3	2·1	9·4
1,000–2,000	21·8	1·0	2·4
4,000–6,000	2·64	—	0·09
4,000–8,000	1·84	0·012	—
6,000–8,000	0·48	—	0·01

Benthos biomass fluctuations from the surface to great depths are even more marked. Even within the limits of the abyssal the benthos biomass may vary by some hundreds of times (*Table 295*).

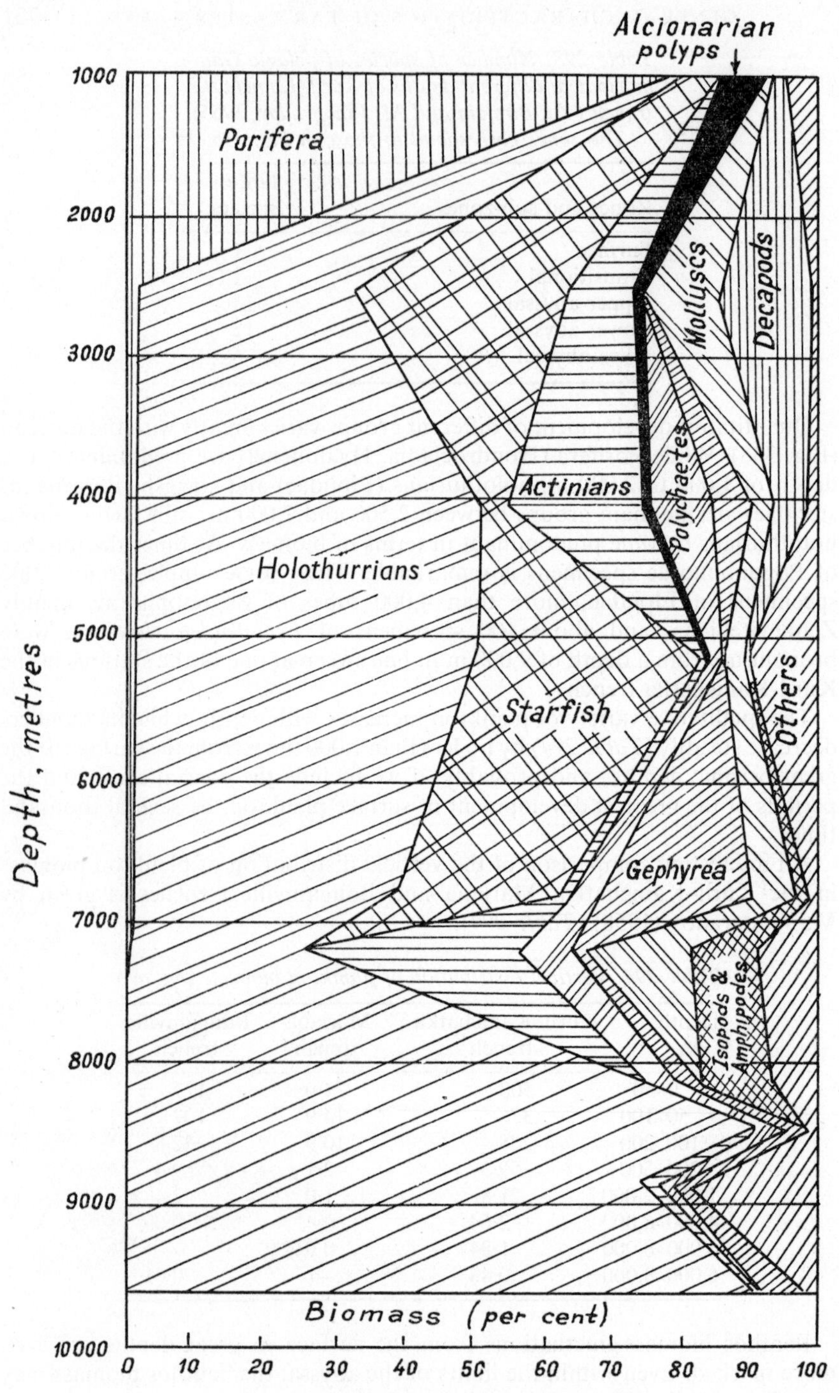

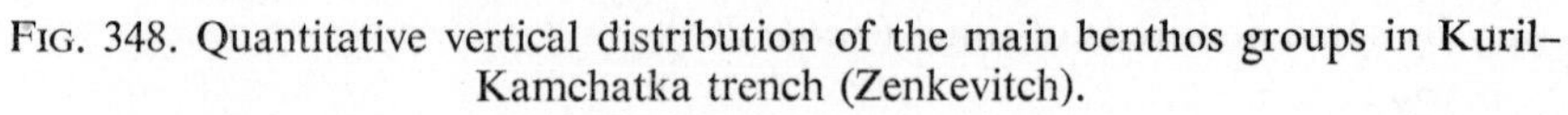

FIG. 348. Quantitative vertical distribution of the main benthos groups in Kuril–Kamchatka trench (Zenkevitch).

Table 295. Changes in benthos biomass with depth (Ya. Birstein and G. Belyaev, 1955) in northwestern part of Pacific Ocean

Depth, m	Coastal zone	50–200	950–4,070	5,070–7,230 Kuril–Kamchatka	8,330–9,250 Kuril–Kamchatka	5,000–6,000 Central part of ocean bed
Biomass g/m²	1,000–5,000	200	6·94	1·22	0·32	0·010

The considerable difference between the variations of the biomass of plankton and of benthos, either in the direction from the coast to the open ocean or from the surface into its depths, is due apparently to the multiplication of benthos being more closely dependent on the shore than is that of zooplankton. The latter depends much more on phytoplankton, the development of which in its turn is determined by the nutrient salts, the system of vertical mixing which brings them from the depths to the surface, and by the general conditions of lighting.

Two diagrams may serve to illustrate this; first the qualitative distribution of life through a cross section of the Kuril–Kamchatka trench (Fig. 349).

The amount of plankton decreases from 400 to 30 mg/m³ from the neretic zone to the oceanic (I). The increase (to 500 mg/m³) corresponds to the increase of plankton biomass towards the zone of convergence of the cold and warm waters. Throughout the same field the benthos biomass (II) decreases

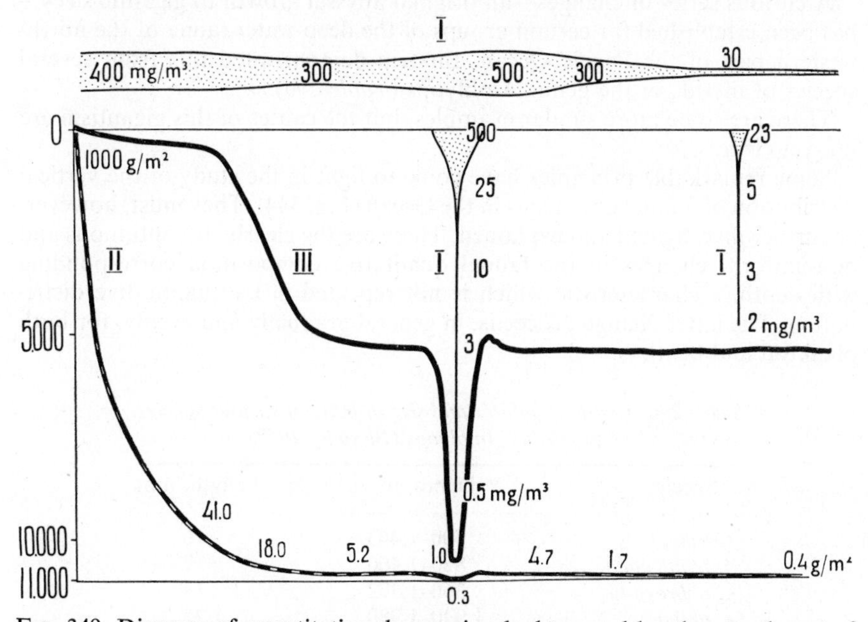

FIG. 349. Diagram of quantitative changes in plankton and benthos south-east of the Kuril chain (Zenkevitch). *I* Plankton; *II* Benthos; *III* Bottom topography (cross section of Kuril–Kamchatka trench).

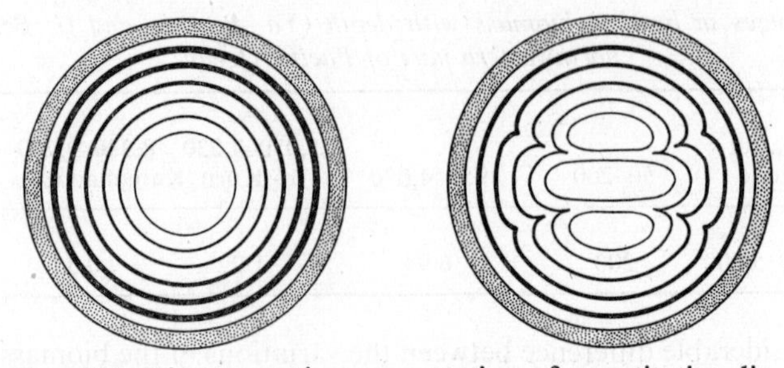

FIG. 350. Diagrammatic representation of quantitative distribution of (right) plankton and (left) benthos in the Ocean.

from 1,000 to 0·4 g/m² with some further decrease in the depths of the Kuril–Kamchatka trench. The curve of benthos biomass does not correspond to the scale of depths given on the left. Bottom relief is represented by curve III. Moreover, the decrease in the amount of plankton with depth for the trench and for the ocean bed is also shown (I).

The second, more abstract diagram (Fig. 350) gives the concentric zonation character of the quantitative distribution of benthos with an amplitude of a million, and the combined zonation (concentric on the periphery and along the latitude) of the qualitative distribution of the surface plankton with an amplitude of 20–50–100.

A curious series of changes—an original abyssal growth to gigantic sizes—has been established for certain groups of the deep-water fauna of the north-western part of the Pacific Ocean. Birstein demonstrated this from several species of mysids of the genus Amblyops (*Table 296*).

There are some more similar examples, but the causes of this gigantism are not yet clear.

Some remarkable principles have come to light in the study of the vertical distribution of animal organisms in the Ocean (Fig. 344). They must, however, be further investigated and explained. These are the clearly discontinuous and non-uniform changes in the faunal qualitative composition corresponding with depth, a characteristic which is not repeated in its quantitative distribution. The latter change proceeds, in general gradually and evenly, for both plankton and benthos.

Table 296. Depth of habitat and size of body of various species of the genus Amblyops (Birstein, 1958)

Species	Depth, m	Length, mm
A. kempi	700–1,463	16
A. tenuicauda	820–1,400	17
A. abbreviata	366–1,372	18
A. chlini	1,940–1,980	25
A. crozeti	2,930	30
A. magna	7,800	38

The most complete and graphic data on this phenomenon are provided by N. Vinogradova (1958), who has examined the vertical distribution of 1,144 species of deep-water animals (below 2,000 m). The first horizon with a pronounced change of bathyal and partly sub-abyssal species lies at a depth of 2,500 to 3,500 m, the second at 4,000 to 5,000 m (Figs. 351A, B and 352A, B). A large number of new species and even new groups appear in both horizons, while those inhabiting higher ones disappear.

Z. Shchedrina (1958) notes also that 'the most luxuriant and varied Foraminifera fauna . . . was recorded on two zones or horizons; at depths of about 3,000 m and at 4,850 to 5,570 m. Between these two zones of maximum Foraminifera variety two more transitional zones, characterized by scarcer Foraminifera fauna, can be distinguished.' With some groups a third horizon of a more marked change can be distinguished at 6,000 to 7,000 m, the threshold of the ultra-abyssal zone. This worker does not explain the cause of such vertical distribution: 'the explanation of this phenomenon should be sought both in the ecology of the animals inhabiting the deepest water, and in the historical causes which promoted their existence'.

It is most interesting that similar kinds of principles in the alterations in the qualitative composition according to depth have been observed also for the pelagic fauna of the Gammaridae (Ya. Birstein and L. Vinogradov, 1955) in the Kuril–Kamchatka trench (*Table 297* and Fig. 353).

Table 297

Zones	Sub-zones	Gammaridae forms
Deep-water, 500–6,000 m	Upper, 500–2,000 m Lower, 2,000–6,000 m	*Cyphocaris challengeri, Cyclocaris guilelmi, Korogam egalops, Paracalanus alberti, Parandania boecki, Eusirella multicalceola, Rhachotropis natator*
	Lower, 2,000–6,000 m	*Cyphocaris richardi, Astyra zenkevitchi, A. bogorovi, Halice aculeata, H. shoemakeri, Cleonardo macrocephala*
Ultra-abyssal, 6,000 m		*Tetronychia gigas, Hyperiopsis laticarpa, Andaniexis subabyssi, Halice quarta, Vitjaziana gurjanovae, Protohyperiopsos arquata*

These workers note also that the number of new forms not found in the higher horizons increases with depth—there are two (15·4 per cent) such forms in the upper deep-water zone; seven (52 per cent) in the lower, and six (100 per cent) in the ultra-abyssal. These last are considered by them as endemic to the Kuril–Kamchatka trench. Moreover, Birstein and Vinogradov arrange their data according to their zoogeography. Among the deep-water Gammaridae they distinguish four main groups: (*1*) Organisms with a pan-oceanic type of distribution (6 species); (*2*) Atlantic–Pacific (amphi-boreal) forms (7 species); (*3*) Arctic forms (1 species) and (*4*) North Pacific forms (2 species).

It is to be noted that the endemic nature of the fauna increases with depth—

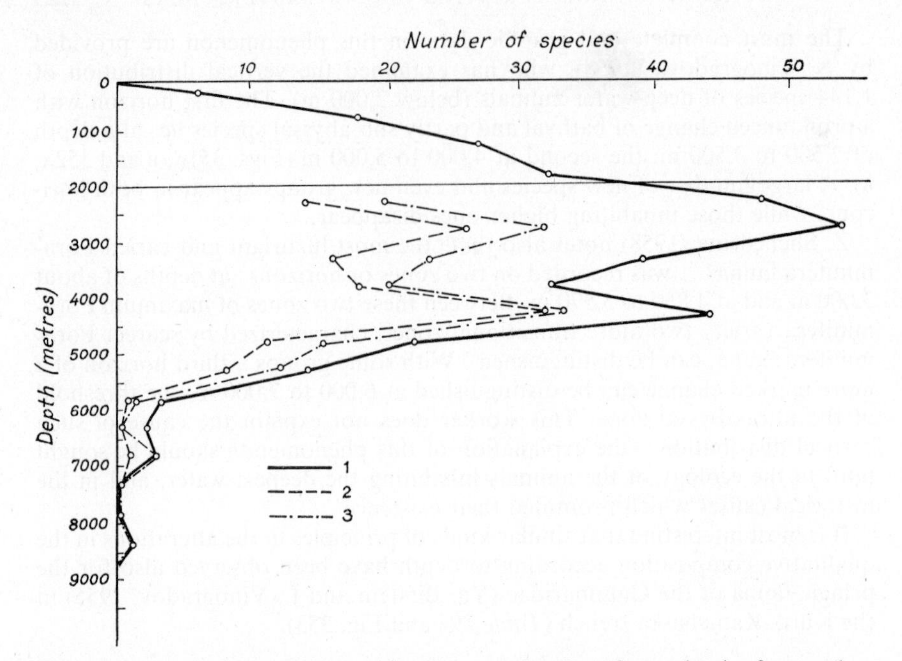

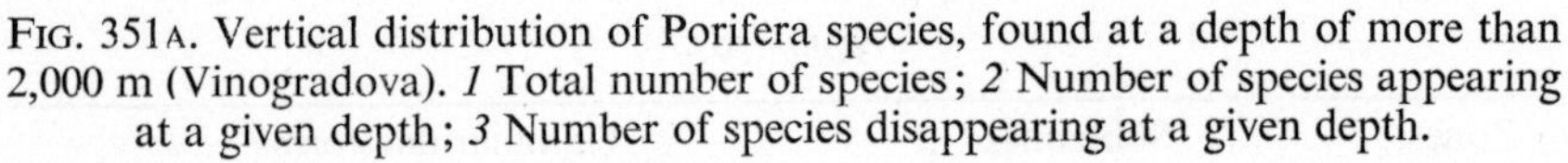
FIG. 351A. Vertical distribution of Porifera species, found at a depth of more than 2,000 m (Vinogradova). *1* Total number of species; *2* Number of species appearing at a given depth; *3* Number of species disappearing at a given depth.

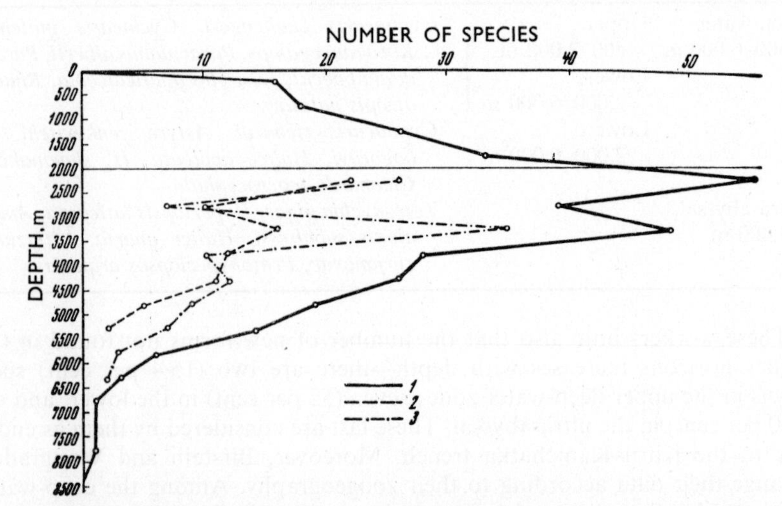

FIG. 351B. Vertical distribution of Elasipoda species, found at a depth of more than 2,000 m (Vinogradova). *1* Total number of species; *2* Number of species appearing at a given depth; *3* Number of species disappearing at a given depth.

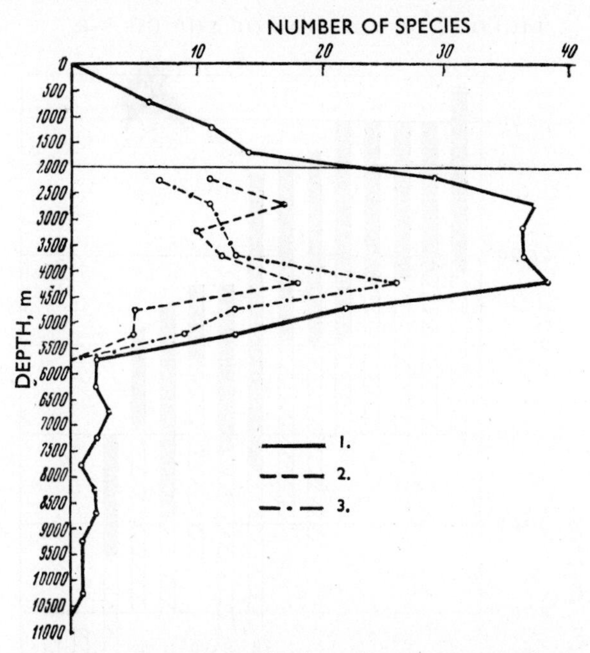

Fig. 352a. Vertical distribution of species Forcipulata, found at a depth of more than 2,000 m (Vinogradova). *1* Total number of species; *2* Number of species appearing at a given depth; *3* Number of species disappearing at a given depth.

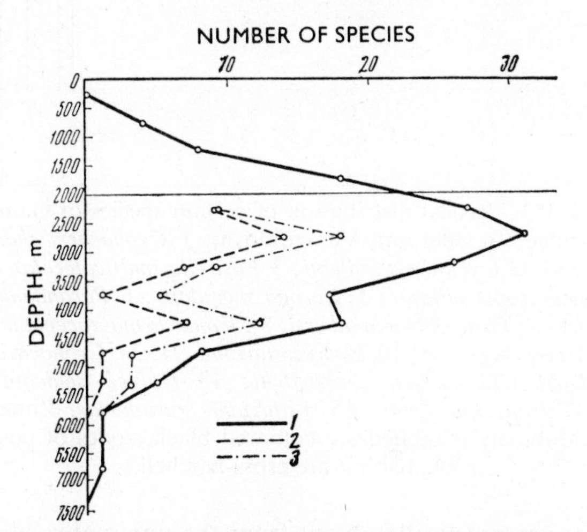

Fig. 352b. Vertical distribution of species Phanerozonia found at a depth of more than 2,000 m (Vinogradova). *1* Total number of species; *2* Number of species appearing at a given depth; *3* Number of species disappearing at a given depth.

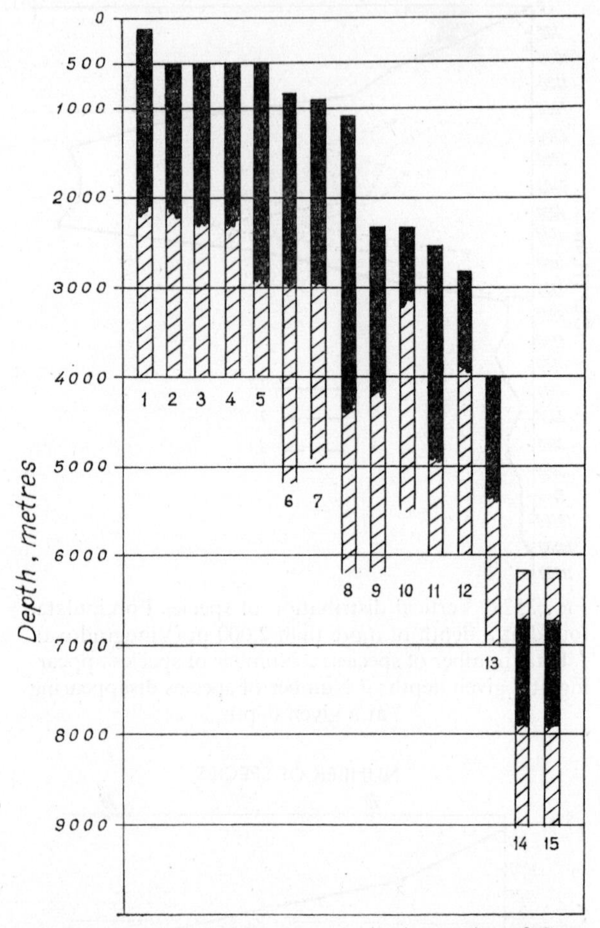

FIG. 353. Vertical distribution of certain species of Gammaridae (Birstein and Vinogradova). 1 *Cyphocaris challengeri*; 2 *Cyclocaris guilemi*; 3 *Eusirella multicalceola*; 4 *Rhachotropis natator*; 5 *Koroga megalops*; 6 *Parandania boecki*; 7 *Paracallisoma alberti*; 8 *Cleonardo mavrocephala*; 9 *Astyra bogorovi*; 10 *Halyce shoemakeri*; 11 *Cyphocaris richardi*; 12 *Astyra zenkevitchi*; 13 *Halyce aculeata*; 14 *Tetronychia gigas*; 15 *Vitjaziana gurjanovae*. Zones undoubtedly inhabited are coloured black, zones of possible habitat are cross-hatched.

endemic species are practically absent from the upper abyssal sub-zone; in the abyssal they constitute 50 per cent, and in the ultra-abyssal 100 per cent. To a certain extent, however, this is accounted for by the deep-water fauna not having been sufficiently studied.

Abyssal plankton of the northern part of the Pacific Ocean contains not only endemic species, but even endemic genera (Lucicutia, Heterorhabdus, Parenchaeta, Bathypontia, Bathycalanus, Spinocalanus, Pachyptilus, Heteroptilus) with a majority of endemic species. Some of these forms penetrate into the Bering and Okhotsk Seas through the deep straits. 'Abyssal species', writes Brodsky, 'are not widely distributed, certain species being endemic to certain areas of the World Ocean'.

Developing his idea further K. Brodsky notes (1948) that a 'series of species of Calanoida are wrongly said to be widely distributed'; this happened because different species were known under the same name. Thus *Metridia pacifica* was classified with *M. lucens*, *M. okhotensis* with *M. longa*, *Calanus pacificus* with *C. finmarchicus*, etc. When these forms were distinguished from one another their habitats naturally became more limited. As a result of the revision of the taxonomic composition of the Far Eastern fauna of the species, Calanoida was found to be 60 per cent, while its cosmopolitan species formed only 1·8 per cent.

A similar vertical distribution of zooplankton in the column of water was traced for other pelagic organisms by M. Vinogradov (1955) from the data obtained from a series of vertical catches of plankton according to horizons, during trawling down to 8,500 m in the region of the Kuril–Kamchatka trench. In the 500 to 1,000 m layer the predominant zooplankton species were *Calanus cristatus*, *C. tonsus*, *Eucalanus bungii* and *Sagitta elegans*. *Hymenodora frontalis* appears at a depth of 200 to 500 m, attaining its greatest numbers within the 500 to 1,000 m horizon. Below 1,000 m it is replaced by *H. glacialis*, and by *Eukronia fowleri* among the Chaetognatha. Among the mysids at a depth of 500 to 2,000 m *Eucopia grimaldi* is predominant, while at 4,000 m *E. australis* and *Gnathophausia gigas* assume this role. Among the Euphausiaceae *Euphasia pacifica* lives at depths down to 500 m, and *Bentheuphausia amblyops* between 3,000 and 4,000 m. Similar pictures are observed with many other species. In the trench itself, below 6,000 m, the usual abyssal species disappear, and plankton comprises mainly the species Copepoda and Amphipoda.

Yet not all the plankton groups have this type of vertical distribution; thus, for example, among the Chaetognatha (Yu. Chinodonova, 1955) only one group of abyssal forms (in the broad sense) can be distinguished (*Sagitta macrocephala*, *S. planctonis*, *Eukronia fowleri* and *Heterekronia mirabilis*).

Qualitative changes with depth of the bottom-living fauna can be determined also by various other biotic and abiotic factors. Such alterations should first be linked with the tropical factor (M. Sokolova, 1956, 1958, 1959). Macro- and micro-zonal distribution of bottom-living fauna is readily explained when this method is applied, and when the properties of the soil (mechanical and chemical), the rates of the movement of bottom-water masses, their content of suspended substances and the general composition of the fauna are taken into account. The detritus-eating group is markedly predominant among the benthos of the abyssal. Sokolova distinguishes among them those which consume the upper layer of the soil indiscriminately, those which discriminate roughly the surface layer of the sea-bed, and those which make a delicate choice of detritus on the surface layer of the sea-bed.

This type of analysis provides us with an interesting scheme of the changes in feeding groups of the sestonophages, detritophages and carnivores. The replacement of one such group by another takes place not once but many times. Within the Kuril–Kamchatka trench it occurs at depths of 3,000, 5,000 and 8,500 to 9,000 m (Fig. 354 and *Table 298*). Moreover, during the replacement the group of biological phyla (according to their feeding) remains the same, but the species may be quite different.

Generally speaking detritus eaters are predominant, the plant-eating

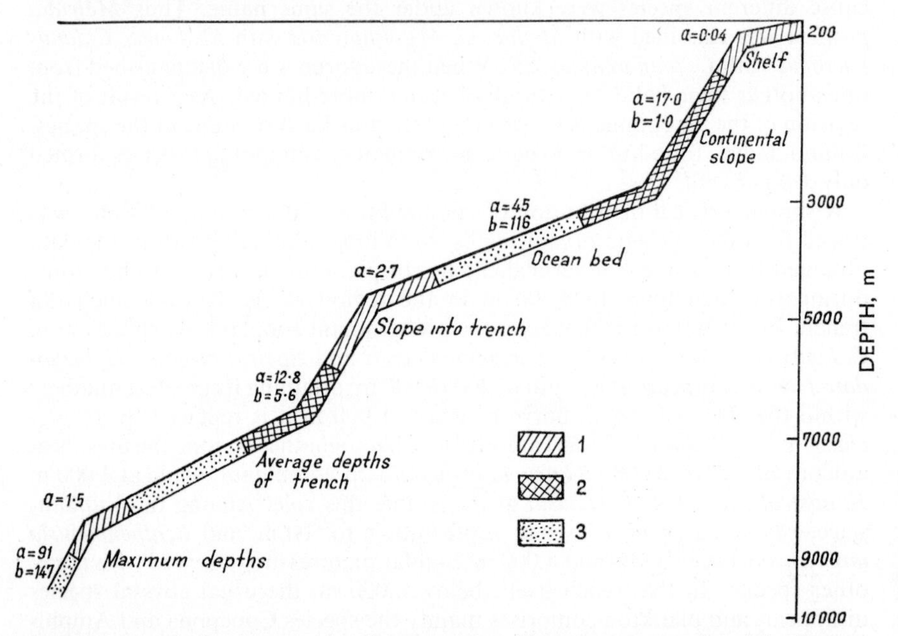

FIG. 354. Correlation between benthos groups and bottom topography of the Ocean. *1* Sestonophage zone; *2* Zone of a considerable development of all three feeding groups; *3* Zone of development of detritus feeders, either only roughly sorting the soil or swallowing it whole A—Ratio by weight of detritus feeders to carnivores (Sokolova).

species are absent from the deep-water fauna, and the deeper the water the more pronounced this becomes.

Among the crustaceans of the Far Eastern Seas the species Crangonidae are carnivores (M. Sokolova, 1957). They feed on worms, crustaceans and molluscs. Ophiuroidae form the main food of *Sclerocrangon derugini*. The diet of the Crangonidae is most varied.

Only a rough picture of the distribution of the bottom biocoenoses of the northwestern part of the Pacific Ocean adjacent to the Kuril Islands and Kamchatka has yet been given (L. Zenkevitch and Z. Filatova, 1958) (Fig. 355). Owing to the steep descent into the Kuril–Kamchatka trench, populated by the ultra-abyssal biocoenosis of holothurians (Elpiidae), Pogonophorae *able 298. Vertical changes in the main feeding groupings of bottom-living fauna in Kuril–Kamchatka trench (M. Sokolova, 1959)*

ominant types of feeding	Zones	Dominant groups of organisms	Ratio of detritophages to sestonophages by weight	Ratio of detritophages to carnivores by weight	Ratio of carnivores to sestonophages by weight
estonophages	*A*	Porifera	0·04	0·77	0·05
	A_1	Madreporaria, Antipataria, Sabellidae, Crinoidea	3·5	26·2	0·07
	A_2	Pogonophora, Crinoidea	2·5	27·5	0·04
estonophages etritophages arnivores	*B*	Molpadonia, Ampharetidae, Decapoda, Actiniaria	17·0	1·0	20·0
	B_1	Molpadonia, Porcellanasteridae, Amapharetidae, Isopoda, Malletiidae, Actiniaria	21·0	7·5	4·0
etritophages	*C*	Gephyrothuriidae, Porcellanosteridae	45·0	116·0	0·38
	C	Elpidiidae, Gephyrothuriidae	—	—	—
	C	Elpiidae	84·0	162·0	0·80

(Zenkevitchiana and others) and different species of Foraminifera, the coastal biocoenosis consists almost exclusively of agglutinating forms (Z. Shchedrina, 1958), Echiuroidea (Vitjazema and Jakobia) and Polychaeta (Macellicephala and Macellicephaloides). Farther to the southeast the Pacific Ocean is characterized for large areas by the biocoenoses of deep-water holothurians (Elpiidae and Psychropotidae), starfish (Porcellanasteridae and Brisingidae), sea-urchins (family Pourtalesiidae, and Echinothuriidae), actinians, single madreporian corals, lilies (Bathycrinus), Polychaeta (families Maldanidae and Ampharetidae), Mollusca (*Spinula oceanica*), and some dozens of species of Foraminifera. The density of the bottom population (Fig. 356) decreases to 10·5 and 1 g/m^2 as one moves southeastwards away from the Kuril Islands. All the huge area of the open parts of the Pacific Ocean is embraced by the 1 g/m^2 isobenth, and by far the greater part of it by the 0·1 g/m^2 isobenth. The benthos biomass of the Ocean bottom in some parts is no higher than 0·01 g/m^2 (Fig. 357).

Some comprehensive studies on the deep-water fish of the northwestern part of the Pacific Ocean are due to P. Schmidt (1948, 1950), A. P. Andriashev (1935) and T. Rass (1954). Andriashev suggested differentiating between ancient and secondary deep-water fish. The first (for instance Stomiatoidei, Opisthoproctoidei and many others) are, as a rule, rare in the waters of the continental shelf seas; the second belong to families widely represented in shallow seas (for instance the families Cottidae, Liparidae, Zoarcidae and others). The boundary between these two groups is probably rather indistinct.

It is more probable that the deep-water fish took a geologically long time to be formed and that the duration of their evolution varies. Rass pointed out the existence of a series of transitional groups (for instance Brotulidae and Moridae). The group of ancient deep-water fish of the Far Eastern Seas and

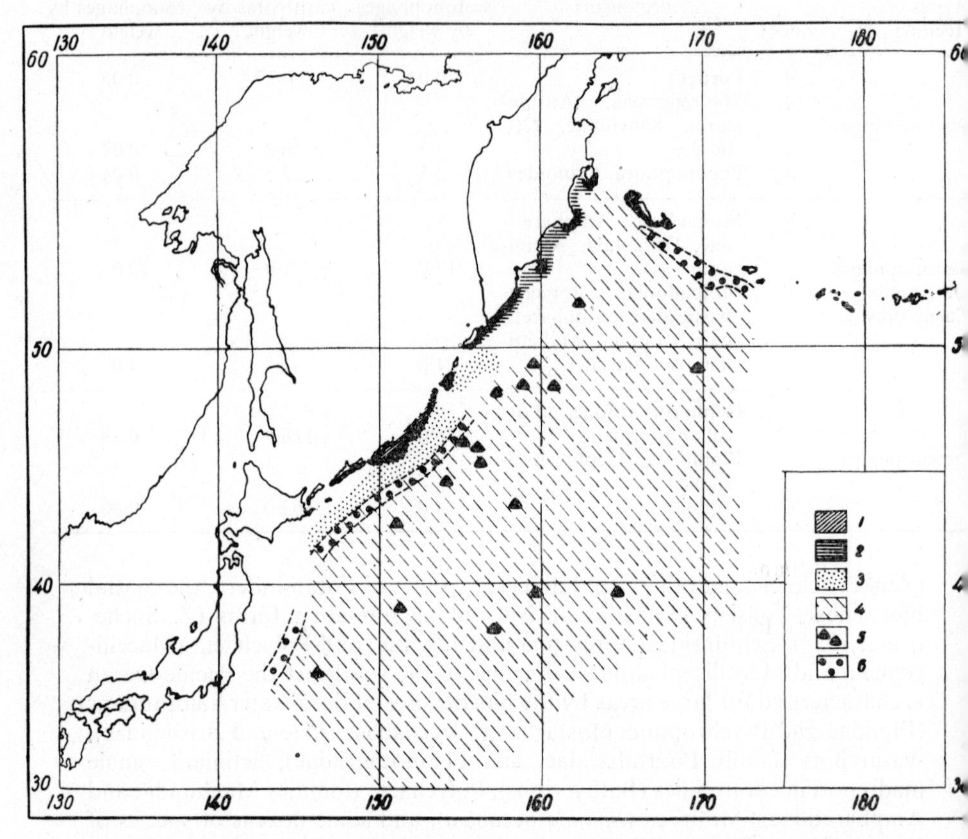

FIG. 355. Distribution of the biocoenoses of bottom-living fauna in northwestern part of Pacific Ocean (Zenkevitch and Filatova). *1* Fouling fauna (Porifera, Bryozoa, Hydroida and others); *2* Biocoenosis *Echinarachnius parma*; *3* Biocoenosis of small bivalves; *4* Biocoenosis Elpidiidae–Psychropotidea–Porcellanasteriidae and others; *5* Biocoenosis Spinula; *6* Biocoenosis Elpidia–Macellicephalis–Thalassema and others.

the adjacent part of the Pacific Ocean includes about 60 species, belonging to 25 families.

T. Rass (1955) gives a list of 46 species belonging to 31 genera of deep-water fish of the Kuril–Kamchatka trench, pointing out that 25 of them are found off the shores of America, 15 or 16 species are recorded in the waters of Japan, 12 in the Sea of Okhotsk, 14 in the Bering Sea and 5 in the Gulf of Panama. Moreover, all the deep-water fish of the Sea of Okhotsk were found in the

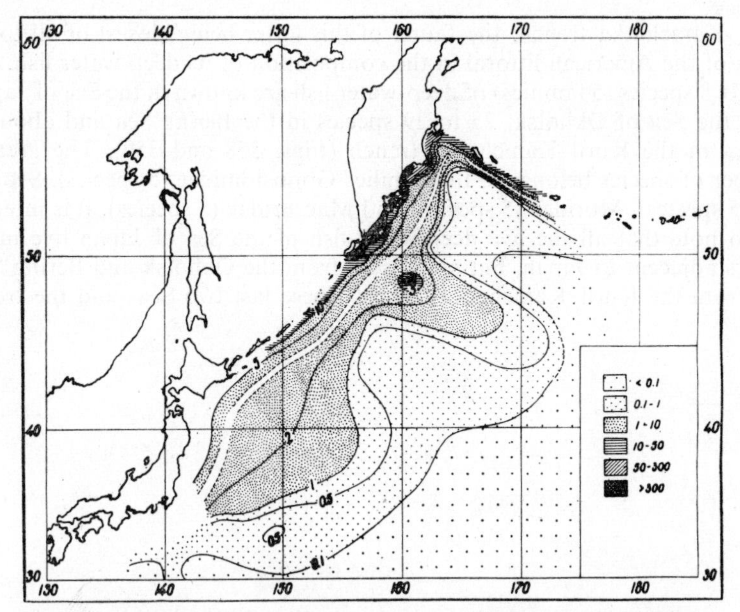

FIG. 356. Quantitative distribution of biomass (g/m²) of bottom-living fauna in northwestern part of Pacific Ocean (Zenkevitch and Filatova).

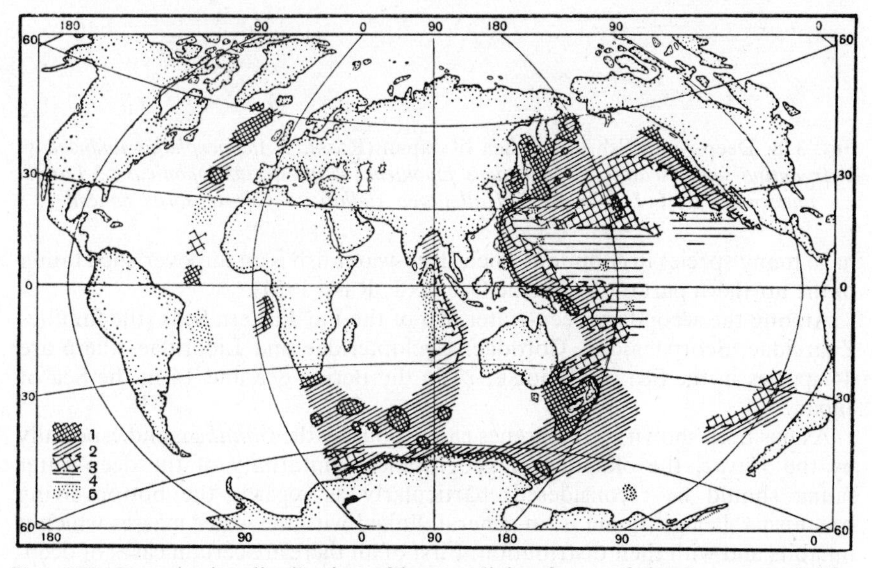

FIG. 357. Quantitative distribution of bottom-living fauna of the Oceans at depths of more than 2,000 m (Belyaev and Zenkevitch). *1* Above 1,000; *2* From 100 to 1,000; *3* From 50 to 100; *4* From 10 to 50; *5* Less than 10 mg/m².

Kuril–Kamchatka trench, the fauna of this latter being closest of all to the fauna of the American littoral in the composition of its deep-water fish.

Only 8 species (5 families) of deep-water fish are known in the Sea of Japan, 12 in the Sea of Okhotsk, 25 to 29 species in the Bering Sea and about 50 species in the Kuril–Kamchatka trench (Figs. 358 and 359). The greatest number of species belongs to the families Gonostomidae (5 species), Scopelidae (5 species), Moridae (5 species) and Macruridae (8 species). It is interesting to note that all the five deep-water fish of the Sea of Japan live in the waters adjacent to Japan, but are absent from the Okhotsk and Bering Seas and from the Kuril–Kamchatka trench. These last two Seas and the trench

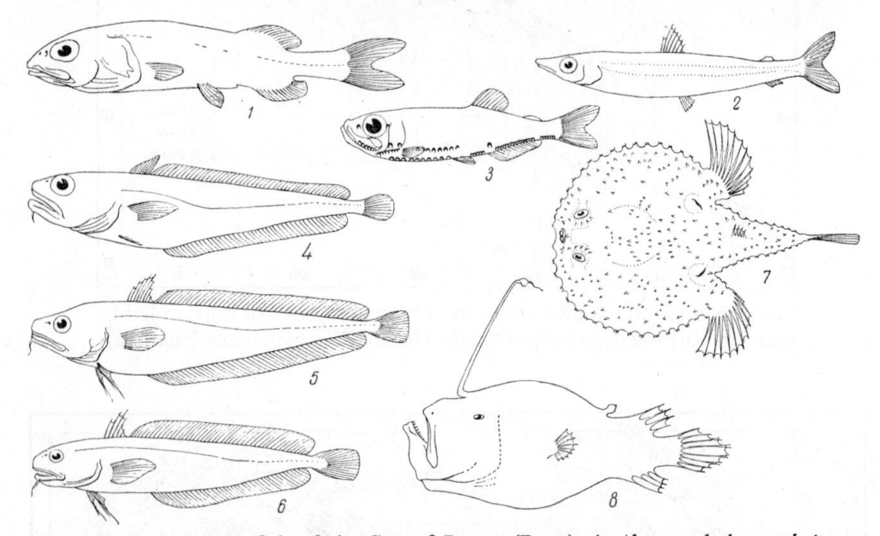

FIG. 358. Deep-water fish of the Sea of Japan (Rass). 1 *Alepocephalus umbriceps*; 2 *Argentina semifasciata*; 3 *Maurolicus japonicus*; 4 *Physiculus japonicus*; 5 *Lotella maximowiczi*; 6 *L. phycis*; 7 *Halleutaea stellata*; 8 *Cryptopsaras couesil.*

have many species in common. Their deep-water fish is an impoverished fauna of the northern part of the Pacific Ocean (T. Rass, 1954).

Among the secondary deep-water fish of the Far Eastern Seas (the families Zoarcidae, Scorpaenidae, Cottidae, Cyclopteridae and Liparidae) there are 44 species in the Sea of Okhotsk, 27 in the Bering Sea and 14 in the Sea of Japan.

As has been shown by researches carried out by the *Galathea*, and especially by the *Vityaz*, the old idea of geographical uniformity of the deep-water fauna should be reconsidered, particularly as regards the bottom-living organisms. Pelagic fauna is, in general, linked with the water masses which it inhabits and with their distribution. First of all there are certain cases of deep-water bottom fauna with most restricted habitats. Certain organisms, moreover, keep strictly to the same horizon. Thus, for example, members of the Monoplacophora were found only in the most easterly part of the Pacific Ocean on a very small sector of the equatorial belt; they occur, however, in

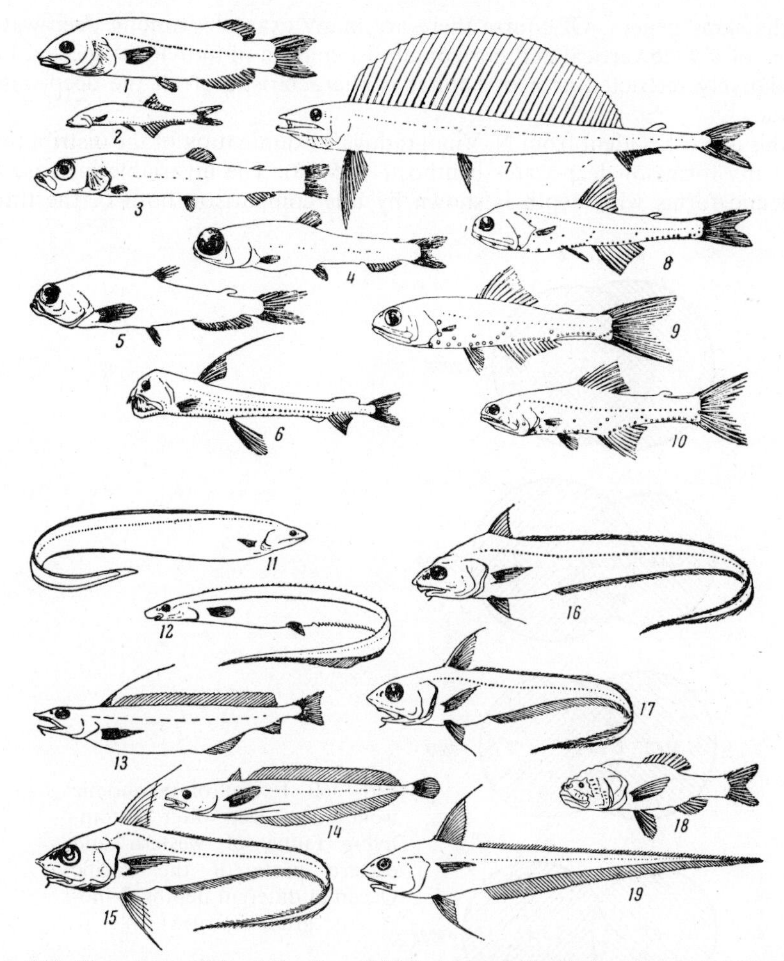

FIG. 359. Deep-water fish of the Sea of Okhotsk and the Bering Sea (some species) (Rass). 1, 8, 9, 11, 12, 13, 18, 19—not found in the Okhotsk Sea. 1 *Ericara salmonea*; 2 *Cyclothone microdon*; 3 *Leuroglossus stilbius schmidti*; 4 *Bathylagus pacificus*; 5 *B. milleri*; 6 *Chauliodus macouni*; 7 *Alepisaurus aesculapius*; 8 *Lampanyctus nannochir*; 9 *L. leucopsarus*; 10 *L. nannochir laticauda*; 11 *Histiobranchus bathybius*; 12 *Polyacanthonotus challengeri*; 13 *Antimora microlepis*; 14 *Podonema longipes*; 15 *Coryphaenoides cinereus*; 16 *C. pectoralis*; 17 *C. acrolepis*; 18 *Melamphaeus nycterinus*; 19 *Coryphaenoides lepturus*.

three different sites, all three at a depth of about 3,000 m. The Echiuroidea *Tatjanellia grandis*, characterized by its bipolar distribution, is found on the same horizon (about 3,000 m) in the northwestern part of the Pacific Ocean and in Antarctic waters. The great variety of the species, genera, families and orders of Pogonophora are found only in the northwestern part of the Pacific Ocean. Every deep trench is characterized by different sub-species and species of the same genera. Of course there are many examples among deep-water fauna of a wide vertical and horizontal distribution of individual species, but a relatively restricted area of habitat is characteristic of all the deep-water fauna.

This is most evident from N. Vinogradova's examination of the distribution of many forms of deep-water benthos (1955–58). The invariable increase of endemic forms with depth is shown by this comparison both of the three

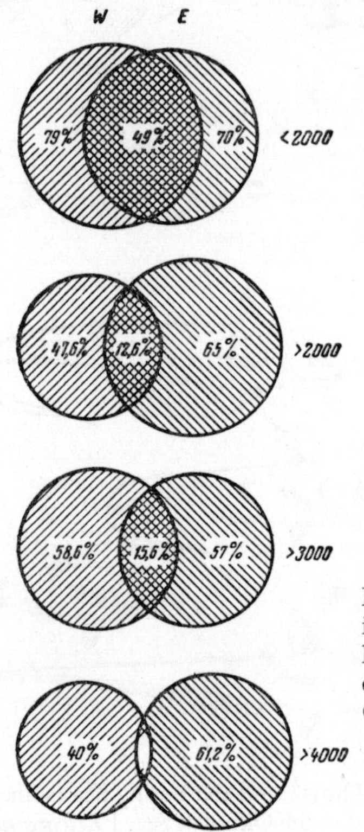

FIG. 360. Extent of taxonomic isolation of deep-water bottom-living fauna of western and eastern parts of the Pacific Ocean at different depths (Vinogradova, 1955).

Oceans and of some individual parts of them. This is well illustrated by the Figs. 360 and 361.

The deep-water fauna of the eastern and western parts of the Pacific Ocean has in the surface zone (<2,000 m) about half of the total number of forms, but at great depths (>4,000 m) less than 10 per cent of them. The same phenomenon was observed from comparison between the northern and southern parts of the oceans and between the oceans themselves. Further research on the deep-water fauna will no doubt weaken the conception of its endemic nature, but will hardly destroy it. The idea of the uniformity and geographical homogeneity of the deep-water fauna was based on the conception of the uniformity, constancy and slight changeability of the conditions of its existence ($t°$, $S‰$, oxygen), and on the absence of any restriction on its

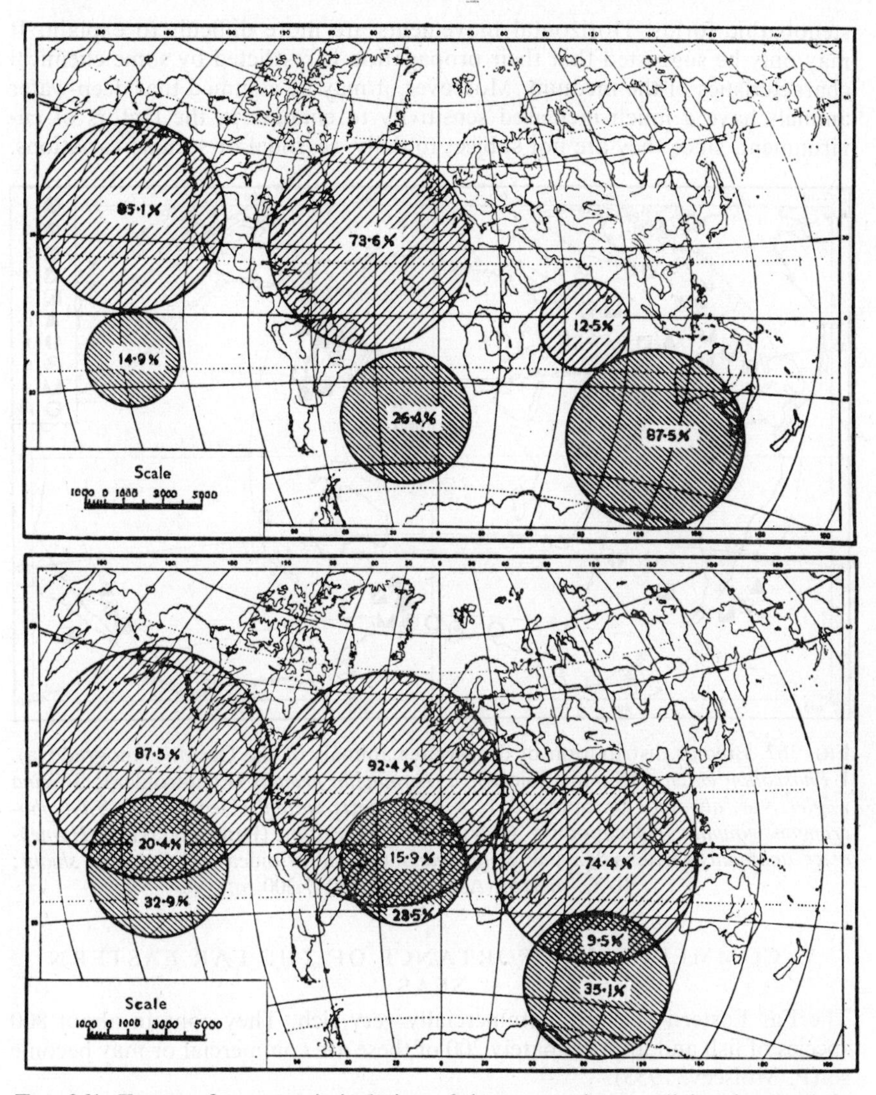

FIG. 361. Extent of taxonomic isolation of deep-water bottom-living fauna of the northern and southern halves of the Oceans. The lower chart for depths less than 2,000 m, upper chart for depths more than 4,000 m (Vinogradova).

horizontal distribution. It is most remarkable that the deep-water fauna is to a great extent both bipolar (Fig. 362) and amphi-boreal in its distribution. The circumtropical distribution of many members of the deep-water fauna also needs some explanation. What factors restrict its distribution southwards and northwards?

Change of pressure may restrict the upward and downward movements of stenobathic forms. Horizontal movements are more difficult to explain. It may only be suggested that their propagation is restricted by some chemical characteristics of the medium. Moreover, it may be assumed that deep-water animals have a much increased sensitivity to changes in the factors of environment, since they are not subject to daily, seasonal or secular variations.

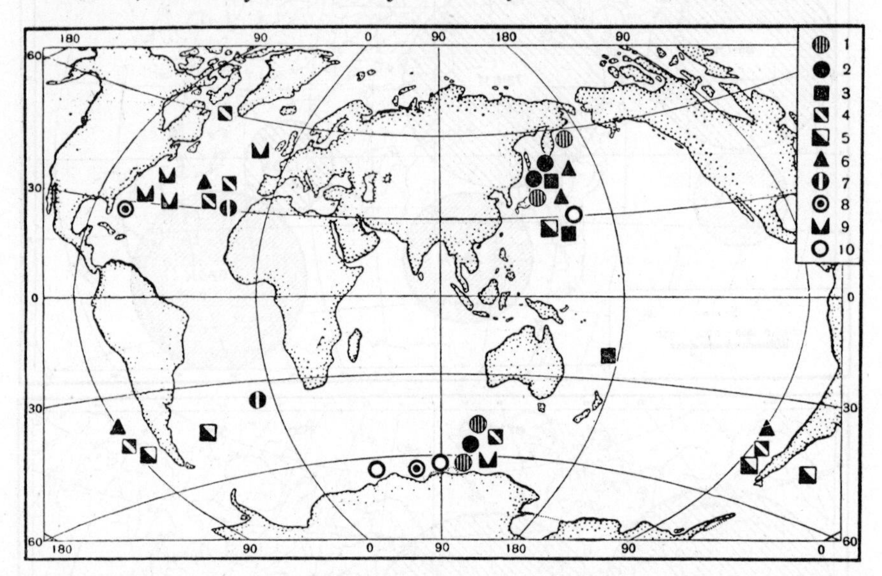

FIG. 362. Bipolar distribution of deep-water animals of the Ocean (Vinogradova). 1 *Phascolion eutense* (Sipunculoidea); 2 *Tatianellia grandis* (Echiuroidea); 3 *Scina wagleri* var. *abyssalis* (Amphipoda); 4 *Munidopsis antonii* (Decapoda); 5 *Glyphocrangon rimapes* (Decapoda); 6 *Nymphon procerum* (Pantopoda); 7 *Hymenaster anomalus* (Asteroidea); 8 *Kolga nana* (Holothurioidea); 9 *Culeolus shumi*; 10 *C. mürrai* (Ascidia). (2,000–7,300 m.)

V. COMMERCIAL IMPORTANCE OF THE FAR EASTERN SEAS

The Far Eastern Seas are commercially very rich. They contain about 800 species of fish and approximately 200 of these are commercial or may become so (P. Moiseev, 1953).

It is to be noted that 60 years ago fishing in Russian waters was confined to river estuaries and the coastal zones. 'More than 96 per cent of the catch was composed of salmon, *Oncorhynchus keta*, *Oncorhynchus gorbusha* and others, which entered the river from the sea for spawning, and about 2·6 per cent was herring, caught in the coastal, low-salinity areas; the remaining yield was composed mostly of *Osmerus spenlanus dentex*, navaga (*Eleginus navaga gracilis*) and the Acipenseridae, also caught in the rivers' (T. Rass, 1955). Now the Acipenseridae constitute no more than a third of the yield, and the fisheries have mostly moved into the open sea. The Salmonidae trade, in particular, has mostly moved into the northwestern part of the Pacific Ocean (Fig. 363A).

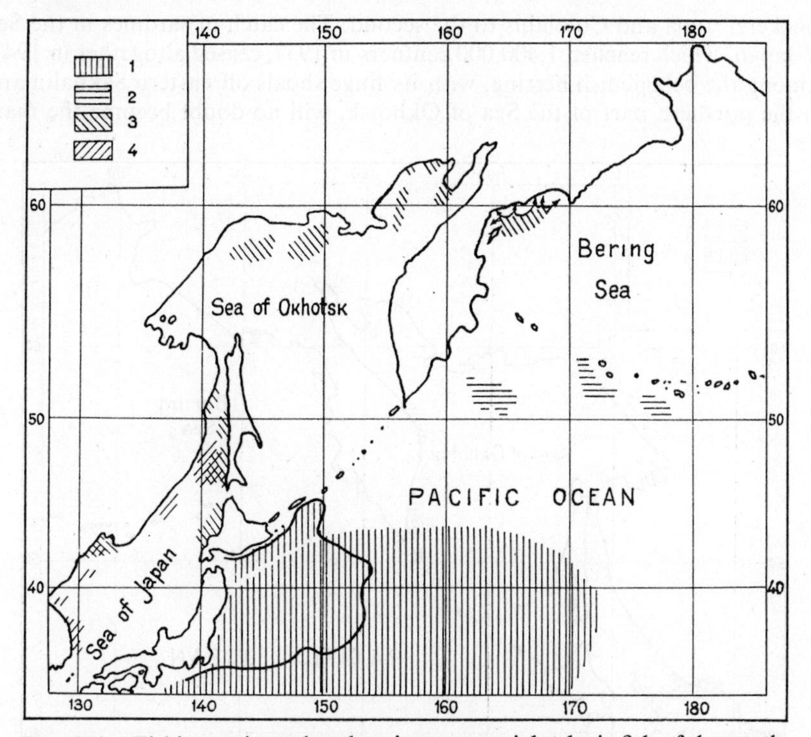

FIG. 363A. Fishing regions abundant in commercial pelagic fish of the north-western part of the Pacific Ocean (Rass). *1* Tuna and Cololabis (outlines); *2* Salmon; *3* Herring; *4* Scomber.

The catch of Kamchatka crab and marine mammals has increased considerably in the last ten years (*Table 299*).

Three biological groups may be distinguished among the commercial fish: transitional, marine pelagic (Salmonidae in their marine period) and the marine bottom-living fish. Far Eastern salmon belongs to the first group; herring,

Table 299. Yield of Soviet marine industry in Far Eastern Seas, 10^3 centners (L. Berdichevsky, 1957)

Year	1913	1930	1940	1950	1953	1954
Salmonidae	954	1,556	1,148	1,102	2,114	1,250
Herring	67	338	500	1,563	2,003	1,246
Gadidae	—	142	112	318	360	440
Pleuronectiformes	—	—	35	326	484	—
Crabs	—	242	158	223	290	393
Whales	—	—	114	530	768	755
Other marine mammals	—	13	11	47	38	65
Total	1,072	3,186	3,093	4,752	2,433	5,240

mackerel, tuna and Cololabis to the second. The catch of sardines in the Sea of Japan, which reached 1,400,000 centners in 1937, ceased altogether in 1941. Among the pelagic fish herring, with its huge shoals off eastern Sakhalin and in the northern part of the Sea of Okhotsk, will no doubt become the main

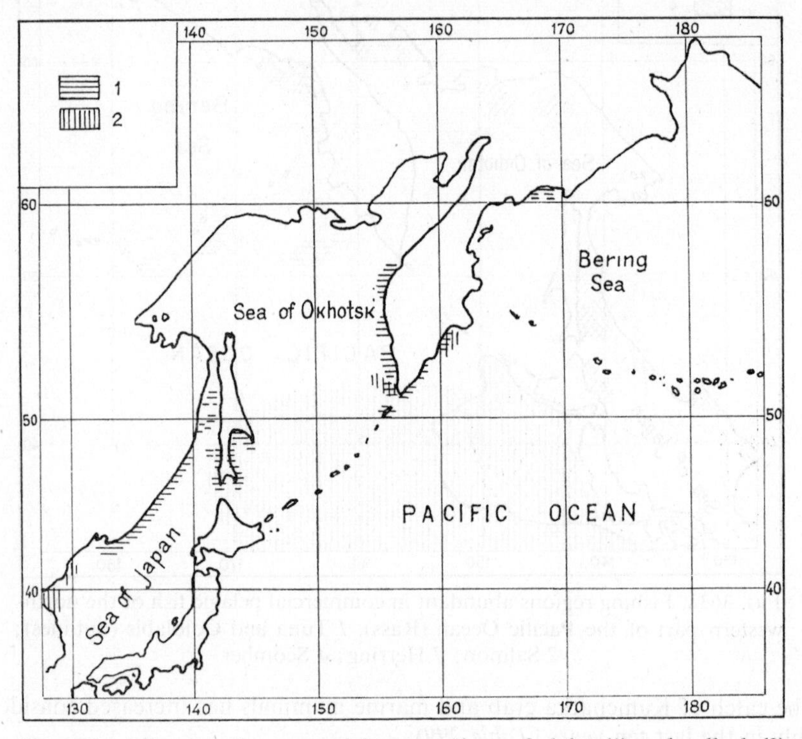

FIG. 363B. Diagram of commercial aggregations of plaice (1) and pollack (2) (Rass, 1955).

object of future fisheries. Mackerel approaches the Primor'e coast for spawning. The tuna Sajra (*Cololabis sajra*) fisheries are still undeveloped in the U.S.S.R.

Among the bottom-living fish the most important are the flatfish (plaice and halibut), the gadoids (cod, alaska-pollack (*Teragra chalcogramma*) and navaga), rock fish (sebastodes) and atka-fish (Pleurogrammus) (Fig. 363B). The shelf zone is poorly developed in the Far Eastern Seas and as a result there is a considerable predominance, as compared with the Barents Sea, of pelagic fish (salmon, herring, sardines, sajra) over the bottom-living fish (cod, flatfish). Owing to the abundance of food in those areas of the Far Eastern Seas open to commercial fish, the latter grow rapidly and get very fat (*Table 300*).

The faunas of the northern parts of the Atlantic and Pacific Oceans have much in common in their amphi-boreal characteristics, Many species of their fish and invertebrates, however, while not showing any essential taxonomic

Table 300. Pacific and Atlantic cod, annual gain in weight, kg (P. Moiseev, 1953)

Sea	Age in years						Fatness (Clark)
	4	5	6	7	8	9	
Bering	1·60	2·62	3·45	5·30	6·80	8·65	1·12
Barents	0·42	0·86	1·40	2·04	3·06	4·53	0·85

differences, vary greatly in their ecology and mass development. Many mass forms found developed in one basin occupy a secondary place in the other. The cod is subject to long distance seasonal migrations in the North Atlantic, but in the Pacific its movements are limited to local seasonal vertical transpositions which are characteristic also of certain other fish and of commercial crabs (Fig. 364).

However, the new data from the results of tagging cod at different points of the eastern coast (I. Polutov, 1952) have shown that cod may migrate from the Avachinsky Bay not only into the Kronotsky Bay, but much farther north to the Olyutor Inlet thousands of kilometres away. However, even such journeys cannot be compared with the long migrations of cod in the Atlantic.

Among the distinguishing features of the seas of the northwestern Pacific as compared with those of the eastern Atlantic P. Moiseev (1953) notes the higher velocities of its currents, leading to the formation of a series of biological peculiarities in the fish. Thus the Pacific cod has the ova of a

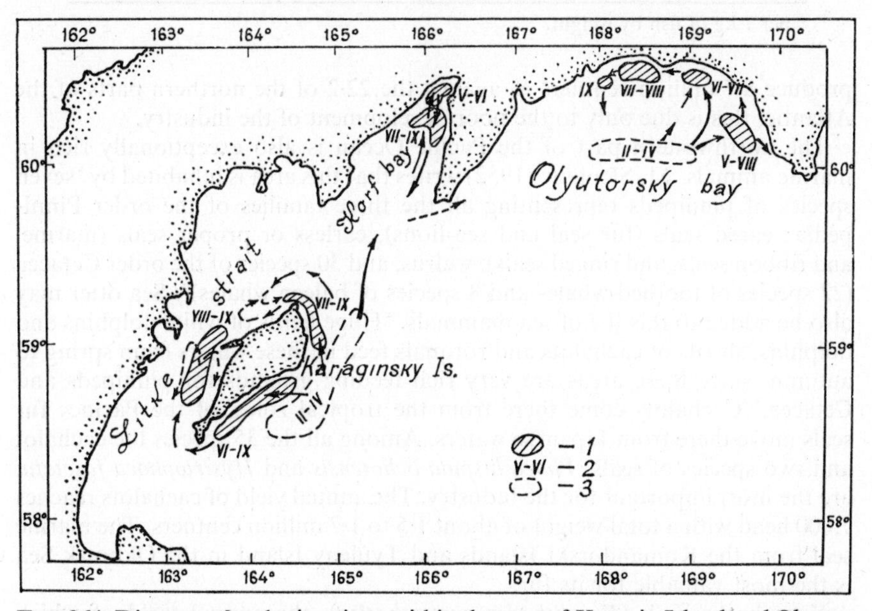

FIG. 364. Diagram of cod migrations within the area of Karagin Island and Olyutor Inlet (Moiseev, 1953). *1* Shoaling of cod; *2* Months of shoaling; *3* Spawning region.

bottom-dweller, and the Atlantic cod the ova of a pelagic fish. Many fish of the Far Eastern Seas move to calm waters for spawning.

P. Moiseev (1953) maintains that a series of biological and morphological peculiarities, in particular an increase in fertility (*Table 301*), spontaneous spawning, bottom ova, a shortening of the incubation period and a higher rate of growth within the first years of life, have developed as a result of the great variety of species of fish in the Far Eastern Seas, including the carnivores.

Moiseev opposes the point of view, formerly held by many ichthyologists, on the poor prospects of the development of fisheries of the near-bottom and bottom-living fish in the Far Eastern Seas; he considers that this industry might yield an output as high as that of the Atlantic Ocean. If, at the moment, the bottom and near-bottom living fish of the northern part of the Pacific

Table 301. Fertility (thousands of ova) of certain Pacific and Atlantic fish (P. Moiseev, 1953)

Species	Pacific Ocean	Atlantic Ocean
Cod	411–763*	170–250
Navaga	25·0–210·0	6·2–63·0
Limanda aspera	626·0–1,133·0	—
L. limanda	—	80·0–140·0
Capelin	15·3–39·9	6·2–13·4
Herring	39·9–92·4	14·8–23·3

* per 1 kg of fish by weight.

produce 8·7 million centners as against the 22·2 of the northern parts of the Atlantic, this is due only to the poor development of the industry.

The northwestern part of the Pacific Ocean is also exceptionally rich in marine animals. M. Sleptzov (1952) writes that this area is inhabited by 'seven species of pinnipeds representing all the three families of the order Pinnipedia; eared seals (fur seal and sea-lions), earless or proper seals (marine, and ribbon seals, and ringed seals), walrus, and 30 species of the order Cetacea (22 species of toothed whales and 8 species of baleen whales)'. Sea otter may also be added to this list of sea mammals. 'Huge herds of white dolphins and dolphins, shoals of cachalots and rorquals feed in these waters from spring to autumn, since these areas are very rich feeding grounds for pinnipeds and Cetacea.' Cachalots come there from the tropical zones of the Pacific; fur seals move there from Japanese waters. Among all the 35 species the cachalot and two species of seals, *Phoca hispida ochotensis* and *Hystriophoca fasciata*, are the most important for the industry. The annual yield of cachalots reaches 7,000 head with a total weight of about 1·5 to 1·7 million centners. The marine seal from the Komandorski Islands and Tyuleny Island in the Okhotsk Sea is the most valuable for its fur.

Kamchatka crab (*Paralithodes camtschatica*), the annual yield of which has risen in recent years to 400,000 centners, occupies a special place among the resources of the Far Eastern Seas. Two other species of the genus (*P. platypus* and *P. brevipes*) are taken (Fig. 365) in small numbers along with the Kamchatka crab. The other two species of this genus are not found in Soviet waters. Only some of the smaller sized true crabs (*Chionoecetes opilio*, *Erimacrus isenbecki* and *Telmessus cheiragonus*) might become important commercially. So far, however, their role in the catch is insignificant. Kamchatka crab is taken almost throughout the whole area of its distribution (L. Vinogradov,

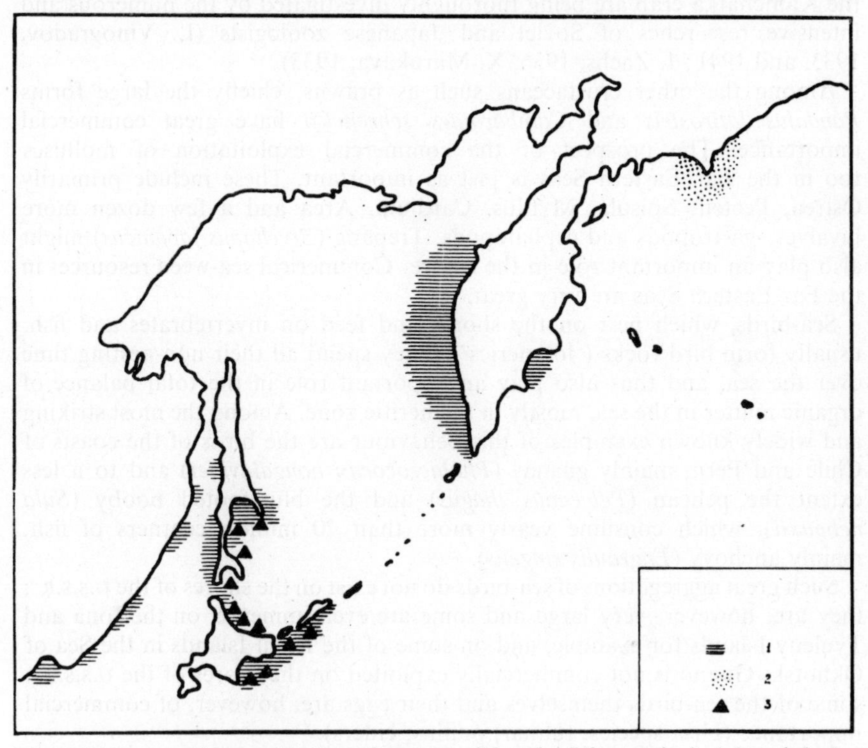

FIG. 365. Places of concentration of commercial crabs (Vinogradov). 1 *Paralithodes camschatica*; 2 *P. platypus*; 3 *P. brevipes*.

1941, 1945). *P. brevipes* has a similar area of distribution. The other four species are found from the Bering Sea to the Sea of Japan. The largest crabs belong to the genus Paralithodes, which forms large aggregations of commercial importance. Kamchatka crab assembles off the shores of the U.S.S.R., Japan and Alaska. The largest yield of this crab is taken off the western coast of Kamchatka. Seasonal migrations of the Kamchatka crab consist of travelling to the coast (at depths of 15 to 70 m) for feeding during the summer, and a return to lower layers (110 to 200 m), and even down to 270 m in the Sea of Japan, where the water is better heated (1·5° to 2·5°) during the cold months when the surface waters are much cooled. The migration routes of the Kamchatka crab cover dozens of miles (up to 100). The average daily distance traversed by the crab during his migration is up to 5 or even 7 miles (L. Vinogradov, 1941). This migration starts when the young begin to appear. New mating takes place in the shallows. After mating crabs cast their shells and for part of the summer and autumn feed intensively on small bivalves, worms, crustaceans and echinoderms (mainly *Echinarachnius parma*). Commercial aggregation of the Kamchatka crab is always repeated at precisely the same places. The biology, migrations and formation of commercial aggregations of the Kamchatka crab are being thoroughly investigated by the numerous and intensive researches of Soviet and Japanese zoologists (L. Vinogradov, 1933, and 1941; I. Zachs, 1936, X. Marukava, 1933).

Among the other crustaceans such as prawns, chiefly the large forms *Pandalus latirostris* and *Cambaroides schrenckii* have great commercial importance. The prospect of the commercial exploitation of molluscs too in the Far Eastern Seas is just as important. These include primarily Ostrea, Pecten, Spisula, Mytilus, Cardium, Arca and a few dozen more bivalves, gastropods and cephalopods. Trepang (*Stychopus japonicus*) might also play an important role in the future. Commerical sea-weed resources in the Far Eastern Seas are very great.

Sea-birds, which nest on the shores and feed on invertebrates and fish, usually form bird rocks ('loomeries'). They spend all their non-nesting time over the sea, and thus also play an important role in the total balance of organic matter in the sea, mostly in the neritic zone. Among the most striking and widely known examples of this behaviour are the birds of the coasts of Chile and Peru, mainly guanay (*Phalacrocorax bougainvillei*) and to a less extent the pelican (*Pelecanus thagus*) and the blue-footed booby (*Sula nebouxii*), which consume yearly more than 20 million centners of fish, mainly anchovy (*Engraulis ringens*).

Such great aggregations of sea-birds do not exist on the shores of the U.S.S.R.; they are, however, very large and some are even immense, on the Iona and Tyuleny Islands for example, and on some of the Kuril Islands in the Sea of Okhotsk. Guano is not commercially exploited on the shores of the U.S.S.R.; some of the sea-birds themselves and their eggs are, however, of commercial importance (Uria species, fulmar, puffins, eiders).

The main breeds of sea-birds of the Soviet Far Eastern shores (S. Uspensky, 1959) are, apart from albatrosses (Diomedea) and shearwaters (Puffinus) which do not form colonies, guillemots (*Uria lomvia* and *U. algae*), puffin (*Fratercula cirrata*, *F. corniculata*), pelagic shag (*Phalacrocorax pelagicus*), kittiwake (*Rissa tridactyla*), petrel (*Fulmarus glacialis*) and others. In the southwestern part of the Sea of Okhotsk and in the Sea of Japan the following are added to this list: *Cerorhinca monocerata*, the black-tailed gull (*Larus crassirostris*), the Ussu cormorant (*Phalacrocorax filamentosus*), the guillemot (*Cepphus carbo*) and others. All this abundant bird population consumes an immense number of small fish and crustaceans (*Tables 302* and *303*).

VI. ZOOGEOGRAPHY OF THE FAR EASTERN SEAS

In estimating the biogeography of the Far Eastern Seas and the adjacent parts of the Pacific Ocean one should proceed from the following premises:

Table 302. Number of colony nesters, in thousands of individuals, in the Far Eastern Seas (S. Uspensky, 1959)

Sea	Group of birds			
	Auks	Tubinares	Gulls	Cormorants
Bering	2,188	2,505	193	71
Okhotsk	3,854	2,106	517	345
Japan	53	1	21	35
Total	6,095	4,612	731	451
	Total of Sea birds 11,889			

(i) Most of the Sea of Japan, the Sea of Okhotsk and the Bering Sea belong to the boreal Pacific sub-region of the boreal region; (ii) In the north the boreal sub-region lies next the Arctic region, and the boundary between them should be established; (iii) To the south it borders the tropical region, and this demarcation line should also be drawn; (iv) Is there reason to distinguish sub-Arctic and subtropical regions or should they be included in a mixed transition zone and, finally, (v) What biogeographical divisions should be established for the boreal Pacific sub-region (provinces, regions, etc.)?

As yet there is no generally accepted scheme for the biogeographical zonation of surface areas of the northwestern part of the Pacific Ocean.*

The separation of the southern and southeastern parts of the Sea of Japan into a subtropical sub-region, or more correctly a South Japanese province of the Indo-West-Pacific sub-region of the tropical region, is generally accepted. Ushakov calls it the Tsushima province. The problem of the boundary between the Arctic and boreal facies in the northern parts of the Bering Sea is the most obscure. The whole southeastern part of the Chukotsk Sea is sometimes included in the boreal region (K. Brodsky, 1955). The northern boundary of the boreal region is at times drawn through the Bering Strait (P. Ushakov, 1953). Most investigators, however, include the northern part of the Bering Sea, to the north of St Lawrence Island, and the greater part

Table 303

Sea	Total annual consumption (thousands of tons)	
	Fish	Invertebrates
Bering	255	247
Okhotsk	299	258
Japan	13	3
Total	567	508

* Zoogeographical zonation of the abyssal is given above.

of the Anadyr Bay in the lower Arctic sub-region of the Arctic region (E. F. Gurjanova, 1935; A. P. Andriashev, 1939; L. Vinogradov, 1948) (Figs. 366 and 367).

N. Vinogradova (1949) characterizes Anadyr Bay and that part of the Bering Sea adjacent to the Bering Strait with St Lawrence Island as its southern boundary, as the low-Arctic region (the presence of ice in winter, near-bottom temperature either below freezing point or just above). L. Vinogradov (1948) includes the bathyal zone of the Bering, Okhotsk and Japan Seas in sub-Arctic regions, and the northern part of the Sea of Okhotsk in the glacial

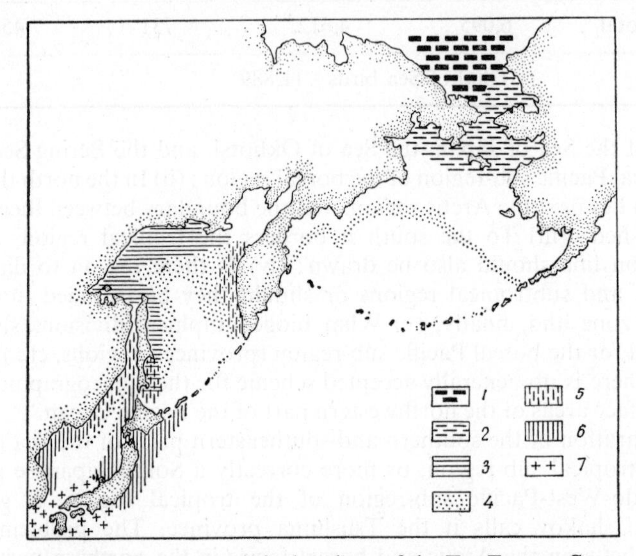

FIG. 366. Zoogeographical regions of the Far Eastern Seas (Vinogradov, 1948). *1* High Arctic; *2* Low Arctic; *3* Glacial; *4* Sub-Arctic; *5* North-boreal; *6* South-boreal; *7* Sub-tropical regions.

regions. A number of investigators recognize the peculiar biogeography of the northern and northwestern parts of the Sea of Okhotsk, with their large number of cold-water, Arctic and Arctic boreal species. Without including these regions in the lower Arctic sub-region a number of investigators give them special biogeographical names—co-arctic (K. Brodsky, 1952), glacial (L. Vinogradov, 1948) and others. The Tartary Strait can to some extent be included in those regions. This problem will be solved when a precise qualitative method is laid down as the basis of the system of zonation, as has been done for the southwestern part of the Barents Sea (Z. Filatova, 1938).

T. Shchapova (1948) uses the geographical distribution of sea-weeds in her division of the north-boreal Pacific sub-region into north-boreal (all the northern part of the Bering Sea and of the Sea of Okhotsk) upper-temperate boreal (southern part of the Bering Sea, Aleutian Islands, central and southern parts of the Sea of Okhotsk and the northern part of the Sea of Japan);

lower-temperate boreal (central parts of the Sea of Japan and the small Kuril Ridge); and south boreal (southern and southeastern parts of the Sea of Japan).

Apart from the larger biogeographical subdivisions of the northwestern part of the Pacific, some further subdivisions are possible for each basin. Thus K. Brodsky (1954) divides the Bering Sea into six main regions according to the zooplankton—the oceanic, the Bering Sea, the north Bering Sea, western neritic, eastern neritic and deep water regions. Brodsky characterizes each of them by their physicogeographical peculiarities and by the list of their

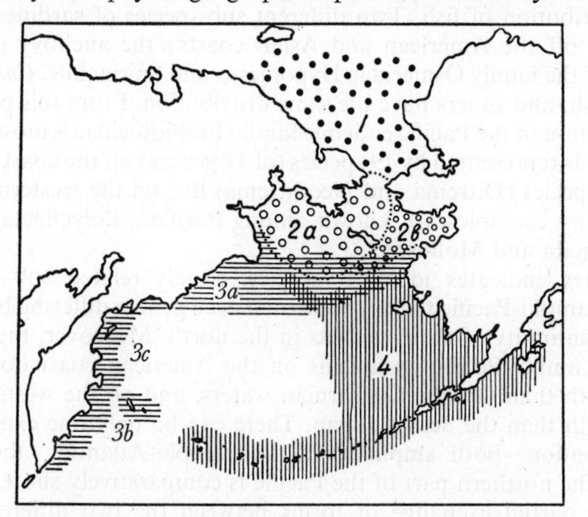

FIG. 367. Zoogeographical division of the Bering Sea (Andriashev). *1* Chukotsk (temperate-Arctic) province; *2a* North Bering (sub-Arctic) region, Anadyr area; *2b* Same, Norton area; *3a* Province of Eastern Kamchatka (boreal), Avachinsk area; *3b* Same, Komandor area; *3c* Same, Koryatzk area; *4* Aleutian (temperate-boreal) province.

forms of zooplankton. Andriashev has distinguished within the Bering Sea temperate boreal province six smaller biogeographical subdivisions.

In a similar manner Savilov divides the Sea of Okhotsk, according to the environment of the habitat and the predominant species, into six ecological zones, each of which in turn might be divided further into more detailed biocoenoses. Six main regions of macrobiocoenoses are distinguishable for the Barents Sea according to its bottom-living fauna. Such microregions could be equally considered as biogeographical and ecological biocoenotic subdivisions. One merges into another.

Amphi-Pacific habitats in the northern part of the Ocean are as characteristic of the distribution of its population as the amphi-Atlantic; Shchapova gives the littoral sea-weeds of the genera Eisenia and Pelvetia as examples of this kind of zonation. Of the five species of Eisenia one (*E. bicyclis*) is distributed along the shores of Japan; three (*E. arborea*, *E. masonii* and *E.*

desmarestioides) off the Californian coast; and the fifth (*E. cookeri*) off the coast of Peru. Four species of the genus Pelvetia are similarly distributed. *P. typica* is found along both Asian and American coasts of the temperate region. *P. wrightii* lives off the Japanese coast, while *P. galapagensis* is found only in the Galapagos Islands, and *P. canaliculata* off the western and northern coasts of Europe. The species mentioned are an example not only of amphi-Pacific but also of amphi-boreal and bipolar distribution.

A. P. Andriashev (1939) gives a large number of examples of the amphi-Pacific distribution of fish. Two different sub-species of sardines (*Sardinops sagax*) live off the American and Asian coasts; the anchovy (Engraoulis) members of the family Osmeridae Hypomesus and Spirinchus, *Cololabis saira*, many flatfish, and others have the same distribution. From this point of view the distribution of the Pacific endemic family Embiotocidae is most interesting. This family is represented by 19 species (of 18 genera) off the coast of America. Only two species (Ditrema and Neoditrema) live on the western side of the Ocean. Many examples are known among Porifera, Polychaeta, Crustacea, Echinodermata and Mollusca.

Andriashev indicates identical species, closely related sub-species, and among the amphi-Pacific forms species and even genera differing by the degree of the discontinuity of their habitats in the north. Moreover, the habitats of a series of amphi-Pacific organisms on the American coast do not extend farther north than Oregon-Californian waters, and on the western coast no farther north than the Sea of Japan. There can be only one explanation for this distribution—both amphi-boreal and amphi-Atlantic: 'the geological history of the northern part of the Pacific is comparatively short. Conditions allowing a partial exchange of forms between the two different faunas—American and Asian—occurred at many different times. At the site of the contemporary fault in the region of the Bering Sea conditions were often, and at different geological periods, very favourable, allowing some individual elements of the two different faunas to spread northwards and to cross over to the opposite sides' (A. P. Andriashev, 1939). Such openings no doubt occurred periodically, beginning in the upper Miocene and especially during the Pliocene, and later during the two inter glacial warm periods. Andriashev rightly notes also that 'when the northern part of the Bering Sea was dry land, the warm branches of the Kuroshio current had a more intense warming effect [on its waters—L.Z.]'.

All groups of the flora and fauna of the northern part of the Pacific are characterized by their great mass development and their marked amphi-boreal distribution. However, as a whole, the flora and fauna of both oceans differ greatly. Thus the amphi-boreal organisms of the population of both oceans alien to its original population belong to a young and newly arrived element. It becomes evident, moreover, that some amphi-boreal groups are of Atlantic origin (among the fish the family Gadidae, among the marine mammals Phocidae) while others, much more numerous, are of Pacific origin (pleuronectiforms among fish, Laminaria among sea-weeds).

Amphi-boreal organisms are represented mostly either by identical or by very similar sub-species and species; this bears evidence of their comparatively recent spread into the new habitat. It can, in general, be considered as an immense experiment in acclimatization by Nature herself—a conquest of vast new habitats, often more spacious than the original ones. This experiment is a good illustration of the actual and potential habitats (L. Zenkevitch, 1940); a comparison of these two concepts should be kept in mind when plans are worked out and measures for trans-oceanic acclimatization are put into effect. A. P. Andriashev (1944) gives 50 cases of amphi-boreal distribution among fish including cod, navaga, herring, several species of flatfish, halibut and others.

Amphi-boreal forms are even more frequent among the invertebrates (crustaceans, polychaetes, echinoderms, molluscs). Among them the following commonly known mass forms may be mentioned: prawn (*Pandalus borealis*), crab (Lithodes), barnacle (*Balanus balanoides*), starfish (*Asterias rubens*), brittle stars (*Ophiura robusta*), holothurians (*Cucumaria frondosa*), molluscs (*Modiola modiolus*), Enteropneusta (*Balanoglossus mereschkowskii*) and many others—more than 100 species in all. It is characteristic that many amphi-boreal organisms, predominant in one ocean, play only a modest role in the other. Thus, for example, the forms dominant in the Bering Sea benthos such as the echinoderms *Ctenodiscus crispatus* and *Strongylocentrotus droebachiensis*; the worms *Phascolosoma margaritaceum*, *Spiochaetopterus typicus* and *Maldane sarsi*; the molluscs *Cardium ciliatum* and many others, become of secondary importance in the Pacific Ocean. *Calanus finmarchicus*, markedly predominant in the plankton of North America, is intensively developed in only a few areas of the Far Eastern Seas. Andriashev is inclined to refer the formation of the amphi-boreal community mainly to the pre-glacial period, when, apparently, the Bering Strait was deeper and wider and the temperature of its waters was (judging by its fossil molluscs) 5° to 10° higher than it is now, and when the whole Arctic basin was considerably warmer. The exchange of faunas could also have taken place, but apparently in a much more restricted form, within the warm interglacial periods and the post-glacial Littorina era.

Whereas the appearance of disconnected habitats along the latitude is linked with the periods of rise of temperature, the bipolar distribution is the result of periods of colder climate, when the organisms of moderate latitudes could penetrate through the somewhat cooled equatorial belt.

The phenomenon of bipolarity is just as marked in the Pacific Ocean as in the Atlantic. Laminariales among sea-weeds and sardines among fish may serve as excellent examples of it. Along the Asian coast Laminaria have only reached the Yellow Sea. They disappear farther south, appearing on the western coast of the ocean only in 30° S latitude. On the eastern side, however, they reach the Galapagos Islands. Their spread so far north along the coast of South America is the result of the cooling effect of the Humboldt current. Laminaria and penguins move with this current to the equator and the Galapagos Islands. The order Laminaria includes only 30 genera and 130 species. In the northern part of the Pacific Ocean 27 genera (90 per cent) and 84 species (65 per cent) of them are found, and in the southern hemisphere only 6 genera (20 per cent) and 22 species (17 per cent). Four species only are recorded for the Yellow Sea.

14
The Sea of Japan

I. PHYSICAL GEOGRAPHY

The area of the Sea of Japan is about 978,000 km²; its volume is 1,713,000 km³; its average depth is 1,752 m and its greatest depth 4,036 m.

Owing to the shallowness of the straits connecting it with the Ocean, the Sea of Japan occupies a special position among the Far Eastern Seas which wash the shores of the U.S.S.R. In spite of this shallowness the isolation of its deep waters is only relative, since in winter, as a result of the sinking of cooled surface waters along its slopes, the deep waters are well aerated; they differ from the adjacent parts of the Ocean and from the Okhotsk and Bering Seas by their lower temperature and by the absence of oxygen deficiency in the middle layers. The cold intermediate layer is also absent from the Sea of Japan. The salinity of the Sea of Japan is practically the same as that of the Ocean (*Table 304*).

Table 304. Vertical distribution of temperature, salinity and oxygen in the central parts of the Seas of Japan and Okhotsk and of the Bering Sea

Depth	Temperature, °C			Salinity ‰			Oxygen, ml/l.		
m	Japan	Okhotsk	Bering	Japan	Okhotsk	Bering	Japan	Okhotsk	Bering
0	18·13	10·72	8·40	34·13	32·57	33·11	6·54	6·38	6·91
50	3·04	−0·62	4·53	34·04	32·97	33·21	6·81	8·05	7·52
100	1·23	−1·44	2·00	34·07	33·11	33·32	6·63	7·58	7·35
150	0·84	−0·15	2·92	34·07	33·35	33·58	6·89	6·55	4·47
250	0·40	1·02	3·65	34·09	33·52	33·97	6·45	3·82	2·07
500	0·15	2·07	3·38	34·09	33·95	34·21	5·78	1·95	1·38
1,000	0·08	2·35	2·75	34·13	34·42	34·42	5·69	0·95	—
3,000	—	—	1·58	—	—	34·72	—	—	2·65

Water exchange in the Sea of Japan is also different from that of the Sea of Okhotsk and the Bering Sea. All the deep waters of the Sea of Japan are isolated from the trenches of the Pacific Ocean and adjacent seas; only the surface waters flow into the Sea of Japan from the neighbouring basins. Warmer deep oceanic waters penetrate freely into the Sea of Okhotsk and the Bering Sea through the deep straits and fill their trenches (Fig. 368).

The Sea of Japan has a varied bottom topography (Fig. 369) (N. Zenkevitch, 1959). Its greatest depth is situated in the northern, deep-water part. The sea-floor is mostly below 3,000 m. Its shelf zone is very narrow except for the Bay of Peter the Great, the northern part of Tartary Bay and the northern coast of Hokkaido Island. Its bathyal zone is comparatively large. The shelf zone forms only about 20 per cent of the total area of the Sea, and the bathyal zone some 40 per cent; the area of the deep-sea floor is also about 40 per cent.

In the southeastern part of the Sea there lies a large submarine range, some of its elevations rising to within 300 to 400 m of sea-level. Moreover, in different parts of the deep-water trench some summits rise to a height of 1,500 to 2,000 m from the sea-floor.

The bottom deposits of the Sea of Japan are mostly aleurites of varying coarseness (Fig. 370). The complete absence of diatomaceous oozes from the Sea of Japan is noteworthy, since they are exceptionally abundant in the Sea of Okhotsk and the ocean adjacent to it.

Almost the whole of the mainland coast of the Sea extends parallel to the

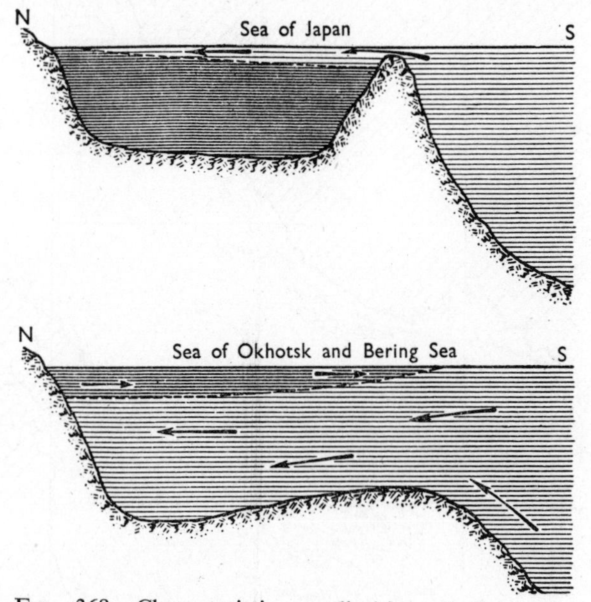

FIG. 368. Characteristic peculiarities of the water exchange of the Seas of Japan and of Okhotsk and Bering with the Ocean.

peaks of the Sikhote-Alin range. The coast there is fairly sheer and coastal features are rare. The character of the coast changes greatly to the south beyond Cape Povorotniy, and it runs at right angles to the axis of the Sikhote-Alin range; its coastal features then become numerous. There are several small, tortuous inlets and two large bays, those of Amur and Ussuriisky.

The coast of Western Sakhalin differs greatly from the mainland coast. It is composed of easily disintegrated chalk and Tertiary rock and has been smoothed throughout most of its length by the process of abrasion. Former river estuaries are filled with alluvium, and some estuaries jut out into the Sea, forming small smooth, prominent deltas. Abrasion has markedly decreased now owing to the formation of a very wide beach along the coast. Although the tide-range is small, the tidal zone is frequently wide.

The Sea of Japan may be divided into two distinct parts according to the

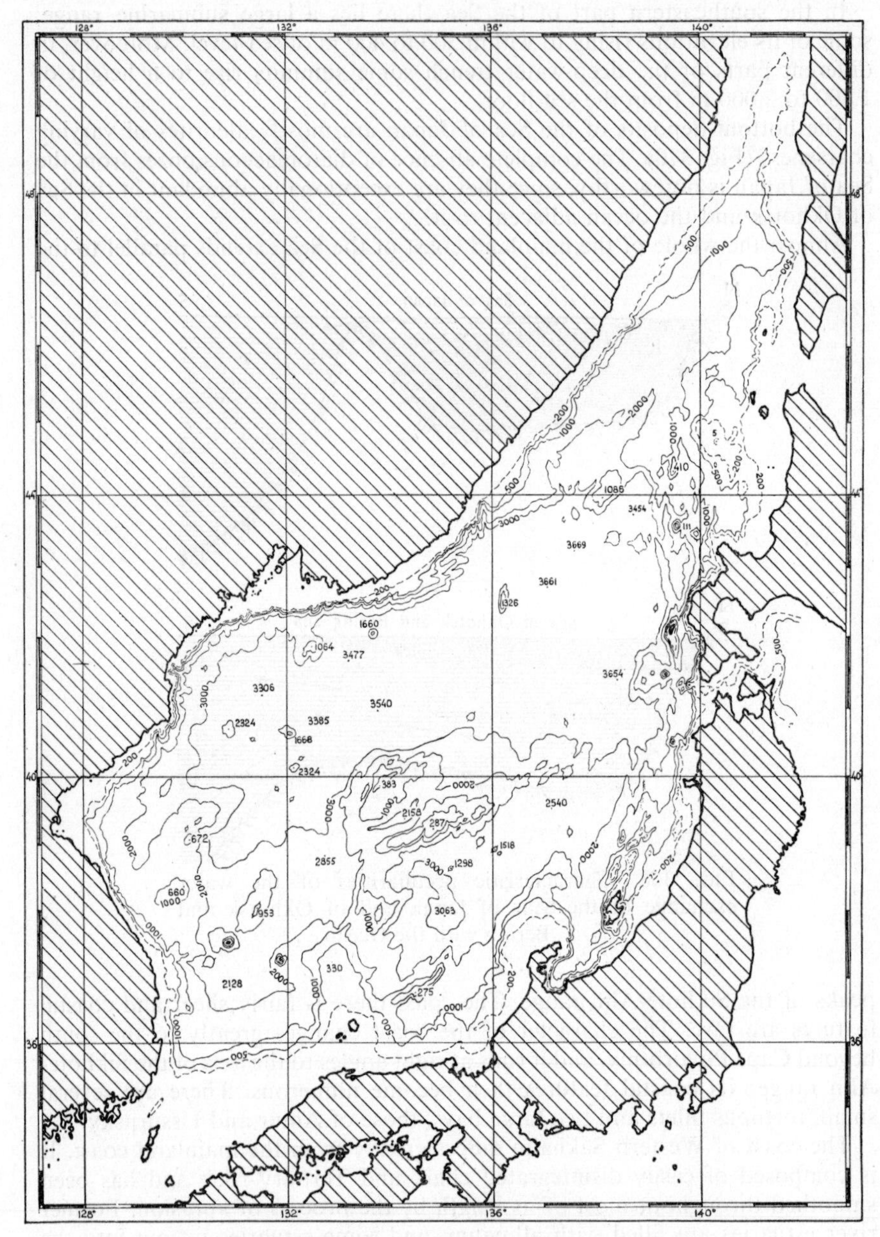

FIG. 369. Sea-bed relief of the Sea of Japan (Zenkevitch).

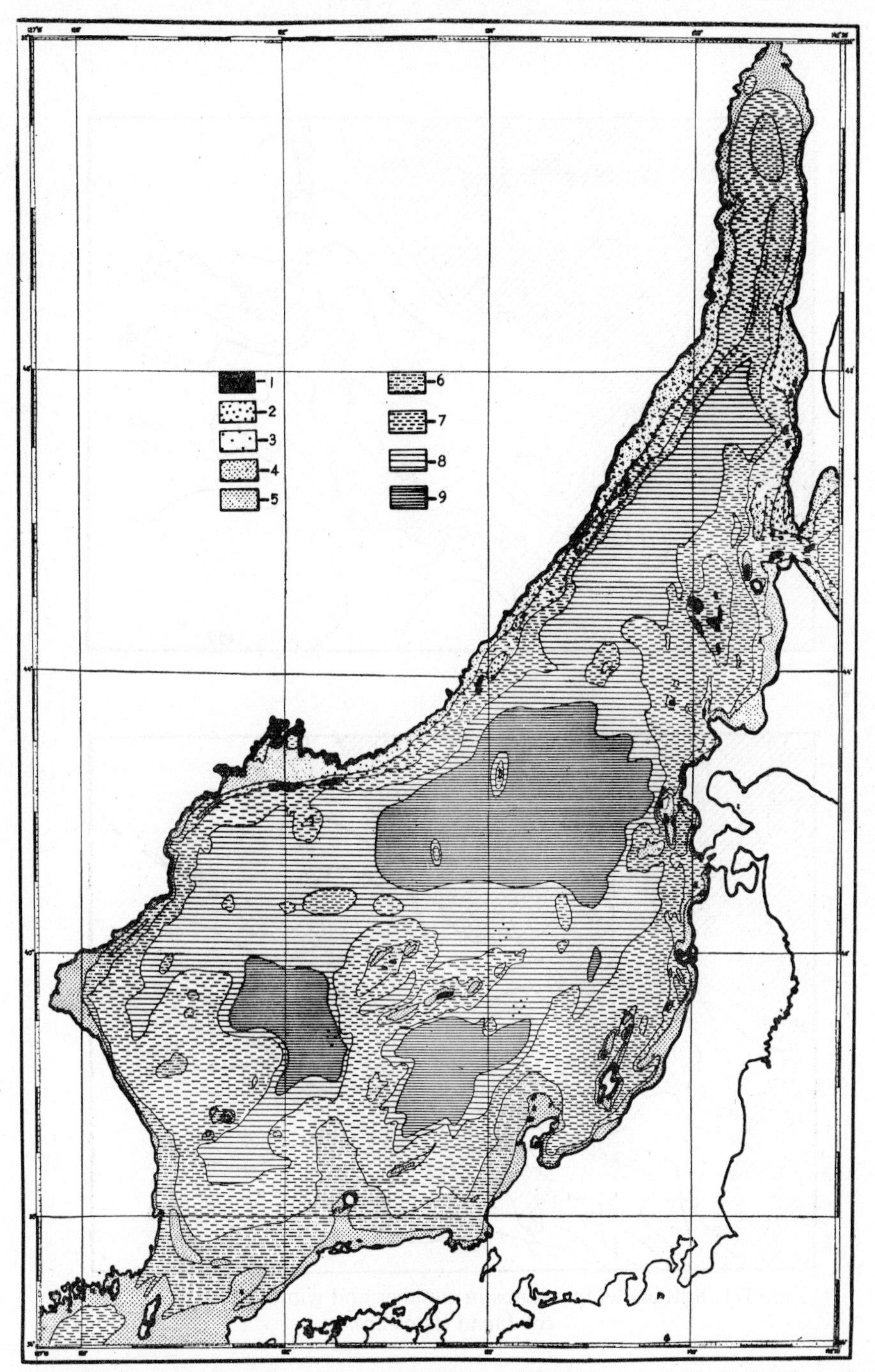

FIG. 370. Bottom deposits of the Sea of Japan (Skornikova). *1* Rock bottom; *2* Shingle–gravel sediments; *3* Scattered shingle–gravel bed; *4*, *5* Sands; *6–8* Aleurites; *9* Ooze.

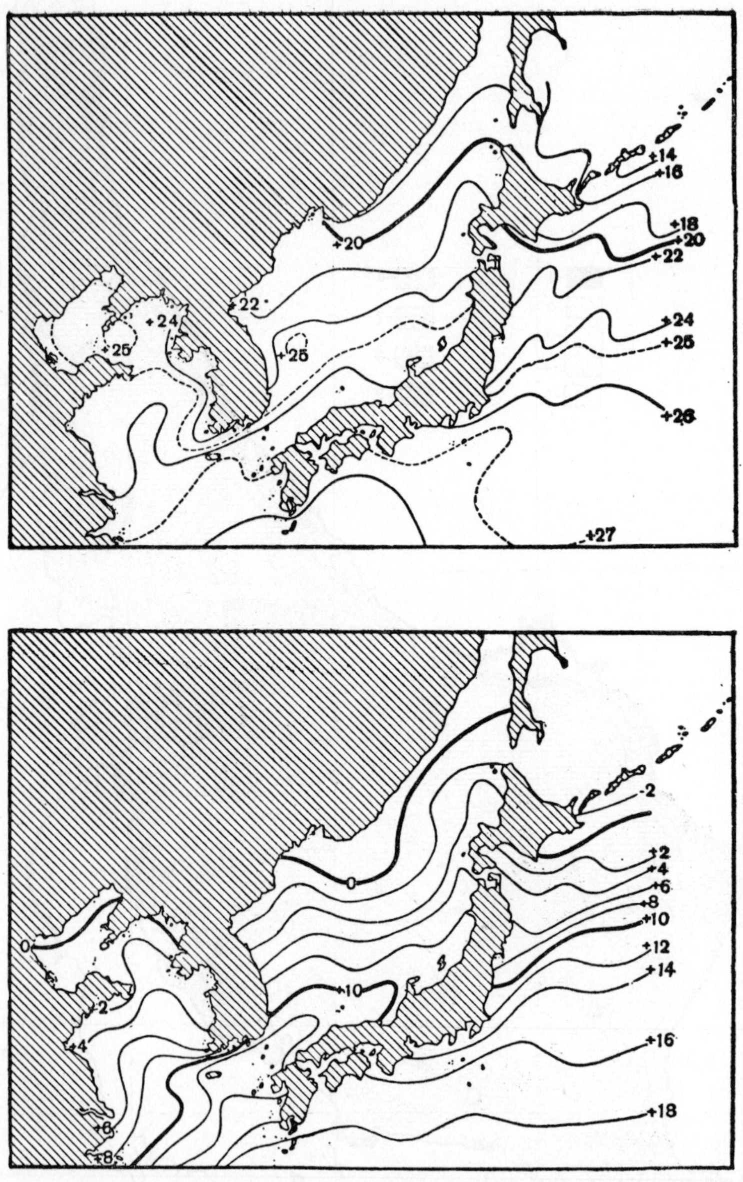

FIG. 371. Surface temperatures in summer and winter of waters of Sea of Japan (Istoshin).

course of its temperature changes (*Table 304*). The isotherm 0° can be taken as their boundary. The temperature of the northwestern part falls sharply in winter and in the Tartary Strait ice is formed from November till April, sometimes reaching great thickness in the northern part.

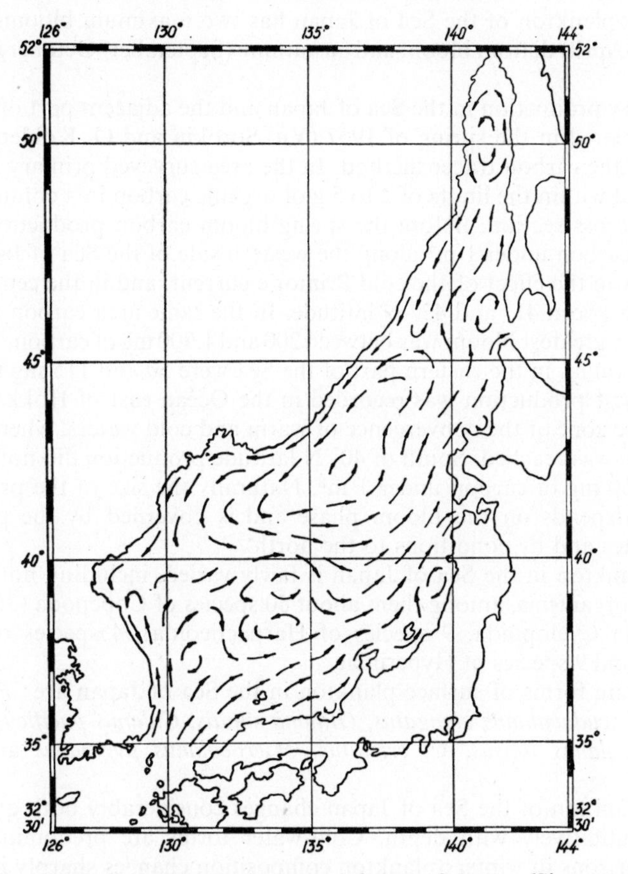

FIG. 372. Surface currents in summer of Sea of Japan (Sizova, 1961).

In the southern part of the Sea the seasonal temperature fluctuations are as high as 14°, and in the northern up to 20° (Fig. 371).

The currents of the Sea of Japan (Fig. 372) have a cyclonic, counter clockwise character, as is usual in seas of the northern hemisphere.

The tidal ranges of the northern and southern parts of the Sea vary considerably. In the most southerly part of the Sea, the Korea Strait, the tidal range is 0·5 m. The tidal range gradually increases in the Tartary Strait, reaching 2·3 to 2·8 m. In the Korea and Tartary Straits the tides are semi-diurnal, in the Primor'e either diurnal or varied. The level of the Sea is subject to fluctuations as a result of the on- and off-shore winds.

II. FLORA AND FAUNA

Four hundred and fifty different plants have been identified in the plankton of the Sea of Japan (Y. Kiselev, 1937, 1947), among them 306 diatoms and 133 peridinians. In contrast with the northern part of the Sea of Okhotsk the phytoplankton of the Sea of Japan has two maximum blooms—a spring (March–April) diatom bloom and an autumn (September–October) peridinean bloom.

Primary production in the Sea of Japan and the adjacent part of the Pacific was estimated in the spring of 1957 (Yu. Sorokin and O. Koblents-Mishke, 1958) by the carbon tracer method. In the area surveyed primary production fluctuated within the limits of 2 to 5 g of organic carbon in a column of water of 1 m^2 cross section. Before the spring bloom carbon production was 2 to 6 mg of carbon under 1 m^2 along the western side of the Sea of Japan, which is subject to the effect of the cold Primor'e current, and in the central part of the Sea between 41° and 42° N latitude. In the same area carbon production during the greatest bloom was between 200 and 1,900 mg of carbon. The corresponding values in the eastern part of the Sea were 50 and 115 mg under 1 m^2. The highest production was recorded in the Ocean east of Hokkaido Island within the zone of the convergence of warm and cold waters, where 5,000 mg of carbon was reached. South of 40° N latitude production did not rise above 100 to 150 mg of carbon under 1 m^2. Naturally the size of the primary production depends on the bloom phase and is governed by the presence of phosphates and by conditions to the north.

Zooplankton in the Sea of Japan is fairly varied, including no fewer than 70 or 80 organisms, among them about 50 species of Copepoda (36 species of Calanoida Cyclopoida, 9 species of Harpacticoida), 4 species of Euphausiaceae, and 9 species of Hyperiidae.

The main forms of surface plankton in the Sea of Japan are: *Paracalanus parvus*, *Pseudocalanus elongatus*, *Oithona similis*, *Calanus pacificus*, *Metridia lucens*, *Calanus tonsus*, *C. cristatus*, *Microcalanus pygmaeus* and *Oncaea borealis*.

The plankton of the Sea of Japan changes considerably both qualitatively and quantitatively with depth. Cold-water forms are predominant in the upper horizons in winter; plankton composition changes sharply in summer. Only eurythermic forms (for example *Oithona similis*) are found here all the year round. There are many Foraminifera and Radiolaria in the plankton of the surface layer during the cold season of the year. Below 500 m *Microcalanus pygmaeus* (K. Brodsky, 1941), the radiolarian *Challengeron* spp. and the ostracoda Conchoecia become the main forms (*Table 305*).

As is shown by the data of *Table 305*, deep-water plankton species are extremely scarce in the Sea of Japan.

In contrast with the northwestern part of the Pacific Ocean (K. Brodsky, 1952) where the number of species of Copepoda increases more than ten times with depth, their number in the Sea of Japan is barely doubled with depth. As regards the number of specimens down to 1,000 m the decrease is five times more rapid in the Pacific Ocean than in the Sea of Japan. This may

Table 305. Number of specimens of individual species of zooplankton in the Sea of Japan according to depth

	Depth, m	0–25	25–50	50–100	100–200	200–500	500–1,000	1,000–2,000
	Mean biomass, mg/m³	540	480	230	120	114	90	0·3
	Organism							
Deep-water	*Gaetanus minor*	—	—	—	—	1	4	9
	Gaidius brevispinus	—	—	—	—	48	18	1
	Euprimno macropus	—	—	—	—	3	4	—
	Eucalanus elongatus var. *bungii*	—	—	—	—	1	2	26
	Euchaeta japonica	—	—	—	5	42	4	—
	Conchoecia spp.	—	—	—	1	380	290	130
	Aulosphaeridae	—	—	—	—	1	60	20
	Dimophyes arctica	—	—	—	15	1	20	3
Eurybathic	*Calanus cristatus*	4	12	22	13	2	2	4
	Parathemisto japonica	—	8	2	—	3	3	1
	Aglantha digitalis	12	12	20	3	2	—	—
	Challengeron spp.	2,000	1,200	1,600	1,800	1,910	370	320
	Scolecithricella minor	—	—	432	365	70	4	—
	Microcalanus pygmaeus	—	400	1,200	750	1,020	1,020	180
Shallow water	*Oithona similis*	38,000	54,400	25,000	1,750	220	—	—
	Pseudocalanus elongatus	5,640	5,600	1,120	250	460	22	—
	Beroe sp.	4	5	2	—	—	—	—
	Calanus tonsus	984	800	620	118	100	8	8
	Metridia lucens	1,600	400	1,400	150	770	70	75

be due to a sufficient oxygen supply in the deep waters of the latter Sea (*Table 306*).

The plankton of the Sea of Japan is divided into definite biogeographical zones (Fig. 373). Its most northern part, adjacent to the Tartary Strait, is occupied by a cold-water biocoenosis with *Calanus finmarchicus*. *Calanus tonsus* is the dominant species in its central part, while the warm-water species *Calanus pacificus*, *Oithona plumifera*, *Paracalanus parvus* and *Coryceus* sp. inhabit the southeastern part of the Sea (M. Kun and I. Meshcheryakova, 1954). A neritic biocoenosis of zooplankton (with Labidocera, Epilabidocera, Centropages, Acartia, Evadne, Podon and the larval forms of bottom-living animals) encircles the Sea.

In K. Brodsky's opinion (1941) the list of warm-water organisms should include *Cladocera* sp., *Paracalanus parvus*, *Oithona brevicornis* and *Calanus pacificus*, and the list of the cold-water organisms—*Calanus cristatus*, *C. finmarchicus*, *C. tonsus*, *Pseudocalanus elongatus* and in part *Oithona similis*.

Table 306. Change in number of species and specimens of Copepoda with depth (K. Brodsky, 1952)

Horizon m	Pacific Ocean, northwestern part		Sea of Japan, northwestern part	
	No. of species	No. of specimens	No. of species	No. of specimens
0–25	7	15,240	5	46,224
25–50	7	8,160	6	61,612
50–100	9	5,040	7	29,794
100–200	10	320	8	3,401
300–5,000	28	84	11	2,734
500–1,000	30	65	11	1,154
1,000–4,000	87	?	—	—
1,000–2,000	—	—	7	303

Plankton is much more developed in the open sea, furnishing a biomass in excess of 1 g/m³ (Figs. 374 and 375).

In winter (December to February) the zooplankton biomass in the 0 to 200 m layer remains fairly well developed in the central part of the Sea throughout the whole layer (30 to 500 mg/m³, Fig. 376) (I. Meshcheryakova, 1954). *Calanus cristatus*, *Thysanoessa raschii*, *Themisto abyssorum* and *Calanus tonsus* are the dominant forms in the southern part. There is also an admixture of *C. finmarchicus* in the coastal areas, and in the southern parts are found also the warm-water *Oithona plumifera*, *Clausocalanus arcuicornis* and others. The boundary between the area of winter conditions and that of spring conditions runs at that season approximately along the fortieth parallel.

Zooplankton distribution in the northern part of the Sea of Japan has some unusual winter features (L. Ponomareva, 1954). The most abundant plankton may be concentrated in the uppermost 25 m layer. Plankton biomass decreases rapidly within the 100 to 200 m layer, and deeper down it becomes considerably richer again (Fig. 377). The layer of decreased biomass coincides with the layer of sudden change. It is of interest to note that the diurnal

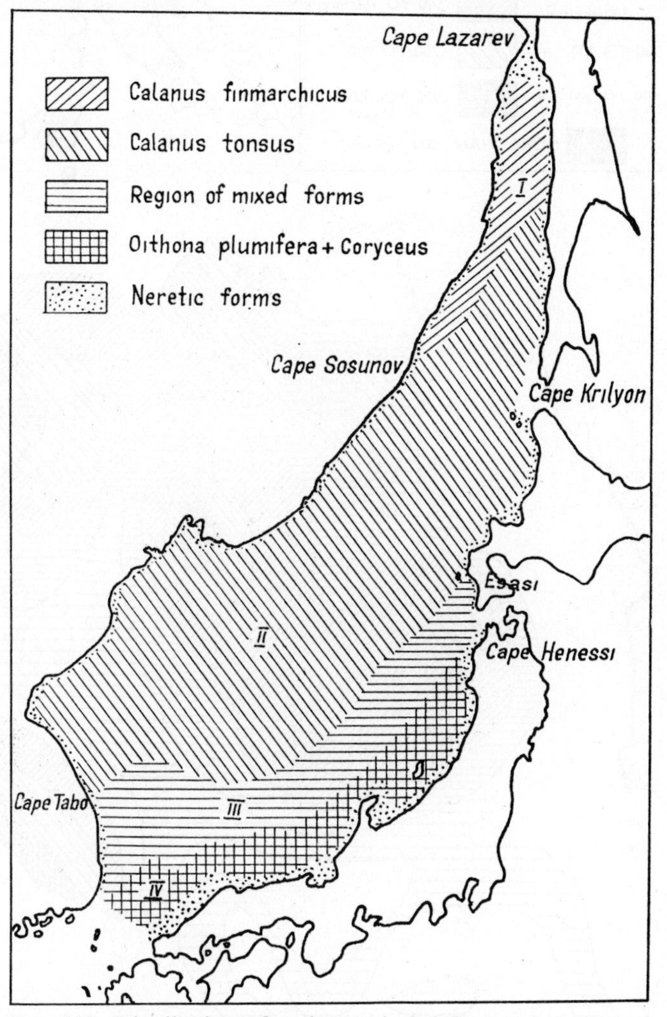

FIG. 373. Distribution of main species of Copepoda in Sea of Japan (Khun and Meshcheryakova, 1954).

vertical migrations of most of the main zooplankton species in the Sea are only feebly developed.

The euphausiids, which at times display a mass development, form a very important group of zooplankton. Members of four species of this group—*Thysanoessa longipes*, *Th. inermis*, *Th. raschii* and *Euphausia pacifica*—are found in the Sea of Japan. The euphausiids form the main food of many commercial fish (herring, mackerel, alaska-pollack, pink salmon) and of whales.

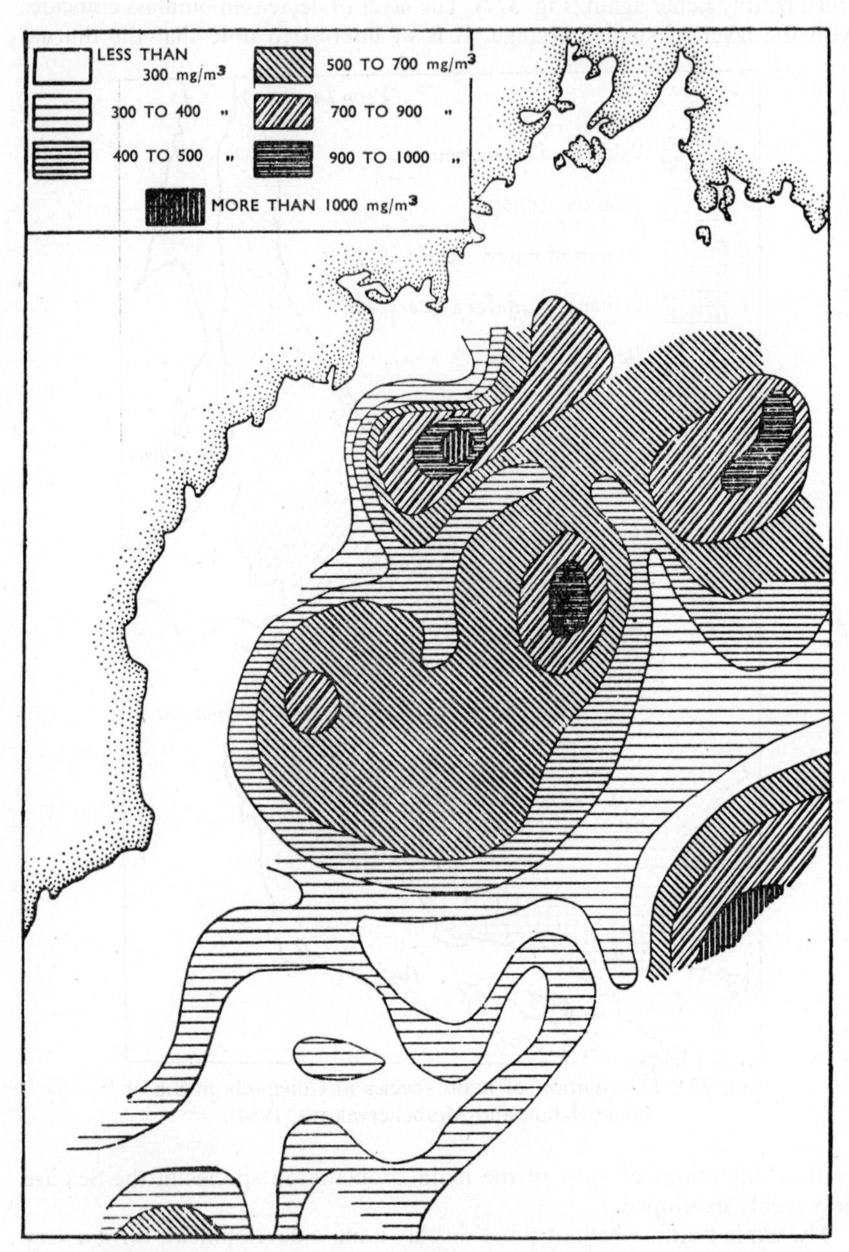

FIG. 374. Horizontal distribution of plankton in Sea of Japan (Kusmorskaya).

They are particularly abundant in the 0 to 50 m layer in January and February (L. Ponomareva, 1955) when their biomass is between 1 and 3 mg/m³ in large areas of the Sea. Euphausiids feed on calanoids with an admixture of various plankton. They are probably the greatest consumers of calanoids.

As a result of some alterations in the Kuroshio system a certain fall of temperature was observed in 1939 in the Sea of Japan, which increased in subsequent years. Sardine fisheries decreased markedly in 1941, and in

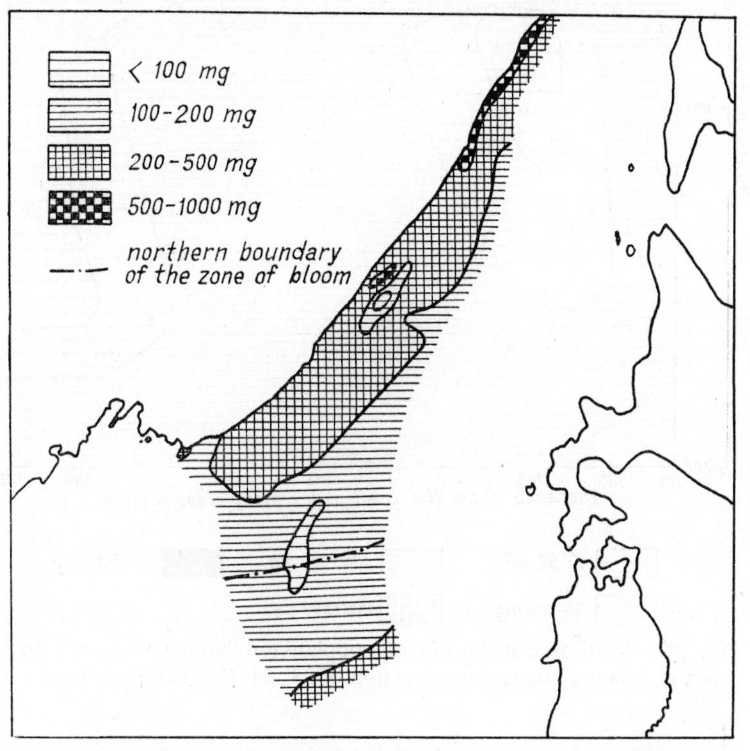

FIG. 375. Distribution of zooplankton biomass (mg/m³) in northwestern part of Sea of Japan between 50 and 200 m, summer 1952 (Meshcheryakova, 1950).

1942 sardines did not enter the Sea of Japan. They were not caught off the Soviet shores of the Sea of Japan for many years after this.

This fall of temperature necessarily affected the plankton, and in May 1941 phytoplankton was still predominant in the northwestern part of the Sea (A. Kusmorskaya, 1950)—mainly the diatoms *Coscinodiscus oculis iridis*. In the eastern part of the region species of the genus *Chaetoceros* were dominant, and in the southern *Thalassiothrix longissima*. *Calanus finmarchicus*, *Pseudocalanus elongatus*, *Oithona similis*, *Metridia lucens* and other cold-water forms were among the most widely distributed zooplankton components in the spring. The mean biomass of zooplankton in May was only 136 mg/m³

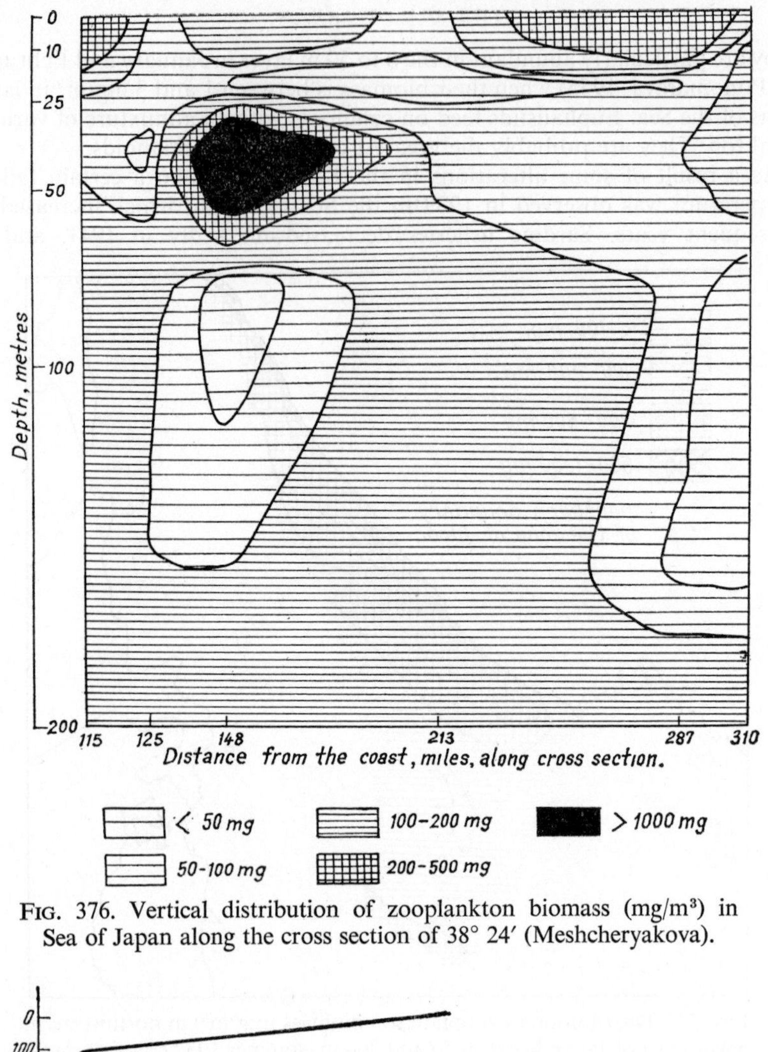

FIG. 376. Vertical distribution of zooplankton biomass (mg/m³) in Sea of Japan along the cross section of 38° 24′ (Meshcheryakova).

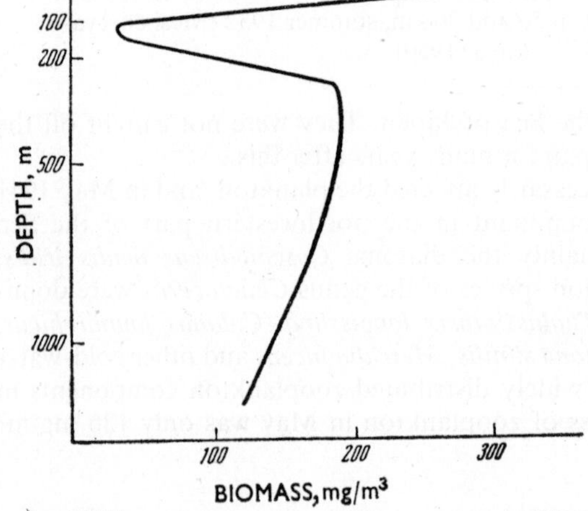

FIG. 377. Vertical distribution of zooplankton biomass (mean data) in northern part of Sea of Japan in January 1950 (Ponomareva).

for the 0 to 100 m layer. *Calanus tonsus* was also greatly developed (45 per cent of the total plankton biomass).

As early as June diatomaceous plankton was replaced by peridinians (some species of the genera *Peridinium* and *Ceratium*); among the zooplankton *Paracalanus parvus* was intensely developed. The amount of zooplankton increased to 350 mg/m³, and with the warming of the surface water *Calanus*

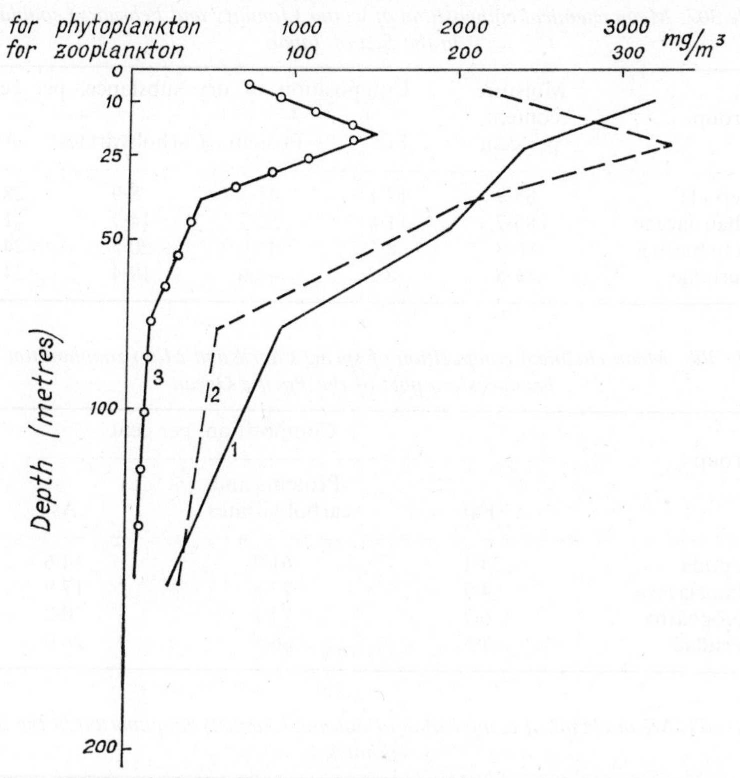

Fig. 378. Vertical distribution of plankton biomass (mg/m³) in Sea of Japan from 31 March to 2 June 1939. 1 Phytoplankton (Coscinodiscus); 2 Zooplankton; *3 Calanus tonsus* (Kusmorskaya, 1950).

tonsus became the main form. In 1937 the zooplankton biomass in the same area, at the same season, was three times greater (1,300 g/m³) (K. Brodsky, 1939), and in 1936 it had even reached 1,640 mg/m³. The greatest concentration of zooplankton is found at a depth of 24 m (Fig. 378). Phytoplankton consists almost exclusively of *Coscinodiscus oculis iridis*, while half the zooplankton consists of *Calanus tonsus*—the main food of sardines in the Sea of Japan. In the opinion of many investigators the sardine catastrophe of 1939 was the result of an exceptional fall of temperature in the sardine spawning area and also of the consequential scarcity of food for the newly-hatched young.

L. Kizevetter (1954) has recorded interesting observations on the chemical composition and food value of the Sea of Japan plankton. He has found that these indices, both of the zooplankton as a whole and of its separate components, may be subject to considerable seasonal variations, their food value being altered as a result (*Tables 307, 308* and *309*).

Table 307. Mean chemical composition of winter (January and February) zooplankton in the Sea of Japan

Group	Moisture content, per cent	Composition of dry substance, per cent			
		Fat	Protein	Carbohydrates	Ash
Copepoda	88·9	17·1	45·3	8·9	28·7
Euphausiaceae	83·7	11·4	52·7	14·9	21·0
Chaetognatha	86·8	8·3	46·9	20·5	24·3
Hyperiidae	86·8	8·3	47·6	19·4	24·7

Table 308. Mean chemical composition of spring (April and May) zooplankton in the northwestern part of the Pacific Ocean

Group	Composition, per cent		
	Fat	Proteins and carbohydrates	Ash
Copepoda	24·1	61·3	14·6
Euphausiaceae	4·3	77·8	17·9
Chaetognatha	6·7	73·1	20·2
Hyperiidae	7·5	66·5	26·0

Table 309. Mean chemical composition of autumn (August) zooplankton in the Sea of Okhotsk

Group	Moisture content, per cent	Composition of dry substance, per cent			
		Fat	Proteins	Carbohydrates	Ash
Copepoda	77·7	38·6	29·6	16·1	15·7
Euphausiaceae	70·2	28·2	54·4	5·6	11·8
Chaetognatha	68·9	19·0	52·5	11·6	16·9
Hyperiidae	69·8	43·9	35·5	8·7	10·9
Phytoplankton	90·86	1·48	29·40	37·52	31·60

Thus the calorific value of 100 g of zooplankton varies from 331·6 to 501·9. The chemical composition of the phytoplankton of the Sea of Okhotsk in August with its lower fat content and higher content of carbohydrates is markedly different from that of the zooplankton.

Copepoda and Euphausiaceae are very important in the diet of plankton-eating fish, and in this respect herring has many rivals. In their turn Euphausiaceae and Chaetognatha consume very large numbers of Copepoda. It is remarkable that the Pacific Ocean herring (*Clupea harengus pallasi*), which lives in the northern part of the Sea of Japan, has the same diet as the Atlantic herring of the Barents Sea (*Thysanoessa inermis*, *Th. raschii* and *Calanus finmarchicus*), but in the Sea of Japan it adds *Sagitta elegans* as a further component of its diet.

The flora of the bottom-living macrophytes of the Sea of Japan has been investigated by the Soviet and Japanese workers E. Zinova (1928–54), G. Gail (1930, 1936), T. Shchapova (1948, 1957), Miyabe (1908), K. Oka (1907–34) and J. Tokida (1957). Three hundred and seventy-nine species of bottom-living macrophytes of the Sea of Japan are listed in *Table 310*.

Table 310. Composition of littoral sea-weeds of the Sea of Japan (T. Shchapova, 1958)

Group	No. of species	Percentage of Primor'e species
Cyanophyceae	9	100
Chlorophyceae	46	96
Phaeophyceae	90	82
Rhodophyceae	172	56
Total	317	68 (202 species)

T. Shchapova has investigated the littoral flora of the Soviet's Primor'e for a number of years (from 1948). The exclusively littoral forms of the bottom flora (including the uppermost horizon of the sublittoral up to 1 m) compose only 25 per cent of the total, e.g. about 72 to 74 species. The marine flora of the Primor'e does not contain Arctic or tropical organisms. Arctic-boreal forms are predominant in the northern part and boreal ones in the southern. *Pylaiella littoralis* and *Dictyosiphon foeniculaceus* are most characteristic of the first group; *Langsdorfii* sp., *Sargassum miyabei*, *Cystoseira crassipes*, *C. hakodatensis*, of the second. They are mainly endemic organisms of the northern part of the Pacific. Apart from them the sea-weeds of the Sea of Japan contain also some amphi-boreal species such as, for example, *Halopteris scoparia*, *Leathesia difformis*, *Ralfsia clavata*, *Colpomenia sinuosa*, and some bipolar ones—*Scytosiphon lomentarius*, *Ilea fascia*. Many organisms are distributed on both sides of the Pacific; on the other hand many of them are endemic forms of the Asian coast—*Nemacystus decipiens*, *Stschapovia flagellaris*, *Cystoseira crassipes* and others. The dominant species of the littoral and of the upper horizon of the sublittoral are the following, which are endemic to the northern part of the Pacific Ocean: *Heterochordaria abietina*, *Pelvetia wrightii* f. *babingtonii*, *Coccophora langsdorfii*, *Sargassum miyabei*, *Cystoseira crassipes*, *C. hakodatensis*. The most profusely developed Laminaria of the Primor'e are *Laminaria japonica*, *L. dentigera*, *Alaria crassifolia*, *A. fistulosa*, which also are endemic to the Pacific Ocean.

Unlike the brown sea-weeds, the red sea-weeds on the Soviet shores of the Sea of Japan belong mostly to the boreal flora. Only *Polysiphonia arctica* might be included among the Arctic forms. The comparative role of the red sea-weeds in the Pacific Ocean is much greater than in the Atlantic.

Two of Shchapova's (1957) diagrams (Figs. 379 and 380) may be used for a

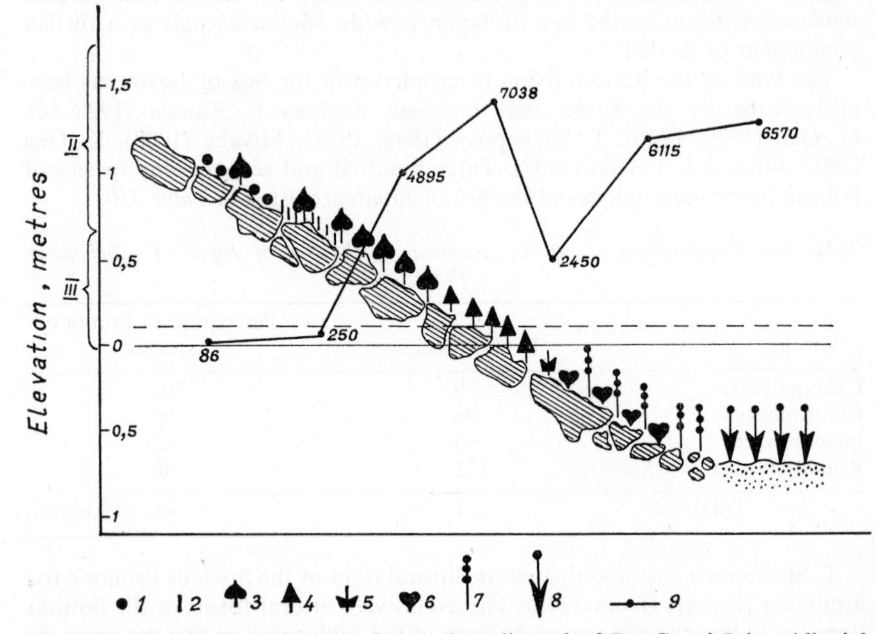

FIG. 379. Distribution of macrophytes along littoral of De Castri Inlet. Alluvial deposit in depth of bight; 1 *Gloiopeltis capillaris*; 2 *Enteromorpha* spp.; 3 *Fucus evanescens*, *Pelvetia wrightii* f. *babingtonii*; 5 *Tichocarpus crinitus*; 6 *Corallina officinalis*; 7 *Cystoseira crassipes*; 8 *Zostera marina*; 9 Biomass distribution curve; *II*, *III* Littoral horizons (Vayan). Summer zero of depth is marked by a broken line; biomass in g/m² (Shchapova, 1957).

comparison of the littoral macroflora of the northern (north of Peter the Great Bay) and the southern regions.

The composition of the littoral macrophytes of the northern part of the western shore of Sakhalin is very similar to that of the northern mainland coast of the Primor'e; that of the southern part, warmed by the warm current, is similar to the southern and central Primor'e.

Vast fields of the commercial marine grass Phyllospadix occur at 0·5 to 15 m depth in some areas of the southern Primor'e (E. Kardakova, 1957); its mean biomass is 2 to 5 kg/m² wet weight (0·4 to 1·0 mg/m² dry weight).

There is a great difference between the northern and southern parts of the Primor'e, principally in temperature. Maximum temperatures of the two parts differ by no less than 10° in certain months; the tides and their character vary a great deal too.

A predominance of perennial forms, with an all-year-round growth, is characteristic of the northern part of the Primor'e (T. Shchapova, 1956). They comprise two species of Fucus and *Pelvetia babingtonii* which, with a biomass of the order of 5 to 7 kg/m³, form continuous homogeneous belts. 'The littoral of the northern Primor'e', writes Shchapova, 'is similar in the

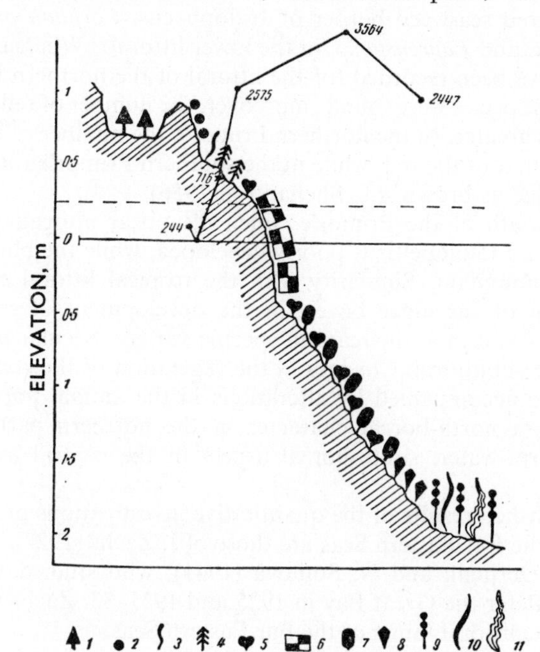

FIG. 380. Cross section through littoral of Olga Inlet off Cape Linden. 1 *Pelvetia wrightii* f. *babingtonii*; 2 *Gloiopeltis capillaris*; 3 *Nemalion helmintoides*; 4 *Rhodomela latix*; 5 *Corallina pillulifera*; 6 Plant mozaic; 7 *Iridea* sp.; 8 *Chondrus pinnulatus*; 9 *Sargassum* sp.; 11 *Phyllospadix scouleri*; 11 *Costaria costata*. Biomass in g/m² (Shchapova).

development and thickness of its fucoid cover to the littoral of the northern Atlantic, the Murman coast and the White Sea.'

As a result of unfavourable winter conditions in the northern Primor'e 'bottom vegetation is absent from the upper half of its littoral; the fucoids frequently sink below zero depth (displacing the fringe of red algae) and there is a general lowering of all the zones'. The formation of a layer of red algae Gloiopeltis above the belts of Fucus and Pelevetia is very characteristic of the Sea of Japan (and of the Bering and Okhotsk Seas). In the upper horizon of the sublittoral brown algae, at times forming large beds, are mixed with the sea-weeds of a northern aspect such as the fucoids, *Myelophucus intestinalis* and *Stictyosiphon tortilis*. This mixture of northern and southern elements in the flora may be considered a consequence of severe winter conditions and a southern geographical situation.

The central and southern Primor'e are characterized by a predominance of annual and seasonal species, by their patchy mosaic-like distribution, by the reduction of the Fucii and Pelvetiae to secondary species, and by the formation of a red sea-weed border of Iridophycus, *Coralina pilullifera* sp. *Rhodomela larix*, and *Laurensia* sp. in the lower littoral. 'Whereas 85 species of sea-weeds have been recorded for the littoral of the northern Primor'e, in the southern 108 species were found; moreover, the number of red algae is one and a half times greater. In the northern Primor'e the number of brown algae species exceeds that of the red, while in the southern Primor'e there are twice as many red algae as brown' (T. Shchapova, 1956).

In the very south of the Primor'e, Fucii disappear altogether, Pelvetiae become scarce and Gloiopeltis is poorly developed, while the blue-green sea-weeds become abundant. Similarity with the tropical littoral exists in the general thinning of the algae cover, in the development of seasonal and ephemeral forms and in an increase in specific variety. Secular macrophytes migrate into the sublittoral. Changes in the vegetation of the coastal strip of the Primor'e are accompanied by alterations in the animal population, the latter acquiring a north-boreal character in the northern part of Tartary Bay, and a warm-water, south-boreal aspect in the central and southern Primor'e.

The first published results of the quantitative investigations of the bottom-living fauna of the Far Eastern Seas are those of I. Zachs (1927), K. Derjugin (1939) and K. Derjugin and N. Somova (1941), who studied the bottom-living fauna in Peter the Great Bay in 1925 and 1931–33. Zachs was the first to investigate the littoral fauna of the Far Eastern Seas.

Peter the Great Bay is a vast shallow which falls away steeply to the great depths of the Sea of Japan. The bottom-living fauna of the Bay (Fig. 381) is distributed according to definite zones. Derjugin distinguishes 41 biocoenoses from the supralittoral down to the greatest depths (Figs. 382 and 383).

The quantitative and qualitative development of the supralittoral and littoral flora and fauna is limited by the small tidal range. The supralittoral zone is characterized by the development of the sea-weeds *Rivularia atra* and at times of *Rhizoclonium riparium*, and among the animals by *Ligia cinerascens* and the small crabs *Brachinotus sanguineus* and *Doclea bidentata*.

In the upper horizon of the littoral zone the rock sea-floor is characterized by growths of *Gloiopeltis capillaris* (funori algae), occasionally by Ulva and Sargassum and frequently by Littorinae (*L. sitchana* and *L. aqualida*), *Patella* sp. and *Turbo sangarensis*; by *Chthamalus challengeri* of the genus *Ligia cinerascens* and the crabs *Brachinotus sanguineus* and *Doclea bidentata*.

The lower horizon of rocky littoral is encircled by a fringe of *Corallina pellulifera* and characterized by a much greater variety of both sea-weeds (*Leathesia difformis*, *Ralfsia*, *Chordaria*) and animals (Hydroida, Actinia, young Ostrea; the Amphipoda *Allorchestres zivellinus* and *Orchestia ochotensis*; the Gastropoda *Thais limoi*; the starfish *Patiria pectinifera* and *Aphelasterias japonica* and others).

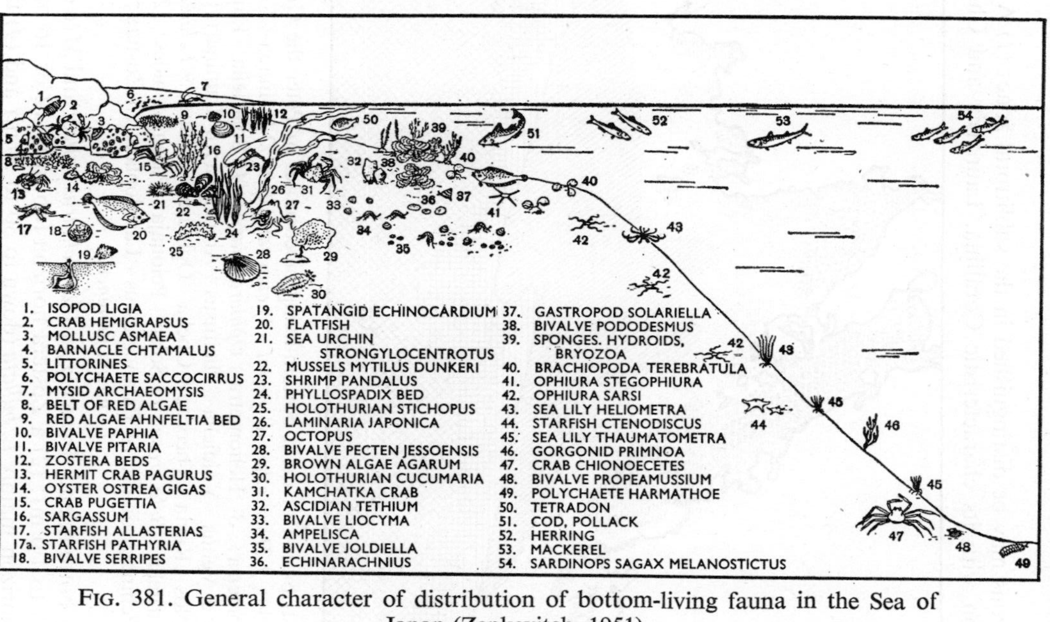

FIG. 381. General character of distribution of bottom-living fauna in the Sea of Japan (Zenkevitch, 1951).

Life is much more abundant on the soft soils of the littoral; the biocoenosis *Arenicola cristata, Mya arenaria, Laternula kamakurana* is found everywhere there. Throughout the littoral there is a large number of the jumping Amphipoda, *Orchestia* sp.; they frequently travel far from the coast into the fields and forests.

Four horizons may be distinguished in the sublittoral zone: (*1*) A transitional horizon with its characteristic Corallina, Laurensia and Chordaria

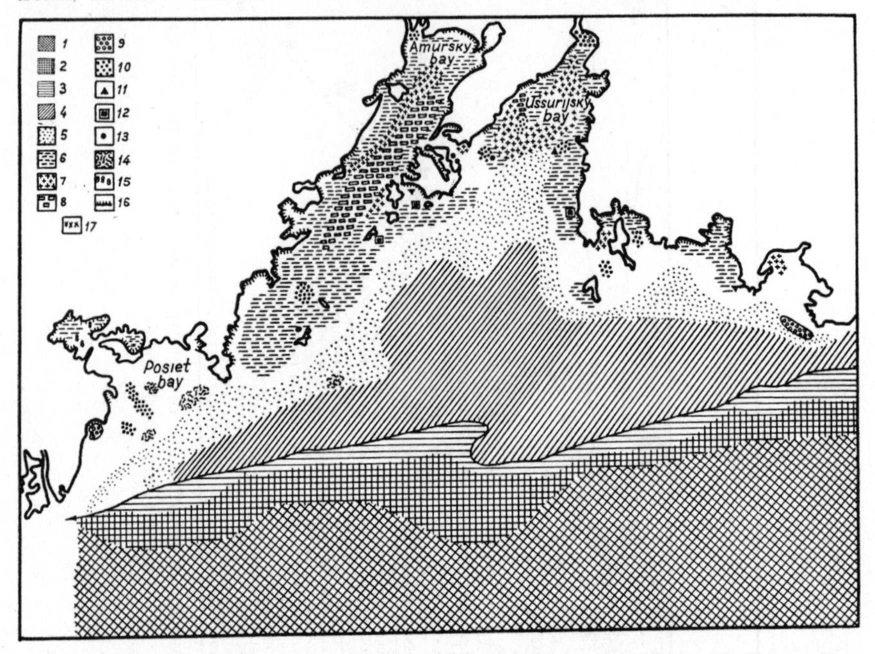

FIG. 382. Distribution of main bottom-living biocoenoses in Peter the Great Bay (Derjugin, 1939). *1 Harmothoe derjugini + Pecten randolphi*; *2* Primnoa + Luidiaster + Thaumantometra; *3* Heliometra + *Ophiura sarsi*; *4* Solariella + Eupyrgus + Stegophiura; *5* Venus + Yoldiella + Plicifusus + Ampelisca; *6* Laminaria; *7* Maldane + Scoloplos + Raeta + Theora; *8* Obelia + Ophiura + Philine; *9 Echinarachnius parma*; *10* Turitella + *Bela erosa*; *11* Solen + Pelonaja + Pareugyrioides; *12* Macrocallista; *13* Echinocardium; *14* Balanoglossus + Labidoplax; *15* Zostera; *16 Corbicula fluminea.*

on the rocky bottom, and *Arenicola pusilla, Echiurus pallasi* and *Mya arenaria* (down to 0·5 to 1·0 m); (2) a Zostera horizon (down to 12 or 16 m); (*3*) a Laminaria horizon mainly *L. bullata* (down to 30 to 50 m) and (*4*) the horizon of the sand plateau (50 to 200 m).

Fields of the sea grass Zostera (*Z. marina* on silt sand, *Z. pacifica* on purer sand) give shelter to abundant fauna. *Phyllospadix scoulleri*, closely akin to Zostera, forms dense growths on cliffs and rocky sea-floors. Biocoenoses inhabiting the leaves and those living in the sea-bed and roots can be distinguished for both Zostera and Phyllospadix. Each of these groups can, in their turn, be divided into two—animals sessile on leaves and animals swimming among leaves in one case, and those crawling over the bottom and living in the soils among Zostera roots in the other. For the Zostera leaves the following are most characteristic: the Mollusca *Lacuna divaricata*, *Alaba vladivostokensis*, *Gibbula derjugini*, *Rissoa* sp., *Pandalus latirostris*, *Botryllus* sp., and *Syngnathus soldatovi*. A great variety of Polychaeta Crustacea, Mollusca and Echinodermata live in the soil among the stems and under the roots. A Zostera biocoenosis has some features in common with that of Phyllospadix. Some other biocoenoses also inhabit this horizon (0 to 10 m): a fine-grain sand biocoenosis with *Mactra sachalinensis*, *M. sulcataria*, *Dosinia japonica*, *Tellina lutea venulosa*, *Echinarachnius parma*, *E. griseus*,

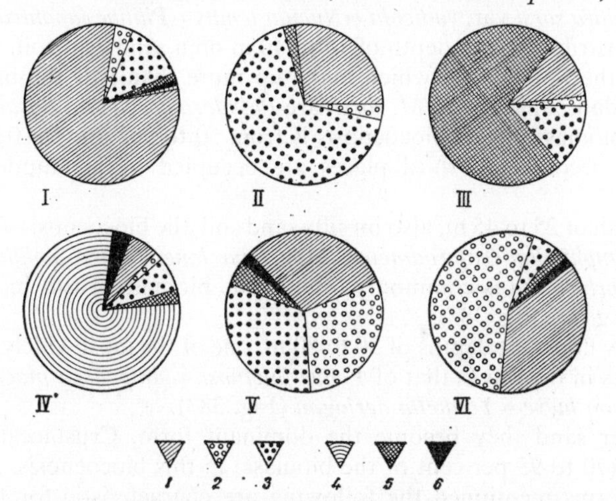

FIG. 383. Composition of bottom biocoenoses in Peter the Great Bay (Derjugin and Somova,) *1* Vermes; *2* Echinodermata; *3* Mollusca; *4* Ascidia; *5* Crustacea; *6* Varia. I *Maldane sarsi* + *Ophiura sarsi vadicola* + *Nucula tenuis* + *Philine japonica*; II *Turitella fortilirata* + *Amphiodia craterodmeta* + *Magelona longicornis* + *Yoldia johanni* + *Axinopsis orbiculata*; III *Venus fluctuosa* + *Ampelisca macrocephala* + *Haploarthron laeve* + *Yoldiella derjugini*; IV *Pareugyrioides japonica* + *Venus fluctuosa* + *Yoldiella derjugini* + *Ampelisca macrocephala*; V *Solariella varicosa* + *Solariella obscura* + *Myriotrochus mitzucuri* + *Stegophiura nodosa* + *S. brachiactis*; VI *Heliometra glacialis* + *Ophiura sarsi* + *Verticordia nadina*.

E. mirabilis; the oyster biocoenosis (*O. gigas*, *O. laperousi*, *O. posjetica*) with many accompanying organisms, among them at times *Rapana bezoar*; the biocoenosis of *Amphiroa cratacea* + *Mytilus* sp. of the type *giganteus*; the seaweed biocoenosis Sargassum, Cystophyllum, Coccophora, Rhodomela and others on the cliff sectors washed by the surf; the biocoenosis *Balanoglossus proterogonius* + *Tellina incongrua* + *Lebidoplax variabilis* on sectors heavily covered with silt at a depth of 3 to 5 m, and a series of others. Somewhat below these (12 to 50 m) lies the horizon of Laminaria (*L. saccharina*, *L.*

bullata and *L. japonica*) and red algae, together with a series of their own biocoenoses. Derjugin distinguishes among them the biocoenosis of *Laminaria thallus*, the rhizoid biocoenosis, and the biocoenosis of the soil with a large number of Polychaeta (*Maldane sarsi*, *Scoloplos armiger*), brittle stars (*Ophiura sarsi* var. *vadicola*, *Amphiodia craterodmeta*), Holothuria (*Cucumaria japonica*, *Stichopus japonicus*), starfish (*Asterias amurensis*, *Distolasterias nipon*), Mollusca (*Pecten swift*, *Modiola modiolus*, *Yoldia johanni*, *Bela erosa*, *Philine japonica*) and a series of other biocoenoses with a rich and varied fauna. K. Derjugin and N. Somova (1941) have given a quantitative description of some of these biocoenoses. In Peter the Great Bay the biocoenosis [*Maldane sarsi*+*Ophiura sarsi* var. *vadicola*+*Nucula tenuis*+*Philine japonica* (Fig. 383)] is widely distributed at a depth of 14 to 40 m on a sandy silt soil.

Among the Polychaeta, which make up more than half the biomass, the most abundant, apart from *M. sarsi*, are *Polydora coeca* and *Sosane gracilior*. The total biomass of this biocoenosis is from 50 to 262 g/m². After the Polychaeta the second and third places are occupied by Echinodermata and Mollusca.

At a depth of 25 to 45 m, also on silty sand soil, the biocoenosis *Turitella fortilirata*+*Amphiodia craterodmeta*+*Magelona longicornis*+*Yoldia johanni*+*Axinopsis orbiculata* is commonly found. The biomass of this biocoenosis is 100 to 200 g/m² (Fig. 383).

On sandy floors, at depths of 50 to 80 m, one of the most widely distributed biocoenoses in the Bay is that of *Venus fluctuosa*+*Ampelisca macrocephala*+*Haploarthron laeve*+*Yoldiella derjugini* (Fig. 383).

On purer sand they become the dominant form. Crustaceans are predominant (70 to 95 per cent of the biomass) in this biocoenosis. Apart from the four forms mentioned the following are characteristic for this biocoenosis: the Ascidians *Pelonaja corrugata* and *Pareugyrioides japonica*; the Crustacea *Byblis gaimardi*; the Polychaeta *Scoloplos armiger*, *Prionospio steenstrupi*, *Euchone olegi*; the Mollusca *Macoma calcarea*, *Montacuta* sp., *Axinopsis* sp., *Crenella decussata* and many others. The mean biomass of this biocoenosis is about 150 g/m², with the number of specimens per 1 m² up to 15,000, mainly Crustacea.

At greater depths (80 to 200 m) the biocoenosis *Venus fluctuosa*-*Ampelisca macrocephala* is replaced by that of *Salariella varicosa*, *S. obscura*+*Myriotrochus mitsukuri*+*Stegophiura nodosa*, *St. brachiactis* (Fig. 383). The total biomass is considerably less (80 to 85 g/m²) and there is qualitative impoverishment. The following should be noted in this biocoenosis apart from the above mentioned brittle stars: *Amphiodia craterodmeta*, the holothurian *Eupyrgus pacificus*, the Mollusca *Yoldiella derjugini*, *Venus fluctuosa*, *Verticordia nadina*, the Amphipoda *Ampelisca macrocephala*, the Polychaeta *Scoloplos armiger*, *Travisia forbesi*, *Asychis punctata* and others.

On the uppermost horizon of the bathyal, on firm sand and boulders, a biocoenosis of the *Heliometra glacialis maxima*+*Ophiura sarsi* with the mollusc *Verticordia nadina* is widely distributed (Fig. 383). It contains also the peculiar Foraminifera Bathysiphon, the Polychaeta *Travisia forbesi*, *Amage anope*, *Lumbriconereis fragilis*, *L. japonica*, *Scalibregma robusta* and others, the brittle star *Amphioplus macraspis*, the mollusc *Yoldiella derjugini*, the Amphipoda *Syrrhoe crenulata*, *Socarnes bidenticulatus*, *Anonyx nugax* and others. The mean biomass of this biocoenosis is 80 to 90 g/m^2, with the number of specimens about 1,000 per m^2. The mean biomass throughout the shelf of Peter the Great Bay is 170 to 200 g/m^2.

In the lower horizon of the bathyal down to 2,000 m the following biocoenosis is equally widely distributed: the lily *Thaumatometra tenuis*, with starfish *Ctenodiscus crispatus* and *Luidiaster tuberculatus*, the coral *Primnoa resedaeformis pacifica* (*Gorgonaria*) (reaching 2 m in height), some single madrepore corals *Caryophyllia clavus*, the hydroid *Lafoeina maxima*, the brachiopods *Terebratulina coreanica*, the polychaetes *Nephthys longisetosa*, *Harmothoe impar* and *Jasmineira pacifica*, the decapods *Nectocrangon dentata*, *Spirontocaris biunguis* and *Chionoecetes elongatus bathyalis*, the Gephyrea *Phascolosoma* spp., and the molluscs *Leda* sp., *Buccinum* sp., and *Pecten randolfi*.

At depths below 2,000 m life becomes qualitatively and quantitatively poor. Derjugin gives the benthos of the abyssal as comprising one single biocoenosis, owing its composition not to the abyssal fauna, but to the bathyal or even the sublittoral. It contains many species of Rhizopoda, *Hyperammina friabilis*, *Haplophragmoides canariensis*, and others; the hydroid *Lafoeina maxima*, the polychaetes *Harmothoe derjugini*, *H. impar*, *Scalibregma inflatum*, *Chaetozone setosa*, *Nephthys malmgreni* and others; the brittle star *Ophiura leptoctenia*; the molluscs *Pecten randolfi*, *Axinus flexuosus gouldi* (?), *Cylichna alba corticata*; the amphipods *Tmetonyx cicada*, *Anonyx ampulloides*; the isopods *Eurycope spinifrons*, *Gnathia elongata*; and the ascidian *Goniocarpa coriacea*.

A considerable admixture of cold-water species is characteristic of the biocoenoses living even at depths of 50 to 80 m in Peter the Great Bay. Many of these are well known as dominant mass forms in Arctic bodies of water: *Maldane sarsi*, *Harmothoe imbricata*, *Pelonaja corrugata*, *Byblis gaimardi*, *Lembos arcticus*, *Haploops tubicola*, *Scoloplos armiger*, *Chaetozone setosa*, *Lysippe labiata*, *Rhodine gracilior*, *Macoma calcarea*, *Crenella decussata*, *Lacuna divaricata*, *Margarita helicina*, *Natica clausa*, *Venus fluctuosa* and *Ophiopholis aculeata*. All these species are present as dominant or characteristic forms in the bottom-living biocoenoses of the Barents Sea.

At depths below 80 to 100 m a number of similar species such as *Ophiura sarsi*, *Ctenodiscus crispatus*, *Heliometra glacialis*, *Ophiocantha bidentata*, *Stegophiura nodosa*, *Travisia forbesi*, *Lysippe labiata*, *Polycirrus medusa*, *Myriochele oculata*, *Lumbriconereis fragilis* and others are also included. On the other hand, in the upper horizons, there is an admixture of tropical species such as the crustaceans *Blephariposa japonica*, *Calianassa* sp. and *Upogebia* sp., *Charybdis japonicus*, the molluscs *Alaba* sp., *Alectrion* sp. and others.

K. Gordeeva (1949) added to Derjugin's description of biocoenoses some supplementary data on the eastern part of Peter the Great Bay. A selection is given in *Table 311*.

The bottom-living fauna of the Sea of Japan becomes markedly poorer in species with increasing depth. Only fifty-three species of macrobenthos are known for depths of 1,000 to 2,000 m, twenty-five for 2,000 to 3,000 m and only five below 3,000 m (21 in the Sea of Okhotsk). Similarly the corresponding

Table 311

Depth, m, and soil	Dominant species of biocoenosis, number of species/m²	Mean biomass, g/m²	Remarks
15–35 sand	*Felaniella olivacea* (438)+*Scoloplos armiger*+*Olivella falgurata*	522·9	Molluscs constitute about three-quarters of biomass, echinoderms about one-quarter
30–35 sand	*Echinarachnius parma*+*Amphiodia rossica*+*Scoloplos armiger*	343·4	Echinoderms constitute about four-fifths of biomass, sipunculids about one-fifth
51–58 silty-sand	*Maldanidae* sp.+*Serripes groenlandicus*+*Lumbriconereis* sp.	398·5	Bivalves constitute four-fifths of biomass. H_2S present in soil
55–64 silty-sand	*Ampelisca macrocephala*+*Lumbriconereis* sp.+*Amphioplus macraspis*+*Plicifusus olivaceus*	182·4	More than half biomass composed of crustaceans, about one-quarter of echinoderms
80–200 firm sand	*Macoma calcarea*+*Ceriantharia*+*Maldanidae* sp.+*Ophiura sarsi*	212·6	Worms, Actinia, molluscs each form 28 per cent of biomass; the remainder are echinoderms
177–238 fine sand and mud	*Ophiopenia tetracantha* + *Ophiura sarsi*+*Verticordia nadina*—*Amphioplus macraspis*	158	Echinoderms form more than half of biomass
340	*Heliometra glacialis maxima*+*Ophiura sarsi*+*Verticordia nadina*	242	Biomass formed almost exclusively of echinoderms

numbers of species of Foraminifera are fifty-two, nine and three (14 in the Sea of Okhotsk). This is much less than in the neighbouring Okhotsk and Bering Seas (O. Mokievsky, 1954). It is well known that the true deep-water fauna is absent from the abyssal in the Sea of Japan. The most eurybathic sublittoral organisms descend into it. The youth of this faunal group is reflected in the fact that it has not yet had time to acquire an endemic character. Only very few deep-water forms can be called endemic (the polychaetes *Harmothoe derjugini* and *Tharix pacifica*; the echinoderms *Pedicillaster orientalis*; and the crab *Chionoecetus angulatus bathyalis*). At the same time a large number of eurybathic species with a wide vertical habitat live in the depths of the Sea of Japan (the polychaetes *Capitella capitata*, *Maldane sarsi*, *Terebellides stroemi*, *Artacama proboscidea*, *Harmothoe impar*, *Spiochaetopterus typicus*, *Chaetozone setosa*; the molluscs *Thyasira flexuosa*; and the echinoderms *Ctenodiscus crispatus* and *Ophiocantha bidentata*). All these forms are also widely distributed in the Arctic seas.

Boreal forms also live in the depths of the Sea of Japan (the polychaetes *Notoproctus oculatus*, *Aricidea succica*; the crustaceans *Nicippe tumida*, *Urothoe denticulata*, *Nectocrangon dentata*, *Eualus biunguis*; the molluscs

Table 312

Depth, m	Biomass, g/m²		
	Mean	Maximum	Minimum
100–200	306	907	6·3
200–500	92	168	15·2
500–1,000	36	138	0·2
1,000–2,000	10	27	0·15
2,000–3,000	2·2	6	0·05
3,000–3,500	0·23	0·45	0·08

Yoldiella derjugini, *Yoldia beringiana*, *Propeamussium randolphi*, *Ruccinum bryani*; the echinoderms *Leptychaster anomalus*, *Synalactes nozamai* and others). In the Sea of Japan the biomass also decreases markedly as depth increases (O. Mokievsky, 1954) (*Table 312*).

As can be seen from *Table 312* the biomass decreases 1,300 times with depth but the range of its fluctuations is considerably curtailed.

K. Derjugin (1933, 1935, 1939) has observed the following characteristics of the fauna (both plankton and benthos) of the great depths of the Sea of Japan: qualitative and quantitative impoverishment, absence of typically abyssal elements, and the sinking to unusual depths of members of the sub-littoral and bathyal fauna. The plankton of the depths of the Sea of Japan (K. Brodsky, 1941; M. Vinogradov, 1953) includes: Radiolaria of the families Challengeridae and Aulospheridae; the Siphonophora *Dymophies arctica*; the Ctenophora *Beroe* sp.; the Copepoda *Gaetanus minor*, *Gaidius brevispinus*, *Eucalanus bungii*, *Pareuchaeta japonica*, *Calanus cristatus*, *C. tonsus* (*plumchrus*), *Scolecithricella minor*, *Microcalanus pigmaeus*, *Metridia lucens* (*pacifica*), *Oncaea borealis*, *Microsatella rosea*; the Ostracoda *Conchaecia* spp.; the Amphipoda *Primno macropa*, *Parathemisto japonica*; the Mysidae *Meterythrops microphthalma*, and the Euphausiidae *Euphausia pacifica*, *Thysanoessa longipes*, *Th. inermis*. A comparison between the zooplankton biomass of the Sea of Japan and of the adjacent regions of the Pacific Ocean shows the considerable poverty of the former (*Table 313*).

M. Vinogradov had approached this problem differently (1959), following

Table 313. Plankton biomass (mg/m³) in the Sea of Japan (K. Brodsky, 1941) and in the Kuril–Kamchatka trench (M. Vinogradov, 1954)

Depth m	Sea of Japan		Kuril–Kamchatka trench, May–June
	Winter	Mean annual	
0–50	313	530	510
50–100	305	230	379
100–200	89	120	288
200–500	147	114	228
500·1,000	89	90	59·3
1,000–2,000	0·3	0·3	21·8

the analogy of the deep-water plankton of the Sea of Japan. While not denying the fact that the penetration of the deep-water plankton forms into the Sea of Japan from the adjacent part of the Pacific Ocean is restricted by the shallowness of the straits leading into it, Vinogradov draws attention also to the contemporary physicochemical characteristics of the Sea of Japan as a possible limiting factor. He confirms the conclusions of previous investigators that only 'those species which, in the adjacent waters of the Pacific Ocean and the Sea of Okhotsk, live at depths of less than 200 to 500 m are found in the deep-water plankton of the Sea of Japan; they rise during their daily migrations at least to 50 to 100 m'. Many of the plankton and benthos species sink down in the Sea of Japan to much greater depths than those which are usual for them in the Pacific Ocean. Qualitatively and quantitatively, however, the deep-water fauna of the Sea of Japan is considerably impoverished. Vinogradov has remarked on the large number of plankton species found in the upper layers of the Ocean in the areas adjacent to the straits which do not penetrate into the Sea of Japan.

The deep waters of the Sea of Japan have a lower temperature (0·12° to 0·22°) and somewhat lesser salinity (34·08 to 34·14‰) than the adjacent parts of the Pacific Ocean and the Bering and Okhotsk Seas (−1·55° to 2·2°; 34·61 to 34·72‰). The main explanation of the absence of a specific deep-water plankton in the Sea of Japan, in Vinogradov's opinion, is associated with this difference in temperature and salinity conditions which might, he thinks, possess the significance of a decisive factor, independently of the geological past of the Sea.

In recent years the littoral fauna of the Sea of Japan has been investigated by O. Mokievsky (1956, 1959), who has found much similarity between the littoral fauna of the northern part of the Tartary Strait and the Sea of Okhotsk, which are characterized by homogeneous colonies of comparatively large-sized, mainly secular species. The rocks of the sublittoral and the supralittoral here are inhabited by *Littorina sitchana subtenebrosa*. Differences are observed in the barnacles of the supralittoral: while mixed colonies of *Balanus balanoides* and *Chthamalus dalli*, with a predominance of the former, are characteristic of the Sea of Okhotsk, in the Sea of Japan the supralittoral is populated almost exclusively by *Chth. dalli*. Lower down live organisms which are also characteristic of the Sea of Okhotsk: *Acmaea testudinalis*, *Littorina squalida*, *Thais lima*, large Gammaridae (*Gammarus locustoides*, *Echinogammarus spasskii* and others), *Idothea ochotensis*; loosely packed soil is inhabited by *Nereis vexillosa*, *Eteone longa*, *Arenicola claparedi* and a few *Macoma baltica*. It is to be noted that these last five species have not been observed in the littoral of the central and southern Primor'e. The fauna of fucii and other sea-weed growths, abundant in the northern part of the Tartary Strait, is very poor both qualitatively and quantitatively. The number of specimens is commonly not more than 100 to 2,000 per m², the biomass being from 25 to 150 g/m².

In the central and southern Primor'e the fauna of the upper horizons of the rocky littoral changes comparatively little. However, Mokievsky describes some marked alterations in the sublittoral. Patchy growths of brown algae are populated by a varied and extremely numerous fauna of small crustaceans: Amphipoda (*Caprella* spp., *Jassa pulchella*, *Ischyrocerus* spp., *Parhyale zibellina*, *Allorchestes* spp., *Pontogensia* spp. and others); Isopoda (*Dynamenella glabra*, *Janiropsis kincaidi*); Polychaeta of the families Syllidae and Nereidae; small Gastropoda (*Cingula* spp., and others), and a number of other groups. Some of these species are altogether absent from the northern part of the Tartary Inlet; others are peculiar only to various biocoenoses of the sublittoral, others again are found only in insignificant numbers. South of the Tartary Strait the number of these inhabitants of the brown sea-weed beds of the sublittoral usually varies from 10,000 to 200,000 specimens per m^2 with a small biomass (usually 50 to 150 g/m^2, rising to 200 to 500 g/m^2 only in Corallina beds). The fauna of the loose soils of the Primor'e also changes considerably.

Mokievsky explains these marked differences in the composition, and especially in the distribution, of the littoral fauna of the two parts of the Sea of Japan not only by the changes of temperature and climatic conditions, but also by differences in its tidal ranges—the range of the tides in the northern part of the Tartary Strait being over 2 m and in the central and southern Primor'e, on the average, 1 m.

Mokievsky maintains that moisture conditions are basically different on littorals with low and high tidal ranges, inasmuch as in the first case the tidal effect on the sea-level is commonly moderated by the swell and by seasonal and sporadic fluctuations of the level; while in the second case there is a precise tidal rhythm—semi-diurnal, diurnal or a mixture of the two. Pointing out that the taxonomic composition of coastal flora and fauna is determined first of all by the temperature factor, Mokievsky attaches very great importance to the character of its moistening (in terms of the height of the tide) in the formation of such features of the littoral as its zonality, the nature of its biocoenoses and the quantitative indices and ratios. On this basis he distinguishes two types of littoral in the Soviet Far Eastern Seas. In his opinion the littoral of the Sea of Okhotsk, of most of the Barents Sea, of the eastern coast of Kamchatka and of almost the whole of the Kuril Range, and also of the northern part of the Tartary Strait, belongs to the type of north-boreal littoral with a long tidal range (from 1·15 m to 10 or even 13 m), while the central and southern Primor'e and the southwestern coast of Sakhalin belong to the south-boreal type with a short tidal range.

In contrast to other Far Eastern Seas the variety of fish in the Sea of Japan is exceptionally great [about 615 species; among them, in the northern part from Peter the Great Bay to Sakhalin and the Tartary Strait, 245 have been distinguished (T. Rass)]. This is a meeting place of cold-water fish and subtropical and tropical fish which have penetrated into the Sea of Japan from the south with the Tsushima current. The tropical and subtropical fish comprise members of the families Gobiidae (30 species), Chaetodontidae, Serranidae (15 species), Pharyngognathi, Balistidae, Monocanthidae, Ostraciidae, Labridae (11 species), Carangidae (12 species) and Tetrodontidae (12 species).

The number of tropical and subtropical fish decreases sharply as one moves northward; and in Peter the Great Bay the dominant forms are already such cold-living families as Pleuronectidae (10 species), Cottidae (37 species), Agonidae (14 species), Liparidae and Cyclopteridae (13 species), Pholidae and Stichaeidae (21 species). However tuna fish, Trichiurus, Geriola, Auxis and others have also been recorded in Peter the Great Bay in summer.

An even more cold-water aspect is acquired by fish in the Tartary Strait, warm-water species being rare there; in summer, however, the hammer-head shark, the ray Trygon akjci, sayra, Trichiurus, and some others enter the Strait. Warm-water fish penetrate much father northward along the eastern side of the Sea of Japan and even through La Perouse Strait into the southern part of the Sea of Okhotsk and to the southern Kuril Islands. Hence the entire Sea of Japan, so far as its ichthyofauna is concerned, may be included in the boreal region, with the possible exception of its most southerly part. The remarkable similarity of the fish of the Sea of Japan and of the Mediterranean Sea has often been noted (A. Gunther, 1880). G. Lindberg (1947) gives a list of 90 families, 63 genera and 12 species common to these two seas.

Until recently only eight oceanic deep-water fish had been recorded in the Sea of Japan (T. Rass, 1954), but it has now been shown that their number is greater, due to some additional species which inhabit the southeastern part.

There are apparently about twenty 'secondary' deep-water fish (in Andriashev's terminology).

About 40 species of the fish in the Sea of Japan are of commercial value. Until recently the Pacific sardine (*Sardinops sagax melanostictus*) was among the most important. Soviet sardine fisheries were rapidly developed in the 'thirties, and by 1937 they were taking 1·4 million centners a year; but they began to decrease in 1940 and during the 'forties ceased altogether. The sardines disappeared from the Sea of Japan as a consequence of a considerable fall in temperature. They ceased to enter their usual spawning-places and abundant grazing groups in the Sea of Japan, and one may suppose that large numbers of sardine fry perished owing to unfavourable temperature conditions and a shortage of food. Pacific herring (Fig. 384) (*Clupea harengus pallasi*) has for a long time occupied an important place in the fisheries there. Herring aggregations are particularly large during their spawning migrations to the coast of Hokkaido and the Primor'e and especially in the waters of southern Sakhalin. The number of herrings approaching the shores is greater than anywhere else in the world . . . 'the approach of the shoals of herring to the shores of southern Sakhalin in April is sighted by the fishermen from far away by the colour and movement of the water and by the behaviour of the sea-birds: flocks of sea-gulls and kittiwakes start circling over the water, filling the air with their cries' (P. Schmidt, 1948). 'The herring lay their eggs on the coastal sea-weeds, in the shallowest patches on the shores. The male herring discharges its milt in such amounts that the water frequently becomes milky white for many hundreds of metres from the coast; since milt is fatty, the swell on the banks is calmed as if oil had been poured on to it, and the surface of the Sea becomes smooth. So many ova are laid that, if there is a storm and the ova are cast up on the shore, they form a regular bank which when it dries out, is turned into a soft carpet some few metres wide, stretching for kilometres along the coast' (P. Schmidt, 1948).

Among the bottom-living fish of the Sea of Japan, the cod *Gadus morrhua macrocephalus* and *Theragra chalcogramma*, and Soleidae, Cynoglossidae and other flatfish except halibut are those usually fished for.

Some pelagic fish enter the Sea of Japan for feeding and reproduction,

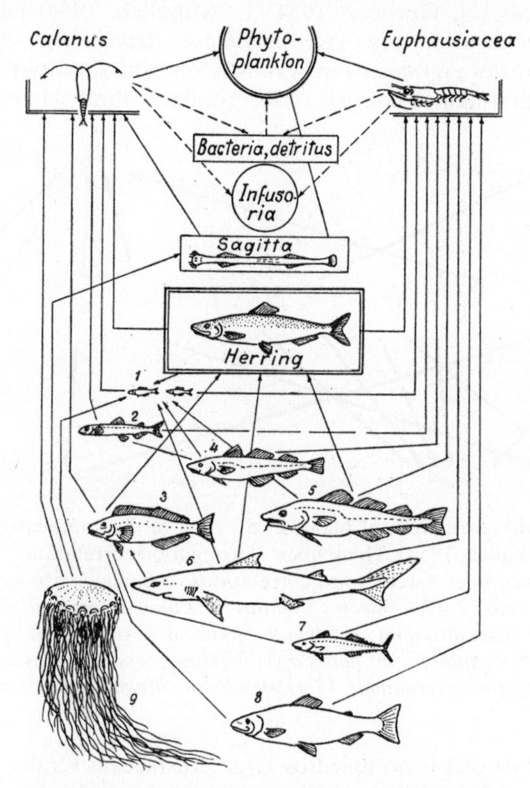

FIG. 384. Diagram of Feeding correlation between the herring and other organisms. *1* Fish fry; *2* Caplin; *3* Starling; *4* Navaga; *5* Cod; *6* Shark; *7* Skumbria; *8* Pink salmon; *9* Jellyfish.

wintering, however, outside its boundaries (sardines, mackerel). In January to March the main mackerel aggregations of the Sea of Japan are concentrated within the area of the Tsushima Strait, at a temperature of 12° to 15°. As the temperature rises mackerel penetrates the Sea of Japan along its eastern and western shores, reaching the Tartary Strait by August and the beginning of September. With the cold autumn weather mackerel moves in the reverse direction. Mackerel spawns in the coastal zone, in inlets and bays, from April to the middle of June, and in Peter the Great Bay in June and July.

Characteristically, mackerel feeds intensively during the period of its spawning migration. After spawning, mackerel concentrates in the northern part of the Sea in large numbers for feeding. It feeds mostly on large copepods (*Calanus tonsus*, *C. finmarchicus*) and euphausiids (*Thysanoessa raschii* and *Th.* sp.) and, as a predator, consumes also fish fry.

The study of the feeding habits of flatfish (Pleuronectidae family) of the Far Eastern Seas (N. Gordeev, 1954; L. Mikulich, 1954) has shown that halibut (*Hippoglossus hippoglossus stenolepis*, *Reinhardtius hippoglossoides matsurae*, *Atherestes evermanni*) lives mostly on fish. Seventy-two per cent of the diet of the first-named consists of fish (pollack, sand-eel and others). The

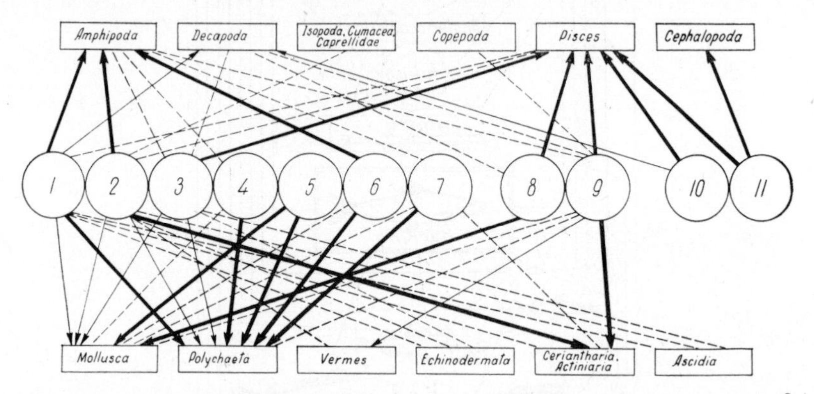

FIG. 385. Food correlation of plaice in the area of the southeastern coast of Sakhalin (Mikulich, 1954). Thick lines—strong food correlations; thin lines—average, broken lines—weak food correlations. 1 *Limanda aspera*; 2 *Platessa quadrituberculata*; 3 *Pleuronectes stellatus*; 4 *Limanda punctatissima proboscidea*; 5 *L. p. punctatissima*; 6 *Glyptocephalus stelleri*; 7 *Pseudopleuronectes yokohamae*; 8 *Acanthopsetta nadeshnyi*; 9 *Hippoglossoides elassodon dubius*; 10 *Atheresthes evermanni*; 11 *Hippoglossus hippoglossus stenolepis*.

second place in its diet is occupied by large crustaceans (crabs, hermit crabs, amphipods, prawns) and large molluscs (*Seripes groenlandicus* and cephalopods).

The majority of the Pacific Ocean flatfish, in contrast to halibut, are benthopages (worms, polychaetes, molluscs, sometimes bottom-living crustaceans and echinoderms). The diet of some flatfish is mixed, both fish and pelagic crustaceans forming at times a considerable part of it (Figs. 385 and 386). Stomach repletion indices of halibut and flatfish are 150 to 200, rising sometimes to 300 or even 600. The nature of the food of the Far Eastern Pleuronectidae, both halibut and flat flounder, is very similar to that of those in the Atlantic.

Owing to the peculiar temperature conditions of the surface water and the narrowness of the shelf zone, the migrations of Pleuronectidae in the Sea of Japan have a destructive character, similar to that of cod and Kamchatka crab (Fig. 387). In summer they feed intensively in the off-shore areas which

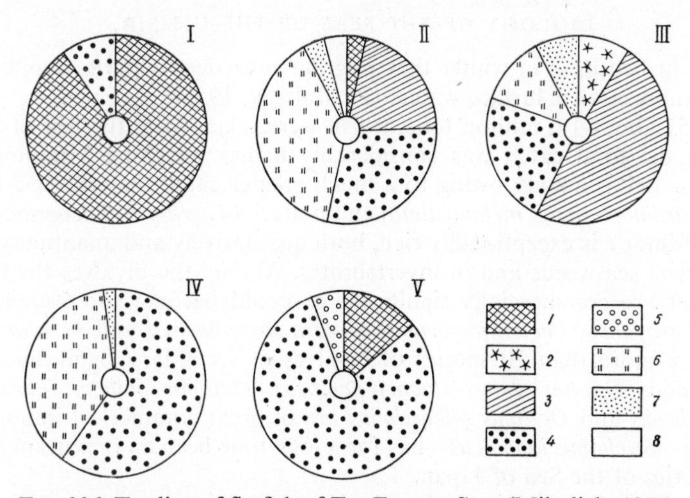

FIG. 386. Feeding of flatfish of Far Eastern Seas (Mikulich, 1951). I *Hippoglosus hippoglossus stenolepis* (Bering Sea); II *Limanda aspera* (southwestern coast of Sakhalin); III *Pseudopleuronectes herzensteini* (southwestern coast of Sakhalin); IV *Pleuronectes stellatus* (western and eastern coast of Sakhalin) ; V *Hippoglossoides elassodon dubius* (Tartary Strait, Syurkum Cape). *1* Pisces; *2* Echinodermata; *3* Mollusca; *4* Crustacea (bottom-living); *5* Crustacea (pelagic); *6* Polychaeta; *7* Varia; *8* Sea-bed.

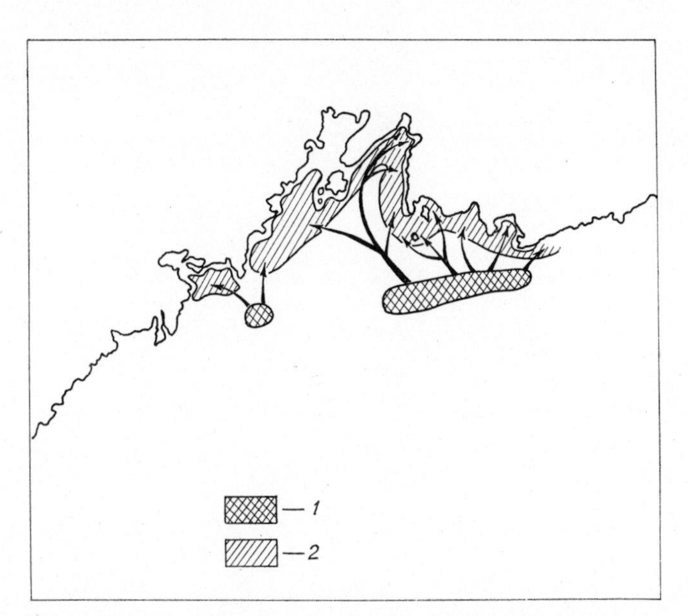

FIG. 387. Plaice migrations in Peter the Great Bay (Moiseev). *1* Winter shoalings; *2* Summer shoalings.

are rich in benthos; in winter they migrate into deeper parts, avoiding the considerably cooled surface waters (P. Moiseev, 1955).

In 1955 about 1·6 million tons of fish were taken from the Sea of Japan. In 1936 the total catch was considerably higher, reaching 3 million tons (T. Rass, 1948), mainly owing to a much greater catch than in 1955 of sardines (*Sardinops sagax melanosticta*) and pollack (*Theragra chalcogramma*).

The Primor'e is exceptionally rich, both qualitatively and quantitatively, in commercial sea-weeds and in invertebrates. Among the bivalves the following either are commercially significant or could become so: *Ostrea gigas. Mytilus grayanus*, *Pecten jessoensis*, *Mactra sachalinensis* and *Mya arenaria*, There are more than 20 species of bivalves of secondary significance. The cephalopods *Ommastrephes sloanei pacificus*, *Octopus dofleini*, *Paroctopus conispadiceus* and *Octopus gilbertianus* are of great commerical importance. Trepang—*Stichopus japonicus*—has for a long time been an important item in the fisheries of the Sea of Japan.

Apart from Kamchatka crab, the decapod crustaceans *Pandalus latirostris*, *Sclerocrangon selebrosa*, *Crangon septemspinosa* and some others are of great importance in the fisheries of the waters of the Primor'e and southern Sakhalin. Stocks of all these invertebrates are very large in the Sea of Japan, and the prospects of their commerical development are immense.

15

The Sea of Okhotsk

I. PHYSICAL GEOGRAPHY

The Sea of Okhotsk is separated from the Pacific Ocean by the Kuril Islands. Numerous deep straits, but none deeper than 2,318 m (Boussole), run between them. The great Kuril range, which rises above sea-level as a chain of islands, forms a submarine barrier—the 'Vityaz ridge'—with its eastern slopes sinking down to 10·3 km into the depths of the Kuril–Kamchatka trench. This geosyncline zone, of the Tertiary or pre-Tertiary Period, runs from southwest to northeast comprising the south Okhotsk trench, the two Kuril ranges divided by a trench, the deep-water Kuril–Kamchatka trench and the bank which borders its southeastern side.

The process of the formation of the geosyncline zone of the Kuril–Kamchatka arch is not yet complete, and it is particularly active in its northern part; it is connected with the phenomenon of the overthrust of the Continental block of Eastern Asia on to the bed of the Pacific Ocean (G. Udintzev, 1955).

The area of the Sea of Okhotsk is 1,590,000 km^2, the volume of its waters 1,365,000 km^3, its maximum depth 3,657 m, and its average depth 859 m. In area the Sea of Okhotsk occupies second place after the Bering Sea among the seas washing the shores of the U.S.S.R., while in volume it is fourth, after the Bering, Japan and Black Seas. Its area is 42 times greater than that of the Sea of Azov and its volume 4,500 times greater. The bottom topography of the Sea of Okhotsk is rich in features (Fig. 388). To the south a deep trench stretches in a latitudinal direction, south of 48° N, demarcated from the northern part of the Sea by the 3,000 m isobath and a steep slope down to the 15,000 m isobath. Its central part is 1,000 to 1,500 m. deep forming, however, some terraced elevations: two at a depth of approximately 1,000 m cutting the central hollow of the Sea into two parts, and a northern ledge at a depth of about 200 m bordering the northern shallows (the shelf proper) on the southern side. The circulation of sea-water (Fig. 389) is greatly influenced by the two terraced elevations, and the distribution of bottom deposits is determined by them (Fig. 391).

Small streams of warm Pacific Ocean surface waters penetrate into the Sea of Okhotsk through the northern Kuril Straits, warming the western shores of Kamchatka, some even reaching Shelekhov Bay in small amounts. The main masses of these warm waters, partly under the effect of the general system of cyclonic rotation, turn westward and break up in a fanlike manner in the central part of the Sea. Warm surface waters can be traced by the presence of the crustacean *Calanus tonsus* (Fig. 390).

Deep Pacific Ocean waters, entering the Sea of Okhotsk mainly through the Kruzenshtern Strait, fill the central hollow of the Sea and, moving northward under the influence of the bottom topography, turn westward at each

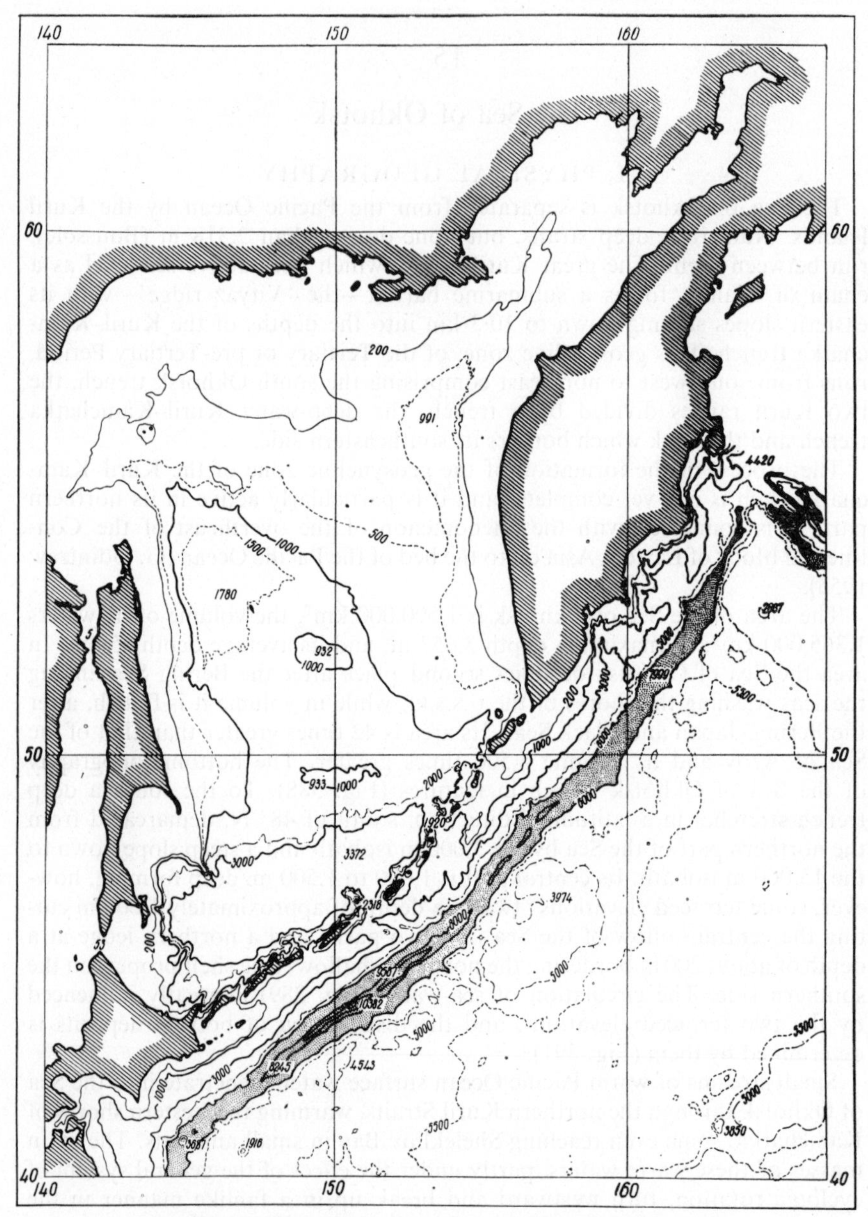

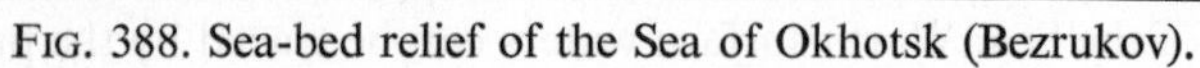
FIG. 388. Sea-bed relief of the Sea of Okhotsk (Bezrukov).

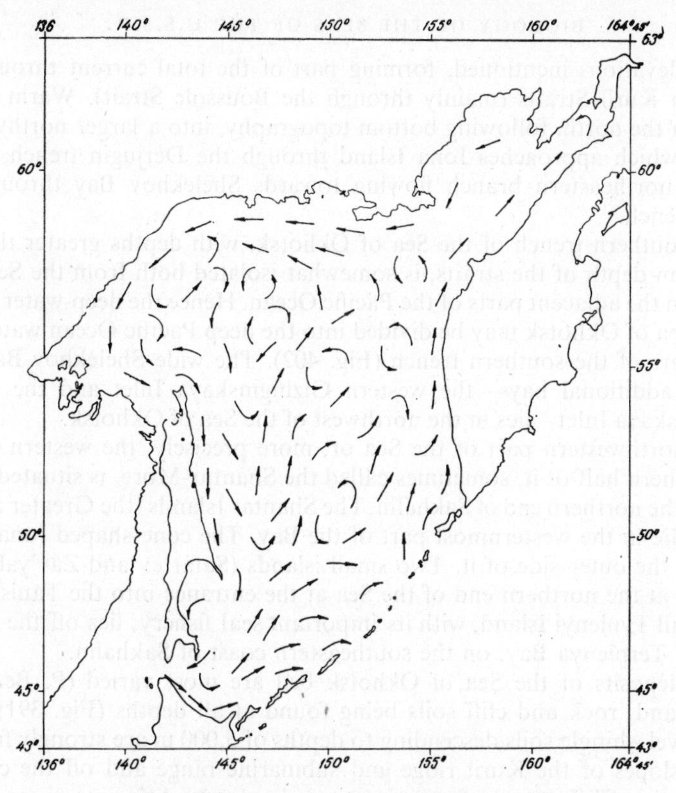

FIG. 389. Currents of Sea of Okhotsk (diagram).

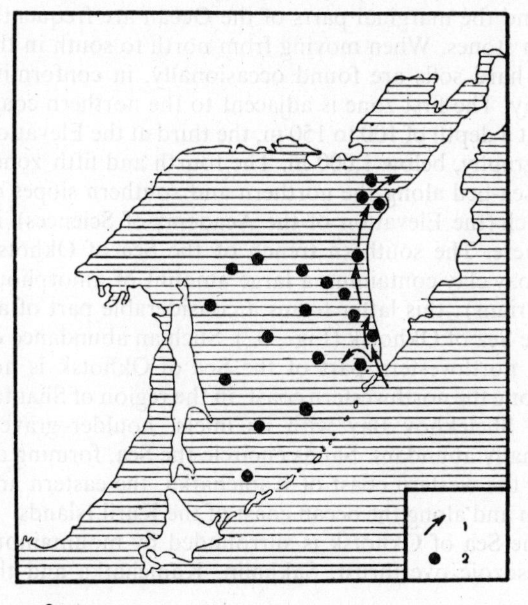

FIG. 390. Distribution of *Calanus tonsus*. *1* Directions of current; *2* Calanus distribution (Lubny-Gertzyk, 1955).

of the elevations mentioned, forming part of the total current through the southern Kuril Straits (mainly through the Boussole Strait). Warm waters divide in the north, following bottom topography, into a larger northwestern branch which approaches Iona Island through the Derjugin trench, and a smaller northeastern branch flowing towards Shelekhov Bay through the Tinro trench.

The southern trench of the Sea of Okhotsk, with depths greater than the maximum depth of the straits, is somewhat isolated both from the Sea itself and from the adjacent parts of the Pacific Ocean. Hence the deep-water masses of the Sea of Okhotsk may be divided into the deep Pacific Ocean waters and the waters of the southern trench (Fig. 402). The wide Shelekhov Bay with its two additional bays—the western Gizhiginskaya Inlet and the eastern Penzhinskaya Inlet—lies in the northwest of the Sea of Okhotsk.

The northwestern part of the Sea or, more precisely, the western part of the northern half of it, sometimes called the Shantar-More, is situated northwest of the northern end of Sakhalin. The Shantar Islands (the Greater and the Lesser) lie in the westernmost part of the Bay. The cone-shaped Iona Island rises on the outer side of it. Two small islands (Safar'ev and Zav'yalov) are situated at the northern end of the Sea at the entrance into the Tauisk Inlet. The small Tyulenyi Island, with its important seal fishery, lies off the eastern coast of Terpienya Bay, on the southeastern coast of Sakhalin.

The deposits of the Sea of Okhotsk bed are most varied (P. Bezrukov, 1955), sand, rock and cliff soils being found at all depths (Fig. 391). Cliffs and gravel–shingle soils descending to depths of 3,000 m are strongly featured on the slopes of the Kuril ridge and submarine range and off the coast of Kamchatka. Cliff outcrop formations may be due to different causes such as volcanic activity, the abruptness of the slopes, or the rapid currents. Even the floor of the Kuril Straits and the marginal parts of the Ocean are frequently covered by coarsely broken stones, When moving from north to south in the Sea of Okhotsk, zones of hard soils are found occasionally, in conformity with the bottom topography. The first zone is adjacent to the northern coast (Fig. 402); the second lies at a depth of 100 to 150 m, the third at the Elevation of the Institute of Oceanography, below 1,000 m. The fourth and fifth zones lie on the elevation of the sea-bed along the northern and southern slopes of the southern Okhotsk trench (the Elevation of the Academy of Sciences), in Boussole Strait and elsewhere. The southern trench of the Sea of Okhotsk is filled with soft ooze or oozy clay containing a large amount of amorphous silica (diatoms and radiolarians); this latter forms a considerable part of all the deposits throughout the Sea of Okhotsk (Fig. 392). Such an abundance of silica as that found in the northwestern part of the Sea of Okhotsk is not known in any other sea. Along the northwestern coast, in the region of Shantar and Iona Islands, and in Shelekhov Bay with its inlets, boulder–gravel–shingle floors are exceptionally abundant. Sands encircle the Sea, forming an especially wide zone along the western coast of Kamchatka, the eastern and northern shores of Sakhalin and along the ocean coast of the Kuril Islands.

On the mainland side the Sea of Okhotsk is surrounded by mountainous formations, mostly of Mesozoic overthrust. Sakhalin, Kamchatka and the

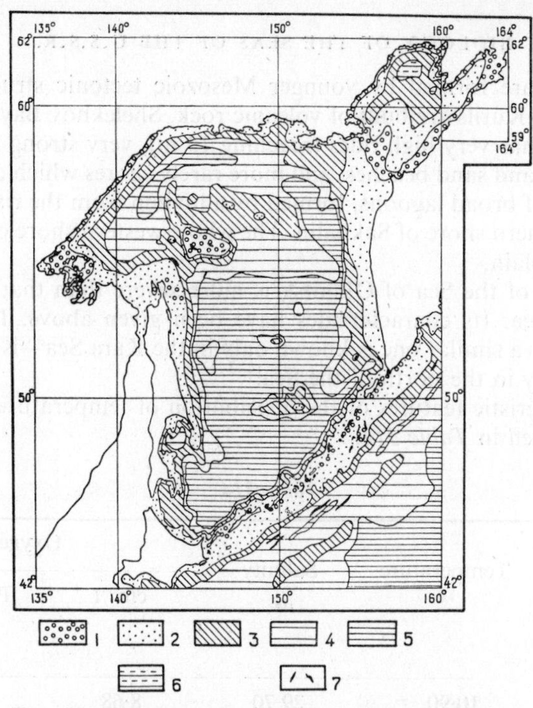

FIG. 391. Bottom soils of Sea of Okhotsk (Bezrukov). *1* Boulder–shingle–gravel deposits; *2* Sands; *3* Aleurites; *4* Aleurites–clay–diatomaceous oozes; *6* Aleurites–clay oozes without silica; *7* Outcrops of rock.

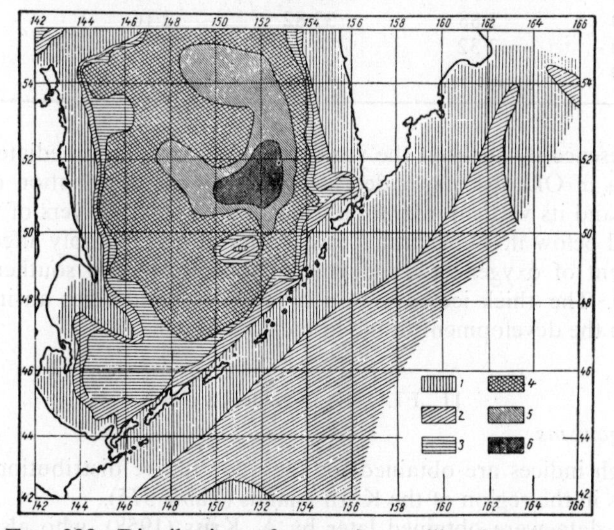

FIG. 392. Distribution of amorphous silica in surface layer of soils of Sea of Ohkotsk. *1* Less than 10 per cent; *2* From 10 to 20; *3* From 20 to 30; *4* From 30 to 40; *5* From 40 to 50; *6* More than 50 per cent (Bezrukov, 1955).

Kuril Islands are formed by younger Mesozoic tectonic structures. Kamchatka and the Kurils are built of volcanic rock. Shelekhov Bay, especially in its inner part, has very high tides (reaching 13 m), very strong tidal currents and wide rock and sand beaches, and more rarely shores which dry out at low tide. A series of broad lagoons, formed by alluvium from the rivers, stretches along the northern shore of Sakhalin. The whole western shore of Kamchatka is an alluvial plain.

The climate of the Sea of Okhotsk is more severe than that of any other Far Eastern Sea. Its characteristics have been given above. Its cold intermediate layer—a similar one is known only in the Kara Sea—is exceptionally wide, especially in the north of the Sea.

The characteristic features of the distribution of temperature, salinity and oxygen are given in *Table 314*.

Table 314

Depth m	Temperature °C	Salinity ‰	Oxygen	
			cm^3/l	Percentage of complete saturation
0	10·90	29·70	8·68	103·2
50	−1·58	32·88	8·10	95·0
75	−1·67	32·97	—	—
100	−1·51	33·04	7·58	89·2
150	0·10	33·33	4·87	60·0
200	0·78	33·46	4·10	51·4
500	1·88	33·82	2·16	28·6
1,000	2·32	—	0·77	10·0
1,500	2·32	34·29	0·70	9·2

The presence throughout the year of a substantial intermediate cold layer in the Sea of Okhotsk has a decisive effect on the distribution of the zooplankton and its vertical migration, since it cuts off the layers of water lying above and below it. The benthos distribution is considerably affected by the low content of oxygen in the depths of the central and southern trenches (Fig. 393). The thick ice cover which forms in winter has an immense influence on the development of life in the coastal zone.

II. FLORA AND FAUNA

Micro-organisms

Fairly high indices are obtained for the quantitative distribution of microorganisms in the region of the Kuril Islands (*Table 315*).

Similar data were obtained later by A. Kriss (1958), who also gives the mean biomass of micro-organisms for the Kuril–Kamchatka trench. It is evident from the data of the two columns in *Table 315* that the number of micro-organisms decreases with depth by some thousands of times (1,500 to 5,500).

Kriss also mentions the immense number (maybe thousands per 1 ml of water) of suspended articles in the water, from a few to a hundred microns

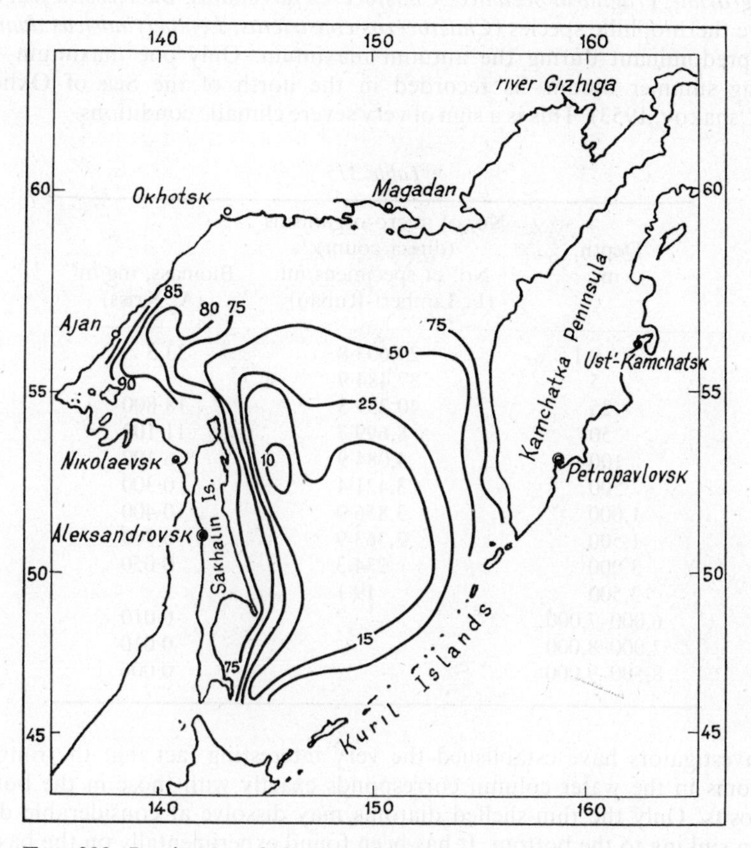

FIG. 393. Isoxigenes of the near-bottom layer of Sea of Okhotsk (Ushakov).

in size. The huge absorption surface of these small bodies is, according to this investigator, most significant for an understanding of the biological and physicochemical processes taking place in the water column.

Plankton

The list of the phytoplankton of the Sea of Okhotsk contains 290 species of diatoms and 58 species of peridineans (P. Ushakov, 1953).

According to the data of A. Zhuze and G. Semina (1955) diatomaceous sea-weeds are markedly predominant in the Sea of Okhotsk phytoplankton, comprising from 70 to 100 per cent of its biomass. This latter may reach

20 g/m^3 with 7 milliards of cells per 1 m^3; this conforms with the abundance of (amorphous) silica in the surface layers of the soil (up to 35 per cent and in some parts of the Sea more than 50). Arctic and Arctic-boreal species are predominant during the spring maximum (*Thalassiosira nordenskiöldii, Th. gravida, Fragilaria oceanica, Chaetoceros furcellatus, Bacterosira fragilis*). More thermophilic species (*Chaetoceros constrictus, Leptoclyindricus danicus*) are predominant during the autumn maximum. Only one maximum—the spring–summer bloom—is recorded in the north of the Sea of Okhotsk (P. Ushakov, 1953). This is a sign of very severe climatic conditions.

Table 315

Depth, m	No. of micro-organisms (direct count) No. of specimens/ml (E. Limbert-Ruban)	Biomass, mg/m^3 (A. Kriss)
0·1	29,603·8	33·3
5	37,484·9	
25	40,259·3	18·800
50	8,699·7	11·100
100	4,084·9	6·100
500	3,421·4	0·300
1,000	3,856·9	0·400
1,500	2,363·9	0·300
3,000	234·3	0·050
3,500	19·1	
6,000–7,000	—	0·010
7,000–8,000	—	0·010
8,500–9,000	—	0·006

Investigators have established the very interesting fact that the range of diatoms in the water column corresponds exactly with those in the bottom deposits. Only the thin-shelled diatoms may dissolve at considerable depth when sinking to the bottom. It has been found experimentally on the basis of the research mentioned, that the distance from the coast can be estimated by the composition of the diatoms in the deposits. In coastal areas neritic diatoms form 78 per cent of the deposits; in oceanic regions the same percentage is composed of oceanic species.

The composition of the diatoms in cores of the soil (16 to 27 m) from great depths of the Bering and Okhotsk Seas was examined by A. Zhuze (1954). The whole thickness of the deposit, taken in the core, does not go beyond the limits of the Quaternary Period; moreover, the composition of the diatoms according to horizons is exactly the same in both Seas. In the uppermost layer (1·5 to 1·8 m) are found all the diatoms now living in the plankton, mainly *Coscinodiscus oculus iridis, C. marginatus, Thalassiothrix longissima* and *Rhizosolenia hebetata*.

The composition of the diatoms in the 1·5 to 5 m layer of the soil is very mixed, with a predominance of neritic, re-deposited and fresh-water species. At depths of 5 to 11 m below the surface of the soil oceanic diatoms again become markedly predominant; there is, however, a considerable admixture of neritic forms. In the fourth horizon (10 to 16·5 m), as in the second, diatoms become scarce, while the neritic (possible glacial) and fresh-water forms are again predominant. Below about 16 m there is again a greater abundance of oceanic species with some neritic ones and some bottom-living diatoms of the Pliocene Age. Zhuze thinks it possible to synchronize the layers rich in oceanic diatoms and those which are poor in them but have an admixture of neritic and fresh-water forms with two periods of glaciation and two inter-glacial periods. The contemporary period has the most 'oceanic' aspect, and exchange between the Okhotsk and Bering Seas and the open Ocean is on a greater scale now than ever. Changes in the Foraminifera in the bottom deposits of the Sea of Okhotsk have also been comprehensively investigated (Kh. Saidova, 1953, 1955). About fifty such species were recorded, including those in the Bering Sea, and almost all of them exist at present. Examination of the successive layers of soil cores led Zhuze to the conclusion that during the deposition of the layer of the sea-bed examined the Sea of Okhotsk trenches underwent a submersion. The numbers of shallow-water and cold-water Foraminifera increase with the depth.

Cold-water organisms are predominant in the summer zooplankton in the north of the Sea of Okhotsk. The greatest plankton biomass (1,000 to 3,000 mg/m^3) was recorded in 1949 in the east of the region at depths of more than 25 m (Fig. 394) at some distance (100 to 150 km) from the coast (M. Kuhn, 1951). There was a considerable predominance of *Metridia* sp., *Oithona similis*, *Pseudocalanus elongatus*, *Microcalanus pygmaeus*, *Acartia longiremis*, *Sagitta* sp. and *Themisto libellula* in the upper horizons (less than 25 m). In the lower, most productive layers (below 25 m) and in addition to the *Metridia* sp. (45 to 50 per cent of the biomass) and *Themisto libellula* mentioned above, there was a predominance of *Calanus finmarchicus*, *C. tonsus*, *C. cristatus* and *Pareuchaeta japonica*. The temperature of these lower horizons is, however, below freezing point in summer. Some zooplankton species (*Metridia* sp., *Themisto libellula* and *Calanus finmarchicus*), in spite of the markedly cold intermediate layer, migrate freely through it.

A considerable admixture of warm-water and partly subtropical members of the Calanoida group appears in two areas of the Sea of Okhotsk. They are brought into the most southwesterly corner of the Sea through La Perouse Strait with branches of the Tsushima current. Warm-water plankton forms are also brought through the Kuril Straits by the warm Pacific waters into the southeastern part of the Sea. Species of the genera Clytemnestra, Claudocalanus, and Pleuromamma can be mentioned among these warm-water forms.

In the most northwesterly part of the Sea (Bay of Sakhalin) not only are estuarine and brackish-water species (*Eurytemora asymmetrica*, *E. herdmani*, *E. americana*, *Acartia bifilosa*, *Totanus derjugini*, *Sinacalanus tenellus*) greatly developed under the effect of the fresh water of the river Amur, but also the true fresh-water groups (Rotifera and Crustacea) are plentiful.

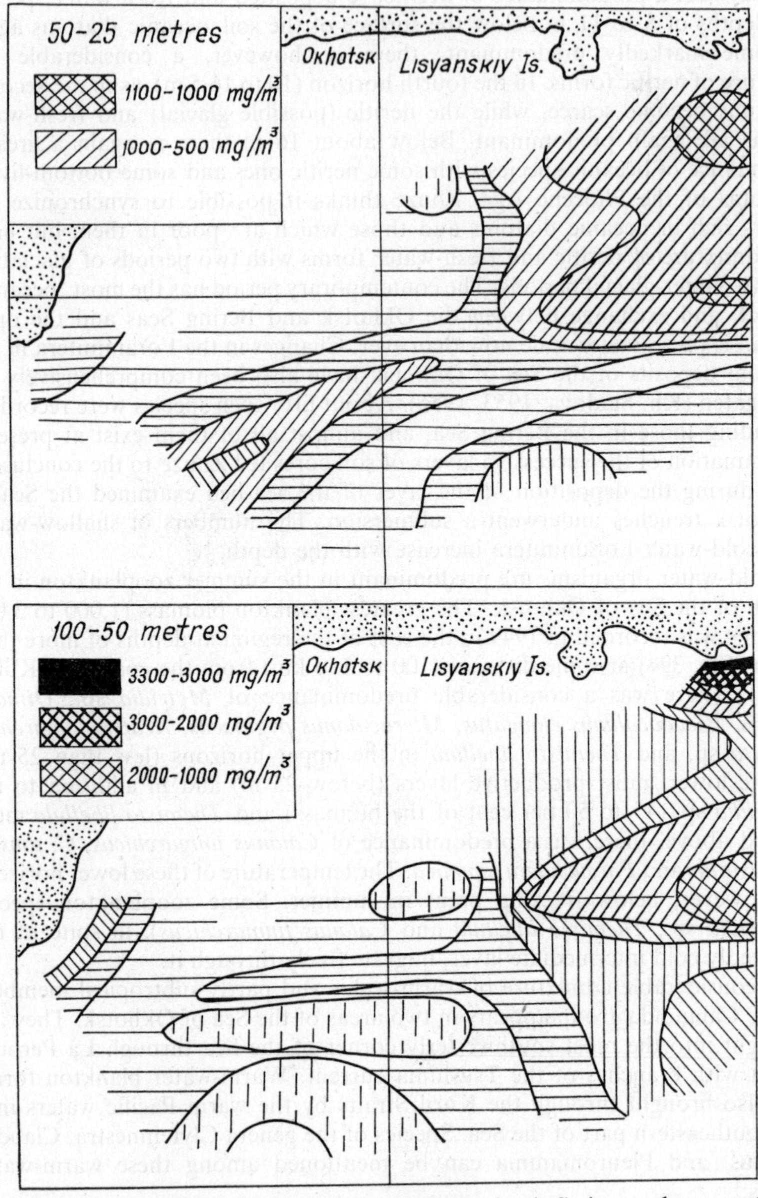

FIG. 394. Distribution of plankton biomass (mg/m^3) in northern part of Sea of Okhotsk in 1949, at the horizons 25 to 50 m and 50 to 100 m (Kusmorskaya).

Table 316. Vertical distribution of phytoplankton biomass and temperature ranges in central part of Sea of Okhotsk during the spring bloom

Depth, m	0	10	25	50
Biomass, mg/m³	1,200	1,600	110	30
Temperature, °C	10·90	—	—	1·58

The vertical distribution of Okhotsk plankton is greatly affected by the presence of the cold intermediate layer. Plankton biomass decreases markedly at depths of 40 to 50 m (*Table 316*), increasing again below the cold layer (at 100 to 150 m). This is clearly seen from specimens collected from the central part of the Sea during the spring bloom (Fig. 395) (M. Vinogradov, 1954).

This vertical distribution of plankton is consistent with the changes of temperature. The sinking of phytoplankton and the vertical migration of zooplankton is restricted by the high range of temperature and density in the upper and lower limits of the cold intermediate layer. *Oithona similis* and *Pseudocalanus elongatus* are adapted to the surface zone (*M. Vinogradov*, 1954). Zooplankton organisms, which are capable of diurnal and seasonal vertical migrations into the upper layer of the Sea, characterize the transitional cold zone. They are composed mainly of *Calanus tonsus* (*C. plumchrus*), *C. finmarchicus* and *C. cristatus*, *Eucalanus bungii*, *Metridia okhotensis* and, to a lesser extent, *M. pacifica* and *Oncea borealis*. The number of species in the deep layers is much higher, and some of them do not penetrate at all into the upper two horizons. These forms may be divided into two groups, those which migrate, and those which do not. The first group includes species living

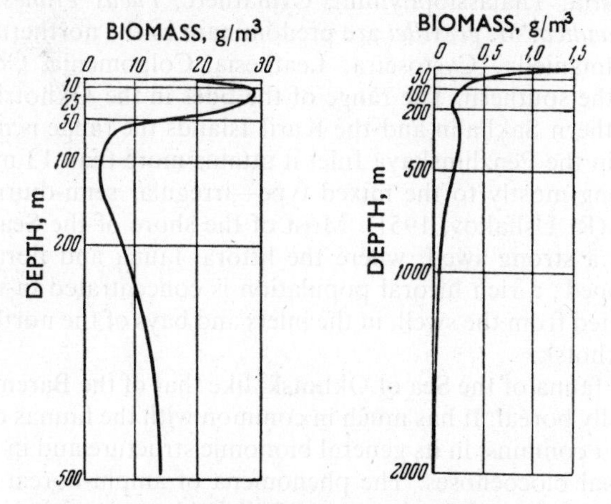

FIG. 395. Vertical distribution of zooplankton biomass (g/m²) in Sea of Okhotsk (left) and Bering Sea (right) (Vinogradov).

above 1,000 m (*Candacia columbiae*, *Racovitzanus antarcticus*, *Heterorhabdus tonneri*, *Pareuchaeta japonica* and others) and those adapted to greater depths (from 2,000 to 3,000 m) (*Pleuromamma scutulata*, *Scolecithricella ovata* and others). The species of the second group do not migrate and do not rise into the upper layer (*Halaptilus*, *pseudooxycephalus*, *Scaphocalanus magnus*, *Pseudociphella spinifera* and others).

The plankton of the Sea of Okhotsk is specially noted for its radiolarians; 81 species have been recorded there.

Benthos (Fig. 396)

The coastal flora of the Sea of Okhotsk comprises about 162 species of sea-weeds. The Kuril Islands flora is considerably richer (*Table 317*).

Table 317. Number of macrophyte species in the Sea of Okhotsk and Kuril Islands

Group	Sea of Okhotsk	Kuril Islands
Phaeophyceae	51	82
Rhodophyceae	80	101
Chlorophyceae	31	44
Total	162	227

The great wealth of species of the sea-weeds of the Kuril Islands is due to the penetration of a series of oceanic and mainly warm-water forms. The Kuril ridge may be divided, according to its coastal sea-weeds, into two regions—a northeastern one embracing all the main ridge, and the southern Islands of Urup, Iturup, Kunashir and all the islands of the small Kuril ridge. Laminaria, Thalassiophyllum, Cymathere, *Fucus evanescens*, *Monostroma groenlandica*, *M. grevillei* are predominant in the northern region, and Pelvetia, Kjelmaniella, Cystoseira, Leathesia, Colpomenia, Chondrus and Neodilsea in the southern. The range of the tides in the Okhotsk Sea is very great: on southern Sakhalin and the Kuril Islands the range is no more than 50 cm, while in the Penzhinskaya Inlet it attains more than 13 m. Moreover, the tides belong mostly to the mixed type—irregular semi-diurnal and irregular diurnal (R. Ushakov, 1951). Most of the shore of the Sea of Okhotsk is exposed to a strong swell, where the littoral fauna and flora are mostly poorly developed; a rich littoral population is concentrated in those coastal sectors protected from the swell, in the inlets and bays of the northern coast of the Sea of Okhotsk.

The littoral fauna of the Sea of Okhotsk, like that of the Barents and White Seas, is typically boreal. It has much in common with the faunas of these Seas, in the species it contains, in its general bionomic structure and in the structure of its individual biocoenoses. The phenomena of amphi-boreal resemblance is reflected in the littoral fauna, most of all in the mass development of its representative species: *Littorina rudis*, *L. sitchana*, *L. littores*, *L. squalida*, *Arenicola marina*, *A. claparedii*, *Nucella lapillus*, *Thais lima* and others. The

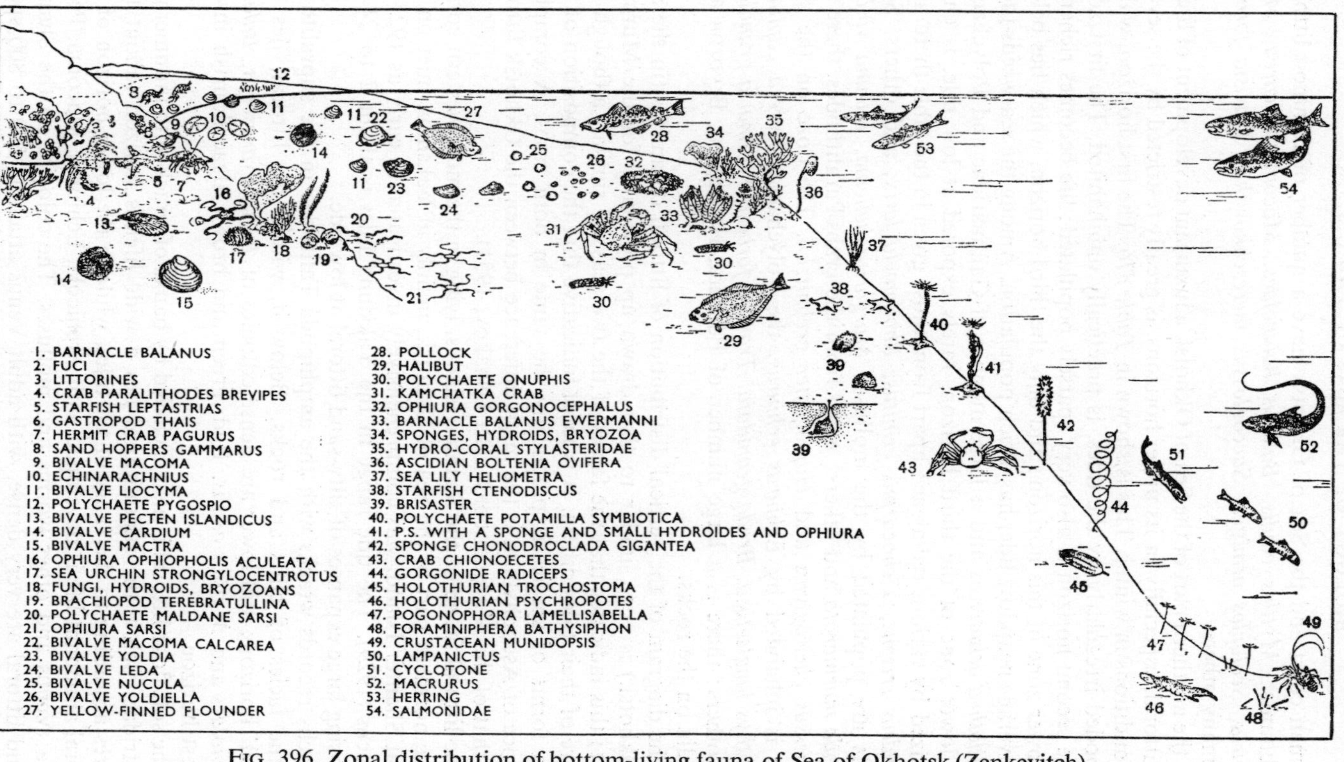
1. BARNACLE BALANUS
2. FUCI
3. LITTORINES
4. CRAB PARALITHODES BREVIPES
5. STARFISH LEPTASTRIAS
6. GASTROPOD THAIS
7. HERMIT CRAB PAGURUS
8. SAND HOPPERS GAMMARUS
9. BIVALVE MACOMA
10. ECHINARACHNIUS
11. BIVALVE LIOCYMA
12. POLYCHAETE PYGOSPIO
13. BIVALVE PECTEN ISLANDICUS
14. BIVALVE CARDIUM
15. BIVALVE MACTRA
16. OPHIURA OPHIOPHOLIS ACULEATA
17. SEA URCHIN STRONGYLOCENTROTUS
18. FUNGI, HYDROIDS, BRYOZOANS
19. BRACHIOPOD TEREBRATULLINA
20. POLYCHAETE MALDANE SARSI
21. OPHIURA SARSI
22. BIVALVE MACOMA CALCAREA
23. BIVALVE YOLDIA
24. BIVALVE LEDA
25. BIVALVE NUCULA
26. BIVALVE YOLDIELLA
27. YELLOW-FINNED FLOUNDER
28. POLLOCK
29. HALIBUT
30. POLYCHAETE ONUPHIS
31. KAMCHATKA CRAB
32. OPHIURA GORGONOCEPHALUS
33. BARNACLE BALANUS EWERMANNI
34. SPONGES, HYDROIDS, BRYOZOA
35. HYDRO-CORAL STYLASTERIDAE
36. ASCIDIAN BOLTENIA OVIFERA
37. SEA LILY HELIOMETRA
38. STARFISH CTENODISCUS
39. BRISASTER
40. POLYCHAETE POTAMILLA SYMBIOTICA
41. P.S. WITH A SPONGE AND SMALL HYDROIDES AND OPHIURA
42. SPONGE CHONODROCLADA GIGANTEA
43. CRAB CHIONOECETES
44. GORGONIDE RADICEPS
45. HOLOTHURIAN TROCHOSTOMA
46. HOLOTHURIAN PSYCHROPOTES
47. POGONOPHORA LAMELLISABELLA
48. FORAMINIPHERA BATHYSIPHON
49. CRUSTACEAN MUNIDOPSIS
50. LAMPANICTUS
51. CYCLOTONE
52. MACRURUS
53. HERRING
54. SALMONIDAE

FIG. 396. Zonal distribution of bottom-living fauna of Sea of Okhotsk (Zenkevitch).

Murman coast and the Sea of Okhotsk have a number of common littoral inhabitants: *Mytilus edulis*, *Balanus balanoides*, *Macoma calcarea*, *Mya arenaria*, *Scoloplos armiger*, *Saccoglossus mereschkowskii*, *Travisia forbesi* and many others.

In the northern part of the Sea of Okhotsk a luxuriant development of life in the littoral, especially in its upper horizons, is greatly restricted by the severe ice conditions in winter. This is shown in *Table 316*. The first horizon, which is flooded irregularly by the tides, is practically uninhabited. The first zone of the second horizon is also very sparsely populated; life becomes richer in the lower zone of this horizon; and only the third horizon, which lies below the average neap low tide, has a rich population. Among the sea-weeds there are *Idothea ochotensis* and a large number of Gammaridae and Polychaeta. The lower zone of the third horizon, rarely exposed at low tide, is characterized by various red algae; apart from those given in the table there are: *Chondrus crispus*, *Tichocarpus crinitus*, *Rhodomela larix*, and others. Seaweeds are populated by the molluscs *Margarita helicina*, *Lacuna vincta*, *Cingula marmorata* and others; apart from the crabs Paralithodes, there are *Telmessus cheirogonus* and *Haplogaster grebnitzkii*. The ooze on the seafloor is inhabited by *Echiurus echiurus*, the Polychaeta *Glycera capitata*, *Nephthys longisetosa*, *Brada granulata*, *Travisia forbesi*, *Pectinaria granulata* and others; there is a large number of Porifera, Hydroidea, Bryozoa and Ascidia on the rocks.

'The diagram of the vertical distribution of littoral organisms (in the Sea of Okhotsk) is very similar to that drawn up previously for the Murman coast; this indicates that the facies of the two seas are similar, although the nature of their tides differs. It is most indicative that the composition of the main forms of species is practically the same in both cases. A complete absence of Ascophyllum is the main difference between the Okhotsk littoral and that of the Murman coast' (R. Ushakov, 1951).

The littoral fauna of the Shantar Islands, lying in the most western corner of the northern part of the Sea of Okhotsk, mainly in Yakshina Inlet on the Great Shantar Island, was comprehensively investigated as early as 1927 by I. Zachs (1929). The tide range in the Yakshina Inlet is about 2 to $2\frac{1}{2}$ m, exposing large expanses of silty-sand littoral at low tide.

Zachs records wracks with the amphipoda Talitridae in the supralittoral on the facies of cliffs and rocks. Below it, within the littoral, lies the 'dead' horizon; still lower are dense colonies of *Fucus evanescens*, *Balanus balanoides* and *Mytilus edulis*. Red, green and brown algae flourish in the lowest horizon.

The soft floor littoral is also encircled by banks of wrack with innumerable Talitridae. Below the supralittoral lies a wide lifeless horizon (about two metres according to the range of the tide), while in the lower horizon of the littoral abundant life is developed with Arenicola, Echiurus, Macoma, Pectinaria, Venus and other worms and molluscs. The colonies on the Shantar Island littoral are very dense, with adult Venus attaining 500 to 800 specimens per 1 m^2 (and even up to 1,375); Pectinaria from 500 to 900 specimens; small polychaetes and mollusc fry in thousands of specimens per 1 m^2;

Macoma baltica, 275 specimens; Amphipoda, 625 specimens per 1 m², with a mean biomass of no less than 1 kg/m².

The upper horizons of the Sea of Okhotsk sublittoral are covered with large sea-weed beds with their accompanying fauna. In the bays at depths of 0 to 5 m grow the Sargassum sea-weeds Cystophyllum and Zostera. Laminaria (*L. agardti*, *L. bullata*, *L. saccharina*, *L. digitata*, *Alaria esculenta*, *A.*

FIG. 397. *Echinarachnius parma* colonies in La Perouse Strait at a depth of 40 m (photographed by Zenkevitch).

membranacea, *A. ochotensis*, *Lessonia laminarioides*) form dense growths somewhat deeper (5 to 20 m).

All these vegetation beds are populated by a varied fauna of Bryozoa, Hydroidea, Mollusca, Polychaeta and Crustacea. Still deeper (from 15 to 30 m) red sea-weeds become significant (*Phycodrya simosa*, *Ph. fimbriata*, *Odonthalia dentata*, *O. ochotensis*, and various *Polysiphonia* sp. and *Ptilota* sp.) with a fauna of Hydroida, Bryozoa, Polychaeta, Crustacea, Echinodermata and Ascidia. At depths below 30 m the macrophytes gradually disappear, and growths of Porifera, Hydroidea and Bryozoans become significant. The originality of the bottom fauna of the Sea of Okhotsk is reflected in some details of its composition and distribution.

The uncommon biocoenosis of *Echinarachnius parma* on pure fine-grain sands at depths of 20 to 60 m (Fig. 397) occupies a special place in the fauna groupings of the upper horizon of the sublittoral of the Far Eastern Seas. The most characteristic among its accompanying species is *Ampelisca macrocephala*, with a population density of some thousands of specimens per m^2.

Echinodermata form a continuous cover at the bottom, at times even with two layers. They feed on vegetable detritus which is easily carried over the compact sand and the aboral sides of the bodies of the Echinodermata. Detritus rolls over the ambulacral grooves to the oral side, and is transported into the mouth-opening.

On the soft soils of the lower horizons of the sublittoral large patches are inhabited by the biocoenosis *Ophiura sarsi*.

A. Savilov has worked out a very interesting picture of the ecological distribution of the bottom fauna on the example of the Sea of Okhotsk (1961). His work is based on the relationship between the character of feeding, the nature of the sea-bed and the speed of the current, and comparing these factors with the structure of the body, the organs of digestion and those used for seizing food.

In his classification of animals according to their manner of feeding Savilov (1961) follows S. Yong (1928), S. Zernov (1949), E. Turpaeva (1948, 1952), J. Allen (1953) and others, distinguishing mobile and sessile sestonophages (on hard and soft beds), mobile and sessile detritus-feeders, which swallow the soil, carnivores and carrion-eaters. Savilov provides a distribution in space, and a quantitative distribution for every ecological group, characterizing in this manner the ecological structure of the bottom-living fauna throughout the Sea of Okhotsk and its separate regions (*Tables 318*, *319* and *320* and Fig. 398).

Savilov has distinguished the following ecological zones of the benthic fauna in the Sea of Okhotsk (Fig. 398):

(1) Zone of predominance of the immobile sestonophages of the hard substratum (Porifera, Hydroidea, Alcionaria, Bryozoa, Cirripedia, Brachiopoda, Ascidia).

(2) Zone of predominance of the mobile sestonophages of the soft substratum (Cardiidae, Astartidae, Mactridae, Veneridae, Ampeliscidae, *Echinarachnius parma*).

(2A) Subzone of predominance of the flat sea-urchin (*Echinarachnius parma*).

(3) Zone of predominance of the detritus-collecting forms (Tellinidae, Nuculidae, Ledidae, Terebellidae, Ampharetidae, *Ophiura* spp.).

(3B) Subzone of predominance of the detritus-collecting bivalves (*Macoma calcarea*, *Yoldia thraciaeformis*, *Y. limatula*, *Leda* spp., *Nucula* spp.).

(4) Zone of predominance of the bottom feeders (Maldanidae, Capitellidae, Brisaster, Ctenodiscus, Molpadiidae).

(5) Zone of predominance of the immobile sestonophages of the soft substratum (Pavonaria, Umbellula, Radiceps, Crinoidea, *Potamilla symbiotica*, Sabellidae, Culeolus, *Lamellisabella zachsi*).

The quantitative distribution of the benthos in the Sea of Okhotsk is very irregular (Fig. 399). The densest benthos colonies, with a predominance of fouling fauna, are found off the northern and eastern shores of the Sea, where

Table 318. *Representation of vertical zonality of littoral organisms in northern part of Sea of Okhotsk* (*P. Ushakov, 1951*). *A–A_1: level of average spring tides* (*high and low respectively*); *B–B_1: level of average neap tides* (*high and low respectively*); *C: high tide*

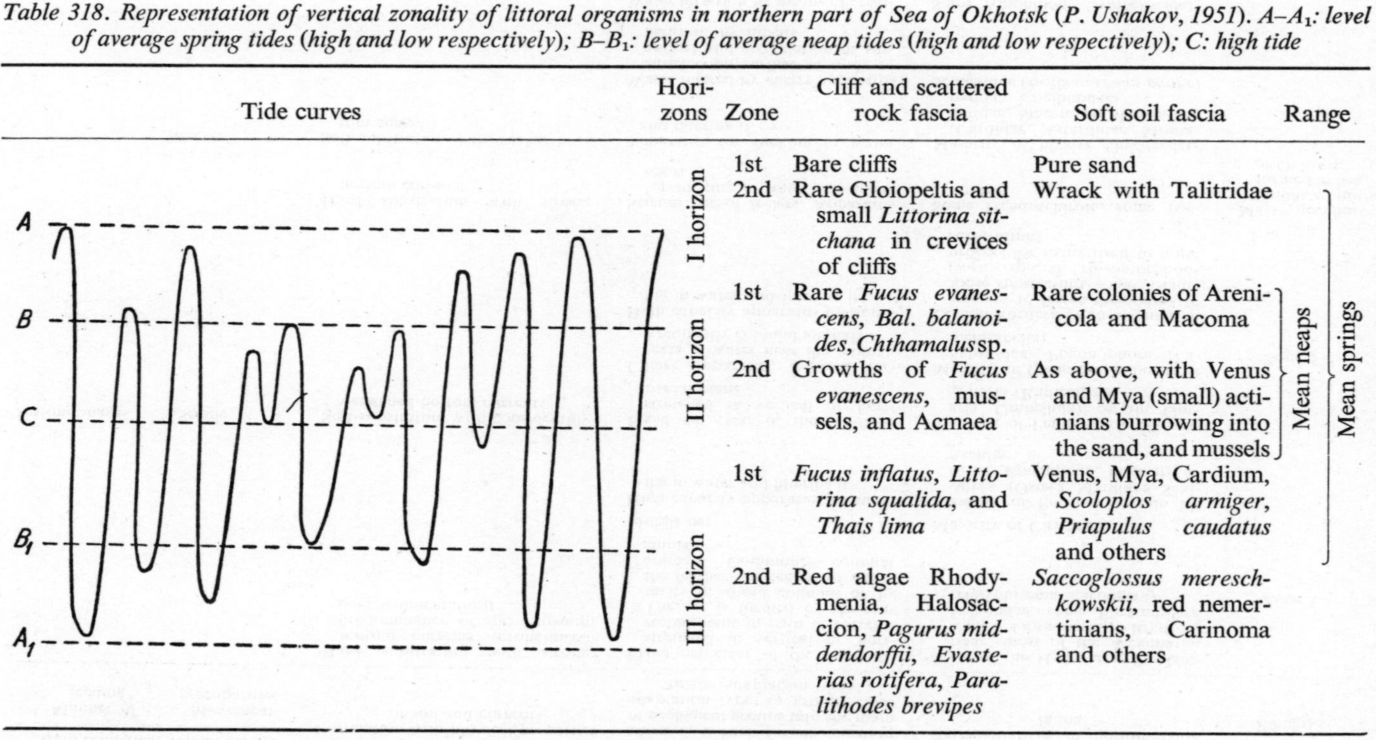

Tide curves	Horizons	Zone	Cliff and scattered rock fascia	Soft soil fascia	Range
	I horizon	1st	Bare cliffs	Pure sand	
		2nd	Rare Gloiopeltis and small *Littorina sitchana* in crevices of cliffs	Wrack with Talitridae	Mean springs
	II horizon	1st	Rare *Fucus evanescens*, *Bal. balanoides*, *Chthamalus* sp.	Rare colonies of Arenicola and Macoma	Mean neaps
		2nd	Growths of *Fucus evanescens*, mussels, and Acmaea	As above, with Venus and Mya (small) actinians burrowing into the sand, and mussels	
	III horizon	1st	*Fucus inflatus*, *Littorina squalida*, and *Thais lima*	Venus, Mya, Cardium, *Scoloplos armiger*, *Priapulus caudatus* and others	
		2nd	Red algae Rhodymenia, Halosaccion, *Pagurus middendorffii*, *Evasterias rotifera*, *Paralithodes brevipes*	*Saccoglossus mereschkowskii*, red nemertinians, Carinoma and others	

Table 319. Classification of bottom-living animals of the Sea of Okhotsk into main ecological groups and adaptation types

Main ecological animal groups		Correlation with physical properties of soil and currents	Special features of feeding mechanism as a basis for classification of ecological groups into the main adaptation types or groups close to the adaptation types	Representatives of bottom-living fauna	Remarks
Manner of feeding	Movement preculiarities				
Sestonophages	Sessile	Hard substratum with strong bottom currents (pronounced predominance of soil erosion over sedimentation)	Fixed net clear of the sea-floor, stretched in vertical or horizontal plane in path of current. The net is formed by the tentacles of zooid colonies or by the feather-like feelers of single animals. Commonly colonial animals	Most of the Hydroidea, Stylaateridae, most of the Alcyonaria, some Gorgonaria, Bryozoa, Serpulidae, some Foraminifera (Halyphisema spiculigera)	Zone 1
			Mobile net	Majority of Cirripedia	
			High capacity apparatus for sucking in water and filtering it	Majority of Porifera, certain bivalves (Ostrea, Mytilidae, Saxicava), Brachipoda, majority of Ascidia	
		Soft substratum with considerably weakened bottom currents	Fixed net clear of the sea-floor stretched in vertical or horizontal plane	Majority of Pennatularia (Pavonaria, Umbellula), certain Gorgonaria (Radiceipes)	Zone 5
			Ciliary apparatus, creating currents of water near the animal. Frequently colonial animals	Majority of Crinoidea, majority of Sabellidae, Pogonophora (Lamellisabella)	
			High capacity apparatus for sucking in water and filtering it	Certain Porifera (with a bunch of spicules to fasten themselves to loose substratum, some Ascidia (with special rhizomorphous process for fixing itself to loose substratum)	
	Mobile	Hard substratum with strong bottom currents	Seizure net of feelers. Apparatus for sucking in water and filtering it	Some Dendrochirota, some Pectinidae	Mass accumulations not formed in Sea of Okhotsk
		Soft substratum with weaker bottom currents	Apparatus for sucking in water and filtering it	Majority of bivalve filter-feeders (Cardidae, Astardidae, Montacutidae, Mactridae, Mydae, Veneridae, Ungilunidae)	
			Water filtered by ciliary apparatus situated on surface of body of animal and coagulation of suspensions by mucus	Scutellidae (*Echinarachnius parma*)	
			Water filtration by means of creating currents of water in special tubular cases	Some Amphipoda (Ampeliscidae, Corophiidae), some Echiuridae (Echiurus, Urechis, Chaetopterus)	

	Sessile	Soft substratum* with weak bottom currents	Greatly elongated feelers and suckers with ciliary grooves, seizing and passing over to the mouth food particles from floor surface	Some Echiuridae (Tatjanella, Alomasoma, Thalassema, Bonnelia) Some Polychaeta (*Spiochaetopterus typicus*)	
			Mostly forms burying themselves in sea-bed and immobile	Some Pogonophora (Sibolglinum)	
			Corona of feelers, collecting detritus from sea-floor surface	Some Psichropotidae, Elpidiidae, Stichopidae, Synallactidae, Cucumaridae, Synaptidae (frequently also found on hard substratum, preferring sand-silt soils)	
Detritus-collecting forms	Mobile	Soft substratum* with weak bottom currents	Elongated lobes and siphons, collecting detritus	Some bivlaves (Nuculidae, Ledidae, Tellinidae)	
			Strong burrowers with an outer calcareous skeleton		
			A series of ambulacral feet on long mobile processes of the organism (arms) seizing and passing particles of food to the mouth (particles of detritus and small animals)	Some Ophiuroidea (species Ophiura, Amphiura, Ophiocantha)	Zone
			Strongly flattened body, easily maintained on the surface of muddy soils		
			Mobile retractable feelers (tentacles) with ciliary groove, seizing food particles and passing them to the mouth	Many Polychaeta (Terebellidae, Ampharetidae, Amphictenidae, Chlorhaemidae, Spionidae, Cirratulidae)	
Soil-swallowing forms	Mobile	Soft substratum with considerably weakened bottom currents (pronounced prevalence of sedimentation over soil erosion)	Absence of organs of choice food-seizure. Short capitula play an auxiliary role—scraping up the soil towards the mouth opening. Mostly almost immobile burrowers	Molpadiidae, Gephyrothuriidae, some Apoda (Myriotrochus), Spatangoidea (Brisaster), Porcellanasteridae (Ctenodiscus)	
				Many Polychaeta (Maldanidae, Opheliidae, Capitellidae, Ariciidae, Scalibregmidae), Sipunculida	
Carnivores and carrion-eaters	Sessile	Hard substratum	Species seizing their prey with feelers. Single, immobile or almost immobile animals	Actinaria	Separate zones are not distinguishable
		Soft substratum			
	Mobile	Hard substratum	Great variety of adaptable types. Commonly with well-developed organs of locomotion and seizure of prey	Numerous Decapoda, numerous Polychaeta (Polynoidae, Glyceridae, Nephthyidae, Aphroditidae, Syllidae, Acoetidae), some Gastropoda (Naticidae), numerous Asteroidea (Asterias, Solaster and others), some Echinoidea (Strongylocentrotus), some Ophiuroidea (Ophiopholis), Nemertini, some Amphipoda	
		Soft substratum			

* Forms adapted to a hard substratum either are absent or do not form mass accumulations in Sea of Okhotsk.

Table 320. Relationship between biomass of different ecological groups of bottom-living animals in different ecological zones in the Sea of Okhotsk

Ecological zones and subzones	No. of stations	Sea area occupied		Mean total benthos biomass g/m²	Ecological groups and their biomass, as percentages						
		km²	percentage of total sea area*		Immobile sestonophages of hard substratum (fouling fauna)	Mobile sestonophages of loose substratum	Detritus consumers	Soil feeders	Immobile sestonophages of loose substratum	Carnivores and carrion eaters	Others†
I. Zone of predominance of immobile sestonophages of hard substratum	51	170,400	10·8	526·4	**57·5**	3·9	3·2	1·2	0·2	31·5	2·5
II. Zone of predominance of mobile sestonophages of soft substratum (including subzone of *Echinarachnius parma*)	28	65,140	4·2	302·0	1·9	**63·9**	14·6	2·5	0·1	10·3	6·7
Echinarachnius parma subzone alone	14	19,700	1·3	355·7	0·7	**85·7**	2·5	0·7	0·3	8·1	2·0
III. Zone of predominance of detritus feeders (including bivalve subzone)	137	653,630	41·4	121·8	0·6	5·2	**55·0**	13·4	2·3	16·0	7·5
Subzone of detritus-consuming bivalves	55	199,670	12·7	177·6	1·2	6·9	**65·2**	9·6	1·7	10·1	5·3
IV. Zone of predominance of bottom feeders	37	246,430	15·6	102·0	1·1	2·6	9·2	**68·4**	0·5	13·0	5·2
V. Zone of predominance of immobile sestonophages of soft substratum	10	230,700	14·5	30·5	10·0	1·5	9·0	3·0	**55·0**	15·0	6·5

* An area of 213,600 km² or 13·5 per cent of the total sea area (1,579,900 km²) is unexplored.
† Species which have not yet been classified in any ecological group.

the total biomass is frequently of the order of 1 kg/m². In the deep trench in the central part of the Sea the benthos biomass is extremely small, as low as 10 mg/m².

The mean benthos biomass throughout the Sea of Okhotsk is about 200 g/m²,

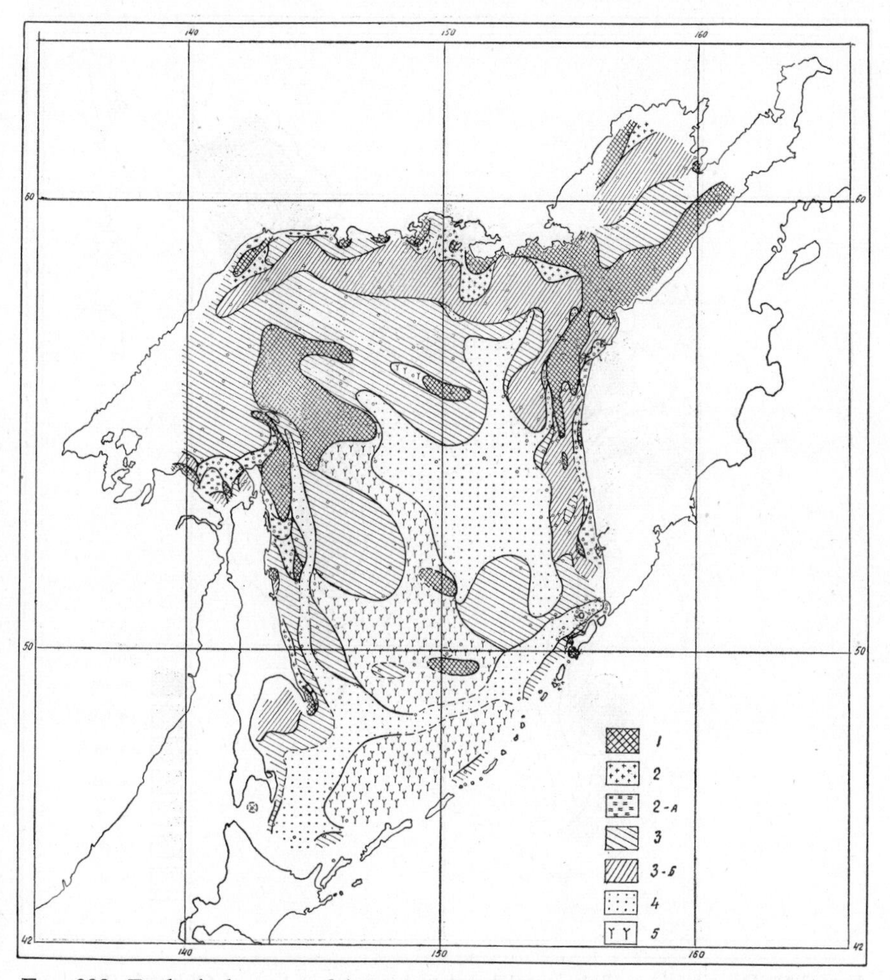

FIG. 398. Ecological zones of bottom-living fauna of Sea of Okhotsk (Savilov, 1961). See page 800–802 for key.

while the general total biomass of bottom-living fauna is about 300 million tons, molluscs occupying the first place among the individual groups.

In some cases biocoenoses acquire an oligomixed character, and under markedly unfavourable life conditions only a few specifically adapted species are able to multiply and develop. Thus, for example, on pure beach sands there is a great and almost exclusive development of the *Echinarachnius parma* population (with mean biomass of 356 g/m², a maximum of 1 kg/m², and 200 specimens per 1 m²) (Fig. 397) which can maintain itself there, feeding on the detritus which is rolled to and fro on the flat, densely packed sand.

Each ecological group comprises a few biocoenoses with various dominant

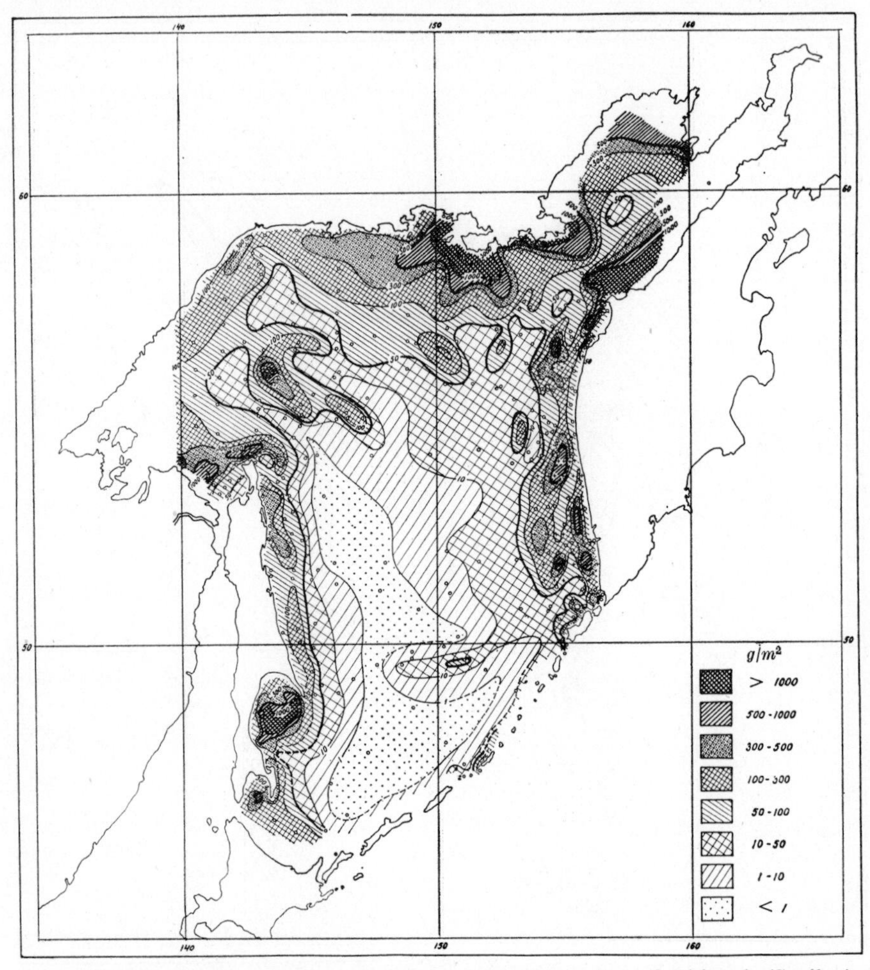

FIG. 399. Distribution of the total benthos biomass in Sea of Okhotsk (Savilov).

forms; this is the result of complex bottom topography, the variety of bottom soils, the complicated system of water circulation and the changes in temperature. 'Bivalve filter-feeders (*Cardium* sp., *Mactra* sp. and others)', writes Savilov, 'are predominant in some areas of development of the mobile sestonophages; in others they are replaced by the sestonophage *Echinarachnius* sp., which in its turn gives place to species of Amphipoda of the family Ampeliscidae.

'The predominant forms in the zone of detritus-collecting organisms are either one or another species of bivalves (species of the genera Macoma, Yoldia, *Leda* and *Nucula* replacing each other) or some mass species of Ophiura (for example *O. sarsi* or *O. leptoctenia*), or detritus-collecting Holothuria or Polychaeta.

'This change in the composition of species of the dominant ecological group of animals within each zone is the result of an alteration in the manifestation of the factors in the environoment to which the ecological animal group is adapted and of the inclusion of some new factors in it.

'A certain consequent replacement of one ecological zone by another in proportion to the distance from the coast and the increase of depth is also observed. Hence there arises the possibility of the occurrence of a certain vertical zonation in the distribution of the ecological groups of bottom-living animals. Rock soils in the coastal areas are commonly predominantly occupied by a fouling fauna. . . . With increase in depth the zone of the predominance of fouling fauna is replaced by that of the predominance of mobile sestonophages. The last is adjacent to the wide zone with a predominance of detritus-collecting forms. . . . Mollusca are replaced by Ophiura, and finally, in the lower horizons of the zone (mainly in the bathyal) where the finest detritus fraction is deposited and the aeration of bottom-water layers becomes less satisfactory, the Polychaeta, as the most eurybiotic forms, acquire a dominant role in the biocoenoses. . . . The group of bottom feeders or sessile sestonophages of soft soils becomes intensely developed in the central deep-water part of the Sea, on diatomaceous oozes rich in plant food.' Thus similar ecological groupings, but having different compositions of species are found in various parts of the Sea at different depths, on more or less common soils and at currents of similar strength.

Quantitative distribution of sessile sestonophages (Fig. 400) and bottom feeders (Fig. 401) could be used for the comparison of the nature of the distribution of Savilov's ecological groups of benthos.

The distribution of Savilov's ecological groups and the total biomass and its connection with bottom topography and currents is most graphically shown in the longitudinal cross section of the Sea of Okhotsk (Fig. 402). This picture is wholly comparable with the ecological profile due to Sokolova, considered above (page 730).

Mollusca occupy the first place (about 30 per cent) in the total benthos biomass of the Sea of Okhotsk; Echinodermata come second (about 25 per cent) and the Polychaeta third (about 12 per cent) (Fig. 403).

Ushakov (1953) gives the simplest diagram of the distribution of bottom biocoenoses in the Sea of Okhotsk on a chart of the Sea and on a latitudinal cross section through the central part of the Sea (Figs. 404 and 405).

Colonies of luxuriant pink hydroid corals of the family Stylasteridae (*St. norvegicus* f. *pacifica*, *St. solidus*, *St. eximius*, *St. scabiosa*, and *Errinopora stalifera*) develop sporadically on rocky bottoms in the uppermost horizon of the bathyal, especially in the area of Iona Island, at the entrance to Shelekhov Bay, at the northern end of Sakhalin and in the area of the Kuril Straits, at depths of 100 to 200 m and somewhat deeper.

P. Ushakov (1953) divides the bathyal into two parts: an upper (200 to 750 m), and a lower (750 to 2,000 m), giving a colourful description of the peculiar fauna of the upper zone of the Sea of Okhotsk bathyal (Fig. 406,

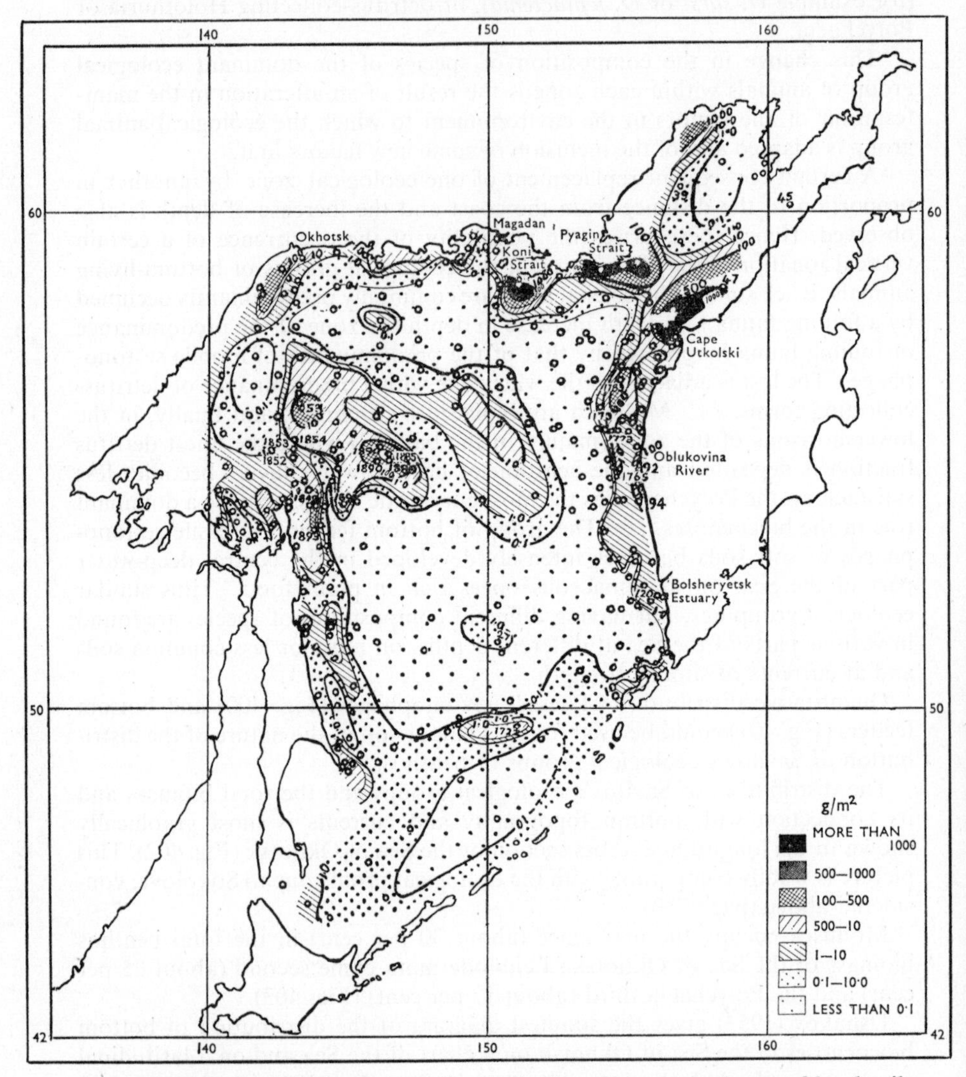

FIG. 400. Quantitative distribution (in g/m²) of sessile sestonophages of hard soils of Sea of Okhotsk (Savilov).

1–5). 'The great *Balanus evermanni* forms large colonies on the steep rocky slopes . . . many Octocorallia, and in particular the large sea-pen *Pavonaria finmarchica*, forming an original biocoenosis with the long-armed ophiura *Asteronyx loveni*. Immense arboreal colonies of *Primnoa resedaeformis* f.

pacifica, reaching 1 m in height, and comparatively small but exquisite fan-like colonies of *Plumarella longispina*, *Caliptrophora ijimai* and others are adapted to the upper division of the continental shelf. On the soft soils of the

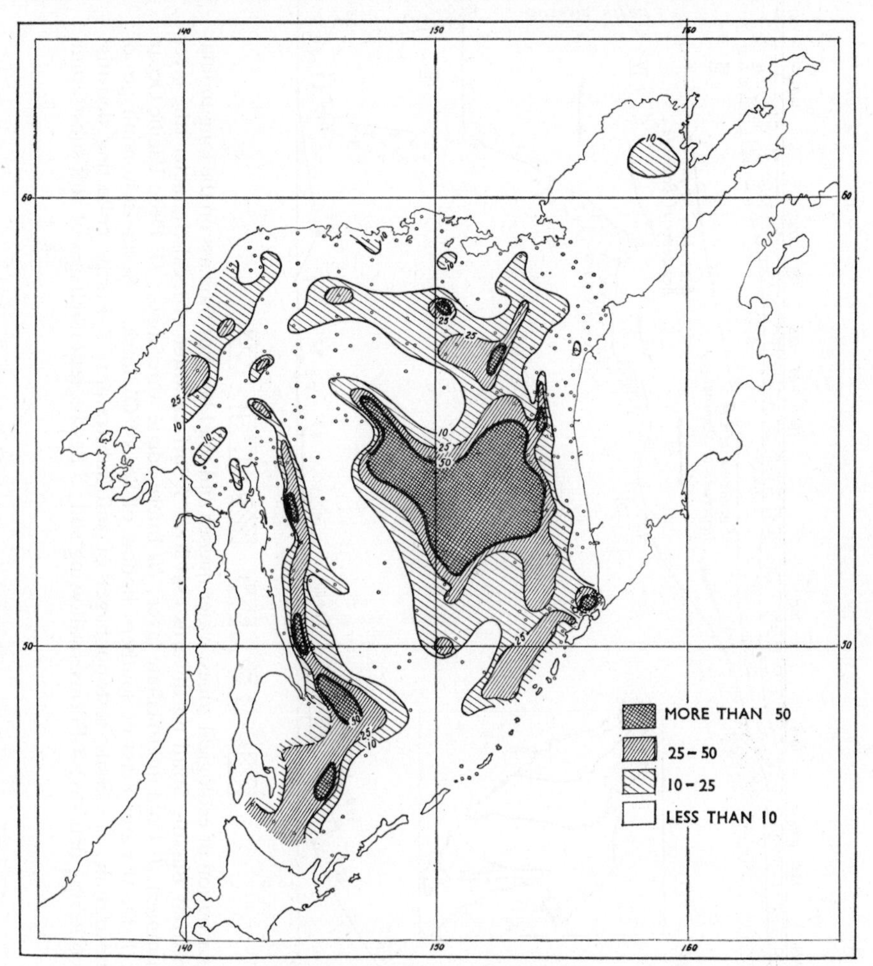

FIG. 401. Quantitative distribution (in g/m²) of soil-swallowing benthic forms of the Sea of Okhotsk (Savilov).

upper horizon large patches are occupied by the *Brisaster latifrons* biocoenosis.'

The fauna of the lower horizon of the bathyal zone (750 to 2,000 m) and of the abyssal zone, considerably impoverished both qualitatively and quantitatively, are characterized also by a series of colourful forms (Fig. 406, 6–11): the Foraminifera Bathysiphon; the Porifera *Cryptospongia enigmatica* pierced by the long tube of the polychaete *Potamilla symbiotica*; the single madreporic coral *Caryophyllia clavus*; the sea-whip *Radiceps verrillii*; the decapod

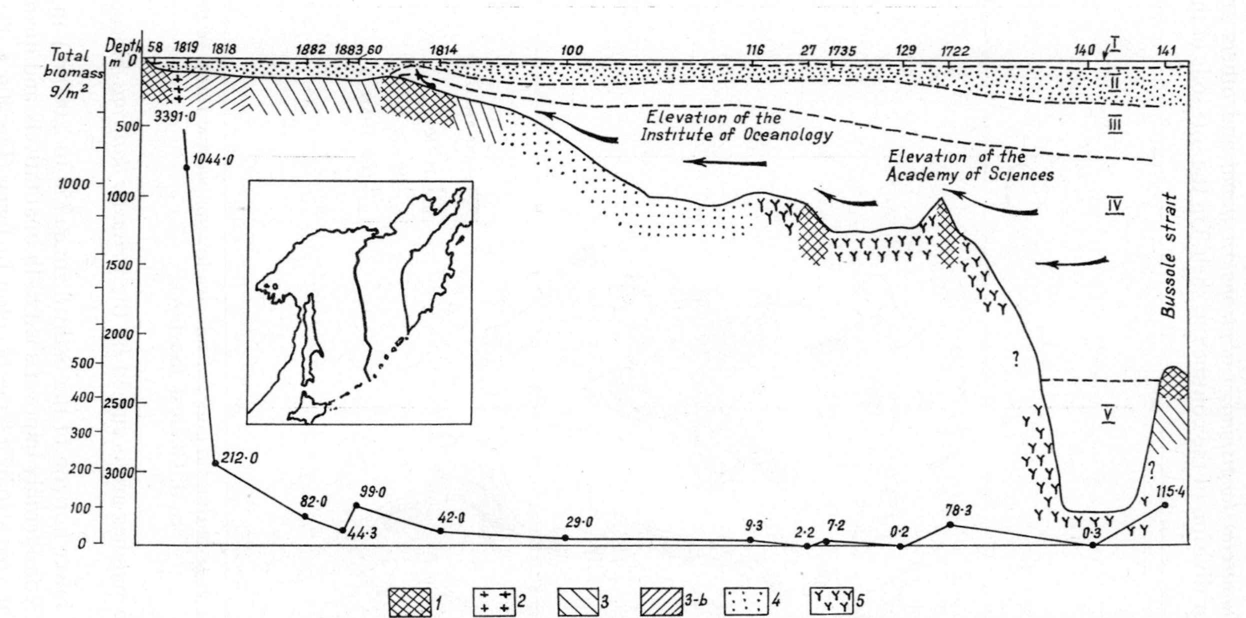

FIG. 402. Distribution of ecological zones, water masses and total benthos biomass on the longitudinal cross section from Bussole Strait northwards (Savilov). *I* Surface water of local character (the layer warmed in summer); *II* Cold intermediate layer; *III* Intermediate water mass; *IV* Deep Pacific Ocean water mass; *V* Deep water mass of southern hollow of Sea of Okhotsk. *1* Sessile sestonophages of the hard substratum; *2* Sessile sestonophages of soft substratum; *3* Forms collecting detritus; *3b* Bivalves collecting detritus; *4* Forms swallowing soil; *5* Sessile sestonophages of soft substratum.

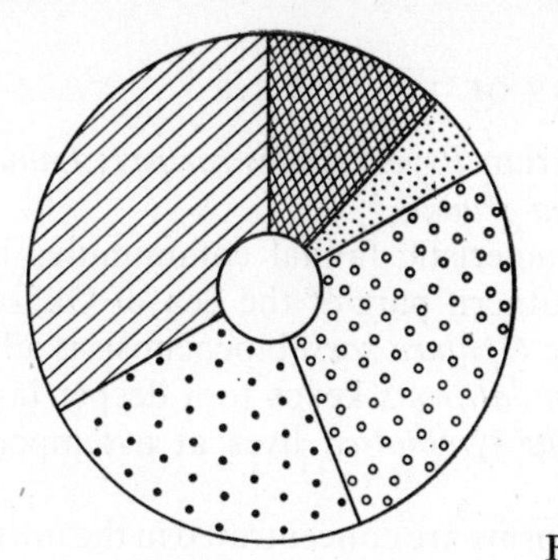

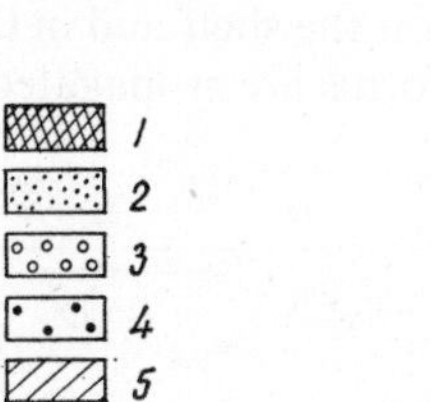

FIG. 403. Total composition of Sea of Okhotsk benthos according to its biomass (Savilov). *1* Polychaeta; *2* Crustacea; *3* Mollusca; *4* Echinodermata; *5* Porifera, Hydroida, Bryozoa and others.

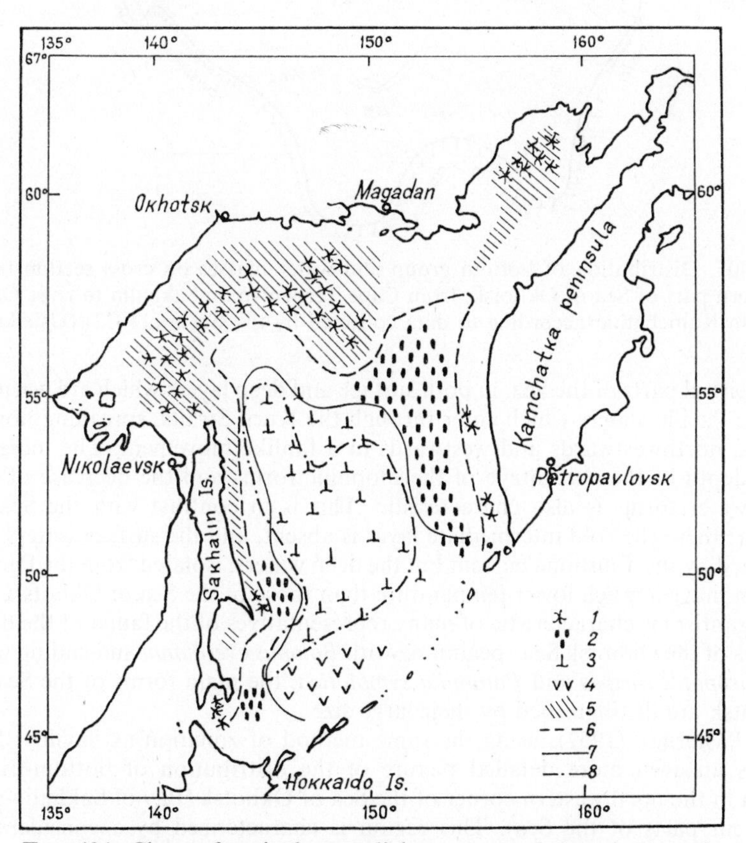

FIG. 404. Chart of main bottom-living groups of Sea of Okhotsk. 1 *Ophiura sarsi*; 2 *Brisaster latifrons*; 3 *Potamilla symbiotica*; 4 *Lamellisabella zachsi*; 5 Temperature always below freezing point; 6 Near-bottom isotherm 0° (winter); 7 Near-bottom isotherm 2°; 8 Near-bottom isoxine 15 per cent (Ushakov, 1953).

crab *Munidopsis beringana*; the holothurian *Psychropotes raripes*; *Lamellisabella zachsi*, and the echiuride *Tatjanellia grandis*.

The vertical distribution of the characteristic faunal communities in the sublittoral and bathyal zones of the southern part of the Sea of Okhotsk is well illustrated in Figs. 404 and 405. The *Ophiura sarsi* biocoenosis is adapted to the coldest layer of the Sea. *Brisaster latifrons* keeps to a deeper layer of warmer water (1° to 2°), and *Potamilla symbiotica* lives at a temperature above 2°.

Cold-water Arctic and Arctic-boreal forms are concentrated in the northern, northwestern and western parts of the Sea on the shelf and in the areas where water has been cooled most. Thermophilic forms are propagated in the eastern

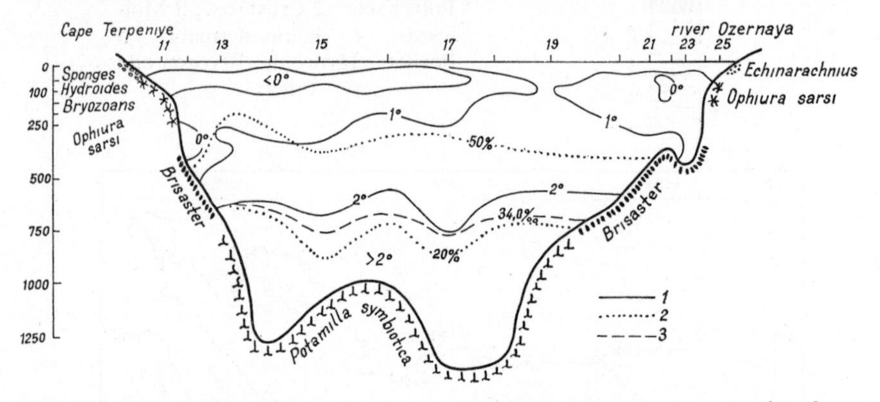

FIG. 405. Distribution of bottom group and water masses on cross section from southern part of Sea of Okhotsk, from Cape Terpeniye on Sakhalin to river Ozernaya in Kamchatka (according to data collected by the *Gagara*, 1932) (Ushakov).

and central parts of the Sea, in both surface and deep layers which are warmed by the Pacific waters which enter through the Kuril Straits, spreading northwards, northwestwards and westwards in a fanlike movement. The increase with depth of the percentage of thermophilic forms and the decrease of the cold-water forms is also characteristic. This is in contrast with the Sea of Japan; there the cold intermediate layer is absent, and the surface waters are warmed by the Tsushima current but the deep waters, isolated from the Pacific Ocean, have a much lower temperature than those of the Sea of Okhotsk.

Gigantism is characteristic of many representatives of the fauna of the deep waters of the Okhotsk Sea; beginning with *Balanus evermanni* and ending with *Psychropotes raripes* and *Potamilla symbiotica*, the main forms of the Sea of Okhotsk are distinguished by their large size.

F. Pasternak (1957), using the same method of zonation as Savilov, furnishes an even more detailed picture of the distribution of bottom-living fauna in the northwestern corner of the Sea of Okhotsk (Bay of Sakhalin and adjacent parts of the Sea). This region is characterized by a considerable complexity in its hydrological conditions. A complex picture of benthos distribution is created by the collision of the lower-salinity and higher-tempera-

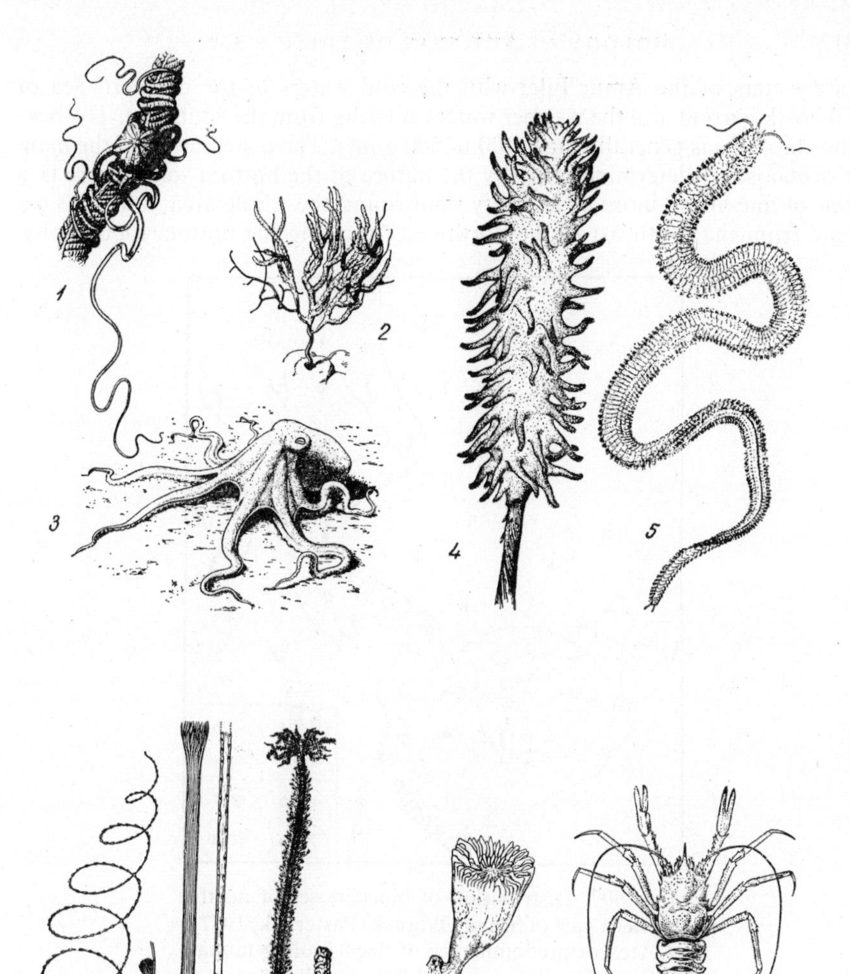

FIG. 406. Members of deep-water fauna of Sea of Okhotsk (Ushakov). Upper series —upper part of the bathyal: 1 *Asteronix loveni*, on marine *Pavonaria finmarchica*; 2 Euplexaura (Octocorallia); 3 *Octopus ochotensis*; 4 *Chondracladia gigantea*; 5 *Leanira areolata*. Lower series—lower part of the bathyal and abyssal: 6 *Radiceps verrillii* (Octocorallia); 7 *Lamellisabella zachsi*; 8 *Potamilla symbiotica*+*Cripto-spongia enigmatica*; 9 *Caryophyllaeus clavus*; 10 *Munidopsis beringana*; 11 *Psychro-potes raripes*.

ture waters of the Amur Inlet with the cold waters of the northern Sea of Okhotsk current and the warmer waters entering from the southeast. The benthos biomass is generally high (100 to 500 g/m^2). The distribution of the main biocoenoses is determined also by the nature of the bottom soils. There is a belt of fine-grain, more or less silty sand round the whole area. Soft soils extend from the southeast to the northwest following the bottom topography.

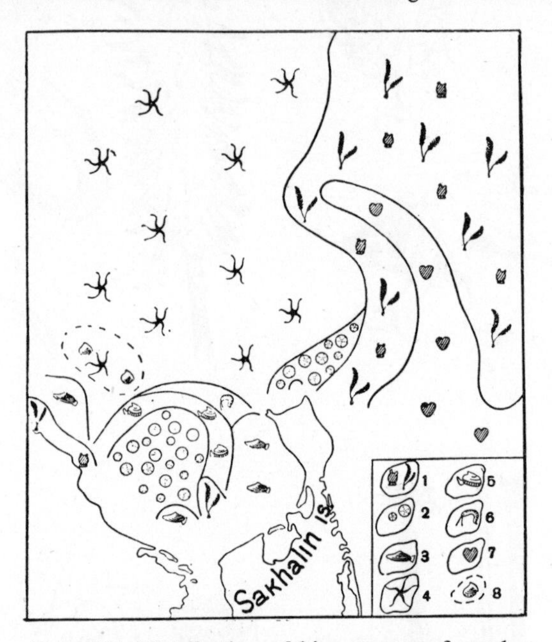

FIG. 407. Distribution of biocoenoses of northwestern part of Sea of Okhotsk (Pasternak, 1957). *1* Area of predominance of fixed fouling fauna; *2* Area of predominance of *Echinarachnius parma*; *3* Area of predominance of large detritus-eating bivalves; *4* *Ophiura sarsi* predominance; *5* Biocoenoses with predominance of filter-feeders; *6* Amphipod predominance; *7* Predominance of forms swallowing detritus with the soil; *8* Area of predominance of small bivalves.

Zones of the predominance of fouling fauna in the northeastern part of the region investigated could be singled out among the biocoenoses of the region (Fig. 407). In the deeper parts of the trench and on its eastern slopes grass Porifera with an admixture of Hydroidea are predominant—Cladocarpus, Sertularia, Bonnevillea, Abiettinaria; the Bryozoa, Smittina and Membranipora; Sabellidae and Actinia like Chondractinia, *Ophiopholis aculeata*, Corophiidae and others.

Large spaces of this region are occupied by forms which collect detritus from the surface of the bed. Hard fine-sand beaches are inhabited by large colonies of *Echinarachnius parma*; silty sands are populated by large-sized bivalves (*Macoma calcarea*, Tellina, *Yoldia traciaeformis*); still siltier sands have an abundance of *Ophiura sarsi* with numerous small Mollusca (*Nucula tenuis*, *Yoldiella derjugini*, Axinopsis and others) and Polychaeta (*Spiochaetopterus typicus*, *Stylarioides plumosa*, *Sternaspis acutata*, *Ampharetidae* and others). Filter-feeder biocoenoses composed of large-sized Mollusca (*Astarte borealis*, *Serripes groenlandicus*, *Cardium ciliatum*, *Mya arenaria*, *M. truncata*, *Liocyma fluctuosa*, *Modiolus modiolus* and others) characterize the region described. Amphipoda (*Ampelisca eschrichti*, *A. macrocephala*, *A. furcigera*) with a biomass of 124·7 g/m² and giving about 3,000 specimens per 1 m² have been found in large numbers in separate patches. The zone of the predominance of organisms which swallow detritus with the soil should also be noted. Pasternak includes in this group the Polychaeta (Maldanidae, Capitellidae, Ariciidae, Scalibregmidae and Opheliidae), Gephyrea, the Holothuria, the urchin *Brisaster latifrons*, the starfish *Ctenodiscus crispatus* and others.

F. Pasternak (1957) describes the zoogeography of one of the most climatically severe regions of the Far Eastern Seas—the northwestern corner of the Sea of Okhotsk. In this region the Arctic and Arctic-boreal species *Ophiura sarsi*, *Praxilella gracilis*, *Pr. praetermissa*, *Spiochaetopterus typicus*, *Scalibragma robusta*, *Chaetozone setosa*, *Terebellides stroemi*, *Myriochele heeri*, *Astarte borealis*, *A. montagui*, *Serripes groenlandicus*, *Mya truncata*, *Macoma moesta*, *M. calcarea*, *M. torelli*, *Liocyma fluctuosa*, *Thyasira gouldi* and *Yoldia myalis* play the dominant role in the fauna. Boreal forms are absent. The northern part of the Sea of Okhotsk cannot be included in the boreal province.

N. Vinogradova (1954) has investigated in detail the bottom-living fauna of the northeastern corner of the Sea.

Shelekhov Bay in the Sea of Okhotsk, thrusting far up into the Chukotsk Peninsula, is the coldest sector of the Far Eastern Seas. It can be compared only with the northwestern area of the Sea and the Gulf of Anadyr in the Bering Sea. This extensive Bay has an area of about 140,000 km². The distribution and composition of its fauna, with its very cold water aspect and a very high mean biomass (470 g/m²) with a predominance of Mollusca, is controlled by the restricted connection of the Bay with the Sea, the feeble penetration of warm waters from the south, its small depth, and the presence of numerous coastal features.

N. Vinogradova (1954), judging by the composition and distribution of the bottom-living fauna of Shelekhov Bay, distinguishes three main biocoenoses disposed from south to north (Fig. 408): 1—a biocoenosis of Balanidae–Hydroidea–Bryozoa–Decapoda; 2—a biocoenosis of *Ophiura sarsi–Macoma calcarea* and 3—a biocoenosis of Leda (pernula type)–*Ophiura sarsi*–Polychaeta. The dominant species of the first biocoenosis are *Balanus evermanni*, *B. rostratus dalli*, *Pagurus pubescens*, *Hyas coarctatus*, and various Hydroidea and Bryozoa. Moreover prawns (Pandalus, Sclerocrangon and others), Echinodermata (*Strongylocentrotus droebachiensis*, *Ophiopholis aculeata*, *Ophiocantha bidentata*, *Gorgonocephalus cargi* and various Asteroidea) and numerous Porifera (*Semisuberites arctica* and others) are well represented in this biocoenosis. Among the Polychaeta *Nephthys coeca*, *N. ciliata*, *Onuphis* sp. and numerous Serpulidae are predominant. Various Buccinidae, Crepidula, *Pododesmus macroshisma*, *Astarte borealis*, *A. banksi*, *Nucula tenuis* and others are predominant among the Mollusca.

The biocoenosis *Macoma calcarea–Ophiura sarsi* is located in the central

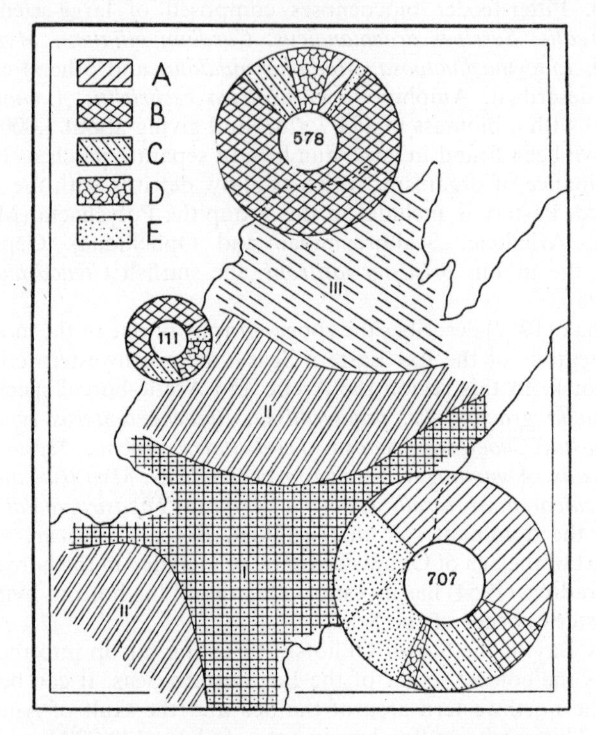

FIG. 408. Distribution of biocoenoses in Penzhina Inlet (Vinogradova, 1954). *I* Balanidae–Hydroidae–Bryozoa–Decapoda biocoenosis; *II Ophiura sarsi* biocoenosis; *III* Leda biocoenosis of the type pernula–*Ophiura sarsi*–Polychaeta. Mean biomass for each biocoenosis indicated in circles, in g/m²; *A*—Crustacea; *B*—Mollusca; *C*—Echinodermata; *D*—Polychaeta; *E*—Others.

part of the Bay. In this biocoenosis the most numerous among the Polychaeta are *Lumbriconereis impatiens*, *Myriochele oculata*, *Praxilella praetermissa*, *Rhodine gracilior*; among the Mollusca *Leda* (*pernula?*), *Macoma moesta*, *M. torelli*, *Musculus corrugatus*, *Yoldia traciaeformis*, and *Nucula tenuis*; there are numerous Crustacea (families Ampeliscidae). Among the Decapoda there are *Chionoecetes opilio*, *Hyas coarctatus*, *Pagurus pubescens*; the Polychaeta Nephthyidae, Aphroditidae; and the starfish *Crossaster papposus*, Pteraster and others.

Table 321. Mean number of specimens and mean biomass of bottom-living fauna of Shelekhov Bay (N. Vinogradova, 1954)

Group	No. of specimens per 1 m²	Biomass, g/m²
Polychaeta	324	28·3
Mollusca	127	210·3
Crustacea	516	94·0
Echinodermata	77	55·8
Sipunculoidea	3	66·0
Others	57	15·1
Total	1,304	469·5

The northern part of the Bay and the Gizigina Inlet are occupied by a biocoenosis in which *Leda pernula(?)*, *Ophiura sarsi*, *Amphiodia craterodmeta*, and *Ophiura maculata* are predominant. Among the Mollusca there is an abundance of *Leda minuta*, *Yoldia myalis*, *Y. limatula*, *Y. traciaeformis*, *Macoma calcarea*, *Saxicava arctica* and *Cardium ciliatum*. Among the Polychaeta the most numerous are *Maldane sarsi*; among the Crustacea Maldanidae, *Myriochele occulata*, *Chaetozone setosa*, *Scoloplos armiger* and *Magelone pacifica* are distinguished by their numbers.

The benthos biomass increases considerably (Fig. 409 and *Table 321*) at the entrance to the Inlet (500, 1,000 g/m³ and more) and in Gizigina Inlet (up to 1,000 g/m²); moreover, Mollusca and Echinodermata are predominant in the north of the Bay.

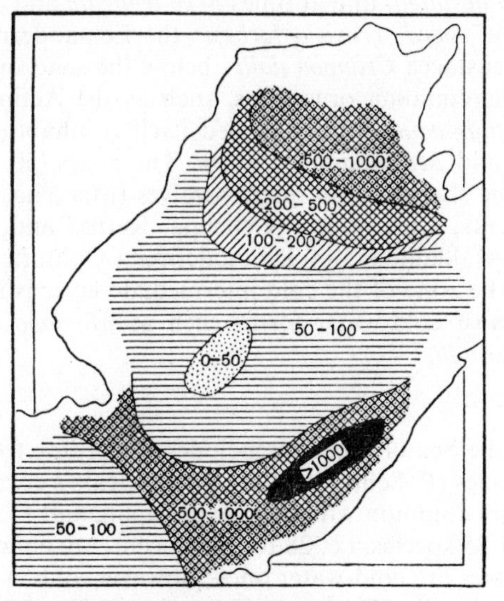

FIG. 409. Distribution of benthos biomass in Penzhina Guba, Sea of Okhotsk, g/m². (Vinogradova).

As may be seen from the lists of the mass forms given, the fauna of Shelekhov Bay has on the whole an Arctic aspect (N. Vinogradova, 1954), boreal forms being predominant in the southeastern part of the Bay (*Venericardia borealis ovata*, *V. crassidens*, *Crepidula* sp. and others); and Arctic-boreal and lower Arctic forms in the northwestern part of it (*Macoma calcarea*, *Leda pernula*, *L. minuta*, *Yoldia myalis*, *Mya truncata*, *Musculus substriatus*, *Axinus gouldi* and others). Arctic and high-Arctic forms are concentrated in the central, deep-water part of the Bay (*Macoma torelli*, *M. loveni*, *M. maesta*, *Musculus corrugatus*, *Axinopsis orbiculata* and others). Although this zoogeographical analysis is adduced only for the bivalves, it reflects the general aspect of the Shelekhov Bay fauna well.

Abundant material on the qualitative and quantitative distribution of the bottom fauna of the most important fishery region of the Sea of Okhotsk—the western Kamchatka shelf—was studied by K. Gordeeva (1948). Spacious feeding grouds of Kamchatka crab, flatfish, cod and others are situated within this area, which is undoubtedly one of the richest regions of life in the Far Eastern Seas. The mean biomass of the whole western Kamchatka shelf is 482·7 g/m^2 and the feeding part of the fauna is on the average 230 to 300 g/m^2.

The surface zone of water heated up to 11° or 12° in summer lies at about 50 to 70 m. The cold intermediate layer is situated at a depth of 70 to 150 m (temperature down to −1·8°). The lower part of the shelf and the edge of the bathyal (150 to 250 m) have a temperature above freezing point; crabs migrate there for wintering.

The most characteristic forms on the sand soil are: the large Mollusca *Siliqua media*, *Tellina lutea*, and at times *Mya truncata* and *Spisula alascana*; the worms *Nephthys coeca*, *Travisia forbesi*; the Echinodermata *Echinarachnius parma*; the Crustacea *Crangon dalli*: below the sand on the gravel bed, there are numerous epifauna organisms, such as the Actinia Halcampella; the Mollusca *Mytilus edulis*; and the bed itself is inhabited by *Mya* spp., *Serripes laperousi* and *Macoma middendorfi*. The oozes (50 to 120 m) of the southern part of the shelf contain many bivalves (Macoma, Nucula, Yoldia, Liocyma and others); Gastropoda (Cylichna, Retusa and others); and an abundance of the Maldanidae; of Echinodermata Ophiura and Holothuria. Still lower down, the zone of the cold intermediate layer is inhabited by biocoenoses of the most cold-water forms such as *Macoma calcarea*, *Nucula tenuis* and *Leda pernula*.

Fish

The list of fish in the Sea of Okhotsk includes, according to Rass, about 300 species and subspecies (P. Schmidt, 1950, with T. Rass's corrections). Among them 140 species are common with the Sea of Japan, and 112 species with the Bering Sea. About 85 species, i.e. 28 to 30 per cent, are endemic.

Most of the species are cold-water ones; however, only a few are properly Arctic forms. The families Cottidae (53 species), Liparidae (43), Zoarcidae (41), Pleuronectidae (21), Stichaeidae (17), Agonidae (15), Cyclopteridae (13) and Salmonidae (10) are the most numerous.

In the southwestern part of the Sea there are south-boreal and even subtropical species of the families Gobiidae (5 species), Clupeidae (2 species), Mugilidae, Carangidae, Oplegnathidae, Tetrodontidae and Pleuronectidae (two species each), and Rhombidae, Engraulidae, Salangidae, Scombresocidae, Syngnathidae, Scombridae, Trididae, Sparidae, Monacanthidae, Rajidae, Lamnidae, Embiotocidae (one species each). There are 29 or 30 such species in all, about 10 per cent of the whole fish fauna.

There are 12 species of deep-water oceanic fish, among them 4 Macruridae, 3 Bathylagidae and one species each of Gonostomidae, Chauliodontidae, Alepisauridae, Scopelidae, and Moridae (T. Rass, 1954). There are 44 secondary deep-water species, among them 27 Liparidae, 10 Zoarcidae, 5 Cottidae, and 2 Scorpaenidae (P. Schmidt, 1950).

There are about 20 species of commercial fish in the Sea of Okhotsk: *Squalis acanthias, Clupea pallasi, Oncorhynchus keta, O. gorbuscha, O. kisutch, O. nerka, Salvelinus malma, Osmerus eperlanus dentex, Cololabis sajra, Gadus macrocephalus, Theragra chalcogramma, Eleginus gracilis, Sebastolobus macrochir, Pleurogrammus azonus, Hippoglossoides elassodon, Lepidopsetta bilineata, Limanda aspera, L. punctatissima, Platessa quadrituberculata, Pleuronectes stellatus.* The most important of them are herring, pink salmon, keta, brook trout, pollack, rock trout and plaice.

About 870 thousand tons of fish were caught in the Okhotsk Sea in 1955. The catch in 1936 was estimated at 700 to 780 thousand tons (T. Rass, 1948); it has increased mainly owing to the development of the herring, plaice, pollack and rock trout fisheries.

In the northern part of the Sea of Okhotsk herring feeds on more or less large plankton (*Themista libellula*, Metridia and *Calanus finmarchicus*).

Commerical crabs (*Paralithodes camtschatica, P. brevipes* and *P. platypus* and *Chionoecetes opilio*) feed in summer (M. Khun and L. Mikulich, 1954) on various mass forms of benthos: Echinodermata (Strongylocentrotus and Echinarachnius, various starfish and Ophiura), Mollusca, especially *Serripes groenlandicus, Cardium ciliatum* and *Macoma calcarea*, various Polychaeta, Ascidia, especially *Pelonaia corrugata* and *Boltenia echinata*, and various Peracardia.

Using A. P. Andriashev's data (1939), L. Vinogradov (1948) distinguishes three zoogeographical regions in the Sea of Okhotsk: the Glacial Okhotsk, the western Kamchatka and the southeastern Sakhalin.

16

The Bering Sea

I. PHYSICAL GEOGRAPHY

The Bering Sea is the largest marine basin of all the seas surrounding the U.S.S.R. Its surface is 2,304,000 km² and its volume 3,683,000 km³. Its greatest depth, in the region of Kamchatka Strait, is 4,420 m, its mean depth 1,598 m. The Bering Sea is divided by the 200 m isobath into two approximately equal parts: the northeastern shelf region, with depths of less than 200 m, and the southwestern part with depths of more than 3,500 m (Fig. 410); this latter in its turn is subdivided by two trenches, a smaller, western one and an eastern one, four times as big. The summits of Shirshov ridge rise to depths of 1,000 to 2,000 m. It is a continuation of the Olyutorsky submarine ridge. Another ridge stretching north of Semisopochny and Gorelov Islands, part of the Aleutian arc, partitions off the southern part of the eastern basin. The Bering Sea is enclosed on the south by the elevation of the Alaska Peninsula and the long Aleutian chain, composed of numerous islands and straits, most of them shallow.

Shirshov ridge does not reach the base of the Aleutian chain, for there is a rather narrow, deep (3,500 m) strait between them connecting (less than 50 km) both parts of the hollow. The bathyal zone in the Bering Sea is comparatively small (*Table 322*).

Table 322. Bottom topography of the Bering Sea (P. Ushakov, 1953)

Zone	Area	
	10³ km²	Percentage
Shelf	1,000	44
Bathyal	289	13
Abyssal	992	43

The Bering Sea is connected with the Pacific Ocean by the deep Kamchatka Strait (4,420m). The trenches of the Strait are connected with each other, and the western one with the Ocean, at all depths. A complete contact of sea and ocean water masses and an identity of their water structure is secured by the depth of certain of the Aleutian Straits. The Bering Sea can be considered as an arm of the Pacific more than can any other sea.

In the north the Bering Sea is connected with the Chukotsk Sea through the Bering Strait. The latter is very shallow (not more than 40 m), and with a width of 85 km its cross section is only 2·5 km².

With rare exceptions (in winter) the movement of water through the Bering Strait is in one direction; about 20,000 km³ of Bering Sea waters enter the Chukotsk Sea through it.

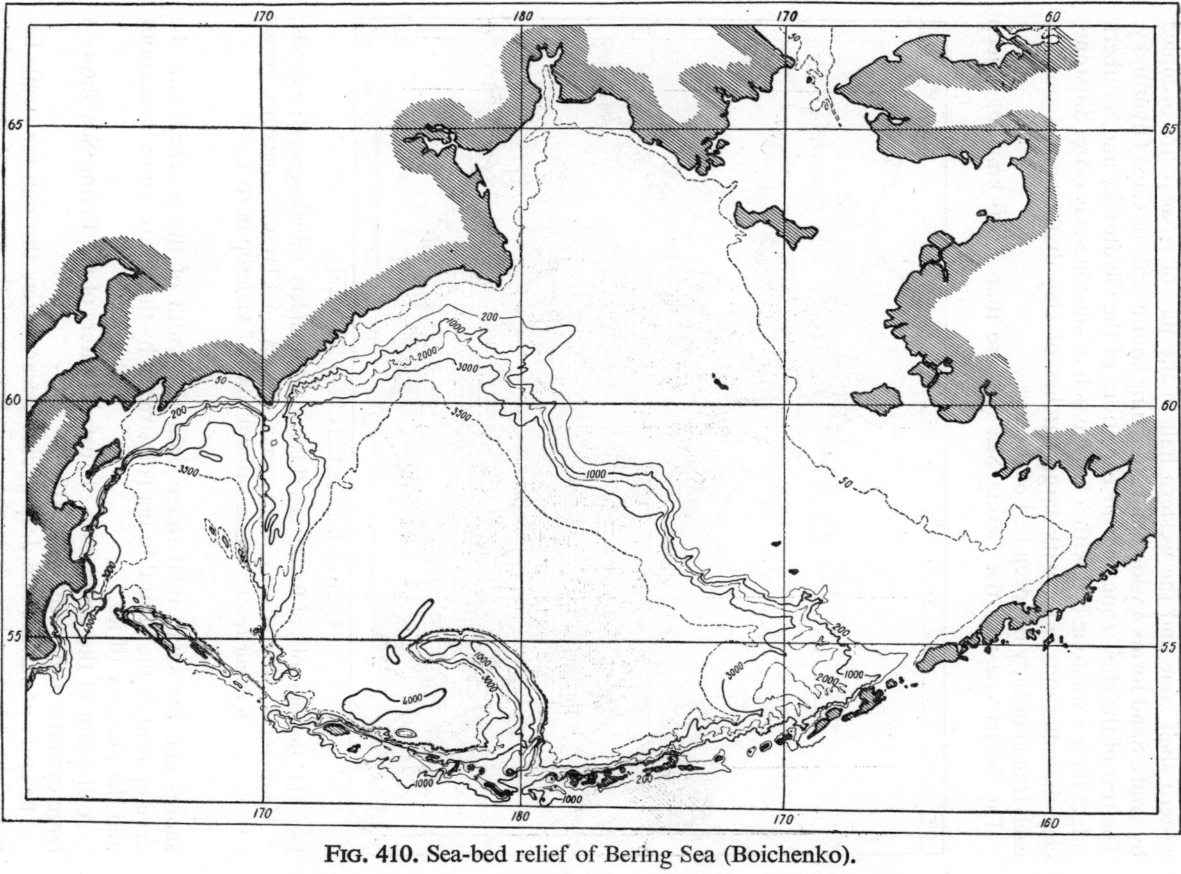

FIG. 410. Sea-bed relief of Bering Sea (Boichenko).

The distribution of soils on the floor of the Sea gives a clear and simple picture (Fig. 411). Large areas of the floor of the northeastern half of the eastern shelf zone and the western half of the Bay of Anadyr are occupied by sands. Sand forms a wide band stretching southwards to Cape Olyutorsky. The rest of the shelf zone and the elevations of the Olyutorsky and Southern ridges have a siltstone bed with a large patch of siltstone-clay ooze. Siltstone-clay diatomaceous ooze with large patches of clay diatomaceous ooze in each trench occupy the deep bed of the Sea.

The Soviet coast of the Bering Sea is more than 5,000 km long. Steep

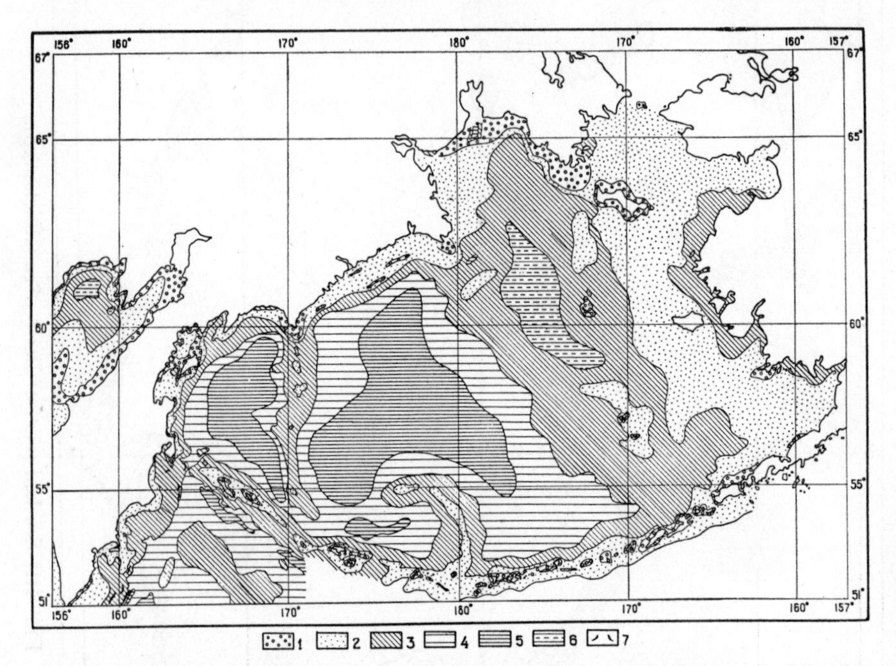

FIG. 411. Bottom soils of Bering Sea (Lisitzin). *1* Boulders–shingle–gravel; *2* Sands; *3* Aleurites; *4* Aleurite–clay–diatomaceous oozes; *5* Clay–diatomaceous oozes; *6* Aleurite–clay oozes without silica; *7* Outcrop of rock.

shores and the small tidal range limit the width of the beaches, and the development of the littoral fauna is restricted by the severe winter conditions and the presence of ice.

A diagram of the circulation of surface waters of the Bering Sea shows a large cyclonic movement (Fig. 412).

The entry of surface and deep Pacific Ocean waters through the straits between the Aleutian Islands is the main feature of the system of Bering Sea currents. The water masses move northward along the eastern side of the Sea creating several anticyclonic and cyclonic rotations on the eastern side, and a circular cyclonic current on the west. Skirting St Lawrence Island on the east, Pacific waters enter the Chukotsk Sea through the Bering Strait, warming its eastern half and creating conditions allowing the penetration of boreal fauna through the Strait. At times, especially in winter, cold waters can enter the Bering Sea through the western side of the Strait and move along the Chukotsk coast. Branches of a warm current, skirting St Lawrence Island, penetrate the Bay of Anadyr from the south, somewhat warming its eastern part.

The anticyclonic movement of water in Anadyr Bay helps as a result of the winter fall of temperature to form the so-called Anadyr cold patch. A similar patch is formed in Olyutorsky Inlet. As a result of all these factors the

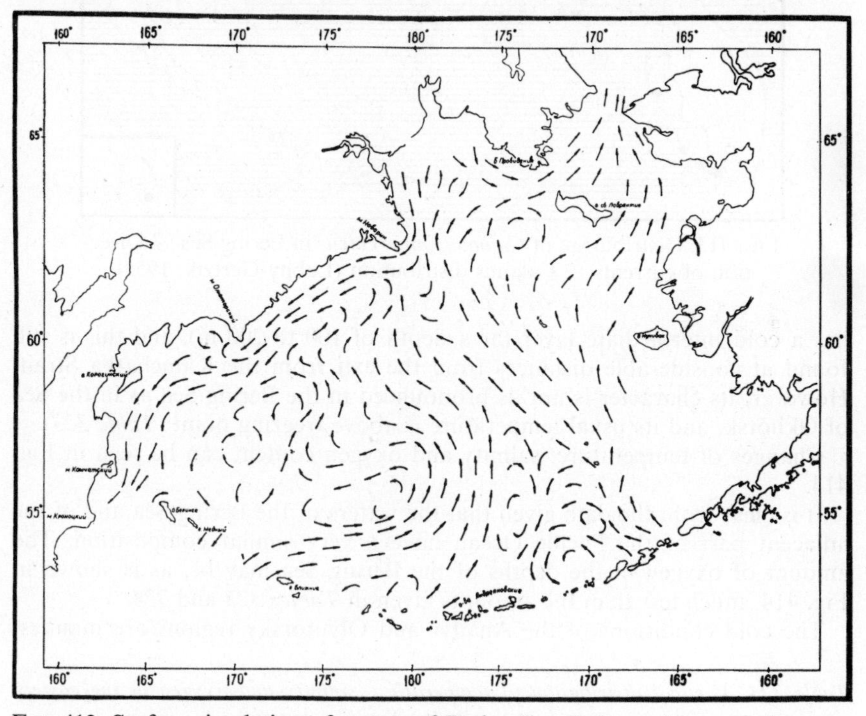

FIG. 412. Surface circulation of waters of Bering Sea (Dobrovolsky and Arsenev, 1959).

western side of the Sea is cooled considerably, so that in winter thick ice is at times formed there.

Strong currents of cold western Bering Sea waters follow into the Pacific Ocean through the Kamchatka Strait, forming the so-called Oyashio current. Certain cold-water plankton organisms serve as good indicators of this cold current, one of them being *Calanus finmarchicus* (Fig. 413).

The actual circulation of water masses in the western part of the Bering Sea is probably much more complex than in the diagram given. The Bering Sea, like the Sea of Okhotsk, is characterized, especially in its western and northern parts, by the severity of conditions on the surface. Even in summer the surface waters down to 30 or 40 m are never warmer than 9° to 10°.

Below the surface layers, especially on the western side of the Sea, there

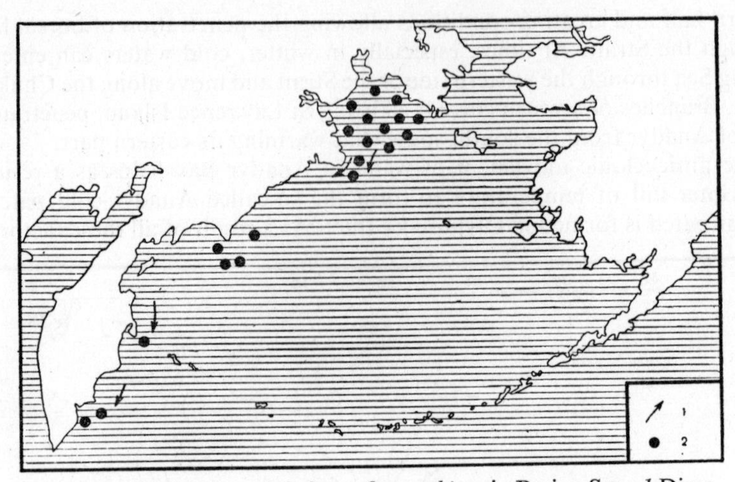

FIG. 413. Distribution of *Calanus finmarchicus* in Bering Sea: *1* Direction of currents; *2* Calanus distribution (Lubny-Gertzik, 1955).

lies a cold intermediate layer (at a depth of 100 to 200 m), and this is still found at considerable distances from the exit from the Kamchatka Strait. However, its character is not as pronounced in the Bering Sea as in the Sea of Okhotsk, and its usual temperature is above freezing point (*Table 323*).

Changes of temperature, salinity and oxygen content can be seen in Fig. 414.

It is clear from the data given that the waters of the Bering Sea and of the adjacent part of the Pacific Ocean have a very similar composition. The amount of oxygen in the depths of the Bering Sea may be, as is shown in Fig. 414, much less than the amounts given in *Tables 323* and *324*.

The cold conditions of the Anadyr and Olyutorsky regions are manifest

Table 323. Vertical distribution of temperature, salinity and oxygen in the eastern trench of the Bering Sea in summer

Depth, m	Temperature °C	Salinity ‰	Oxygen	
			ml/l	Percentage of saturation
0	8·90	32·52	—	—
50	1·41	33·40	5·94	75·30
100	0·80	33·40	5·31	66·40
200	0·68	33·40	—	—
300	3·55	33·82	6·09	81·90
500	3·44	34·05	1·25	16·80
1,000	2·80	34·42	0·45	16·90
2,000	1·91	34·01	1·44	20·10
3,000	1·65	34·72	1·65	21·40

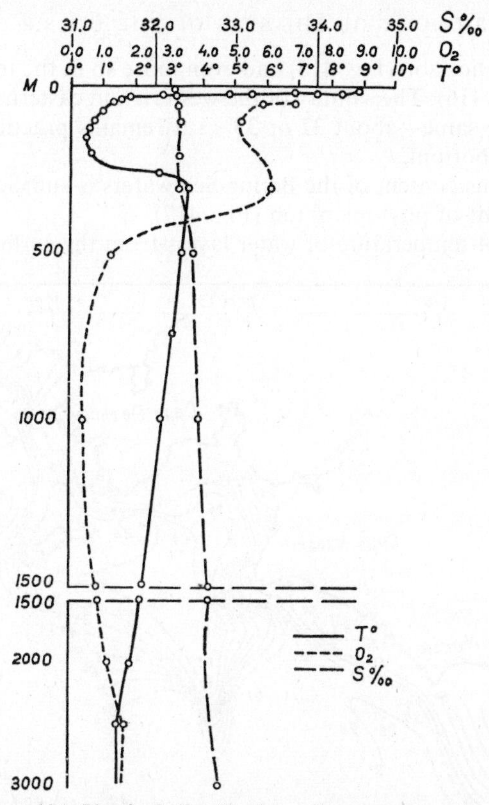

FIG. 414. Vertical distribution of temperature (continuous line), oxygen (short dashes) and salinity (long dashes) in summer 1932 (Ratmanov).

Table 324. Oxygen and phosphorus in the Bering Sea and Pacific Ocean

Depth, m	Bering Sea				Pacific Ocean	
	Kamchatka Strait August, 1950		Central part of Sea September, 1950			
	Oxygen per cent	Phosphorus mg/m³	Oxygen per cent	Phosphorus mg/m³	Oxygen per cent	Phosphorus mg/m³
0	103	54	99	34	99	24
25	104	55	99	42	94	27
50	88	79	93	63	89	38
100	83	85	87	73	85	50
150	57	93	82	75	73	69
300	14	101	22	85	9	75
500	10	100	12	102	7	77
1,000	9	100	4	101	8	77
1,500	11	104	10	100	15	68
2,000	17	103	14	98	22	69
2,500	26	95	—	—	—	—

even at the 25 m horizon (Fig. 415) and even more so in the temperature near the bottom (Fig. 416). The salinity of the western and eastern parts of the Sea is practically the same—about 32 or 33‰; it remains practically unchanged from surface to bottom.

The phosphorus content of the Bering Sea waters is sufficient for the luxuriant development of phytoplankton (Fig. 417).

The changes of temperature of water layers from the surface to the 200 to

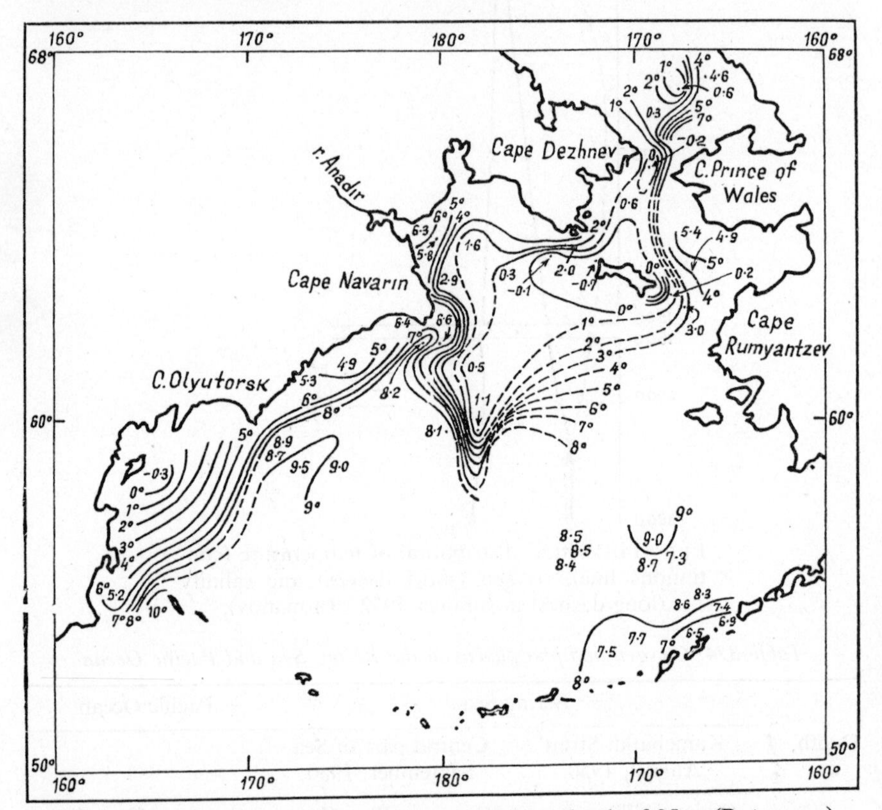

FIG. 415. Isotherms of the Bering Sea in 1932 at a depth of 25 m (Ratmanov).

300 m level are clearly shown on the cross section from Cape Africa eastward. Cold Kamchatka waters are pushed to the western side. At a depth of 300 to 400 m these differences are already indistinct (Fig. 418).

The water masses of the Bering Sea may be divided into four layers according to their chemical properties (V. Mokievskaya, 1956): (*1*) the surface layer, most exposed to seasonal fluctuations of temperature, salinity and chemical properties; (*2*) the transition zone, which becomes thicker in spring and summer (50 to 200 m) while its boundaries become less pronounced; (*3*) a third layer, characterized by a lower oxygen content, down to 10 to 15 per cent of saturation, and the highest phosphorus content (over 100 mg/m³) lying beneath the transition zone: this third layer extends down to 1,500 m; (*4*) the fourth layer stretches from 1,500 m down to the sea-bed: its oxygen content rises to 20 per cent of saturation and its phosphorus content decreases to 90 mg/m³. The upper two layers, formed in the Bering Sea itself, are the most characteristic. The lower two layers are similar to the Pacific waters, to which they owe their origin, since they penetrate freely into the Bering Sea through the straits.

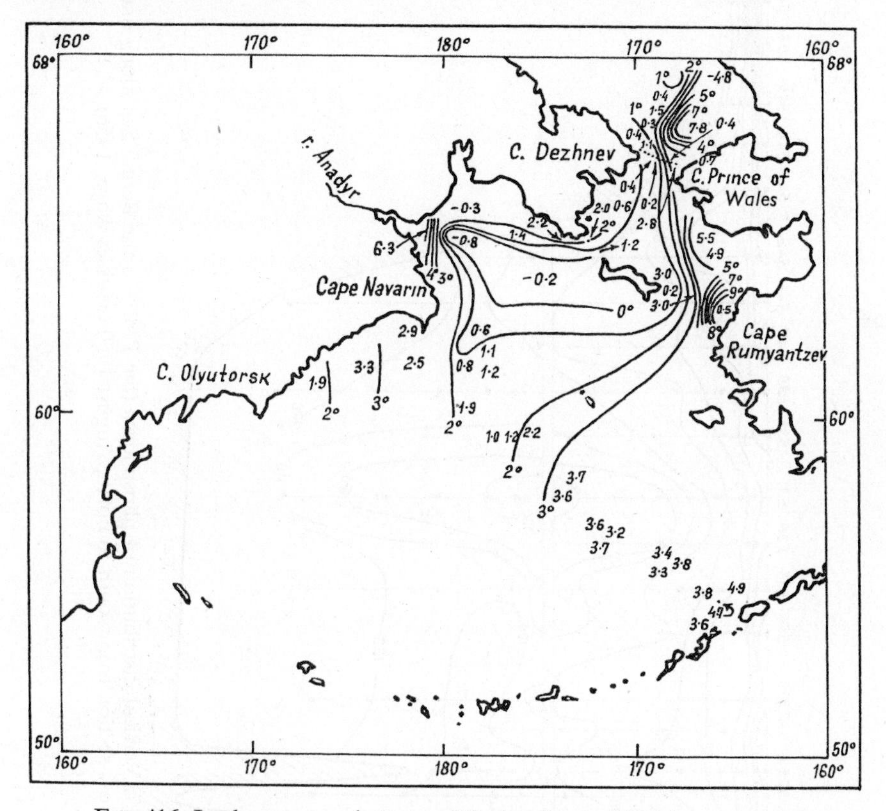

FIG. 416. Isotherms near bottom of Bering Sea in 1932 (Ratmanov).

A comparison of the structures of the column of water of the Bering Sea and of the adjacent Pacific Ocean is most significant (*Table 324*).

The amount of phosphorus in the Bering Sea is higher than that in the Pacific Ocean, while its oxygen content is lower at depths of 1,000 to 2,000 m.

The Bay of Anadyr and the adjacent shallows have, as a result of the vigorous autumn and winter vertical circulation, a uniform distribution of oxygen and other elements. During the period of intense development of phytoplankton (June) the amount of oxygen increases, that of phosphorus decreases to 20 mg/m³, and that of silica may amount to 100 mg/m³.

A high concentration of plant food in the upper layer of the Sea is

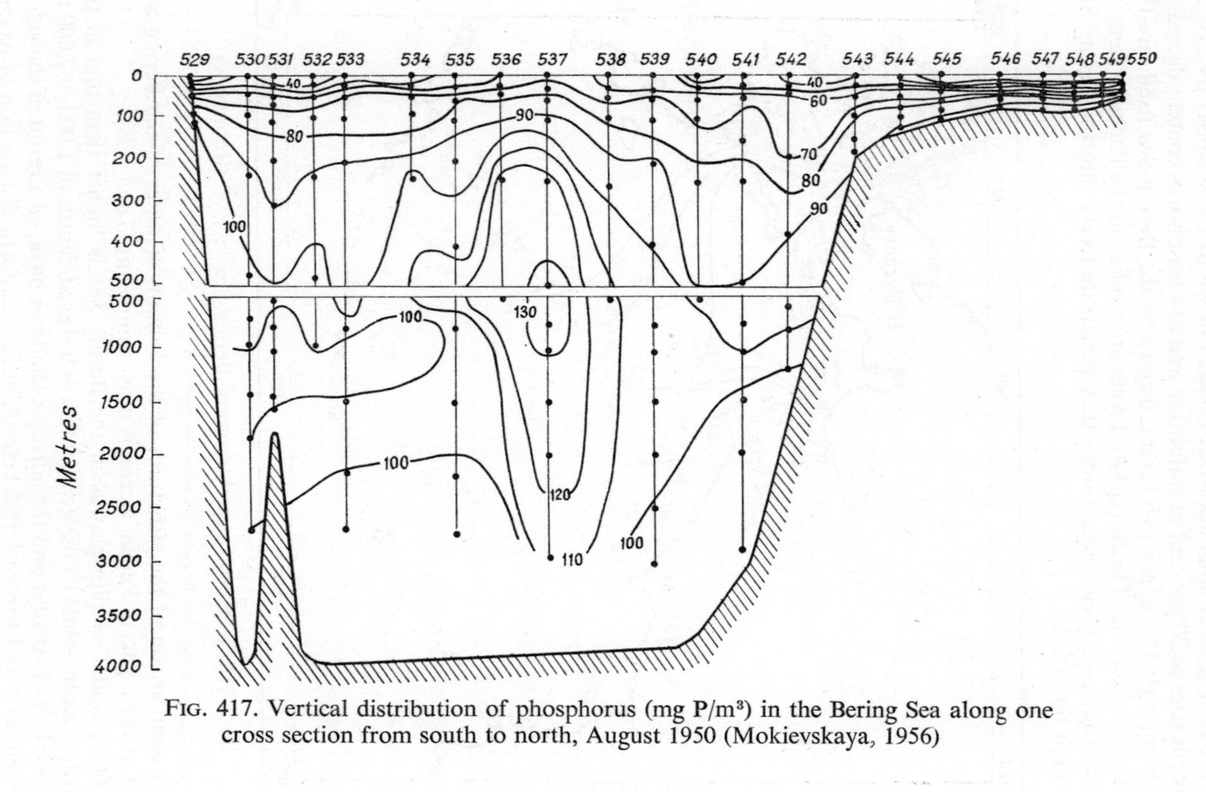

FIG. 417. Vertical distribution of phosphorus (mg P/m³) in the Bering Sea along one cross section from south to north, August 1950 (Mokievskaya, 1956)

characteristic of the Bering Sea, in contrast to the Seas of Okhotsk and Japan. Their amounts are not reduced to a minimum by the development of phytoplankton. However, a sharp decrease of nutrient salts is at times observed in the surface waters (*Table 325*). The curves of phosphate

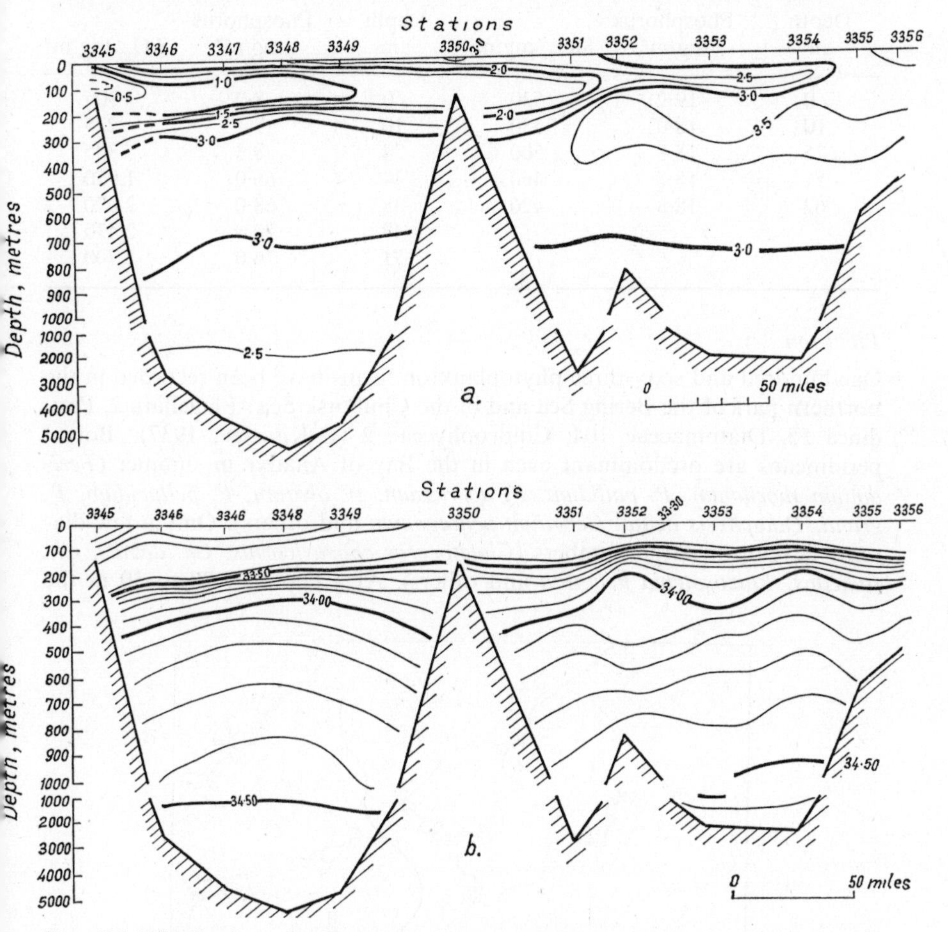

FIG. 418. Distribution of temperature (a) and salinity (b) on the cross section Cape Africa to Attu Island (Burkov, 1958).

distribution show a dome-like rise in the central part of the Sea; this is the result of the cyclonic movement of waters in the Bering Sea.

II. FLORA AND FAUNA

A biogeographical division into cold western and warm eastern zones characterizes the surface horizons throughout the Bering Sea. This division is particularly pronounced in the northern part of the Sea (Fig. 419).

Table 325. Two types of distribution of nutrient salts in the northern shallows of the Bering Sea (V. Mokievskaya, 1956)

First type (Kamchatka coast)			Second type (Bay of Anadyr in summer)		
Depth, m	Phosphorus mg/m³	SiO_2, mg/m³	Depth m	Phosphorus mg/m³	SiO_2, mg/m³
0	19·2	530	0	8·0	305
10	18·0	530	10	7·1	275
25	18·8	500	24	8·3	305
51	18·8	460	34	66·0	1,950
62	18·8	420	38	68·0	2,070
			48	70·0	2,430
			71	76·0	2,700

Plankton

One hundred and sixty-three phytoplankton forms have been recorded in the northern part of the Bering Sea and in the Chukotsk Sea: Flagellata 2, Peridinea 55, Diatomaceae 104, Chlorophyceae 2 (I. Kisselev, 1937). Boreal peridineans are predominant even in the Bay of Anadyr in summer (*Peridinium thorianum, P. pallidum, P. depressum, P. ovatum, P. pellucidum, P. granii, Dinophysis acuta, Ceratium pentagonum* and others). Only a few diatoms develop in large numbers (*Chaetoceros concavicornis, Ch. debilis, Ch. radicans, Rhizosolenia hebetata* and others). At a depth of 20 to 30 m the

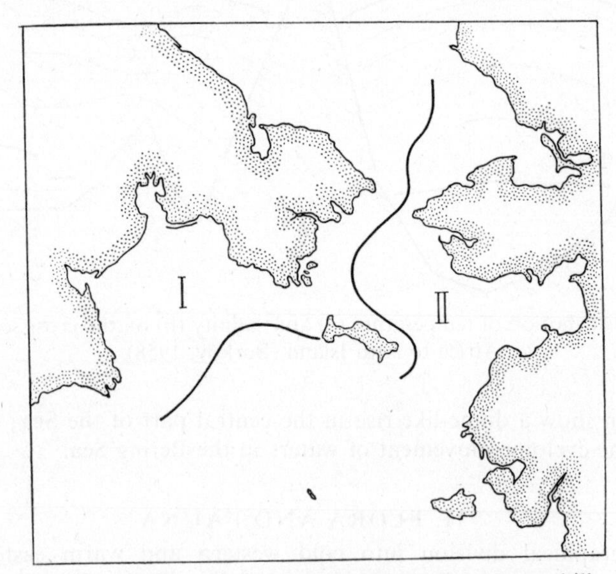

FIG. 419. Limit of zones of cold water (*I*) and thermophilic fauna (*II*) in northern part of the Bering Sea.

diatoms, however, become markedly predominant (*Thalassiosira nordenskiöldi*, *Th. gravida*, *Fragillaria oceanica*, *Amphiprora hyperborea*, *Porosira glacialis*, *Coscinosira polychorda* and others.) Anadyr phytoplankton, however, is mainly Arctic or Arctic-boreal, the boreal forms being predominant only in the surface layer in summer.

The same pronounced difference is observed between the phytoplankton compositions in the western and eastern sides of the Bering Strait, Arctic and Arctic-boreal forms being predominant in the first and boreal in the second.

The phytoplankton of the eastern side of the northern half of the Bering Sea is characterized by the predominance of boreal forms with an admixture of brackish-water and neritic species (*Thalassiosira japonica*, *Coscinodiscus granii*, *Actynoptychus undulatus*, *Rhizosolenia alata*, *Ditylum brightwellii*, *Actinocyclus ehrenbergii*, *Bellerochea malleus*, *Asterionella japonica*, *Peridinium excentricum*). Arctic and Arctic-boreal species are just as characteristic of the western side (*Thalassiosira nordenskiöldi*, *Th. gravida*, *Chaetoceros socialis*, *Ch. radians*, *Porosira glacialis*, *Bacterosira fragilis*, *Eucampia groenlandica* proceeding from cold-water to warm-water forms) (I. Kisselev, 1937). Apart from these zoogeographical changes seasonal alterations are observed in summer, especially in the surface layer of the western part of the Sea.

The Bay of Anadyr phytoplankton is characterized by the predominance of Arctic and Arctic-boreal species even in summer (except for its warmed surface layer). It is possible, however, that small, terminal branches of warm Pacific waters enter the Bay of Anadyr and currents stimulate a rich development of boreal forms in summer.

Four main groupings of zooplankton may be distinguished in the Bering Sea according to their distribution (K. Brodsky, 1954; M. Vinogradov, 1956) (Fig. 420).

The southern Bering Sea oceanic group in the 200 m surface layer is characterized by a selection of forms similar to those of the surface waters of the northwestern part of the Pacific Ocean; they penetrate into the Bering Sea with the warm Pacific waters. *Calanus cristatus*, *C. tonsus* and *Eucalanus bungii* are the mass forms of this group; *Racovitzanus antarcticus*, *Scolecithricella minor*, *Parathemisto japonica*, *Oncaea borealis* and others are added to them in smaller numbers. This group penetrates far to the north and into the Chukotsk Sea. The northern Bering Sea group lives on the shelf in the northern part of the Sea, partly overlapping the first group. *C. cristatus*, *C. tonsus*, *Primno macropa* and other warm-water forms are completely absent there, while *Calanus finmarchicus* and *Parathemisto libellula* become abundant. Certain cold-water species of this group move southwards with the cold waters along the coast of the Chukotsk Peninsula and Kamchatka almost to the southern end of the latter, forming the western neritic group together with some neritic species; this third group is very similar in its composition to the eastern neritic group. *Podon leuckarti*, *Centropages mamurrichi*, *Acartia clausi* and *A. longiremis* play an important role in the plankton of the most shallow regions of low salinity. This group, with the Oceanic and northern groups, penetrates into the Chukotsk Sea. A deep-water Bering Sea group lives in the southern part of the Sea below 200 m; it is an impoverished deep-water plankton of the Pacific Ocean.

There are considerable seasonal changes in the vertical distribution of plankton of the southern Bering oceanic group (Fig. 421). The cold intermediate layer of the Bering Sea is not so pronounced as that of the Sea of Okhotsk (its temperature is usually above freezing point); it has less influence on the vertical distribution of plankton and does not separate to the same extent

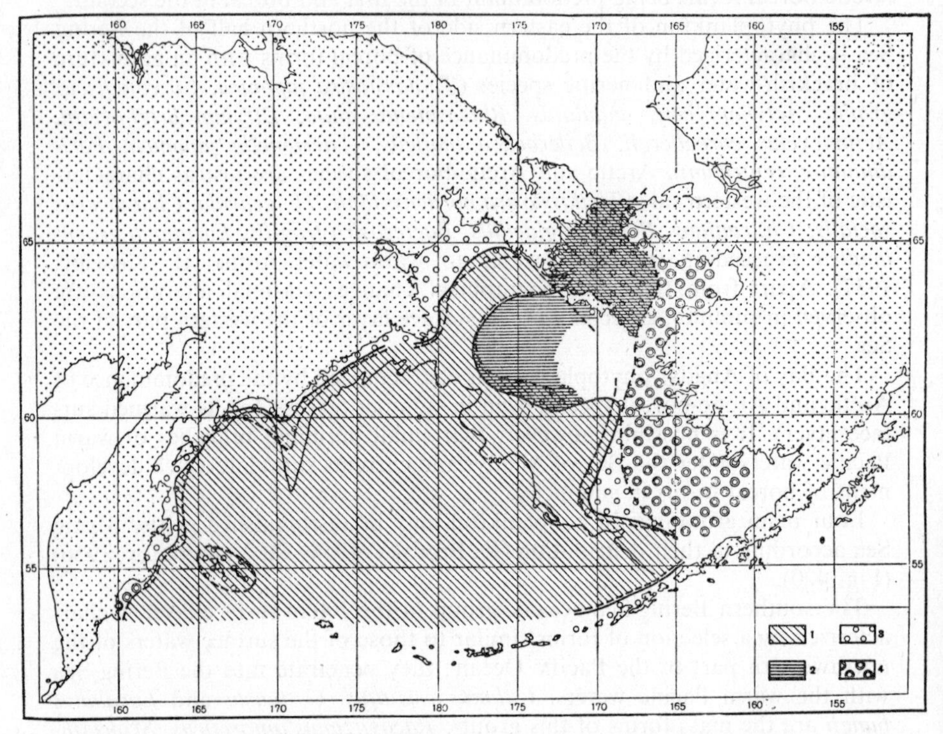

FIG. 420. Faunal grouping of zooplankton in Bering Sea in summer. *1* South Bering Sea grouping; *2* North Bering Sea oceanic grouping; *3* West neritic grouping; *4* East neritic grouping (Vinogradov, 1951).

the surface and subsurface plankton. The main mass of plankton is retained below the 200 m surface layer by a considerable fall of temperature in winter. In spring and summer, when the surface layer is warmed, zooplankton moves upwards, concentrating mostly in the uppermost 100 m for feeding and multiplication (*Eucalanus bungii*, *Calanus tonsus* and *C. cristatus*), frequently forming a biomass of from 1,500 to 2,500 mg/m^3 in the 10 to 100 m layer; the three species of Copepoda mentioned constitute up to 90 per cent of the total biomass in summer.

A very intensive development of phytoplankton (up to 15 or 20 g/m^3) has been recorded in the northern shallows in spring, while zooplankton is only feebly developed (M. Vinogradov, 1956). The Copepoda are concentrated in the lower horizons (Fig. 422).

As in the Sea of Okhotsk, but to a lesser extent, the cold intermediate layer influences the vertical migration of zooplankton, dividing it into three groups: those migrating above the cold layer (*Calanus tonsus*, *C. cristatus*, *Eucalanus*

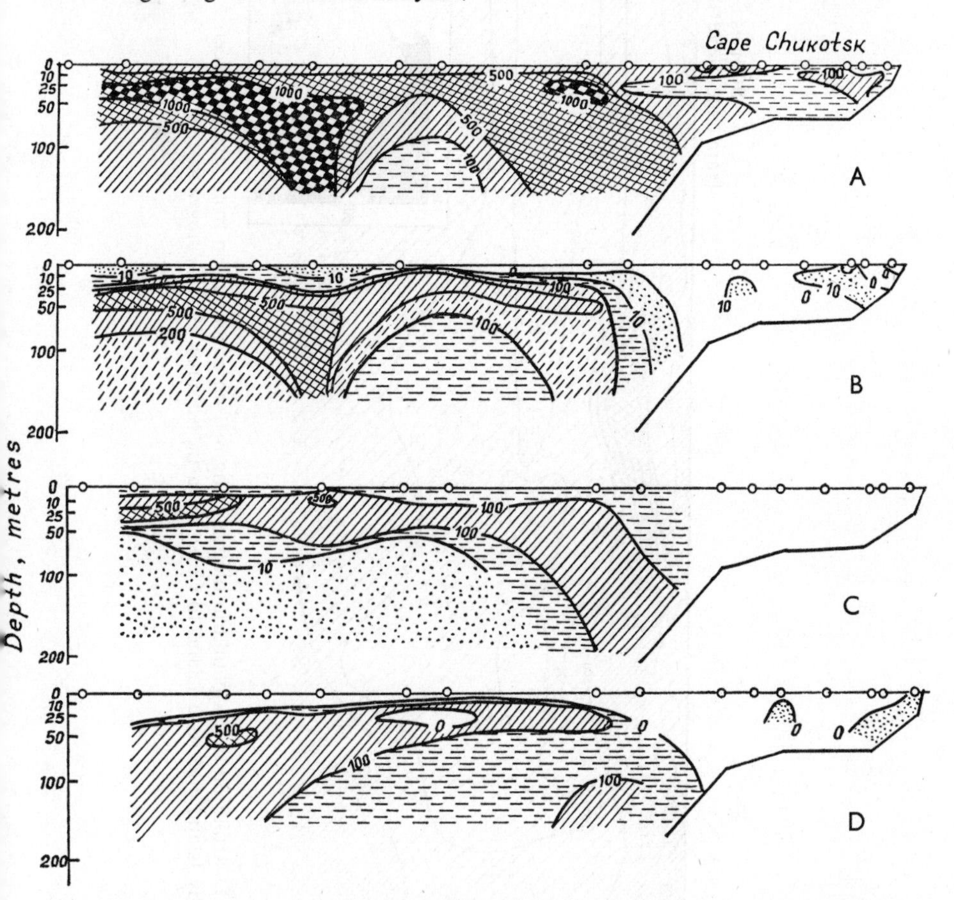

FIG. 421. Distribution of zooplankton biomass (mg/m²) on cross section through the Bering Sea, spring 1952). A Total zooplankton biomass; B *Eucalanus bungii* biomass; C *Calanus tonsus* biomass; D *C. cristatus* biomass (Vinogradov).

bungii), forms migrating through it (*Metridia pacifica*, *Pleuromamma scutulata*, *Candacia columbiae* and others), and those for which in their migrations the cold layer serves as a 'ceiling'. When the boundaries of the cold intermediate layer become less definite in summer the migration system becomes complete. *Calanus cristatus*, and *C. tonsus* and later the cold-water *Eucalanus bungii* sink down in autumn when the surface layer gets colder.

M. Vinogradov (1956) notes a characteristic peculiarity in the vertical

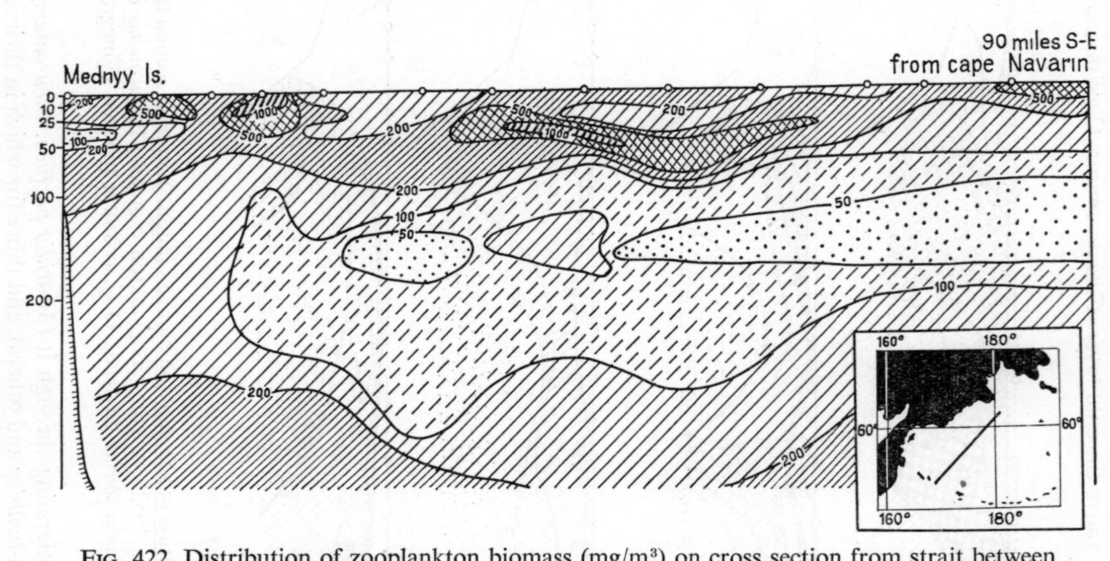

FIG. 422. Distribution of zooplankton biomass (mg/m³) on cross section from strait between Medny Island and Attu Island to Cape Navarin, Summer 1950 (Vinogradov, 1956).

distribution of the three dominant species of Copepoda: each species is predominant in a certain horizon, therefore, although they feed on the same species of diatoms, their competition for food is less intense since their main habitats belong to different horizons.

Eurythermic species—*Oithona similis*, *Sagitta elegans*, *Calanus finmarchicus*, *Parathemisto libellula*—become predominant in winter as a result of the cooling of the upper layer (down to 1,000 m) in the western part of the Sea and the total zooplankton biomass is considerably reduced. It increases again by the second half of the summer (Fig. 423), Eucalanus alone producing a biomass of 200 to 1,000 mg/m³. The amount of zooplankton decreases considerably

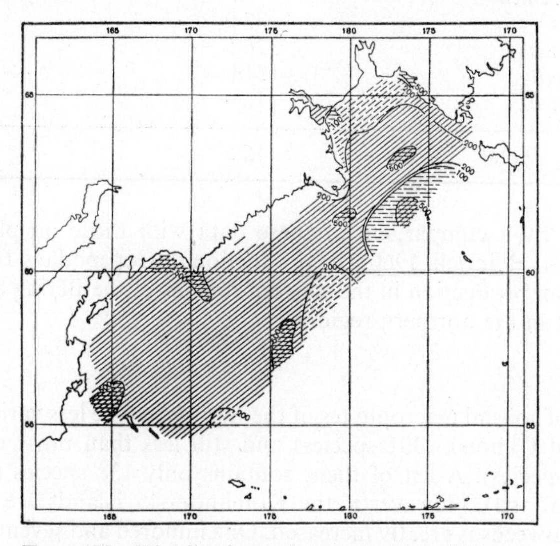

FIG. 423. Distribution of zooplankton biomass (mg/m³) in the 0 to 100 m layer in June 1952 (Vinogradov).

again in autumn. In the Bay of Anadyr, however, zooplankton reaches its highest development in autumn only, mainly on account of *Eucalanus bungii*. In the north of the Bering Sea the biomass remains low throughout the year, only at certain places does *Calanus finmarchicus* form great concentrations with a density of up to 100 mg/m³, and 400 specimens per 1 m².

The mass forms of the plankton Calanoida multiply at different times in the Bering Sea, thus making the best use of the food resources available (A. Geinrich, 1955). The multiplication of *Calanus finmarchicus* takes place at the beginning of the greatest phytoplankton development; *Eucalanus bungii* develops somewhat later, followed by *Calanus tonsus* (small race). The multiplication of *Calanus tonsus* (large race) is not connected with phytoplankton vegetation. The multiplication of *Metridia pacifica* proceeds throughout May to November, while *Calanus cristatus* spawns in December to February. Most of the forms mentioned produce only one generation annually (monocyclic), but in the southwestern part of the Sea the copepod stages of the second generation appear in *Calanus tonsus* in the autumn. *Metridia pacifica* produces several generations (up to four) during the summer.

A. Heinrich (1956) gives an estimate of the annual production of the main species of Copepoda from data on the cycle of their development (*Table 326*).

Table 326. Annual production of Copepoda in the Bering Sea, g/m², down to 500 m

Species	Western regions	Northern regions
Calanus finmarchicus	—	5·2
Calanus tonsus	22·0	—
Calanus cristatus	26·5	—
Eucalanus bungii	51·0	1·6
Metridia pacifica	16·0	3·3
Total	115·5	10·1

As shown by a comparison of these data with those on phytoplankton production (A. Heinrich, 1960) the production of Copepoda is 1/12 to 1/19 of phytoplankton production in the western regions of the Bering Sea, and only 1/200 of that in the northern regions.

Benthos

The species of coastal macrophytes of the Bering Sea are less varied than those of the Sea of Okhotsk (301 species) and still less than those of the Sea of Japan (379 species). A list of them contains only 138 species (25 green, 46 brown and 67 red). However if the Komandorski Islands are included the variety of sea-weeds is greatly increased. One hundred and seventy-one species of macrophytes have been recorded off the coast of these islands, especially off their southern side. There are huge forests of immense Alaria (reaching to 10 to 15 m in length) and *Nereocystis luetkeane* in the deepest places. Sea-weed growths give shelter to a rich fauna.

An elaborate investigation of the zoobenthos of the Bay of Anadyr was carried out by N. Vinogradova (1954).

The Bay of Anadyr is the coldest place in the Bering Sea (the Anadyr cold patch); only the waters of its western coast are somewhat warmed by small branches of warm currents entering it. Like Shelekhov Bay, the Bay of Anadyr has a quantitatively very rich fauna, on the average 426·5 g/m³, and is similar to the former in number and variety of species. The bottom biocoenoses of the Bay of Anadyr are more varied than those of Shelekhov Bay; moreover, they have a circular distribution (Fig. 424). The most characteristic biocoenoses are common to both bays. Fouling fauna (epifauna) develops intensely on the rocks and cliffs along the shores. It is composed of *Balanus balanus*, *B. crenatus*, *B. rostratus dalli*; the Porifera *Phakellia* sp.; the Bryozoa *Myriozoum* sp., *Membranipora flustra* and others; the Ascidia *Boltenia ovifera*, *B. echinata* and *Tethyum aurantium*. Starfish (*Leptasterias polaris* and others), brittle stars (*Gorgonocephalus* sp., *Ophiopholis aculeata*), sea-urchins (*Strongylocentrotus* sp.), very numerous prawns (*Nectocrangon lar*, *N. crassa*, *Hetairus fasciata*, *Spirontocaris* sp.), crabs (*Chionoecetes opilio*, *Hyas coarctatus* and

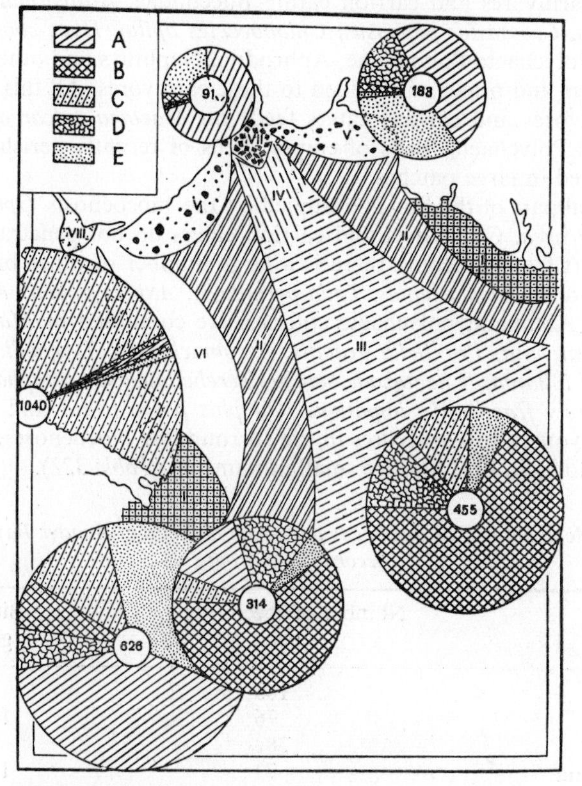

FIG. 424. Distribution of benthos biocoenoses in Bay of Anadyr (Vinogradova). *I* Balanidae–Hydroida, Bryozoa–Porifera biocoenosis; *II* Decapoda biocoenosis; *III Ophiura sarsi–Macoma calcarea* biocoenosis; *IV Yoldia limatula–Nucula tenuis* biocoenosis; *V* Ampeliscidae–Polychaeta biocoenosis; *VI Echinarachnius parma* biocoenosis; *VII Myriotzochus–Ophiura sarsi*–Polychaeta biocoenosis; *VIII Musculus discors–Potamilla reniformis–Terebellides stroemi* biocoenosis.

Encircled numerals denote average biomass (g/m³).

A—Crustacea; B—Mollusca; C—Echinodermata; D—Polychaeta; E—Others.

hermit crabs), Polychaeta (Polynoidae, Glyceridae, Nephthys), and Mollusca (*Saxicava arctica*) all live among the strongly developed growths.

The southwestern corner of the Bay gives shelter to a number of thermophilic fish; cod comes there in large numbers. On the sands of the western side of the Bay *Echinarachnius parma* lives in huge numbers; it is absent from other parts of the Bay. Within the fouling and *Echinarachnius parma* biocoenoses there lies a wide belt with the biocoenosis *Macoma calcarea—Ophiura sarsi*, with carnivores and carrion eating Buccinidae, *Natica clausi*, *Leptasterias polaris*, *Crossaster papposus*, *Chionoecetes opilio*, *Hyas coarctatus*, the large-sized Polychaeta Polynoidae, Aphrodita, Nephthys and others. Numerous Paguridae and prawns are added to these carnivores. All this huge number of carnivores and carrion eaters feeds on *Macoma calcarea* and other bivalves and Polychaeta. Beds of empty shells of recently perished bivalves are distributed in large patches.

The central part of the Bay is occupied by the biocoenosis *Ophiura sarsi–Macoma calcarea*. Carnivores and carrion eaters do not penetrate into this region. Apart from Macoma there is a large number of other bivalves here (*Yoldia limatula*, *Nucula tenuis*, *Leda pernula*(?), *Axinus gouldi*, Astarte and Periploma). Abundant polychaete colonies are composed of *Maldane sarsi*, *Axiothella catenata*, *Praxilella gracilis*, *Nicomache* sp., *Terebellides stroemi*, *Scalibregma inflatum*, *Chaetozone setosa*, *Terebellidae* sp., *Ampharetidae* sp., *Lumbriconereis fragilis*, *L. impatiens*, *Onuphis parvastriata* and others, i.e. all forms devoured by carnivores in the surrounding biocoenoses. Other biocoenoses, shown in Fig. 424, are small in numbers (*Table 327*).

Table 327. Mean number of specimens and mean biomass of Anadyr Bay biocoenoses according to groups

Group	Number of specimens per 1 m²	Biomass g/m²
Polychaeta	168	33·6
Mollusca	76	101·1
Crustacea	382	55·7
Echinodermata	73	188·6
Others	11	47·6
Total	710	426·6

The fauna of the Bay of Anadyr has an even greater tendency to gigantism than that of Shelekhov Bay. The greatest benthos biomass is adapted to the eastern and western coasts and to the region of the cold patch (500 to 1,000 g/m² and more).

The largest gatherings of Mollusca and Polychaetes have been recorded in the central part of the Bay; Echinodermata are most numerous in the western and Crustacea in the eastern part. The whole central part of the Bay, occupied by the biocoenosis *Ophiura sarsi–Macoma calcarea*, has a benthos biomass of 100 to 200 g/m² (Fig. 425). There is a sector in the middle of the region with a considerably increased biomass, even exceeding 1,000 g/m², on account of carnivores gathered on the dense colonies of *Macoma calcarea* (starfish, Gastropoda Mollusca, and crabs). The biomass is increased off the northeastern coast by the epifauna, and off the southwestern by *Echinarachnius parma*.

Data on the qualitative and quantitative distribution of benthos in the eastern part of the Bering Sea are given in A. Neiman's paper (1960). This investigator has drawn a picture of the biocoenotic distribution of bottom-living fauna (Fig. 426).

There is a considerable difference in the composition and quantitative distribution of the population between the northwestern shallow, the only

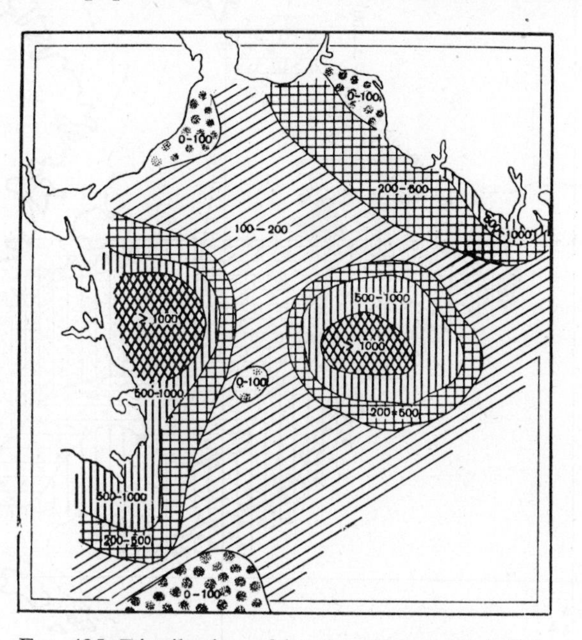

FIG. 425. Distribution of benthos biomass (g/m²) in the Bay of Anadyr (Vinogradova, 1954).

large shallow in the Far Eastern Seas, and the southwestern and southern deep parts of the Sea. The main bottom-living population of the Bering Sea shelf is composed of bivalves, then come the Echinodermata (mainly Ophiura) and Polychaeta. The oozes south and southwest of St Lawrence Island have the richest population, reaching at times a biomass of 500 g/m² at depths of 50 to 150 m. The population of the sands is scarce, furnishing a biomass of less than 50 g/m².

The eastern and western sides of the Bering Sea have a similar fauna. At a temperature not higher than 3° the predominant forms are as follows: among Mollusca *Macoma calcarea*, *Leda pernula*, *Nucula tenuis*, *Serripes groenlandicus*, *Yoldia hyperborea*, *Y. traciaeformis* and *Cardium ciliatum*; among Echinodermata *Ophiura sarsi*, *Echinarachnius parma*, *Brisaster* sp., *Ctenodiscus crispatus* and *Cucumaria calcigera*.

It has been possible to draw a general chart of the quantitative distribution

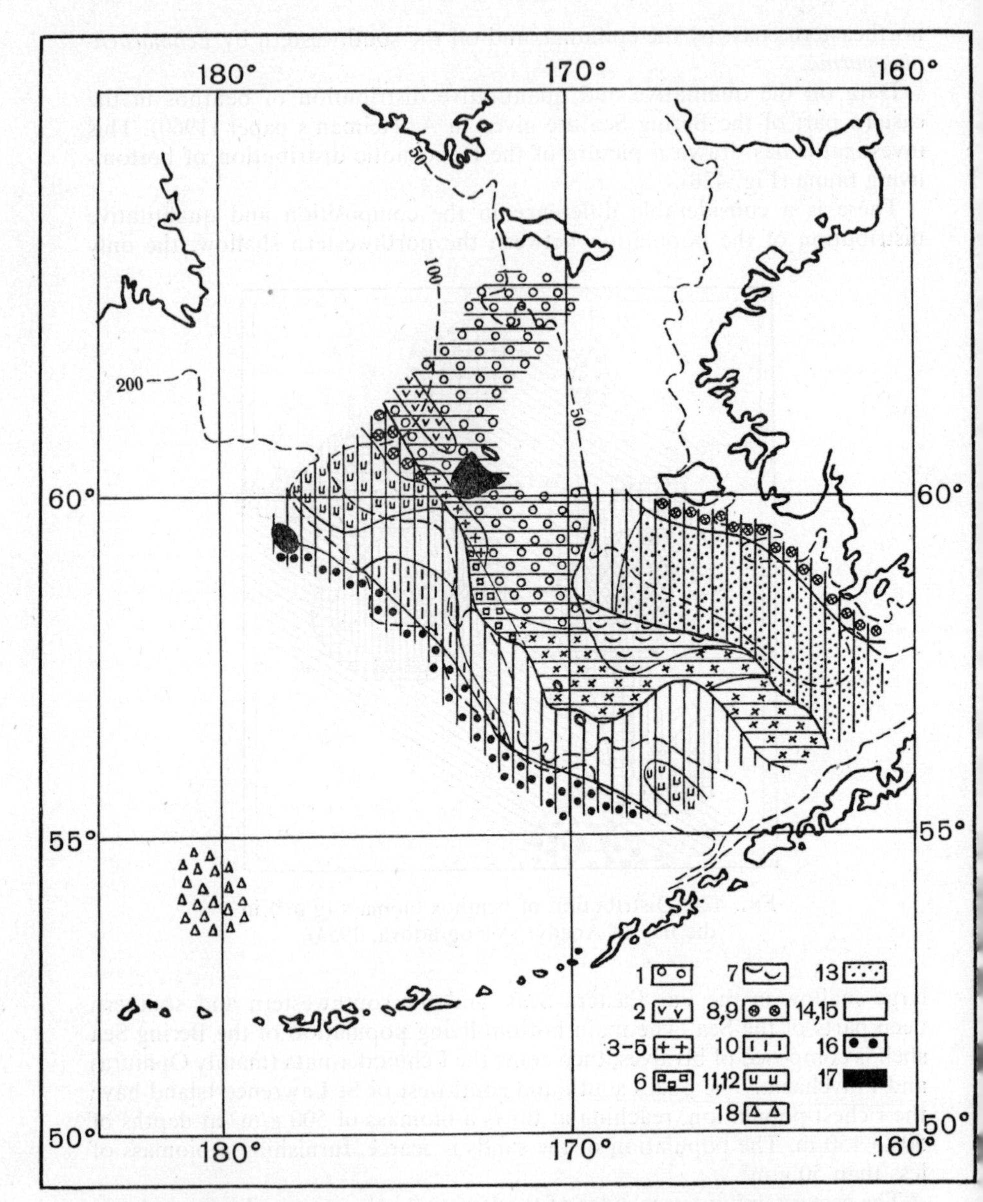

FIG. 426. Distribution of benthos biocoenosis in eastern part of Bering Sea (Neiman, 1960). 1 *Macoma calcarea*; 2 *Leda pernula*; 3, 4 *Ophiura sarsi*; 6 *Serripes groenlandicus*; 7 *Cucumaria calcigera*; 8, 9 *Echinarachnius parma*; 10 *Chiridota* sp.; 11 *Yoldia traciaeformis*+*Ctenodiscus crispatus*; 12 *Ctenodiscus crispatus*; 13 *Cardium* sp.; 14, 15 Polychaeta; 16 *Ophiura leptoctenia*; 17 Fouling; 18 Glass Porifera.

of the bottom-living fauna throughout the Bering Sea from all the data collected on this problem (Fig. 427).

Fish

The Bering Sea contains about 315 species of fish (A. Andriashev, 1939, with T. Rass's corrections); 112 of them are common with the Sea of Okhotsk. Most of the species are cold-water boreal forms but certain true Arctic species are recorded among them. Three main fauna elements can be distinguished (A. Andriashev, 1935); the Asian element: 122 species, genetically linked with the fauna of the other Far Eastern Seas; the American: 107 species, connected with the fauna of the American coast; and the Polar element: composed of 5 to 7 Arctic species (*Ulcina olriki*, *Boreogadus saida* and others). South-boreal species, for example *Sardinops sagax melanosticta* and *Engraulis japonicus*, enter the southwestern part of the Sea singly.

The following families, constituting about 70 per cent of all the fish, are the richest in species: Cottidae (65 species), Liparidae (46), Zoarcidae (24), Pleuronectidae (23), Stichaeidae (18), Agonidae (14), Salmonidae (12), and Scorpaenidae (10).

The Bering Sea has about 30 deep-water oceanic spieces of fish, among them Macruridae (7), Gonostomidae (4), and Scopelidae (4) (T. Rass, 1954). There are 48 secondary deep-water species, among them Liparidae (24), Zoarcidae (8), Cottidae (5), and Scorpaenidae (4).

Approximately 25 species are of commerical value; among the most important are herring (*Clupea pallasi*) and salmon (*Oncorhynchus keta*, *O. gorbuscha*, *O. nerka*. *O. tschawytscha*, *O. kisutch*, and *Salvelinus malma*); frostfish (*Osmerus eperlanus dentex*, *Hypomesus olidus*); cod (*Gadus macrocephalus*); navaga (*Eleginus gracilis*); halibut and flatfish (*Hippoglossus stenolepis*, *Reinhardtius matsuurae*, *Hippoglossoides robustus*, *Limanda aspera*, *Platessa quadrituberculata*, *Lepidopsetta bilineata*); sterling (*Pleurogrammus monopterygius*) and others. So far the fisheries of the Bering Sea proper are poorly developed, less than those in the adjacent waters of eastern Kamchatka and southwestern Alaska. The fish stocks of this body of water should not be estimated by the present fish yield. Much greater numbers of plaice, halibut, sea bass (Sebastes), sterling, cod, frostfish and capelin could be taken in this sea (T. Rass, 1955).

As a result of a zoogeographical analysis of the Bering Sea fauna Ya. Birstein and M. Vinogradov (1952), taking Decapoda as an example, came to the conclusion that the influence of the Arctic conditions is perceptible: 32·4 per cent of the species are found to be pan-Arctic, low-Arctic, Arctic-boreal, low Arctic-boreal, sub-Arctic and sub-Arctic-boreal. This applies to the decapod fauna (about a hundred species) throughout the Sea. The percentage rises to 38·1 if the species recorded only off Unalashka Island are excluded. The Arctic aspect of the fauna stands out even more sharply in the northern part of the Sea. These two investigators have made an interesting comparison of their data (obtained for the Bering Sea) with those for the Sea of Okhotsk (*Table 328*).

The amphi-Pacific character of the fauna distribution is fairly pronounced

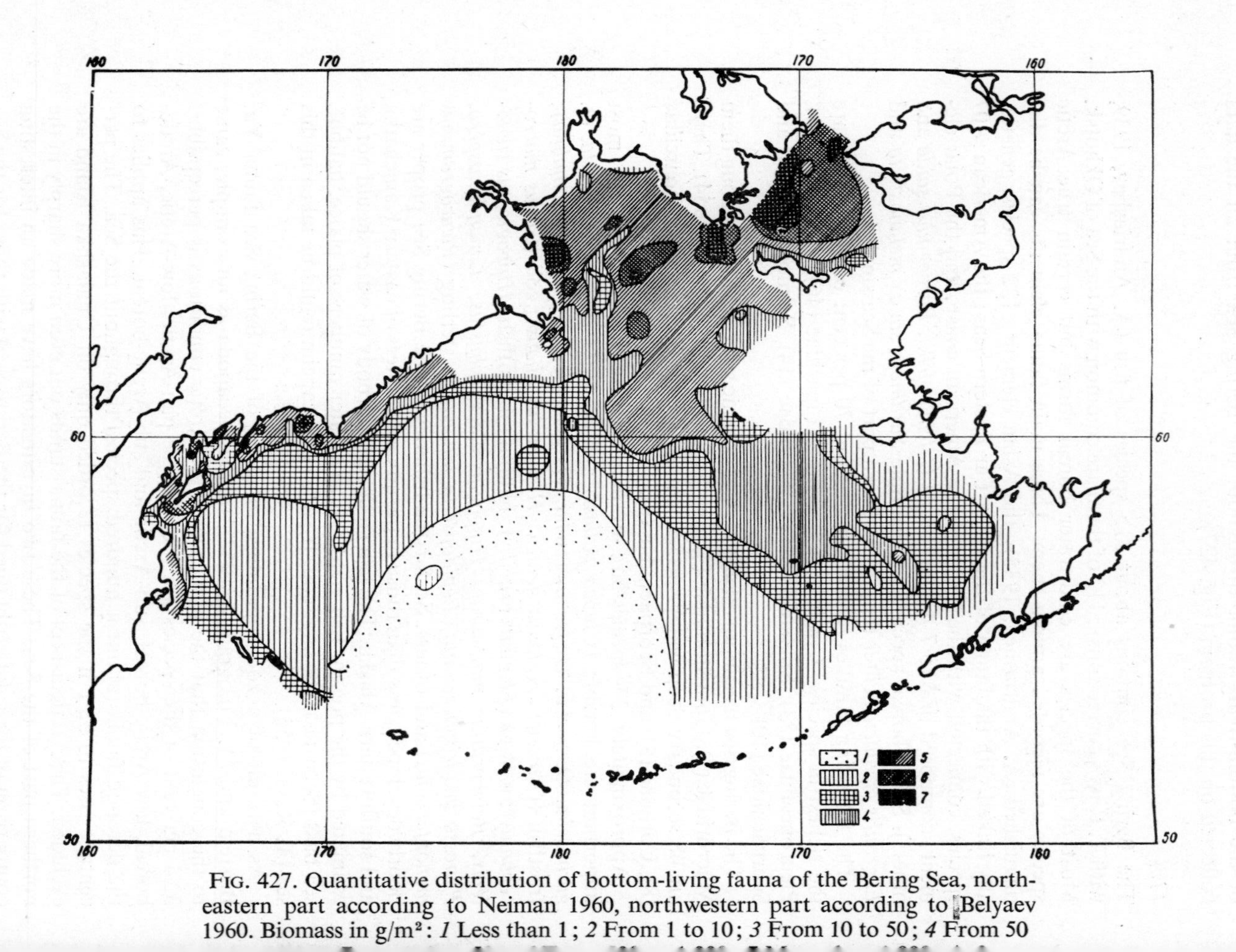

FIG. 427. Quantitative distribution of bottom-living fauna of the Bering Sea, north-eastern part according to Neiman 1960, northwestern part according to Belyaev 1960. Biomass in g/m²: *1* Less than 1; *2* From 1 to 10; *3* From 10 to 50; *4* From 50

Table 328. Comparison of percentage composition of fauna of decapod Crustacea in Akhotsk and Bering Seas

Group	Sea of Okhotsk	Bering Sea, excluding Unalashka Island
Pan-Arctic, low Arctic, Arctic-boreal and low Arctic-boreal	36·4	33·7
Sub-Arctic and sub-Arctic-boreal	10·4	4·4
Pacific Ocean-glacial	7·8	3·4
Total	54·6	41·5
Boreal (including subtropic-boreal for Sea of Okhotsk)	45·4	58·5
Total	100	100

in the Bering Sea. Decapod crustaceans and fish may be given as an example (*Table 329*).

Many other groups have great qualitative variety in the eastern part of the Ocean. The fact that not all of them do so is interesting. Certain deep-water groups are greatly varied in the eastern part of the Ocean. Pogonophora and Echiuroidea certainly belong to these groups, and possibly some others.

The great age and permanency of the Oceanic trenches, especially the Pacific Ocean trenches, is proved, we think, by all the data given in this book, particularly by the data on the Pacific Ocean fauna. Otherwise we would have been unable to explain many phenomena which fully support this suggestion, primarily the indubitable age of the geographical uniformities connected with the temporary distribution of oceanic basins and of that of the oceanic flora and fauna.

The greater richness of Pacific flora and fauna compared with those of the Atlantic; the ancient, primitive aspect of its deep-water fauna, amphiboreal and bipolar phenomena; the ancient aspect of the uniformity of the vertical distribution of fauna; the harmony of the whole system of geographical zonation, in other words of the biological structure of the Ocean: all these indicate the long existence of the main features of the contemporary geographical distribution of the water masses of this ocean.

Table 329. Distribution of decapod Crustacea and fish on eastern and western sides of Bering Sea

Distribution	Decapod Crustacea	Fish
Common to western and eastern coast	52·5	46·1
Off western coast only	8·9	19·9
Off eastern coast only	38·6	34·0

REFERENCES

The reference list is composed along the following lines.

The names of the authors are given in transcription adopted by the authors. In many instances the Russian authors spell their names in various ways: the spelling varies in regard to the specific language in which the paper or the summary is presented. For example, the same name may be spelled as: Zinova and Sinova, Vodyanitzky and Wodianizky, Virketis and Wirkettiss, Tchugunov and Tschugunoff, Stschapova, Scapova and Schapova, Ouchakoff and Uschakov etc. Owing to this discrepancy the author places other versions of spelling in brackets. These are followed by the translation of each paper's title into English. To reduce the general size of the reference part the author has made provisional abbreviation attached to the titles of journals, proceedings, institutes, laboratories etc. which frequently appear in the text of the book. The abbreviations are adopted in accordance with the initial letters commonly referred to in Russian scientific papers. The next symbol introduced into brackets is R — which shows that the paper is written only in Russian; E.s. — which indicates that an English summary is available; F.s. — which indicates that a French summary or G.s. — German summary is available. Ed. stands for Edition.

A list of abbreviations in regard to institutions, journals, proceedings etc. is given, and figures following the title of the journal, proceedings or symposia reflect the volume and issue; for example, *Z.J.* **18**, 2 should be read as follows: *Zoological Journal*, Vol. 18, Issue 2.

In the course of compiling the reference list the author was guided by the fact that the Russian language is little known abroad and, hence, the papers written in Russian are not widely read or used in the course of scientific bibliographies; in many cases papers in Russian are frequently not mentioned at all. This fact should be ascribed partly to linguistic difficulties and partly to the difficulty of finding the Russian papers scattered in various publications.

The author hopes that this book and the reference list included will help to disseminate knowledge about the advances of marine biology in Russia.

The reference list of Russian works is incomplete. An overwhelming number of papers devoted to classification, the faunistics and the biology of marine fauna and flora, ichthyology and commercial fisheries, the physical and chemical oceanography and marine geology are not included into the list. The total coverage of the vast literature throughout the last forty years should run as high as 10,000 titles.

A more complete, and in some cases a more exhaustive, list can be found in a series of books and papers included in scientific periodicals. For information it is advisable to refer to K. Derjugin's (1936) and L. Zenkevich's (1937) works on the period covering the entire number of the water reservoirs of the USSR; the southern seas are reviewed in N. Maximov's (1958) and V. Nikitina's (1934, 1939–40) reference list and also in N. Romanova's (1955) and

K. Vinogradov's (1958) reference list; the seas of the Soviet Far East are mentioned in the work of E. F. Guryanova and G. Lindberg (1937) and in N. Romanov's (1959) reference list. Above all, an extensive literature is attached to the monographs devoted to the studies of separate seas or separate groups of organisms. It is worth mentioning the Bibliographic Index for the Study of the Barents Sea (1941), the Reference Book on the Hydrology of the Seas of the USSR, the works of K. Derjugin devoted to the fauna of the Kola Gulf (1915) and to the White Sea fauna (1928). Also worthy of note are P. Ushakov's work on the fauna of the Okhotsk Sea (1953) and the fauna of the Chukotsk Sea (1952); A. Sinova on the brown (1953) and red (1955) algae; V. Vorobiev on the benthos of the Azov Sea (1949), S. Brujewicz on the hydrochemistry of the mid and southern part of the Caspian Sea (1937); V. Datzko devoted to the organic matter in the waters of the Southern Seas of the USSR (1959); A. Andriashev on the fishes of the Northern Seas of the USSR (1954); M. Klenova on marine geology (1948) and on the geology of the Barents Sea (1960); N. Knipovich on marine hydrology (1932), brackish waters (1938), the hydrology of the Black and Azov Seas (1932).

Literary references are also to be found in the numerous monographs of N. Subov (1938, 1940, 1945, 1947, 1950); in P. Ushakov's works on the Polychaetae; in L. Berg's work on the fresh-water fishes (1948–9); in P. Schmidt's work on the fishes of the eastern seas (1904) and in the study devoted to the fishes of the Okhotsk Sea (1950); in L. Zenkevich's work on the fauna and the biological productivity of the sea (1947 and 1951); in J. H. Segerstrale's study devoted to the Baltic Sea (1957); in H. Caspers' work (1957) on the Black and Azov Seas and in many others.

ABRIKOSOV, G. 1959. Bryozoa in the Caspian and Aral Seas. *Z.J.* **38**, 5 (E.s.)

ABRIKOSOV, G. and SOKOLOVA, N. 1948. The study of the littoral in the White Sea. *Bull. Moscow Univ., Biology*, **2** (R)

Acclimatization of the Nereis in the Caspian Sea. 1952. *Ed. M.O.I.P.* (R)

Acclimatization of fishes and feeding-organisms (for fish) in the seas of the USSR. 1960. *I. Tr. V.N.I.R.O.* **43** (R)

AGENOROV, V. 1946. On the dynamics of the waters in the Barents Sea. *Ed. G.O.I.* (R)

AGENOROV, V. 1947. On the water masses in the Barents Sea in summer. *Tr. G.O.I.* **1** (3) (R)

AKSENOV, A. 1955. Morphology and dynamic of the northern coast in the Azov Sea. *Tr. G.O.I.* **29** (41) (R)

ALEKIN, O. 1947. On the problem of the origin of the salt composition in the waters of the Aral Sea. *Meteorologia and Hydrologia*, **4** (R)

ALEXANDROV, A. 1927. The anchovy in the Azov–Black basin, their origin and systematic position. *Tr. kerch Sci. Fisheries Station*, **1**, 2–3 (R)

ANDREEVA, I. and UDINTZEV, G. 1958. The bottom structure of the Sea of Japan, according to research done aboard *Vityaz. Bull. Acad. Sci. USSR, geol.* **10** (R)

ANDRIASHEV, A. 1935. Geographical distribution of the edible sea food of the Bering Sea and the problems raised. *Expl. des mers de l'URSS*, **22** (E.s.)

Andriashev, A. 1939. On the amphipacific (Japan-Oregonian) distribution of marine fauna in the northern part of the Pacific Ocean. *Z.J.* **18**, 2 (E.s.)

Andriashev, A. 1939. *The fish of the Bering Sea and neighbouring waters, its origin and zeogeography*. Leningrad University Press (E.s.)

Andriashev, A. 1953. The ancient and secondary deep-sea fish and their significance for zoogeographical analysis. *Survey in general problems of Ichthyology* (R)

Andriashev, A. 1954. Fishes of the Northern Seas of the USSR. *Ed. Acad. Sci. USSR* (R)

Andriashev, A. 1935. On a new Liparid fish from a depth over 7,000 metres. *Tr. IOAN*, **12** (R)

Andrusov, N. (Andrusoff, N.), 1888. A survey in the history of the development of the Caspian Sea and its inhabitants. *Bull. Imp. Russ. Geogr. Soc.* 24 (R)

Andrusov, N. 1888. Essay on the history of the Caspian Sea. *Bull. Russ. Geog. Soc.* **42**, 2 (R)

Andrusov, N. 1894. On the hydrogen sulphide contamination of the Black Sea. *Mém. Acad. Imp. Sci. St. Pétersbourg, physico-mathématique*, **8**, 1 (R)

Andrusov, N. 1897. The fossil and living Dreissensidae of the Evrasia. *Trav. Soc. Natur. Pétersbourg*, **25** (R)

Andrusov, N. 1911. On the age and the stratigraphic position of the Akchagil strata. *Mem. Miner. Soc.* **48**, 1 (R)

Andrusov, N. 1911. On the age and stratigraphical position of the Akchagil strata. *Mem. Miner. Soc.* **47**, 1.

Andrusov, N. 1917. *The Pontic stage: Geology of Russia*, 4, 2. *Ed. Geological Committee* (R)

Andrusov, N. 1918. Geological construction of the Kerch Strait. *Bull. Acad. Sci. Russ.* (R)

Andrusov, N. 1918. The interrelation of the Euxin and Caspian basins in neogen. *Bull. Russ. Acad. Sci.* **12**, 8 (R)

Andrusov, N. 1926. Geology and history of the Kerch Strait. *Bull. M.O.I.P., géologique*, **4**, 3–4 (R)

Andrusov, N. 1929. Das obere Pliocen des Schwarzmeer-Beckens. *Geology of the USSR*, 4, 2, 3. *Ed. Geological Committee* (R)

Annenkova, N. and Palenichko, Z. 1947. The finding of the boreal polychaete in the White Sea. *Priroda*, **4** (R)

Antews, E. 1928. Shell beds of the Skagerrack. *Geol. Foren. Forhandl., Stockholm*, **50**.

Antipa, G. 1910. *Das Ueberschwammungsgebiet der unteren Donau, Bucuresti.*

Antipa, G. 1931. Les bases biologiques de la production des pêcheries dans la région Nord-Ouest de la Mer Noire. *Rapp. proc. verb. comm. intern. explor. Méditerranée*, **6**.

Antipa, G. 1941. Marea Neagra. *Bucuresti Academia Româna*, Publ. Fond. V. Adamachi, **10**, 55.

Aphanasiev, G. 1938. Some data on the weight relationship of organs in the Black Sea Lamellibranchia. *Z.J.* **17**, 4 (E.s.)

APOLLOV, B. 1954. The future of the Caspian Sea. Symposium: Level changes of the Caspian Sea. *Acad. Sci. USSR* (R)

APOLLOV, B. 1956. *The Caspian Sea and its basin.* (R)

APPELLÖF, A. 1912. Invertebrate fauna of the depths of the Norwegian Sea and North Atlantic. In Murray & Hjort. *The Depths of the Ocean.*

ARCHANGELSKY, A. (Archanguelsky, Arkhangelsky). 1926. Hydrogen sulphide contamination of some Tertiary sea basins of the Crimea and Caucasus regions and its connection with the origin of petroleum. *Petroleum Ind.* **10**, 4 (E.s.)

ARCHANGELSKY, A. 1927. On the sediments of the Black Sea and their importance for the study of sedimentary rocks. *Bull. M.O.I.P., géologique,* **5**, 3–4 (E.s.)

ARCHANGELSKY, A. 1932. The geological structure of the USSR. Moscow.

ARCHANGELSKY, A. 1932. Introduction to the study of the geology of European Russia. Leningrad.

ARCHANGELSKY, A. and BATALINA, M. 1928. Knowledge of the history of the development of the Black Sea. *Bull. Acad. Sci. USSR.*

ARCHANGELSKY, A. and STRAHOV, N. 1932. Geological history of the Black Sea. *Bull. M.O.I.P., géologique* **10** (R)

ARCHANGELSKY, A. and STRAHOV, N. 1938. Brief outline of the geological history of the Black Sea. *Acad. Sci. USSR, Moscow* (E.s.)

ARNOLDI, L. 1938. On the question of the zooplankton distribution in the Caspian Sea. *Trans. Complex Study Caspian Sea,* **5** (R)

ARNOLDI, L. 1941. New data on quantitative study of the zoobenthos in Karkinitsky Bay. *Proc. Inst. Biol. Acad. Sci. USSR* (1940).

ARNOLDI, L. 1948. On the littoral in the Black Sea. *Tr. S.B.S.* **6** (R)

ARNOLDI, L. and FORTUNATOVA, E. 1941. The experimental study of the fish-feeding. *Tr. Z.I.N.* **7**, 2.

ATKINS, W. 1925, 1926. Seasonal changes in the phosphate content of sea water in relation to the growth of the algal plankton during 1923 and 1924 (Part 2). *J. Mar. Biol. Assoc.* **13**, 14.

ATKINS, W. 1930. Seasonal variations in the phosphate and silicate content of sea water to the phytoplankton. *Ibid.* **14**, 3.

AURIVILLIUS, C. 1896. Das Plankton des Baltischen Meeres. *K. Svenska Vet. Akad. Handl.* **21**, **4**, 8.

AURIVILLIUS, C. 1898. Vergleichende tiergeographische Untersuchungen über die Planktonfauna des Skagerraks. *Ibid.* **30**, 3.

BACESCO, M. 1940. Les Mysidacés des eaux roumaines. *Ann. Sci. Univ. Jassy,* **26**, 2.

BACESCO, M. 1948. Quelques observations sur la faune benthonique du défilé Roumain du Danube. (e.c.) *Ann. Sci. Univ. Jassy,* **31**, 2.

BACESCO, M. 1954. Mysidacea. Fauna Republicii populare Romine. *Crustacea,* **4**, 3.

BACESCO, M. 1957. Les sables à Corbulomya (Aloidis) maeotica, Mill. base trophique de premier ordre pour les poissons de la Mer Noire. *Tr. Mus. hist. nat.* ("Gr. Antipa"), **1**.

BADIGIN, K. 1940. *On board the* George Sedov *across the Arctic Ocean* (R)

De Beauchamp, P. 1914. Aperçu sur la répartition des êtres dans les zones des marées à Roscoff. *Bull. Soc. Zool. Fr.* **39**.

De Beauchamp, P. and Zachs, I. 1913. Esquisse d'une monographie bionomique de la plage de Terrénès. *Mém. Soc. Zool. Fr.* **26**.

Behning, A. 1924. Zur Erforschung der am Flussboden der Wolga lebenden Organismen. *Monogr. Biolog. Wolga-Station Naturforscher-Gesellsch. Saratov*, **1** (G.s.)

Behning, A. 1934. Hydrologische und hydrobiologische Materialien zu einer Fischerei Karte des Aralsees. *Tr. Ar. V.N.I.R.O.* **3** (R)

Behning, A. 1935. Die Materialien zu einer Fischerei Karte des Aralsees. *Ibid.* **4** (R)

Behning, A. 1936, 1941. Miscellanea Aralo-Caspica. *IRHH*, **33**, **39**.

Behning, A. 1938. The principal food series of the Caspian Sea Pelagial. *Priroda*, **9** (R)

Behning, A. 1938. Caspian relics in the fauna of the Usboy lakes. *DAN, USSR*, **21**, 6 (R)

Beklemischev, C. The feeding habits of *Nereis pelagica* and the functional significance of its mandibular apparatus. *DAN, USSR*, **73**, 5 (R)

Beklemischev, C. and Burkow, W. 1958. Verbindung der Plankton-verteilung mit der Verteilung der Wassermassen in der Zone der Meeresfronten des Nordwestlichen Teiles des Stillen Ozean. *Tr. IOAN*, **27** (R)

Beklemischev, W. 1915. On the Turbellarian fauna in the Caspian Sea. *Trav. Soc. Natura. Pétersbourg*, **46**, 1 (F.s.)

Beklemischev, W. 1922. New data on the fauna of the Aral Sea. *R.H.J.* **1**, 9–10 (G.s.)

Beklemischev, W. 1923. On the question of the river-Peracarida in the Ponto-Caspian basin. *R.H.J.* **2** (G.s.)

Beklemischev, W. 1953. Turbellaria of the Caspian Sea. *Bull. M.O.I.P., Biol.* **58**, 6 (R)

Beklemischev, W. and Baskina, W. 1938. Einige experimentelle Prämissen zur ökologischen Zoogeographie der südrussischen Binnenmeere. II. Die Hauptursache der schwächeren Giftigkeit von Aralseewasser fur Cladoceren im Vergelich mit dem Kaspisee- und Schwarzmeerwasser. *Tr. de l'Inst. Rech. biol. Stat. biol. Univ. Perm.* **8**, 9–10 (G.s.)

Belyaev, G. (Beliayev, Belyayev). The quantitative distribution of the bottom fauna in the north-western part of the Bering Sea. *Ibid.* **34** (R)

Belyaev, G. 1952. The biology of *Nereis succinea* in the northern part of the Caspian Sea. In "Acclimatization of *Nereis* in the Caspian Sea". *Bull. M.O.I.P. Moscow* (R)

Belyaev, G. 1959. A diagram of vertical biological zonality of the ocean. *DAN, USSR*, **129**, 3 (R)

Belyaev, G. and Birstein, A. 1940. Osmoregulation of some Caspian invertebrates. *Z.J.* **19**, 4 (E.s.)

Belyaev, G., Vinogradova, N. G. and Filatova, Z. A. 1960. Investigation of the bottom fauna in the deep water trenches of the Southern Pacific. *Tr. IOAN*, **41** (R)

BERDICHEVSKY, L. 1957. The state and methods of raising valuable commercial fish stock in the waters of the USSR. *Probl. Ichthyology*, **9** (R)

BERG, L. 1908. Der Aralsee. Versuch einer physischgeographischen Monographie. *Mitt. Turkestan. Abteil. Keiserl. Russ. Geogr. Gesellsch.* **5** (R)

BERG, L. 1916. On the distribution of the fish *Myoxocephalus quadricornis* from the family Cottidae (e.c.). *Bull. Acad. Imp. Sc.* (R)

BERG, L. 1918. On the causes of similarity between the fauna of the northern part of Atlantic and Pacific Oceans. *Bull. Acad. Sci. Russ.* **16** (R)

BERG, L. 1920. Bipolar distribution of organisms and the Glacial Period. *Bull. Acad. Sci. Russ.* (R)

BERG, L. 1928. On the origin of the northern elements in the fauna of the Caspian Sea. *DAN, USSR*, **14**, 3 (R)

BERG, L. 1932. On the level of the Aral Sea. *Mem. State Hydrol. Inst.* **8** (R)

BERG, L. Niveau de la mer Caspienne dans les temps historiques. *Probl. phys. geogr.* **1** (F.s.)

BERG, L. 1934. Distribution amphiboréale (disjointe) de la faune marine dans l'hémisphère septentrionale. *Izv. Soc. Russ. Géogr.* **66**, 1 (R)

BERG, L. 1939. Appearance of boreal fish in the Barents Sea. (Volume in honour of N. M. Knipovich) *VNIRO* (E.s.)

BERG, L. 1940. Rise of temperature in 1919–1938 in the north and its effect on fish and fisheries. Reports, Jubilee Session 25 years of the Institute of Lakes and River fisheries (R)

BERG, L. 1948–9. Fresh water fish of the USSR and neighbouring countries—1, 2, 3. *Acad. Sci. USSR*, **4** (R)

BERNSTEIN, T. 1934. Zooplankton des nördlichen Teiles des Karischen Meeres. *Trans. Arctic Inst.* **9** (G.s.)

BEZRUKOV, P. 1955. On the distribution and rate of the siliceous deposits in Okhotsk Sea. *DAN, USSR*, **103**, 3 (R)

BEZRUKOV, P. 1955. Bottom deposits in the Kurile–Kamchatka Trench. *Tr. IOAN*, **12** (R)

BEZRUKOV, P. 1960. Sedimentation in North-western Pacific Ocean. *Internat. Geol. Congr.* (XXI Session). *Repts. Soviet geol.* Problem 10 *Marine Geology* (E.s.)

BEZRUKOV, P. *et al.* 1957. New data on the regularities of the morphology of submarine relief. *DAN, USSR*, **116**, 5 (R)

BIRSTEIN, J. 1935. Materialen zur geographischen Verbreitung der Wassertieren der USSR (Zur Frage über die Herkunft der marinen Crustazeen in den Flüssen des Ponto-Kaspischen Bassins). *Z.J.* **14**, 4 (G.s.)

BIRSTEIN, J. 1936. Growth and distribution of *Cardium edule* in the bays of Mertviy Kultuk and Kaidak in the Caspian Sea related to the salinity. *DAN, USSR*, **4**, 4 (R)

BIRSTEIN, J. 1939. The benthos in the northern part of the Caspian Sea. *Z.J.* **18**, 3 (R)

BIRSTEIN, J. 1945. Annual variations in the benthos of the northern part of the Caspian Sea. *Z.J.* **24**, 3 (E.s.)

BIRSTEIN, J. 1946. Notes. Some observations on the geographical distribution of Ponto-Caspian Amphipoda. *Bull. M.O.I.P., biol.* **51**, 3 (E.s.)

BIRSTEIN, J. 1952. The history of the crab. *Priroda*, **9** (R)

BIRSTEIN, J. 1952. Nourishment of Caspian benthos-feeding fish in 1948–1949 and the use of *Nereis* as feeding material. Acclimatization of the *Nereis* in the Caspian Sea. *Bull. M.O.I.P., Moscow* (R)

BIRSTEIN, J. 1956. Résultats de l'acclimatisation de *Nereis succinea* dans la Mer Caspienne et leur critique. *Bull. M.O.I.P., biol.* **61**, 1 (F.s.)

BIRSTEIN, J. and BELIAEV, G. 1946. Action of the Balchash water on the Caspian invertebrates. *Z.J.* **25**, 3 (R)

BERSTEIN, J. and SPASSKY, N. 1952. Bottom fauna of the Caspian Sea before and after the introduction of *Nereis* in Caspian Sea. Acclimatization of the *Nereis* in Caspian Sea. *Bull. M.O.I.P., Moscow* (R)

BIRSTEIN, J. and TCHINDONOVA, J. 1958. Deep-sea mysids in the north-western part of the Pacific ocean. *Tr. IOAN*, **27** (R)

BIRSTEIN, J. and TCHINDONOVA, J. 1958. Die Tiefsee-Mysiden des nordwestlichen Teiles des Stillen Ozeans. *Tr. IOAN*, **27** (R)

BIRSTEIN, J. and VINOGRADOV, L. 1934. Fresh-water Decapoda USSR and their geographical distribution. *Z.J.* **13**, 1 (R)

BIRSTEIN, J. and VINOGRADOV, M. 1955. The pelagic gammarids of the Kurile–Kamchatka Trench. *Tr. IOAN*, **12** (R)

BIRSTEIN, J. and VINOGRADOV, M. Pelagische Gammariden des nord-westlichen Teiles des Stillen Ozean. *Tr. IOAN*, **27** (R)

BLACKER, R. Benthic animals as indicators of hydrographic conditions and climatic change in Svalbard waters. *Fishery Investigations*, **20**, 10.

BLINOV, L. 1950. On the evaporation of sea-salts in the atmosphere and on the significance of the wind in salt-balance of the Caspian Sea. *Tr. GOI.* **15**, 27 (R)

BLINOV, L. 1956. *The Hydrochemistry of the Aral Sea.* Leningrad (R)

BOGATSCHEV, V. (Bogatchew). 1928. Mytilaster im Kaspischen Meere. *R.H.J.* **7**, 8–9 (G.s.)

BOGATSCHEV, V. 1932. Leading fossils of the Apsheron peninsula section. *Tr. AZNII.* **4** (R)

BOGATSCHEV, V. 1933. Report on the study of the tertiary fish in the Caucasus. *Tr. AzNII*, **15** (R)

BOGDANOVA, A. 1959. Water exchange through the Bosporus and its role in mixing the Black Sea waters. *Tr. S.B.S.* (R)

BOGDANOVA, A. 1959. Multiannual changes of the level and continental drainage as factors of the changes in hydrographical conditions in the water masses in the Black Sea. *Priroda* (R)

BOGDANOVA, A. 1960. Multiannual changes of the level and the continental discharge as factors determining the hydrological changes in the Black Sea. *Tr. S.B.S.* **13** (R)

BOGOJAVLENSKY, A. 1955. Chemistry of the Kurile–Kamchatka Trench waters. *Tr. IOAN*, **12** (R)

BOGOROV, V. 1932. Materials on the biology of the Copepods of the Barents and the White Seas. *Bull. GOIN*, **4** (E.s.)

BOGOROV, V. 1934. Investigations on nutrition of plankton-consuming fish. *Bull. VNIRO*, **1** (E.s.)

Bogorov, V. 1938. Diurnal vertical distribution of plankton under polar conditions (in the south-eastern part of the Barents Sea). *Tr. PINRO*, **2** (E.s.)

Bogorov, V. 1938. The biological seasons in the Polar Seas. *DAN, USSR*, **19**, 8.

Bogorov, V. 1939. The characteristics of seasonal phenomena in the plankton of Arctic seas and their significance in ice forecastings. *Z.J.* **18**, 5 (E.s.)

Bogorov, V. 1939. Diurnal vertical migration of *Eurytemora grimmi* in the Caspian Sea. (Volume in honour of N. M. Knipovich.) *Bull. VNIRO* (E.s.)

Bogorov, V. 1943. Diurnal vertical migration of the zooplankton in the Polar seas. *DAN, USSR*, **40**, 4 (R)

Bogorov, V. 1944. Distribution of brackish water plankton fauna in the Siberian Polar Seas. *DAN, USSR*, **44**, 5 (E.s.)

Bogorov, V. 1945. The role of biological indications in the study of the hydrological regime of the Sea. *Repts. Arctic Inst.* (R)

Bogorov, V. 1946. Zooplankton collected by the Sedov Expedition 1937–1939. *Tr. drift-expedition on ice-breaker* G. Sedov *1937–1940* (E.s.)

Bogorov, V. 1957. Standardization of marine plankton investigations. *Tr. IOAN*, **24** (R)

Bogorov, V. 1957. Uniformity of plankton distribution in the north-west Pacific. *Proc. UNESCO Symp. phys. Oceanogr. Tokyo*, 1955.

Bogorov, V. 1958. Biogeographical regions of the plankton of the north-western Pacific Ocean and their influence on the deep-sea. *Deep-sea Research*, **5**, 9.

Bogorov, V. 1959. The biological structure of the Ocean. *DAN, USSR*, **128**, 4 (R)

Bogorov, V. 1960. Geographical zones in the pelagial of the central Pacific. *Tr. IOAN*, **41** (R)

Bogorov, V. and Preobrajenskaya, E. 1934. On the mass and characteristics of the plankton organismus of the Barents Sea. II. Copepoda. *Bull. VNIRO*, **2** (E.s.)

Bogorov, V. and Vinogradov, M. 1955. Some essential features of zooplankton distribution in the north-western Pacific. *Ibid.* **18** (R).

Bogorov, V. and Vinogradov, M. 1960. Distribution of zooplankton biomass in the central part of the Pacific Ocean. *Tr. V.G.O.* **10** (R)

Bogorov, V. and Vinogradov, M. 1960. The distribution of zooplankton in the Kurile–Kamchatka region of Pacific. *Tr. IOAN*, **34** (R)

Bojenko, M. 1936. Hydrogeological and hydrochemical investigations. *Sivash. Arch. All-Union Geol. Inst. Leningrad* (R)

Bokova, E. 1946. Fodder value of the benthos in the North Caspian Sea. *Z.J.* **25**, 6 (E.s.)

Bokova, E. 1955. The feeding habits of the young *Clupeonella delicatula delicatula* in the Sea of Azov. *Probl. Ichthyology*, **4** (R)

Bokova, E. 1958. Findings in support of the biological basis for the acclimatization of some species of the northern Caspian *Cumacea* and *Corophiidae* in Aral and Baltic Seas. Annotations to works by *VNIRO*, 3 (R)

Boldovsky, G. 1936. Feeding habits of *Mallotus villosus* in the Barents Sea. *Fish industry of the North*, **4** (R)

Boldovsky, G. 1937. Warm-water *Euphasiidae* near Murman coast. *DAN, USSR*, **17**, 1–2 (R)

Boldovsky, G. 1941. The food and feeding of the Barents Sea Herrings. *Tr. PINRO*, **7** (E.s.)

Borcea, J. 1924. Faune survivante du type caspien dans les limans d'eau douce de Roumanie. *Ann. Sci. Univ. Jassy*, **13**, 1–2.

Borcea, J. 1926. Données sommaires sur la faune de la Mer Noire (littoral roumain). *Ibid.* **14**, 3–4.

Borcea, J. 1927. Faune des limans roumains en relation avec problème de l'adaptation des êtres marins d'eau douce et données sommaires sur la faune de la Mer Noire. *X Congrès Intern. Zool. Budapest*, **2**.

Borcea, J. 1931. Nouvelles contributions à l'étude de la faune bentonique dans la Mer Noire, près du littoral roumain. *Ann. Sci. Univ. Jassy*, **16**, 3–4.

Borisov, P. and Bogdanov, A. 1955. Resources of the USSR fish-industry, Moscow (R)

Borodin, N. 1901. Results of the zoological expedition through the Sea of Azov on the ice-breaker *Donskich Girl*, **6** (R)

Borschov, I. 1877. Algae of the Aral Sea. *Trans. Aral-Caspian Exped. Supplem. 2* to note of W. Alenitzin "Aral Sea" (R)

Brandes, C. 1939. Über die raumlichen und zeitlichen Unterschiede in der Zusammensetzung des Ostseeplanktons. *Mitt. Hamburg. Zool. Mus. Inst.* **48**.

Brandt, K. 1897. Die Fauna der Ostsee, insbesondere die der Kieler Bucht. *Verhandl. Deutsch. Zool. Gesellsch.*

Brandt, K. 1897. Das Vordringer mariner Thiere in den Kaiser-Wilhelm-Kanal. *Zool. Jahrb., Syst.* **9**.

Braun, M. 1884. Physikalische und biologische Untersuchungen im westlichen Theil des finnischen Meerbusens. *Arch. Naturkunde Liv. Ehst. und Kurlands*, ser. **2**, 10.

Bregman, G. and Michalevsky, A. 1935. The water-balance of the Caspian Sea in connection with *Greet Wolga* (R)

Briskina, M. 1939. Feeding of non-commercial fishes of the Barents Sea. *Tr. VNIRO*, **4** (E.s.)

Broch, H. 1927. Methoden der marinen Biogeographie. *Handbuch der biologischen Arbeitsmetoden.* Abt. **10**, 5, 1.

Broch, H. 1933. Einige Probleme der biogeographische Abgrenzung der arctischen Region. *Mitt. Zool. Mus. Berlin*, **19**.

Brodsky, K. 1937. Plankton investigations in the north-eastern part of the Japan Sea, *Bull. TINRO*, **12** (E.s.)

Brodsky, K. 1941. The plankton of the deep-waters of the Japan Sea. *Investigations of the far-eastern seas of USSR*, **1** (E.s.)

Brodsky, K. 1941. A review of quantitative distribution and components of zooplankton in the north-western part of the Japan Sea. *Tr. Inst. Zool. Acad. des Sci. URSS*, **7**, 2 (E.s.)

BRODSKY, K. 1948. The free-living copepods in the Sea of Japan. *Bull. TINRO*, **26** (R)

BRODSKY, K. 1948. On the zoogeography of the depth in the north-western part of the Pacific ocean. *DAN, USSR*, **60**, 6 (R)

BRODSKY, K. 1950. The copepods (Calanoidae) in the far-eastern seas of the USSR and in the Polar basin. *The keys for the fauna of USSR*, **35** (R)

BRODSKY, K. 1954. The fauna of Copepods (*Calanida*) and the zoogeographical zonation of the north-western part of the Pacific ocean. Leningrad (R)

BRODSKY, K. 1955. The zoogeographical zonation of the pelagial in the Far-East seas and in the northern part of the Pacific ocean (on example of Calanida). *DAN, USSR*, **102**, 3 (R)

BRODSKY, K. 1955. On the fauna of the Copepoda (Calanoidae) of the Kurile–Kamchatka Trench. *Tr. IOAN*, **12** (R)

BRODSKY, K. 1956. The life in the Polar basin waters. *Priroda*, **5** (R)

BRODSKY, K. 1956. Life in the water column of the Polar basin. *Priroda*, **5** (R)

BRODSKY, K. 1956. The Copepods (Calanidae) and zoogeographical zonation of the northern part of the Pacific ocean. *Acad. Sci. USSR* (R)

BRODSKY, K. 1959. Zooplankton of sea waters of the South Sakhalin and South Kuril Islands. *Investigations of the far-eastern seas of USSR*, **6** (R)

BROTSKY, V. (Brotzky, Brotskaia). 1930. Materials for the quantitative evaluation of the bottom fauna of the Storfjord (East Spitzbergen). *Ber. Wissenschaftl. Meeres Inst.* **4**, 1 (E.s.)

BROTSKY, V. 1931. Report on the feeding of cod. *Rep. of the First Session of the State Oceanogr. Inst.* **4** (E.s.)

BROTSKY, V. 1951. Microbenthos of the littoral in the White Sea. *Tr. VGO*, **3** (R)

BROTSKY, V. and NEZENGEVITCH, M. 1941. The distribution of *Mytilaster lineatus* in the Caspian Sea. *Z.J.* **20**, 1 (E.s.)

BROTSKY, V. and ZENKEWITCH, L. 1932. A quantitative evaluation of the bottom fauna of the Cheshkay bay. *Tr. GOIN*, **2**, 2 (E.s.)

BROTSKY, V. and ZENKEWITCH, L. 1939. Quantitative evaluation of the bottom fauna of the Barents Sea. *Tr. VNIRO*, **7** (E.s.)

BROTSKY, V., ZHDANOVA, N. and SEMYONOVA, N. 1962. Bottom fauna of the Velikaya Salma and the adjoining regions of the Kandalaksha Bay of the White Sea. *Tr. Kandalaksha State Reserve*, **5** (R)

BRUJEWICZ, S. (Brouievitch). 1931. Hydrochemical works of the State Oceanographic Institute in the Barents sea in 1927–1930. *Repts. First Session State Oceanogr. Inst.* **1** (E.s.)

BRUJEWICZ, S. 1937. Hydrochemistry of the Middle and South Caspian (after the investigations of 1934). *Tr. Complex studies of the Caspian Sea*, **4** (E.s.)

BRUJEWICZ, S. 1938. On the question of the fluctuation of level of the Caspian Sea. *Meteorologia and Hydrologia*, **3** (R)

BRUJEWICZ, S. 1939. Le dynamisme de la composition chimique de la Mer Caspienne dans la période de l'abaissement de son niveau (1933–1937). *Izv. Soc. Géogr. URSS*, **71**, 6 (R)

BRUJEWICZ, S. 1939. The distribution and dynamics of the living substance in the Caspian Sea. *DAN, USSR*, **25**, 2 (R)

BRUJEWICZ, S. 1939. The age of the recent lake-period in the Caspian Sea and the metamorphosis of the discharge of river salts into the sea. *Ibid.* **23**, 7 (R)

BRUJEWICZ, S. 1941. The distribution of matter among different groups of organisms inhabiting the Caspian Sea. Elements of the chemical balance of the Caspian Sea. *Tr. of the complex studies of the Caspian Sea*, **14** (E.s.)

BRUJEWICZ, S. 1941. The hydrochemical aspect of the Caspian Sea in 1938. *Ibid.* (E.s.)

BRUJEWICZ, S. 1950. On the salt-composition of the Black Sea water. *Memory of J. M. Shokalsky*, **2** (R)

BRUJEWICZ, S. 1950. On dynamics of the chemical composition of water in the Northern part of the Caspian Sea (1932–1940). *Ibid.* (R)

BRUJEWICZ, S. 1952. Trapped water pockets of dilute salinity under recent deposits in the Black Sea. *DAN, USSR*, **84**, 3 (R)

BRUJEWICZ, S. 1953. The chemistry and biological productivity of the Black Sea. *Tr. IOAN*, **7** (R)

BRUJEWICZ, S. 1960. Water and salinity equilibrium of the Black Sea. *Ibid.* **42** (R)

BRUJEWICZ, S. 1960. Hydrochemical investigations on the White Sea. *Ibid.* (R)

BRUJEWICZ, S., BOGOYAVLENSKY, A. and MOKIEVSKAYA, V. 1960. Hydrochemical features of the Okhotsk Sea. *Ibid.* (R)

BRUUN, A. 1954. On the distribution and origin of the deep-sea bottom fauna. *Int. Union Biol. Sci., ser. B*, **16**.

BRUUN, A. 1956. The fauna of the deep: ecology, distribution and origin. *Nature*, **177**.

BRUUN, A. 1957. Deep-sea and abyssal depths. *Tr. Mar. Ecol. Paleoecol. Geol. Soc. America, Memoir 67*, **1**, Ecology.

BRUUN, A. and TORBEN, WOLFF. 1961. Abyssal benthic organisms: nature, origin, distribution and influence on sedimentation. *Oceanogr. Ed. Mary Sears.*

BUCH, K. 1915. Bestimmungen des Ammoniakgehaltes im Wasser der Finland umgebenden Meere. *Oefv. Finska. Vet-Soc. Forh.* **57**, Afd. A, 21.

BUCH, K. 1929. Ueber die Bestimmungen von Stickstoffverbindungen und Phosphaten im Meerwasser. *Rapp. Proc. Verb.* **53**.

BUCH, K. 1931. Eine biologisch-chemische Studie im Hafenwasser von Helsingfors. *Ibid.* **75**.

BUJOR, P. 1904. Nouvelle contribution à l'étude des lacs salés de Roumanie. *Ann. sci. univ. Jassy*, **3**, 1.

BURKOW, W. 1958. Gebiets des Stillen Ozeans in der Zeit des Frühlings. *Tr. IOAN*, **27** (R)

BURKOW, W. and ARSENIEW, W. 1958. Versuch einer Aufgliederung der Wassermassen in der Berührungszone Kuroschio und Kurilenstrom. *Tr. IOAN*, **27** (R)

BUTKEVITCH, V. 1938. On the bacterial population in the Caspian and Azov Seas. *Microbiologia*, **7** (R)

BYCHOWSKY, B. 1931. Parasites of the Aral Sea fishes. *Bull. Inst. Ichthyology*, **12**, 2 (R)

CARAUSU, S. 1943. Amphipodes de Roumanie, I. Gammaridés de type Caspien. Monographia. *Inst. de Certetari piscicole al Roumaniniei*, **1.**

CASPERS, H. 1949. Biologie eines Limans an der bulgarischen Küste des Schwarzen Meeres (Varnaer See). *Verh. deutsch. Zool. Mainz.*

Caspers, H. 1951. Quantitative Untersuchungen über die Bodentierwelt des Schwarzen Meeres im Bulgarischen Küstenbereich. *Arch. Hydrobiol.* **45.**

CASPERS, H. 1957. *Black Sea and Sea of Azov in Treatise on Marine Ecology and Paleoecology*, Vol. 1.

CAULLERY, M. 1914. Sur les Siboglinidae, type nouveau d'invertébrés recueilli par l'expédition du "Siboga". *C. R. Acad. Sci. Paris*, **158.**

CHAJANOVA, L. 1936. The feeding habits of the plankton feeding fishes of the Caspian Sea. *Tr. All-Caspian Sci. Conf.* **1** (R)

CHAJANOVA, L. 1959. Reproduction and development of the Black Sea pelagic Copepoda. *Tr. Karadag Biol. station*, **10** (R)

CHAJANOVA, L. The feeding habits of the herring in the White Sea. (Volume in honour of N. M. Knipovich.)

CIGIRIN, N. (Tschigirine). 1930. Phosphorus in the water of the Black Sea. *Tr. S.B.S.* **2** (E.s.)

CIGIRIN, N. 1930. The distribution of oxygen in the Black Sea. *Proc. Second Hydrolog. Congr. of USSR* (R)

CIGIRIN, N. 1930. The hydrogen ion concentration, alkalinity and free carbonic acid in the Black Sea. *Ibid.* (R)

CIGIRIN, N. 1939. Carbonic acid in the waters of the North Polar Basin and in the Greenland Sea. *Tr. of the First high-latitudinal expedition "Sadko", 1935*, **1**, 1 (R)

CIGIRIN, N. and DANILCENKO, P. P.T. De l'azote et ses composés dans la Mer Noire. *Tr. S.B.S.* **2** (F.s.)

Commercial fish of the bottom of the Barents Sea. 1944. *Tr. PINRO*, **8** (E.s.)

Commercial fish of the Barents and White Seas. 1952. *PINRO. Leningrad* (R)

CREDNER, R. 1888. Die reliktenseen, 2. *Peterm. Mitt. Ergänzh.* **89.**

DALY, K. 1935. The changing world of the Ice Age.

DANILCENKO, P. (Daniltchenko) and CIGIRIN, N. 1926. Sur l'origine de l'hydrosulfure dans la Mer Noire. *Tr. lab. zool. station biol. Sébastopol, série* 2, No. 10 (F.s.)

DANILCENKO, P. and CIGIRIN, N. 1929. Materials on the chemistry of the Black Sea. Nitrogen and its compounds. *Tr. Krim. Sci. Inst.* **2**, 2 (R)

DANILCENKO, P. and CIGIRIN, N. 1929. Sur la question de l'échange de matière dans la Mer Noire. *Bull. de la Soc. Naturalist et Amis Nature en Crimée*, **11** (F.s.)

DANILCENKO, P. and PONIZOVSKY, A. 1954. Hydrochemistry of the Sivash. *Acad. Sci. USSR* (R)

DATZKO, V. 1951. On the causes of fish mortality in the Sea of Azov. *Tr. Az.-Cher. NIRO*, **15** (R)

DATZKO, V. 1954. Some chemical indicators of productivity in the Black Sea. *Tr. VNIRO*, **28** (R)

DATZKO, V. 1955. The tentative balance of the organic substances in the Sea of Azov (e.c.) *Tr. Az.-Cher. NIRO*, **16** (R)

DATZKO, V. 1959. Organic substance in the waters of the South Seas of the USSR. *Acad. Sc. USSR* (R)

DAVIS, F. 1923. Preliminary investigation of the Dogger Bank. *Fishery Investigations* (*Ser.* 2), **6**, 2.

DEKTEREVA, A. 1931. The feeding of haddock. *Rep. First Session of the State oceanogr. Inst.* **4** (E.s.)

DEMEL, K. 1927. Granica i Podzial naturalny Baltyku (Delimination et régions naturelles de la Baltique). *Arch. Hydrobiol. Ichtyol.*

DEMEL, K. 1933. Wykaż bezkręgcowów i ryb Baltyku naszego (Liste des invertébrées des eaux polonaises de la Baltique). *Fragm. Faun. Mus. Zool. Polon. Warszawa*, **2**, 13.

DEMEL, K. 1935. Studia nad fauną denną i jej rozsiedleniem w polskich wodach Baltyku (Etudes sur la faune bentique et sa répartition dans les eaux polonaise de la Baltique). *Arch. Hydrobiol. i Rybactwa Suwalki*, **9**, 3–4.

DEMEL, K. and MAŃKOWSKI, W. 1950. Studia nad fauną denną Baltyku poludniowego (Investigations on the Bottom Fauna of the Southern Baltic.) Biuletyn Morskiego Instituta Rybackiego w Gdyni. *Bull. Inst. pêches marit. Gdynia*, **5**.

DEMEL, K. and MAŃKOWSKI, W. 1951. Ilościowe studia nad fauną denną Baltiku poludniowego (Quantitative Investigations on the Bottom Fauna in the Southern Baltic). Prace Morskiego Institutu Rybackiego w Gdyni. *Bull. Inst. pêches marit. Gdnyia*, **6**.

DEMEL, K. and MULICKI, Z. 1954. Studia ilościowe nad wydajnością biologiczną dna poludniowego Baltiku (Quantitative Investigations on the biological bottom-productivity on the South Baltic). *Ibid.* **7**.

DENGINA, R. 1957. Hydrological surveying of the Bay of Adjibai of Aral Sea in 1953. *Tr. of the Lake study laboratory. AN*, *USSR*, **4** (R)

DERJAVIN, A. (Derzhavin). 1912. Kaspische Elemente der Fauna des Wolgabassins. *Arbeiten des Ichtyologischen Laboratoriums der Kaspi-Wolgaschen Fischerei-Verwaltung*, **25** (G.s.)

DERJAVIN, A. 1915. Feeding of the *Rutilus rutilus caspicus* Jac. *Tr. du Laboratoire ichtyologique d'Astrakhan*, **3**, 4 (F.s.)

DERJAVIN, A. 1918. 1. Feeding of the *Abramis brama*. 2. Feeding of the herrings. *Ibid.* **4**, 3 (F.s.)

DERJAVIN, A. 1922. The stellated sturgon (*Acipenser stellatus Pallas*), a biological sketch. *Bull. of Ichthyol. Lab. Baku*, **1** (E.s.)

DERJAVIN, A. 1925. Materials of the Ponto-Azov Carcinofauna (Mysidacea, Cumacea, Amphipoda). *R.H.Z.* **4**, 1–2 (E.s.)

DERJAVIN, A. 1939. Mysidae of the Caspian Sea. Baku (E.s.)

DERJAVIN, A. 1951. Papers from the "Animals of the Azerbaydzan". Baku.

DERJUGIN, K. (Deriugin). 1915. Fauna of the Kola Gulf and its environmental conditions. *Mém. Acad. Imp. Sci.* **34**, 1 (R)

DERJUGIN, K. 1915. Explorations hydrologiques et hydrobiologiques de la baise de la Néva. (1)—Hydrologie et bentos. (4)—Die Hydrologie und benthonische Bevölkerung des östlichen Teiles des finnischen Meerbusens. *Etudes de la Néva et de son bassin*, **2** (G.s.)

DERJUGIN, K. 1924. Das Barents-Meer langs dem Kola-Meridian. *IRHH*, **12**.

DERJUGIN, K. 1925. Investigations of the Barents and White Seas and Novaya Zemlya in 1921–1924. Arkhangelsk (R)

DERJUGIN, K. 1925. Die negativen Charakterzüge der Benthos-Fauna des Weissen Meeres und deren Ursachen. *R.H.Z.* **4**, 7–9 (G.s.)

DERJUGIN, K. 1927. La distribution bipolaire des organismes marins. *Bull. Inst. Océanogr. Monaco*, **495**.

DERJUGIN, K. 1928. Der Reliktensee Megilnoje. *Fauna Arctica*, **5**, 2.

DERJUGIN, K. 1928. Fauna des Weissen Meeres und ihre Existenzbedingungen. *Expl. des mers de l'URSS*, **7–8** (G.s.)

DERJUGIN, K. 1932. The Benthos of the R. Lena estuary. *Ibid.* **15** (G.s.)

DERJUGIN, K. 1933. Hydrology of the White sea. *Mémoirs Hydrogr.* **47** (R)

DERJUGIN, K. 1933. Pacifische Expedition des Hydrologischen Staatsinstituts im Jahre 1932. *Expl. des mers de l'URSS*, **19** (G.s.)

DERJUGIN, K. 1935. Materials of the Pacific ocean expedition. *Ibid.* **22** (G.s.)

DERJUGIN, K. 1936. Advances of Soviet Hydrobiology in the Study of the Sea. *Advanc. Mod. Biol.* **5**, 1 (E.s.)

DERJUGIN, K. 1939. Zonen und biocönosen der Bucht Peter des Grossen (des Japanische Meer). (Volume in honour of N. M. Knipovich.) *VNIRO* (G.s.)

DERJUGIN, K. and IVANOV, A. 1937. Preliminary Survey of benthos investigations in the Bering and Chukotsk seas. *Invest. of the far-eastern seas*, **5** (E.s.)

DERJUGIN, K. and SOMOVA, N. 1941. Contributions to quantitative estimate of the benthonic population of Peter the Great Bay (Japan sea). *Ibid.* **1** (E.s.)

DIUNINA, K. 1949. Some data on *Nereis* from the Greater and Lesser Kirov Bays (Kzil-Agach). *Fishery*, **8** (R)

DJAKONOW, A. 1926. Stachelhäuter des Barentz-Kara- und Weissen meeres. *Tr. L.O.E.* (*C.R. séances*), **56**, 2 (R)

DJAKANOW, A. 1945. On the interrelation between the Arctic and the northern Pacific marine fauna based on the zoogeographical analysis of the Echinodermata. *J. Gen. Biol.* **6**, 2 (E.s.)

DJAKANOW, A. 1950. Sea-stars of the Seas of USSR (USSR Fauna Keys). *Zool. Inst. Acad. Sci. USSR*, **34** (R)

DJAKANOW, A. 1952. Echinoderms of the Chukotsk Sea and the Bering strait. "Extreme North" (R)

DMITRIEV, N. 1957. The results of investigations in the White Sea. Materials for the complex study of the White Sea (R)

DOBROVOLSKY, A. 1933. The dynamic map of the eastern part of the Black Sea. *Tr. of the Hydrometeorol. Inst. Black and Azov Seas*, **1** (R)

DOBROVOLSKY, A. 1948. Isotherm maps of the northern Pacific. *Tr. IOAN*, **2** (R)

DOBROVOLSKY, A. and ARSENIEV, V. 1959. On the problem of the currents of the Bering Sea. *Probl. of the North*, **3** (R)

DOBRZANSKAYA, M. 1954. On the problem of phytoplankton production in the Black Sea by photosynthesis. *Tr. S.B.S.* **8** (R)

DOBRZANSKAYA, M. 1958. The principal features of the distribution and dynamics of phosphates in the Black Sea. *Tr. S.B.S.* **10** (R)

DOGIEL, V. 1938. Parasites of the Caspian fish. Caspian Sea Research Commission. Complex studies of the Caspian Sea, *AN, USSR*, **7** (E.s.)

DOGIEL, V. 1939. Influence of fish acclimatization on the spreading of fish epizootics. *Bull. Inst. Fresh-water fisheries*, **21** (E.s.)

DOGIEL, V. and BYCHOWSKY, B. 1934. Die Fischparasiten des Aral Seas. *Mag Parasitol. Inst. Zool. Acad. Sci. URSS*, **4** (G.s.)

DOROFEEW, S. and FREIMANN, S. 1928. Versuch einer quantitativen Schätzung des Bestandes der Weissmeerherde des grönländischen Seehunds durch aerophotographische Aufnahmen. *Repts. Sci. Invest. Fisheries*, **2**, 1 (G.s.)

DRAPKIN, E. 1953. A new mollusc of the Black Sea. *Priroda*, **9** (R)

DUNBAR, M. 1951. Eastern Arctic waters. *Fisch. Res. Bd. Can. Bull.* **88.**

DUNBAR, M. 1953. Arctic and subarctic marine ecology: Immediate problems. *Arctic*, **6**, 2.

DU TOIT. 1939. The Origin of the Atlantic-Arctic Ocean. *Geol. Rundschau*, **30**, 1–2.

DVOICHENKO, P. 1925. The geological history of the Krimea. *Bull. Soc. Natur. et Amis nature Crimée*, **8** (F.s.)

DYBOWSKY, B. 1938. Gastropods of the Caspian Sea. *Tr. AzNII*, **16**, 8 (R)

EBERZIN, A. 1940. The Middle and Upper Pliocene layers of the Black Sea region. *Stratigraphy of USSR*, **12**. Neogene of the USSR. (E.s.)

EGUNOV, M. 1900. The bioanisotropic basins. *Ann. geol. mineral. Russ.* **4.**

EKMAN, S. 1913. Artbildung bei der Copepodengattung *Limnocalanus* durch akkumulative Ferwirkung einer Milieuveränderung. *Zschr. indukt. Abstamm.-Vererbungsl.* **11.**

EKMAN, S. 1915. Vorschläge und Erörterungen zur Reliktenfrage in der Hydrobiologie. *Ark. f. Zool.* **9.**

EKMAN, S. 1916. Systematische und tiergeographische Bemerkungen über einige glacialmarine Relikte des Kaspischen Meeres. *Zool. Anz.* **47.**

EKMAN, S. 1913, 1918, 1919, 1920. Studien über die marinen Relikte der nordeuropäischen Binengewässer. II. Die Variation der Kopfform bei *Limnocalanus grimaldii* und *L. macrurus*. V. 1st *Pallasea quadrispinosa* in den nordeuropäischen Binnenseen ein marines Relikt? VI. Die morphologischen Folgen des Reliktwerdens. VII. Fortpflanzung und Lebenslauf der marin-glacialen Relikte und ihrer marinen Stammformen. *IRHH*, **6**, 8.

EKMAN, S. 1930. Die Sudbaltischen marin-glaziale Relikte und die Stauseetheorie. *IRHH*, **24**, 3–4.

EKMAN, S. 1931. Vorschlag zu einer naturwissenschaftlichen Einteilung und Terminologie des Baltischen Meeres. *Ibid.* **25.**

EKMAN, S. 1935. *Tiergeographie des Meeres*. Leipzig.

EKMAN, S. 1935. *Zoogeography of the sea*. London.

EKMAN, S. 1940. Die schwedische Vernreitung der glacial-marine Relikte. *Verhandl. Intern. Verein. theor. angew. Limnol.* **9**.

EPSTEIN, L. 1957. Zooplankton of the Onega Gulf and its importance for feeding of herring and young fish. *Mat. Invest. White Sea,* **1** (R)

ESAKOVA, E. and SOLDATOVA, I. 1959. The introduction of the Teredinidae in the Sea of Azov. *Priroda,* **6** (R)

ESSIPOV, V. 1952. The fishes of the Kara sea. *Acad. Sci. USSR* (R)

FEDOROV, B. 1928. The comparative survey of the littoral of the Solovetzky Islands in the White Sea. *Tr. 3rd Congr. Zool. Anatom. Histol. USSR* (R)

FEDOSOV, M. 1952. The rate of deposition on the bottom of the Sea of Azov. *DAN, USSR,* **84**, 3 (R)

FEDOSOV, M. 1955. The chemical basis of feeding in the Sea of Azov (e.c.). *Tr. VNIRO,* **31**, 1 (R)

FEDOSOV, M. 1958. Secondary phenomena following the formation of the bottom deposits in the Sea of Azov. *Ann. VNIRO,* **2** (R)

FEDOSOV, M. and VINOGRADOVA, E. 1955. The basic characteristics of the hydrochemical regime in the Sea of Azov. *Tr. VNIRO,* **31**, 1 (R)

FESENKO, E. 1955. Feeding of the young pike, perch and bream in the lower reaches of the River Don. *Tr. VNIRO,* **31**, 1 (R)

FESENKO, E. and SHEININ, M. 1955. The feeding base of commercial fish in the river Don and eastern part of the Taganrog bay. *Tr. VNIRO,* **31**. *The reconstruction of the fisheries of the Sea of Azov,* **1** (R)

FILATOVA, Z. 1938. The quantitative evaluation of the bottom fauna of the south-western part of the Barents Sea. *Tr. PINRO,* **2** (E.s.)

FILATOVA, Z. 1957. Some new molluscs of family Astartidae (Bivalvia) from the far eastern seas. *Tr. IOAN,* **23** (R)

FILATOVA, Z. 1957. General aspect of the marine bivalve fauna of the northern seas of the USSR. *Ibid.* **20** (R)

FILATOVA, Z. 1957. Zoogeographical division of north seas into districts (regarding the distribution of bivalve molluscs). *Ibid.* **23** (R)

FILATOVA, Z. and ZENKEVITCH, L. 1957. Quantitative distribution of the bottom fauna in the Kara Sea. *Tr. V.G.O.* **8** (R)

FLEROV, B. 1932. Algues des côtes de la Nouvelle Zemble. Distribution des algues sur les côtes de la Nouvelle Zemble. *Tr. GOIN,* **2**, 1 (F.s.)

FLEROV, B. and KARSAKOFF, N. Liste des algues de la Nouvelle Zemble. *Ibid.* (F.s.)

FLEROV, B. 1925. Les algues de la région sud-est de la mer de Barents (Mer de Petchora). *Tr. MNT.* **15** (F.s.)

FRIEDRICH, H. 1938. *Polychaeta. Die Tiervelt der Nord und Ostsee,* **32**, 6b.

GAIL, G. 1930. Essay on the algae-zone in the sea-shore of Primorje in connection with some general questions of their utilization. *Bull. TINRO,* **4**, 2 (R)

GAIL, G. 1950. Key for the phytoplankton of the sea of Japan. *Bull. TINRO,* **33** (R)

GALADZIEW, M. 1948. Zusammensetzung, Verbreitung und quantitative Wechselbeziehungen des Zooplanktons der Bucht von Karkinitsk und des offenen Meeres in Gebiet der südlichen Krim-Küste. *Tr. S.B.S.* **6** (R)

GAMS, E. 1929. Die Geschichte der Ostsee. Sammelreferat über die neuere Literatur. *IRHH*, **22**.

DE GEER, G. 1910. Quaternary Sea-bottom in Western Sweden. *Geol. Fören. Stockholm Förhandl.* **32**.

DE GEER, G. and HULT, E. 1954. Skandinaviens Geokronologi. *Geol. Fören. Förhandl.* **76**, 299.

GEINRIKH, A. 1956. On seasonal rates of the *Calanus tonsus* in the Bering Sea. *DAN*, *USSR*, **109**, 2 (R)

GEINRIKH, A. 1960. Copepoda production in the Bering Sea. *Ibid.* **3**, 1 (R)

GENERALOVA, V. 1951. Sea vegetation of the Utljuk-liman and Arabatsk "strelka" in the sea of Azov. *Tr. Az.-Cher. NIRO*, **15**.

GERASIMOV, I. and MARKOV, K. 1939. *Quaternary geology. The glacial period in the territory of the USSR* (R)

GERTCHENSTEIN, C. 1885. Materials on the fauna of the Murman and White Seas. I. Molluscs. *Tr. Soc. Imp. Natur. St.-Pétersbourg*, **16**, 2 (G.s.)

GESSNER, ER. 1933. NO_3, P and Plankton in Arkonabecken. *J. Cons.*

GESSNER, ER. 1933. Die Produktionbiologie der Ostsee. *Die Naturwissenschaften*, **21**.

GESSNER, ER. 1933. Die Planktonproduktion der Brackwässer in ihrer Beziehung zur Produktion der Offenen See. *Verhandl. Internat. Verein. Limnol.* **6**.

GESSNER, ER. 1937. Hydrographie und Hydrobiologie der Brackwässer Rügens und des Darss. *Kieler Meeresforschungen*, **2**.

GESSNER, ER. 1940. Productionsbiologische Untersuch. in Arkonabecken und in den Binnengewassern vom Rügen. *Kieler Meeresforsch.* **3**.

GESSNER, ER. 1957. *Meer und Strand.*

GILSEN (Hülsen), K. 1908. Die Bedenproben des Aralsees. Mitteilungen der Turkestanischen Abteilung der Keiserlichen Russischen Geographischen Gesellschaft, **8**, 1 (R)

GOLENCHENKO, A. 1947. The determination of the anchovy stock with the aid of aeroplanes. *Fisheries*, **7** (R)

GOLOLOBOV, J. 1949. On the age of the recent stage of the Black Sea. *DAN*, *USSR*, **66**, 3 (R)

GORBUNOV, G. 1925. The "Loomeries" of Novaya Zemlya. *Tr. of Inst. Sci. Expl. North*, **26** (E.s.)

GORBUNOV, G. 1934. Biological indicators and their importance in the study of the Arctic. *Arctica*, **2** (E.s.)

GORBUNOV, G. 1937. The hydrobiological investigations in the northern seas of the USSR for 20 years. *Bull. Acad. Sci. USSR* (R)

GORBUNOV, G. 1937. The bottom fauna (benthos) of the Kara Sea as the indicator of the water's origin. *Priroda*, **5** (R)

GORBUNOV, G. 1939. Bottom population of the Soviet Arctic seas. *Probl. of the Arctic*, **7–8** (R)

GORBUNOV, G. 1940. Bivalvian mollusc Portlandia arctica as indication of the continental waters distribution in the Siberian seas. *Ibid.* **11** (R)

GORBUNOV, G. 1946. Bottom life of the Novosiberian shallow waters and the Central Part of the Arctic Ocean. *Tr. drift-expedition on ice-breaker* G. Sedov, *1937–1940*, **3**. *Biology* (E.s.)

GORDEEV, V. 1949. The state and prospects of the trawler-fishing industry in the far-east. *Tr. TINRO*, **29** (R)

GORDEEVA, K. 1948. Materials on the quantitative evaluation of the zoobenthos in the West-Kamchatka shelf. *Bull. TINRO*, **26** (R)

GORDEEVA, K. 1949. New data on the distribution of the benthos in the eastern part in the Bay of Peter the Great. *Ibid.* **31** (R)

GORDEEVA, K. 1952. Feeding of Cod in the northern part of the Bering sea. *Ibid.* **37** (R)

GORDEEVA, K. 1954. Feeding of halibut in the Bering Sea. *Ibid.* **39** (R)

GORSHKOVA, T. 1937. Organic matter and carbonates in the sediments of the Barents Sea. *Ibid.* **4**, 1 (E.s.)

GORSHKOVA, T. 1938. Organischer Stoff in den Sedimenten des Motovskij Busens. *Tr. VNIRO*, **5** (G.s.)

GORSHKOVA, T. 1955. Organic substance in the deposits of the sea of Azov and in the Taganrog Bay. *Tr. VNIRO*, **31**, 1 (R)

GORSHKOVA, T. 1955. Chemical composition of ground-waters in the sea of Azov and in Taganrog Bay. *Ibid.* (R)

GORSHKOVA, T. 1957. Organic substance and carbonates in the deposits of the White Sea. Materials on complex-study of the White Sea. I. *AN, USSR* (R)

GORSHKOVA, T. 1957. Deposits of the Kara Sea. *Tr. VGO*, **8** (R)

GORSHKOVA, T. 1958. Organic matter and carbonates in the sediments of the Barents Sea. *Tr. PINRO*, **10** (R)

GORSKY, N. 1936. The ventilation of the near-bottom waters in the Caspian Sea. *Probl. Phys. Geogr.* **3** (R)

GOSTILOVSKAJA, M. 1957. Bryozoa of the White Sea. Materials for the complex study of the White Sea. (R)

GRAN, H. 1927. The production of plankton in coastal waters off Bergen. *Rep. Norweg. Fish. Invest.* **3**.

GREBNITZKY, N. 1874. Preliminary report on the affinity of the Black Sea fauna. *Mém. Soc. natur. Nouvelle-Russe*, **2**, 2 (R)

GRIMM, O. 1876. The Caspian Sea and its fauna. *Tr. Aralo-Caspian exped.* **2**, 1–2 (G.s.)

GRIPENBERG, S. 1934. A study of the sediments of the North Baltic and adjoining seas. *Merentutimuslait. julk.* (*Havsforskningsinstit. Helsinki*) *Helsingfors skr.* **96**.

GUBKIN, I. 1931. The problem of the Akchagil in the light of new data. *Acad. Sci. USSR* (R)

GURWITSCH, G. 1934. Die Verteilung der Tierwelt im Littoral und Sublittoral des "Babje More". *Expl. mers l'URSS*, **20** (R)

GURWITSCH, G. and IVANOV, I. 1939. A quantitative evaluation of the bottom fauna in the Umba River district. *Tr. G.G.I.* **8** (R)

GURWITSCH, G. and MATVEEVA, T. 1939. Materials for the study of supralittoral in the White Sea. *Ibid.* (R)

GURWITSCH, G. and SOKOLOVA, E. 1939. On the study of relict basins in the White Sea. *Ibid.* (R)

GURYANOVA, E. (Gurianova). 1925. Fauna der "Dwori" am Kola-Fjorde. *Tr. L.O.E.* **54**, 1 (G.s.)

GURYANOVA, E. 1927. To the fauna of the Kola-Fjord, Barents Sea, Kara Sea, and White Sea and Novaya Semlya. *Ibid.* **57**, 1 (E.s.)

GURYANOVA, E. 1928. The fauna of the Cheshskaya bay. *Proc. Third Congr. Russ. Zool. Anat. Histol.* (R)

GURYANOVA, E. 1929. The composition and distribution of the benthos of the Cheshskaya bay. *Tr. of the Institute for the study of the North.* **43** (R)

GURYANOVA, E. 1929. Über die Fauna der Crustacea-Malacostraca der Jenissej-Mündungen. *R.H.J.* **8**, 10–12 (G.s.)

GURYANOVA, E. 1930. On the fauna of the Crustacea-Malacostraca of the Barents Sea, White Sea, and Kara Sea. *Tr. L.O.E.* (*C.R. Séances*), **59**, 1 (E.s.)

GURYANOVA, E. 1932. Some contribution to the fauna of Crustacea of the Brothers Laptev's sea (Nordenskjold's sea). *Expl. mers l'URSS*, **15** (E.s.)

GURYANOVA, E. 1933. On the fauna Crustacea Malacostraca of Ob-Yenissey Gulf. *Invest. Seas USSR*, **18** (R)

GURYANOVA, E. 1934. Crustacean fauna of the Kara-sea and routes of penetration of the Atlantic sea fauna into the Arctic. *DAN, USSR*, **3**.

GURYANOVA, E. 1934. Zoogeographical study of the Arctic Isopods. *Arctica*, **2** (E.s.)

GURYANOVA, E. 1935. Contribution to the Zoogeography of the far-eastern seas. *Bull. Acad. Sci. URSS.* (sér. 7), **8–9** (E.s.)

GURYANOVA, E. 1935. Commandor Islands and its sea-coastal fauna. *Priroda*, **11** (R)

GURYANOVA, E. 1936. The zoogeography of Kara Sea. *Bull. Acad. Sci. URSS, Biol.* **2–3** (E.s.)

GURYANOVA, E. 1938. On the problem of the composition and origin of the abyssal fauna in the Polar basin. *DAN, USSR*, **20**, 4 (R)

GURYANOVA, E. 1939. Contribution to the origin and history of the fauna of Polar Basin. *Bull. Acad. Sci. URSS, Biol.* **5** (E.s.)

GURYANOVA, E. 1946. Individual and age variability of the marine assel Mesidothea entomon and its importance in evolution of the genus Mesidothea Rich. *Tr. Inst. Zool. Acad. Sci. URSS*, **8** (E.s.)

GURYANOVA, E. and LINDBERG, G. Attainments of hydrobiological researches in the seas of the far-east. *Bull. Acad. Sci. URSS, Biol.* **5** (E.s.)

GURYANOVA, E. and OUCHAKOFF. 1927. Travaux hydrobiologiques près de la côte Tersky de la mer Blanche en 1926. *Bull. Inst. Hydrol.* **18** (R)

GURYANOVA, E. and OUCHAKOFF. 1928. Zur fauna der Tschernaja Bucht auf der Nowaja Semlja. *Expl. mers d'URSS*, **6** (G.s.)

GURYANOVA, E. and OUCHAKOFF. 1929. Das littoral des östlichen Murmanküste. *Ibid.* **10** (G.s.)

GURYANOVA, E., SACHS, J. and USCHAKOV, P. 1925. Das Litoral des Kola-Fjords. *Tr. de la Stat. Biol. Murman Soc. Natur. Léningrad*, **1** (R)

GURYANOVA, E., SACHS, J. and USCHAKOV, P. 1928, 1929, 1930. Das Littoral des Kola Fjords. *Tr. L.O.E., Zool. Physiol.* **58**, 2; **52**, 2; **60**, 2 (G.s.)

GURYANOVA, E., SACHS, J. and USCHAKOV, P. 1930. The littoral (tidal) zone of West Murman coast. *Expl. mers l'URSS*, **11** (E.s.)

GURYEVA, T. 1948. A qualitative and quantitative characteristic of the littoral populations in the stony grounds of the bay Dalne Zelenetzkaya (Eastern Murman). *Tr. M.B.S.* **1** (R)

HAAS, F. 1938. Bivalvia, in *Bronns Klassen und Ordnungen des Tierreichs*, **3**, 3 (Teil 2, Lief 2)

HAGMEIER, A. 1926. Die Arbeiten mit dem Petersenschen Bodengreifer auf der Ostseefahrt. April 1925. *Ber. Deutsch. Wiss. Komm. Meeresf. N.F.* **11**, 4.

HAGMEIER, A. 1930. Die Bodenfauna der Ostsee im April 1929 nebst einigen Vergleichen mit April 1925 und Juli 1926. *Ibid.* **5**, 3.

HAGMEIER, A. 1930. Eine Fluktuation von Mactra (Spisula) subtruncata da Costa an der Ostfriesischen Kuste. *Ibid.* **3**.

HARIN, N. 1939. Hydrobiological sketch of the salted limans near Azov Sea. *Tr. Novocherkassk Zoo-vet. Inst.*

HARIN, N. 1951. Zoobenthos and zooplankton of the Kuban River limans and its changes under dilution. *Tr. Az.-Cher. NIRO*, **15** (R)

HARVEY, H. 1926. Nitrate in the Sea. *J. Mar. Biol. Assoc.* **14**.

HARVEY, H. 1928. *Biological chemistry and physics of sea water.*

HARVEY, H. 1945. *Recent advances in the chemistry and biology of sea water.*

HEDGPETH, J. 1957. Concepts of Marine Ecology. *Treatise on Marine Ecology and Paleoecology*. Vol. 1.

HEDGPETH, J. 1957. Marine Biogeography. *Ibid.*

HEDGPETH, J. 1957. Estuaries and Lagoons. Biological Aspect. *Ibid.*

HELLAND-HANSEN, B. 1912. The ocean waters. *IRHH Suppl.* **1**, *ser.* 2.

HERTLING, H. 1929. Die Nahrung der Ostseefische. *Mitt. Deutsch. Seefisch. Ver.* **45**.

HESSLAND, J. 1946. On the Quaternary Mya period in Europe. *Arkiv Zool.* **37A** (8)

HESSLE, C. 1924. Bottenboniteringar i inre Östersjön (Quantitative investigations into the bottom fauna of the inner Baltic). *Meddel. K. Lantbruksstyre.* **250**.

HESSLE, C. 1946. On the Quaternary Mya period in Europe. *Arkiv Zool.* **37** (2)

HESSLE, C. and VALLIN, S. 1934. Undersökningar över plankton ochdess växlingar i Östersjön under aren 1925–27 (Investigations of plankton and its fluctuation in the Baltic during the years 1925–1927). *Sv. Hydrogr.-biol. Komm. Stockholm Skr. N.S. Biologi*, **1** (5)

HOFFMAN, C. 1943. Salzgehalt des Seewassers als Lebensfactor mariner Pflanzen. *Kieler Blätter*, **3**.

HOFSTEN, N. 1915. Die Echinodermen des Eisfjords. *Kungl. Sv. Vetensk. Acad. Handl.* **54**, 2.

HOFSTEN, N. 1916. Die Decapoden Crustaceen des Eisfjords. Zool. Erg. der Sved. Exped. nach Spitzbergen 1908. *Ibid.* **54**, 7.

HÖGBOM, A. 1917. Über die arktische Elemente in der aralo-kaspischen Fauna, ein tiergeographisches Problem. *Bull. Geol. Inst. Uppsala*, **14**.

IDELSON, M. 1929. On the Nourishment of the Food-Fish in the Barents Sea. *R.H.J.* **8**, 10–12.

IDELSON, M. 1930. A preliminary quantitative evaluation of the bottom fauna of the Spitzbergen bank. *Ber. MNI*, **4**, 3.

IDELSON, M. 1934. Materials for the quantitative evaluation of the bottom fauna of the Barents, White and Kara Seas. Distribution of the benthos biomass in the Southern Barents Sea. The influence of different factors on the density of the sea bottom population. *Tr. GOIN*, **3**, 4 (E.s.)

IDELSON, M. 1941. The plankton of the Caspian Sea. (In press.) (R)

ILGAZ, O. 1944. Karadenizden Istanbul bogazine giren sulari ingildendiran bazi notlar (Notes on the exit of water from the Black Sea into the Bosphorus) Türk. *Cogr. Derg.* (*Turkish Geogr. Mag.*), **7**, 6.

ILYIN, B. 1930. Some data on the distribution of the Crustacea and Gobiidae in the estuaries (limans) of the Kuban. *Tr. Az.-Cher. NIRO*, **7**.

ILYIN, B. 1933. Halistatic community in the Black Sea. *Priroda*, **7** (R)

ISSATCHENKO, B. 1914. Recherches sur les microbes de l'océan Glacial Arctique. *L'Expédition Scientifique pour l'Exploration des pêcheries de la côte Mourmane* (R)

ISSATCHENKO, B. 1924. Sur la fermentation sulphyrique dans la Mer Noire. *C.R. Acad. Sci.* **178**, 26.

ISSATCHENKO, B. 1925. Über die bacteriallen Processe im Azowschen und Schwarzen Meeren. *Tr. First All-Russian Hydrolog. Congr.* (1924).

ISSATCHENKO, B. 1929. Die Charakteristik der bakteriologischen Prozesse im Schwarzen und Azowschen Meeren. *Proc. Intern. Congress Plant. Sci.* (New York).

ISSATCHENKO, B. and EGOROVA, A. 1939. On the "bacterial plate" in the Black Sea. (Volume in honour of N. M. Knipovich.) *VNIRO* (E.s.)

ISSATCHENKO, B. and EGOROVA, A. 1945. On the problems next in turn microbiological study of the water and ground of the Sea. *Repts. Arctic Inst.* (R)

IVANOV, A. 1957. Neue Pogonophora aus dem nordwestlichen Teil des Stillen Ozean. *Zool. Jahrb. Abt. Syst. Ökol. u. Geogr. d. Tiere*, **85**, 4–5.

IVANOV, A. 1959. Pogonophora. Fauna of the USSR. *AN, USSR* (R)

IVANOV, A. 1960. Pogonophora. *Traité de Zoologie*, **5**, 2.

IVANOV, C. 1946. Hydrochemical regime in the northern part of Caspian Sea. (In press.) (R)

IVANOVA, S. 1957. The qualitative and quantitative characteristic of the benthos in the Onega Bay in the White Sea. Materials on complex study of the White Sea, 1. *AN, USSR* (R)

JABE, H. and TOYAMA, R. 1934. Bottom relief of the seas bordering on the Japanese Islands and Korean Peninsula. *Bull. Earthquake Research Inst. Tokyo, Imp. University*, **12**.

JAECKEL, S. 1950. Die Mollusken der Schlei. *Arch. Hydrobiol.* **44**.

JAKOVLEVA, A. 1952. Loricata (Mollusca) in the seas of the USSR. *AN, USSR* (R)

JAKUBOVA, L. (Jacubova). 1935. Concerning the division into districts of the Black Sea on the basis of composition and distribution of its benthos fauna. *DAN, USSR*, **1**, 4 (E.s.)

JAKUBOVA, L. 1948. Biology of the Subbosporus area of the Black sea. *Tr. S.B.S.* **6** (R)

JAKUBOVA, L. 1948. On the question of the distribution of Modiola phaseolina (Phil.) in the Black Sea. *Ibid.* (R)

JAKUBOVA, L. and MALM, E. 1931. Die Beziehungen einiger Benthos-Formen des Schwarzen Meeres zum Medium. *Biol. Zbl.* **51**, 3.

JAMADA, T. 1933. Report on the distribution of the Plankton in the neighbouring seas of Tyosen in June 1932. *Z. Exp. St. Husan.*

JAROSHENKO, M. 1950. Genesis and development of the Dniester bottom land (flood plain). *Sci. Mem. Moldavian filial of the Acad. Sci. USSR*, **3** (R)

JASHNOV, V. (Jaschnov). 1927. Das Zooplankton des Karischen Meeres. *Tr. MNI*, **2**, 2 (G.s.)

JASHNOV, V. 1938. Plankton of the Caspian Sea. *Tr. First All-Caspian Sci. Fishery Conf.* **2** (R)

JASHNOV, V. 1939. Plankton productivity of the Caspian sea. I. The distribution of the titre and the plankton biomass of the Caspian Sea, according to the materials of 1934–35. *Bull. Acad. Sci. USSR, biol.* **5** (E.s.)

JASHNOV, V. 1939. On the biology of *Calanus finmarchicus* of the Barents Sea. Reproduction and seasonal variations in the distribution of stages. *Tr. VNIRO*, **4** (E.s.)

JASHNOV, V. 1939. Plankton productivity of the south-western part of the Barents Sea. *Ibid.* (E.s.)

JASHNOV, V. 1940. Plankton productivity of the northern seas of the USSR. *M.O.I.P.* (E.s.)

JELTENKOWA, M. (Zheltenkova). 1938. Food preference of the North Caspian and composition of the benthos. *Z.J.* **17**, 1 (E.s.)

JELTENKOWA, M. 1939. Feeding of *Rutilus rutilus caspicus Jak.* in the northern part of the Caspian Sea. *Tr. VNIRO*, **10** (E.s.)

JELTENKOWA, M. 1955. The feeding and utilization of the nutritional material with demersal fishes in the Sea of Azov. *Tr. VNIRO*, **31**, 1 (R)

JENSEN, A. 1939. Concerning a change of climate during recent decades in the Arctic and subarctic regions (e.c.). *Dethgl. Danske Widensk. Kabernes Selskab. Biologiske Meddelelser*, **14**, 8.

JENSEN, A. and HARDER, P. 1910. Post-glacial changes of climate in Arctic regions as revealed by investigations on marine deposits. *Die veränd. d. Klimas u.s.w. hrsg. vom XI Intern. Geologenkongr. Stockholm.*

JESPERSEN, P. 1923. On the quantity of macroplankton in the Mediterranean and the Atlantic. *Rep. Danish Oceanogr. Exp.* 1908–1910, **7**

JHDANKO, S. 1940. Aral Sea currents. *Meteorologia and Hydrologia*, **1–2** (R)

JIJCHENKO, B. 1940. Lower Miocene. Middle Miocene. *Stratigraphy of USSR*, **12**. Neogene of USSR (E.s.)

JOHANSEN, A. 1918. Oversigt over Dyreliveti Randers Fjord (Survey of the fauna of the Randers Fjord). *Randers Fjords Naturhistorie*. **5**, A.

JONGE, C. 1928. Feeding mechanism in the invertebrates. *Biol. Rev.* **3**.

JOUSE, A. 1954. Tertiary diatoms in the bottom deposits of the far-eastern seas. *Tr. IOAN*, **9** (R)

JOUSE, A. 1954. A comparative study of the results in diatomaceous analysis of the Okhotsk and Bering Seas deposits. *DAN, USSR*, **98**, 1 (R)

JOUSE, A. 1957. Diatoms in bottom deposits of the Bering Sea. *Bull. Comiss. étude Quaternaire*, **13** (R)
JOUSE, A. and SECZKINA, T. 1955. Diatom algae in the deposits of the Kurile–Kamchatka Trench. *Tr. IOAN*, **12** (R)
JOUSE, A. and SEMINA, G. 1955. The general patterns in the distribution of diatoms in the plankton of the Bering sea and on the layer surface of the deposits. *DAN*, *USSR*, **100**, 3 (R)
JUKOV, M. 1945. Pliocenian and quaternary history in the northern near-Caspian depression. *Probl. of the Western Kazakhstan*, **2** (R)
JUKOVA, A. 1954. The role of microorganisms in the feeding of *Nereis succinea* in the Caspian Sea. *Microbiology*, **23**, 1 (R)
JUKOVA, A. 1955. The biomass of microorganisms in the deposits of the northern Caspian sea. *Microbiology*, **24**, 3 (R)
JURAVEL, P. 1952. On the Fauna in the limans of the lower reaches of the River Dnieper. *Bull. Hydrobiol. Inst.* **9**. Dniepropetrovsk (R)
JURAVEL, P. 1950. On the problem of enriching the food resources in the reservoirs of the south-eastern Ukraine. *Z.J.* **29**, 2 (R)
KALLE, K. 1932. Phosphat-Gehaltsuntersuchungen in der Nord- und Ostsee im Jahre 1931. *Ann. Hydr. mar. Met.* **1**.
KALUGINA, A. 1958. Benthos algae of the White Sea. Authoreferate of the dissertation (R)
KAMSHILOV, M. 1955. Materials on the biology of the *Calanus finmarchicus* in the Barents and White Seas. *Tr. M.B.S.* **2** (R)
KAMSHILOV, M. 1957. Some new data on the Zooplankton of the White Sea. "Materials on the complex study of the White Sea." *Acad. Sci. USSR* (R)
KAMSHILOV, M. 1957. Zooplankton in the coastal zone of the Barents Sea. *Tr. M.B.S.* **3** (R)
KARDAKOVA, E. 1957. The state of commercial processing *Phyllospadix* in southern Primorje. *Bull. TINRO*, **45** (R)
KARPEVITCH, A. 1952. The level of the nutritional material in the southern seas from the standard discharge of the rivers' water. *Tr. All-Union Conf. Fishery* (December 17–26, 1951), **1**. *Acad. Sci. USSR*, *Moscow* (R)
KARPEVITCH, A. 1953. The relation of Bivalvia in the northern Caspian Sea to the change of environmental salinity. Summary of dissertation. Moscow (R)
KARPEVITCH, A. 1955. The relation of the Invertebrates of the Azov Sea to the change of salinity. *Tr. VNIRO*, **31**, 1 (R)
KARPEVITCH, A. 1957. The influence of a decreased discharge on the regime and fauna of the Sea of Azov. (Annotations to works undertaken by *VNIRO*, **4** (R).)
KARPEVITCH, A. 1957. The possible changes in the Azov Sea fauna in the standard discharge of the River Don and ways of increasing the stock of commercial fishes. *Probl. Ecology*, **1** (R)
KARPEVITCH, A. 1958. The biological basis of the acclimatization of mysids in the Aral Sea and Lake Balkhash. (Annotations to works undertaken by *VNIRO*, **3** (R).)

KARPEVITCH, A. 1958. Survival reproduction and respiration of *Mesomysis kowalewskyi* (*Paramysis lacustris kowalevskyi Czern.*) in brackish waters of the USSR. *Z.J.* **37**, 8 (E.s.)

KARPEVITCH, A. 1960. Influence of the variable river discharge and regime of the Sea of Azov on its fishery and food provision. *Tr. AzNIIRH*, **1**, 1 (R)

KARPEVITCH, A. and BOKOVA, E. 1936–1937. The rate of digestion in marine fishes. *Z.J.* **15**, 1 (R); **16**, 1 (E.s.)

KARPEVITCH, A. and OSADCHIH, V. 1952. The influence of salinity, the gas regime and the nature of the bottom deposits on *Nereis*. Acclimatization of *Nereis* in the Caspian Sea. *M.O.I.P.* (R)

KESSLER, K. 1860. The Journey with a zoological purpose to the coasts of the Black Sea and Krimea in 1858.

KESSLER, K. 1877. The fishes living in Aral–Caspian–Pontic ichthyology region. *Tr. Aralo-Caspian Exped.* **4** (R)

KHMISNIKOVA, V. (Khmiznikova, Khmisnikova, Chymsnikowa, Chmysnikova). 1931. Materials for the study of the zooplankton in the Matochkin Shar area. (Works of the Novaya Zemlya expedition.) *G.G.I.* **7** (R)

KHMISNIKOVA, V. 1936. The individuals that comprise the zooplankton of the Kara Sea. *Northern Sea Waterway*, **4** (E.s.)

KHMISNIKOVA, V. 1936. Zooplankton des südlichen und südöstlichen Teiles des Karischen Meeres. *Expl. Mers URSS*, **24** (G.s.)

KHMISNIKOVA, V. 1937. Distribution of the biologic indicators in Shokalsky and Vilkitsky straits (after the materials of the expedition on the ice-breaking steamer *Russanov* in 1932). *Tr. Arctic Inst. USSR*, **82** (E.s.)

KHMISNIKOVA, V. 1947. Distribution of plankton in the White Sea basin, as a hydrographical indicator of the poles of warmth and cold. *Tr. G.O.I.* **1**, 13 (R)

KHUSAINOVA, N. 1958. The biological features of some invertebrates found on the bottom of the Aral Sea used by fish as food. *Alma-Ata* (R)

KINALEW, N. 1937. The nutrition of Gobies (Gobüdae) in the northern Caspian. *Z.J.* **16**, 4 (E.s.)

KIREEVA, M. (Kireieva, Kirejeva). 1958. Quantitative evaluation of the bottom algae in the Baltic Sea. (Annotations to the works by *VNIRO*, **3** (R).)

KIREEVA, M. and SCHAPOVA, T. 1933. Report on stationary works for the study of iodine-bearing algae. *Tr. GOIN*, **3**, 3 (E.s.)

KIREEVA, M. S. and SCHAPOVA, T. 1938. Rates of growth, age and spore-bearing of *Laminaria saccharina* and *L. digitata* in Kola fjord. *Tr. VNIRO*, **7** (E.s.)

KIREEVA, M. and SCHAPOVA, T. 1939. Végétation benthique de la Mer Caspienne. (La côte Est.) *Bull. M.O.I.P., biol.* **48**, 5–6 (F.s.)

KIREEVA, M. and SCHAPOVA, T. 1939. Stock and commercial treatment of the sea-grass. *Fishery Ind.* **3** (R)

KIREEVA, M. and SCHAPOVA, T. 1939. La végétation marine de la partie nord-est de la Mer Caspienne. *Bull. M.O.I.P., biol.* **48**, 2–3 (F.s.)

KIREEVA, M. and SCHAPOVA, T. 1957. Materials on systematical composition and biomass of the seaweeds and the highest vegetation of the Caspian Sea. *Tr. IOAN*, **23** (R)

KIREEVA, M. and SCHAPOVA, T. 1957. The bottom vegetation of the Krasnovodsk Gulf. *Ibid.* (R)

KIRKEGAARD, J. 1956. Pogonophora. First records from the Eastern Pacific. *Galathea Rep.* **2**.

KISELEVICH, K. 1923. The clupeids of the Caspi-Volga district. Part I. Systematic. *Tr. Astrakhan Sci. Commercial Exped.* 1914–1915 (R)

KISSELEW, J. (Kiselev). 1925. Das Phytoplankton des Weissen Meeres. *Expl. Mers URSS*, **2** (G.s.)

KISSELEW, J. 1928. On the question of distribution and composition of the phytoplankton in the Barents Sea. *Tr. Arctic Inst.* **37** (R)

KISSELEW, J. 1931. Bestand und Verteilung des Phytoplanktons im Amur Liman. *Ibid.* **14** (G.s.)

KISSELEW, J. 1932. Beiträge zur Mikroflora des süd-östlichen Teiles des Laptev Meers. *Ibid.* **15** (G.s.)

KISSELEW, J. 1937. Zusammensetzung und Verteilung des Phytoplanktons im nördlichen Teil des Beringmeeres und im südlichen Teil des Tschuktschen-Meeres. *Ibid.* **25** (G.s.)

KISSELEW, J. 1947. The Phytoplankton of the far-eastern seas as an indicator of some peculiarities of its hydrological regime. *Tr. GOI*, **1**, 13 (R)

KIZEVETTER, J. 1954. On the fodder value of the plankton in the Okhotsk and Japan Seas. *Tr. TINRO*, **39** (R)

KJELMAN, F. 1877. Über die Algenvegetation des Murmanschen Meeres. *Nova Acta Beg. Soc. Sci. Uppsala*, **3**.

KLENOVA, M. 1936. The deposits of the Kara Sea. *DAN, USSR*, **4**, 4 (R)

KLENOVA, M. 1938. Colouring of the deposits of the Polar Seas. *Ibid.* **19**, 8.

KLENOVA, M. 1940. The deposits of the Barents Sea. *Ibid.* **26**, 8 (R)

KLENOVA, M. 1948. *Geology of the Sea. Moscow* (R)

KLENOVA, M. 1960. The geology of the Barents Sea. *Acad. Sci. USSR* (R)

KLOTCHKO, M. 1937. The "lake-age" of the Caspian Sea (e.c.). *DAN, USSR*, **16**, 1 (R)

KLOUMOV, S. 1937. Morue polaire (Boreogadus saida) et son importance pour certains procès vitaux de l'Arctique. *Bull. Acad. Sci. URSS, biol.* **1** (F.s.)

KLUCHAREV, K. 1948. On the question on the reproduction and development of some Copepods in the Black Sea. *DAN, USSR*, **1** (R)

KNIPOWITSCH, N. (Knipovic). 1900. Über die postpliocänen Mollusken und Brachiopoden von Spitzbergen. *Bull. Acad. Sci. St.-Petersb.* **5** (G.s.)

KNIPOWITSCH, N. 1906. Grundzüge der Hydrologie Europäischen Eismeeres. *Bull. Soc. géogr. Russ.* **42** (G.s.)

KNIPOWITSCH, N. 1907. Zur Ichtyologie des Eismeeres. *Mem. Acad. Imp. Sci.* **18**, 5 (G.s.)

KNIPOWITSCH, N. 1921. Hydrological investigations in the Caspian Sea in the years 1914–1915. *Tr. Caspian exped.* 1914–1915, **1** (R)

KNIPOWITSCH, N. 1921. On the temperature conditions in the Barents Sea at the end of May 1921 (R). *Bull. Russ. Hydrol. Inst.* **9** (R)

KNIPOWITSCH, N. 1923. *The Caspian Sea and its fisheries* (R)

KNIPOWITSCH, N. 1924. Über die Verteilung des Lebens im Schwarzen Meere• *R.H.J.* **3**, 8–10 (G.s.)

KNIPOWITSCH, N. 1929. On the hydrology of the brackish-waters. *USSR Bull. GGI.* **24** (R)

KNIPOWITSCH, N. 1930. Vertikale Zirkulation und Verteilung des Sauerstoffs im Schwarzen und im Kaspischen Meer. *Bull. Inst. Hydrol.* **31** (G.s.)

KNIPOWITSCH, N. 1931. Rasche Veränderungen hydrologischer und biologischer Verhältnisse im Barents-Meer. *Bull. Commiss. étude Quaternaire*, **3** (G.s.)

KNIPOWITSCH, N. 1931. Hydrologische Untersuchungen im Azowschen Meere. *Abhandl. wissenschaftl. Fischerei-Exped. im Azow. Schwarzen Meer*, **5** (G.s.)

KNIPOWITSCH, N. 1932. Hydrologische Untersuchungen im Schwarzen Meere. *Ibid.* **10** (G.s.)

KNIPOWITSCH, N. 1933. Hydrological investigations in the Black Sea. *Tr. Azov-Black Seas sci. fisheries exped.* **10**.

KNIPOWITSCH, N .1938. Hydrography of the Seas and Brackwater. Moscow.

KOLBE, R. 1927. Zur Oekologie, Morphologie und systematik der Brackwasser Diatomeen. *Die Kieselalgen des Sperenterger Salzgebiets. Pflanzeforschung*, **7**.

KOLESNIKOV, B. 1939. On the problem of the origin of the Caspian Sea molluscs. *DAN, USSR*, **25**, 5 (R)

KOLESNIKOV, B. 1940. The Upper Miocene. The Lower, Middle and Upper Pliocene. *Stratigraphy of USSR*, **12**. Neogene of USSR (E.s.)

KOLESNIKOV, B. 1941. On the cyclic development of the tertiary fauna. *DAN, USSR*, **31**, 1 (R)

KOLESNIKOV, B. 1941. The development of depressions in the Caspian Sea. *Ibid.* **32**, 3 (R)

KOLOKOLOV, A. 1940. The biogenous components in the deposits of the Caspian Sea. *Zemlevedenie* (New Series), **1**, 41 (R)

KOMAROVA, I. 1939. Feeding of the long-rough dab in the Barents Sea in connection with food resources. 50 cruises of the research ship *Persey. Tr. VNIRO*, **4** (E.s.)

KONDAKOV, N. 1941. Cephalopods of the far-eastern seas of USSR. *Invest. far-eastern seas of USSR*, **1** (E.s.)

KONOPLEV, G. 1937. The seasonal changes of the zooplankton in the Odessa bay. *Tr. Odessa State Univ., biol.* **2** (R)

KONOPLEV, G. 1938. The zooplankton in the Odessa bay. *Ibid.* **3** (R)

KONOVALOV, P. 1958. The acclimatization of the Caspian Sea stellated sturgeon in the Aral Sea. *Priroda*, **7** (R)

KORNILOVA, V. 1955. The feeding of the Azov anchovy. *Tr. VNIRO*, **31**, 1 (R)

KOSTUCHENKO, V. 1955. The feeding of *Clupeonella* and its use of the feeding material in the Sea of Azov. *Ibid.* (R)

KOSYAKINA, E. 1936 (1937). Die Jahreszeitveränderungen des Zooplanktons in der Novorossijsk Bucht. *Works of the V. M. Arnoldi biological station of Novorossiysk*, **1**, 6 (G.s.)

KOSYAKINA, E. 1940. The quantitative study of the plankton in Novorossijsk-bay. *Ibid.* **2**, 3 (R)

KOYEWNIKOW, G. 1889. Vertical distribution of the vertebrates at Russian coasts in the Baltic Sea. *Repts. Zool. Dept. Moscow Soc. Natur. Hist. Anthrop. and Ethnogr.* **2** (R)

KOYEWNIKOW, G. 1892. La faune de la Mer Baltique orientale et les explorations prochaines de cette faune. *Congr. Intern. Zool.*

KREPS, E. and VERYBINSKAYA, N. 1930. Seasonal changes in phosphate and nitrate content in the Barents Sea. *J. Cons.* **5**.

KREPS, E. and VERYBINSKAYA, N. 1932. The consumption of nutrient salts in the Barents Sea. *Ibid.* **7**.

KRISS, A. 1958. *Marine microbiology. Moscow.*

KROPOTKIN, P. 1954. A brief survey of the tectonics and the paleogeography of the southern part of the Soviet Far East. *Probl. Asiatic Geol.* **1** (R)

KROPOTKIN, P. 1956. Brief survey of neotectonics in the Sichote-Aline. *Bull. Acad. Sci. USSR, géol.* **3** (R)

KROTOV, A. 1949. *Life in the Black Sea* (R)

KUDELIN, N. 1914. De la distribution géographique des animaux de la Mer Noire en rapport avec la question sur l'origine des animaux d'eau douce. *Mem. soc. natur. Nouvelle Russ.* **39** (R)

KULIK, N. 1926. About Northern Postpliocene. *Geol. Herald*, **5**, 1–2 (R)

KULLENBERG, B. 1954. On the presence of sea water in the Baltic ice lake. *Tellus*, **6**, 3.

KUN, M. 1942. Some data on the feeding of *Cololabis*. *Tr. TINRO*, **21** (R)

KUN, M. 1951. The feeding of the mackerel in the Sea of Japan in 1948–1949. *Ibid.* **34** (R)

KUN, M. 1951. The distribution of the plankton and the feeding of Herring in northern part of the Okhotsk Sea. *Ibid.* **35** (R)

KUN, M. and MIKULICH, L. 1954. The food composition of the far-eastern fishery of crabs during the summer period. *Ibid.* **41** (R)

KUN, M. and MESHCHERIAKOVA, T. 1954. The distribution of the plankton types in the Sea of Japan. *Ibid.* **39** (R)

KUSAKIN, O. 1956. The littoral fauna and flora of the Kunashir Island. (Tr. of problems and thematic symposiums of the Zoological Institute.) *AN, USSR*, **6** (R)

KUSAKIN, O. 1961. Some characteristics of the fauna and flora distribution on the tidal zone in South Kurile Islands. *Invest. Far East Seas USSR*, **7** (R)

KUSMORSKAYA, A. (Kusmorsky, Kousmorskaya, Kousmorskaja). 1938. The zoobenthos in the Northern Caspian. Dissertation. (In press.) (R)

KUSMORSKAYA, A. 1940. The zooplankton of Mertvy Kultuk and Kaidak. *Z.J.* **19**, 6 (E.s.)

KUSMORSKAYA, A. 1940. Changements saisonniers du plancton de la Mer d'Okhotsk. *Bull. MOIP, biol.* **49**, 3–4 (F.s.)

KUSMORSKAYA, A. 1950. On the zooplankton of the Black Sea. *Tr. Az.-Cher. NIRO*, **14** (R)

KUSMORSKAYA, A. 1950. The composition and distribution of the plankton in the north-western part of the Sea of Japan in the first half of summer 1941. *Tr. VGO*, **2** (R)

KUSMORSKAYA, A. 1954. Zooplankton in the Black Sea and the commercially valuable fish who eat it. *Tr. VNIRO* (R)
KUSMORSKAYA, A. 1955. The seasonal and annual changes in the zooplankton of the Black Sea. *Tr. VGO*, **6** (R)
KUSMORSKAYA, A. State of the feeding material of the Black Sea anchovy and its larval forms in summer 1953–1954. (Annotations to works fulfilled by *VNIRO* (R).)
KUSNETZOV, A. (Kusnetsov). 1959. Distribution of the bottom-fauna in the North-Kuril waters. *Tr. IOAN*, **36** (R)
KUSNETZOV, A. 1960. Data concerning quantitative distribution of bottom fauna of the bed of the Atlantic. *DAN, USSR*, **130**, 6 (R)
KUSNETZOV, V. 1948. The bioecological characteristics of the mass forms of the marine invertebrates, *Tr. M.B.S.* **1** (R)
KUTCHEROVA, Z. 1957. Diatoms in marine fouling and its species composition. *Tr. S.B.S.* **9** (R)
LAKOWITZ, K. 1927. *Die Algenflora der gesamten Ostsee.*
LAVROV-NAVOZOV, N. 1939. A Black Sea shrimp in the Caspian Sea. *Z.J.* **18**, 3 (E.s.)
LEBEDEVA, M. 1953. *The numeral characteristic and the biomass of microorganisms in the Black Sea* (R)
LEBEDINZEV, A. 1892. Preliminary account of the chemical investigations of the Black and Azov Seas in the summer of 1891. *Bull. Russ. geogr. soc.* **28**, 1.
LEIBSON, R. 1939. Quantitative evaluation of the bottom fauna of the Motovskij Bay. *Tr. VNIRO*, **4** (R)
LEIVISKA, J. 1905. Ueber die Kusten . . . des Bottnischen Meeresbusens. *Fennia*, **23**, 1.
LEONOV, A. 1947. Water masses of the Bering Sea and the currents on its surface. *Meteorologia and Hydrologia* (Information reports), **2** (R)
LEONTIEV, O. 1955. *The geomorphology of the sea shores and the bottom.*
LEVANDER, K. 1899. Materialien zur Kenntnis der Wasserfauna in der Umgebung von Helsingfors (e.c.). *Acta Soc. F. Fl. Fenn.* **17**, 4.
LEVANDER, K. 1900. Ueber das Herbst- und Winter-plankton im Finnischen Meeresbusen und in der Alandsee. *Acta Soc. F. Fl. Fenn.* **18**, 5.
LEVANDER, K. 1901. Zur Kenntnis des Plankton und der Bodenfauna einiger seichten Brackwasserbuchten. *Ibid.* **20**.
LEVANDER, K. Ueber die Zusammensetzung des Zooplanktons. *Finn. Meeresbusen. Forh. vid. nord. Naturf. och läraremöted in Helsingfors*. 1902.
LEVANDER, K. 1915. Zur Kenntnis der Bodenfauna und des Plankton der Pojowick. *Atlas de Finland*, **25**, 2.
LIMAREV, V. 1957. The type of the coasts in Aral sea. *Tr. Oceanogr. Commission*, **2** (R)
LIMBERG-RUBAN, E. 1952. The number of bacteria in the water and grounds in the north-western part of the Pacific. *Invest. far-eastern Seas USSR*, **3** (R)
LINDBERG, G. 1947. The fish fauna in the Sea of Japan and the history of its development. *Proc. Acad. Sci. USSR*, **51**.

LINDBERG, G. 1948. The past of the Pacific ocean in the light of biological data. (In memory of Academician S. A. Zernov.) (R)
LINDBERG, G. 1953. The pattern of distribution of fish and the geological history of the far-eastern seas. Essays on the general questions of the Ichthyology. *AN, USSR* (R)
LINDBERG, G. 1955. Quaternary period in the light of the biogeographic data. *Acad. Sci. USSR* (R)
LINDBERG, G. 1956. On the quaternary history of the far-eastern seas. *DAN, USSR*, **111**, 2 (R)
LINDHOLM, V. 1937. *Mollusca. The Animal kingdom of the USSR*, **1** (R)
LINKE, O. 1939. Die Biòta des Jadebusenwattes. *Helgoländer Wissensch. Meeresunters*, **1**, 3.
LINKO, A. 1907. Investigations on the composition and life of the plankton in the Barents Sea. *L'expédition scientifique pour l'exploration des pêcheries de la côte Mourman.*
LINKO, A. 1908. Schizopoda of the Russian northern Seas. *Ibid., Zool.* **1**, 8 (R)
LINKO, A. 1913. The zooplankton in the Siberian area of the Arctic Ocean (e.c.). *Mém. Acad. Imp. Sci.* **8**, 29, 4 (R)
LISITSIN, A., MIKHALTSEV, I, SYSOEV, N. and UDINTSEV, G. B. 1957. New data on the thickness conditions of soft deposits in the north-western part of the Pacific. *DAN, USSR*, **115**, 6 (R)
LIVANOV, N. 1912. Fauna in Glubokaia (Dolgaia) Bay of the Solovetzky Islands. (Supplements to the Protocols meeting of the Natural History Society of the Kazan University.)
LOBSA, N. 1945. The salt composition of the water in the Kara Sea and its change under the influence of the river discharge. *Repts. Arctic Inst.* (R)
LOGVINENKO, B. 1959. "Newcomer"-species in the Caspian Sea. *Priroda*, **2** (R)
LOMAKINA, N. 1952. The origin of the glacial relict Amphipods in connection with the problem of the late-glacial junction between White and Baltic Seas. *Sci. Mem. Karelo-Finnish Univ. Biol.* **4**, 3. *Petrozavodsk* (R)
LOVEN, S. 1861. *Öfversigt Vetenskaps Akademiens Handlingar*, **18**.
LOVEN, S. 1861. Om nägra i Vettern och Venern fauna Crustaceer. I. *Ofv. Konigl. vetensk. Akad. Forhandl.* **6**.
LOVEN, S. 1862. Till fragan om ishafsfaunas fordna ütstrackning öfveren del af Nordens fastland. *Ibid.*
LOVEN, S. 1864. *Om ostersjön Föredrag vit Scand. Naturf.-Sellsk. Stockholm.*
LUBNI-GERTZIK, E. 1955. The plankton indicators of the currents. *Tr. IOAN*, **13** (R)
LUKONINA, N. 1957. The feeding resources of the plankton-eating fish of the Aral Sea. (Annotations to works undertaken by *VNIRO*, **4** (R))
LUKONINA, N. and JABLONSKAYA, E. 1958. The feeding resources of plankton-eating fish in the Aral Sea and its utilization. *Ibid.* **3** (R)
LUTHER, A. 1909. Über eine Littorina-Ablagerung bei Tvärminne. *Acta Soc. F. Fl. Fenn.* **32**.
LUTHER, H. 1951. Verbreitung und Ökologie der höheren Wasserpflanzen im Brackwasser der Ekenäs-Gegend in Süd-Finland. *Acta Bot. Fenn.* **49**, 50.

MADSEN, H. 1936. Investigations on the shore fauna of East Greenland with a survey of the shores of other Arctic Regions. *Medd. om Grönland*, **8**.

MAISKY, V. 1939. The influence of the raptores on the fish population in the Sea of Azov. *Z.J.* **18**, 2 (R)

MAISKY, V. 1940. On the method of studying fish productivity in the Sea of Azov. *Tr. Az.-Cher. NIRO*, **12** (R)

MAISKY, V. The fish distribution and fish number in the Sea of Azov before the discharge of the River Don. *Tr. VNIRO*, **31**, 2 (R)

MAISKY, V. 1955. The feeding and the feeding material of the pike and perch in the Sea of Azov. *Ibid.* **31**, 1 (R)

MAISKY, V., LINDER, L. and DORMENKO, V. 1950. *Clupeonella delicatula cultriventris* in the Sea of Azov. *Simferopol.* (R)

MAJOROVA, A. 1934. The taxonomic standing of the anchovy near the coasts of the Georgia. *Tr. station piscicole et biol. Georgia*, I, **1**.

MAKAROV, A. 1938. On the distribution of some Crustacea (Mysidacea, Cumacea) and lagun molluscs in the mouth of rivers and open estuaries of the northern shore of the Black Sea. *Z.J.* **17**, 6 (Fr.s.)

MAKAROV, A. 1940. A new shrimp of the Caspian Sea. *Priroda*, **4** (R)

MAKAROV, S. and ENIKEEV, D. 1937. Preliminary results of the physico-chemical investigations in the north-eastern bays of the Caspian Sea (Komsomoletz and Kaidak). Bays of the Caspian Sea. *AN, USSR*, **1**, 1 (R)

MAKAROV, V. 1937. Materials for the quantitative evaluation of the bottom fauna of the north part of the Bering Sea and the south part of the Chukchee Sea. *Expl. mers URSS*, **25** (E.s.)

MAKAROV, V. 1941. *Invest. far-east seas USSR*, **1** (E.s.)

MAKAROVA, I. 1957. Diatoms algae in the plankton of the middle and southern Caspian Sea.

MAKAROVA, I. 1957. The diatomaceous plankton algae in the middle and south parts of the Caspian Sea. *Autoref. Dissertation. Leningrad* (R)

MAKAROW, S. 1885. On the water exchange between the Black and Mediterranean seas. *Mém. Acad. Imp. Sci.* **51** (*Supplement* 6) (R)

MAKAROW, S. 1894. Le "Vitiaz" et l'Océan Pacifique. Vol. I, St.-Pétersbourg (F.s.)

MALEVICH, I. 1951. Materials on the study of the Oligochaeta fauna in the White Sea. *Tr. Zool. Mus. Moscow Univ.* **7** (R)

MALIANZ, A. 1933. Microbiological investigation of the soil in the Caspian Sea (middle and southern parts). *Tr. Azerbaidjan Oil Inst.* (AzNIII), **18** (Geological depart.) (R)

MALYATZKY, S. 1934. The migration of the anchovy in the Sea of Azov and the balance of the organic material in the Black Sea. *Fisheries USSR*, **5** (R)

MALYATZKY, S. 1940. Materials on the ecology of the pelagic population in the Black Sea. *Works of the V. M. Arnoldi biological station of Novorossijsk*, **2**, 3 (R)

MANKOWSKI, W. 1950. Badania planktonowe w Baltyku poludniowym W. R. 1948. (Plankton investigations in the Southern Baltic in 1948.) *Biul. Morskiego Inst. Rybackiego w Gdynia*, **5**.

MANKOWSKI, W. 1950. Macroplankton zatoki Gdanskief W.R. (Macroplankton of the Gulf of Gdansk in 1947.) *Ibid.*

MANTEUFEL, B. 1938. A short essay of changes of plankton in the Barents Sea. *Tr. PINRO*, **1** (E.s.)

MANTEUFEL, B. 1939. The zooplankton of the coastal waters of the Western Murman (materials collected in 1931–32). *Tr. VNIRO*, **4** (E.s.)

MANTEUFEL, B. 1939. The plankton of one of the Bays in the Western part of the Murman coast. (Volume in honour of N. M. Knipovich.) *VNIRO* (E.s.)

MANTEUFEL, B. 1941. The plankton and the herring in the Barents Sea. *Tr. PINRO*, **7** (E.s.)

MARKOVSKY, Ju. 1953–1955. Invertebrate fauna in the lower stream of the rivers in the Ukraine, its environmental conditions and its utilisation. (I–III parts.) *Kiev. Acad. Aci. Ukr.SSR* (R)

MARSHALL, S. and ORR, A. 1955. Biology of a marine Copepod *Calanus finmarchicus* (*Gunnerus*).

MARTI, J. 1936. On the question of the research methods in fisheries. *Fisheries USSR*, **5** (R)

MARTINOV, A. 1924. On the knowledge of the relict crustaceans in the lower Don, their etiology and distribution. *Ann. Zool. Mus. Acad. Sci. USSR*, 25 (R)

MARTINOV, A. 1924. On the knowledge of the relict crustaceans in the lower stream of the Don and their ethnology and distribution. *Year-book Zool. Mus. Acad. Sci. USSR*, **25** (R)

MARTINSEN, G. 1933. Distribution of the capelan (*Mallotus villosus Mülle*) in the Barents Sea. *Tr. GOIN*, **4** (E.s.)

MARTO, V. 1934. The role of the fauna of the Sea of Azov as a food for some fish in the eastern part of the Azov–Black Sea basin. *Fisheries USSR*, **3** (R)

MARTO, V. 1940. Acclimatization of the grey mullet in the Caspian Sea. *Priroda*, **1** (R)

MARTO, V. 1941. New facts about the acclimatization of the grey mullet in the Caspian Sea. *Ibid.* **3** (R)

MARUCAWA, H. 1928. On the plankton of the Japan Sea. *Annot. Oceanogr. Research*, **7**, 1.

MARUCAWA, H. 1933. Biological and fishery research on the Japanese crab *Paralithodes camtschatica. J. Fish. exptl. station*, **4**.

MARUMO, R. 1955. Distribution of plankton diatoms in the sea area east of Honshu in the summer of 1954. *Reg. Oceanogr. Works Japan*, **2**, 2.

MASLOV, N. 1944. The fish of the bottom of the Barents Sea and their fisheries. *Tr. PINRO*, **8** (E.s.)

MATVEEVA, T. 1948. Seasonal changes of the littoral populations in the stone facies in the Dalne–Zelenetskaya Bay. *Tr. M.B.S.* **1** (R)

MAXIMOV, I. 1936. On the hydrology of the Laptev sea. *Tr. Arctic Inst. Hydrol.* **68** (E.s.)

MAXIMOV, N. 1913. A list of works on the hydrology, fishery and ichthyology of the Azov–Black Sea basin, 1831–1912. *Mat. study Russ. fisheries*, **2**, 10.

MEISNER, V. 1908. Mikroskopische Wassertiere des Aralsees und der einmünden den Flüsse, im Zusammenhang mit der Frage über deren Verbreitungsbedingungen. *Wissenschaftl. Ergebn. Aralsee-exped.* **8** (R)

MEISNER, V. 1933. *The fisheries Ichthyology* (R)

MESHCHERYAKOVA, I. 1951. New data on the Zooplankton of the Sea of Japan. *Tr. TINRO*, **34** (R)

MESHCHERYAKOVA, I. 1954. Winter plankton of the central part of the Sea of Japan. *Ibid.* **39** (R)

MESYATZEV, I. 1923. Beiträge zur Zoogeographie der russischen nordlichen Meere. *Ber. MNI*, **1**, 13 (G.s.)

MESYATZEV, I. 1931. Mollusken des Barentsmeeres. *Tr. GOIN*, **1**, 1 (R)

MEYER, C. 1925. Le Sivache (Mer Putride) et sa flore algologique. *Bull. Inst. Hydrol. Russ.* **15** (F.s.)

MEYER, C. 1933. The account of the expedition for determination of the algal resources in the White Sea. *Tr. GOIN*, **3**, 3 (G.s.)

MEYER, C. 1937. Sur les dépôts d'Algues. *Tr. Jardin botan. Univ. Moscow*, **1** (Fr.s.)

MEYER, C. 1938. Data on Algae flora of the White Sea. *Tr. VNIRO*, **7** (E.s.)

MICHALEVSKI, A. 1931. Schême des courants de la mer Caspienne. *Mém. Hydrogr.* **66** (R)

MIKHAILOVSKAYA, Z. 1936. Phytoplankton of the Novorossijsk Bay and its vertical distribution. *Tr. Novorossijsk biol. station*, **2**, 1 (R)

MIKULITCH, L. 1954. Feeding of the dabs near the Southern Sakhalin and Southern Kuril Islands. *Tr. TINRO*, **39** (R)

MILOSLAWSKAYA, N. 1939. Zur Oekologie der Gammaroidea des Schwarzen Meeres in Verbindung mit der Entstehung ihrer Fauna. *Tr. Karadag biol. station*, **5** (G.s.)

MILOSLAWSKAYA, N. 1939. Zum Studium der Amphipoda Gammaroidea des Schvarzen und Azovschen Meeres. *Ibid.* (G.s.)

MÖBIUS, K. 1871. Die Fauna der Ostsee. *Deutsch. Naturforsch.*

MÖBIUS, K. 1871. Das Tierleben am Boden der deutsche Ost- und Nordsee Samme. *Gem. Wissensch. Vortr. v. Virchow und Holzendorff.*

MÖBIUS, K. 1873. Die Wirbellosen Tiere der Ostsee. *Jahresb. Comm. wiss. Unters. deutschen Meere in Kiel.*

MÖBIUS, K. and HEINKE, P. 1883. Die Fische der Ostsee. *Ibid.*

MOISEEV, P. A. 1953. Cod and dabs of the far-eastern seas. *Tr. TINRO*, **40** (R)

MOKYEVSKAYA, V. 1956. Some data on the chemistry of the biogen elements of the Bering Sea. *Tr. IOAN*, **17** (R)

MOKYEVSKY, O. 1949. Fauna of unconsolidated sediments of the littoral of the West Crimea. *Ibid.* **4** (R)

MOKYEVSKY, O. 1954. Quantitative distribution of the deep-sea bottom fauna of the Japan Sea. *Ibid.* **8** (R)

MOKYEVSKY, O. 1956. Some characteristics of the littoral fauna of the Sea shore of Sea of Japan. *Tr. probl. thematic conf. Zool. Inst. Acad. Sci. USSR* (R)

MOKYEVSKY, O. 1960. The littoral fauna of the north-western coast of the Japan Sea. *Ibid.* **34** (R)

MORDUKHAI-BOLTOVSKOY, F. (Morduchai-Boltowskoi). 1937. Die Verteilung der Bodenfauna im Golfe von Taganrog. *Repts. Dono-Kuban Station of the Az.-Cher. NIRO*, **5** (G.s.)

MORDUKHAI-BOLTOVSKOY, F. 1938. To the study of the plankton in the Sea of Azov. *Tr. Rostov. biol. Soc.* **2** (R)

MORDUKHAI-BOLTOVSKOY, F. 1939. On yearly changes in the benthos of the Taganrog Bay. *Z.J.* **18**, 6 (E.s.)

MORDUKHAI-BOLTOVSKOY, F. 1939. On the relict fauna in the lower Don area. *Tr. biol. Soc. Rostov-on-Don*, **3** (R)

MORDUKHAI-BOLTOVSKOY, F. 1946. Concerning the origin of Caspian fauna in the Ponto-Azov basin. *Z.J.* **25**, 2 (E.s.)

MORDUKHAI-BOLTOVSKOY, F. 1948. On the benthos distribution in the Dnieper delta. *Ibid.* **27**, 5 (R)

MORDUKHAI-BOLTOVSKOY, F. 1948. On the seasonal dynamics of the zoobenthos in the Taganrog Bay. *Sci. works Ivanovsky Agric. Inst.* **5** (R)

MORDUKHAI-BOLTOVSKOY, F. 1952. On the introduction of the new species of the crab in the River Don. *Priroda*, **1**.

MORDUKHAI-BOLTOVSKOY, F. 1953. The influence of hydrotechnic reconstruction of the River Don on the biological features of the Sea of Azov. *Tr. V.G.O.* (R)

MORDUKHAI-BOLTOVSKOY, F. 1953. The ecology of the Caspian fauna in the Azov–Black Sea basin. *Z.J.* **32**, 2 (R)

MORDUKHAI-BOLTOVSKOY, F. 1960. The Caspian fauna in the Azov–Black Sea basin. *Inst. biol. reservoirs Acad. Sci. USSR* (R)

MORDUKHAI-BOLTOVSKOY, F. 1960. The Caspian fauna in the Azov–Black Sea Basin. *Acad. Sci. USSR* (R)

MOROSHKIN, K. 1955. Water masses of the north-western Pacific and the Kurile–Kamchatka Trench region. *Tr. IOAN*, **12** (R)

MOROSOVA-WODYANITZKAYA, N. (Morosova-Vodyanitskaya). 1927. Die Beobachtungen über die Oecologie der Algen der Bucht von Noworossijsk. Shriften des Kuban-Schwarzmeerischen Institut für Wissenschaftlichen Forschungen, 52. *Arb. Biol. Station in Noworossijsk* (G.s.)

MOROSOVA-WODYANITZKAYA, N. 1930. Saisonwechsel und "Migration" der Algen in der Bucht von Noworossijsk. *Arb. Biol. Station in Noworossijsk* (namens W. M. Arnoldi), **4** (G.s.)

MOROSOVA-VODYANITZKAYA, N. 1936. Essai d'une évaluation quantitative de la végétation du fond de la mer Noire. *Tr. S.B.S.* **5** (F.s.)

MOROSOVA-VODYANITZKAYA, N. 1936. Phytobenthos des Karkinitzky Busens. *Ibid.* (G.s.)

MOROSOVA-VODYANITZKAYA, N. 1937. Some data on the vegetation productivity in the Black Sea. *DAN*, **14**, 8 (R)

MOROSOVA-VODYANITZKAYA, N. 1939. Zostera as a harvestable object in the Black Sea. *Priroda*, **8** (R)

MOROSOVA-VODYANITZKAYA, N. 1941. Materials bearing on the vegetative productivity of the Black Sea. *Tr. Z.I.N.* **7**, 2 (E.s.)

MOROSOVA-VODYANITZKAYA, N. 1948. 1954. Phytoplankton of the Black Sea (Parts I and II). *Tr. S.B.S.* **6** and **8** (R)

MOROSOVA-VODYANITZKAYA, N. 1957. Phytoplankton of the Black Sea and its quantitative development. *Ibid.* **9** (R)

MOROSOVA-VODYANITZKAYA, N. and BELOGORSKAYA, E. 1957. On the significance of the coccolithophorids, especially the Pontosphaera, in the plankton of the Black Sea. *Ibid.* (R)

MOSEVITCH, N. (Mosevic). 1928. Contributions à la systématique, l'écologie et la distribution de Yoldia arctica Gray récente et fossile. *Mat. commission étude Républ. Autonome Soviétique Socialiste Yakoute*, **19** (G.s.)

MOSENTZOVA, T. 1939. The seasonal changes in the microplankton in the Barents Sea. *Tr. PINRO*, **4** (E.s.)

MOSKALEV, L. 1961. Pogonophora in the Barents Sea. *DAN, USSR*, **137**, 3 (R)

MUNTHE, H. 1910. Studier over Gotlands senkvartära historia. *Sver. Geol. Under.* **4**.

MUNTHE, H. 1927. Studier over Ancylussjöns avlopp. *Ibid.* **346**.

MUNTHE, H. 1929. Nägra till den fennoskandiska geokronologien och isavmaltningen Knutna frägor. *Ibid.* **358**.

MUNTHE, H. 1931. Litorinahavet, Clypeushavet och Limnaeahavet. *Geol. Fören. i Stockholm Förhandl.* **53**.

MURATOV, M. 1957. On the origin of the oceanic depressions. *Bull. MOIP, géol.* **32**, 5 (R)

MUSHKETOV, N. 1895. General geological map of Russia. Geological investigations in the Kalmik steppe. *Tr. Geol. Comm.*

NANSEN, F. 1902. The oceanography of the North Polar Basin. *Norweg. North Polar Exped.* 1893–1896. *Sci. Res.* **3**.

NANSEN, F. 1906. *The Northern Waters.*

NANSEN, F. 1915. *Spitzbergen Waters.*

NEBOLSINA, T. 1959. The crab of the Caspian sea. *Priroda*, **6** (R)

NEIMAN, A. 1960. Quantitative distribution of benthos in the eastern part of the Bering Sea. *Z.J.* **39**, 9 (E.s.)

NEUMANN, G. 1942. Die absolute Topographie des Physicalischen Meeresniveaus und die Oberflächenströmungen des Schwarzen Meeres. *Ann. Hydr. Marit. Meteorol.* **70**, 9.

NEUMANN, G. 1943. Über die Stabilität der Wasserschichtung im Schwarzen Meer. *Ibid.* **2**.

NEUMANN, G. 1943. Über den Aufbau und die Frage der Tiefenzirkulation des Schwarzen Meeres. *Ibid.* **71**, 1.

NEUMANN, G. 1944. Das Schwarze Meer. Ein oceanographischer Uberlick. *Zeitschr. Erdkunde*, **3–4**.

NICHALLS, A. 1933. On the biology of *Calanus finmarchicus*. *J. Mar. Biol. Ass. N.S.* **19**.

NIKITIN, V., NIKITIN, B. and NIKITIN, W. 1924. Concerning the question of the vertical distribution and the lower limit of extension of the plankton in the Black Sea. *C.R. Acad. Sci. USSR* (E.s.)

NIKITIN, V., NIKITIN, B. and NIKITIN, W. 1926. La distribution verticale du plancton dans la mer Noire. I. Copepoda et Cladocera. *Tr. Lab. zool. Station biol. Sébastopol*, **2**, 5–10 (F.s.)

NIKITIN, V., NIKITIN, B. and NIKITIN, W. 1928. On the question of the influence of the Oxygen regime on the vertical distribution of the zooplankton in the Black Sea. *Proc. Setchenov Inst. Sebastopol*, **2** (E.s.)

NIKITIN, V., NIKITIN, B. and NIKITIN, W. 1929. La distribution verticale du plancton dans la mer Noire. II. Zooplancton (les Copépodes et les Cladocèros exceptés), *Tr. S.B.S.* **1** (F.s.)

NIKITIN, V., NIKITIN, B. and NIKITIN, W. 1929. Les migrations verticales saisonières des organismes planctoniques dans la Mer Noire. *Bull. Océanogr. Monaco*, **257**.

NIKITIN, V., NIKITIN, B. and NIKITIN, W. 1929. The influence of temperature on the seasonal vertical migration of the zooplankton in the Black sea. *Tr. Crim. Sci. Inst.* **2** (E.s.)

NIKITIN, V., NIKITIN, B. and NIKITIN, W. 1930. Die untere Planktongrenze und derne verteilung im Schwarzen Meere. *IRHH*, **25**, 1–2.

NIKITIN, V., NIKITIN, B. and NIKITIN, W. 1933. Oysters, mussels and shrimps as commercial objects in the Black and Azov Seas. *Fisheries USSR*, **3** (R)

NIKITIN, V., NIKITIN, B. and NIKITIN, W. 1934. The Gudaut oyster bank. (Essay of ecological and fishery investigations.) *Tr. station piscicole biol. Georgie*, **1**, 1 (E.s.)

NIKITIN, V., NIKITIN, B. and NIKITIN, W. 1938. The lower boundary of the benthic fauna and its distribution in the Black Sea. *DAN, USSR*, **21**, 7 (R)

NIKITIN, V., NIKITIN, B. and NIKITIN, W. 1939. The plankton of Batumi bay and its changes in animal population. (Volume in honour of scientific activity of N. M. Knipovich.) (E.s.)

NIKITIN, V., NIKITIN, B. and NIKITIN, W. 1945. La distribution de la biomasse du plancton dans la mer Noire. *Ibid.* **47**, 7 (R)

NIKITIN, V., NIKITIN, B. and NIKITIN, W. 1946. Feeding of anchovies (*Engraulis encrasicholus*) in the Black Sea at the Georgian shores. *Tr. Inst. zool. Acad. Sci. RSSG.* **6** (E.s.)

NIKITIN, V., NIKITIN, B. and NIKITIN, W. 1948. The communities and the quantitative distribution of the bottom fauna in the eastern part of the southern coast of the Black Sea. *Tr. S.B.S.* **6** (R)

NIKITIN, V., NIKITIN, B. and NIKITIN, W. 1949. Basic conditions for the distribution of life in the Black Sea. *Tr. IOAN*, **3** (R)

NIKITIN, V., NIKITIN, B. and NIKITIN, W. 1950. The boundaries of vertical distribution of organisms in the Black sea. (In memory of J. M. Shokalsky.) **2** (R)

NIKITIN, V. and MALM, E. 1934. L'influence de l'oxygene, des ions hydrogène et de l'acide carbonique sur la distribution verticale du plankton de la Mer Noire. *Ann. Inst. Océanogr. Monaco*, **14**, 4.

NIKITIN, V. and SKVORTZOV, E. 1925. Hydrological sections made in August and November 1923 and in March 1924. *Mem. Hydrogr.* **48**.

NIKITINA, V. 1934. Bibliographie ichtyologique de la mer Noire et de la mer d'Azov. *Tr. station piscicole biol. Géorgie*, **1**, 1 (R)

NIKITINA, V. 1939. Bibliographie ichtyologique de la mer Noire et de la mer Azov. (*Supplément*) *Ibid.* **2** (F.s.)

NIKITINA, V. 1940. List of literature of the fauna and flora of the Black Sea and Sea of Azov for the years 1773–1937. (With the exception of the Pisces and Mammalia.) (R) *Acad. Sci. USSR. Tbilisi, Georgia.*

NIKITINSKI, W. 1933. Quantitative Bestimmung der Bodenfauna der offenen Stellen des Aral Sees. *Referat Aral Sea sci. station fisheries*, **1** (G.s.)

NIKOLAEV, I. 1949. On the advancement of the warm water and brackwater elements of the fauna and flora in the inner (eastern) part of Baltic. *DAN, USSR*, **68**, 2 (R)

NIKOLAEV, I. 1951. Arctic element of the phytoplankton in Baltic Sea. *Tr. V.G.O.* **3** (R)

NIKOLAEV, I. 1951. On the new habitants in the fauna of Northern and Baltic Seas from distant districts. *Z.J.* **30**, 6 (R)

NIKOLAEV, I. 1957. On the fluctuations in the biological productivity of the Baltic Sea. *Tr. Latvian VNIRO*, **2** (R)

NIKOLAEV, I. 1957. The biological seasons in the Baltic Sea. *Ibid.* (R)

NIKOLAEV, I. and KRIEVS, K. 1957. Productivity and the conditions of the plankton development in central Baltic and in the Riga bay in 1955–1956. *Ibid.* (R)

NIKOLSKY, G. 1940. The fishes of the Aral Sea. *Mat. study fauna flora USSR.* New Series, *Div. zool.* **1**, 16, *Ed. MOIP* (E.s.)

NOVOYILOVA, A. 1955. The zooplankton changes in the Sea of Azov in condition of the changed regime. *Tr. VNIRO*, **31**, 1 (R)

NOVOYILOVA, A. 1958. The characteristic of the zooplankton in the Sea of Azov in conditions of the regulation discharge of the Don river. (Annotations to works undertaken by *VNIRO*, **1** (R).)

NORDMANN, M. 1840. Voyage dans la Russie etc. Vol. III. Observation sur la faune pontique.

NORDQUIST, O. 1890. Bidrag till kännedomen om Bottnisca vikens. och norra Ostersjöns evertebratfauna (Contributions to the Invertebrate fauna of the Gulf Bothnia and Northern Baltic). *Medd. Soc. F. Fl. Fenn.* **17**.

OKUL, A. 1940. On the method of quantitative study of plankton in the Sea of Azov. *Publ. Azov–Black Sea Sci. Inst. Marine Fisheries Oceanogr.* **12** (E.s.)

OKUL, A. 1941. Some materials on the productivity of the plankton of the Azov sea. *J.Z.* **20**, 2 (E.s.)

OKUL, A. Feeding of the plankton-eating fishes in the Sea of Azov. *Ibid.* **20**, 4–5.

ORTMANN, A. 1896. *Grundzüge der marine Tiergeographie.*

OSADCHIKH, V. 1958. The state of the feeding basis for the commercial fishes in the north Caspian Sea in 1956. *An. VNIRO*, **3** (R)

OSTROUMOV, A. 1892. Preliminary report on the participation in the Black Sea and deep-sea expedition 1891. *Bull. Russ. Geogr. Soc.* **28**, 1 (R)

OSTROUMOV, A. 1892. An account of the participation in the scientific voyage on the Azov Sea on the transport-ship *Kazbek* in the summer of 1891. *Mém. Acad. Imp. Sci. St.-Pétersbourg*, **69** (*Supplément* 6) (R)

OSTROUMOV, A. 1893. Voyage to the Bosphorus (e.c.). *Ibid.* **72** (*Supplement* 8) (R)

OSTROUMOV, A. 1894. Supplement au catalogue des mollusques de la Mer Noir et d'Azov, observés jusqu'à ce jour à l'état vivant. *Zool. Anz.* **17**.

OSTROUMOV, A. 1896. Preliminary report on the biological investigations of the Sea of Marmara. *Papers Russ. Imp. Geogr. Soc.* **33**, 2 (R)

PAKHULSKY, A. 1951. The fish-eating birds in the southern seas of the USSR and their harm. Materials for study of the fauna and flora USSR. *New Series, Div. zool.* **30**, 45. *Ed. MOIP* (R)

PALENITCHKO, Z. 1943. The edible invertebrates in the White Sea. Arkhangelsk (R)

PALENITCHKO, Z. 1957. The results of the complex investigations in Onega Bay (White Sea). *Mat. Complex Study White Sea,* **1** (R)

PALLAS, P. 1811. *Zoographia rosso-asiatica.* **3**. Petropoli.

PANKRATOVA, V. 1935. Data on the feeding of fish in the Aral Sea. Reports of the Aral-Sea division of the Institution of marine fisheries. *VNIRO*, **4** (R)

PANOV, D. 1937. Esquisse géomorphologique du littoral de la mer de Barentz. *Izv. Soc. Russ. Géogr.* **69**, 6 (R)

PANOV, D. 1940. The paleogeography of the Soviet Arctic in the quaternary period. *Tr. Geogr. Inst.* **36** (R)

PANOV, D. (1943) 1945. The problem of origin of the central polar basin. *Probl. Arctic,* **3** (R)

PASPALEV, G. 1933. Hydrobiologische Untersuchungen über den Golf von Varna. *Trud. Biol. Station Varna,* **2**.

PASTERNAK, F. 1957. Quantitative distribution and faunistic composition of benthos in the Sakhalin Gulf and adjacent parts of the Sea of Okhotsk. *Tr. IOAN,* **23** (R)

PAULI, V. 1927. On the history of the fauna in the Sea of Azov. *Proc. Second Congr. Zool. Anat. Histol. USSR* (1925, Moscow) (R)

PAULI, V. 1939. Sea of Azov as an eutrophical basin. (Volume in honour of scientific work of N. M. Knipovich.) *VNIRO* (R)

PAULI, V. 1954. The free-living isopods in the Black Sea. *Tr. S.B.S.* **8** (R)

PAULI, V. 1957. Key of the mysids of the Azov–Black Basin. *Tr. S.B.S.* **9** (R)

PELSH, A. 1936. On the autotrophic hydrogen sulphide bacteria Hydrogen-thiobacteria. Volume of the works on the hydrochemistry of the Kara-bugaz Bay of the Caspian Sea. Transactions of the salt-laboratory. *AN, USSR,* **5**.

PEREYASLAVTZEVA, S. 1886. Protozoaires de la Mer Noire. *Mém. Soc. Natur. la Nouvelle-Russie,* **10**, 2 (R)

PEREYASLAVTZEVA, S. 1892. Monographie des Turbellariés de la Mer Noire. *Ibid.* **17** (F.s.)

PERGAMENT, T. (1944–1945.) The benthos in the Kara Sea. *Probl. Arctic,* **1** (R)

PERZOV, N. 1952. The mass-littoral invertebrates in the White Sea as the components of fish and bird diets and the methods for the determination of their average size and weight. *Tr. V.G.O.* **4** (R)

PETERS and PUNNING, 1933. Die chinesische Wollhandkrabbe in Deutschland. *Zool. Anz. Erg. H. zu Bd.* **104**.

PETERSEN, C. 1913. Evaluation of the Sea. The animal communities of the Sea bottom and their importance for marine zoogeography. *Rep. Dan. Biol. Station*, **21**.

PETERSEN, C. 1914. Notes to Charts I and II. Appendix to Report 21. *Ibid.* **22**.

PETROVA-GRINKEVICH, N. 1944. Struggle for food between the Cod and the Haddock in the Barents Sea. *Tr. PINRO*, **8** (E.s.)

PETTERSSON, O. 1914. Die Feränderungen der Ostsee und ihre Einfluss auf das Fischleben. 2. *Nordeurop. Fischhändler- und Hochseefischereikongress.* Malmö.

PETTIBONE, M. 1953. A new species of polychaete worm of the family Ampharetidae from Massachusetts. *J. Wash. Acad. Sci.* **43**, 11.

PFANNENSTIEL, M. 1944. Die Diluvialen Entwicklungstadien und die Urgeschichte von Dardanellen, Marmarameer und Bosphorus. *Geol. Rundschau*, **34**, 7–8.

PFANNENSTIEL, M. 1951. Quartäre Spiegelschwankungen des Mittelmeeres und des Schwarzen Meeres. *Vierteljahrschr. Naturf. Gesellsch. Zurich*, **96**, 2.

PIROZHNIKOV, P. 1937. The question of the origin of the northern elements of the fauna in the Caspian Sea. *DAN, USSR*, **15**, 8 (R)

PITSYK, G. 1950. On the quantitative development and horizontal distribution of phytoplankton in the western part of the Black Sea. *Tr. Az.-Cher. NIRO*, **14** (R)

PITSYK, G. 1951. On the phytoplankton in the Sea of Azov. *Ibid.* **15** (R)

PITSYK, G. 1954. On the quantitative composition and distribution of the phytoplankton in the Black Sea. *Tr. VNIRO*, **28**.

PITSYK, G. and NOVOZHILOVA, A. 1951. On the dynamics of the zooplankton in the Sea of Azov. *Tr. Az.-Cher. NIRO*, **15** (R)

PODLESNIY, A. 1941. Geographical distribution of the *Stenodus leucichthys* and their origin in the Caspian Sea Basin. *Z.J.* **20**, 3 (R)

POLIANSKY, J. 1955. Data on the parasitology of the fish in the Northern Seas of the USSR. The parasites of the fishes in the Barents Sea. *Tr. ZIN AN, USSR*, **19** (R)

POLUTOV, I. 1952. Fresh data on the cod migrations near the eastern coasts of Kamchatka. *Tr. TINRO*, **37** (R)

PONOMAREVA, L. 1954. The winter zooplankton in the north part of the Sea of Japan. *Tr. IOAN*, **9** (R)

PONOMAREVA, L. 1955. Feeding and distribution of the Euphausiidae in the Sea of Japan. *Z.J.* **34**, 1 (R)

PONOMAREVA, L. 1959. Euphausiidae of the Sea of Okhotsk and Bering Sea. *Tr. IOAN*, **30** (R)

POPOV, A. 1932. Hydrobiological explorations in the Nordenskjöld Sea (Sea of the Brothers Laptev). *Expl. Mers URSS*, **15** (E.s.)

PORTENKO, L. 1931. The productive forces of the ornithofauna in the Novaya Zemlya. *Tr. Biogeochem. lab. Supplement*, **2** (R)

POST, L. 1929. Svea, Göta och Dana älvar. *Ymer*, **49**.

PRATJE, O. 1931. Einfuhrung in die Geologie der Nord und Ostsee. *Tierw. Nord-Ostsee.*

PRISHLETZOV, V. 1940. L'évaporation de la Mer Caspienne. (Preliminary report.) *Zemlevedenie*, **1** (Fr.s.)
PROBATOV, A. 1934. The materials on the scientific and industrial exploration of the Kara Bay. Northern department. *VNIRO* (R)
RADZICHOVSKAYA, M. 1961. The water-masses in the Japan Sea and the water- and thermal balance of the Japan sea. *The fundamental features of the geology and hydrography of the Sea of Japan*, **2** (R)
RASS, T. 1948. *World Fisheries of the aquatic animals. Moscow* (R)
RASS, T. 1949. Ichthyofauna of the Black Sea and its utilization. *Tr. IOAN*, **4** (R)
RASS, T. 1951. Ichthyofauna of the Caspian Sea and some queries on its history. *Ibid.* **6** (R)
RASS, T. 1954. The deep-sea fish of the far-eastern seas. *J.Z.* **33**, 6 (R)
RASS, T. 1955. Deep-sea fish of the Kurile–Kamchatka Trench. *Tr. IOAN*, **12** (R)
RASS, T. 1955. New regions and fisheries objective in the far-eastern seas. *Probl. Ichthyol.* **4** (R)
RASS, T. 1959. Biogeographical fishery complex of the Atlantic and Pacific oceans and their comparison. *J. Cons.* **24**, 2.
RASS, T. 1960. Biogeographical fishery complex of the Atlantic and Pacific oceans and their comparison. *Tr. IOAN*, **31** (R)
RATHKE, H. 1837. Zur fauna der Krym. *Mém. prés. Acad. Imp. St.-Pétersburg*, **3**.
RATMANOFF, G. 1930. Zur Hydrologie des Ostsibirischen Meeres. *Expl. mers URSS*, 13 (G.s.)
RATMANOFF, G. 1937. Contributions to the Study of the Hydrology of the Bering and Chukchee seas. *Ibid.* **25** (E.s.)
RATMANOFF, G. 1937. On water interexchange in the Bering Strait. *Ibid.* (E.s.)
RATMANOFF, G. 1939. Chukotsk Sea. *Soviet Arctic*, **9** (R)
RAVICH-SHERBO, J. (Ravic-Scerbo). 1930. On the question of the thin bacterial layer in the Black Sea according to the hypothesis of Prof. Egunoff. *Tr. S.B.S.* **2** (E.s.)
RAZIN, A. 1934. The sea commercial molluscs of the Southern Primorje. *Khabarovsk* (R)
REDEKE, H. 1922. Zur Biologie der niederländischer Brackwassertypen. *Bijdr. Dierk. Amsterdam*, **22**.
REIBISCH, J. 1914. Die Bodenfauna von Nord- und Ostsee. *Verch. Deutsch. Zool. Gesellsch.* **24**.
REMANE, A. 1933. Verteilung und Organisation der benthonischen Microfauna der Kieler Bucht. *Wiss. Meeresunters. Abt., Kiel*, **21**, 2.
REMANE, A. 1934. Die Brackwasserfauna. *Zool. Anz. Suppl.* **7**.
REMANE, A. 1940. Einfuhrung in die zoologische Ökologie der Nordund Ostsee. *Tierwelt Nord- und Ostsee*, **34**, 1a.
REMANE, A. 1952. Die Besiedelung des Sandbodens im Meere und die Bedeutung der Lebensformtypen für die Ökologie. *Zool. Anz. Suppl.* **16**.
REMANE, A. 1955. Die Brackwassersubmergenz und die Umcomposition der Coenosen in Belt- und Ostsee. *Kieler Meeresforschung*, **11**.

RIECH, F. 1926. Beitrage zur Kenntnis der littoralen Lebensgemeinschaften in der poly- und mesohalinen Region des Frischen Haffs. *Schrift. Phys. Oeconom. Gesellsch. Köningsberg*, **55**.

ROMANOV, N. 1955. Guide to commercial fisheries literature of the southern basins of USSR for the years 1918–1953. *Moscow Ed. Acad. Sci. USSR* (R)

ROMANOV, V. 1959. Guide to commercial fisheries literature of the Far Eastern Seas of USSR for the years 1923–1956. *Moscow Ed. Acad. Sci. USSR* (R)

ROMANOVA, N. 1956. Variations of the biomass of higher Crustacea in the northern Caspian Sea, as observed in the course of several years. *DAN, USSR*, **109**, 2 (R)

ROMANOVA, N. 1958. Distribution and ecological description of North Caspian Amphipoda and Cumacea. *Ibid.* **121**, 3 (R)

ROMANOVA, N. 1960. Benthos distribution in Central and Southern Caspian. *Z.J.* **39**, 6 (E.s.)

ROSSOLIMO, L. 1922. Tintinnoidea of the Black Sea. *Arch. Russ. Protistol. Soc.* **1**, 22 (G.s.)

SADOVSKY, A. (Ssadowsky). 1929. Biologische Untersuchungen des Schlamms der Bucht von Krasnovodsk. *Proc. Centr. Hydrometeorol. Bur.* **9** (G.s.)

SADOVSKY, A. 1934. Über die intermediäre Stellung einiger Schwarzmeer-mollusken zwischen atlantischen und mediterrannean Formen. *Tr. Zool. Sect. of the transcaucasian branch AN, USSR*, **1** (G.s.)

SAENKOVA, A. 1941. The change of the composition and benthos biomass in the northern Caspian Sea 1935–1940. The reconstruction of the fauna in the Caspian Sea (R)

SAENKOVA, A. 1956. New forms in the fauna of the Caspian Sea. *Z.J.* **35**, 5 (R)

SAIDOVA, K. 1953. On the significance of the benthos foraminifera for the stratigraphy of the quaternary marine deposits. *DAN, USSR*, **93**, 1 (R)

SAIDOVA, K. 1957. Quantitative distribution of Foraminifera in the deposits of the Okhotsk sea. *Ibid.* **114**, 6 (R)

SAIDOVA, K. 1960. Distribution of foraminifera in the bottom sediments of the Okhotsk Sea. *Tr. IOAN*, **32** (R)

SAIDOVA, K. 1960. Stratigraphy of sediments and palaeogeography of the north-east sector of Pacific Ocean according to the number of sea-bottom foraminifers. *Intern. geol. congr. XXI session. Repts. soviet geologists. Probl.* **10** (E.s.)

SAKS, V. 1945. The Seas of the Soviet Arctic in the quaternary period. *Repts. Arctic Inst.* (R)

SAKS. V. 1948. The quaternary period in the Soviet Arctic. *Tr. Arctic Inst.* **201** (R)

SAMOYLENKO, B. 1947. The immediate future of the Sea of Azov. *Tr. GOI*, **3**, 15 (R)

SAMOYLOFF, J. and GORSHKOWA, T. 1924. The deposits of the Barents and Kara Seas. *Ber. M.N.I.* **14** (E.s.)

SAMUELSSON, G. Die Verbreitung der höheren Wasserpflanzen in Nord-europa. *Acta Phytogeogr. Suec. Uppsala*, **6**.

SARS, G. 1927. Notes on the Crustacean fauna of the Caspian Sea. (Volume in honour of scientific activity of N. M. Knipovich, Moscow.)
SAURAMO, M. 1929. The quaternary geology of Finland. *Bull. Comm. Geol. Finland*, **86**.
SAURAMO, M. 1953. Das Rätsel des Ancylussees. *Geolog. Rundschau*, **41**.
SAURAMO, M. 1956. Pelagic community in the Pacific ocean. *Priroda*, **3** (R)
SAVILOV, A. 1953, 1957. Invertebrates of the White Sea, *Mytilus edulis, Mya arenaria, Balanus balanoides; their growth and its changes.* Parts I, II. *Tr. IOAN*, **7** and **23** (R)
SAVILOV, A. 1961. Ecologic characteristics of the bottom communities of invertebrates in the Okhotsk Sea. *Ibid.* **46** (R)
SCHLIEPER, C. 1932. Die Brackwassertiere und ihre Lebensbedingungen vom physiologischen Standpunkt aus betrachtet. *Verh. int. Ver. Limnol.* **6**.
SCHLIEPER, C. 1956. Über die Physiologie der Brachwassertiere. *Verh. int. Ver. Limnol. Helsinki.*
SCHMIDT, P. 1904. Pisces marium orientalium Imperii Rossici. *Ed. Soc. géogr. Russ. St.-Péterburg* (R)
SCHMIDT, P. 1934. On the zoogeographical distribution of the main commercial fishes in the western part of the North Pacific. *Bull. Pacific Comm. Acad. Sci. USSR*, **3** (R)
SCHMIDT, P. 1947. Migrations of the fishes. *Acad. Sci. USSR. Moscow* (R)
SCHMIDT, P. 1948. The fishes of the Pacific Ocean. Moscow. *Ed. Pistchepromisdat* (R)
SCHMIDT, P. 1950. The fishes of the Okhotsk Sea. *Tr. Pacific Comm. AN, USSR*, **6** (R)
SCHORYGIN, A. 1926. Die Echinodermen des Weissen Meeres. *Ber. M.N.I.* **2**, 1 (G.s.)
SCHORYGIN, A. 1928. Die Echinodermen des Barents Meeres. *Ibid.* **3**, 4 (G.s.)
SCHORYGIN, A. 1939. Food and food preference of some Gobiidae of the Caspian Sea. *Z.J.* **18**, 1 (E.s.)
SCHORYGIN, A. 1945. Changes in the quantity and composition of the benthos in the northern part of the Caspian Sea in the course of the years 1935–1940. *Z.J.* **24**, 3 (E.s.)
SCHORYGIN, A. 1948. The annual dynamics of competition for food of the fish. *Ibid.* **27**, 1 (R)
SCHORYGIN, A. 1952. The feeding and food-interrelation of the fishes in the Caspian Sea (Acipenseridae, Cyprinidae, Gobiidae, Percidae and predatory herrings). Moscow. *Ed. Pistchepromisdat* (R)
SCHORYGIN, A. and KARPEVITCH, A. 1948. The new inhabitants of the Caspian Sea and their importance in the biology of this basin. Krimea. *Ed. Krimizdat* (R)
SCHULEIKIN, V. 1925. Hydrodynamic of the huge tide in the White Sea. *Mem. Hydrogr.* **1** (R)
SCHULZ, B. 1932. Einführung in die Hydrographie der Nord- und Ostsee. *Tierw. Nord.- und Ostsee*, **21**.
SCHURIN, A. 1957. The feeding grounds of the *Pleuronectes flesus trachurus* Dunker in the Riga Bay. *Tr. Latvian Depart. VNIRO*, **2** (R)

Seas Atlas. 1951–1954, **1–3** (R) (Leningrad).

SEGERSTÅLE, S. 1932. Quantitative Studien über den Tierbeschtand der Fucus Vegetation in den Scheren von Pellinge. *Comm. Biol. Soc. Sci. Fenn.* **3**, 2.

SEGERSTÅLE, S. 1933. Studien über die Bodentierwelt in Südfinnländischen Küstengewässern. *Ibid.* **4**, 8.

SEGERSTÅLE, S. Übersicht über die Bodentierwelt mit besonder Berücksichtigung der Produktionsverhältnisse. *Ibid.* **4**, 9.

SEGERSTÅLE, S. 1938. Zur Fortpflantzungsbiologie des Amphipoden Pontoporeia femorata. *Ibid.* **7**, 5.

SEGERSTÅLE, S. 1939. Ein Planktonprofil Pellinge-Lill-Pernaniken im August 1937. *Ibid.* **7**, 10.

SEGERSTÅLE, S. 1944. Weitere Studien über die Tierwelt der Fucus-Vegetation an der Südküste Finlands. *Ibid.* **9**, 4.

SEGERSTÅLE, S. 1949. The brackish-water fauna of Finnland. *Oikos*, **1**, 1.

SEGERSTÅLE, S. 1951. The recent increase in salinity of the coasts of Finnland and its influence upon the fauna. *J. Cons.* **17**, 2.

SEGERSTÅLE, S. 1957. On the immigration of the glacial relics of Northern Europe with comments on their Prehistory. *Soc. Sci. Fenn. Commentat. Biol.* **16**, 16.

SEGERSTÅLE, S. 1957. Baltic sea. *Treatise on Marine Ecology and Paleoecology*, **1**.

SEGERSTÅLE, S. 1957. On the immigration of the glacial relics of Northern Europe with comments on their Prehistory. *Soc. Sci. Fenn. Commentat. Biol.* **46**, 16.

SEGERSTÅLE, S. 1958. On an Isolated Finnish Population of the Relict Amphipod *Pallasea quadrispinosa* G. O. Sars showing striking morphological reduction with remarks on other cases of morphological reduction in the species. *Soc. Sci. Fenn. Commentat. Biol.* **17**, 5.

SEMINGA, G. 1955. On the problems of the vertical distribution of phytoplankton in the Bering Sea. *DAN, USSR*, **101**, 5 (R)

SEMINA, G. 1958. Verbreitung der phytogeographischen zonen im Pelagial des Nord-Westlichen Teiles des Stillen Ozeans mit der Verteilung der Wassermassen in diesem Gebiet. *Tr. IOAN*, **27** (R)

SENKEVITCH, L. (*see* ZENKEVITCH, L.)

SERNOV, S. (*see* ZERNOV, S.)

SETCHKINA, T. 1959. Diatoms in the long core from the Sea of Japan. *DAN, USSR*, **126**, 1 (R)

SHEININ, M. 1957. Plankton of the Don and east part of Taganrog Bay. *AN, VNIRO*, **4** (R)

SHIRSHOV, P. 1936. The plankton as an indicator of the ice regime of the sea. Scientific results of the expedition on the ice-breaker *Krassin* in 1953.

SHIRSHOV, P. 1937. Seasonal changes of the phytoplankton of the Polar Seas in connection with Ice Regime. *Tr. Arctic Inst. USSR*, **82** (E.s.)

SHIRSHOV, P. 1938. Determination of the plankton productivity in the Polar Seas by photosynthesis. *Scientific results of the works of the expedition "Cheluskin" and in the camp of Schmidt*, **1** (R)

SHIRSHOV, P. 1944. The scientific results of the drift-station of "North Pole". The general conference *AN, USSR* in 1944 (R)

SKOPINTZEV, B. 1939. Organic matter in the waters of the Barents, Polar and Kara Seas. *Ibid.* **19**, 4.

SKOPINTZEV, B. 1944. On the deposits in the Okhotsk Sea. *Repts. G.O.I.* **33** (R)

SKOPINTZEV, B. and GUBIN, F. 1955. Some results of the hydrological investigations in the Black Sea in 1952–1953. *Tr. Hydrophys. Inst. of the Sea. AN, USSR*, **5** (R)

SKORIKOV, A. 1903. Modern distribution of *Dreissena polymorpha* in Russia. *Tr. Soc. natur. Saratov*, **3**, 2 (R)

SKVORTZOV, E. 1929. On the question on the currents in the Black Sea. *Tr. Krimea Sci. Inst.* **2**, 2 (R)

SLASTENENKO, E. 1938. Catalogue of fish of the Black and Azov Seas. *Works of the V.M. Arnoldi biological station of Novorossiysk*, **2**, 2 (R)

SLASTENENKO, E. 1939. Les poissons de la Mer Noire et de la Mer d'Azov. *Ann. Sci. Univ. Jassy*, **25**, 1.

SLASTNIKOV, G. 1939. New species of Nereis in the White Sea. *Priroda*, **1** (R)

SLASTNIKOV, G. The Polychaeta fauna in the Onega Bay (White Sea). *Mat. Complex Study White Sea*, **1** (R)

SLEPTZOV, M. 1952. Crustaceans in the far-eastern seas. *Bull. TINRO*, **38** (R)

SMETANIN, D. 1958. Hydrochemie im Gebiet des Kurilen-Kamtschatka tiefsee Grabens. I. Einige Frage der Hydrologie und Chemie der unteren subarktischen Gewässer in Gebiet des Kurilen-Kamtschatka Grabens. *Tr. IOAN*, **27** (R)

SMETANIN, D. 1959. Hydrochemistry of Kuril–Kamchatka Deep-Sea Trench. II. On hydrology and chemistry of the upper subarctic water in the district of the Kurile–Kamchatka trench. *Ibid.* **33** (R)

SMIRNOV, A. (Smirnoff). 1938. Distribution of anchovy (*Engraulis encrasicholus maeoticus*) in the Azov Sea and its food. *Tr. Az.-Cher. NIRO*, **11** (E.s.)

SMIRNOV, S. 1947. New species of Copepoda Harpacticoida from the Arctic ocean. *Tr. drift-exped. on ice-breaker* G. Sedov, *1937–1940*, **3**, biol. (E.s.)

SMIRNOVA, L. 1956. The phytoplankton of the north-western part of the Pacific. *DAN, USSR*, **109**, 3 (R)

SOKOLOV, A. 1932. Dynamic chart of Barents Sea. *Tr. GOIN*, **2**, 2 (E.s.)

SOKOLOV, A. 1936. The contemporary conception on the hydrology of the Barents Sea. *Priroda*, **7** (R)

SOKOLOVA, E. 1934. Data on the hydrology of the Bobje-Sea. *Invest. Seas of USSR*, **20** (R)

SOKOLOVA, M. 1956. On the distribution pattern of deep-sea benthos. The influence of the macro-relief and distribution of suspension upon the edaphic groups of bottom invertebrates. *DAN, USSR*, **110**, 4 (R)

SOKOLOVA, M. 1957. Feeding of some carnivorous benthic deep-sea invertebrates of the far-eastern seas. *Tr. IOAN*, **20** (R)

SOKOLOVA, M. 1958. Erhährung der wirbellosen Tiere auf dem Tiefseeboden. *Ibid.* **27** (R)

SOKOLOVA, M. 1959. Some specificities of deep-sea bottom fauna ecology. *Intern. Oceanogr. Congr., New York*, 1959.
SOKOLOVA, M. 1960. The distribution of the groupings (biocenoses) of the bottom fauna of the deep-sea trenches in the north-western Pacific. *Tr. IOAN*, **34.**
SOKOLOVA, N. 1952. The feeding of the acipenserids in the Northern Caspian Sea after the introduction of *Nereis. Acclimatization of* Nereis *in the Caspian Sea* (R)
SOKOLOVA, N. 1957. The littoral fauna of the islands of the Kandalaksha reservation area. *Tr. V.G.O.* **8** (R)
SOLDATOV, V. and LINDBERG, G. 1930. A review of the fish of the seas of the far-east. *Bull. TINRO*, **5** (E.s.)
SOLOVYEV, V., KULAKOVA, L. and AGAPOV, G. 1958. The submarine mountain-ranges on the bottom of the southern Caspian Sea area. *Priroda*, **8** (R)
SOROKIN, J. and COBLENTZ-MISHKE, O. 1958. Primary production in the Japan Sea and the Pacific near Japan in spring 1957. *DAN, USSR*, **122,** 6 (R)
SOVINSKY, V. 1902 and 1904. An introduction to the study of fauna in the Ponto–Caspian–Aral Marine Basin (e.c.). *Mem. Kiev. Natur. Hist. Soc.* **18.**
SPASSKY, N. 1945. Discovery of the annelid *Nereis succinea* in the North Caspian. *Z.J.* **24**, 1 (E.s.)
SPASSKY, N. 1948. The state and changes of the benthos in the Northern Caspian area in 1940–1945. *Ibid.* **27**, 3 (R)
SPETHMANN, H. 1912. Der Wasserhaushalt der Ostsee. *Z. Gesellsch. Erdkunde. Berlin.*
STAMP, L. and DUDLEY. 1936. The Geographical Evolution of the North Sea Basin. *J. Cons.* **11**, 2.
STARK, I. 1950. The oysters' raw matter base and their distribution in the Gudaut Bank oyster ground. *Tr. Az.-Cher. NIRO*, **14** (R)
STARK, I. 1951. The fluctuations of the benthos state in the Taganrog Bay in connection with salinity. *Ibid.* **15** (R)
STARK, I. 1951. The state of basic food of the benthos-feeding fishes in the north-eastern part of Sea of Azov. *Ibid.* **15** (R)
STARK, I. 1955. The benthos variations in the Sea of Azov under conditions of changeable regime. *Tr. VNIRO*, **31**, 1 (R)
STARK, I. 1958. The influence of the river discharge change on the feeding base of benthos feeding fishes and the prediction of its future state. (Annotations to the works undertaken by *VNIRO* in 1956, **1** (R))
STARK, I. 1959. *Nereis succinea* in the Sea of Azov. *Z.J.* **38**, 11 (E.s.)
STARK, I. 1960. The yearly and seasonal benthos dynamics in the sea of Azov. *Tr. of the fisheries Azov Institute*, **1**, 1 (R)
STOCKMANN, V. 1938. Investigation of currents cinematic at west coast of the central part of the Caspian Sea. *Tr. Azerbaidjan Sci. Invest. Fishery Station*, **1** (E.s.)
STOCKMANN, V. 1944. On the water-masses in the central part of the Arctic Ocean. *Probl. Arctic*, **2** (R)

STRAKHOV, N. 1941. On the significance of the gaseous regime of a basin in the accumulation of organic matter in its sediments. *Bull. Acad. Sci. USSR. geol.* **4–5** (E.s.)

STSCHAPOVA, T. (Scapova, Schapova). 1938. The bottom vegetation of the Komsomoletz (Mertvy Kultuk), and Kaidak Basy. *J. Botan. URSS*, **23**, 2 (E.s.)

STSCHAPOVA, T. 1946. On the amphipacific distribution of certain species of Phaeophyceae. *DAN, USSR*, **52**, 2 (E.s.)

STSCHAPOVA, T. 1948. Geographical distribution of the ordnung Laminariales in the northern part of the Pacific ocean. *Tr. IOAN*, **2** (R)

STSCHAPOVA, T. 1953. On the systematics of the Black Sea Cystoseira. *Ibid.* **7** (R)

STSCHAPOVA, T. 1957. Littoral flora of the continental coast of the Japan Sea. *Ibid.* **23** (R)

STSCHAPOVA, T., MOYEVSKY, O. and PASTERNAK, F. 1957. Flora and fauna of the littoral of Western Sakhalin. (Preliminary report.) *Ibid.* **23** (R)

STSCHAPOVA, T. and VOSZHINSKAYA, V. 1960. The algal flora of the littoral of the Western Sakhalin coast. *Ibid.* **34** (R)

STSCHEDRINA, Z. (Schjedrina). 1938. On the distribution of the Foraminifera in the Kara Sea. *DAN, USSR*, **19**, 4 (R)

STSCHEDRINA, Z. 1952. Foraminifera in the Chukotsk and Bering Seas. The extreme north-east of the USSR, **2** (*F. Fl. Chukotsk Sea*) (R)

STSCHEDRINA, Z. 1956. The fauna of the Foraminifera in the Far East Seas. Tr. of the problem and thematic conferences in the Zoological Institute, *AN, USSR*, **6** (R)

STSCHEDRINA, Z. 1958. Die Foraminiferenfauna des Kurilen–Kamtschatka Grabens. *Tr. IOAN*, **27** (R)

STUXBERG, A. 1882. Evertebratfauna i Sibiriens. Ishaf, *Vega Expedit. Vetensk. Jaktagesker.* **1**.

STUXBERG, A. 1886. Faunar pä och Kring Novaja Zemlja. *Ibid.* **5**, 5.

SUBOV, N. (*see* ZUBOV, N.).

SUESS, E. 1888–1909. Das Antlitz der Erde.

SVESHNIKOV, V. 1958. Polychaetes species, new to the White Sea. *Z.J.* **37**, 1 (E.s.)

SVETOVIDOV, A. 1937. The fish of Komsomoletz (Mertvyi Kultuk) and Kaidak Bays (Caspian Sea). *Tr. Complex Study Caspian Sea. Acad. Sci. USSR.* **1**, 1 (E.s.)

SVETOVIDOV, A. 1943. On the Clupeoid-fish of the Caspian and Black Seas. (Genera Caspialosa and Clupeonella) and on the conditions of their development. *Z.J.* **22**, 4 (E.s.)

SVETOVIDOV, A. Gadoidea. Fauna of the USSR. *ZIN AN USSR*, **9**, 4 (R)

SVETOVIDOV, A. On some similar features of the fish fauna in the Caspian and Black Seas and in the northern parts of the Pacific and Atlantic oceans. *DAN, USSR*, **62**, 5 (R)

SVETOVIDOV, A. 1952. Clupeidae. Fauna of the USSR. *ZIN AN USSR* (new series), **2**, 1 (R)

SVETOVIDOV, A. 1957. On the reasons for difference in the rate of growth of the Clupeonides of the Caspian, Black and Azov Seas. *Z.J.* **36**, 11 (E.s.)

SYSOEV, N., UDINTZEV, G. and ANDREEVA, I. 1958. The results of the seismic-acoustic exploration of the bottom of Japan Sea. *DAN, USSR*, **119**, 3 (R)

SZIDAT, L. 1926. Beiträge zur Faunistik und Biologie des Kurischen Haffs. *Schr. Phys.-Oekonom. Gesellsch. Königsberg*, **61**.

TANASICHCUK, N. (Tanasijtchuk). 1927. Sur quelques espèces des animaux nouveaux et rares, recueillis dans le golfe de Kola (Mourman). *DAN, USSR*, **14** (R)

TANASICHCUK, N. 1928. Zoological results of the cruise on the Kola meridian in the years 1925 and 1927. *Proc. Third Congr. of the Russ. Zool. Anat. Histol.* (R)

TANASICHCUK, N. 1929. Beiträge zur Kenntniss der fauna des Barents-Meeres. *Tr. station Biol. Murman*, **3** (G.s.)

TARANETZ, A. 1937. Handbook for identification of fishes of Soviet Far East and adjacent waters. *Bull. TINRO*, **11** (R)

TARASOV, N. 1927. On the hydrobiology of the Sivash. *Proc. G.G.I.* **18** (R)

TARASOV, N. 1940. A survey of the Sea of Japan. *Marine Symp.* **8** (R)

TARASOV, N. and ZEVINA, G. 1957. *Cirripedia Thoracica of the USSR Seas* (R)

TCHERNJAVSKY, V. 1867–1868. Materials for comparative zoogeographical studies of Pont (e.c.). *Tr. First Russ. Congr. Natur. Physic.* (R)

TCHOKHURI, N. 1939. To the question of diurnal vertical migrations of plankton in the Bay of Batumi. *Tr. station Piscicole biol. Géorgie*, **2** (E.s.)

TCHUGUNOV, N. (Tschugunoff, Tchougounov). 1918. The study of feeding habits of young fishes in the Caspian–Volga district. Part I. Vobla. *Ibid.* **3**, 6 (E.s.)

TCHUGUNOV, N. 1921. Über das Plankton des nördlichen Teiles des Kaspisees. *Arb. Biol. Wolga-Station*, **6**, 3 (G.s.)

TCHUGUNOV, N. 1923. Essay on the quantitative investigation of the benthos-production in the North part of the Caspian sea and of the typical bassins in the Volga delta. *Rept. Ichthyol. Lab. Astrakhan*, **5**, 1 (R)

TCHUGUNOV, N. 1926. Vorläufige Ergebnisse der Untersuchungen über die Productivität des Asowschen Meeres. *Abhandl. Wissenschaftl. Fischerei Exped. im Azowschen und Schwarzen Meer*, **1** (G.s.)

TCHUGUNOV, N. 1928. The biology of the young food-fishes in the Volga–Caspian district. (To the study of the biological basis of Fisheries.) *Rept. Astrakhan Sci. Fisheries Station*, **6**, 4 (E.s.)

TCHUGUNOV, N. 1932. The marine investigations of the All-Caspian expedition. *Bull. All-Caspian Exped.* **3–4**, **5–6** (R)

TCHUGUNOVA, N. and EGERMAN, F. F. 1932. Gobiidae and Crayfishes. *Bull. All-Caspian Fisheries Exped.* **5–6** (R)

THIENENMANN, A. 1928. Die Reliktenkrebse Mysis relicta, Pontoporeia quadrispinosa und die von ihnen bewohnten norddeutschen Seen. *Arch. Hydrobiol.* **19**.

THULIN, G. 1922. Dottenboniteringar i Sodra Ostensjon i sambamd mad fiskralningar. Svenska Hydr.-Biol. Komm. Skrifter, **6**.

TICHONOV, V. 1951. *The fish of the Black Sea. Simferopol* (R)

TICHY, M. 1916. The planctonic hydroid of the Caspian Sea. *Tr. Soc. Imp. Natur. Pétrograd*, **47**, 1, 4 (E.s.)

TIMONOV, V. 1925. On the question on the hydrological conditions in the "Gorlo" of the White Sea. *Invest. Russ. Seas*, **1**.

TIMONOV, V. 1947. The pattern of the general water circulation in the White Sea basin and the origin of its deep-waters. *Tr. GOI*, **1**, 13 (R)

TIMONOV, V. 1950. The principal features of the hydrological regime of the White Sea. (In Memory of J. M. Shokalsky.) **2** (R)

TOKIDA, J. 1934. The marine algae of Southern Saghalin. *Mem. faculty fisheries*, **2**, 1.

TROFIMOV, A. 1938. Twilight in the upper (0–70 m.) horizon of the Caspian Sea. *Meteorologia and Hydrologia*, **3** (E.s.)

TROFIMOV, A. and GOLUBCHIK, J. 1947. The pre-spring hydrochemical regime of the White Sea. *Tr. GOI*, **1**, 13 (R)

TURPAEVA, E. 1948. The feeding of some bottom invertebrates in the Barents Sea. *Z.J.* **27**, 6 (R)

TURPAEVA, E. 1953. The feeding and food grouping of the benthic invertebrates. *Tr. IOAN*, **7** (R)

TURPAEVA, E. 1957. Food interrelations between the dominant species in marine bottom biocoenoses. *Ibid.* **20** (R)

UDA, M. 1955. On the subtropical convergence and currents in the North-western Pacific. *Ibid.* **2**, 1.

UDA, M. 1955. Research on the fluctuation of the North Pacific circulation. *Rec. Oceanogr. Works Japan*, **2**, 2.

UDINTZEV, G. 1955. Topography of the Kurile–Kamchatka Trench. *Tr. IOAN*, **12** (R)

UDINTZEV, G. 1955. The origin of the bottom relief in the Okhotsk Sea. *Ibid.* **13** (R)

UDINTZEV, G. 1957. Bottom relief of the Okhotsk Sea. *Ibid.* **22** (R)

UDINTZEV, G. 1960. Bottom topography and tectonics of the Western Pacific. *Intern. Geol. Congr., XXI session. Reports of Soviet geologists. Probl.* **10** (E.s.)

ULLYOTT, P. and ILGAZ, O. 1946. Observations on the Bosporus, **3**. The degree of turbulence. *Rev. fac. sci. Univ. Instanbul. ser. B*, **2**.

ULLYOTT, P. and ILGAZ, O. 1946. The Hydrography of the Bosporus. *Geogr. Review*, **36**, 1.

ULYANIN, V. 1871. 1. Account on the zoologic journey to the Black Sea. 2. On the pelagic fauna of the Black Sea. *Bull. Moscow Soc. Natur. anthropol. ethnogr.* **8**, 1 (R)

URAZOV, G. and POLIAKOV, V. 1954. Hydrochemical study of the Kara-Bogaz Bay. Level fluctuations in the Caspian Sea. *Acad. Sci. USSR*, **2** (R)

USATCHEV, P. (Ussachev, Usatschev). 1926. On the phytoplankton of the Sea of Azov. *J. All-Union Congr. Botan. Moscow* (R)

USATCHEV, P. 1927. The phytoplankton of the Azov Sea. (Volume in honour of N. M. Knipovich.) (E.s.)

USATCHEV, P. 1928. On the phytoplankton in north-west part of the Black Sea. *J. All-Union Congr. Botan. Leningrad* (R)

USATCHEV, P. 1935. Die Zusammensetzung und Verteilung des Phytoplanktons des Barentsmeeres im Sommer 1931. *Tr. Arctic Inst.* **21** (G.s.)

USATCHEV, P. 1941. *Phytoplankton of the Caspian Sea.* (In press.) (R)

USATCHEV, P. 1946. Phytoplankton collected by the *Sedov* Expedition 1937–1939. *Tr. drift-exped. on ice-breaker* G. Sedov, *1937–1939*, **3**, *biol.* (E.s.)

USATCHEV, P. 1946. Biological indicators of the origin of ice-floes in the Kara sea and sea of Brothers Laptev and the Strait of the Franz-Josef Land Archipelago. *Tr. IOAN*, **1** (E.s.)

USATCHEV, P. 1947. General characteristics of the phytoplankton of the Seas of USSR. *Recent Advanc. Biol.* **23**, 2 (R)

USATCHEV, P. 1948. Quantitative fluctuations of phytoplankton in the northern Caspian Sea area. *Tr. IOAN*, **2** (R)

USCHAKOV, P. (Uschakow, Ouchakoff). 1924. Season-changes in the littoral of the Kola fjord. *Tr. L.O.E.* **59**, 1.

USCHAKOV, P. 1931. Biocönosen der Meeresstrasse Matotschkin Schar auf Nowaja Semlja. *Expl. Mers URSS*, **12** (G.s.)

USCHAKOV, P. 1934. Some particularities of fauna and hydrographical conditions on the Okhotsk Sea. *Priroda*, **11** (R)

USCHAKOV, P. 1936. On the benthic fauna of the Chukotsk Sea. *Sci. results Exped. on the ice-breaker* Krassin *in 1935* (R)

USCHAKOV, P. 1940. The Okhotsk Sea. *Marine volumes*, **1** (R)

USCHAKOV, P. 1945. Bottom life in the Tchuktchi Sea, as flow-indicator. *Repts. GOI*, **31**, 32 (R)

USCHAKOV, P. 1949. The system of vertical zones in the Okhotsk-Sea. *DAN, USSR*, **68**, 4 (R)

USCHAKOV, P. 1951. The littoral of the Okhotsk Sea. *Ibid.* **76**, 1 (R)

USCHAKOV, P. 1952. The Tchuktchi Sea and its bottom-fauna. *Extreme north-east of the USSR*, **2** (R)

USCHAKOV, P. 1953. The fauna of the Okhotsk Sea and its life conditions. *Ed. ZIN Acad. Sci. USSR* (R)

USCHAKOV, P. 1955. Polychaetes of the far-eastern seas of the USSR. *Ibid.* (R)

USCHAKOV, P. 1955. On the importance of the Laperouse strait in the formation of the fauna in south-western part of the Okhotsk Sea. *DAN, USSR*, **105**, 6 (R)

USPENSKY, S. 1959. Colonial sea breeding birds of the Northern and far-eastern seas of the USSR, their biotopic distribution, number and role as plankton and benthos consumers. *Bull. MOIP, biol.* **64**, 2 (E.s.)

VÄLIKANGAS, I. 1926. Planktologische Untersuchungen im Hefengebiet von Helsingfors. *Acta. Zool. Fenn.* **1**.

VÄLIKANGAS, I. 1933. Über die Biologie der Ostsee als Brakwassergebiet *Verhandl. Intern. Verein. theor. angew. Limnol.* **6**.

VASNETZOV, W. 1931. Hydrology of the Kara Sea. *Tr. GOIN*, **1**, 2–3 (R)

VASNETZOV, W. 1936. Materials on the hydrology of the Kara Sea in the connection with the influence of the Atlantic waters on its regime. *Ed. Glavsermorput* (R)

VELOKUROV, N. and STAROV, D. 1946. *Hydrometeorological characteristic of the Black Sea. Moscow* (R)

VEREŠČAGIN, G. 1926. Vorläufige Betrachtungen über den Ursprung der Fauna und Flora des Bajkalsees. *DAN, USSR* (G.s.)

VEREŠČAGIN, G. 1940. Origine et histoire du Baikal, de sa faune et de sa flore. *Tr. station limnol. Lac Baikal,* **10** (F.s.)

VEREŠČAGIN, G. 1941. On the question on the origin and history of the fauna and flora of the Bajkal. *Tr. commiss. étude lac Bajkal,* **3** (G.s.)

VINOGRADOV, K. 1948. On the question of the utilization of the polychaetes as the fish-food. *DAN, USSR,* **7** (R)

VINOGRADOV, K. 1958. A historical survey of Russian hydrobiological investigations in the Black Sea. Kiev. *AN Ukr. SSR* (R)

VINOGRADOV, L. 1941. The Kamchatka crab (*Paralithodes kamchatica*). Vladivostok (R)

VINOGRADOV, L. 1945. The Year cycle in the life and the migrations of the *Paralithodes Kamchatica* in the northern part of the west Kamchatka shelf. *Bull. TINRO,* **19** (R)

VINOGRADOV, L. 1946. The geographical distribution of the Kamchatka crab. *Paralithodes Kamchatica* (Til.). *Bull. TINRO,* **22** (E.s.)

VINOGRADOV, L. 1948. On the zoogeographical zonation of the far-eastern seas. *Ibid.* **28** (R)

VINOGRADOV, L. 1950. A key-guide for shrimps, crayfish and crabs of the Far-East. *Ibid.* **33** (R)

VINOGRADOV, L. 1955. On the position of *Nereis succinea* in the benthos of the northern part of the Caspian Sea. *Bull. MOIP, biol.* **60**, 6 (R)

VINOGRADOV, M. 1954. Diurnal vertical migrations of the zooplankton in the Far East Seas. *Tr. IOAN,* **8** (R)

VINOGRADOV, M. 1954. The vertical distribution of Zooplankton biomass in the Kurile–Kamchatka trench. *DAN, USSR,* **96,** 3 (R)

VINOGRADOV, M. 1955. Pattern of the vertical zooplankton distribution in the waters of the Kurile–Kamchatka Trench. *Tr. IOAN,* **12** (R)

VINOGRADOV, M. The vertical migrations of the zooplankton and its role in the feeding of the deep-sea pelagic fauna. *Ibid.* **13** (R)

VINOGRADOV, M. 1956. The distribution of the zooplankton in the western areas of the Bering Sea. *Tr. V.G.O.* **7** (R)

VINOGRADOV, M. 1959. On the vertical distribution of deep-sea plankton in the western part of the Pacific ocean. *XV Intern. Congr. Zool. Sect. 3,* Paper 31.

VINOGRADOV, M. 1960. On the plankton of deep waters in the sea of Japan. *Z.J.* **39**, 4 (E.s.)

VINOGRADOV, M. 1960. Quantitative distribution of deep-sea plankton in the western and central Pacific. *Tr. IOAN,* **4** (R)

VINOGRADOVA, E. 1955. The hydrochemical conditions of the Azov Sea in 1951–1953. *Tr. VNIRO,* **31**, 1 (R)

VINOGRADOVA, N. (Winogradowa). 1954. Materials on the quantitative evaluation of the bottom fauna in some bays of the Okhotsk and Bering Seas. *Tr. IOAN,* **9** (R)

VINOGRADOVA, N. 1955. Some peculiarities in the distribution of the deep-sea fauna. *Ibid.* **13** (R)

VINOGRADOVA, N. 1956. Zoogeographical subdivision of the abyss of the World's oceans. *DAN, USSR*, **111**, 1 (R)

VINOGRADOVA, N. Some pattern in the vertical distribution of the bottom fauna of the abyss of the World's Oceans. *DAN, USSR*, **110**, 4 (R)

VINOGRADOVA, N. Die Vertikalverbreitung der Tiefsee bodenfauna des Ozeans. *Tr. IOAN*, **27** (R)

VINOGRADOVA, P. 1954. Grounds of the Barents Sea. (*Sci.-tech. Bull.*) *PINRO*, **4** (R)

VINOGRADOVA, P. 1957. New data on the bottom configuration of the Barents Sea. *Tr. PINRO*, **10** (R)

VIRKETIS, M. (Wirketis, Wirketiss). 1926. Das Zooplankton des Weissen-Meeres. *Expl. Mers URSS*, **3** (G.s.)

VIRKETIS, M. 1929. On the zooplankton distribution in the Gorlo of the White Sea. *Tr. Inst. North Study*, **40** (R)

VIRKETIS, M. 1932. Some data on the zooplankton south-east part of the Laptev Sea. *Invest. Seas USSR*, **15** (R)

VIRKETIS, M. 1941. Quantitative Angaben über das Plankton des Japonischen Meeres. *Invest. Seas USSR*, **1** (G.s.)

VIRKETIS, M. 1943 (1944). Zooplankton of the B. Wilkitsky Strait as an indicator of the hydrological region. *Probl. Arctic*, **2** (R)

VIRKETIS, M. 1946 (1947). 25 Years of plankton investigation in the Arctic. *Ibid.* **3** (E.s.)

VIRKETIS, M. 1952. Zooplankton of the Sea of Tchukcha and Bering Straits. The extreme north-east of the USSR. 2. Fauna and Flora of the Sea of Tchukcha. *Ed. Acad. Sci. USSR* (R)

VODYANITZKY, W. (Wodyanitzky, Wodianizky, Wodjanitzky). 1930. On the question on the origin of the Black Sea fish; *Works V. M. Arnoldi Novorossijsk Biol. Station*, **4** (R)

VODYANITZKY, W. Observations on the pelagic eggs of the fish in the Black Sea. *Tr. S.B.S.* **5** (R)

VODYANITZKY, W. 1940. On ecology and history of the fish of the Black Sea. *Works V. M. Arnoldi Novorossijsk Biol. Station*, **2**, 3 (R)

VODYANITZKY, W. 1941. Contribution à la connaissance de la production biologique de la Mer Noire. *Tr. ZIN*, **7**, 2 (F.s.)

VODYANITZKY, W. 1945. On the biological productivity of inland waters. (A note about W. I. Jadin's theory.) *Z.J.* **24**, 2 (E.s.)

VODYANITZKY, W. 1948. The basic water exchange in the history of the formation of salinity in the Black Sea. *Tr. S.B.S.* **6** (R)

VODYANITZKY, W. 1954. On the problem of the biological productivity of reservoirs and particularly of the Black Sea. *Ibid.* **8** (R)

VODYANITZKY, W. 1958. Is it permissible to dump radioactive wastes into the Black Sea? *Priroda*, **2** (R)

VOROBIEFF, V. 1937. The feeding of bream in the Azov Sea. *Z.J.* **16**, 1 (E.s.)

VOROBIEFF, V. 1938. Mussels of the Black Sea. *Az.-Cher. NIRO*, **11** (E.s.)

VOROBIEFF, V. 1940. Hydrobiological outline of the eastern Sivash and its possible utilization for economic fisheries. *Ibid.* **12**, 1 (R)

VOROBIEFF, V. 1949. The benthos of the Azov Sea. *Ibid.* **13** (R)

VORONICHIN, N. 1908. On the distribution of the algae in the Black Sea near Sebastopol. *Bull. Petersbourg Natur. Soc.* **37**, 3.

VORONKOV, P., URALOV, N. and CHERNOVSKAJA, E. 1948. The fundamental peculiarities of the hydrochemical regime in the coastal region of the Barents Sea in the Central Murman. *Tr. M.B.S.* **1** (R)

VOROSHILOVA, A. and DIANOVA, E. 1937. The role of the plankton in the reproduction of the microorganisms in isolated samples of the sea-water. *Microbiology*, **6**, 6 (R)

WAERN, M. 1952. Rocky-shore algae in the Öregrun archipelago. *Acta Phytogeogr. Svec. Uppsala*, **30**.

WAGNER, N. 1885. *Invertebrates of the White Sea*, **1** (R)

WIESE, V. 1922. Sur l'hydrologie de la mer de Kara. *Bull. Inst. Hydrol. Russ.* **4** (G.s.)

WIESE, V. 1926. A hydrological sketch of the sea of the Brothers Laptev and of the East Siberian sea. *Mat. commiss. étude Républ. Autonome Soviétique Socialiste Yakoute*, **5** (E.s.)

WILLER, A. 1925. Studien über das Fische *Haff. Zeitsch.* **23**.

WILLER, A. 1931. Vergleichende Untersuchungen an Strandgewässern *Verh. Intern. Ver. theor. angew. Limnol.* **5**.

WITTING, R. 1912. Die Hydrographie der Ostsee. *Z. Gesellsch. Erdkunde. Berlin.*

WITTING, R. 1912. Zusammenfassende Übersicht der Hydrographie des Bottnischen und Finnischen Meerbusen und der nordlichen Ostsee. *Finn. Hydrograph.-biol. Unters.* **7**.

WOLFF, TORBEN. 1960. The hadal community—an introduction. *Deep-Sea Research*, **6**.

WRIGHT, W. 1914. *The Quaternary Ice Age*. London.

YABE, H. 1929. The latest land connection of the Japanese Islands to the Asiatic continent. *Proc. Imp. Acad. Tokyo*, **5**, 4.

YABE, H. and TAYAMA, R. 1929. On some remarkable examples of drowned valleys found around the Japanese Islands. *Records of Oceanographic Works in Japan*, **2**, 1.

YABLONSKAYA, E. 1952. Feeding of *Nereis* in the Caspian Sea. Acclimatization of *Nereis* in the Caspian sea. *Ed. MOIP* (R)

YABLONSKAYA, E. 1955. Possible changes of food-material for fishes in the sea of Azov during the discharge regulation of the rivers. *Tr. VNIRO*, **31**, 1 (R)

YABLONSKAYA, E. 1957. The hydrographical and hydrochemical regime of the Sea of Azov, the condition of the feeding basis for fishes in 1955 and character of its changes. (Annotations to works of *VNIRO*, **4** (R))

YABLONSKAYA, E. 1958. The distribution of the bottom communities and the benthos biomass in the Aral-sea. *Ibid.* **3** (R)

YABLONSKAYA, E. and STARK, I. 1955. On the interrelations between *Nereis succinea* and other forms of benthos organisms. *Bull. MOIP, biol.* **60**.

YAKOVLEV, S. 1926. The alluvium and the relief of the city Leningrad and environs. *Proc. sci. meliorative Inst.* (R)

ZACHS, I. 1927. Preliminary data on the distribution of fauna and flora in the coastal zone of Peter the Great Bay in the Sea of Japan. *1st Conf. study Far East productivity forces*, **4** (R)

ZACHS, I. 1929. Upon the bottom communities of the Shantar sea (S-W Okhotsk Sea). *Bull. Pacific Sci. Fishery Research Station*, **3**, 2 (E.s.)

ZADULSKAYA, E. and SMIRNOV, K. 1939. Diurnal process of feeding cod in the fishing grounds of the Barents Sea. *Tr. VNIRO*, **4** (E.s.)

ZAGOROWSKY, N. (Zagorovsky). 1928. Das Gestern und Heute der Bucht von Odessa. *Mém. Soc. Natur. Odessa*, **44** (G.s.)

ZAGOROWSKY, N. 1930. Comparative-hydrobiological investigations of the "limans" in the northern areas of the Black Sea. *Tr. 2nd Hydrol. congr.* (R)

ZAGOROWSKY, N. and RUBINSTEIN, D. 1916. Matériaux relatifs au système des biocénoses du golfe d'Odessa. *Mém. Soc. Imp. agric. Russ. mérid.* **86**, 1 (F.s.)

ZAIKOV, B. 1946. Recent and future water balance of the Aral Sea. *Tr. Sci. Inst. Hydrometeorol. Service, series 4*, **39** (R)

ZAITZEV, G. 1946. Variations in Salinity in the North Caspian area in 1935–1943 and causes of their origin. *Meteorologia and Hydrologia*. Informative symposium, **4** (R).

ZAITZEV, G. 1960. On the water exchange between the Arctic Basin and the Pacific and Atlantic Oceans. *Priroda* (R)

ZAITZEV, G. 1961. On the exchange of waters between the Arctic Basin and the Pacific and Atlantic Oceans. *Oceanology*, **4** (R)

ZALKIN, V. 1938. The distribution of the endemic Black Sea dolphin (*D. delphis L.*) during the summer–autumn period. *Tr. Az.-Cher. NIRO*, **11** (R)

ZATSEPIN, V. (Zatzepin). 1946. Arctic-boreal bottom colonies *Modiolus modiolus—Pecten islandicus* and *Mactra elliptica* of the Murman coast of the Barents Sea and their comparative zoogeographical characteristics. *Bull. Moscow Univ.* **2** (E.s.)

ZATSEPIN, V., ZENKEVITCH, L. and FILATOVA, Z. 1948. Materials for the quantitative evaluation of the littoral fauna in the Kola-fjord. *Tr. GOI*, **6**, 18 (R)

ZATSEPIN, V. and PETROVA, N. 1939. The feeding of the Cod in south part of the Barents Sea. *Tr. PINRO*, **5** (E.s.)

ZELINSKY, N. 1893. Sur la fermentation sulfhydrique dans la Mer Noire. *J. soc. phys.-chim. russ.* **25**, 5 (R)

ZENKEVITCH, L. (Zenkevich, Zenkevitsch, Senkevitsch). 1927. Materialien zur quantitativen Untersuchungen der Bodenfauna des Barents und Weissen Meeres. *Ber. M.N.I.* **2**, 4 (G.s.)

ZENKEVITCH, L. 1931. A quantitative evaluation of the bottom-fauna in the sea region about the Kanin peninsula. *Ber. M.N.I.* **4**, 3 (E.s.)

ZENKEVITCH, L. 1931. Fish-food in the Barents Sea. *Repts. first session State Oceanogr. Inst.* **4** (E.s.)

ZENKEVITCH, L. 1931. On the aeration of the bottom waters through vertical circulation. *J.C.* **6**, 3.

ZENKEVITCH, L. 1933. Beiträge zur Zoogeographie des nördlichen Polarbassins im Zusammenhang mit der Frage über dessen paläogeographische Vergangenheit. *Z.J.* **12**, 4 (G.s.)

ZENKEVITCH, L. 1937. On the problem relative to the acclimatization of new animal species in the Caspian and Aral Seas. *Ibid.* **16**, 3 (E.s.)

ZENKEVITCH, L. 1937. Achievements in the sea-fauna study of the USSR for twenty years. *Ibid.* **16**, 5 (R)

ZENKEVITCH, L. 1938. The influence of Caspian and Black Sea waters of different concentrations upon some common Black Sea invertebrates. Part I. Survival and body weight changes. Part 2. The change of internal salinity. *Ibid.* **17**, 5–6 (E.s.)

ZENKEVITCH, L. 1940. Sur l'aclimatisation dans la mer Caspienne de nouveaux invertébrés alimentaires (pour les poissons) et sur les prémisses théoriques concernant cette aclimatation. *Bull. MOIP, biol.* **49**, 1 (F.s.)

ZENKEVITCH, L. 1947. *Fauna and the biological productivity of the sea.* **2,** Moscow (R)

ZENKEVITCH, L. 1949. La structure biologique de l'océan. *13 Congr. Intern. Zool.*

ZENKEVITCH, L. 1951. *Fauna and the biological productivity of the sea,* **1,** Moscow (R)

ZENKEVITCH, L. 1951. Some biogeographical problems of the sea as part of general geography. *Questions of the Geography,* **24** (R)

ZENKEVITCH, L. 1951, 1955. *The seas of the USSR their Fauna and Flora.* Moscow (R)

ZENKEVITCH, L. 1952. The theoretical basis for acclimatization. Acclimatization of *Nereis* in Caspian sea. *Bull. MOIP* (R)

ZENKEVITCH, L. 1954. Erforschungen der Tiefseefauna im nordwestlichen Teil des Stillen Ozeans. *Union intern. sci. biol. Série* B, **16.**

ZENKEVITCH, L. 1957. New genus and two new species of the deep-water Echiurids from the far-eastern seas and the north-west part of Pacific Ocean. *Tr. IOAN,* **23** (R)

ZENKEVITCH, L. 1958. Die Tiefsee-Echiuriden des Nord-Westlichen Teiles des Stillen Ozeans. *Tr. IOAN,* **27** (R)

ZENKEVITCH, L. 1959. The classification of brackish-water basins as exemplified by the seas of the USSR. *Estratto dall-Archivio di Oceanographia e Limnologia,* **10,** *Supplemento.*

ZENKEVITCH, L. 1961. Special Quantitative Characteristics of the Ocean Bottom Life. Oceanography. I *Intern. Oceanogr. Congr.*

ZENKEVITCH, L., BARSANOVA, N. and BELYAEV, G. 1960. Quantitative distribution of bottom fauna in the abyssal area of the World Ocean. *DAN, USSR,* **130,** 1 (R)

ZENKEVITCH, L., BELYAEV, G. and BIRSTEIN, J. 1954. Study of the fauna from the Kurile–Kamchatka Trench, *Priroda,* **2** (R)

ZENKEVITCH, L. and BIRSTEIN, J. 1934. On possible methods of raising the productivity of the Caspian and Aral Seas. *Fisheries USSR,* **3** (R)

ZENKEVITCH, L. and BIRSTEIN, J. 1937. On the problem relative to the acclimatization of new animal species in the Caspian and Aral Seas. *Z.J.* **16,** 3(R)

ZENKEVITCH, L. and BIRSTEIN, J. 1960. On the problem of the antiquity of the deep-sea fauna. *Deep-Sea Research*, **7**, 1.

ZENKEVITCH, L., BIRSTEIN, J. and BELYAEV, G. 1955. The bottom fauna of the Kurile–Kamchatka Trench. *Tr. IOAN*, **12** (R)

ZENKEVITCH, L., BIRSTEIN, J. and KARPEVICH, A. 1945. First steps in reconstruction of the Caspian fauna. *Z.J.* **24**, 1 (E.s.)

ZENKEVITCH, L. and BROTZKAYA, V. 1939. Ecological depth-temperature areas of benthos mass-forms in the Barents Sea *Ecology*, **20**, 1.

ZENKEVITCH, L. and BROTZKAYA, V. 1939. Quantitative evaluation of the bottom fauna of the Barents sea. *Tr. VNIRO*, **4** (E.s.)

ZENKEVITCH, L., BROTZKY, V. and IDELSON, M. 1928. Materials for the study of the productivity of the sea-bottom in the White, Barents and Kara Seas. *J. Cons.* **3**, 3.

ZENKEVITCH, L. and FILATOVA, Z. 1957. Quantitative distribution of bottom fauna in the Kara Sea. *Tr. V.G.O.* **8** (R)

ZENKEVITCH, L. and FILATOVA, Z. 1958. Allgemeine Charakteristik der quantitativen Verbreitung der Bodenfauna der fernöstlichen Meeren der USSR und des nord-westlichen Teiles des Stillen Ozeans. *Tr. IOAN*, **27** (R)

ZENKEVITCH, N. 1957. Bottom relief of the northern part of the Japan Sea. *Ibid.* **22** (R)

ZENKEVITCH, N. 1959. New data on the bottom relief of the Sea of Japan. *Bull. Acad. Sci. USSR, geogr.* **3** (R)

ZENKOVITCH, V. 1962. Principles of the study on the development of the sea shores. *Acad. Sci. USSR* (R)

ZERNOV, S. (Sernov). 1901. Plankton of the Sea of Azov and their limans. *Ann. Zool. Mus. Acad. Sci.* **6** (R)

ZERNOV, S. 1913. On the question of the knowledge of the life of the Black Sea. *Zap. A.N. Series 8*, **32**, 1 (R)

ZERNOV, S. 1934 (2nd ed. 1949). *General Hydrobiology*. Moscow-Leningrad (R)

ZEVINA, G. 1957. Balanus improvisus Darwin and B. eburneus Gould, observed in fouling on ships and hydrotechnical constructions in the Caspian Sea. *DAN, USSR*, **113**, 2 (R)

ZEVINA, G. 1958. The fouling of the ships and hydrotechnical constructions in the Caspian Sea. (*Autoreferat of the dissertation*) (R)

ZEVINA, G. 1959. The appearance of new fouling organisms in the Caspian Sea after the Volga–Don Canal began to operate. *Priroda*, **7**.

ZEVINA, G. and TARASOV, N. 1954. New Balanidae species in the Soviet waters of the Black Sea. *Tr. S.B.S.* **8** (R)

ZHELTENKOVA, M. (*see* JELTENKOVA, M.)

ZIKOV, W. 1903. Materials on the fauna of the Volga and hydrofauna of the Saratov district. *Bull. MOIP*, **1** (R)

ZINOVA, A. 1950. On some peculiarities of the flora in the White Sea. *Tr. V.G.O.* **2** (R)

ZINOVA, A. 1953. The key of the Phaeophyta of the Northern Seas. *AN, USSR* (R)

ZINOVA, A. 1955. The key of the Rhodophyta of the Northern Seas. *AN, USSR* (R)

ZINOVA, A. 1957. Seaweeds in the Eastern part of the Soviet sector of the Arctic. *Tr. IOAN*, **23** (R)

ZUBOV, N. 1931. On the ventilation of the sea bottom waters. *Expl. Mers URSS*, **12** (E.s.)

ZUBOV, N. 1938. *The Sea waters and the sea-ice* (R)

ZUBOV, N. 1940. *In the centre of the Arctic.* Moscow-Leningrad. *Ed. Glavsevmorput* (R)

ZUBOV, N. 1945. The ices of the Arctic. Moscow. *Ed. Glavsevmorput* (R)

ZUBOV, N. 1950. A basic science for studying Straits. *All-Union Geogr. Soc. New Series*, **2** (R)

INDEX

INDEX OF LATIN NAMES

SUBJECT INDEX